W9-CRV-201

Handbook of Hot Atom Chemistry

Exclusive sales rights for Japan, Taiwan, Hong Kong, Republic of Korea and People's Republic of China:
Kodansha Ltd., 12-21, Otowa 2-chome, Bunkyo-ku, Tokyo 112-01 (Japan)
Distribution for
Switzerland: VCH Verlags AG, P. O. Box, CH-4020 Basel (Switzerland)
Great Britain and Ireland: VCH Publishers (UK), Ltd., 8 Wellington Court, Wellington Street, Cambridge CB1 1HZ (Great Britain)
USA and Canada: VCH Publishers, Suite 909, 220 East 23rd Street, New York, NY 10010-4606 (USA)
for all other countries: VCH Verlagsgesellschaft, P.O.Box 101161, D-6940 Weinheim (Federal Republic of Germany)

ISBN3-527-29001-X VCH Verlagsgesellschaft
ISBN1-56081-271-0 VCH Publishers
ISBN4-06-205851-0 Kodansha Ltd.

Handbook of Hot Atom Chemistry

Edited by
Jean-P. Adloff
Peter P. Gaspar
Masashi Imamura
Alfred G. Maddock
Tatsuo Matsuura
Hirotoshi Sano
Kenji Yoshihara

Tokyo

Weinheim · New York
Cambridge · Basel

Prof. Jean-P. Adloff
University Louis Pasteur,
and Centre de Recherches
Nucléaires, 67037 Strasbourg
Cédex, France

Prof. Peter P. Gaspar
Department of Chemistry,
Washington University,
Saint Louis, MO 63130, USA

Prof. Masashi Imamura
Tokyo University of
Information Sciences,
Chiba 265, Japan

Prof. Emeritus
Alfred G. Maddock
University of Cambridge,
Cambridge CB2 1EW, UK

Prof. Tatsuo Matsuura
Institute for Atomic Energy,
Rikkyo University,
Yokosuka 240-01, Japan

Prof. Hirotoshi Sano
Tokyo Metropolitan
University,
Tokyo 192-03, Japan

Prof. Kenji Yoshihara
Department of Chemistry,
Faculty of Science,
Tohoku University,
Sendai 980, Japan

Library of Congress Card No. applied for

A CIP catalogue record for this book is available from the British Library.

Die Deutsche Bibliothek - CIP-Einheitsaufnahme
Handbook of hot atom chemistry / ed. by J.-P. Adloff...- Tokyo
: Kodansha ; Weinheim ; New York ; Cambridge ; Basel : VCH, 1992
ISBN 3-527-29001-X (VCH, Weinheim...)
ISBN 1-56081-271-0 (VCH, New York...)
ISBN 4-06-205851-0 (Kodansha)
NE : Adloff Jean-Pierre 〔Hrsg.〕

Published jointly by
Kodansha Ltd., Tokyo(Japan),
VCH Verlagsgesellschaft mbH, Weinheim(FRG) and
VCH Publishers Inc., New York, NY(USA)

Printed in Japan

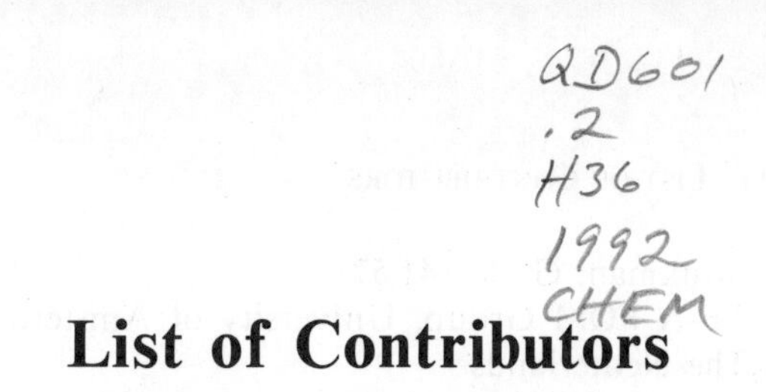

List of Contributors

Numbers in parentheses refer to the pages on which a contributor's paper begins.

Ache, H. J. (488)
Institut für Radiochemie, Kernforschungszentrum Karlsruhe GmbH, D-5700 Karlsruhe, Germany

Adloff, J.-P.(571,627)
University Louis Pasteur, and Centre de Recherches Nucléaires, 67037 Strasbourg Cédex, France

Aratono, Y. (35,412,663)
Department of Chemistry, Japan Atomic Energy Research Institute, Tokai, Ibaraki 319-11, Japan

Arnikar, H. J. (423)
Department of Chemistry, University of Poona, Pune - 411 007, India

Arseneau, D. J. (232)
TRIUMF and Department of Chemistry, University of British Columbia, Vancouver, B. C., Canada, V6T 2A3

Asano, T. (533)
Research Institute for Advanced Science and Technology, University of Osaka Prefecture, Sakai 591, Japan

Baragiola, R. A. (156,461)
Department of Nuclear Engineering and Engineering Physics, University of Virginia, Charlottesville, VA 22903, USA

Berei, K. (80,286)
Central Research Institute for Physics, Hungarian Academy of Sciences, H-1525 Budapest, Hungary

Blotcky, A. J. (383)
General Medical Research, V. A. Medical Center, Omaha, NE 68105, and Department of Chemistry, University of Nebraska, Lincoln, NE 68588-0304, USA

Boring, J. W. (156,461)
Department of Nuclear Engineering and Engineering Physics, University of Virginia, Charlottesville, VA 22903, USA

Brinkman, G. A. (41,57)
TF-A-FOM Group, University of Amsterdam, c/o NIKHEF-K, 1009 DB Amsterdam, The Netherlands

Bulbulian, S. (320)
Instituto Nacional de Investigaciones Nucleares, Deleg. Miguel Hidalgo, México, D. F. 11801, México

Collins, C. H. (320)
Instituto de Química, Universidade Estadual de Campinas, 13081 Campinas, SP, Brasil

Collins, K. E. (378)
Instituto de Química, Universidade Estadual de Campinas, 13081 Campinas, SP, Brasil

Continetti, R. E. (133)
Department of Chemistry, University of California, Berkeley, and Materials and Chemical Sciences Division, Lawrence Berkeley Laboratory, Berkeley, CA 94720, USA

Duplâtre, G. (334)
Laboratoire de Chimie Nucléaire, Centre de Recherches Nucléaires, 67307 Strasbourg Cédex, France

Ebihara, H. (378)
Department of Chemistry, Tsukuba University, Tsukuba 305, Japan

Endo, K. (473)
Laboratory of Physical Chemistry, Showa College of Pharmaceutical Sciences, Tokyo 194, Japan

Ferrieri, R. A. (114,176)
Department of Chemistry, Brookhaven National Laboratory, Long Island, NY 11973, USA

Fleming, D. G. (232)
TRIUMF and Department of Chemistry, University of British Columbia, Vancouver, B.C., Canada, V6T 2A3

Funabashi, K. (247)
Kawai Institute for Culture and Education, Nagoya 464, Japan

Gaspar, P. P. (85)
Department of Chemistry, Washington University, Saint Louis, MO 63130, USA

Halpern, A. (550)
Institute of Chemistry 1, Research Center Jülich, D-5170 Jülich, Germany

Hashimoto, T. (423,443)
Department of Chemistry, Faculty of Science, Niigata University, Niigata 950-21, Japan

Hatano, Y. (167)
Department of Chemistry, Tokyo Institute of Technology, Tokyo 152, Japan

Heyl, M. (226)
Institut für Radioastronomie der Universität Bonn, D-5300 Bonn, Germany

Hoffman, D. C. (27)
Nuclear Science Division, Lawrence Berkeley Laboratory, University of California, Berkeley, CA 94720, USA

Ikuta, S. (419)
General Education Department, Tokyo Metropolitan Universtiy, Tokyo 192-03, Japan

Imamura, M. (419,434)
Tokyo University of Information Sciences, Chiba 265, Japan

Ito, Y. (488)
Research Center for Nuclear Science and Technology, University of Tokyo, Tokai, Ibaraki 319-11, Japan

Itoh, N. (449)
Department of Physics, Faculty of Science, Nagoya University, Nagoya 464-01, Japan

Iwata, R. (515)
Cyclotron and Radioisotope Center, Tohoku University, Sendai 980, Japan

Johnson, R. E. (156,461)
Department of Nuclear Engineering and Engineering Physics, University of Virginia, Charlottesville, VA 22903, USA

Kaji, H. (506)
Department of Chemistry, Faculty of Science, Tohoku University, Sendai 980, Japan

Koura, K. (210)
Aerodynamics Division, National Aerospace Laboratory, Tokyo 182, Japan

Kudo, H. (647)
Department of Radioisotopes, Japan Atomic Energy Research Institute, Tokai, Ibaraki 319-11, Japan

Kuroda, P. K. (584)
Department of Chemistry, University of Nevada, Las Vegas, NV 89154, USA

Lazzarini, E. (488)
Instituto di Ingegneria Nucleare-CESNEF Politecnico, 20133 Milano, Italy

Lee, Y. T. (133)
Department of Chemistry, University of California, Berkeley, and Materials and Chemical Sciences Division, Lawrence Berkeley Laboratory, Berkeley, CA 94720, USA

Liu, M. (156)
Department of Nuclear Engineering and Engineering Physics, University of Virginia, Charlottesville, VA 22903, USA

Maddock, A. G. (3,320)
Professor Emeritus, University of Cambridge, Cambridge CB2 1EW, UK

Matsuura, T. (305)
Institute for Atomic Energy, Rikkyo University, Yokosuka 240-01, Japan

Miyazaki, T. (395)
Department of Applied Chemistry, Faculty of Engineering, Nagoya University, Nagoya 464, Japan

Müller, H. (354)
Institute of Inorganic and Analytical Chemistry, University of Freiburg, D-7800 Freiburg, Germany

Newton, G. W. A. (351)
Chemistry Department, Manchester University, Manchester M13 9PL, UK

Niisawa, K. (126)
Tanaka Kikinzoku Kogyo K. K., Tokyo 103, Japan

Ogasawara, M. (402)
Faculty of Engineering, Hokkaido University, Sapporo 060, Japan

Ohno, S. (412,663)
Department of Chemistry, Japan Atomic Energy Research Institute, Tokai, Ibaraki 319-11, Japan

Oohashi, K. (35)
Department of Chemistry, College of Arts and Sciences, Chiba University, Chiba 260, Japan

Patil, S. F. (423)
Department of Chemistry, University of Poona, Pune - 411 007, India

Rack, E. P. (66,176,383)
Department of Chemistry, University of Nebraska-Lincoln, Lincoln, NE 68588-0304, and General Medical Research, V. A. Medical Center, Omaha, NE 68105, USA

Rao, B. S. M. (41,57)
Department of Chemistry, University of Poona, Pune - 411 007, India

Roessler, K. (226,265,571,601)
Institut für Nuklearchemie, Forschungszentrum Jülich GmbH, D-5170 Jülich, Germany

Saeki, M. (637)
Department of Chemistry, Japan Atomic Energy Research Institute, Tokai, Ibaraki 319-11, Japan

Sakai, Y. (257)
Department of Chemistry, Daido Institute of Technology, Nagoya 457, Japan

Sakanoue, M. (17)
Professor Emeritus, Kanazawa University, Kanazawa 920, Japan

Sano, H. (473)
Tokyo Metropolitan University, Tokyo 192-03, Japan

Sasaki, K. (305)
Faculty of General Education, Rikkyo University, Tokyo 171, Japan

Sekine, T. (344)
Department of Chemistry, Faculty of Science, Tohoku University, Sendai 980, Japan

Senba, M. (232)
TRIUMF and Department of Chemistry, University of British Columbia, Vancouver, B. C., Canada, V6T 2A3

Sensui, Y. (105)
Faculty of General Education, Rikkyo University, Tokyo 171, Japan

Shizgal, B. (210)
Department of Chemistry, University of British Columbia, Vancouver, B. C., Canada, V6T 1Y6

Shoji, H. (354)
Department of Chemistry, Tsukuba University, Tsukuba 305, Japan

Taki, K. (126)
Professor Emeritus, Kitasato University, Kanagawa 228, Japan

Urch, D. S. (35,500)
Department of Chemistry, Queen Mary and Westfield College, University of London, London E1 4NS, UK

Valencich, T. (188)
Department of Chemistry and Biochemistry, California State University, Los Angeles, CA 90032, USA

Vasâros, L. (80)
Central Research Institute for Physics, Hungarian Academy of Sciences, H-1525 Budapest, Hungary

Welch, M. J. (105)
Division of Radiation Sciences, Washington University Medical Center, Saint Louis, MO 63110, USA

Willard, J. E. (21)
Professor Emeritus, University of Wisconsin, Madison, WI 53706, USA

Wolf, A. P. (176,515)
Department of Chemistry, Brookhaven National Laboratory, Long Island, NY 11973, USA

Yoshihara, K. (344,506)
Department of Chemistry, Faculty of Science, Tohoku University, Sendai 980, Japan

Contents

Chapter 6 Relation to Other Nuclear Techniques

Chapter 7 Correlation with Life-, Geo-, and Space Sciences

Chapter 8 Hot Atom Chemistry and Energy and Environmental Problems

Preface

The goal of this book is to make the methods, findings, and point of view of hot atom chemists available to workers in many fields. It is also our hope that directions for future work in the field will be apparent from what has been written by each author. If this volume can function as a guidepost to the future as well as a record of the past, it will be a living work of reference, the true handbook of our dreams.

Richard Wolfgang explained in 1964 that hot atom chemistry "is an aspect of a large but little explored field of physical chemistry dealing with those chemical reactions which occur above the threshold or activation energy. At the threshold only one reaction path will be open to the system, but as the energy increases other paths leading to other products will in general become successively available. It is the province of high energy or hot atom chemistry to study reactions over this entire range and to provide an understanding of their mechanisms."[1] Wolfgang himself made notable experimental and theoretical contributions to the discovery of new hot atom reactions and their understanding.

Twenty years after his untimely death, we would modify Wolfgang's description of the field only by broadening it to include inorganic, organic, and theoretical chemistry, and, of course, radiochemistry. It should also be pointed out that hot atom chemistry provides by far the most convenient and powerful techniques for studying the atomic reactions of virtually any desired element at energies above (and at) threshold.

Garman Harbottle expressed his belief in 1979 "...that the study of the chemical effects of nuclear transformation has developed to the point where its results ought to be of interest not only to its own specialists but to the scientific community at large, by reason both of its intrinsic content and of its connections with many other fields of physics and chemistry."[2] That is certainly the view of the present editors, and this book sets out to clarify many of the connections between hot atom chemistry and other fields.

What hot atom chemistry has in fact accomplished in nearly 60 years of activity has been to reveal what reactions free atoms undergo, including what exotic products they can form, what their reaction mechanisms are down to the details of their reaction dynamics, how reaction probabilities depend on the kinetic and electronic energy of an atom and how the energy distribution of recoiling atom is established and how it changes.

The symbiosis between hot atom chemistry experiments and other kinds of chemical and physical endeavors has been striking. Hot atom experiments have provided information about the distribution of vibrational excitation energies of product molecules, and thus have helped to test theoretical predictions about energy transfer, reaction cross sections, and recoil atom relaxation dynamics. The products detected in gas-phase hot atom experiments have suggested the nature of reactive intermediates formed in the primary reactions of polyvalent atoms, and chemical generation of suspected reactive intermediates in hot atom reaction sequences has provided new criteria for their intervention. In some cases hot atom reactions have served as models for chemical synthesis and have been "scaled up" by factors as large as 10^{12} ! The direct synthesis by recoil reactions of small molecules labelled with short-lived radioisotopes has given nuclear medicine the starting materials for radiopharmaceuticals that are in wide use as diagnostic and therapeutic agents, and as probes in biochemistry and biomedical research. The potential of hot atom experiments for answering fundamental questions about the chemistry and physics of solids has begun to be realised by a combination of physical techniques such as ion implantation and *in situ* spectroscopic experiments, with chemical identification of products.

It is a tragic quirk in the history of contemporary science that few subdisciplines encompass such a broad area of interest and application as hot atom chemistry, and yet are so little recognized. While textbooks do contain some results from the field,[3] hot atom chemistry has largely been a shrinking violet, unappreciated and poorly publicized, despite the fruitful work in the area. Hot atom chemistry has had a very wide sweep, ranging from the basic contributions to the understanding of bond-making, bond-breaking, and energy transfer in atomic collisions that are at the heart of the subject, to important applications in fields as diverse as geochemistry, reactor technology and the chemistry of comets and interstellar grains.

It is an irony shared with its parent discipline radiochemistry, that as the need for chemists trained in hot atom chemistry has increased, because its techniques have become firmly entrenched in a number of allied disciplines such as nuclear medicine, the number of students being trained as hot atom chemists has decreased precipitously.

Perhaps Richard Wolfgang's 1964 description of hot atom chemistry as an *aspect* of physical chemistry (which we would now broaden by adding organic, inorganic, theoretical and radiochemistry) exemplifies the dilemma. Rather than etching a clear profile of a subdiscipline, the achievements of hot atom chemistry, and hot atom chemists themselves, have been identified primarily with those fields that they have influenced.

This book attacks directly one of the reasons for the neglect of hot atom chemistry, the lack of a clear delineation of its goals, its techniques, its findings, its applications, and its links with other fields. We thank the authors for providing this in abundant measure. Much work remains to be done, however, and the new opportunities for future work in hot atom chemistry are stressed in many of the following chapters. The creation of new theoretical tools and the computer power to implement them, the development of techniques for the creation, manipulation, visualization and interrogation of individual atoms and ions, in solids, in the gas phase, and on surfaces, have created unprecedented opportunities to obtain and to utilize the results of hot atom chemistry and to answer the questions that have led a diverse group of scientists to practice hot atom chemistry.

As one of the editors of this book I want to make it clear that this project is the brainchild of Professor Tatsuo Matsuura, whose enthusiasm and tireless efforts have brought it to fruition. His vision and leadership were essential catalysts, and it has been a pleasure and a privilege to work with him.

References

1. R. Wolfgang, *Progress in Reaction Kinetics*, 1964, **3**, 97.
2. G. Harbottle, *Chemical Effects of Nuclear Transformations in Inorganic Systems* (G.

Harbottle and A. G. Maddock, eds.), North-Holland, Amsterdam, 1979, p.9.
3. The chemistry of nucleogenic carbon atom is included in; W. J. le Noble, *Highlights of Organic Chemistry, an advanced textbook*, Marcel Dekker, New York, 1974, pp. 853-858. A section is devoted to hot atom chemistry in the undergraduate text: J. Nicholas, *Chemical Kinetics, a modern survey of gas reactions*, John Wiley & Sons, New York, 1975, pp. 215-219.

December, 1991

Peter P. Gaspar

Note and Acknowledgments

Among human endeavors, the development of basic science in various fields is of particular importance, independently of whether practical applications can be found in a near future. Hot atom chemistry, or the study of chemical effects of nuclear transformations, is a relatively accessible branch of basically attractive academic fields and provides openings towards the solutions of problems of actual and potentially practical concern. This field also furnishes many challenges that are appropriate for training young students in nuclear science and engineering, for which a shortage of manpower is feared in coming years.

It is unfortunate that the number of researchers engaged in hot atom chemistry has decreased recently, in contrast to the flourishing era of the 1960's. The purpose of this book is to help counteract this world-wide situation. It is a sincere pleasure for the Editors to publish this book with the collaboration of many expert scientists, following "Hot Atom Chemistry-Recent Trends and Applications in the Physical and Life Sciences and Technology", which appeared in 1984.

The Editors wish to express their thanks to all the contributors, who kindly encouraged and supported the idea of this project and cooperated in writing their fine manuscripts. In particular, we are deeply grateful to the following renowned scientists, who immediately responded to our request: Professor Yuan T. Lee of University of California, Berkeley, Professor Darleane C. Hoffman of the same university, Professor Emeritus John E. Willard of the University of Wisconsin, and Professor Paul K. Kuroda of Nevada University.

The writer of this Note would like to express his sincere thanks to the six co-Editors who cooperated with him. Among them, the three veteran Editors, Professor Jean-Pierre Adloff, Professor Peter P. Gaspar and Professor Alfred G. Maddock kindly assisted the Japanese Editors in various ways, especially in their linguistic correction of many manuscripts. He also wishes to thank the members of the Advisory Board: Dr. Mitio Inokuti, Professor Paul K. Kuroda, Professor Gerhardt Stoecklin, Dr. Alfred P. Wolf, Professor Nobufusa Saito, and Professor Masanobu Sakanoue; and the members of the Editorial Board: Dr. Gerald A. Brinkman, Professor Carrol H. Collins, Professor Kenneth

E. Collins, Dr. Gilles Duplâtre, Dr. Alexander Halpern, Professor Horst Mueller, Dr. G. W. A. Newton, Professor Edward P. Rack, Dr. Kurt Roessler, Dr. John W. Root, Dr. David S. Urch, Dr. Hiroshi Kudo, Dr. Shin-ichi Ohno, and Dr. Enzo Tachikawa. He very much appreciates their valuable assistance in providing useful advice and encouragement, and by acting as referees. He also appreciates that several of these foreign colleagues frequently contributed much of their time and money dealing with the necessary international correspondence.

Finally, the writer of this Note expresses his gratitude to the Japan Society for Promotion of Science (JSPS), that encouraged us by supporting this project as one of the international joint research programs in the fiscal years 1989 and 1990. This aid was based on the policy of Japanese Government to support basic science.

December, 1991

Tatsuo Matsuura

Chapter 1

Historical Development of Hot Atom Chemistry and Prospects

1.1 Outline of History

Alfred G. MADDOCK
University Chemical Laboratory, Lensfield Road, Cambridge, U.K.

The substantial recoil accompanying a particle emission in radioactive decay was observed early in the study of radioactivity [1]. Although some of the physical effects associated with such recoil were investigated, no attention to the chemical effects was forthcoming until the discovery of artificial radioactivity. The much smaller recoil associated with the capture radiation during the (n,γ) reaction was shown to rupture the molecule containing the affected atom [2a,b]. The same year the chemical changes accompanying β decay in the series ^{210}Pb, ^{210}Bi, ^{210}Po were explored [3].

Early work

Many of the pre-World War II studies were directed towards enhancing the low specific activities of the products of the (n,γ) reaction due to the small neutron fluxes then available [4a,b]. But an interest in the more fundamental aspects of the reactions also developed. A study of the (n,γ) reaction in gaseous and liquid alkyl halides showed that although the nuclear reaction probably ruptured more than 98 % of the affected molecules, the recoiling radioactive atom might i) reform the parent chemical species because of a cage effect, or ii) reform the parent species by a replacement reaction involving a nearby inactive parent molecule; iii) react with the parent species to form new compounds, iv) or survive in the elemental form[5]. These experiments also provided the first evidence of hot reactions of the translationally excited recoiling atom [6] (v. also J.E. Willard, Chapter 1.3).

These data led to the proposal of a "Billiard Ball" interpretation of the reaction processes. Naturally the proportion of the radioactive product found in the parent chemical form, soon called the retention, tended to be higher for irradiated solids. A key paper interpreting these phenomena was published by Libby [7]. A further paper extending this analysis appeared soon after the end of World War II [8].

Another important discovery of this early period was that deep ionization, such as arises after internal conversion, could also lead to chemical changes, even when any associated recoil appeared to be negligible [9].

The second World War interrupted such studies for a few years, but immediately it was over, stimulated by the newly available high neutron fluxes, research recommenced. The subject soon began to subdivide. It is convenient to treat it largely according to the phase in which the nuclear reactions occur.

Effects in solids

With solid matrices the distribution of the radioactive product amongst the different chemical forms in which it is found could be changed by various treatments of the solid prior or, particularly, subequent to the nuclear events. Nuclear reactions leading to isotopic products, the (n,γ), (n,2n) and (γ,n) reactions attracted the most attention. Since the solids nearly always had to be dissolved before analysis to determine the distribution of the radioactive product there was some uncertainty as to the relation between the species found in the solution and those existing in the irradiated solid. Surprisingly few attempts have been reported to detect unstable products present in the solid by using scavenging techniques during solution [10)].

The large recoil following the (n,2n) and (γ,n) reactions was found to give somewhat similar distributions to those found for the much smaller recoil after the (n,γ) process. This suggested that the terminal environment of the recoiling atom was not very different in the two cases [11a,b)].

The primary effect of the recoil was bond rupture producing ligand deficient species. However re-attachment of ligands or capture from the surroundings often follows the primary event. As might be expected from free space considerations, the recoiling atom sometimes forms di- or polynuclear complexes in the solid [12)]. Thus irradiated orthophosphates were found to contain radioactive pyro- and polyphosphates [13a,b)]. Whether such species are formed in the solid and whether they survive on solution of the irradiated solid depended on the purely chemical properties of the system[14)]. The specific chemical properties of the target material often obscured any generalisations about the effects of recoil.

The recoil effects were structure sensitive so that the same disintegrating entity, for example a complex anion like MnO_4^-, gave different distributions of the products in different salts [15a,b)]. Rather remarkably, different radioisotopes formed in a single irradiation of a compound of a polyisotopic element gave quantitatively different distributions of the radioactive products. It was suggested that this might be due to differences in the extent of internal conversion of photons from low-lying states at the bottom of the capture cascade [16)]. Indeed clear-cut separation of ionization and recoil effects has rarely been achieved. But it is also possible that differences in the recoil energy spectra for the two isotopes may be responsible, although these differences were not expected to be very great [17a,b)].

Annealing processes

Post nuclear event treatments of the solid by heating [18a,b)], ionizing radiation [19a,b)], U.V. illumination [20a,b)] and compression [21a,b)] all led to increases in the retention. In addition the initial distribution of the radioactive product and the effects of all the above treatments depended on the concentration and nature of the defects present in the solid [22a,b)]. These effects made it difficult to achieve reproducibility with different samples of the same compound and between measurements in different laboratories [23].

It was also reported that the annealing (heating) process was affected by the ambient atmosphere [24a,b]. Although numerous investigations of the role of the defects and of the ambient atmosphere have appeared, it cannot be said that a thorough understanding of them has yet been reached [25a,b].

Thermal annealing in salts of anions of the type ML_6^{n-} sometimes led to sequential re-attachment of ligands [26]; but in other cases only a single step could be observed [27]. A noteworthy feature of the annealing process in cis and trans isomers was its stereospecificity [26,28]. The kinetics of the thermal annealing were expected to be first order but it was immediately apparent that they did not conform to a simple first order process. The data could be fitted by a combination of first order processes with different energies of activation [29]. Several other interpretations were advanced but the rather limited precision possible for the experimental data, usually not better than ±1%, left the interpretation uncertain and provided little insight into the mechanism of the process [30].

Exchange processes

Significant progress was made when it was shown that exchange could take place if crystals of the inactive target compound were doped with one of the radioactive products found in the neutron irradiated material, for example if inactive iodate crystals were doped with traces of radioactive iodide [31] or chromate with radioactive chromic ions [32]. This exchange process also displayed the unusual kinetics found for the annealing reactions. A difficulty with this kind of experiment was that the environment and even the identity of the dopant species was usually uncertain. Some years later it was shown that similar exchange reactions with similar kinetics could also take place between regular lattice species, for example between the Tl(I) and Tl(III) atoms in Tl_4Cl_6 [33] or the chloride ions and the ligand chlorine in $Co(NH_3)_5Cl.Cl_2$ [34a,b]. These exchange reactions took place in the same temperature range as the higher temperature annealing, so that it has been suggested that they involve similar mechanisms. The low temperature annealing processes may well involve recombination of geminate fragments [35,52]. In some cases exchange was only appreciable after an ionizing irradiation [36].

Ion implantation

Another way of simulating the neutron irradiated systems was by ion implantation using radioactive ions [37]. Similar results could be obtained using recoiling atoms from a source in which a reaction such as (γ,n) was taking place and arranging for them to impinge on an inactive target compound [38]. These systems gave qualitatively but not quantitatively the same behaviour as the neutron irradiated solids, even to the extent of some stereospecificity [39a,b]. It was shown that $^{51}Cr^+$ ions implanted in K_2BeF_4 or K_2SO_4 stabilised as Cr^{2+} suggesting that the recoil chromium in the lattice might be Cr^0 or a low charge cation [40].

Not surprisingly recoil species were found to react with radiolytic entities formed in the same matrix. The radiolytic products also underwent annealing reactions [41]. Indeed it was possible that radiation annealing was due to incipient radiolytic decomposition of the matrix followed by reformation of the parent species incorporating the radioactive fragment [42].

Double complexes

All the work so far described suffered from the limitations imposed by the presence of only one kind of complex and dilution of affected species was impossible. Additional information could be obtained by the use of double complexes as target materials. The tiny yield of the ion $^{51}Cr(NH_3)_6^+$ found with $(Co(NH_3)_6)_2(CrO_4)_2$ suggested that billard ball replacements were rare events [43]. Such a process would be a real hot atom reaction and rather few truly hot atom processes in solids have been identified. With the compound $(Coen_2(NO_2)_2)(CoEDTA).3H_2O$ the kinetics of annealing of the *Co to reform both the cationic and anionic species were shown to be related, with similar structures to their annealing isochronals.[44] The ambient atmosphere effect during annealing was particularly marked with cobalt complexes [45]. The use of isotopically labelled double complexes was also explored. In $(Fe(bipy)_3)_3(Fe(CN)_6)_2$ labelled separately with ^{58}Fe only in the anion or the cation, no annealing to give $(Fe(CN)_6)^{3-}$ was observed, but $(^{59}Fe(bipy)_3)^{2+}$ was formed irrespective of the origin of the ^{59}Fe [46].

Solid solutions studies

Perhaps the most informative series of experiments were those conducted with mixed crystals. The idea that geminate reformation processes might be distinguished from reactions of the recoil atom more remote from its origin dated from the earliest period of these studies [47a,b]. But the most fruitful results came from work using mixed crystals of the type $A_2MX_6/A_2M'Y_6$ and A_2MX_6/A_2MY_6 [48a,b]. (v. Müller, Chapter 4.8). Both the active halogen and metal distributions can be measured after neutron irradiation.

The effects of a very small recoil (< 25 eV) were explored by studying the proportions of $(M^*X_nY_{6-n})^{2-}$ species following isomeric transition in the bromine in the K_2ReBr_6/K_2ReCl_6 system. The high proportion of species with the higher values of n even at very low concentrations of K_2ReBr_6 showed that the bromine atom remained in its original unit cell and a relatively small number of halogen atoms competed to reform the halorhenate anion. The lattice was hardly disordered [49]. In contrast to this result the effect of a very large recoil (> 1 keV) was studied using the (γ,n) reaction in K_2ReBr_6/K_2SnCl_6 crystals. The yield of $^*ReBr_6^{2-}$ approached zero as the mole fraction of K_2ReBr_6 in the crystals fell to zero, showing that the primary retention (failure of nuclear process to effect rupture) was about zero. The recoil rhenium atom moved further from its origin, perhaps 104 pm, and became thermalised in a larger and more disordered zone. The distribution of the $^*ReBr_nCl_{6-n}^{2-}$ species was close to the statistical distribution determined by the proportions of bromine and chlorine in the crystals. Billard ball replacement of tin by rhenium atoms was sufficiently rare that it had little effect on the distribution [50].

For the intermediate case of more modest recoils (about 100 eV), typical of the (n,γ) reaction, the distribution of products in the K_2ReBr_6/K_2SnCl_6 system was far from the statistical values found for the (γ,n) reaction [51]. The data were explained by the recoil atom only moving a few lattice units and becoming thermalised in a relatively small zone that was not heavily disordered. About 25 atoms were disturbed. The data indicated that recoil of partially ligand stripped fragments was unimportant. The pattern was complicated by the fact that most (n,γ) recoil energy spectra included a low energy tail which behaved as in the first situation considered above.

About one third of the annealable *Re in the K_2ReBr_6/K_2SnCl_6 system reformed $ReBr_6^{2-}$, the remainder formed $ReBr_nCl_{6-n}^{2-}$ species. The $ReBr_6^{2-}$ reformation was substantially due to recombination of geminate fragments [52].

The rather simple crystal structure of these mixed crystals allowed a Monte Carlo calculation of the fate of the recoil atoms to be carried out. The results were in substantial agreement with the experimental data and the models proposed above [53a,b].

Direct measurement of the minimum recoil energy needed to bring about molecular rupture, not to be followed by rapid recombination of fragments, was made by varying the recoil energy in the excitation of nuclear isomers by the (γ,γ') reaction [54]. The results were in reasonable agreement with theoretical estimates. Unfortunately the method was of limited applicability and precision [55].

<u>Effects in the alkali halides</u>

Turning to other nuclear reactions one might have hoped the production of ^{35}S and ^{32}P in alkali halide crystals by the (n,p) and (n,α) reactions respectively would show rather simple behaviour. This proved to be an illusion. Firstly it was found that the ^{35}S and ^{32}P must be present in the crystals in several different forms. Analytical methods had to be developed to separate and distinguish these forms [56a,b,c]. Secondly the behaviour of the sulphur and phosphorus was very sensitive to the presence of traces of OH^- or O_2^- in the crystals [57a,b,c]. Finally the concentration and nature of the defects in the crystals used were important [57,58a,b]. Indeed it proved possible to study the reactions between the sulphur and phosphorus species and the defects, which were usually present in higher concentration [58a,b, 59].

Monte Carlo calculations on the fate of these recoil atoms have not been reported though the systems seem well suited to such a study.

<u>Isomeric transition effects</u>

In the absence of internal conversion of the de-excitation radiation in isomeric transition the recoil is usually very small (about 5eV) and molecular rupture was found not to occur [60]. However, since the excitation energy was small, internal conversion was generally substantial and isomeric transition resembled orbital electron capture in producing a vacancy, usually in the K or L shell of the atom.

It was proposed that the Auger cascade immediately following a deep ionisation would produce a high positive charge on the atom. Bonding electrons might be lost and the positive charge would quickly spread to the peripheral atoms of the molecule and a coulombic explosion would ensue [61]. The fragments would acquire some recoil energy dependent on their mass [61,63]. This model was validated by experiments on gaseous methyl iodide, producing the K vacancy by X-ray irradiation.

It was noted that the electrons ejected in the Auger cascade have rather small energies and might cause local radiolysis of the matrix [64]. In fact the effects of radiolysis and isomeric transition on the solid were similar, although the effects of isomeric transition, unlike the radiolytic damage did not depend simply on the crystal free space [65]. Much depended on the surroundings of the affected atom since these determined the speed and extent of neutralisation of the positive charges [66]. In $[M(NH_3)_5{}^{80m}Br]X_2$ the yield of free $^{80}Br^-$ was very much influenced by the nature of X [67]. Surprisingly isomeric transition seldom led to oxidation. The small zone affected by the transition made thermal annealing rather easy. Geminate recombination occurred readily. Such annealing was unaffected by the defects in the bulk of the crystal matrix because of the high local density of holes and trapped electrons [68]. More detailed information about isomeric transition and orbital electron capture was obtained by Moessbauer emission spectroscopy (v. inf.).

Beta decay effects

Pure beta decay only led to a small average recoil that was unlikely to rupture the molecule, especially in solid matrices. An electron count suggested beta decay should lead to oxidation [69] and this might be enhanced by shake-off In fact in most systems more or less bond rupture occurs and although a lot of work has been reported the magnitude of the fragmentation is not well understood.

Such studies began at an early date [70a,b] but some of the earlier work has required revision (v. e.g. [71a,b]). Some evidence has been obtained that positively charged species produced by beta decay play a part in the rupture mechanism [71b]. Where oxidation occurs, a charge balancing defect must be produced in the lattice. The lattice will only tolerate a limited amount of such defects so that if a macroscopic amount of the target is transformed such oxidation is not observed [72].

An interesting discovery was the application of beta decay to the synthesis of new compounds. Thus beta decay of ^{99}Mo yielded the species $C_5H_5{}^{99m}Tc(CO)_3$ and $(C_5H_5)_2{}^{99m}Tc^+$ derivatives [73]. The technique was also employed extensively to obtain compounds of ^{210}Po, such as $^{210}Po(C_6H_5)_2$, in tracer amounts [74].

In situ studies

All the above investigations had an Achilles heel -- the relation of the products found on solution to those existing in the solid. But good progress has been made in the development of in situ methods of investigation. The most successful of these was the use of Moessbauer emission spectroscopy. Unfortunately there were no systems in which a direct comparison with radiochemical methods was possible.

A first work with ^{57}CoO, studying the emission from the ^{57m}Fe formed by orbital electron capture, noticed chemical effects, called "after effects" [75]. Most of the data relate to iron or tin systems, in both cases the chemical effects arise from deep ionisation due to orbital electron capture or internal conversion. The data confirmed and considerably extended existing conclusions about these processes (v. sup.). Oxidation often took place [76a,b] and was influenced by the defects in the source material. Oxidation also followed beta decay in ^{193}Os as was revealed by the ^{193m}Ir spectrum of labelled osmium compounds [77]. But reduction was also possible with ligands like oxalate [78]. The emission spectra from ^{57}Co labelled complexes, or ^{57}Co-doped iron complexes resembled the absorption spectra of the radiolysed iron complexes [79]. In hydrated cobalt salts Fe^{3+} production could be associated with OH° radicals, arising from local radiolysis by the Auger electrons [79]. The ^{57m}Fe remained in the lattice site occupied by the ^{57}Co [80]. The ^{57m}Fe emission spectrum, reflecting its oxidation state and environment took place about 10^{-7} s after the orbital electron capture by the cobalt and by this time the state of the iron was established [81]. But when the Moessbauer nucleus was produced with a very large recoil, for example ^{237m}Np by α decay of ^{241}Am, the Moessbauer fraction increased with time as was shown by time resolved Moessbauer spectroscopy [82a,b]. This probably reflected local heating at the end of the recoil track.

Confirmation of the model for the effects of deep ionisation was obtained in experiments on cobalt complexes with different kinds of ligands. With ligands that are very resistant to radiolysis, such as bibenzoylmethane, the Auger electrons quickly returned and neutralised the positive charges left by the Auger cascade; the emission spectrum seen was like the absorption spectrum of the iron complex. Magnetic relaxation was relatively slow and modest cooling of the source gave a magnetically split emission spectrum. But with ligands susceptible to radiolysis, such as acetylacetone, the high local concentration of radicals, due to Auger electron radiolysis, led to faster relaxation by a spin-spin mechanism and magnetic splitting did not occur until much lower temperatures were reached [83a,b].

A number of other in situ methods were proposed. Differential perturbed angular correlation was, perhaps, the most favourable, but the method was limited to a small number of systems (for review v. 84). The half-life of the daughter species from radioactive decay was known to depend, in principle, on its oxidation state and environment; but the changes are small and the interpretation difficult [84,85]. Nuclear resonance fluorescence was also proposed for in situ studies [86].

Liquid systems

Much work has been reported on effects in liquids and solutions. The interpretation of the results was always difficult. Solids gave rather strong cage effects and diffusive effects were negligible; by contrast, in liquids, cage effects were weaker and the radioactive product atom could diffuse after thermalisation into the liquid medium. Details of this area of investigation can be found in the Chapter 1.3 contributed by J.E. Willard.

Gas phase studies

Studies in the gas phase were, by contrast, amongst the most significant in this field. Here one could identify real hot atom reactions. Although it was not possible to extract all the fundamental quantitities from the experimental data that one might hope, nonetheless these studies provided the earliest and certainly the cheapest information on the subject.

It was soon realized that radiolytic effects would dominate the results unless the deposition of energy from ionising radiation in the system was kept very small. This precluded the use of ^{14}C from the (n,p) reaction on nitrogen.

Hot tritium

Hot tritium was studied extensively. Mixtures of ^{3}He, a reactant and a moderator were irradiated with slow neutrons. Very energetic tritium atoms were generated by the (n,p) reaction. Although the initial product was a triton, in most gaseous systems neutralisation and electronic de-excitation took place before the tritium reached the hot atom reaction energy region, 0.5-40 eV (v. e.g. 87). The number of collisions of the reactant with the hot tritium, and hence the yield of hot products, could be changed by the addition of inert gas moderators [87]. Scavengers, such as iodine or oxygen, could be added in small amounts to mop up thermalised atoms and radicals [87].

The earlier hard sphere collision model [88] for hot reactions was refined and quantitative expressions obtained relating the total hot reaction yield to the mole fraction of the reactant in the mixture, the average energy loss by the tritium atoms on collisions, α, and a reactivity integral, I, which measured the liability of the reactant to the hot reaction [89]. The theory was extended to mixtures of reactants [90a,b]. Unfortunately the treatment did not give the hot reaction energy range, although the order of hot reaction ranges for different reactions might be inferred [91a,b]. Subsequently computer studies of such systems were made [92a,b] as well as other approaches to the theory of these processes (v.e.g. 93).

The hot reactions identified in this way included some reactions known in thermalized systems, such as hydrogen abstraction from alkanes to give HT, while others, such as hydrogen substitution to give the tritium labelled alkane, were not [94a,b]. Replacement by tritium was found to take place with retention of configuration [95]. Rather surprisingly the HT yields depended on the bond energy of the R-H bond replaced [96]. Various explanations were proposed [87,97].

An important development was the discovery that vibrationally excited products were sometimes obtained [98a,b,c]. More vibrational excitation was found when T replaced a heavy atom, or radical, than for H abstraction or substitution [99]. The excited products sometimes decomposed and the fragments were identified by their reaction with the scavenger [100]. The proportion of the excited species undergoing dissociation or isomerisation was dependent on the pressure [98,101]. The data indicated an excitation of about 5 eV.

The hot HT/RT ratio for alkanes increased with the complexity of the alkane [102]. The data seemed compatible with the abstraction reaction taking place by attack along the R-H axis, while substitution took place by attack normal to this axis [87]. Tritium was found to add to the double bond in alkenes [98a].

With alkyl halides as reactants, T/H reaction yields increased; but T for halogen yields were low. The lower yields for T replacement of heavy atoms or groups suggested inertial effects [103]. All the hot tritium events were fast, 10^{-13}

to 10^{-14} s, even compared with bond vibration periods. Thus the hot atom behaviour of tritium was fundamentally different from that of the halogens, for instance.

Hot halogens

At the same kinetic energy the lightest halogen, fluorine, travelled much slower than the tritium. In hot halogen reactions excitation of the labelled products was greater and their decomposition more frequent. Unlike tritium the excitation on replacement of hydrogen or chlorine by hot chlorine was much the same [104]. Yields of hot products were generally less for the halogens.

Hot Cl/Cl replacement took place with retention of configuration [105]. But it was possible that products formed with inversion were more highly excited and decomposed. This was compatible with the much lower stereospecificity found in the liquid phase. Complexes between chlorine atoms and aromatic compounds were invoked to explain results obtained with chlorobenzene in the liquid phase [106a,b].

Most of the studies of hot chlorine used ^{38}Cl from the (n,γ) reaction and the electronic state of the atom when it reached hot reaction energies was less certain than in the case of tritium. For hot bromine, where the (n,γ) reaction was also used extensively, the situation was even less sure because of the isomeric states. It was important to distinguish hot reactions from ionic processes. A study of the liquid systems $CCl_4/^{82m}BrBr$ and neutron irradiated CCl_4/Br_2 revealed an enhanced reactivity of the ^{82g}Br formed by isomeric transition [107]. Charged species were also involved in $^{80m}BrBr$/benzene, toluene or halobenzene systems [108]. The earliest demonstration of ionic or electronically excited species in reactions initiated by the (n,γ) reaction was the high yield of methyl iodide for iodide in methane [109].

Hot fluorine

Hot ^{18}F atoms could be obtained by the $^{19}F(\gamma,n)^{18}F$ reaction. Ethylene-iodine, methane and perfluoropropylene were used as scavengers [110]. Inert gases, CF_4 and SF_6 were suitable moderators [111]. Hot fluorine reactions provided interesting similarities and contrasts to the hot tritium systems. Although the $^{18}F/F$ replacement reaction was identified in CF_4 and other perfluorocarbons [110,112a,b] it was necessary to develop techniques permitting determination of $H^{18}F$ and ^{18}FF yields before a reasonably detailed picture of hydrocarbon reactions could be obtained [113].

In partially fluorinated hydrocarbons, hydrogen abstraction was the dominant reaction, but some $^{18}F/H$ and $^{18}F/F$ replacements also occurred, as well as attack at C-C bonds [113]. Attack at the C-C and C-F bonds was relatively more important than in the tritium systems.

Excitation accompanying hot reactions was large, as much as 10 eV following $^{18}F/F$ replacements. Thus in CF_4, $:C^{18}FF$ was produced in similar yield to $C^{18}FF_3$ [112a]. Polymeric products were found with the larger hydrocarbons and perfluorocarbons [114]. The large excitation led to considerable differences between the same compounds in the gaseous and liquid phases.

With ethylene the primary $°CH_2CH_2{}^{18}F$ decomposed both by C-C and C-H rupture [111] giving $:CH_2$ and $°CH_2F$, identified by their reaction with HI scavenger. But acetylene gave the rather stable $°CH{=}CH^{18}F$ which captured hydrogen to yield vinyl fluoride [115].

$^{18}F/F$ replacement in CFClHCHFCl took place with retention of configuration [116].

Experiments with hot fluorine enabled some distinction to be made between the effects of pressure and of the cage effect in liquid systems [117].

Atomic carbon

The hot reactions of polyvalent atoms were more difficult to disentangle. Studies of recoil O, S, Se, N, P and As have been reported. But the most important work in this area was the exploration of the reactions of hot and thermal carbon atoms.

To avoid undue radiolytic effects ^{11}C was used. A suitable preparation was by a nuclear stripping reaction $^{12}C(X,n)^{11}C$ brought about by passing a high energy beam of $^{12}C^{6+}$ through a thin platinum foil [118a,b]. Because of the three low lying electronic states of carbon, the state of the hot atom was uncertain. The high reactivity of the carbon atom made it difficult to find a really satisfactory scavenger, but thermalised ground state atomic carbon reacted extremely efficiently with oxygen giving carbon monoxide [119]. This reaction took place so readily that in earlier studies ^{11}CO was often reported as a product even in oxygen free reactants [120].

Carbon atoms were so reactive that hot and thermal atoms often showed the same reactions.

In hydrocarbon systems, acetylene and other unsaturated hydrocarbons were always the major products, but a substantial yield of polymeric material was always observed [121a,b].

The data were interpreted in terms of insertion of carbon atoms, methyne, CH, or methylene, CH_2; thus

$$[RCH_2\text{-}^{11}\ddot{C}\text{-}H]^* \rightarrow R° + H° + H\text{-}C{=}^{11}C\text{-}H$$

Singlet and triplet carbon atoms were expected to react differently [122a,b]. With singlet atoms the insertion product shown above gave but-1-ene which was also found. The production of acetylene involved an intramolecular reaction as was shown using mixtures of C_2H_6 and C_2D_6 as reactants. However with 1.1. dideuterocyclopropane as reactant some 25% of C_2HD was found [123a,b]. The yield of acetylene in oxygen scavenged systems did not extrapolate to zero for 100% moderator, indicating some formation from thermalized singlet carbon [124].

Ethylene production involved singlet methylene insertion into the C-H bond of a $-CH_3$ group [125a,b,c]. The yield of ethylene was enhanced by the presence of hydrogen and depended on the number of methyl groups in the reactant. It was suggested that the hot carbon atoms could react with hydrogen to produce :CH and $:CH_2$.

Singlet recoil carbon added across a double bond so that ethylene gave a reasonable yield of $H_2C{=}^{11}C{=}CH_2$ [126]. With heavy inert gas moderators the acetylene to allene ratio increased with moderation due to a reduction in the population of singlet excited atoms [127].

Compounds with more carbon atoms than the reactant were formed by $:CH_2$ insertion and by the reaction of the excited primary products with the reactant [128].

A reaction of practical importance was that with nitrogen. This was analogous to the reaction with oxygen, attack on one nitrogen atom. The immediate product decomposed to give a cyanogen radical, $^{11}CN^{\circ}$ which abstracted hydrogen - if available- to form $H^{11}CN$ [129]. In ammonia $^{11}CH_2{=}NH$ and $^{11}CH_3NH_2$ were formed [130a,b]. The distribution of products was very sensitive to the radiation dose received by the system.

Conclusion

Although a great deal of work has been published on recoils in solids, in very few cases has it proved possible to reach a definitive picture of the events that take place. In gases the situation is rather better but it looks as though the future, in this field, lies in the beam experiments rather than in classical hot atom studies.

References

1. Brooks, H.: Nature, 170, 270 (1904).
2. a. Szilard, L., Chalmers, T.A: Nature, 134, 494 (1934).
   b. Amaldi, E., D'Agostino, O., Fermi, E., Pontecorvo, B., Rasetti, F., Segre E. : Proc. Roy. Soc. (Lond.), A149, 522 (1935).
3. Mortensen, R.A., Leighton, P.A.: J. Amer. Chem. Soc., 56, 2397 (1934).
4. a. Erbacher, O., Philipp, K.: Z. Physik. Chem., A176, 169 (1936).
   b. Majer, V.: Naturwiss., 25, 252 (1937).
5. Glueckauf, E., Fay, J.W.J.: J. Chem. Soc. (Lond.), 390 (1936).
6. Lu, C.S., Sugden, S.: J. Chem. Soc. (Lond.), 1273 (1939).
7. Libby, W.F.: J. Amer. Chem. Soc., 62, 1930 (1940).
8. Libby, W.F.: J. Amer. Chem. Soc., 69, 2523 (1947).
9. Seaborg, G.T., Kennedy, J.W.: Phys. Rev., 55, 410 (1939)
10. Lindner, L.: Thesis, Amsterdam (1958).
11. a. Maddock,A.G., Treloar, T.E.: Disc. Nuclear Chem. AERE/M. 1078 (1962).
    b. Saito, N., Ambe, F., Sano, H.: Nature, 205, 688 (1965).
12. Maddock, A.G., Collins, K.E.: Can. J. Chem., 46, 3924 (1968).
13. a. Fiskell, J.G.A.: Science, 113, 244 (1951).
    b. Borland J.W., MacKenzie, A.J., Hill, W.L.: Ind. Eng; Chem., 44, 2726 (1952).
14. Van Ooij, W.J., Houtman, J.P.W.: Radiochimica Acta, 20, 21 and 27 (1973).
15. a. McCallum, W.J., Maddock, A.G.: Trans. Farad. Soc., 49, 1150 (1953).
    b. Cleary, R.E., Hamill, W.H., Williams, R.R.:J. Amer. Chem. Soc., 74, 4675 (1952).
16. Jones, C.H.W.: Inorg. Nucl. Chem. Letts., 3, 363 (1967).
17. a. Apers, D.J., Capron, P.C., Gilly, L.J.: J. Inorg. Nucl. Chem., 5, 23 (1957).
    b. Jach, J., Harbottle, G.: Trans. Faraday Soc., 54, 520 (1958).
18. a. Green, J.H., Maddock, A.G.: Nature, 164, 788 (1949).
    b. Aten, A.H.W., Van Berkum, J.G.M.: J. Amer. Chem. Soc., 72, 3273 (1950).
19. a. Williams, R.R.: J. Phys. Chem., 52, 603 (1948).
    b. Cobble, J.W., Boyd, G.E.: J. Amer. Chem. Soc., 74, 1324 (1952).
20. a. Herr, W.: Z. Elektrochem., 56, 911 (1952).
    b. Claridge, R.F.C., Maddock, A.G.: Nature, 184, 1932 (1959).
21. a. Andersen, T., Maddock, A. G.: Trans. Farad. Soc., 59, 1641 (1963).
    b. Kacena, V., Maddock, A.G.: Chemical Effects of Nuclear Transformations, IAEA, (Vienna), 2, 255 (1965).
22. a. Maddock, A.G., Vargas, J.I.: Nature, 184, 1931 (1959).

b. Andersen, T., Maddock, A.G.: Nature, 194, 371 (1962).
23. Andersen, T., Maddock, A.G.: Trans. Farad. Soc., 59, 2362 (1963).
24. a. Nath, A.: Indian J. Chem., 2, 232 (1964).
b. for review v. Venkateswarlu, K.S.: Indian At. En. Rep., BARC, 446 (1969).
25. a. Odru, P., Vargas, J.I.: Inorg. Nucl. Chem. Letts., 7, 379 (1971).
b. Glentworth, P., Nath, A. in " Specialist Periodical Report, Radiochemistry", Newton, G.W.A., Ed., Chem. Soc.(London), 2, 74 (1975).
26. Rauscher, H., Harbottle, G.: J. Inorg. Nucl. Chem., 4, 155 (1957).
27. Saito, N., Tominaga, T., Sano, H.: Bul. Chem. Soc. Japan, 33, 20 (1960).
28. Dimotakis, P. N., Maddock, A.G.: Chemical Effects of Nuclear Transformations, IAEA, (Vienna), 1, 365 (1961).
29. Maddock, A.G., in Physical Chemistry, Vol. 7, "Reactions in the Condensed Phase", Eyring H., Ed., Academic Press (New York and London), (1979).
30. Vargas, J.I., Maddock, A.G. in " Chemical Effects of Nuclear Transformations in Inorganic Systems", Harbottle, G., Maddock, A.G., Eds, North Holland (Amsterdam), (1979), p. 476.
31. Kaucic, S., Vlatkovic, M.: Croatica Chim. Acta, 35, 305 (1963).
32. Apers, D.J., Collins, K.E., Collins, C.H., Ghoos, Y.F., Capron, P.C.: Radiochimica Acta, 3 , 18 (1964).
33. Fernandez Valverde, S., Duplâtre, G., Maddock, A.G.: J. Inorg. Nucl. Chem., 40, 900 (1978).
34. a. Schmidt, G.B., Roessler, K. : Radiochimica Acta, 5, 123 (1966).
b. Passaglia-Schuch, A.M., Maddock, A.G.: Inorg. Chim. Acta, 63, 27 (1982).
35. Ackerhalt, K.E.: Thesis, State Univ. of New York at Buffalo, (USA), (1970).
36. Lazzarini, E., Fantola-Lazzarini, A.L.: J. Inorg. Nucl. Chem. 37, 467 (1975).
37. Croatto, U., Giacomello, G.: Acta 45th Congress of SIPS, Naples (1954).
38. Ackerhalt, P., Ellerbe P., Harbottle, G.: Radiochimica Acta, 18, 73 (1972).
39. a. Andersen, T., Langrad, T., Sorensen, G.: Nature, 218, 1158 (1968).
b. Andersen, T., Langrad, T., Sorensen, G.: Nature, 219, 544 (1968).
40. Mohanty, S.R., Maddock, A.G.: Nature, 183, 1797 (1958).
42. Albarran, G., Archundia, C., Maddock, A.G.: Radiochimica Acta, 30, 199 (1982).
43. Ikeda, N., Saito, K., Tsuji, K.: Radiochimica Acta 13, 90 (1970).
44. Lazzarini, E., Fantola-Lazzarini, A.L.: J. Inorg. Nucl. Chem., 34, 817 (1973).
45. v. ref. 24 b.
46. Siekierska, K.E., Fenger J., Maddock, A.G.: J. Chem. Soc. (Dalton), 1086 (1973).
47. a. Rieder, W., Broda, E., Erber, J.: Monatsch. Chem., 81, 657 (1950).
b. Green, J.H., Harbottle, G., Maddock, A.G.: Trans. Farad. Soc., 49, 1413 (1953).
48. a. Müller, H.: Naturwiss., 49, 182 (1962).
b. Müller, H.: Radiochimica Acta, 9, 167 (1968).
49. Müller, H., Cramer, D.: Radiochimica Acta, 14, 78 (1970).
50. Müller, H.: J. Inorg. Nucl. Chem., 31, 1579 (1969).
51. Müller, H.: J. Inorg. Nucl. Chem., 27, 1745 (1965).
52. Müller, H.: " Nukleare Methoden in der Festkörperchemie", Jülich, Conf. 22 (1976) p. 88.
53. a. Robinson, M.T., Roessler, K., Torrens, I.M.: J. Chem. Phys., 60, 680 (1974).
b. Roessler, K., Robinson, M.T., in "Atomic Collisions in Solids", Datz, S., Appleton, B.R., Moak, C.D., Eds, Plenum Press, (New York), (1974) p. 237.
54. Yoshihara, K., Kudo, H.: J. Chem. Phys., 52, 2950 (1970).
55. Yoshihara, K., Misusawa, T.: Radiochem. Radioanal.Letts., 9, 263 (1972).
56. a. Meyer, J.P.: Thesis, Univ. Strasbourg (France), (1970).
b. Kasrai, M., Maddock, A.G.: J. Chem. Soc. (London) A, 1105 (1970).
c. Maddock, A.G., Mahmood, A.J.: Inorg. Nucl. Chem. Letts., 9, 509 (1972).
57. a. Bracokova, A., Cifka, J.: J. Inorg. Nucl. Chem., 32, 365 (1970).
b. Baptista, J.L., Newton, G. W. A., Robinson, V.J.: Trans. Farad. Soc., 66, 213 (1970).
c. Andersen, T., Baptista, J.L.: Trans. Farad. Soc., 67, 1213 (1970).
58. a. Caillat, R., Süe, P.: Compt. Rend., 230, 1666 and 1864 (1950).
b. Maddock, A.G., Mirsky, R.M.: Chemical Effects of Nuclear transformations, IAEA, (Vienna), 2, 41 (1966).
59. Bogdanov, R.V., Murin, A.N., Olevsky, E.B.: Radiokhimiya, 11, 612 (1969).

60. Kennedy, J.W., Seaborg, G.T., Segre, E.: Phys. Rev., 56, 1095 (1939).
61. Carlson, T.A., White, R.M., J. Chem. Phys., 44, 4510 (1966).
62. Wexler, S. in "Actions Chimiques et Biologiques des Radiations", Haissinsky, M. Ed., Masson, Paris, 8, 105 (1965).
63. Kazanjian, A.R., Libby, W.F.: J. Chem. Phys., 42, 2778 (1965).
64. Geissler, P., Willard, J.E.: J. Phys. Chem., 67, 1675 (1963).
65. Johnston, E.R., in "Radiation Induced Decomposition of Inorganic Molecular ions", Gordon and Breach, New York, (1970) p. 17.
66. Maddock, A.G., in "Artificial Radioactivity", Proc. Symposium Poona (1985), Tata-McGraw Hill, (1986) p. 319.
67. Schmidt, G.B., Herr, W.: Z. Naturwiss., 18A, 505 (1963).
68. Halpern, A., Dancewicz, D.: Nature, 203, 145 (1964).
69. v. ref. 62.
70. a. Edwards, R.R., Coryell, C.: US AEC Report, AECU 50 (1948).
    b. Davies, T.: J. Phys. Coll. Chem., 52, 595 (1948).
71. a. Glentworth, P., Betts, R.H.: Can. J. Chem., 39, 1049 (1961).
    b. Glentworth, P., Wright, C.L.: J. Inorg. Nucl. Chem., 31, 1263 (1969).
72. a. Young, J.P., Haire, R.G., Peterson, J.R., Ensor, D.D., Fellows, R.L.: Inorg. Chem. 19, 2209 (1980).
    b. Young, J.P., Haire, B.G., Petreson, J.R., Ensor, D.D., Fellows, R.L.: Inorg. Chem. 20, 3979 (1981).
73. Baumgartner, F.: Chemical Effects of Nuclear Transformations, IAEA, (Vienna), 2, 507 (1965).
74. Murin, A.N., Nefedov, V.D., Kirin, I.S., Zaitsev, V.V., Pakulov, G.: Radiokhimiya, 7, 629 (1965).
75. Werheim, G.K.: Phys. Rev., 124, 764 (1961).
76. a. Blomquist, J., Grapengiesser, S., Söderquist, R.: Phys. Stat. Sol., 44, 435 (1971)
    b. Friedt, J.M.: J. Inorg. Nucl. Chem., 32, 2123 (1970).
77. Rother, P., Wagner, F., Zahn, U.: Radiochimica Acta, 11, 203 (1969).
78. Siekierska, K.E., Fenger, J.: Radiochimica Acta, 14, 93 (1970).
79. Gütlich, P., Odar, S., Fitzsimmons, B.W., Erickson, N.E.: Radiochimica Acta, 10, 147 (1968).
80. Nath, A., Agarwal, R.S., Mathur, P.K.: Inorg. Nucl. Chem. Letts., 4, 161 (1968).
81. Trifthäuser, W., Craig, P.P.: Phys. Rev., 162, 274 (1967).
82. a. Hoy, G.R., Wintersteiner, P.P.: Phys. Rev. Letts., 28, 877 (1972).
    b. Jones, C.H.W., Warren, J.L.: J. Chem. Phys., 53, 1740 (1970).
83. a. Sakai, Y., Endo, K., Sano, H.: Bull. Chem. Soc. Japan, 53, 1317 (1980).
    b. Endo, K., Sano, H., Wei,H.H.: Radiochem. Radioanal. Letts., 50, 29 (1981).
84. Vargas, J.I in "MTP International Review of Science, Inorganic Chemistry, Series one", Vol.8, Maddock A.G. Ed., Butterworth, London, p. 45.
85. Daudel, R.: Rev. Sci., 87, 162 (1947).
86. Adloff, J.P.: Radiochimica Acta, 15, 135 (1971).
87. Wolfgang, R.: Progr. Reaction Kinetics, 3, 97 (1965).
88. Miller, J.M., Gryder, J.W., Dodson, R.W.: J. Chem. Phys., 18, 579 (1950).
89. Estrup, P.J., Wolfgang, R.: J. Amer. Chem. Soc. 82, 2665 (1960).
90. a. Milman, M.: Radiochimica Acta, 2, 180 (1964).
    b. Johnston, A.TJ.: Thesis, London Univ. (1966).
91. a. Seewald, D., Wolfgang, R.: J. Chem. Phys., 47, 143 (1967).
    b. Westhead, C., Urch, D.S.: Chem. Comm., 403 (1971).
92. a. Rowland, F.S., Coulter, P.: Radiochimica Acta, 2, 163 (1964).
    b. Malcolme Lawes, D.J.: Thesis, London Univ. (1969).
93. Brodsky, A.M., Temkin, A.Y.: Khim. Vys. Energ., 1, 4 (1964).
94. a. Henchman, M., Urch, D.S., Wolfgang, R.: Can. J. Chem., 38, 1722 (1960).
    b. Rowland, F.S., Lee, J.K., Musgrave, B., White, R.M.: Chemical Effects of Nuclear Transformations, IAEA, (Vienna), 2, 67 (1961).
95. Henchman, M., Wolfgang, R.: J. Amer. Chem. Soc., 83, 2991 (1961).
96. Breckenridge, W., Root, J.W., Rowland, F.S.: J. Chem. Phys., 39, 2374 (1963).
97. Arthy, R.: M. Phil. Thesis, London Univ. (1965).
98. a. Urch, D.S., Wolfgang, R.: J. Amer. Chem. Soc., 81, 2025 (1959).

b. Lee, E.K.C., Rowland, F.S.: J. Amer. Chem. Soc., 85, 897 (1963).
c. Ting, C.T., Rowland, F.S.: J. Phys. Chem., 72, 763 (1963).
99. Tang, Y.N., Lee, E.K.C., Rowland, F.S.: J. Amer. Chem. Soc., 86, 1280 (1964).
100. Johnston, A.J., Malcolme Lawes D., Urch, D.S., Welch, M.J.: Chem. Comm., 187 (1966).
101. Lee, J.K., Musgrawe, B., Roland, F.S.: J. Amer. Chem. Soc., 82, 3545 (1960).
102. Urch, D.S., Wolfgang, R.: J. Amer. Chem. Soc., 83, 2982 (1961).
103. Odum, R., Wolfgang, R.: J.Amer. Chem. Soc., 83, 4668 (1961).
104. Tang, Y.N.., Smith, W.S., Williams, J.L., Lowery, K., Rowland, F.S.: J. Phys. Chem., 75, 440 (1971).
105. Wai, C.M., Rowland, F.S.: J. Phys. Chem., 71, 2752 (1967).
106. a. Kontis, S.S., Urch, D.S.: Radiochimica Acta, 15, 21 (1971).
b. Berei, K., Stöcklin, G.: Radiochimica Acta, 15, 39 (1971).
107. Collins, K.E., Robinson, G.B., Collins, C.H.: J. Phys. Chem., 76, 3331 (1972).
108. Cacace, F., Stöcklin, G.: J. Amer. Chem. Soc.,; 94, 2518 (1972).
109. Loberg, M.D., Welch, M.J.: J. Amer. Chem. Soc., 95, 1075 (1973).
110. Colebourne, N., Todd, J.F.J., Wolfgang, R.: Chemical Effects of Nuclear Transformations, IAEA, (Vienna), 1, 149 (1965).
111. Williams, R.L., Rowland, F.S.: J. Phys. Chem., 76, 3509 (1972).
112. a. Tang, Y.N., Smail, T., Rowland, F.S.: J. Amer. Chem. Soc., 91, 2130 (1969).
b. Smail, T., Miller, G.E., Rowland, F.S.: J. Phys. Chem., 74, 3464 (1970).
113. Parks, N.J., Krohn, R.A., Root, J.W.: J. Chem. Phys., 55, 2690 and 5771 (1970).
114. Dulmen, A.A., Aten, A.H.W.: Radiochimica Acta, 15, 34 (1971).
115. Williams, R.L., Rowland, F.S.: J. Amer. Chem. Soc., 94, 1047 (1972).
116. Palino, G.F., Rowland, F.S.: Radiochimica Acta, 15, 57 (1971).
117. Manning, R.G., Root, J.W.: J. Phys. Chem., 79, 1478 (1975).
118. a. MacKay, C., Wolfgang, R.: Radiochimica Acta, 1, 42 (1962).
b. Dubrin, J.,MacKay, C., Wolfgang, R.: J. Inorg. Nucl. Chem., 26, 2113 (1964).
119. Pandow, M., MacKay, C., Wolfgang, R.: J. Inorg. Nucl. Chem., 14, 153 (1960).
120. v.e.g. Schrodt, A.G., Libby, W.F.: J. Amer. Chem. Soc., 78, 1267 (1956).
121. a. Stöcklin, G., Wolf, A.P.: J. Amer. Chem. Soc., 85, 229 (1963).
b. Dubrin, J., MacKay, C., Wolfgang, R.: J. Amer. Chem. Soc., 86, 4747 (1964).
122. a. MacKay, C., Pandow, M., Polak, P., Wolfgang, R.: Chemical Effects of Nuclear Transformations, IAEA, (Vienna), 2, 17 (1961).
b. MacKay, C., Wolfgang, R.: J. Amer. Chem. Soc., 83, 2399 (1961).
123. a. Ache, H.J., Wolf, A.P.: Chemical effects of Nuclear transformations, IAEA, (Vienna), 1, 107 (1965).
b. Ache, H.J., Christman, D.R., Wolf, A.P.: Radiochimica Acta, 12, 121 (1969).
124. Finn, R.D., Ache, H.J., Wolf, A.P.: Radiochimica Acta, 17, 131 (1972).
125. a. Stöcklin, G., Wolf, A.P.: Chem. Ind. (London), 46 (1964).
b. Stöcklin, G., Wolf, A.P.: Chemical Effects of Nuclear Transformations, IAEA, (Vienna), 1, 121 (1965).
c. Nicholas, J., MacKay, C., Wolfgang, R.: J. Amer. Chem. Soc., 88, 1065 (1966).
126. Marshall, M., MacKay, C., Wolfgang, R.: J. Amer. Chem. Soc., 86, 4741 (1966).
127. Nicholas, J., MacKay, C., Wolfgang, R. J. Amer. Chem. Soc., 88, 1064 (1966).
128. MacKay, C., Wolfgang, R.: J. Amer. Chem. Soc., 83, 2399 (1966).
129. Ache, H.J., Wolf, A.P.: Radiochimica Acta, 6, 32 (1966).
130. a. Yang, J.Y., Wolf, A.P.: J. Amer. Chem. Soc., 82, 4488 (1960).
b. Cacace, F. Wolf, A.P.: J. Amer. Chem. Soc., 87, 5301 (1965).

1.2 Hot Atom Chemistry of Naturally Occurring Radionuclides

Masanobu SAKANOUE
Professor Emeritus, Kanazawa University, 14-20, Miyanocho, Takarazuka, 665 Japan

The first report of a new phenomena (later recognized as the recoil of a hot atom) was made in the early stages of studies on natural radioactive elements. In 1904, Miss Harriett Brooks (1876-1933, later Mrs. Pitcher), working under the guidance of Ernest Rutherford (1871-1937) at McGill University in Montreal, reported that the decay products of the emanation "X" of radium, when deposited on a solid body, appears slightly volatile even at ordinary temperatures. [1] Thus, when a copper plate on which the daughter nuclides of radon were deposited from a hydrochloric acid solution was placed inside a testing vessel and removed after one minute, a temporal activity, as high as one or two percent of the plate activity, was found on the walls of the vessel.

The explanation of this phenomenon was proposed in the next year by E. Rutherford in his book[2] : " Since radium A breaks up with an expulsion of an α particle, some of the residual atoms constituting radium B, may acquire sufficient velocity to escape into the gas and are then transferred by diffusion to the walls of the vessel ". In modern terms, due to the recoil effect following α decay of ^{218}Po(Ra A) the hot daughter atoms ^{214}Pb(Ra B) are projected onto the walls of the vessel. Later in 1909, by utilizing such an effect as a means for a very rapid separation (with "zero" time delay)· O. Hahn and L. Meitner discovered a new short-lived (1.32 min) naturally occurring radionuclide, Ra C" (^{210}Tl).

Another important hot atom effect with key implication in geochemistry was discovered by V. V. Cherdyntsev (1912-1971) during his collaboration with P. I. Chalov at Kazakhstan from 1944 to 1960. In 1955 [3] the authors reported at the Academy of Science of USSR on the abnormal activity ratio of the two natural uranium isotopes, ^{238}U and ^{234}U.

These two uranium isotopes had been discovered in 1907 independently by several investigators (H. N. McCoy and W. H. Ross: B. B. Boltwood, R. B. Moore and H. Schlund) and were called U I and U II respectively. Following the recognition of the displacement laws by F. Soddy and A. S. Russel and K. Fajans in 1913 , the genetic relation between the two isotopes could be established.

Normally the two uranium isotopes in nature are in secular equilibrium and the activity ratio (AR) of $^{234}U/^{238}U$ is equal to unity because the intermediary nuclides in the chain are very short lived with respect to geological time scales, and chemical fractionation of the two uranium isotopes is excluded.

Thus it was a great surprise when in the mid 50's Cherdyntsev and his colleague found for the first time an abnormal AR of 3.7 ± 0.5 in a secondary uranium sulfate mineral, Schroekingerite.[3] They also observed that the AR was above unity in the aqueous extracts from zircon and monazite. Following these first observations, the AR values were measured in the USSR for various minerals, quaternary deposits as well as for river waters and other aqueous systems. These investigations lead to interesting geochemical application, as e.g. the geochronology of a high mountain lake in Kirgizskaya.[4]

These studies were also widely pursued in other countries, using first α spectrometry with a grid ionization chamber and later on with surface barrier semiconductor detectors. But it is interesting to note that Cherdyntsev's discovery [3] was made with a very primitive method, by using thin paper filters as absorbers in order to discriminate the lower energy α rays of ^{238}U from the more energetic rays of ^{234}U .[13]

In 1962, D. L. Thurber of the Lamont Geological Observatory at Columbia University, reported that even uranium dissolved in oceanic water was enriched in ^{234}U by 15% with respect to the activity of ^{238}U.[5] This finding was applied for dating atoll corals from the Pacific. It was used to revise previous age determinations by ^{230}Th / ^{238}U activity ratio and to establish an independent dating based on the decay of the excess ^{234}U.[6]

At the same laboratory, T. L. Ku established a dating method of pelagic sediments [7] based on the $^{234}U/^{238}U$ AR, while J. N. Rosholt et al. of the U. S. Geological Survey Laboratory investigated the fractionation of uranium isotopes in sandstone deposits. [8]

An AR of 2.3 ± 0.1 was measured in England for water sample from a deep boring core.[9] In Japan, the AR values for several mineral spring waters and for other samples were reported by us in 1964. [10] Our studies were extended to uranium ore deposits and the behaviour of several α emitters in these ores was investigated. [11] We found an exceptionally high AR of about 15 in a maghemite sample collected from the altered clay zone of a mine in Japan.[12] This high value may have resulted from the deposit of recoiling ^{234}Th from an aqueous system onto the mineral and from the subsequent β decay of the nuclide on the surface of the maghemite.

In 1969, Cherdyntsev published a book [13] which covered all available data as well as the principles underlying in the disequilibrium of uranium isotopes. About one decade later, J. K. Osmond et al. reviewed the topic [15] with particular emphasis on terrestrial hydrogeochemistry, a field which they had started to investigate at the Florida State University.[14]

In 1983 the same authors wrote a review[16] on uranium isotope disequilibrium in ground waters together with M. Ivanovich who published in the U. K., a book [17] on $^{234}U/^{238}U$ disequilibrium. In 1983, K. Rössler gave a comprehensive review of this subject in the Gmelin Handbook.[18]

From the hot atom chemistry point of view, the most interesting question is the mechanism which causes the abnormal $^{234}U/^{238}U$ AR in nature. Since the first finding of the phenomenon, the recoil effect due to the α decay of ^{238}U has been pointed out to be at the origin of the isotopic fractionation.[13] Leaching experiments of uranium from ores and from minerals with various weak chemical solutions have shown that ^{234}U is more soluble than ^{238}U. This leads to consider that ^{234}U formed by decay of recoiling ^{234}Th finds itself in an "unusual" lattice position and would be less firmly bound than ^{238}U in a normal lattice site. This ^{234}U is more liable to dissolution in water, in particular if due to its unstable chemical state it is oxidized from the U^{4+} valency state to U^{6+}, i. e. to the uranyl cation $UO_2{}^{2+}$.[8][13]

On the other hand, from his own experiments, K. Kigoshi proposed a model suggesting that the recoiling ^{234}Th atoms are directly ejected in the aqueous phase.[19] However, we could not find any appreciable amount of ^{234}Th in natural hot spring waters despite an AR of 10.[20] In this case, the ^{234}Th atoms ejected into the aqueous phase may be subsequently adsorbed on the surface of minerals where they decay to ^{234}U. This deposit accumulating over a long time may be the reason for the high AR for hot spring water sucked out a short time after boring to a depth of 600m.

R.L. Fleischer proposed another model based on nuclear recoil tracks measurements in solid materials. The α-recoiling ^{234}Th atoms produce along their track in the solid mineral various fragments and radiation damage. Subsequent etching or loosening of the damaged zones releases the ^{234}U formed at the end of the ^{234}Th track and lead to a high enrichment of ^{234}U in the solution.[21] A sensitive test of this mechanism was carried out with a ^{239}Pu source to simulate ^{238}U and by detecting the recoiled ^{235}U by neutron irradiation.[22] In this work, the implications for the storage of α emitting radioactive waste and for radon emanation were mentioned.

Recently, K. Rössler and J. P. Adloff elaborated a new hot atom chemical model. The latter was presented at several radiochemical meetings (Lindau 1984, Nancy 1985, Beijing 1986) and published in a paper.[23] This model emphasizes a recoil induced oxidation of ^{234}U and is based on computer simulation of the collisions of uranium recoil atoms in selected compounds. According to the authors, their model appears more plausible complementary to the direct ejection of recoil ^{234}Th and to the radiation damage mechanisms which are not well compatible with the actual dissolution rate of the uranium minerals.

Besides these topics, other hot atom chemical effects in the natural radioactive series have been well discussed by J. P. Adloff.[24] They include the rupture of radioactive equilibrium in the thorium series, the behaviour of recoil atoms in mineral, the spontaneous fission of ^{238}U and the hot syntheses of fission xenon compounds in uranium ore, the possible chemical bonding of radon in natural sample, the chemical form of radon daughters, etc. Hot atom effects also intervene in the chemical state of cosmogenic nuclides and in the synthesis of interstellar molecules.

These topics are considered in Chapters 7.4, 7.6 and 8.1 of this book.

References

1. Brooks, H.: Nature, 70, 270 (1904).
2. Rutherford, E.: " Radioactivity " Cambridge University Press., Cambridge,1904, p. 392.
3. Cherdyntsev, V.V., Chalov, P.I., Khitrik, M.E., Mamebetov, D.M., Khaidarov, G.Z.: Transactions of the 3rd Session of Committee for Determination of Absolute Ages of Geologic Formations, Izv. Akad. Nauk SSSR, 175-233 (1954-55).
4. Chalov, P.I., Tuzova T.V., Musin, Ya.A.: Geokhimiya, 405-413, (1964); [in Japanese] Sakanoue M.: J. Ocean. Soc. Jap., 22, 61-65 (1966).
5. Thurber, D.L.: J. Geophys. Res., 67. 4518-4520 (1962).
6. Thurber, D.L., Broecker, W.S., Blanchard, R.L., Potratz, H.A.: Science, 149 , 55-58 (1965).
7. Ku, T.-L.: J. Geophys. Res.,70, 3457-3474 (1965).
8. Rosholt, J.N., Shield, W.R., Garner, E.L.: Science. 139 , 224-226 (1963).
9. Hill, C.R., Crookall, J.O.: J. Geophy. Res. 68, 2358 (1963).
10. Sakanoue, M., Hashimoto, T.: Nippon Kagaku Zashi (J. Chem. Soc. Jap.), [in Japanese] 85, 622-627 (1964).
11. Sakanoue, M., Yoneda, S., Onishi, K., Koyama, K., Komura, K., Nakanishi, T: Geochem. J. [Japan], 2, 71-86 (1968).
12. Sakanoue, M., Komura, K.: Nature, Phys. Sci., 233 , 80-81 (1971).
13. Cherdyntsev, V.V.: " Uran-234 " [in Russian] Atomizdat Moscow, 1969. pp1-304; " Uranium-234 " [in English] Israel Program for Scientific Translations, Jerusalem, 1 971.
14. Osmond, J.K., Rydell, H.S., Kaufmann, M.I.: Science, 162 . 997-999 (1968).
15. Osmond, J.K., Cowart, J.B.: At. Energy Rev.,14, 621-679 (1976).
16. Osmond, J.K., Cowart, J.B., Ivanovich, M.: Int. J. Appl. Radiat. Isot., 34, 283-308 (1983).
17. Ivanovich, M., Harmon, R.S.(Ed.): " Uranium Series Disequilibrium; Applications to Environmental Problems in the Earth Sciences " Clarendon Press, Oxford, (1982).
18. Rössler, K.: Uranium Recoil Reactions, in " Gmelin Handbook of Inorganic Chemistry, 8th Edition, Uranium, Supplement Volume A6 " Springer Verlag, Berlin, pp135-163 (1983).
19. Kigoshi, K.: Science, 173 . 47-48 (1971).
20. Sakanoue, M., Hashimoto, T.: "Hot Atom Chemistry" Kodansha, Tokyo. pp460-471 (1984).
21. Fleischer, R.L., Raabe, O.G.: Geochim. Cosmochim. Acta, 42, 973-978 (1978).
22. Fleischer, R.L.: Science, 207 ,979-981 (1980).
23. Ordonez Regil, E., Schleiffer, J.J., Adloff, J.P., Rössler, K.: Radiochim. Acta, 47, 177-185 (1989).
24. Adloff, J.P.: Radiochim. Acta, 29, 5-8 (1981).

1.3 Early Nuclear Hot Atom Chemistry

John E. WILLARD

Department of Chemistry, University of Wisconsin, Madison, Wisconsin, USA

This chapter will note the origin of the use of "hot atom chemistry" to designate the phenomena discussed in this book, will note similarities in the processes of hot atom chemistry and radiation chemistry, and will outline the evolution of knowledge of the mechanism of the hot atom chemistry of the halogens in organic media.

The term "hot atom chemistry" originated as an informal synonym for "chemical effects of nuclear transformations". It received formal recognition at the first symposium in the field, which was held at Brookhaven National Laboratory in 1948 with the title "Chemical Effects of Nuclear Transformations (Hot Atom Chemistry)", - and shortly thereafter, as the title of a paper in the Journal of Chemical Physics - "The Hot Atom Chemistry of the Propyl Bromides" [1]. For the next decade or so "hot atom" usually connoted an atom freshly formed by a nuclear process. With time, and increased interest in producing atoms with controlled energies above chemical bond energies by various means, it came to mean any atom with such translational or electronic energy.

Some 50 papers in the field were published between 1934 (the time of the Szilard-Chalmers[2] demonstration of the separation of ^{128}I from C_2H_5I by the $^{127}I(n,\gamma)^{128}I$ reaction) and 1942. There was a lull during World War II. Starting in 1946 the rate of production increased, reaching about 34 in 1950, and 70 in 1958.

Like radiation chemistry nuclear hot atom chemistry deals with chemical events caused by the deposition in single atoms of energy much greater than chemical bond and ionization energies. It may be considered a branch of radiation chemistry. The types of energy conveyed to the atom, and thence to the surrounding atoms and molecules by the nuclear processes are: 1) the kinetic energy of recoil from gamma ray or particle emissions (typically of the order of 100 eV from the (n,γ) process and 100,000 eV from the (n,p) process); 2) the energy of coulombic repulsion generated when the high positive charge acquired by an atom as a result of internal conversion of a γ ray, followed by Auger electron emission, spreads over the atom in a molecule; 3) the energy of ionization and molecular excitation conveyed to molecules of the medium by γ rays, X rays, and high energy electrons emitted in nuclear processes. The recoil energy and massive coulombic repulsion are different initiators of reactions than those found in radiation chemistry, but the reactions of electrons, atoms, radicals and ions following the primary energy deposition are similar. Another unique feature of activation by nuclear processes is that both the recoil and internal conversion atoms which initiate reactions are usually radioactive so that the stable molecules into which they are incorporated at the end of the reaction can be distinguished from all other reaction products. It would be useful to know what the non radioactive products are, but since the number of nuclear events in the system is typically 10^{-12} mole fraction their concentration is usually too low for anlysis. In addition the concentration of these products of the nuclear processes is greatly exceeded by the decomposition products resulting from the background radiation, if the nuclear process is produced by radiation from an outside source.

When Szilard and Chalmers irradiated C_2H_5I with neutrons, with the idea that the momentum imparted to an I atom by an impinging neutron could cause rupture of the C-I bond, they probably had no thought of the recoil, charging, and ionizing processes noted above. The first step toward a better understanding came when Fermi and coworkers [3], having observed that the rupture can occur with slow neutrons (which impart insufficient energy for bond rupture) suggested that it must result from recoil from the γ ray emitted in the (n,γ) process. This concept, that the atom is ejected with high translational energy, led to the "billard ball collision hypothesis" of Libby [4] which postulated that the radioactive recoiling atom may reenter stable combination as the result of a head-on collision with a bound atom of the same mass, leaving the recoil atom in the solvent cage vacated by the knocked-on atom. Thus ^{128}I produced by the $^{127}I(n,\gamma)^{128}I$ process in liquid C_2H_5I was thought to rupture its parent C-I bond and then lose its large excess energy by head-on collision with an I in another C_2H_5I molecule, leaving the ^{128}I in the cage with the C_2H_5 to form $C_2H_5{}^{128}I$. This was thought to account for the 40% "organic yield" of the newly formed ^{128}I. Conservation of momentum considerations preclude the recoil I atom from remaining in the cage after giving enough energy to an H atom to break a C-H bond. The 60% of the ^{128}I atoms found in inorganic combination were presumed to have combined with I atoms knocked out by the recoil atom. The billard ball collision hypothesis predicted that all recoil atoms which reenter organic combination do so as the parent compound (e.g., $C_2H_5{}^{128}I$ for ^{128}I in C_2H_5I.). It was found however (using fractional distillation of neutron irradiated samples, with added carriers for different molecular species), that H atoms in hydrocarbons and organic halides can be replaced by heavy recoil atoms, and also that carbon-carbon bonds are sometimes broken. This led to the suggestion [1] that when a recoil atom has been moderated to about 10 eV it may give up energy to molecules as a whole, rather than only to single atoms, exciting them sufficiently to cause rupture of C-H and C-C bonds. This was called the "billard ball collision-epithermal collision hypothesis". It was still an over-simplification for several reasons:

1. The assumption that the momentum transfer events which a recoil atom with high energy experiences in a condensed phase are identical to those between isolated atoms in the gas phase fails to consider that the struck molecule is backed by a wall of other molecules. 2. It was shown that many of the recoil

atoms in alkyl halides enter stable combination only after diffusion in thermal equilibrium with the medium. 3. It was shown that inorganic as well as organic compounds may be formed before the recoil atom has undergone thermal diffusion.

These considerations led to the "random fragmentation hypothesis"[5]. Its postulates are as follows. When a halogen atom in a molecule in the liquid or solid phase acquires several hundred eV or more of recoil energy it starts moving rapidly, but having traveled less than a molecular diameter encounters a solvent molecule. If this were an isolated molecule the energetic atom would transfer momentum to an atom in an elastic collision and would continue on its way. In the condensed phase this cannot happen because the struck molecule is backed by and surrounded by a close packed and sometimes intertwined wall of other molecules. The result is that the energy is dissipated by breaking bonds in a rather indiscriminate fashion in the immediate vicinity of the energetic atom. When the energy of the atom has been reduced below bond breaking energies it finds itself in, or adjacent to, a pocket of high local concentration of organic radicals and inorganic atoms. It may combine with one of these after it has been moderated to an energy where combination is possible but before it has had opportunity to diffuse in the system as a thermal atom. Alternatively, it may encounter a reactive partner with which it can enter stable combination only after diffusion in thermal equilibrium with the medium. These two types of events have been dubbed "hot processes" and "thermal processes". They can be distinguished by the use of low concentration of "scavengers"[5] which react with the diffusing atoms before the latter encounter one of the fragmentation radicals or atoms. For example, 0.5 mole % of Br_2 reduces the "organic yield" from C_2H_5Br from 32% to 25% and 0.1 mole % 1,2-dibromoethylene, which does not react with Br_2 but scavenges Br atoms into organic combination [7], raises it to 60%. This indicates that the "hot" (i.e., combination before diffusion) organic yield in this system is 25% and the hot inorganic yield 40%. In the absence of scavengers, 35% of the recoil atoms must react with organic radicals, Br, Br_2, or HBr in diffusive encounters.

Consistent with the random fragmentation hypothesis, it was found, with the advent of gas chromatography, that over 20 different organic bromides containing the ^{82}Br produced by the $^{81}Br(n,\gamma)^{82}Br$ reaction could be identified in a drop of neutron irradiated n-C_3H_7Br [8].

The next step in the evolution of thinking about processes which might lead to the multiplicity of products from (n,γ) activation and other nuclear processes was the "Auger electron reaction hypothesis"[9]. It postulates that the fate of the radioactive recoil atoms is determined in whole or in part by combination with the products of radiolysis of the immediately surrounding medium by the internal conversion and Auger electrons emitted from the atoms in the process of nuclear stabilization. Consistent with this hypothesis it was found that the relative yields of the various ^{131}I labeled products from a γ irradiated solution of ^{131}II in C_2H_5I are similar to the relative yields of ^{128}I products from the $^{127}I(n,\gamma)^{128}I$ process in neutron irradiated C_2H_5I [9]. The high yield of stabilization as the parent molecule is consistent with the high probability of formation of the parent radical by processes such as

$C_2H_5I + e^- \dashrightarrow C_2H_5 + I^-$ and $C_2H_5I + H \dashrightarrow C_2H_5 + HI$.

Furthermore, great similarity in product distributions produced by different nuclear reactions of the same element have been observed in each of several liquid media [10]. For iodine, nuclear process compared include: $^{127}I(n,\gamma)^{128}I$, $^{127}I(\gamma,n)^{126}I$, $^{127}I(d,p)^{128}I$, and $^{127}I(n,2n)^{126}I$ in alkyl iodides. For bromine they include $^{80m}Br \dashrightarrow {}^{80}Br$, $^{79}Br(n,\gamma)^{80}Br$, $^{81}Br(n,\gamma)^{82}Br$, $^{79}Br(n,2n)^{78}Br$ in alkyl and aromatic bromides. The observations show that nuclides of a given element activated by drastically different nuclear processes may give both the same organic yield and same product distribution. If all the nuclear processes produce nuclei which pass through low lying metastable levels which decay by internal conversion, the similarity of products may result either from the similarity in the charging and neutralization processes at the end of all recoil tracks or from the radiolytic effects postulated by the Auger radiation hypothesis discussed above.

About four years after the first demonstration of chemical activation by the (n,γ) reaction, Segre, Halford and Seaborg[11] reasoned that it should be possible to separate nuclear isomers by the Szilard-Chalmers method, as a result of recoil from the low energy γ rays or conversion electrons emitted in the isomeric transition or, if these energies were less than bond energies, as a result of chemical activation of reactions such as hydrolysis. They demonstrated separation, using the $^{80m}Br(4.4h) \dashrightarrow {}^{80}Br(18\ min)$ transition of ^{80m}Br in t-$C_4H_9{}^{80m}Br$ in aqueous CH_3OH. Similar separations in other systems were obtained by others. Experiments in our laboratory [12] showed, unexpectedly, that when $^{80m}BrBr$ is dissolved in the "inert" solvent CCl_4, 40% of the ^{80}Br daughter activity appears in organic combination and cannot be extracted with aqueous reducing agent. Since the recoil energy of the ^{80}Br from either the conversion electron or the unconverted γ-ray is too small to cause replacement of Cl in CCl_4 by Br, it was apparent that the reaction must occur by a mechanism dependent on the positive charge given the atom by the emission of a conversion electron. The magnitude of the charge was not known at that time. Results of this type stimulated mass spectrometric charge collection experiments which showed that the Auger process which follows emission of a conversion electron generates large charges on the ^{80}Br daughter. For example, when the ^{80m}Br is present as gaseous $CH_3{}^{80m}Br$, charged states of ^{80}Br ions from +1 to +13, as well as CH_2Br^+, CH_3^+, CH_2^+, CH^+, C^+, C^{2+}, C^{3+}, H_2^+ and H^+ are observed[13] indicating massive fragmentation as the result of Coulomb repulsion when the high charge has spread over the molecule. Other dramatic examples are the production of charges from +1 to +22 on the ^{131}Xe daughters from the isomeric transition of ^{131m}Xe [14], and the observation that production of L shell vacancies in the I of gaseous CH_3I by X-rays leads to decomposition of the molecules almost entirely into H^+, C^{n+} and I^{n+} with the C^{2+} ions having a recoil energy of 50 eV.[15]

The production of $CBr_3{}^{80}Br$ by the isomeric transition of ^{80m}Br in solutions of 25 mol % CCl_4 in Br_2 [16] indicates that in the condensed phase the charge built up by the transition may cause major decomposition of molecules adjacent to the atom which develops the charge.

These results on activation by isomeric transition turned attention to the possibility that atoms activated with translational energy from the (n,γ) process might also develop high charge as a result of internal conversion of low energy capture γ-rays. Neutron irradiation of gold and indium foils [17] under conditions where the atoms recoiling from the surface were collected on negatively charged plates showed that such charging occurs and indicated that the charging is delayed relative to the recoil. If it were instantaneous, neutralization would occur before escape from the surface. Findings such as these indicated that "coulombic explosions" following Auger charging of recoil atoms must in many cases contribute to the nest of radicals (and ions) which determines the form of chemical stabilization of recoil atoms.

In the condensed phase discussed above, any unique types of reaction of the recoil atoms are obscurred by the "soup" of potential reaction partners in which the atoms find themselves when they have been moderated. In the gas phase, however, where the recoil atom or ion escapes from any fragments formed in moderating collisions, specific new types of reaction inaccessible by thermal activation were discovered. These included: 1) the formation of $CH_3{}^{128}I$ by the recoil ^{128}I from the $^{127}I(n,\gamma)^{128}I$ reaction on I_2 in CH_4 [18], and similar reactions of chlorine [19,20] and bromine [18]; 2) numerous replacements of H and D, by T from the $^{6}Li(n,\alpha)T$ [21] and $^{3}He(n,p)T$ [22] processes.

Studies with additives with lower ionization potential than I, and with additives capable of removing electronic excitation, indicated that positive charge, electronic excitation and translational energy each contribute to the unusual ^{128}I reactions [23,24]. Extensive information on the products, mechanisms and energy dependence of the reactions of recoil T atoms has been obtained by using an inert gas to moderate them to a known average energy in the epithermal range before collision with dilute target molecules [25].

There are review articles which discuss in much greater depth, with many additional references, the subjects which have been treated in brief historical perpective here [5, 25-35]. These include discussions of inorganic systems and of activation by additional types of nuclear processes.

References

1. Friedman, L., Libby, W.F.: J. Chem. Phys., 17 , 647 (1949).
2. Szilard, L., Chalmers, T.A.: Nature,134 , 462 (1934).
3. Amaldi, E., D'Agostino, O., Fermi E., Pontecorvo, B., Rasetti, F.,Segre, E.: Proc.Roy Soc., A146, 483 (1934).
4. Libby, W.F. : J. Am. Chem. Soc. 62 , 1930 (1940).
5. Willard, J.E.: "Chemical Effects of Nuclear transformations", Annual Review of Nuclear Science, Annual Reviews, Inc., Stanford, CA, 1953, P.198.
6. Goldhaber, S., Willard, J.E.: J. Am. Chem. Soc., 74 ,318 (1952)
7. Hamill, W.H., Williams, R.R., Schwarz, H.A.: J.Am. Chem. Soc. 72 ,2813,(1950).
8. Evans, J.B., Willard, J.E.: J.Am. Chem. Soc., 78 , 2908 (1956).
9. Geissler, P.R., Willard, J.E.: J. Phys. Chem., 67 , 1675 (1963).
10. Schuler R.H., McCauley, C.E.: J. Am. Chem. Soc. 79 , 821 (1957); McCauley, C.E., Hilsdorf, G.J., Geissler, P.R., Schuler, R.H.: J. Am. Chem. Soc., 78 3246 (1956).
11. Segre, E., Halford, R.S., Seaborg, G.T.: Phys.Rev., 55 , 321 (1939).

12. Willard, J.E.: J. Am. Chem. Soc., 62 , 256 (1940).
13. Wexler, S., Anderson, G.R.: J. Chem. Phys., 62 , 850 (1960).
14. Pleasonton, F., Snell A.H.: Proc. Roy. Soc. (London), A211 , 141 (1957).
15. Carlson, T.A., White, R.M.: "Explosion of Multicharged Molecular Ions: Chemical Consequences of Inner Shell Vacancies in Atoms", Chemical Effects of Nuclear Transformations, International Atomic Energy Agency, Vienna, 1965, Vol. I, p.23.
16. Hornig, J.F., Willard, J.E.: J. Am. Chem., 75 , 461 (1953).
17. Yosim. S., Davies, T.H.: J. Chem. Phys., 56 , 599 (1952).
18. Hornig, J.F., Levey, G., Willard, J.E.: J. Chem. Phys., 20 , 1556 (1952).
19. Chien, J.C.W., Willard, J.E.: J. Am. Chem. Soc., 75 , 6160 (1975).
20. Gordus, A.A., Willard, J.E.: J. Am. Chem. Soc., 79 , 4609 (1957).
21. Wolfgang, R., Eigner, J., Rowland, F.S.: J. Phys. Chem. 60 , 1137 (1956).
22. Gordus, A.A., Sauer, M.C., Willard, J.E.: J. Am. Chem. Soc.,79 , 3284 (1957); El-Sayed, M.F.A., Wolfgang, R.: J. Am. Chem. Soc.79 , 3286 (1957).
23. Levey, G., Willard, J.E.: J. Chem. Phys. 25 , 904 (1956).
24. Rack, E.P., Gordus, A.A.: J. Chem. Phys., 34 , 1855 (1961); 36 , 287 (1962); J. Phys. Chem. , 65 , 944 (1961).
25. Wolfgang. R.: "The Hot Atom Chemistry of Gas Phase Systems", Progress in Reaction Kinetics, (G. Porter, ed.) Pergamon Press, New York 1965.`
26. Willard, J.E.: "Radiation Chemistry and Hot Atom Chemistry", Annual Review of Physical Chemistry, Annual Reviews, Inc., Stanford, CA, 1955, p. 141.
27. Willard, J.E.:"Chemical Effects of Nuclear Transformations of Halogen Atoms in Organic Halides", Chemical Effects of Nuclear Transformations, International Atomic Energy Agency, Vienna, 1961, Vol. I, p. 215.
28. Willard, J.E.: "Chemical Effects of Nuclear Transformations of Halogens in Organic Media", Chemical Effects of Nuclear Transformations, International Atomic Energy Agency, Vienna, 1965, Vol.I. p.221.
29. Campbell, I.G.: "Chemical Effects of Nuclear Activation in Gases and Liquids", Advances in Inorganic Chemistry, Academic Press, Inc., New York, 1963, p. 135.
30. Siuda, A.: "Chemical Effects of Nuclear Transformation" (a bibliography from 1914-1962), Information Center of the Polish Atomic Energy Commission, Warsaw, 1963.
31. Wolf, A.P.: "Labeling of Organic Compounds by Recoil Methods", Annual Review of Nuclear Science, Annual Reviews Inc., Stanford, CA, 1960, p.259..
32. Wolf, A.P.: "The Reactions of Energetic Tritium and Carbon Atoms with Organic Compounds", Advances in Physical-Organic Chemistry, Academic Press, Inc.,New York, 1964, p. 201.
33. Harbottle, G.: "Chemical Effects of Nuclear transformations in Inorganic Solids", Annual Review of Nuclear Science, Annual Reviews Inc., Stanford, CA, 1965, p. 89.
34. Wexler, S.: "Primary Physical and Chemical Effects Associated with Emission of Radiation", Actions Chimiques et Biologiques des Radiations, (M.Haissinsky, ed.) Masson et Cie, Paris 1965, p. 107.
35. Rowland, F.S.: "Hot Atom Chemistry", Molecular Beams and Reaction Kinetics, Academic Press, New York, 1970, p. 108.

1.4 Discovery of New Elements and Hot Atom Chemistry

Darleane C. HOFFMAN

Nuclear Science Division
Lawrence Berkeley Laboratory, University of California
Berkeley, CA 94720 U.S.A.

Hot atom chemistry has been of vital importance in the separation and discovery of the heaviest elements. A recoil technique has been used in the discovery of all the heavy elements from mendelevium (101) through element 109, the heaviest element currently known. As discussed by Seaborg[1], this technique, which takes advantage of the fact that when a target is bombarded with high energy ions the resulting products of the nuclear reaction have sufficient energy that many of them will recoil out of the target, was first applied in the discovery of mendelevium. In this "recoil" method a relatively thin target is deposited on an appropriate backing and the projectile beam from the accelerator first passes through the backing and then into the target. Because of the momentum imparted to the products of the nuclear reactions they are ejected from the target material and can be collected on a thin "catcher" foil which is removed for subsequent chemical processing and analysis. This technique becomes especially important when rare and expensive targets such as separated stable isotopes or very radioactive isotopes which are difficult to handle and are available in only microgram or even smaller quantities must be used. The target can be used over and over again and the recoiling products need only be separated from the catcher foil. Furthermore, there is no need to re-enter the irradiation area as the method lends itself to remotely controlled rapid removal of the foil and is applicable to the "atom-at-a-time" study of nuclides with very short half-lives. Extensions of this technique include shuttle or pneumatic rabbit systems and a host of other mechanical devices for removing the samples. Moving tape systems have also been used to collect the recoiling reaction products and measure their half-lives.

Alternatively, gas transport systems incorporating a variety of different gases (He, Ar) and aerosols (KCl, NaCl, water vapor) can be used[2,3] This method is rapid (fractions of a second) and highly efficient and was used in the subsequent discoveries of all of the rest (elements 102 through 109) of the known heavy elements.

In the discovery of the next element, nobelium, another application of "hot atom" chemistry was used! Isotopes of nobelium were produced[4] via $^{244,245}Cm(^{12}C,x,n)$ reactions. Positive identification of the new element was based on chemical separation and detection of the daughter, a known Fm isotope. When the No alpha decays to Fm, the recoil energy of the Fm daughter of more than 100 keV is sufficient to eject the Fm daughter from the sample containing the No. It can then be collected in an appropriate catcher foil for subsequent chemical separation and/or measurement of its half-life and decay.

The discovery of lawrencium (element 103) by Ghiorso et al.[5] in 1961 utilized a long metallized mylar tape to collect atoms recoiling from the interaction of boron beams with a californium target. The tape was moved past a series of detectors for measuring the emitted alpha particles.

A variety of sophisticated instrumentation has been developed for collecting recoiling alpha decay products directly on detectors and then collecting subsequent alpha decays on clean detectors for measurement of half-lives and establishment of genetic relationships. In the "double-recoil" method the original recoiling product of the reaction may be deposited via a gas-transport system onto a wheel, drum, moving tape, or similar device which can be stepped in front of alpha detectors at selected time intervals. Alpha-decay of the collected product causes the recoiling daughter to implant itself in the radiation detector--this detector can then be moved in front of a clean detector. If the daughter activity decays via alpha-emission, the recoiling "granddaughter" activity is then collected on this second detector. Consequently, if the decay characteristics of the daughter and granddaughter activities are known and they are detected and measured, a genetic link is established and the atomic number and mass of the parent activity can be assigned. Variations of this technique have been used in the discovery of a number of elements.

In 1965 Donets et al.[6], used a double recoil technique to identify the daughter and granddaughter of ^{256}Lr and thus identify the atomic number of Lr by linking it genetically to its known alpha-decay daughter, ^{252}Md, which then decays via electron capture to the known isotope, ^{252}Fm.

Elements 104 and 105 were unambiguously identified[7,8] by measuring the time-correlation between alpha particles emitted by the parent (element 104 or 105) and the known No or Lr daughter activities. Positive identification of both the Z and A of element 106 in the isotope $^{263}106$ produced via the $^{249}Cf(^{18}O,4n)$ reaction was obtained by Ghiorso et al.[9] by showing that it decays by alpha emission to the known $^{259}104$ which then decays via alpha emission to the known isotope, ^{255}No.

The gas transport technique coupled with mechanical transport to detectors cannot be used for activities with half-lives much less than 0.1 second. Therefore, techniques for directly separating the products recoiling from the target have been developed. The velocity filter SHIP (Separator for Heavy Ion reaction Products) built at the UNILAC accelerator at GSI in Germany enabled Münzenberg et al.[10-13] to identify elements 107, 108, and 109 which were produced in "cold fusion" reactions between stable lead or bismuth targets and heavy ions. (So-called "cold fusion" reactions are those in which targets near the very stable, doubly magic ^{208}Pb configuration are used together with the appropriate heavy ion beam in order to make compound nuclei which are relatively "cold", i.e., have less excitation energy and therefore are more likely to undergo only a 1 neutron out reaction. This method was proposed by

Oganessian et al.[14]. The recoiling products of these compound nucleus reactions were separated in times of the order of microseconds from the transfer and deeply inelastic products based on the difference in their velocities and angular distributions. Again, however, the atomic number and mass number were determined by observing the time (and position) correlation between alpha decay of the new element and its known decay products. The half-life is obtained from the time intervals between subsequent events. The power of this technique is demonstrated in that these discoveries were based on the observation of the decay of only 5 atoms of element 107 in the initial experiments (a total of 38 by 1988), only 4 atoms (in two separate experiments) of element 108, and only 3 atoms (in two separate experiments) of element 109. Yet these discoveries have found widespread acceptance because of the compelling evidence for the assignment based on the genetic link to known daughter activities. The species first discovered and their half-lives are: $^{262}107$, 5 ms; $^{265}108$, 1.8 ms; $^{266}109$, 3 ms.

The foregoing examples illustrate the importance to date of "hot atom" chemistry in the discovery of new elements and the study of the decay properties of the heaviest element isotopes. What are the prospects for the future? The experimental results showing that the half-lives of the known isotopes of elements 107, 108, and 109 are all of the order of milliseconds and that their alpha-decay half-lives are shorter than their spontaneous fission (SF) half-lives is extremely encouraging because it indicates that the fission barriers have not decreased precipitously. The odd Z elements 107 and 109 might be expected to have somewhat longer SF half-lives due to the known odd proton hindrance, but the further finding that the partial half-life for SF of the even-even isotope $^{264}108$ is at least 5 ms is quite unexpected and indicates that microscopic shell effects are large enough to overcome the decreases in the liquid-drop fission barriers. Furthermore, several calculations[15-18] have indicated a deformed subshell in the region of 162-164 neutrons. This has prompted a number of investigators to propose experiments to produce element 110 with neutron numbers in this region.

Several other devices besides SHIP for the purpose of detecting heavy element isotopes have also been constructed. These include gas-filled separators such as the Small Angle Separating System (SASSY)[19,20] at Lawrence Berkeley Laboratory and the recently improved version SASSY-II[21], and the electrostatic separator, VASSILISSA,[22] at the Dubna laboratory in the U. S. S. R. which can analyze complete fusion reaction products as short as microseconds. In SASSY the nuclei recoiling from the target are deposited in detectors placed in the focal plane and are identified via their alpha-decay and genetic correlation with daughters. Although these separators (and SHIP) can analyze very short-lived products they are not efficient for detecting non-compound nucleus products which are emitted at larger angles with respect to the beam direction although SASSY-II has a somewhat larger acceptance angle and higher efficiency than SHIP. Attempts to produce and identify element 110 are planned or in progress at the various laboratories. Armbruster et al.[23] prefer the reaction $^{208}Pb(^{64}Ni,n)^{271}110$ while Ghiorso et al. propose to use the reaction $^{209}Bi(^{59}Co,2n)^{266}110$. Unfortunately, the cross sections are expected to be only of the order of picobarns and the half-lives may be only microseconds in the case of the more neutron-deficient products. Another complication is that decay via some mode other than alpha emission, e.g., electron capture or spontaneous fission may predominate, making positive identification nearly impossible using these techniques.

A consortium of U. S. labs has also proposed[24] the Large Einsteinium Activation Program (LEAP) to produce the largest ever ^{254}Es target (40 micrograms) and use it in reactions with lighter ions to produce new heavy elements and even superheavy elements using reactions such as $^{254}Es(^{48}Ca, xn)^{302-x}119$ which would give a product with neutron number near the predicted spherical shell at 184 neutrons. More neutron-rich isotopes of lighter Z elements can also be produced by direct transfer reactions and have been successfully used to produce the new, unexpectedly long-lived species ^{261}Lr (40 minutes) and ^{262}Lr (3.6 hours) via transfer reactions from ^{22}Ne projectiles[25]. Again, if the desired product decays via spontaneous fission and is not long enough for chemical and mass separation, positive identification of Z and A is nearly impossible using the presently available systems. However, a system called HEFT (Heavy Element Fission Tracker) was proposed by Wilhelmy et al.[26] in which an array of modules, each designed to measure the velocity, energy loss, total energy, and position of fission fragments is used. An array of five pairs of these modules should permit efficient detection of coincident fission fragments and make it possible to make definitive assignments based on 10 to 100 detected events. On-line measurements of half-lives as short as nanoseconds is envisioned. Off-line measurements of longer-lived nuclides could be performed using the gas-jet technique and a rotating wheel system.

Currently, the biggest obstacle to the discovery of additional new elements and superheavy elements appears to be finding synthesis reactions by which they can be produced with detectable cross sections and additional effort should be invested in attaining a better understanding of the reaction mechanisms involved. However, both on the basis of theoretical predictions of nuclear stability and the demonstrated ingenuity of the experimentalists in designing new devices with ever increasing efficiencies, the prognosis for the identification of a number of new elements and even superheavy elements is quite promising.

References

1. Seaborg, G. T.: "Hot Atom Chemistry" (T. Matsuura, Ed.) Kodansha, Tokyo (and Elsevier, Amsterdam), 1984, p. 7.
2. Ghiorso, A., Sikkeland, T., Nurmia, M., Phys. Rev. Lett., 18, p. 401 (1967).
3. Macfarlane, R. D., McHarris, W. C., "Nuclear Spectroscopy and Reactions A" (J. Cerny, Ed.) Academic Press, New York and London,, 1974, p. 244.
4. Ghiorso, A., Sikkeland, T., Walton, J. R., Seaborg, G. T., Phys. Rev. Lett., 1, 18 (1958).
5. Ghiorso, A., Sikkeland, T., Larsh, A. E., Latimer, R. M., Phys. Rev. Lett., 6, 473 (1961).
6. Donets, E. D., Schegolev, V. A., Ermakov, V. A., Atom. Energ., 19, 109 (1965); English translation, Sov. J. At. Energy, 19, 995 (1965).
7. Ghiorso, A., Nurmia, M., Harris, J., Eskola, K., Eskola, P., Phys. Rev. Lett., 22, 1317 (1969).
8. Ghiorso, A., Nurmia, M., Eskola, K., Harris, J., Eskola, P., Phys. Rev. Lett. 24, 1498 (1970).
9. Ghiorso, A., Nitschke, J. M., Alonso, J. R., Alonso, C. T., Nurmia, M., Seaborg, G. T., Hulet, E. K., Lougheed, R. W., Phys. Rev. Lett., 33, 1490

(1974).
10. Münzenberg, G. et al., Z. Phys., A300, 107 (1981).
11. Münzenberg, G. et al., Z. Phys., A309, 89 (1982); A315, 145 (1984).
12. Münzenberg, G. et al., Z. Phys., A317, 235 (1984); A328, 49 (1987).
13. Münzenberg, G. et al., Z. Phys., A330, 435 (1989).
14. Oganessian, Y. T., Iljinov, A. S., Demin, A. G., Tretyakov, S. P., Nucl. Phys., A239, 353 (1975).
15. Möller, P., Leander, G, A., and Nix, J. R., Z. Physik A: At. Nucl., 323, 41 (1986).
16. Möller, P., Nix, J. R.and Swiatecki, W. J.., Nucl. Phys., A492, 349 (1989).
17. Boening, K., Patyk, K., Sobiczewski, A., and Cwiok, S., Z. Phys. A: At. Nucl., 325, 479 (1986).
18. Cwiok, S., Pashkevich, V. V., Dudek, J., and Nazarewicz, W., Nucl. Phys., A410, 254 (1983).
19. Leino, M. E., Yashita, S., Ghiorso, A., Phys. Rev. C 24, 2370 (1981).
20. Ghiorso, A., Yashita, S., Leino, M., Frank, L., Kalnins, J., Armbruster, P., Dufour, J. P., Lemmertz, P. K., Nucl. Instr. Meth. A269, 192 (1988).
21. Ghiorso, A., J. Radioanal. Chem., 124, 407, (1988).
22. Yeremin, A. V. et al., Nucl. Instr. Meth., A274, 528 (1989).
23. Armbruster, P., Ann. Rev. Nucl. Part. Sci., 35, 135 (1985).
24. Ghiorso, A., Hoffman, D. C., Hulet, E. K., Keller, O. L., Seaborg, G. T., Lawrence Berkeley Laboratory Publication No. Pub-5118 (1984).
25. Lougheed, R. W., Moody, K. J., Dougan, R. J., Wild, J. F., Hulet, E. K., Dupzyk, R. J., Henderson, C. M., Gannett, C. M., Henderson, R. A., Hoffman, D. C., Lee, D. M., Sümmerer, K., Hahn, R. L., Lawrence Livermore Laboratory Nuclear Chemistry Division FY87 Annual Report, UCAR-10062/87, 1987, p. 4-2.
26. J. B. Wilhelmy, Los Alamos National Laboratory Isotope and Nuclear Chemistry Division Annual Report FY84, LA-10366-PR, 1985, p.147.

Chapter 2

Hot Atom Chemistry of Specific Elements

2.1 Hot Atom Chemistry of Tritium

Yasuyuki ARATONO,[1] Kunio OOHASHI[2] and David S. URCH[3]

(1) Japan Atomic Energy Research Institute, Tokai, Ibaraki, 319-11 Japan
(2) Department of Chemistry, College of Arts and Sciences, Chiba University, Yayoi, Chiba, 260 Japan
(3) Department of Chemistry, Queen Mary and Westfield College - University of London, Mile End Road, London, E1 4NS, England

1. Introduction

The basic reactions of recoil tritium and reviews of its chemistry up to 1980 have been considered in the previous edition of this book[1]; other reviews of recoil tritium chemistry have also been published.[2,3]. Gas-phase studies of the reactions of recoil tritium have not been pursued as actively as during the two decades 1960-1980 but research in this field is still progressing with interest more concentrated on relative rates of hot atom reactions. $^3He(n,p)^3H$ is used as the source of recoil tritium and the reactions can be modified by factors such as scavenger, pressure or the amount of moderator (inert bath gas) so that vibrationally excited states and specific hot reactions can be distinguished. Furthermore, the analysis of tritium labelled products is facilitated by the use of radio gas chromatography. Rather less information is available for condensed phase reactions because of the difficulties of interpreting the experimental results in terms of simple atom-molecule collisions. Both the $^6Li(n,\alpha)^3H$ and $^3He(n,p)^3H$ nuclear processes can be used as a source of recoil tritium and recent studies have concentrated not only on reactions in aromatic systems but also on the effect of change of phase on hot atom reactions. Studies of the reactions of recoil tritium have been extended to include water and solid alkanes, reflecting the development of pile and nuclear fusion reactor technologies, but very few reactions have been reported with inorganic compounds. In order to avoid repetition, the reactions of recoil tritium will be considered in this review according to molecular type rather than phase. This will also facilitate the discussion of phase change studies.

2. Reactions with Hydrogen

The reactions of recoil tritium with hydrogen isotopes are a very basic field of hot reaction kinetics and have been studied intensively. As is well known, hydrogen has two spin isomers ortho-H_2(o-H_2) and para-H_2(p-H_2). Hawke et al.[4] studied the difference between these isomers for recoil tritium reaction in the system of p-H_2 enriched mixtures of H_2 with D_2. The results are shown in Table 1. As is seen in the Table, the $(p_{HT}/p_{DT})_{normal}/(p_{HT}/p_{DT})_{p\text{-}enriched}$ is 1.09 for an unmoderated and unscavenged system, suggesting that hot reaction is independent of the spin state of H_2. On the other hand, the values for moderated but unscavenged systems are 1.26 and 1.23 and agree well with $(o\text{-}H_2)_{normal}/(o\text{-}H_2)_{p\text{-}enriched}$ values of 1.25 and 1.23. These results show the preference of o-H_2 for the reaction with tritium in the thermal-epithermal region. These differences were supposed to be due to the long collision time of thermal or epithermal tritium, that is, the o-H_2 can polarize the tritium atom such that its nuclear spin is aligned parallel to that of the o-H_2.

Table 1 Specific Ratio, p_{HT}/p_{DT}, for Normal and p-Enriched H_2 Reaction Systems

<table>
<tr><td>Moderator</td><td>None</td><td colspan="2">Ar</td><td colspan="2">Xe</td></tr>
<tr><td>Scavenger</td><td>None</td><td>None</td><td>I_2</td><td>None</td><td>I_2</td></tr>
<tr><td>$(p_{HT}/p_{DT})_{normal}$</td><td>1.54</td><td>2.16</td><td>1.13</td><td>2.11</td><td>-</td></tr>
<tr><td>o-H_2/p-H_2</td><td colspan="5">75/25</td></tr>
<tr><td>$(p_{HT}/p_{DT})_{p\text{-}enriched}$</td><td>1.41</td><td>1.72</td><td>1.11</td><td>1.71</td><td>1.04</td></tr>
<tr><td>o-H_2/p-H_2</td><td>(a)</td><td colspan="2">60/40</td><td colspan="2">61/39</td></tr>
<tr><td>$\frac{(p_{HT}/p_{DT})_{normal}}{(p_{HT}/p_{DT})_{p\text{-}enriched}}$</td><td>1.09</td><td>1.26</td><td>1.02</td><td>1.23</td><td>-</td></tr>
<tr><td>$\frac{(o\text{-}H_2)_{normal}}{(o\text{-}H_2)_{p\text{-}enriched}}$</td><td>-</td><td>1.25</td><td>1.25</td><td>1.23</td><td>1.23</td></tr>
</table>

(a) not given but supposed to be 60/40 or 61/39.

3. Reactions with Simple Hydrides

The reaction of recoil tritium with water in the solid[5], liquid[6] and gas[7] phases has been extensively studied: an investigation initiated to elucidate the behavior of tritium in both conventional and fusion nuclear reactors. The labelled products are HT and HTO in all phases and the major part of the yields is due to hot reactions. The yield of HT falls from 18.7% in the gas to 12% in the liquid and decreases with increasing irradiation time in the solid. This trend in the solid phase is in agreement with the assumption that the

HT yield was reduced by its reaction with hydroxyl radicals produced by the radiolysis of water. The enhanced HT yield in the gas phase is attributed to the dissociative de-excitation of $[HTO]^*$ molecules produced by the hot labelling reaction. Similar studies have been made of aqueous solutions.[8] The threshold kinetic energy of tritium to produce the excited $[HTO]^*$ species was estimated to be about 7 eV from thermodynamic calculations.

The reactions of recoil tritium with ammonia and perdeutero-ammonia have also been investigated.[9] Again the products are HT or DT and labelled parent molecule. RRK theory was used to calculate a rate constant for the unimolecular dissociation of $[NH_2T]^*$ formed by the hot T-for-H replacement reaction, but the theoretical value $(4.7 \pm 0.8) \times 10^{11}$ s^{-1} proved to be an order of magnitude greater than observed (presumably due to the assumptions inherent in RRK theory not being fulfilled by a localized, fast, T-for-H reaction).

The hot substitution yields in simple hydrides such as PH_3, AsH_3, H_2S and HCl were compared with CH_4, SiH_4, GeH_4, NH_3, H_2O from the viewpoint of bond energies and the bond angle between hydrogens and central atom.[10,11] The yield of the substitution product did not depend on the bond energies, but decreased with bond angle for the compounds of the same period in the periodic table. The effect of the bond angle was ascribed to the difference of the electron density on the central atom brought by the lone pairs electron on the central atom, i.e., the increase of H-M-H bond angle, where M means the central atom, causes a decrease of electron density on the central atom and resulted in a decrease in reactivity for the incoming T atoms.

4. Reactions with Aliphatic Compounds

The extensive studies of the reactions of recoil tritium with adsorbed hydrocarbons have continued, e.g., ethane on zeolites.[12] As in the gas phase the major products are HT and labelled parent molecules. In the case of ethane adsorbed onto silica gel[13] it was possible to show that the average vibrational energy of newly labelled molecule, $[C_2H_5T]^*$ was about 2 eV. Solid ethane has also been studied[14] when dispersed in a rare gas matrix. This circumstance proved very similar to the gas phase, the major yields were HT and C_2H_5T with the former being produced by both hot and thermal atoms whilst labelled ethane was only made by hot T atoms. However, large isotope effects were observed[14,15] in the formation of HT or DT by abstraction from solid C_2H_6 or C_2D_6(HT:DT $\sim$3.5:1). This was ascribed to quantum-mechanical tunneling. The formation of vibrationally excited species as a result of the hot T-for-H process[16] has been studied in detail for ethyl fluoride and also ethyl alcohol. In the case of C_2H_5F, a pressure range of six orders of magnitude was investigated(1-10^6 Pa) covering the change of state from gas to liquid.[17] At the lowest pressures only 5% of $[C_2H_4TF]^*$ became stabilized by collision; this rose to 91% in liquid ethylfluoride. From these results, and in the light of RRK of calculations, it was concluded that 95% of the $[C_2H_4TF]^*$ molecules were formed with an average vibrational excitation energy of 2.8 eV. But the high pressure and liquid phase results indicated that about 15% of the recently labelled molecules had quite high excitation energies, showing that the excitation function had a very long and narrow tail to high energies.

In a similar way the formation of highly vibrationally excited molecules, following the T-for-H reaction or the T-for-OH reaction in ethyl alcohol, has been postulated[18] to rationalize the observed pressure dependence of labelled ethane from $[C_2H_4TOH]^*$ and $[C_2H_5T]^*$. Studies of the T-for-H replacement reaction in substituted ethylenes (1,2-difluoroethylene[19] and 1,2-dichroloethylene[20,21] have shown that the original cis- or trans-configuration is retained to more than 80% and that the retention is greater[20] in the liquid than the gas phase. This is ascribed to the formation, in some cases, of a vibrationally excited species which, if not rapidly moderated by collision, as would happen in a liquid, would have sufficient energy to change its geometric configuration unimolecularly.

5. Reactions with Aromatic Systems

Studies of the reactions of recoil tritium in liquid benzene showed[22] that hot tritium gave yields of HT (15%), C_6H_5T (45%) and C_6H_6T (35%). In substituted benzenes the hot T-for-H substitution reaction at aromatic H sites is remarkably uniform (toluene)[23] and appears to be independent of phase. When excess hexafluorobenzene or water is added to toluene[23], benzonitrile[24], or lithium β-phenylproplonate[25], greater selectivity is observed, usually favoring the ortho- and para-positions. As hexafluorobenzene or water presumably acts as a moderator for hot tritium atoms these results indicate a greater selectivity on the part of lower energy recoil T atoms, as could be expected. Recently, non-uniform tritium distributions were found in the T-for-H substitution with naphthalene[26], its derivatives, pyrroles, and uracil[27], the rings of which were considered to be strongly activated. The orientation of the substitution agreed with that of an electrophilic reaction in the case of aniline, and was interpreted by assuming an intermediate complex formed in the lower energy region in the hot atom reaction. In 5,10,15,20-tetraphenylporphyrine, the benzene ring was substituted by recoil tritium in a higher energy region than for the pyrrole ring, in agreement with the above findings.[28]

When the relative reactivities of different hydrogen sites were studied as is possible in molecules such as benzoic acid, acetanilide, phenyl ethyl alcohol[29] and porphyrine[30] it was found that the order is NH(pyrrole) > CH(pyrrole) > CH(benzene) > CH(aliphatic). The order, at least for CH sites, was established[31] in experiments using benzene, hexane, cyclohexane and perdeuterocyclohexane: in these experiments it was found that aromatic sites were three times more likely to be labelled by tritium than aliphatic ones.

6. Reactions with Inorganic Compounds

The neutron irradiation of lithium salts is the principal source of tritium and recent investigations have centered upon determining the final chemical state of tritium. In the case of lithium fluoride[32] or lithium fluoride -

beryllium fluoride mixtures[33] much of the tritium is found as TF whilst the irradiation of oxy-metal lithium salts(i.e., $LiAlO_2$, Li_2MoO_4 and Li_2WO_4)[34] leads to the formation of both metal-tritium and oxygen-tritium bonds. The reactions of recoil tritium with graphite[35,36] and boron carbide[37] have also been investigated. The reactive surface of graphite leads to a variety of labelled compounds being formed whose nature can be varied by changes in the annealing procedures.

7. Conclusion

Experiments carried out during the past 30 years have clearly established the basic reactions of the hot atom chemistry of recoil tritium and have given an indication of the relative energies involved in some reactions. But tritium production in the nuclear reactor can be accompanied by undesirable effects such as the decomposition of the reactant and reaction products by in-pile gamma rays and/or through the recoil energy degradation process. This makes the interpretation of the experimental results difficult. Even so evidence from studies the reactions of recoil tritium with solid mixtures of n-$C_{10}D_{22}$, n-$C_{10}H_{22}$ or neo-C_5H_{12}, iso-C_4H_9D showed[38-40] that most recoil atoms react within their own track and that the thermal diffusion of tritium atoms in the bulk matrix are of little importance. These results also indicate that gross decomposition can usually be ignored. A further problem in the interpretation of tritium results is, of course the complete lack of any direct information about the energy of the atom when it reacts.

Recently, laser technology has developed very rapidly and its application to research on hot atom chemistry has becoming interesting. The production of intensive and monochromatic hydrogen beam by laser photolysis will make studies under very well-defined experimental condition possible. In addition, the analysis of the internal state(electronic, vibrational, rotational and translational) and distribution of the products by laser will clarify the elementary processes of hot atom reactions. The crossed beam experiment combining the superiority of laser technique and the measurement of angular distribution of the products by a rotatable mass spectrometer has been carried out by Lee et al..[41]

References

1. Urch, D. S.: "Hot Atom Chemistry" (T. Matsuura Ed.) Kodansha, Tokyo (and Elsvier, Amsterdam), 1984, p. 128.
2. Tominaga, T., Tachikawa, E.: "Modern Hot Atom Chemistry and Its Applications" Springer-Verlag, Berlin Heidelberg New York 1981.
3. Saeki, M.: "CRC Handbook of Radiation Chemistry" (Y. Tabata Ed.) CRC Press, Boca Raton, Ann Arbor, Boston, 1991, p. 525.
4. Hawke, J. G., Sueda, A. A., Lukey, C. A.: J. Chem. Soc., Chem. Commun., 1986, 499.
5. Aratono, Y., Tachikawa, E.: J. Inorg. Nucl. Chem., 39, 555 (1977).
6. Tachikawa, E., Aratono, Y.: ibid, 38, 193 (1976).
7. Koutit, A., Paulus, J. M.: Radiochimica Acta, 30, 89 (1982).
8. Aratono, Y., Nakashima, M., Tachikawa, E.: J. Inorg. Nucl. Chem., 39, 1473 (1977).

9. Koutit, A., Paulus, J. M.: Radiochimica Acta, 40. 119 (1986).
10. Castiglioni, M., Volpe, P.: ibid, 34, 165 (1983).
11. idem: Polyhedron, 2, 225 (1983).
12. Tsetskhladze, T. V., Cherkezishvili, L. I., Tsibakhasivlli, N. Ya.: Zh. Fiz. Khim, 58, 1214 (1984).
13. Salukvadze R. E.: Khim Vys Ehnerg, 20, 371 (1985); High Energy Chem.(Engl. Trans.), 20, 287 (1986).
14. Lee, K. P., Ito, Y., Fujitani, Y., Miyazaki, T., Fueki, K., Aratono, Y., Saeki, M., Tachikawa, E.: J. Phys. Chem., 90, 5343 (1986).
15. Aratono, Y., Tachikawa, E., Miyazaki, T. Nagata, S., Fujitani, Y., Fueki, K.: ibid, 87, 1201 (1983).
16. Tang, Y. N.: "Isotopes in Organic Chemistry"(E. Buncel and C. C. Lee, Ed.) Elsevier, 1979, Vol. 4, p. 85.
17. Tang, Y. N., Wu, E. C., Anderson J. W., Clark, R. R.: J. Chem. Phys., 79, 2181 (1983).
18. Jiunnguang, L., Jongchen, N.: J. Radioanal. Nucl. Chem., 97, 237 (1986).
19. Siefert, E. E., Smith, D. D., Tricca, R. E., Ayoub, P. M., Tang, Y. N.: J. Am. Chem. Soc., 105, 330 (1983).
20. King, W. G., Wai, C. M.: Radiochem. Radioanal. Letters, 30, 27 (1977).
21. Veenboer, J. Th., Brinkman, G. A.: Radiochim. Acta, 30, 193 (1982).
22. Brinkman, G. A., Veenboer, J. Th.: ibid, 29, 21 (1981).
23. Oohashi, K., Morikawa, N.: Radioisotopes(Tokyo), 33, 601 (1984).
24. Oohashi, K., Takiguchi, H., Morikawa, N.: ibid, 33, 747 (1984).
25. Oohashi, K., Morikawa, N.: ibid, 33, 444 (1984).
26. Muramatsu, Y., Izawa, G., Yoshihara, K.: Radiochim. Acta, 38, 5 (1985).
27. Murano, Y., Akimoto, J., Yoshihara, K.: ibid, 38, 11 (1985).
28. Izawa, G., Shiraihashi, K.,Murano, Y., Yoshihara, K.: ibid, 46, 191 (1989).
29. Nogawa, N., Oohashi, K., Matuoka, H., Moki, T., Moriya, T. Morikawa, N.: J. Radioanal. Nucl. Chem. Letters, 106, 47 (1986).
30. Shiraishi, K. Izawa, G., Yoshihara, K.: ibid, 105, 257(1986).
31. Oohashi, K., Nogawa, N., Tanno, N., Morikawa, N.: J. Radioanal. Nucl. Chem. Letters, 128, 181 (1988).
32. Aratono, Y., Nakashima, M., Saeki, M., Tachikawa, E.: Radiochim. Acta, 37, 101(1984).
33. Moriyama, H., Maeda, S., Ohmura, T., Moritani, K., Oishi, J.: "Chemical Aspects of Down-Stream for Thorium Fuel Cycle" (S. Suzuki, T. Mitsugashira, M. Hara, I. Satoh and Y. Shiokawa, Ed.) Atomic Energy Society of Japan, Tokyo, 1987, p. 125.
34. Kurilenko, L. N., Serebryakova, N. V., Saunin, E. I., Gromov, V. V., Sokolova, N. P.: Zh. Fiz. Khim, 6, 3093 (1987).
35. Vietzke, E., Philipps, V.: Radiochim. Acta, 43, 75 (1989).
36. (a)Tsetskhladze, T. V., Cherkezishvill, L. I., Tsibakhashvili, N. Ya.: Zh. Fiz. Kim. 62, 1690 (1988).; (b) Saeki, M., Masaki, N. M.: Radiochim. Acta, 46, 163 (1989).
37. Barnov, V. A., Bobokhidze, K. Sh., Nadirashvili, L. Sh., Tsetskhiadze, T. V.: At. Ehnerg, 64, 441 (1988).
38. Aratono, Y., Tachikawa, E., Miyazaki, T., Sakurai, M., Fueki, K.: Bull. Chem. Soc. Jpn., 54, 1627 (1981).
39. Aratono, Y., Tachikawa, E., Miyazaki, T., Fueki, K.: ibid, 55, 1957 (1982).
40. Aratono, Y., Tachikawa, E., Miyazaki, T., Kawai, Y., Fueki, K.: J. Phys. Chem., 86, 248 (1982).
41. Continetti, R. E., Balko, B. A., Lee, Y. T.: Proc. Int. Symp. on Advanced Nucl. Energy Res., -Near Future Chemistry in Nuclear Energy Field-, Oarai, 1989, p. 14.

2.2 Hot Atom Chemistry of Chlorine

G.A. BRINKMAN [a] AND B.S.M. RAO [b]

[a] TF-A - FOM Group, University of Amsterdam, c/o NIKHEF-K, P.O. Box 41882, 1009 DB Amsterdam, The Netherlands

[b] Chemistry Department, University of Poona, Pune - 411 007, India

1. Introduction

The most commonly used chlorine isotopes for hot atom chemistry research are:

a) ^{34m}Cl ($t_{1/2}$ = 32 min) produced via (γ,n), (n,2n) and (p,d) reactions from ^{35}Cl,

b) ^{38}Cl ($t_{1/2}$ = 37 min) produced via (n,γ) and (d,p) reactions from ^{37}Cl, via (γ,pn) and (d,α) from ^{40}Ar as well as via β-decay of ^{38}S and

c) ^{39}Cl ($t_{1/2}$ = 56 min) via the (γ,p) reaction from ^{40}Ar.

When these isotopes are produced from $^{35,37}Cl$ atoms which are part of a chlorinated molecule, the recoil energies that they receive as a consequence of their nuclear formation are sufficient to rupture the chemical bonds.

After slowing down, the recoil Cl atoms are thought to reach the chemical reactive zone (< 20 eV) as neutral ground-state atoms and then can react as hot atoms [1]. However, in most systems the majority of these recoil atoms lose their translational energy by elastic collisions: they will react as thermal Cl atoms via H-abstraction and addition to alkenes and arenes [2]. Reactions of hot and thermal Cl atoms can lead to the formation of the same labelled products and a discussion of hot atom reactions must therefore include the contribution of thermal atoms.

The research into the reactions of recoil T and ^{18}F atoms is mainly focused on gaseous systems, but in the case of recoil Cl atoms most of the investigations have dealt with liquid compounds. This is quite understandable, as the nuclear reactions for the production of ^{34m}Cl or ^{38}Cl require a compound containing Cl: a vast proportion of these are liquids at room temperature. In general, experiments in the gaseous phase are more straightforward than in the condensed phases, where cage reactions may be involved. At the end of the track of the relaxed recoil particle, ions, radicals and excited products are formed that may easily react with less energetic or thermalized Cl atoms and as a consequence, these liquid phase reactions do not lend themselves to theoretical modelling.

The discussion of the reactions of recoil Cl atoms will be based on two types of experiments:

1) the determination of total organic yields in mixtures of liquid halocarbons with hydrocarbons and high π-electron density scavengers, and
2) studying the four main reaction channels (abstraction, substitution, fragmentation and addition) and covering the three aggregation states of simple organic compounds (methanes [3a]), alkanes, cycloalkanes, alkenes [3b]) and arenes [3c])).

A special feature of gas phase experiments is the possibility of determining the extent of excitation energy that remains in a labelled molecule after a hot substitution reaction. This can be achieved by measuring the products formed via decomposition or isomerization (i.e. cycloalkanes). Stereochemical investigations of the substitution of an atom bound to an asymmetric C atom (retention versus inversion) can furnish information regarding the approach of the recoil atom and the course of the reaction. In highly moderated systems, thermal reactions of radioactive Cl atoms can be studied and rate constants can be measured.

The major interest in liquid phase hot atom chemistry (LPHAC) arises from the availability of a great number of compounds, high product yields and the possibility of probing the mechanistic aspects of the reactivity of hot and thermal Cl atoms with arenes. The experiments deal mainly with the determination of the formed labelled compounds and their yields, and their dependence upon the nature and concentration of additives (i.e. radical scavengers).

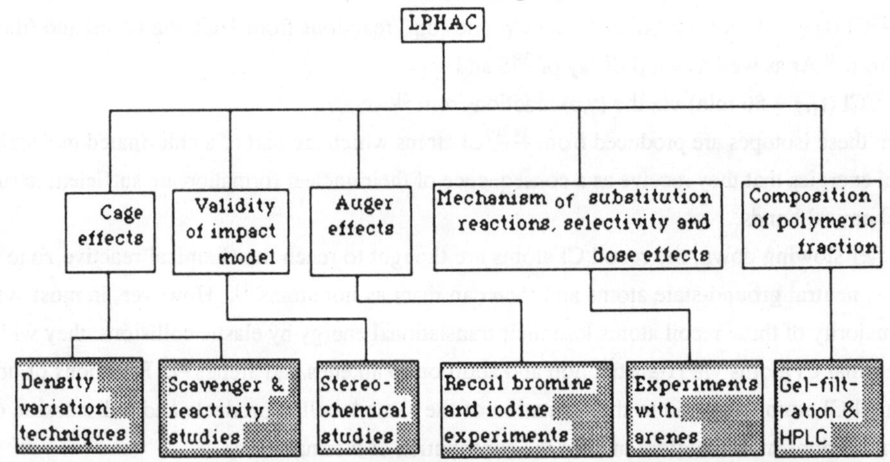

The diagram above gives a schematic overview of the basic problems associated with recoil halogen atom chemistry in the liquid phase and the types of experiments that are performed to gain further insight into their reaction mechanisms. Some of these aspects are discussed in more detail elsewhere in this book.

Product yields measured for solid compounds are generally higher than those in the liquid phase: thermalized recoil Cl atoms and radicals can barely escape from the cage in the solid medium.

In order to evaluate the relative reactivities of recoil halogen atoms, Kontis and Urch [4]) developed a theory that is based on the existence of different cross-sections (σ) for the formation of organic labelled compounds in mixtures of two components (A,B). When both compounds are aliphatic, the organic yields are derived from a single hot zone either through hot substitution or via caged radical reactions. However, a second stage is operative for aromatic compounds, in which recoil halogen atoms react with the arenes through a thermal, diffusive exchange reaction. Relative cross- sections for both the hot ($S = \sigma_A/\sigma_B$) and thermal ($S^1 = \sigma^1{}_A/\sigma^1{}_B$) processes and the organic yields in the pure compounds due to hot (Y_A or Y_B) and thermal $Y^1{}_A$ or $Y^1{}_B$) reactions have been evaluated. From the work of Kontis *et al.* [4,5] and Rao *et al.* [6], experimental data are given in the following Table:

	X	Y	Y^1	S	S^1
Additive: c-C_6H_{12}					
CH_2Cl_2, $CHCl_3$, CCl_4	14	40	-	15	-
C_2Cl_4	13	47	-	5	-
C_6H_5Cl	14	24	38	2	33
$C_6H_5CH_2Cl$	18	17	20	2	4
2,4-$C_6H_3Cl_2CH_2Cl$	21	24	30	2	10
Additive: $C_6H_5NH_2$					
C_6H_5Cl	8	7	54	1	220
o-$C_6H_4Cl_2$	11	26	42	6	320

X: Organic yield (%) of the pure additive (A).

Y, Y^1: Organic yields (%) of the pure substrate (B), due to hot (Y_B) and thermal (Y, Y^1B) reactions.

S, S^1: Relative cross-sections (σ_A/σ_B) for hot and thermal reactions.

One of the results is that for mixtures of chlorobenzenes with hydrocarbons and alcohols, the S values (1-3) are much lower than for corresponding mixtures of chloromethanes and chloroethanes (S = 10-15), indicating that hot reactions are more predominant in the case of arenes. Very high S^1 values are observed in mixtures of chlorobenzenes with aniline and other high π-electron density compounds, which is attributed to a more efficient H-elimination from the p-complex formed between a Cl atom and these molecules. This model provides only a guideline to help determine whether a one- or two-stage mechanism is operative, but does not impart any real quantitative significance to the absolute values of the different parameters.

2. Abstraction

The abstraction of a hydrogen or a halogen atom (X) by a recoil Cl atom leads to the formation of inorganic products (HCl, XCl.) The yield of this fraction is normally determined by shaking the irradiated organic (chlorinated) compound with an aqueous solution containing an amount of Cl^- (as a carrier) and $SO_3^=$ (for the reduction of XCl.) This inorganic fraction also contains products that are formed via abstraction reactions of thermalized recoil Cl atoms, as well as Cl atoms that have not reacted with the organic matrix but rather, are reduced by impurities or radiolytically-produced radicals, or are absorbed on the walls of the irradiation vessel. Many experiments were performed in the presence of traces of I_2 as a scavenger of thermalized Cl atoms which, in general, resulted in an increase of the inorganic fraction. The number of radioactive Cl atoms in the inorganic fraction therefore decline utterly to provide any indication of the true yields of hot (and thermal) abstraction reactions.

Hydrogen abstraction by hot and thermal recoil Cl atoms from aliphatic compounds is also possible as these processes are exothermic, in contrast with aromatic H-abstraction by thermal Cl atoms. The average inorganic yields for several liquid chloromethanes and chloroethanes are identical at 63%, despite the possibility of the elimination of HCl from excited chloroethane molecules [7)]. The inorganic yields for a series of liquid chloroethylenes are in the order of 32% [7)]: these data cannot be explained by H-abstraction, as a similar yield was also measured for C_2Cl_4. For both the alkanes and ethylenes, the inorganic yields are not greatly affected by the addition of I_2, contrary to the results obtained for halobenzenes where the inorganic yields are doubled [8,9)]. The presence of a CH_3 group in chlorobenzenes does not lead to an increase in the inorganic yield, indicating that benzylic H-abstraction does not play an important role [6,10)]. However, in the case of $C_6H_4ClNH_2$ isomers and other high π-electron density compounds, the inorganic yields (85%) are far higher than for all other substituted arenes [6,11)]. What appears to be relevant is not the presence of a substituent containing H, but rather the existence of an electron-donating group.

There is some evidence that hot halogen abstraction reactions are very rare. Lee and Rowland [12)] placed an upper limit of probability of 5% on hot halogen abstraction from gaseous CF_2Cl_2 (by activity balance), but the actual yield is more likely to be in the vicinity of <1%. Mudra [13)] measured a yield of 1% $C_2H_4Cl^{38}Cl$ in gaseous CCl_4 containing 2.4 mol% C_2H_4; this yield was purported to be the result of addition by $Cl^{38}Cl$. In a similar type of experiment, Brinkman and Visser [14)] found a yield of 6% 1,2-$C_6H_{12}Cl^{34m}Cl$ in gaseous CCl_4 containing 10% 1-C_6H_{12}. (A yield of 12% 1,2-$C_6H_{12}Cl^{34m}Cl$ measured in liquid CCl_4 containing traces of 1-C_6H_{12} may be partly due to cage reactions [15)]).

Apart from the abstraction of hydrogen and halogen atoms, the abstraction of methylgroups was also observed. In liquid $C_6H_5CH_3$, some 3% $CH_3{}^{38}Cl$ was measured (this may be somewhat overstated, as the yield of polymers was not determined), whereas 1% $CF_3{}^{38}Cl$ was found in liquid $C_6H_5CF_3$ [16)]. Neither compound was formed via caged recombination reactions, as their yields in mixtures containing CCl_4 decrease linearly with CCl_4 concentrations. In liquid chloroethanes, some small percent of labelled chloromethanes were detected [7a].

Rate constants for thermal abstraction reactions can be measured in highly moderated systems. A special investigation dealt with the reactions of recoil ^{38}Cl atoms with H_2 and D_2: experimentally, no distinction could be made between abstraction and substitution leading to the formation of $H^{38}Cl$ or $D^{38}Cl$ [17]. At low energies (high moderation) an isotope effect of $k(H_2)/k(D_2) = 2.3$ was found, which corresponds to a temperature of 1,200K, according to non-radioactive kinetic data. At higher ^{38}Cl reaction energies however, there is a cross-over to an opposite isotope effect of 0.8. This behaviour was interpreted by a non-Boltzmann rate constant formalism.

Lee and Rowland [18] measured rate constants for the abstraction of H atoms by thermal ^{38}Cl atoms from CH_4 and C_2H_6: $(1.9 \pm 0.4)10^7$ and 2.7×10^{10} L mol^{-1}s^{-1}, respectively. These data are in good accord with recommended values for thermal non-radioactive Cl atoms (243K): 2.2×10^7 and 3.2×10^{10} L mol^{-1}s^{-1}, respectively [19]. Thermal abstraction of CH_3 was observed from $(CH_3)_4Pb$: the yield of $CH_3{}^{38}Cl$ was 18% and the rate constant at room temperature was $(1.8 \pm 0.3)10^{10}$ L mol^{-1}s^{-1} [20].

3. Methanes

The yields for the substitution of hydrogen and halogen (X) atoms in gaseous CH_nX_{4-n} compounds by recoil Cl atoms are in the order of only 1-2% per atom (see Table XII in Ref. 3a for a virtually complete survey). In the CH_nCl_{4-n} series, the total yields of hot substitution reactions decrease with enhanced chlorination and the Cl atoms are preferentially displaced [21]. Substitution of the heavier atoms in the CF_nCl_{4-n} series is also favoured [22]; the energy deposited after such a reaction is higher than in the case of the CH_4Cl_{4-n} series and consequently more decomposition of the excited molecules occurs. In the presence of traces of I_2, the replacement of two atoms can be established by the detection of $CX_2{}^{38}ClI$; the yields are also in the order of 1-2% [3a]. The substitution of even three atoms in CH_2Cl_2 (one H and two Cl) was confirmed by the detection of c-$C_3H_5{}^{38}Cl$, which is formed through the addition of $CH^{38}Cl$ to some added C_2H_4 [23].

In the presence of C_2H_4 and I_2 scavengers, the hot ^{38}Cl-for-H,D substitution in gaseous CH_4 and CD_4 extrapolate to zero at infinite dilution with Ar. In the 60-90% moderator concentration range, the yield ratios for single (CH_3Cl/CD_3Cl) and double (CH_2Cl/CD_2Cl) displacement reactions are constant: 1.8 and 1.6, respectively [24]. The origin of these hot isotope effects is primarily reactive in nature and is not a result of unimolecular decomposition of excited intermediates.

The substitution yields for liquid chloromethanes are far greater than those measured for the gaseous compounds. For recoil ^{34m}Cl atoms, the following yields (%) were reported [3a,7a]:

	CH_2Cl_2	$CHCl_3$	CCl_4	CCl_4 (solid) [25]
Cl substitution	15	16	34	63
H substitution	6	6	-	-
Ethylenes	1	2	3	3
Ethanes	2	4	6	12

These high substitution yields are not as the result of hot one-step replacement reactions but are mainly due to caged recombination reactions. In the case of CCl_4, only 3% $CCl_3{}^{34m}Cl$ is formed via direct ^{34m}Cl-for-Cl substitution, whereas 32% is produced through a reaction between ^{34m}Cl atoms and CCl_3 radicals. The production of labelled ethylenes and ethanes can only be explained by the replacement of more than one atom: for the formation of 3% $C_2Cl_3{}^{34m}Cl$ in liquid CCl_4, five C-Cl bonds in two CCl_4 molecules have to be broken. For solid CCl_4, the yields of $CCl_3{}^{34m}Cl$ and $C_2Cl_5{}^{34m}Cl$ are even greater than those measured in the liquid phase: radicals and thermalized ^{34m}Cl atoms can barely escape from the cage in this rigid medium.

In liquid mixtures of CCl_4 and C_6F_6, the $CCl_3{}^{38}Cl$ yield decreases with increased C_6F_6 concentrations [26]. However, in frozen mixtures the $CCl_3{}^{38}Cl$ yield remains constant, even upon a twenty-fold dilution. Below are the yields in %:

Molar Ratio	$CCl_3{}^{38}Cl$		$C_6F_5{}^{38}Cl$	
$CCl_4 : C_6F_6$	liquid	solid	liquid	solid
100 : 0	34	61	-	-
10 : 90	2.9	57	16	0.1
5 : 95	1.3	61	16	0.2

These results were interpreted by the formation of CCl_4 clusters (or micro-crystals) in the frozen mixtures. Recoil ^{38}Cl atoms produced in these crystals will react before they have the chance to escape from the cluster - the low yields of $C_6F_5{}^{38}Cl$ in these frozen mixtures strengthen this conclusion. Similar behaviour was observed in frozen aqueous mixtures of CH_3Cl: the $CH_3{}^{38}Cl$ yield remained constant (6%) over a CH_3Cl concentration range of between 10-1 and 10-3 molair, whereas in liquid mixtures the yield diminished from 3.3 to 0.4% over the same concentration range [27].

An increase of a factor of two in the organic yields when going from the liquid to the solid phase was found for $CHCl_3$ [28] and CCl_2Br_2 [29].

4. Other Alkanes

The reactions of recoil Cl atoms with ethanes (and other higher alkanes) lead, apart from H- and X-replacement reactions, to C-C bond scission. The labelled products arising in gaseous C_2H_5Cl from the reactions of recoil ^{38}Cl [30] and ^{39}Cl [21] atoms are C_2H_5Cl (2-3%), CH_2Cl_2 (0.7%) and CH_3Cl (0.6-1.3%). The ^{38}Cl-for-H substitution reaction in C_2H_5Cl results in the formation of highly excited $C_2H_4Cl_2$ molecules that yield 90% C_2H_3Cl [23] via unimolecular decomposition. The decomposition of excited $C_2H_5{}^{38}Cl$ (formed by ^{38}Cl-for-Cl substitution) cannot be measured as the reaction product (C_2H_4) has no radioactive label. However, this reaction channel may be quite important, as labelled CH_3CHCl_2 (produced via Cl substitution in CH_3CHCl_2) decomposes to the extent of 82% into C_2H_3Cl. For liquid C_2H_5Cl the product yields are far higher: 8% C_2H_5Cl, 3% $C_2H_4Cl_2$, 3% C_2H_3Cl, 2% CH_3Cl and 2% CH_2Cl_2 [30]; the total organic yield is 23% (for solid C_2H_5Cl, the organic yield is 62% [31]).

Brinkman *et al.* [3a,7a] investigated the reactions of recoil ^{34m}Cl recoil atoms with liquid chloroethanes. The product yields (%) are given below:

	11-$C_2H_4Cl_2$	12-$C_2H_4Cl_2$	111-$C_2H_3Cl_3$	112-$C_2H_3Cl_3$	1112-$C_2H_2Cl_4$	1122-$C_2H_2Cl_4$	C_2HCl_5
Methanes	3	3	4	7	6	8	8
Ethylenes	3	1	6	5	8	9	10
Cl-substitution	9	8	8	12	12	10	9
H-substitution	6	5	nm	6	1	3	2

The three main reaction channels are similar to those observed in the gas phase experiments:

4.1 ^{34m}Cl-for-Cl substitution.

The yield of the labelled parent compound is independent of the number of Cl atoms in the molecule and averages some 9%. The initial yield is 15%, but almost half of the excited molecules decompose by HCl (and $H^{34m}Cl$) elimination.

4.2 ^{34m}Cl-for-H substitution.

Corrected for HCl elimination, the initial yield for this reaction decreases with a decreasing number of H atoms - from 7% for $C_2H_4Cl_2$ to 3% for C_2H_5Cl. (The degree of decomposition of compounds formed after ^{34m}Cl-for-H substitution is greater than that after ^{34m}Cl-for-Cl substitution because of the higher excitation energy deposited in the molecule in the former process).

4.3 ^{34m}Cl-for CH_xCl_{3-x} substitution, with an average yield of 4%.

However, there are some more complex reaction channels that lead to the formation of 1.5% $CH_2Cl^{34m}Cl$ from 1,1-$C_2H_4Cl_2$ and 1,1,1-$C_2H_3Cl_3$, of 1.5% $CHCl_2{}^{34m}Cl$ from 1,2-$C_2H_4Cl_2$ and 1,1,1,2-$C_2H_2Cl_4$ and of 2% $C_2Cl_5{}^{34m}Cl$ from 1,1,2,2-$C_2H_2Cl_4$. Furthermore, on the average, 20% of products containing three or more C atoms are formed. The reactions leading to these compounds must by nature be rather complex and require multiple bond rupture. Berei *et al.* [32)] also mentioned a 1,2-hydrogen shift in the irradiation of dichloroethanes, as 1,1-$C_2H_4Cl^{38}Cl$ was found in irradiated liquid and crystalline 1,2-$C_2H_4Cl_2$.

The organic yields measured for solid chloroethanes (65%) are a factor of two higher than for the liquid phase [25,28)]; this effect was explained by cluster formation.

The total ^{38}Cl-for-H displacement yield in gaseous 2-C_4H_9Cl is some 4% and the substitution pattern is almost statistical [33)]. In liquid 1- and 2-C_4H_9Cl the total Cl-for-H displacement yield is at least a factor of 5 higher, due to caged recombination between ^{38}Cl atoms and butyl radicals, but the distribution is still statistical.

Thermally excited c-C_3H_5Cl isomerizes to CH_2=CH-CH_2Cl; the unimolecular decomposition of c-$C_3H_5{}^{38,39}Cl$, formed by the reaction of $^{38,39}Cl$ atoms with gaseous c-C_3H_6, also leads to the formation of CHCl=CH-CH_3 [23)]. In similar experiments with c-C_4H_8 a value of 1.6 was measured for the C_2H_3Cl/c-C_4H_7Cl ratio; this means that after the Cl-for-H substitution, most of the molecules posses an excitation energy of over 2.6 eV, the activation energy for decomposition to C_2H_3Cl+C_2H_4.

5. Ethylenes

An important reaction of recoil Cl atoms with ethylenes is the addition to the unsaturated bond. Three reaction channels are available for excited or thermalized labelled chloroethyl radicals:

1. loss of a Cl atom to give (labelled or unlabelled) ethylene,
2. abstraction of an H or Cl atom from another molecule to yield an ethane and
3. addition to another ethylene molecule to form a dimer; this process may befollowed by subsequent polymerization reactions.

The product yields (%) for these reactions deduced with recoil ^{34m}Cl atoms with liquid chloroethylenes are as follows [7b)]:

	Ethylenes	Ethanes	Polymers	Inorganic
1,1-$C_2H_2Cl_2$	5	3	29	62
cis $C_2H_2Cl_2$	19	6	43	27
trans $C_2H_2Cl_2$	16	5	47	29
C_2HCl_3	20	7	51	20
C_2Cl_4	23	6	37	32

The low yield of ethylenes in the case of 1,1-$C_2H_2Cl_2$ is due to the preferred addition of the ^{34m}Cl atom to the CH_2-site, followed by the elimination of the same atom:

$$^{34m}Cl + CH_2{=}CCl_2 \rightarrow CH_2{}^{34m}Cl\text{-}{\bullet}CCl_2 \rightarrow {}^{34m}Cl + CH_2{=}CCl_2,$$

whereas barely any addition at the CCl2-site takes place:

$$^{34m}Cl + CH_2{=}CCl_2 \rightarrow {\bullet}CH_2\text{-}CCl_2{}^{34m}Cl \xrightarrow{(67\%)} Cl + CH_2{=}CCl^{34m}Cl.$$

This behaviour is in concurrence with the assumption that thermal Cl atoms preferentially add to the less substituted end of the olefin [34]. No elimination of an H atom of chloroethyl radicals occurs, as the yields of labelled ethylenes containing one Cl atom more than the irradiated compound are negligible.

Further proof of the Cl-addition/elimination sequence stems from the results of experiments with cis- and trans-1,2-$C_2H_2Cl_2$. In pure and moderated gaseous systems the trans : cis ratio is 34 : 66 from the irradiation of either or both isomers [35]. (The total yield is almost 30%.) For liquid 1,2-$C_2H_2Cl_2$ the original configuration is preserved in a ratio of about 60 : 40 for both isomers [36,37]. (The sum of the yield is 16%.) From the liquid phase data it was concluded that direct hot ^{34m}Cl-for-Cl substitution accounts for 3% of the retention of the original configuration, and the labelled isomers that are formed by addition of ^{34m}Cl, followed by complete racemization, contribute the remaining 13%. (For gaseous $CF_3CCl{=}CCl\text{-}CF_3$, moderated with (rather unreactive) CF_2Cl_2, the total ^{38}Cl-for-Cl substitution yield is almost 95% [37]; the cis : trans ratio measured from both isomers is 44 : 56, similar to the photo-stationary equilibrium value of either the cis- or trans-isomer.) For solid cis- and trans-1,2-$C_2H_2Cl_2$, the retention of the original configuration in ^{38}Cl-for-Cl substitution (70% for both isomers) is much higher than for the liquid phase [36]. This effect may be due to a comparable time scale for the addition/elimination reaction of the ^{38}Cl atoms and the rotation around the C-C bond in the $C_2H_2Cl_2{}^{38}Cl$ radical.

The low yield of 0.2% $C_2HCl_2{}^{38}Cl$ detected for gaseous 1,2-$C_2H_2Cl_2$ is an upper limit for hot ^{38}Cl-for-H substitution [36]; a yield of 8% $C_2Cl_3{}^{34m}Cl$ measured for gaseous C_2Cl_4 containing 10% cycloheptatriene seems an upper limit for hot ^{34m}Cl-for-Cl substitution and a hot addition/elimination reaction [7b].

Although the total organic yield for solid C_2Cl_4 (93%) is higher than for the liquid phase (70%) [38], the polymer yield in the solid phase (20%) is much lower than for the liquid phase (37%), reflecting the rigid nature of the solid phase in which chain reactions are hindered.

6. Arenes

In the recoil chemistry of Cl atoms with arenes, three main reaction channels can be distinguished: H substitution, ipso substitution and polymerization.

In gaseous C_6H_5F (295K) the ^{38}Cl-for-F displacement yield is 2.5%, whereas the substitution yield per H atom is only 0.3% [39]. This latter yield decreases linearly to zero upon moderation with Ar, whilst the o : m : p ratio (38:38:24) remains constant. The yields for both F- and H-substitution do not change over the C_6H_5F pressure range (at 473K) of between 1.3 kPa and 1.3 MPa. These results clearly demonstrate the existence of a single substitution mechanism for the gas phase, whereas excitational decomposition and collisional stabilization are of minor importance. Over the same pressure range, the yield of polymers increases from almost zero to 50% (at the expense of the inorganic yield), indicating the relevance of the addition of Cl atoms leading to the formation of a chlorocyclo- hexadienyl radical which, at higher pressures, can add to another aromatic molecule.

The predominant research effort has been focused on liquid phase experiments. The Table below gives averaged yields (%) for the principal products detected for unscavenged mono-substituted benzenes (C_6H_5X) and the relative o : m : p H-substitution yields (40 : 40 : 20 statistically) 39-42).

			Substitution				
X	Inorganic	Polymers	X	H	o :	m :	p
F	60	25	3	6	40	30	30
Cl	34	25	29	5	40	30	30
Br	35	46	14	3	37	35	28
I	62	20	9	2	37	40	23
CH_3	70	22	2	3	40	29	31
NO_2	62	25	13	2	24	47	29
NH_2	92	5	1	2	44	22	38

Aromatic H-substitution is primarily a hot process, as the yields are not particularly dependant upon the presence of scavengers [43]. This conclusion is also supported by the fact that the isomer distribution is close to statistical and that the Hammett ρ^+ value for the one-step process is only -0.56 [39]. This data is absolutely different from that which is characteristic of thermal electrophilic or homolytic chlorination. It is assumed that the hot reaction proceeds via the direct formation of a s-complex [39], but it must be kept in mind that rearomatization takes place via H-elimination, whereas the loss of the radioactive Cl atom may be a more noteworthy process [44].

The replacement of aromatic substituents (X) by recoil Cl atoms is a hot process for endothermic reactions (X = F, CH_3, CF_3, NH_2), but for thermoneutral (X = Cl) and exothermic (X = Br, I, NO_2) reactions, thermal ipso substitution also takes place. The Table below gives yields (%) for both hot and thermal recoil Cl-for-X substitution reactions (Table IX in Ref. 3c).

X =	F	Cl	Br	I	NO_2	CH_3	CF_3	NH_2
Hot	3	5	2	4	4	2	1	1
Thermal	_	24	12	4	9	_	_	_

Extensive studies were made to elucidate the mechanism of ^{34m,38}Cl-for-Cl substitution reactions in C_6H_5Cl and C_6H_4ClX. These exchange reactions can only be studied using enriched (^{35,37}Cl) or radioactive Cl isotopes. The yield of the thermal substitution reaction is very sensitive to the radiation dose [44,45]: for C_6H_5Cl it increases from some 24% at low doses to almost 50% at higher doses. This effect is explained by radiation-induced thermal exchange reactions.

Berei et al. [46] found , via intermolecular competition experiments in I_2-scavenged 1 : 1 mixtures of C_6H_5Cl and C_6H_4ClX, that the Hammett ρ^+ value for the hot ^{38}Cl-for-Cl substitution reaction is -0.48, one that is close to the -0.56 measured by Coenen et al. [39] for hot ^{38}Cl-for-H substitution. The energy range of the reacting ^{38}Cl atoms in the Cl replacement reaction is assumed to be no higher than 1-2 eV. Hot and thermal ^{34m,38}Cl - for - Cl substitution yields were measured by Veenboer et al. [44] in 1:1:1 mixtures of o, m, p-C_6H_4ClX (X = Cl, F, CH_3, CF_3) compounds. (The thermal contributions were perceived as the difference between pure- and I_2-scavenged experiments.) The ρ^+ value for the thermal Cl substitution reactions was determined to be -1.56, quite similar to the -1.43 found by Coenen et al. [39] for thermal ^{38}Cl-for-H substitution. (The value of ρ^+ for thermal chlorination in C_6H_5X compounds with Cl_2/HAc is -10.0 [47].) The hot versus thermal Cl-for-Cl substitution is also illustrated by the relative o:m:p ratios in 1:1:1 mixtures of the three isomeric C_6H_4ClX compounds [44]:

	Hot			Thermal		
	o	m	p	o	m	p
C_6H_4ClF	38	26	36	55	1	44
C_6H_4ClCl	35	25	40	42	2	56
$C_6H_4ClCH_3$	46	20	34	55	6	39
$C_6H_4ClCF_3$	42	22	36	30	47	23

The hot data are not very different from the statistical 33:33:33 distribution, whereas the thermal data are more in accord with the thermal electrophilic and homolitic Cl-for-H substitution: mainly o- and p-replacement for X = F, Cl, CH_3 and enhanced m-replacement for X= CF_3.

The replacement of a Cl atom or an X atom (or group) in disubstituted benzenes by recoil ^{38}Cl atoms depends upon the nature of X. The highest yield is found for the atom or group with the lowest bond energy [48]. The following yields are in % per atom:

	^{38}Cl-for-Cl	(+ I_2)	^{38}Cl-for-X	(+ I_2)
o-$C_6H_4Cl_2$	15	5	–	–
o-C_6H_4ClF	24	9	3	9
o-$C_6H_4ClNO_2$	4	1	16	9

Parent yields (^{38}Cl-for-Cl substitution) for the three a-chlorotoluenes ($C_6H_5CH_2Cl$, $C_6H_5CHCl_2$ and $C_6H_5CCl_3$) are in the order of 15% [49]. However, aliphatic H-substitution in the C_6H_4CH3 isomers accounts - per H atom - for only 0.5%: almost the same yield as for aromatic H-substitution [50]. Aliphatic H-abstraction from the CH_3 group in $C_6H_5CH_3$ is also a minor process, as the inorganic yield (60%) is the same as for C_6H_6 [51]. In contrast, the inorganic yields for $C_6H_5NH_2$ (92%) [39] and $C_6H_4ClNH_2$ (88%) [11] are much higher, probably due to H-abstraction from the NH_2 group.

High-boiling labelled products represent a large proportion in recoil Cl chemistry with aromatic compounds. Sephadex gel chromatography showed the presence of dimers, trimers and higher polymers in liquid chlorobenzes [45,50].

The organic yields measured for the reactions of recoil ^{38}Cl atoms with chlorobenzenes increase somewhat when going from the liquid to the solid phase - for C_6H_5Cl from 61 to 65% and for o-$C_6H_4Cl_2$ from 68 to 77% [53]. The ^{38}Cl-for-H substitution yield in p-$C_6H_4Cl_2$ is equal (4-5%) for both condensed phases (also in the presence of 0.5 mol% I_2 in the liquid phase), indicating the occurrence of hot reactions [53]. The yield of ^{38}Cl-for-Cl substitution in liquid o- and m-$C_6H_4Cl_2$ is approximately 35%, but decreases to 20% when traces of I_2 are present. The latter value is not very different from the solid phase yield. These comparable results were also explained by hot substitution reactions in both phases. The non-appearance of thermal substitution reactions in the pure solid compounds was ascribed to hindered radical recombination as a consequence of a lack of mobility [54]. However, such an explanation disagrees with formerly-mentioned conclusions drawn from the increase of labelled parent compounds in solid CCl_4 (Chapter 3).

7. Stereochemistry

An important aspect of hot atom chemistry concerns the stereo- chemistry of substitution reactions: whether they proceed via retention of configuration or via (Walden) inversion. A review of this topic is given in Ref. 2, and the retention values for tritium-for-hydrogen and halogen-for-halogen are given in Ref. 54.

In gaseous meso- and dl-$(CH_3CHCl)_2$ there is > 93% retention of configuration when traces of butadiene are present as a scavenger. In the liquid phase the yields are ten times higher and the retention only 72%, whereas the retentions are even lower in the solid phase: 62% for the meso- and 50% for the dl-isomers. These findings were attributed to the caged recombination of a ^{38}Cl atom with a $CH_3CHCl^{\bullet}CHCH_3$ radical [55]. Similar results were obtained with meso- and dl-$(CHFCl)_2$: the retention in the gas phase was 90% and only 70% in the liquid phase; the yields were higher by a factor of three [56,57].

When the approach of the recoil Cl atom to the Cl atom to be substituted is sterically hindered, a much lower degree of retention is observed: in gaseous d- and l-$CH_3CHClCOCl$ (where the gauche prime confirmation is present in high concentrations) a relatively unhindered approach to an attack of the asymmetric C atom from the rear is a real possibility, resulting in 81% inversion [58,59]. This interpretation is supported by the finding that in $(CH_3)_2CHCHClCOCl$, where this type of approach is sterically hindered, the degree of inversion is only 41%. Not only does steric hindrance predict the retention/inversion ratio, but also the mass of the departing atom. The degree of inversion for ^{34m}Cl-for-X substitution at the chiral carbon in $CH_3CHXCOX$ is 71% (X = F), 81% (X = Cl) and 78% (X = Br) [60].

Another example of the effect of hindered approach is the observation that in gaseous d- and l-$CH_3CHClCH_2OH$, the inversion decreases from 80% at a pressure of 38 kPa to 42% at 100 kPa [61]. Infrared spectroscopy demonstrates that an increase in the pressure results in a decrease of free molecules and in the formation of dimeric species - formed through hydrogen bonding - which diminish the unhindered rear attack.

Changes in the retention/inversion ratios in liquid d- and l- $(CH_3CHCl)_2$ [56], $(CHFCl)_2$ [62], $(CH_3CHCl)_2CH2$ [63] and $CH_3CHClCH_2OH$ [64] were observed upon dilution with several compounds. These effects were ascribed to the dielectric properties of these additives, causing differences in the solute-solvent interactions. (A strong interaction prevents the intermediate radical from attaining planarity, maintaining the configuration that is obtained in the primary substitution step [64].) For liquid cis- and trans-1,2- dichlorohexafluorocyclobutane, no dependence for the retention/inversion ratio was found on the magnitude of the dielectric constants of the various solvents containing hydrogen [65]. This was attributed to a far higher activation energy being required for achieving planarity for the c-C_4F_6Cl radical than for the above-mentioned radicals.

8. Acknowledgements

Mr. J.F. Wilkinson is thanked for his advice on English usage. Ms M. Oskam-Tamboezer is thanked for the preparation of the manuscript. This manuscript was mainly researched at the National Institute for Nuclear Physics and High-Energy Physics (NIKHEF-K) and is made possible by financial support from the Foundation for Fundamental Research on Matter (FOM) and the Netherlands Organization for Scientific Research (NWO).

9. References

1. Brinkman, G.A. Int. J. Appl. Rad. Is. 34, 985 (1983)
2. Brinkman, G.A. Adv. Inorg. Radiochem. 28, 101 (1984)
3. Brinkman, G.A. Chem. Rev, (a) 84, 299 (1984); (b) 82, 245 (1982); (c) 81, 267 (1981)
4. Kontis, S.S.; Malcolme-Lawes, D.J.; Urch, D.S. Radiochim. Acta 24, 87 (1977)
5. Kontis, S.S. et al., Radiochem. Acta 36, 103 (1984); J. Radioanal. Nucl. Chem., Articles 102, 15 (1986); 102, 321 (1986)
6. Rao, B.S.M. et al., Radiochim. Acta 27, 143 (1980); 28, 145 1981); 30, 189 (1982); 31, 13 (1982); 33, 81 (1983); 35, 65 (1984); 36, 163 (1984); 39, 5 (1985); 42, 19 (1987); 46, 25 (1989)
7. Brinkman, G.A.; Gerritsen, G.A.V.; Visser, J. Radiochim. Acta (a) 27, 203 (1980); (b) 27, 137 (1980)
8. Brinkman, G.A. et al., Radiochim. Acta 26, 85 (1979); 28, 61 (1981)
9. Berei, K.; Stöcklin, G. Radiochim. Acta 15, 39 (1971)
10. Bhave, R.N.; Brinkman, G.A.; Rao, B.S.M.; Halteren, B.W. van Radiochim. Acta 31, 185 (1982)
11. Rao, B.S.M.; Brinkman, G.A.; Veenboer, J.Th. Radiochim. Acta 35, 61 (1984)
12. Lee, F.S.C.; Rowland, F.S. J. Phys. Chem. 81, 1229 (1977)
13. Mudra, K. Radiochim Acta 19, 16 (1973)
14. Brinkman, G.A.; Visser, J. Radiochim. Acta 27, 91 (1980)
15. Brinkman, G.A.; Gerritsen, G.A.V.; Visser, J. Radiochim. Acta 26, 153 (1979)
16. Stöcklin, G.; Tornau, W. Radiochim. Acta 9, 95 (1968)
17. Stevens, J.D.; Spicer, L.D. J. Phys. Chem. 82, 627 (1978)
18. Lee, F.S.C.; Rowland, F.S. J. Phys. Chem. 81, 86 (1977)
19. Baulch, D.L.; Cox, R.A.; Hampson Jr., R.F.; Kerr, J.A.; Troe, J.; Watson, J.; J. Phys. Chem. Ref. Data, 13, 1259 (1984)
20. Kikuchi, M.; Lee, F.S.C.; Rowland, F.S. J. Phys. Chem. 85, 84 (1981)
21. Spicer, L.D.; Wolfgang, R. J. Am. Chem. Soc. 90, 2426 (1968)
22. Lee, F.S.C.; Hower, C.O. J. Phys. Chem. 75, 2685 (1971)
23. Tang, Y.N.; Smith, W.S.; Williams, J.L.; Lowery, K.; Rowland, F.S. J. Phys. Chem. 75, 440 (1971)
24. Spicer, L.D.; J. Am. Chem. Soc. 95, 51 (1973)
25. Dulmen, A.A. van; Aten Jr., A.H.W. Radiochim. Acta 15, 26 (1971)
26. Berei, K.; Vasáros, L.; Ache, H.J. J. Phys. Chem. 84, 1063 (1984)

27. Opelanio-Buencamino, L.R.; Rack, E.P. Radiochim. Acta 38, 87 (1985)
28. Gigoo, S.S.; Agrawal, A.S.; Bhave, R.N.; Rao, B.S.M. Radiochem. Radioan. Lett. 53, 195 (1982)
29. Goldhaber, S.; Chiang, R.S.H.; Willard, J.E. J. Am. Chem. Soc. 74, 318 (1952)
30. Willard, J.E. "Chemical effects of nuclear transformations" IAEA, Vienna, I, 215 (1961)
31. Goldhaber, S.; Willard, J.E. J. Am. Chem. Soc. 74, 318 (1952); Chien, J.C.W.; Willard, J.E. ib. 75, 6169 (1953)
32. Berei, K.; Vasáros, L.; Kiss, I. J. Chem. Soc. Far. Trans. I, 82, 3003 (1986) Berei, K. J. Phys. Chem. 90, 717 (1986)
33. Wai, C.M.; Rowland, F.S. J. Phys. Chem. 72, 3049 (1968)
34. Nonhebel, D.C.; Walton, J.C. "Free-radical chemistry." 166 (1974)
35. Smith, W.S.; Daniel, T.H.; Tang, Y.N. J. Phys. Chem. 76, 2711 (1972)
36. Wai, C.M.; Rowland, F.S. J. Am. Chem. Soc. 91, 1053 (1969)
37. Stevens, D.J.; Spicer, L.D. J. Am. Chem. Soc. 100, 3295 (1978)
38. Aten Jr., A.H.W.; Raaphorst, J.G. van "Chemical effects of nuclear transformations" IAEA, Vienna, I, 203 (1961)
39. Coenen, H.H.; Machulla, H.J; Stöcklin, G. J. Am. Chem. Soc. 99, 2892 (1977)
40. Berei, K.; Stöcklin, G. Radiochim. Acta 15, 39 (1971)
41. Stöcklin, G.; Tornau, W. Radiochim. Acta 9, 95 (1968)
42. Brinkman, G.A.; Veenboer, J.Th.; Visser, J.; Kaspersen, F.M.; Lindner, L. Radiochim. Acta 26, 85 (1979)
43. Berei, K.; Vasáros, L. Radiochim. Acta 43, 61 (1983)
44. Veenboer, J.Th.; Halteren, B.W. van; Brinkman, G.A. Radiochim. Acta 40, 129 (1986)
45. Brinkman, G.A.; Kaspersen, F.M.; Veenboer, J.Th. Radiochim. Acta 28, 61 (1981)
46. Berei, K.; Vasáros, L.; Norseyev, V.; Sutyor, J. Radiochim. Acta 42, 13 (1987)
47. Stöcklin, G.; Brown, H.C. Adv. Phys. Org. Chem. 1, 35 (1963)
48. Berei, K.; Kardos, Zs.; Vasáros, L. Radiochim. Acta 38, 83 (1985)
49. Chandrasckhar, N.; Bhave, R.N.; Rao, B.S.M. Radiochim. Acta 39, 5 (1985)
50. Bhave, R.N.; Brinkman, G.A.; Rao, B.S.M.; Halteren, B.W. van Radiochim. Acta 31, 185 (1982)
51. Stöcklin, G.; Tornau, W. Radiochim. Acta 6, 86 (1966)
52. Gigoo, S.S.; Agrawal, A.S.; Bhave, R.N.; Rao, B.S.M. Radiochem. Radioan. Lett. 53, 195 (1982)
53. Berei, K.; Ache, H.J. J. Phys. Chem. 85, 986 (1981)
54. Firouzbakht, M.L.; Ferrieri, R.A.; Wolf, A.P.; Rack, E.P. J. Phys. Chem. 90, 5339 (1986)
55. Wai, C.M.; Rowland, F.S. J. Phys. Chem. 74, 434 (1970)
56. Vasáros, L.; Machulla, H.J.; Stöcklin, G. J. Phys. Chem. 76, 501 (1972)
57. Machulla, H.J.; Stöcklin, G. J. Phys. Chem. 78, 658 (1974)

58. Wolf, A.P.; Schuler, P.; Pettijohn, R.P.; To, K.C.; Rack, E.P. J. Phys. Chem. 83, 1237 (1979)

59. Rack, E.P.; Ferrieri, R.A.; Wolf, A.P. Radiochim. Acta 43, 92 (1988)

60. To, K.C.; Wolf, A.P.; Rack, E.P. J. Phys. Chem. 87, 4929 (1983)

61. To, K.C.; Rack, E.P.; Wolf, A.P. J. Phys. Chem. 74, 1499 (1981)

62. Acciani, T.R.; Su, Y.; Ache, H.J.; Rack, E.P. J. Phys. Chem. 82, 975 (1978)

63. Wu, J.; Ache, H.J. J. Am. Chem. Soc. 99, 6021 (1977)

64. Wu, J.; Booth, T.E.; Ache, H.J. J. Chem. Phys. 68, 5285 (1978)

65. Acciani, T.R.; Ache, H.J. J. Phys. Chem. 82, 1465 (1978)

2.3 Hot Atom Chemistry of Bromine

G.A. BRINKMAN [a] AND B.S.M. RAO [b]

[a] TF-A - FOM Group, University of Amsterdam, c/o NIKHEF-K, P.O. Box 41882, 1009 DB. Amsterdam, The Netherlands.

[b] Chemistry Department, University of Poona, Pune - 411 007, India.

1. Introduction

The chemical reactions of recoil tritium, fluorine and chlorine are straightforward in the sense that only the reactions of energetic and thermal neutral atoms in their electronic ground state need be considered. Depending upon the type of nuclear reaction utilized for the production of radioactive recoil bromine, iodine and astatine, energetic and thermal ions can contribute to the final formation of stable labelled compounds (particularly in the gaseous phase [1]), whilst electronically excited ions can also be involved.

Various types of nuclear reactions can lead to the production of radioactive Br atoms and ions:

1. Thermal neutron activation of $^{79,81}Br$ resulting in energetic ground state 80,82Br and metastable $^{80m,82m}Br$ species.
2. Isomeric transition of $^{80m,82m}Br$ to ground state $^{80,82}Br$; as these transitions are highly converted, the ground state Br particles are multiply- charged Br^{n+} ions. The metastable isotopes are in general incorporated in compounds such as HBr, Br_2, CH_3Br and CF_3Br.
3. Electron capture decay of ^{76}Kr yields 100% multiply-charged $^{76}Br^{n+}$ ions. The decay of ^{77}Kr (β^+ = 84% and EC = 16%) gives rise to 60% $^{77}Br^-$, 20% Br^o and 20% Br^{n+} particles.
4. Proton irradiation of Se produces several Br isotopes that react as neutral atoms with high kinetic energies.
5. Fission of ^{235}U leads to the direct formation of $^{84-89}Br$ isotopes with high kinetic energies and to their indirect formation through b- decay of the corresponding Se isotopes, resulting partly in the production of Br^+ ions.

Urch [2] and Brinkman [3] have published several review articles on hot atom chemistry which also detail the reactions of recoil Br species.

2. Alkanes

Most of the research into the reactions of recoil Br-species has been performed with CH_4 [3c] and C_2H_6 [2]. The total organic yields measured in gas phase experiments are quite low (5-12%) for both (n,γ) and IT reactions; the main product arises from Br*-for-H substitution. The organic yields derived from the isomeric $^{80m}Br \rightarrow {}^{80}Br$ transition in CH_4 are between 0 and 8%, depending upon which type of molecule contained the ^{80m}Br atom. The isomeric transition leads to the formation of highly charged $^{80}Br^{n+}$ ions (n<12) [4]. After charge distribution to the other atoms within the molecule, it will explode due to coulombic repulsion. The kinetic energy of the repelled Br ion depends upon both the charge distribution and the masses of the other atoms. For $H^{80m}Br$, the recoil energy is 1 eV and the organic yield <0.1%, whereas for recoil energies above 10eV ($CCl_3{}^{80m}Br$, $CH_3{}^{80m}Br$, $Br^{80m}Br$) the organic yields are 8% [5].

The ^{80}Br-for-H substitution in C_3H_8 - induced by the $^{80m}Br(IT)^{80}Br$ process - leads, per C-H bond, to a ratio of (1.1 ± 0.1) for n-$C_3H_7{}^{80}Br$ / i-$C_3H_7{}^{80}Br$. This ratio decreases with dilution, meaning that at lower energies the secondary C-H bond is more subject to substitution than the primary bond [6].

It has been shown that for (n,γ) activation in gaseous CH_4 [7] and CH_3F [8], all the product yields drop to zero upon 100% moderation with rare gases, indicating that the reactions occur as a result of the kinetic energy of Br atoms. However, for the (IT) decay in CH_4 / $Br^{82m}Br$, the yield of $CH_3{}^{82}Br$ drops from 6 to 1% on high moderation with Ar, whereas the $CH_2Br^{82}Br$ yield remains constant at 1%. To explain similar results in CH_4 / $H^{80m}Br$, $H^{82m}Br$, Yagi and Kondo [9] suggested that a (CH_4Br^+) charged complex gives rise to the formation of ion clusters with surrounding molecules, thus generating the final products. In CH_3X / $CF_3{}^{80m}Br$ systems the formation of an (CH_3XBr^+) ion, which can react via halide- or proton-transfer, was proposed in order to explain that moderator curves do not extrapolate to zero, but to 0.4% [10].

SYSTEM	REACTION	PRODUCTS	H/D EFFECT	REF.
CH_4/CD_4	$^{79}Br(n,\gamma)^{80}Br$	Organic Yield	1.9	11)
	$^{80m}Br(IT)^{80}Br$	Organic Yield	1.5	11)
	"	$CH_3(CD_3)^{80}Br$	2.7	12)
	"	$CH_2(CD_2)Br^{80}Br$	1.0	12)
CH_3F/CD_3F	$^{79}Br(n,\gamma)^{80}Br$	Organic Yield	1.5	8)
	$^{82m}Br(IT)^{82}Br$	Organic Yield	1.9	8)

The table above sets out measured H/D isotope effects. The isotope effect of 2.7 for $CH_3(CD_3)^{80}Br$ is due to reactions of energetic Br atoms, as was shown by moderator experiments; the yields of $CH_2(CD_2)Br^{80}Br$ remained constant (1.1% for both compounds) on moderation with Xe, establishing that these products are formed by thermal $^{80}Br+$ ions.

The proton irradiation of CH_4 + 20% H_2Se results in the formation of labelled CH_3Br with yields of 5.5, 6.8 and 3.1% for ^{76}Br, ^{77}Br and ^{82}Br (all formed via Se(p,xn)Br reactions), respectively [13]. These Br isotopes react as neutral atoms with high kinetic energies. The yields of Br^*-for-H substitution in CH_3F, CH_3Cl and CH_3Br are approximately 5, 2 and 1%, respectively in mixtures with H_2Se, $(CH_3)_2Se$ and $(CF_3)_2Se$; however, the Br^*-for-X substitution reactions were difficult to interpret as substantial radiolysis occurred during the irradiations.

The substitution yields of hydrogen and halogen by $^{76,77}Br$ isotopes that were produced via the decay of $^{76,77}Kr$ are in the order of 1-2% (Table XXVI in Ref. 3c). On the basis of scavenger and moderator effects, it was deduced that the substitution of halogens occurs via reactions of Br^- and (excited) Br^+ ions, whereas the substitution of H atoms is merely due to reactions of Br^+ ions. The addition of H_2S, CH_3SH, $(CH_3)_2S$, H_2Se or CH_3OH leads to a dramatic increase in the $^{76,77}Br$-for-Br substitution in CH_3Br - 20% H_2S results in a 65% yield of $CH_3{}^{77}Br$. This effect was explained by Br^+ or Br^- and the gas molecules forming gas phase clusters; HBr^* can be formed in such clusters [14].

Frost et al. [15] also performed experiments with $^{76,77}Br$ isotopes. In gaseous CH_4 (2.5 MPa) the yields of both $CH_3{}^{76}Br$ and $CH_3{}^{77}Br$ were 4.5%. (In gaseous C_2H_6 the $^{76,77}Br$-for-H substitution yields are 0.7 and 2.7% [16].) As the recoil energies of the $^{76,77}Br^+$ ions are too low to explain the CH_4 results via a direct reaction

$$Br^+ + CH_4 \rightarrow CH_3Br + H^+,$$

it was suggested that proton transfer between an excited molecule and CH_4 occurs:

$$(CH_4Br^+)^{¥} + CH_4 \rightarrow CH_3Br + CH_5{}^+.$$

The CH_3Br yield decreases upon moderation, but above 80 mol% of Ar or Kr the yield of $CH_3{}^{76}Br$ increases to 12%, thought to be through the reactions of brominating compounds such as $ArBr^+$ and $KrBr^+$ [15]. The product yields increase at pressures above 3MPa and reach maximum values in the condensed phase, i.e., 37% $CH_3{}^{76}Br$ from CH_4 and 30% $C_2H_5{}^{76}Br$ from C_2H_6. These results were explained by the onset of cage reactions due to auto- radiation effects caused by electrons emitted after the EC event. (Similar results were obtained for the gas-to-condensed phase transitions in C_2H_6 for the $^{79}Br(n,\gamma)^{80}Br$ and $^{82m}Br(IT)^{82}Br$ transitions [17].) From $^{82m}Br(IT)^{82}Br$ experiments with liquid and frozen aqueous solutions of haloalkenes - the organic molecules tend to aggregate in such mixtures - it was also concluded that interactions with Auger electrons (and charge neutralization) predict product formation [18].

High organic yields were also measured in liquid and solid halo- methanes, i.e., 40 and 75% for the $^{79}Br(n,\gamma)^{80}Br$ reaction in CCl_2Br_2 (Table XXVII in Ref. 3c). Organic yields increase in direct proportion to the chain length of the homologeous series of $C_nH_{2m+1}Br$ (n = 1 to n = 6) [19] and with enhanced bromination of liquid ethane: from 32% for C_2H_5Br to 42% for $CHBr_2CHBr_2$ [20]. For solid C_2H_5Br, the organic yield is even higher at 77% [21].

By using varying amounts of Br_2 in liquid C_2H_5Br, the yields of products formed by highly energetic Br^* atoms and via diffusive processes could be determined [22]: for $C_2H_5Br^*$ these yields are 8 and 14% respectively.

Apart from single substitution reactions, double displacement reactions were also observed, i.e., in liquid CF_2Cl_2 and $CFCl_3$ mixtures with Br_2 [23]. In liquid CH_3F, products were found that were formed through the displacement of 2, 3 and 4 atoms; yields, as a percentage, are given below [24]:

	CH_2Br_2	$CHBr_3$	$CFBr_3$	CBr_4
$^{79}Br(n,\gamma)^{80}Br$	3.8	2.4	0.1	0.5
$^{82m}Br(IT)^{82}Br$	2.8	5.8	0.1	3.6

3. Cycloalkanes

Wai and Jennings [25] were the first to notice that the reactions of recoil Br atoms with gaseous c-C_3H_6 barely yielded any c-C_3H_5Br but that n-C_3H_5Br, formed via the isomerization of excited c-C_3H_5Br, was the main organic compound. More extensive data were obtained by Saeki and Tachikawa [26] using the $^{79}Br(n,\gamma)^{80}Br$ reaction in gaseous c-C_3H_6 and c-C_3H_5Br with traces of CH_3Br (as the ^{80}Br source) and I_2 (as a scavenger). The product yields (as a percentage) of three interesting species were found to be:

PRESSURE	c-$C_3H_5{}^{80}Br$	CH_2=CH-$CH_2{}^{80}Br$	$CH_2{}^{80}BrI$
12kPa c-C_3H_6	0.8	0.8	12.5
110kPa	1.5	5.3	8.2
12kPa c-C_3H_5Br	<0.4	3.0	3.0
120kPa	<0.4	12.0	2.0

These results demonstrate that the ^{80}Br-for-H substitution in c-C_3H_6 and the ^{80}Br-for-Br substitution in c-C_3H_5Br lead to the formation of excited c-$C_3H_5{}^{80}Br$ that can isomerize to excited CH_2=CH-$CH_2{}^{80}Br$, which in turn can decompose to $\bullet CH_2{}^{80}Br$; this radical will, in the presence of I_2, form $CH_2{}^{80}BrI$. At higher pressures there is enhanced collisional stabilization of both excited species. In the case of c-C_3H_5Br, the ^{80}Br-for-Br substitution also leads to excited species, but the excess of energy in n-$C_3H_5{}^{80}Br$ is less than when it is formed from c-C_3H_6. Experiments with c-C_4H_{10} and c-C_4H_9Br underline this conclusion, in that a higher level of excitation energy is imparted after Br-for-H than after Br-for-Br substitution [27]. In liquid c-C_3H_5Br there is an even higher degree of stabilization, the relative yields of the three compounds being 1 : 2 : 0.2.

Experiments with c-C_3H_6 were also performed with $^{76,77}Br$, produced through the decay of $^{76,77}Kr$. In the gaseous phase all the yields of identified products were below 1%, whereas the major contribution to the organic yield was made by high-boiling unidentified compounds, for which the $^{77}Br/^{76}Br$ product yield ratio was (0.46 ± 0.08) for both pure and highly moderated c-C_3H_6 [28]. This ratio is close to that of 0.35 for Br^{n+} ions resulting from the $^{77}Kr/^{76}Kr$ decay. The high-boiling compounds are therefore thought to be formed by cationic polymerization reactions, initiated by c-$C_3H_6Br^+$ ions. In the case of solid c-C_3H_6, a low yield (1-3%) of c-C_3H_5Br was detected with no trace of n-C_3H_5Br, but high yields of C_2H_5Br (13%) and i-C_3H_7Br (21%) were found [15]. These results were explained by reactions involving (excited) radicals and rearrangements of products within a cage formed by the charged and energetic recoil species. The observation that only i-C_3H_7Br (and no n-C_3H_7Br) is formed has been explained by the reactions of $^{76,77}Br$ with a rearranged allyl radical (•CH_2 - •CH - CH_3), produced from the allene structure (•CH_2 - CH_2 - CH_2•) after the ring opening of c-C_3H_6.

4. Arenes

The first experiments on the gas phase bromination of arenes were performed in highly moderated (95% Ar) systems [29-31]. By using $CH_3{}^{80m}Br$ as the source for the $^{80m}Br(IT)^{80}Br$ decay, it was ensured that only electrophilic substitution reactions by $^{80}Br^+$ ions took place. Above 50 mole % of Ar moderator, the relative ortho- and para-substitution yields in C_6H_5F decrease, whilst the meta yield increases. This effect was attributed to a competition between two reaction channels of the arenonium ions that are formed by ortho- or para-attack:

1) stabilization, or
2) (at high Ar concentrations) enhanced isomerization to the thermo- dynamically more stable meta-isomer [30]:

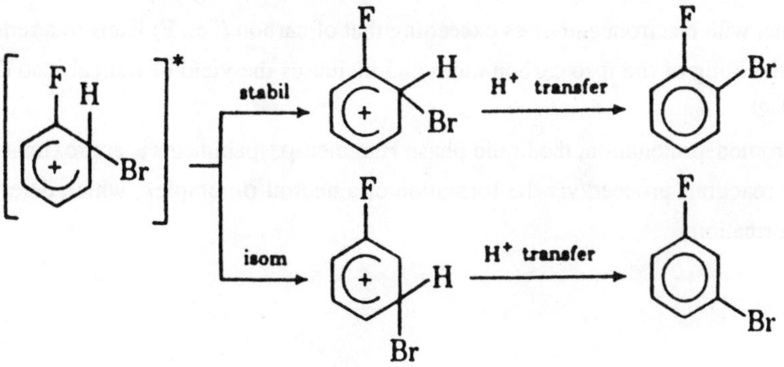

The ^{80}Br-for-F substitution yield is not greatly affected by the moderator concentration, indicating the absence of high-kinetic-energy processes. In p-$C_6H_4F_2$, considerable isomerization also occurs: at 95% Ar the relative o:m:p $C_6H_4F^{80}Br$ yields are 55:31:14 [30)]. The primary attack of $^{80}Br^+$ not only occurs at the π-electron system but also at the F-substituent, the location of the highest electron density. Gas phase experiments with several substituted benzenes at high Ar moderation gave linear Hammett equation plots with a slope of $\rho^+ = -0.9$ [31)]. From the experiments it was concluded that the naked gaseous $^{80}Br^+$ ions follow a mechanism similar to that of the solvated ions in the liquid phase.

The same type of experiment was also performed with $^{76,77}Br$, produced from the decay of $^{76,77}Kr$. In unmoderated C_6H_6 the principal reaction pathway is H-substitution by $^{76,77}Br$ atoms [32a)], whereas in Kr-moderated C_6H_5F and p-$C_6H_4F_2$ these reactions proceed via Br^+ ions [33a)]. In contrast to the above-mentioned $^{80m}Br(IT)^{80}Br$ system, the moderation of C_6H_5F results in an increase in the yield of para-substitution and in a decrease in the ortho- and meta-yields. Furthermore, only para- and meta- C_6H_4FBr were detected (in a 1:3 ratio) in gaseous p-$C_6H_4F_2$, but not the ortho-isomer. To explain these differences in behaviour, it was stated that when using $CH_3{}^{80m}Br$ the reacting species is $CH_3{}^{80}Br^+$, rather than $^{80}Br^+$. The organic compounds found in gaseous C_6H_5F are formed from $C_6H_5BrF^+$ arenium intermediates, either via the π-complex or the (C_6H_5-F-Br^+) n-complex. A very substantial proportion of the inorganic yield (94%) may also be formed through BrF elimination from the n-complex [32a,33)]. Further studies at higher moderator pressures showed an increase in the $^{76,77}Br$-for- H substitution yields (up to 14% at 1.4 MPa Kr), indicating that the reaction proceeds via a very reactive Kr_nBr^+ cluster [34)].

For the liquid phase, Berei et al. [35)] found that the ^{82}Br-for- halogen substitution yields are inversely proportional to the C-X bond energies: the yields increase from 1.4% for X=F to 19% for X=Br. A similar bond energy effect for halobenzenes was also measured for reactions of $^{76,77}Br$ recoil atoms [32b,33b)]. It therefore appears that direct hot halogen replacement reactions must be excluded from consideration; ipso substitution is described in terms of a two-step addition-elimination reaction in which bond breakage determines the product. Substitution yields of other groups (OH, CH_3, CF_3, NO_2, NH_2, OCH_3) are all very low (0.4 - 2%) and it is not possible to reach conclusions regarding the electronic effects of these groups. However, adding more substituents with electronegativities exceeding that of carbon (i.e., F) leads to a reduction in the π-electron shielding of the ipso carbon atom and increases the yield of radical ipso displacement of fluorine [32b)].

For bromodeprotonation, the liquid phase Hammett-ρ^+ parameter is approximately -0.5 [32b,33b)] and these reactions proceed via the formation of a neutral σ-complex, which determines the final product formation.

For gaseous C_6H_6 the principal pathway for $^{76,77}Br$ species is substitution; the yield is 1.2% [32a]. In the liquid phase this yield increases (on average) to 14% for both isotopes, which is attributed to increased density and collisional stabilization of the σ-complex intermediate. In the liquid phase, polymers are also found (12%). For solid C_6H_6 the substitution yield is 19% and polymers are again present (20%), but extensive fragmentation also occurs to the extent of 34% (almost equal amounts of C_2H_5Br, C_3H_7Br and C_4H_9Br). These brominated fragments are possibly formed in caging reactions generated from the decay of charged substrate molecules.

5. Stereochemistry

Rowland et al. [36] found that the $^{79}Br(n,\gamma)^{80m}Br$ reaction in gaseous and liquid $(CH_3CHCl)_2$ led to the almost complete retention of configuration for both the dl- and meso-compounds. For (IT)-induced reactions in liquid $(CH_3CHCl)_2$ the retention/inversion ratio is almost unity [37]. For the $^{80m}Br(IT)^{80}Br$ transition in gaseous $(CH_3CHCl)_2$ the retention/ inversion ratios are 2.5 for both isomers, but extrapolation to 100 mol% Ar moderation results in a ratio of 3.3 for the meso- and 0.3 for the dl-compounds [38]. Front attack of the thermal Br^+ ion leads, in the case of the meso-compound, to a thermodynamically stable erythreo form of the intermediate halocarbocation, whereas in the dl system the less stable threo diastereomer is formed, which readily leads to racemization.

The inversion of configuration for the Br-for-X substitution reaction at the asymmetric carbon atom of halopropionyl halides ($CH_3CHXCOX$) were studied with ^{75}Br recoil atoms, produced via the $^{75}As(^3He,3n)^{75}Br$ reaction in gaseous mixtures with AsH_3 [39]. The degrees of inversion, equal for both the (-)-2R and (+)-2S isomers, were 65, 73 and 83% for X=F, Cl and Br, respectively. With regard to retention values for ^{18}F and ^{34m}Cl atoms with (+)-2S-$CH_3CHClCOCl$, it was concluded that the bond strength of the displaced atom was not relevant in controlling the configuration change, but rather the reduced mass: $m_1m_2/(m_1+m_2)$ and, in part, the lifetime of the intermediate complex.

6. Acknowledgements

Mr. J.F. Wilkinson is thanked for his advice on English usage. Ms M. Oskam-Tamboezer is thanked for the preparation of the manuscript.
This manuscript was mainly researched at the National Institute for Nuclear Physics and High-Energy Physics (NIKHEF-K) and is made possible by financial support from the Foundation for Fundamental Research on Matter (FOM) and the Netherlands Organization for Scientific Research (NWO).

7. References

1. Kanzanjan, A.R.; Libby, W.F. J. Chem. Phys. 42, 2778 (1965)
2. Urch, D.S. "Hot atom chemistry." Ed. T. Matsuura, 142 (1984)
3. Brinkman, G.A. Chem. Rev. a) 81, 267 (1981); b) 82, 245 (1982); c) 84, 299 (1984)
4. Wexler, S.; Anderson, G.R. J. Chem. Phys. 33, 850 (1960)
5. Gordus, A.A.; Willard, J.E. J. Am. Chem. Soc. 79, 4609 (1957)
6. Numakura, K.; Tachikawa, E. Bull. Chem. Soc. Japan 46, 346 (1973)
7. Rack, E.P.; Gordus, A.A. J. Phys. Chem. 65, 944 (1961)
   Nicholas, J.B.; Rack, E.P. J. Chem. Phys. 48, 4085 (1968
8. Helton, R.W.; Yoong, M.; Rack, E.P. J. Phys. Chem. 75, 2072 (1971)
9. Kondo, K.; Yagi, M. Bull. Chem. Soc. Japan 51, 1284 (1978); 52, 225 (1979)
10. Daniel, S.E.; Ache, H.J. Radiochim. Acta 19, 132 (1973)
11. Spicer, L.D.; Gordus, A.A. "Chemical effects of nuclear transformations." Vol. I, 185. IAEA, Vienna (1965)
12. Tachikawa, E. et al. Bull. Chem. Soc. Japan 42, 1293 (1970)
13. Jong, D. de; Brinkman, G.A.; Halteren, B.W. van Int. J. Appl. Rad. Is. 34, 1597 (1983)
14. Jong, D. de Ph.D. Thesis, University of Amsterdam (1982)
15. Frost, J.J.; Moerlein, S.M.; Welch, M.J. J. Am. Chem. Soc. 103, 4332, 4337 (1981)
16. Jong, D. de; Brinkman G.A.; Halteren, B.W. van Radiochem. Radioanal. Lett. 56, 165 (1982)
17. Loventhal, A.; Berg, M.E.; Rack, E.P. Radiochim. Acta 24, 91 (1977)
18. Rack, E.P. et al. Radiochim. Acta 37, 191 (1984); 38, 87 (1985); 46, 65 (1989)
19. Karamyan, A.S. Doklady Akad. Nauk. U.S.S.R. 69, 787 (1949)
20. Milman, M.; Shaw, P.F.D. J. Chem. Soc. 1317 (1957)
21. Goldhaber, S.; Willard, J.E. J. Am. Chem. Soc. 74, 318 (1952)
22. Milman, M.; Shaw, P.F.D. J. Chem. Soc. 1303 (1957)
23. Tominaga, T.; Iwata, R.; Makide, Y. Bull. Chem. Soc. Japan 46, 1882 (1973)
24. Berg, M.E.; Grauer, W.M.; Helton, R.W.; Rack, E.P. J. Phys. Chem. 79, 1327 (1975)
25. Wai, C.M.; Jennings, R.L. J. Phys. Chem. 75, 2698 (1971)
26. Saeki, M.; Tachikawa, E. Trans. Far. Soc. I 71, 2121 (1975)
27. Su, Y.; Metcalfe, Ch.; Ache, H.J. Radiochem. Radioanal. Lett. 18, 349 (1974).
28. Jong, D. de; Brinkman G.A.; Halteren, B.W. van Radiochim. Acta 34, 93 (1983)
29. Cacace, F.; Stöcklin, G. J. Am. Chem. Soc. 94, 2518 (1972)
30. Knust, E.J.; Halpern, A.; Stöcklin, G. J. Am. Chem. Soc. 96, 3733 (1974)
31. Knust, E.J. J. Am. Chem. Soc. 99, 3037 (1977)
32. Moerlein, S.M.; Welch, N.J.; Wolf, A.P. a) Radiochim. Acta 35, 29 (1984);
    b) J. Am. Chem. Soc. 105, 5418 (1983)

33. Coenen, H.H.; Machulla, H.J.; Stöcklin, G. Radiochim. Acta a) 33, 13 (1983); b) 33, 21 (1983)

34. Backhausen, H. Diss. D38, University of Cologne. Jül. 1918 (1984).

35. Berei, K.; Stöcklin, G. Radiochim. Acta 15, 39 (1971)

36. Rowland, F.S.; Wai, C.M.; Ting, C.T.; Miller, G. "Chemical effects of nuclear transformations." Vol. I, 333. IAEA, Vienna (1965)

37. Su, Y.; Ache, H.J. J. Phys. Chem. 80, 659 (1976)

38. Daniel, S.H.; Ache, H.J.; Stöcklin, G. J. Phys. Chem. 78, 1043 (1974)

39. Firouzbakht, M.L.; Ferrieri, R.A.; Wolf, A.P.; Rack, E.P. J. Phys. Chem. 90, 5339 (1986)

2.4 Hot Atom Chemistry of Iodine

Edward P. RACK
Department of Chemistry, University of Nebraska-Lincoln, Lincoln, Nebraska 68588-0304 and Medical Research, Department of Veterans Affairs Medical Center, Omaha, Nebraska 68105, U.S.A.

1. Introduction

In 1934 L. Szilard and T.A. Chalmers[1] reported the first study of hot atom chemistry when they showed that, after the thermal neutron irradiation of liquid ethyl iodide, most of the iodine activity formed could be extracted from ethyl iodide with water. Evidently the iodine-carbon bond was broken when an iodine-127 nucleus was transformed by neutron capture to iodine-128. They hypothesized that the incident neutron imparted enough energy to the iodine nucleus to cause the iodine-carbon bond rupture. A year later Amaldi and co-workers[2] proposed that the bond rupture was not due to the direct transfer of momentum of the captured thermal neutron but rather due to the emission of gamma rays as a result of the de-excitation of the compound nucleus and thus the nucleus received some recoil energy in this process. Glueckauf and Fay[3] demonstrated that new carbon-halogen bonds could be formed when activated recoil halogens are allowed to react with various alkyl iodides. If Szilard and Chalmers are the fathers of hot atom chemistry, then iodine is the mother of all hot atoms.

Since 1934 hundreds of iodine hot atom chemistry papers have been published. Review articles pertaining to the reactions of these recoil atoms in gaseous and condensed organic systems have been written by Willard[4-8], Wolfgang[9], Maddock and Wolfgang[10], Filatov[11,12], Campbell[13], Wolf[14], Urch[15], and Rowland[16]. The first book dedicated entirely to hot atom chemistry has been written by Stöcklin[17]. Papers concerning solid state reactions of nuclear activated species have been published by Campbell[18], Walton[19], Mueller[20], Harbottle[21], and Anderson[22]. A complete bibliography of all publications in hot atom chemistry through 1962 has been collected by Siuda[23]. Through the efforts of Adloff[24] an annual listing was made available through 1980. A review on hot atom chemistry for the year 1976 was prepared by Adloff[25].

Iodine hot atoms can be produced in nuclear reactors or cyclotrons employing various nuclear reactions. The most often studied is the $^{127}I(n,\gamma)^{128}I$ reaction. Other reactions include $^{129}I(n,\gamma)^{130m}I$ + ^{130}I, $^{130m}I(I.T.)^{130}I$, $^{127}I(\gamma,n)^{126}I$, $^{127}I(d,p)^{126}I$, and U(n, fission)^{131}I, ^{133}I, ^{135}I, and $^{123 \text{ or } 125}Xe \xrightarrow{E.C.} {}^{123 \text{ or } 125}I$, which has importance in nuclear medicine and radiobiology. Reactions of these hot atoms have been studied in liquid, solid, and gas phase organic systems as well as inorganic crystals and solutions. This chapter will restrict its discussion to reactions of energetic atoms employing the bulb technique in gas-phase organic systems and to reactions in the gas to condensed-phase transition. Bulb techniques, where the reaction system containing the radioactivatable atom is exposed to reactor neutrons or cyclotron particle bombardment, are multi-collisionally oriented. The kinetic energy imparted to atoms or ions is the result of nuclear recoil activation. While some nuclear activation modes produce atoms, ions or radicals within narrow kinetic energy limits, the multi-collisional nature of the technique results in collisional "cooling" of the "hot" entities, producing a broad spectrum of kinetic energies.

Extrinsic properties such as product yields and dependence on the physical state of a reaction system can be readily measured (the hot species or medium taken in bulk) and intrinsic properties such as reaction pathways are inferred. New reaction channels (both exo- and endoergic) can be observed and characterized employing radio-gas chromatography. Although molecules cannot be oriented, the ease of product identification (including diastereomers and enantiomers) permits study of reaction dynamics. Therefore, the effects of the molecular environment on the reaction systems from low pressure gas to solid state gases and crystals can be easily studied in bulb experiments.

The moderator technique employing rare gas additives at varying concentrations in the gas phase system, as developed by Estrup and Wolfgang[26] for tritium atom reactions with methane and refined by Rack and Gordus[27] for the study of iodine-128 reactions in methane, can be employed to determine the relative importance of kinetic-energy activated and thermal reactions, especially involving electronically-excited species. In the period of greatest activity from the early fifties to the early eighties, research groups led by Willard, Gordus, Wolfgang and Rack made important contributions to the hot atom chemistry of iodine. This author will not rehash previous reviews but, from his experience of thirty years in iodine hot atom chemistry, will lead the reader through important experiments attempting to define the reactivity of iodine in organic systems. Throughout the discussion the following questions will be addressed: (1) How has iodine hot atom chemistry contributed to general chemical knowledge or to applications in other fields such as nuclear medicine, or did it scavenge chemical knowledge to perpetuate understanding of the area; (2) Is iodine too complex an atom/ion to derive meaningful and clear-cut information? and (3) Is there a viable future for continued study of iodine hot atom chemistry?

2. Nature of Activated Iodine

Depending on the nuclear reaction, iodine hot atoms can be born with kinetic energy anywhere from a few eV[28] up to the MeV energy range.[29] As will be shown in the following sections, iodine can react as a positively charged ion in ground or excited states, and as an iodocarbene[30,31] from ^{235}U fission.

The most commonly studied iodine isotope has been ^{128}I born via radiative neutron capture. Because of the nature of the radiative neutron capture process (n,γ), monoenergetic atoms and ions of large initial kinetic energies are not produced. Instead, a distribution ranging from zero to some maximum value (in the hundreds of electron volts for halogens) is produced. The nature of this distribution may be critical or important for several reasons. A significant fraction of hot atoms can be born with kinetic energies too low for effective organic chemical stabilization. A statistically well-defined distribution of energies in the chemically reactive zone may not be obtained, which would violate assumptions of the kinetic theory.[32]

Yoong et al.[33] calculated the ^{128}I kinetic energy spectrum because of its importance in the understanding of ^{128}I hot reactions. Their calculations of the ^{128}I kinetic energy spectrum utilized previously derived closed general solutions of the probability distribution function for the three dimensional random-walk processes reported by Hsiung and Gordus[34]. For each of the two-, three-, and four random step gamma-ray emissions following neutron capture, they generated 20,000 possible combinations. Of these 20,000 combinations, only the allowed combinations were used in their calculations. The allowed combinations of γ-ray energies are those combinations of energies whose sums are equal to the neutron binding energy associated with the $^{128}I(n,\gamma)^{128}I$ activations. The kinetic energy spectrum obtained as a sum of the two-, three- and four-step processes behaved in the same manner as that of the two-step process at the low-recoil energy range, but reached a maximum at 152 eV. The maximum recoil energy was 194 eV. The significance of these spectra was that they demonstrated that a substantial fraction of the ^{128}I atoms or ions are born in or near the chemically reactive energy zone, which is roughly estimated to be 10-80 eV for iodine reactions.

There is increasing interest in the consequences of the Auger effect, especially in condensed organic or biochemical systems. For example, the isotope iodine-125, which decays by nearly 100% electron capture via the $^{125}Xe(EC)^{125}I$ process, demonstrates chemical reactivity associated with the Auger effect. The consequences of an iodine-125 label on a biological molecule can be quite severe biologically because of recoil electronic excitation, charge build-up, chemical identity change, and internal radiation effects[35]. These effects account for the experimental evidence that decay of ^{125}I in DNA (incorporated into DNA as a label of thymidine analogue 5-iododeoxyuridine) may be 1-100 times more effective in inactivating cells and phage than is the decay of ^{3}H in DNA[36].

A description of the primary physical and chemical processes associated with the Auger effect can be found elsewhere[35]. For example, the internal conversion coefficient, i.e., the ratio of conversion electrons to gamma rays emitted for ^{130m}I, is 400[37], indicating that nearly all of the iodine atoms are involved in the charging event. Carlson and White[38] have induced the Auger effects in the iodine atom by bombarding CH_3I with X-rays. As a result of an initial L vacancy, a vacancy cascade is initiated when the L vacancy is filled by an clectron from an outer shell. The energy difference between the two shells is subsequently emitted as an X-ray, or is transferred to another electron, i.e., an Auger electron, which acquires enough energy to be emitted. At this point the atom is doubly charged as a result of the two vacancies. The initial internal conversion followed by the successive Auger electrons in cascade dissipates the energy of excitation towards the valence shell.

The time required for the Auger process to occur with the removal of Auger electrons (10^{-16}-10^{-15} sec) is very short compared to the time of a molecular vibration (10^{-14}-10^{-12} sec). Carlson and White[38] observed a subsequent charge build-up on the iodine; of +5 the most abundant, relative to a distribution of charges ranging from +1 to +11. The molecular explosion model[39] predicts that the iodine atom in the methyl iodide molecule undergoes intramolecular charge transfer with the other atoms in its parent molecule, resulting in a Coulombic explosion that imparts kinetic energy to the resultant ions. The iodine species may exchange charge, lose energy, and react as a hot or thermal ion or atom. It is important to realize that the "Auger explosion" model is only valid for gaseous systems; that is, the physical and chemical consequences of the Auger effect are still quite obscure for condensed phase systems[35].

Berg[40] and Rack[41] calculated the kinetic energy spectra for $^{130m}I(I.T.)^{130}I$ reaction in I_2, CH_3I and HI employing a "selective electron collapse" model. The spectra appear discontinuous, going through many maxima and exhibiting zero probability at several points. This is the result of discrete energies generated by the transfer of electrons. It is important to note that collisional cooling of the halogen ions with system molecules will rapidly redistribute the kinetic energies and "smooth" the distribution. These kinetic energy spectra range from a minimum value of zero eV to a maximum of 0.65, 21, and 80 eV, respectively, for HI, CH_3I, and I_2, the most probable energies being 0.218, 4, and 15 eV, respectively. It appears that I_2 is the most significant source of translationally excited iodine ions.

From a qualitative evaluation of the kinetic energy spectra for (n,γ)-activated ^{128}I and (I.T.)-activated ^{130}I, it would appear that these activations are not suitable for producing energetic species with sufficient energy to obey kinetic theory assumptions[32].

3. Iodine Reactivity in Methane

In this author's opinion the two most important studies in iodine hot atom chemistry, and perhaps in hot atom chemistry are the two classical papers by Willard et al.[42,43] Prior to 1952, it was generally assumed that the extent of hot atom reactivity in the gas phase was minimal. Willard and his group[42] shattered this myth. They found about 50 percent of the ^{128}I atoms formed by the $^{127}I(n,\gamma)^{128}I$ reaction in gaseous mixtures of 0.2 torr of iodine and 400 torr of methane react to form mainly ^{128}I-labelled methyl iodide. This was a unique reaction ($^{128}I + CH_4 \dashrightarrow CH_3I + H$) in that iodine hot atoms reacted by an I-for-H displacement reaction. Indeed these experiments ushered in the era of gas-phase hot atom chemistry. In a subsequent study[43] Levey and Willard employed the rare gas additives helium, argon and xenon in an attempt to determine the importance of kinetic energy of the iodine in its reaction. They showed that the yield of ^{128}I-labelled methyl iodide was decreased, but not to the extent expected if activation energy were solely supplied by the kinetic energy of ^{128}I. These authors were the first to employ the moderator technique in gas phase systems which have been a mainstay of hot atom chemistry.

Willard and Levey's[43] attempt at determining the mechanism for the $I^{128} + CH_4$ reaction by employing the moderator technique (determining the influence of various additives on the reaction) did not suggest a reaction mechanism for the following reasons: (1) In many of the reaction systems no halogen scavenger (for radicals produced by radiation damage) was present, invalidating the results; (2) the error spread in the data was quite large; and (3) the technique of comparing additives having an ionization potential lower than iodine with rare-gas additives having an ionization potential higher than iodine to ascertain the relative importance of kinetic energy and charge is not entirely valid.

It remained for Rack and Gordus[27] to refine the moderator technique. By having, in the reaction system, the target molecule methane, diiodine scavenger and rare gas moderator at varying concentrations and 0.5 torr of methyl iodide as the major source of iodine hot atoms, large scatter in data was eliminated.

On the basis of the moderator studies it was concluded that of the 54.4 ± 0.5% I^{128} found in organic product molecules:

18.4 ± 2% is formed by a hot reaction or reactions. The experimental evidence, however, is insufficient to conclude whether the hot I^{128} species is an ion or an atom.

25 ± 3% is formed as a result of the $I^+(^1D_2) + CH_4$ reaction. Considering the energy requirements, if the reaction is a simple H displacement, then the reaction must be $I^+(^1D_2) + CH_4 \dashrightarrow CH_3I^+ + H$.

11 ± 2% is formed as a result of the reaction of I^{128} ions (or excited atoms). Either $^3P_2$, $^3P_1$, or $^3P_0$ I^+ ions are involved since, as stated above, ions in energy states greater than the $^1D_2$ would not exist in the CH_4 environment. If the ionic reaction taking place involves H displacement then, considering the energy available, the reaction must also be $I^+ + CH_4 \dashrightarrow CH_3I^+ + H$.

The significance of the Rack-Gordus experiments was the demonstration that in the simplest of all organic systems, methane, ^{128}I reactivity is quite complex. In the truest sense, it is a mix brew of ion-molecule reactions, where both kinetic energy and electronic excitation energy play a part in the formation of ^{128}I-labelled methyl iodide. Indeed, in terms of its primary physical and chemical properties, ^{128}I hot atoms are "messy". Their kinetic energy is not monoenergetic but a spectrum of energies from zero to 194 eV. A significant population is born with a positive charge. Even with these limitations, ^{128}I was an interesting hot atom for study.

Nicholas et al.[44] studied the reactions of ^{130m}I + ^{130}I activated by radiative neutron capture and ^{130}I activated by the reaction $^{130m}I(I.T.)^{130}I$ in gaseous CH_4 and CD_4. As in the reactions of ^{128}I with CH_4, the reactions of ^{130m}I + I and ^{130}I via (I.T.)-activation are complex, not only involving iodine atoms or ions possessing excess kinetic energy, but also translationally-thermalized and electronically-excited ions. A comparison of the contributions of hot and thermal yields leading to methyl iodide formation is shown in Table 1.

Table 1. Contributions of hot and thermal yields for the reactions of (n,γ)-activated ^{128}I, (n,γ)-activated ^{130}I + ^{130m}I, and (I.T.)-activated ^{130}I with CH_4 and CD_4

Systems	Total (%)	Total hot yield	Total thermal yield	Thermal Yield $I^+(^1D_2)$	Thermal Yield $I^+(^3P_1,^3P_0)$
$(n,\gamma)^{128}I + CH_4$ [a]	54.5±2.0	18.5±2.0	36.0±2.0	25.0±2.0	11.0±2.0
$(n,\gamma)^{130}I + CH_4$ [b]	42.5±2.0	16.5±2.0	26.0±2.0	9.5±2.0	16.5±2.0
$(I.T.)^{130}I + CH_4$ [b]	25.6±2.0	9.7±2.0	15.9±2.0	5.6±2.0	10.30±2.0
$(n,\gamma)^{130}I + CD_4$ [b]	41.3±2.0	15.3±2.0	26.0±2.0	9.5±2.0	16.5±2.0
$(I.T.)^{130}I + CD_4$ [b]	26.4±2.0	10.5±2.0	15.9±2.0	5.6±2.0	10.3±2.0

[a] Values taken from reference 27.
[b] Values taken from reference 44.

As can be seen in Table 1 (I.T.) hot organic yield (9.7±2.0%) was much lower than the (n,γ)-induced organic yield (16.5±2.0%). The organic yields for the ^{128}I, ^{130m}I + I, and I.T.(activated)^{130}I were varied. These results suggested that the (n,γ)-activated ^{130}I + ^{130m}I hot reactions occur mainly as the result of kinetic energy imparted to the recoil iodine atom or ions following γ-ray cascade, while the isomeric-transition induced hot reactions occurred by virtue of kinetic energy following Coulombic repulsions. Apparently the "Auger explosion" model is applicable in 1-atm gas systems. Since the hot ^{128}I and ^{130m}I + I organic yields are much higher than the ^{130} I yield (I.T.), it is reasonable to assume that the hot iodine atoms or ions acquire their kinetic energy mainly by the radiative neutron capture process. There appears to be no isotope effect between CH_4 and CD_4.

In a systematic study of ^{128}I reactions activated by radiative neutron capture in various gaseous methyl halides, Yoong et al.[33] found that the formation of ^{128}I-labelled organic products proceeded entirely by hot reactions, unlike the reactions of ^{128}I with CH_4 as previously discussed. The author's results showed a progressive decrease in hot organic yield for $CH_4 > CH_3F > CH_3Cl > CH_3I$. It appeared that the only factor consistent with the yield trend is the system's energy degradation factor. The energy degradation factor $\Delta E_{max}/E_{initial} = 4M_1M_2/(M_1 + M_2)^2$, where the ΔE_{max} is the maximum energy lost during degradation; $E_{initial}$ is the kinetic energy of the incident hot atom; M_1 is the mass of the incident hot atom; and M_2 is the mass of the target molecule. As pointed out in a previous section, a significant fraction of the ^{128}I atoms or ions were born in or near the reactive energy zone. For atoms or ions born with these low kinetic energies such as (n,γ)-activated ^{128}I or (I.T.)-activated ^{130}I ions, the energy degration factor can become significant because one or two collisions with a halomethane molecule may result in an iodine atom having an energy below the reactive zone, removing it from organic combination. Berg et al.[45] found a similar trend for bromine reactions activated by radiative neutron capture and isomeric transition with halomethanes. It is important to note that for atoms born with higher kinetic energies such as the (n,γ)-activated ^{38}Cl, or tritium ($\sim 10^5$ eV) or ^{34m}Cl one would not expect or would find the energy degradation factor to be of any importance.

In an interesting approach, of general interest and application to nuclear medicine, Welch and his coworkers[46-48] studied the reactions of ^{123}I activated by the nuclear process $^{122}Te(^3He,2n)^{123}Xe$ (2.08 hr half-life) ------> (E.C./β^+) ^{123}I (13.3 hr half-life) in CH_4 and C_2H_6 by the moderator technique and the gas to liquid to solid transition. These iodine species can possess kinetic energy because of the emission of a neutron or a positron with a maximum kinetic energy of 34.3 and 20.2 eV in the case of the electron capture and positron modes, respectively. Similar to ^{128}I or ^{130}I, the ^{123}I atoms possess not only kinetic energy but electronic energy and a wide range of charges exist. Based on moderator studies[47] in the reactions of ^{123}I with CH_4, the authors concluded that the effect of additives cannot be explained simply by the direct reaction of two or more excited states of iodine positive ions as employed previously by Rack and Gordus[27], but by molecular ion complexes of the form AI^+ where A can be CH_4, Xe, Ne, Ar, Kr, or N_2. It is believed that these species undergoes ion-molecular reactions to form organic products. However, for the ^{123}I/ethane system, the data could be explained by the Rack and Gordus model[27]. In a subsequent study, Welch et al.[48] reacted ^{123}I with CH_4 and C_2H_6 with and without additives over the density range 10^{-4} to 0.5 g/mL. Major differences were observed between the behavior of CH_4 and C_2H_6 as would be expected from their previous study. In CH_4 the yield of organic products drops from 50 to 10% while the yield in ethane increases over the comparable range. The authors suggest ion-molecule reactions predominate in the low density range and radical recombination reactions are important in the higher density reaction systems.

Saeki and Tachikawa[49] studied the reactions of ^{125}Xe(EC)^{125}I with CH_4. The main ^{125}I-labelled product was CH_3I. Employing the moderator technique these authors found 8.7±6.7% CH_3I yield, 35.8±8.0% by $^{125}I^+$ in the $^1D_2$ stable and 31.5±2% by $^{125}I^+$ in the ^3P states. These data are similar to the reactivity of ^{128}I and ^{130}I discussed previously. These authors suggested that electron scavengers such as I_2, SF_6 and O_2 played an important role and may account for differences found in similar systems[46-48].

Probably the most difficult iodine species to study are those produced by nuclear fission. The thermal neutron induced fission of ^{235}U produces ^{135}I (0.482 direct fission yield, 0.519 indirect fission yield), ^{133}I (0.977 indirect fission yield) and ^{131}I (0.997 indirect fission yield)[30,31]. The directly produced ^{135}I have a kinetic energy in excess of 21 MeV, while indirectly produced ^{135}I, ^{133}I and ^{131}I have a maximum kinetic energy of 2 eV. Kikuchi and Church[30,31] studied these reactions in CH_4. Indeed, the systems are complex because of the mixed bag of iodine isotopes, and the fraction of these species with MeV and eV energies. These authors mainly studied the unimolecular decomposition process occurring after iodine substitution upon CH_4. It was speculated that unimolecular decomposition of excited CH_3I leads to iodocarbons, CHI which can be chemically scavenged with ethylenes. Their reactions were similar to methylene and other halocarbenes.

As can be noted from the complexity of iodine reactions with a simple target molecule such as CH_4, little information of value to general chemical knowledge could be obtained. There are too many different kinds of reactive species depending on the mode of activation. The reverse is true. General chemical knowledge was employed in an attempt to understand the reactions of iodine. However the results obtained in these studies are important for developing chemical procedures important in applied areas such as nuclear medicine. Rather than studying iodine isotope reactions with CH_4, activated by nuclear reactions leading to ion formation, it would have been better to employ, for example, such reactions as $^{127}I(\gamma,n)^{126}I$[51], producing true hot atoms in the 10-100 KeV range. There is a strong probability that the ^{126}I will be atomic when it reaches the reaction energy range, rather than a mixture of electronically excited positive ions/atoms. Unfortunately, Cross and Wolfgang used this activation reaction only to study gaseous methyl iodide rather than CH_4.[51]

4. Iodine Reactivity in Alkanes, Alkenes and Alkynes

It was shown by us and others that the reactions of iodine are complex, occurring by virtue of kinetic energy acquired in the activation event, positive charge and electronic excitation energy. The activation of ^{128}I was employed by us in order to learn about the electrophilic reactions of alkanes, alkenes and alkynes employing the moderator technique and the gas-to condensed-phase transition. The work of Richardson and Wolfgang[52] (in the now familiar study of the $^{18}F + CH_3F$ system in the gas, high pressure, liquid and solid states) led us to a renewed interest in condensed-phase hot atom chemistry. More importantly, other groups mainly those led by Root[53] have utilized the density-variation technique to study the gas-to condensed-phase transition and have demonstrated the general sigmoidal character of yield versus pressure reported by Richardson and Wolfgang. The main purpose of the Rack group for employing this technique was to assist in determining iodine reaction pathways involving substitution and iodine addition to double and triple bonds of alkenes and alkynes. One limitation arises in heavy halogen studies. The rapid thermal exchange between the hydrogen iodide and diodine, I, for iodine precludes the quantitation of these products. As a consequence a total isotope balance cannot be determined for individual inorganic products making a total mechanistic determination highly improbable. While complete separation and characterization of molecular and enhancement reactions require a knowledge of the system kinetics a realistic approximation can be made by postulated reaction schemes utilizing all probable product formation routes.

To determine the validity of a product formation route, all data available were considered and compared to find a reaction or reactions consistent with the observed behavior of the product of interest. These data can include information obtained by the use of radical scavengers such as O_2, I_2, etc., rare gas moderators, product ratios and the density-variation techniques to show the dependence of product formation on a collapsing molecular environment. This was the approach initiated by Rack and his coworkers in their study of ^{128}I reactivity in ethane[54], ethylene[55], propylene[55], isomers of butene[56,57], isomers of pentene[58,59], acetylene[60], propyne[61] and butyne isomers[62].

4.1 Reactions of ^{128}I with Ethane and Alkene Systems

Summarized in Table 2 are gas-phase iodine reactions with ethane and all the alkenes through the isomers of pentene, and the nature of the liquid state enhancement, if one is observed. Several trends become apparent which can assist us in understanding recoil ^{128}I reactions with π-bond systems. The iodine reactions with alkenes are exceedingly complex, dominated mainly by $^{128}II^{+}$ and/or I^{+}-dependent ion-molecule reactions. 1-Butene is unlike the other alkenes in that its reactions occur mainly due to excess kinetic energy. It was suggested that for olefins through the isomers of butene, direct substitution products (I for H) only occur for straight chain olefins with terminal methylene groups. There was no evidence for direct substitution in the 1-pentene, *cis*-2-pentene, and 2-methyl-2-butene systems consistent with the trend.

Summarized in Table 2 are gas and liquid phase reactions of recoil iodine-128 with olefins through the isomers of pentene. Although the reactions of iodine with alkenes are indeed complex, the following observations, can be made:

1. Preferential electrophilic attack by recoil iodine-128 occurs at or near the π-bond, mainly with the formation of reaction intermediates or complexes.
2. I_2-dependent ion-molecule reactions may show an inverse trend with rare gas additives; that is, helium is the most effective reaction quencher.
3. Organic products may be formed by diverse reaction channels, even for the same system.
4. For I_2-dependent ion-molecule reactions, the CH_3I yield increases with carbon chain length through isomers of butene.
5. Collapsing the molecular environment decrease the attack angle on the double bond by interposition of bath molecules.
6. When the center of mass is centered on or along the line bisecting the double bond, attack at the double bond results in bond cleavage and/or molecular translation rather than rotation.
7. There appears to be no simple systematic trend with chemical and physical parameters.

Table 2. Summary of Iodine Reactions with Ethane and Selected Alkenes

Reaction	Organic Yield %	Products	Product Yield %	% Hot	% Total Thermal	Total Reaction	Liquid state Enhancement
$^{128}I+C_2H_6$ [(a)]	1.1	CH_3I	0.06	-----	-----	substitution	caged radical
		C_2H_3I	0.46	-----	-----	complex formation	non-observed
		C_2H_5I	0.57	-----	-----	complex formation	caged complex
$^{128}I+C_2H_4$ [(b)]	18.0	CH_3I	10.0	0	10.0	ion-molecule/ decomposition	------------
		C_2H_3I	4.0	0	4.0	ion-molecule/ elimination	------------
		C_2H_5I	4.0	4.0	0	ion-molecule/ decomposition	------------

$^{128}I + C_3H_6$(b)	24.1	CH_3I	18.7	0	18.7	ion-molecule decomposition	------------
		C_2H_3I	0.3	-----	-----	-------------	------------
		C_2H_5I	0.1	-----	-----	-------------	------------
		$CH_3CI=CH_2$	4.0	-----	-----	-------------	------------
^{128}I + 1-butene(c)	21.4	CH_3I	8.6	5.6	3.0	substitution	caged radical
		C_2H_3I	2.7	2.7	0	complexation/ decomposition	decrease
		C_2H_5I	0.8	0.8	0	substitution and complexation	increase
		C_3H_7I	0.2	0.2	0	substitution	increase
		$C_2H_5CH=CHI$	1.8	1.8	0	complexation/ elimination	increase
		C_4H_9I	7.3	7.3	0	abstraction of H	caged complex
^{128}I + *cis*-2-butene(d)	60.5	CH_3I	47.0	0	47.0	ion-molecule (multiple)	multiple product routes
		C_2H_3I	11.5	0	11.5	ion-molecule	not present
		C_2H_5I	2.0	0	2.0	ion-molecule	not present
^{128}I + *Trans*-2-butene(d)	23.8	CH_3I	13.6	0	13.6	ion-molecule	disappears
		C_2H_3I	9.4	0	9.4	ion-molecule/ decomposition	increase
^{128}I + methyl-propene(d)	58.4	CH_3I	33.8	0	33.8	ion-molecule/ decomposition	-------------
		C_2H^5I	18.7	0	18.7	ion-molecule	decrease
		1-C_4H_9I	5.9	0	5.9	ion-molecule	decrease
^{128}I + 1-Pentene(e)	69	CH_3I	14.0	0	14.0	ion-molecule/ decomposition	decrease
		C_2H_3I	14.0	0	14.0	ion-molecule/ decomposition	decrease
		C_2H_5I	10.0	0	10.0	ion-molecule/ decomposition	decrease

		C_3H_5I	5.7	0	5.7	ion-molecule/ decomposition	decrease
^{128}I + 1-pentene[e]		C_3H_7I	10.0	0	10.0	ion-molecule/ decomposition	decrease
		1-C_5H_nI	4.2	0	4.2	ion-molecule/ abstraction of H	decrease
		2- & 3-C_5H_nI	11.0	0	11.0	ion-molecule/ abstraction of H	decrease
*^{128}I + *cis*-2-pentene[f]	69	CH_3I	22.0	0	22.0	ion-molecule/ decomposition	decrease
		C_2H_3I	17.0	0	17.0	ion-molecule/ decomposition	decrease
		C_2H_5I	13.0	0	13.0	ion-molecule/ decomposition	decrease
		C_3H_5I	8.8	0	8.8	ion-molecule/ decomposition	decrease
		C_3H_7I	1.5	0	1.5	ion-molecule/ decomposition	decrease
		1-C_5H_nI	0.6	0	0.6	ion-molecule/ stabilization and abstraction	increase
		2- & 3-C_5H_nI	6.0	0	5.0	ion-molecule/ stabilization and abstraction	increase
^{128}I + 2-methyl-2-butene[e]	72	CH_3I	16.0	0	16.0	ion-molecule	decrease
		C_2H_3I	11.0	0	11.0	ion-molecule	decrease
		C_2H_5I	12.0	0	12.0	ion-molecule	decrease
		$(CH_3)_2C{=}CHI$	6.8	0	6.8	ion-molecule	decrease
		$(CH_3)_2CH\text{-}CH_2I$	7.6	0	7.6	ion-molecule	decrease
		1-C_5H_nI			9.6	ion-molecule/ abstraction of H	decrease
		2- & 3-C_5H_nI			4.9	ion-molecule/ abstraction of H	decrease

(a) See Reference 54
(b) See Reference 55
(c) See Reference 56
(d) See Reference 57
(e) See Reference 59
(f) See Reference 58

4.2 Reactions of ^{128}I with Alkyne Systems

Summarized in Table 3 are gas phase iodine reactions with acetylene[60] and propyne[61], and the nature of the liquid state enhancement, if any is observed. Suggested product formation routes were determined by the experimental approach discussed in the preceeding section. It is interesting to observe that the reaction of ^{128}I with acetylene occur primarily through an addition channel forming an electronically excited reaction intermediate. In their study of energetic ^{38}Cl-for-Cl exchange in *dl-* and *meso*-1,2-dichloro-1,2-difluoroethane, Machulla and Stöcklin[63] suggested that enhancement of the configuration inverted product yield could be explained by postulating a caged intermediate, the lifetime of which is effectively prolonged by the surrounding molecules (caged-complex model). If the ^{128}I reaction with acetylene proceeded by some form of complex, it would present an excellent opportunity to study caging properties of a complex.

Table 3. Summary of Gas Phase Iodine Reactions with Propyne and Acetylene

Reaction	Organic Yield %	Products	Product Yield %	% Hot	% Total Thermal	Total Reaction	Liquid state Enhancement
$^{128}I+C_3H_4$ [a]	22.90	CH_3I	3.23	1.23	2.0	decomposition[b]	decrease
		C_2H_5I	2.04	1.04	1.0	decomposition[b]	diminish to nondetectable
		CH_3CHICH_3	10.0	9.01	1.0	abstraction of H[b]	caged complex
		$C_2H_5CHICH_3$	7.61	6.61	1.0	decomposition[b]	liquid cage radical
		n-C_3H_7I	0	0	0	-------------	liquid cage radical
		$CH_3C{\equiv}CI$	0	0	0	-------------	liquid cage radical
		n-C_4H_9I	0	0	0	-------------	liquid cage radical
$^{128}I+C_2H_2$ [c]	14.9	CH_3I	0.49	0	0.49	decomposition[b]	(d)
		CH_2I_2	0.70	0	0.70	decomposition[b]	(d)
		C_2H_3I	0.40	0	0.40	stabilization and abstraction of H[b]	(d)
		C_2H_5I	9.30	3.6	5.70	stabilization and abstraction of H[b]	caged complex
		1-C_3H_7I	2.70	0	2.71	addition/ decomposition[b]	(d)
		$C_2H_5CHICH_3$	1.10	0	1.10	addition[b]	(d)
		$CH_3(CH_2)_3I$	0.20	0	0.20	addition[b]	(d)

(a) See Reference 61
(b) Complex formation
(c) See Reference 60
(d) Product is not present in liquid state

In an excess of gaseous acetylene, at 1 atm, 14.9 ± 0.6% of ^{128}I is stabilized as organic activity as CH_3I, 0.49%; CH_2I_2, 0.70%; C_2H_3I, 0.40%; C_2H_5I, 9.30%; i-C_3H_7I, 2.71%; $CH_3CH_2CHICH_3$, 1.10%; and $CH_3(CH_2)_3I$, 0.20%. The effects of rare-gas additives in moderating ^{128}I with gaseous C_2H_2 were determined in an effort to ascertain the nature of the activation process. Only the C_2H_5 ^{128}I yield is decreased by the presence of rare gases, suggesting that both hot ^{128}I ions and thermal $I^+(^1D_2)$ and other excited ions are involved in the primary addition to acetylene. The gas-to condensed-phase studies showed a depletion of all C_1, vinyl iodide, C_3, and C_4 ^{128}I labelled products; the only product observed in high pressure gas and condensed phase system was C_2H_5 ^{128}I. As can be seen in Table 3, the reaction scheme would involve creation of the iodine-acetylene complex, decomposition of the complex to form CH_3I or CH_2I_2, addition of a second C_2H_2 molecule to form butyl iodides or decomposition to propyl iodide, and the formation of a vinyl iodide secondary intermediate which may stabilize on abstract H to form ethyl iodide. In the liquid state the only product C_2H_5I displays yield by enhancement. This behavior suggests that a complex can be caged and have behavior similar to that predicted for radical reactions. Therefore, it is our contention that unless systematic studies such as described in the previous sections are performed and consideration given to all possible reaction channels, it cannot be concluded that yield enhancements are primarily the result of a cage radical or caged-complex reaction. The non-inclusion of an enhancement reaction expression in the model suggests that caged-complex reactions may be an extention of simple molecular processes.

Unlike acetylene, propyne provides both a π-bond site and carbon-carbon σ-bond sites. The question we can ask is, what is the effect of the additional carbon in propyne on the formation of an excited reaction intermediate, and, if an intermediate is formed, does this reaction occur in preference to substitution at the π-bond sites? As can be seen from Table 3, the reactions of ^{128}I with propyne occur primarily through an addition channel forming an electronically excited reaction intermediate. In an excess of gaseous propyne at 700 torr pressure 22.9%, the ^{128}I is stabilized as CH_3I, 3.23%; C_2H_5, 2.05%; CH_3CHICH_3, 10.0%; and $C_2H_5CHICH_3$, 7.61%. Rare-gas additive studies suggest that the iodine reaction with propyne occurs mainly by virtue of its kinetic energy. This is unlike the acetylene system. Oxygen additive and gas to condensed phase transition experiments suggest that the iodine-propyne complex is highly excited, undergoing decomposition, addition to propyne and stabilization and hydrogen abstraction reactions. The major stabilization product is CH_3CHICH_3 suggesting preferential electrophilic iodine site attack on the central carbon of propyne. This product exhibits enhancement in the liquid state suggesting caging of the electronically excited complex. As seen in Table 3, unlike the acetylene system, there is evidence for caged radical reactions for the formation of n-C_3H_7I, $CH_3C{\equiv}CI$ and n-C_4H_9I. It is important to point out how meaningless it is proposing general models for liquid state systems. For the propyne system evidence exists for both caged-complex and caged-radical routes.

Study of reactions of recoil ^{128}I with isomers of butyne[62] in the gas, high pressure and condensed phase, employing the density variation technique and rare gas moderators in low pressure systems, and in the presence and absence of I_2 and O_2 radical scavengers suggested that the ^{128}I reactions were initiated by thermal electronically excited I^+ species for both the

1-butyne and 2-butyne systems. The diverse and complex nature of the reactions could not be explained by simple chemical arguments. However a comparison among the alkyne systems studied demonstrated a preferential attack of iodine at the triple bond resulting mainly in electronically excited intermediates.

5. Conclusions

The field of iodine hot atom chemistry was active for the better part of three decades. Since 1981, no further progress has been made in understanding its reactivity with organic gas phase systems. The question as to whether iodine hot atom chemistry contributed to general chemical knowledge must be answered with an emphatic no. This is mainly the result of the complex nature of reactive iodine; an ion, an atom, kinetically excited or electronically excited. One major mistake was that no real attempt was made to study energetic iodine atoms by techniques minimizing formation of ions. What would be important for future studies would be to generate these hot iodine atoms and to study their stereochemistry as was done for fluorine, chlorine and bromine, as discussed in other sections of this book. Another area to study would be the application of iodine hot atom chemistry to nuclear medicine and radiobiology. What is needed is more research groups, worldwide to enter into these ventures.

References

1. Szilard, L., Chalmers, T.A.: Nature, 134, 462 (1934).
2. Amaldi, E., Fermi, E., Pontecorvo, B., Rosetti, F., Segre, E.: Proc. Roy. Soc. (London), A149, 522 (1935).
3. Glueckauf, E., Fay, J.W.J.: J. Chem. Soc., 390 (1936).
4. Willard, J.E.: Ann. Rev. Nuc. Sci., 3, 193 (1953).
5. Willard, J.E.:Chemical Effects of Nuclear Transformations, Vol.1, p.221, IAEA, Vienna (1965).
6. Willard. J.E.: Ann. Rev. Phys. Chem., 6, 141 (1955).
7. Willard, J.E.:Chemical Effects of Nuclear Transformations, Vol.1, p.215, IAEA, Vienna (1965).
8. Willard, J.E.: Nucleonics, 19, 61 (1961).
9. Wolfgang, R.: Ann. Rev. Phys. Chem., 16, 15 (1965).
10. Maddock, A.G., Wolfgang, R.: "Nuclear Chemistry", Vol. 2, L. Yaffe, ed., Academic Press, New York, p. 185-248, 1968.
11. Filatov, E.S.: Russ. Chem. Rev., 31, 382 (1962).
12. Filatov, E.S.: Russ. Chem. Rev., 34, 680 (1965).
13. Campbell, I.G.: Advan. Inorg. Chem. Radiochem., 5, 135 (1963).
14. Wolf, A.P.: "Advances in Physical Organic Chemistry", Vol. 2, V. Gold, ed., Academic Press, New York, p. 202-207, 1964.
15. Urch, D.S.: MTP International Review of Science--Inorganic Chemistry Series One, 8, 149 (1972).
16. Rowland, F.S.: ibid. - Physical Chemistry Series One, 9, 109 (1972).
17. Stöcklin, G.: "Chemie Heisser Atome", Verlag Chemie, Weinheim, 1969.
18. Campbell, I.G.: Nukleonika, 3, 43 (1958); AEC-Tr-4112 (translation).
19. Walton, G.N.: Radiochim. Acta, 2, 201 (1964).
20. Müller, H.: Angew. Chem. (Int. Ed.), 6, 133 (1967).

21. Harbottle, G.: Ann. Rev. Nucl. Sci., 16, 89 (1966).
22. Anderson, T.: "Experimental Investigations of Chemical Effects Associated with Nuclear Transformations in some Inorganic Solids", Aarhus University, Denmark, 1968.
23. Siuda, A.: Information Center of the Polish Atomic Energy Commission, Review Rept. No. 6 (1963).
24. Adloff, J.P.: "Effets Chimiques Des Transformations Nucleaires Bibliographie", Laboratoire de Chimie Nucleaire, Strasbourg, France (1980).
25. Adloff, J.P.: "Hot Atom Chemistry 1976", Radiochimica Acta, 23, 137 (1976).
26. Estrup, P.J., Wolfgang, R.: J. Am. Chem. Soc., 82, 2661 (1960).
27. Rack, E.P., Gordus, A.A.: J. Chem. Phys., 34, 1855 (1961).
28. Halpern, A., Sochacka, R.: Inorg. Nucl. Chem., 23, 7 (1961).
29. Aras, N.K., Menon, M.P., Gordon, G.E.: Nucl. Physics, 69, 337 (1965).
30. Kikuchi, M., Church, L.B.: Radiochim. Acta, 19, 128 (1973).
31. Kikuchi, M., Church, L.B.: Radiochim. Acta, 20, 81 (1973).
32. Wolfgang, R.: J. Chem. Phys., 39, 2983 (1963).
33. Yoong, M., Pao, Y.C., Rack, E.P.: J. Phys. Chem., 76, 2685 (1972).
34. Hsiung, C.H., Hsiung, H.-C., Gordus, A.A.: J. Chem. Phys., 34, 535 (1961).
35. Halpern, A., Stöcklin, G.: Rad. Environm. Biophys., 14, 167 (1977).
36. Feinendegen, L.E.: Hot Atom Chemistry Status Report, IAEA, Vienna, 285 (1975).
37. Wilkey, D.D., Willard, J.E.: J. Chem. Phys., 4, 970 (1966).
38. Carlson, T.A., White, R.M.: J. Chem. Phys., 44, 4510 (1966).
39. Carlson, T.A., White, R.M.: Chemical Effects of Nuclear Transformations, IAEA, Vienna, 23 (1965).
40. Berg, M.E.: Ph.D. Thesis, University of Nebraska-Lincoln, (1977).
41. Rack, E.P.: Radiochim. Acta, 28, 221 (1981).
42. Hornig, J.F., Levey, G., Willard, J.E.: J. Chem. Phys., 20, 1556 (1952).
43. Levey, G., Willard, J.E.: J. Chem. Phys., 25, 904 (1956).
44. Nicholas, J.B., Yoong, M., Rack, E.P.: Radiochim. Acta, 19, 124 (1973).
45. Berg, M.E., Grauer, W.M., Helton, R.W., Rack, E.P.: J. Phys. Chem., 79, 1327 (1975).
46. Welch, M.J.: J. Am. Chem. Soc., 92, 408 (1978).
47. Loberg, M.D., Welch, M.J.: J. Am. Chem. Soc., 95, 1075 (1973).
48. Loberg, M.D., Krohn, K.A., Welch, M.J.: J. Am. Chem. Soc., 95, 5496 (1973).
49. Saeki, M., Tachikawa, E.: Bull. Chem. Soc. Japan, 50, 1762 (1977).
50. Schroth, F., Adloff, J.P.: J. Chim. Phys., 61 1373 (1964).
51. Cross, R.J., Wolfgang, R.L.: Radiochim. Acta, 2, 112 (1964).
52. Richardson, A.E., Wolfgang, R.L.: J. Am. Chem. Soc., 92, 3480 (1970).
53. Manning, R.G., Root, J.W.: J. Phys. Chem., 79, 1478 (1975).
54. Berg, M.E., Loventhal, A., Adelman, D.J., Grauer, W.M., Rack, E.P.: J. Phys. Chem., 81, 837 (1977).
55. Pettijohn, R.R., Rack, E.P.: J. Phys. Chem., 76, 3342 (1972).
56. To, K.-C., Berg, M.E., Rack, E.P.: J. Phys. Chem., 81, 1239 (1977).
57. To, K.-C., Berg, M.E., Rack, E.P.: J. Phys. Chem., 82, 761 (1978).
58. El-Amri, F.A., Firouzbakht, M.L., Rack, E.P.: Radiochim Acta, 29, 125 (1981).
59. El-Amri, F.A., Firouzbakht, M.L., Rack, E.P.: Radiochim Acta, 29, 185 (1981).
60. To, K.-C., Berg, M.E., Grauer, W.M., Rack, E.P.:J. Phys. Chem., 80, 1411 (1976).
61. Garmestani, S.K., Rack, E.P.: J. Phys. Chem., 83, 2316 (1979).
62. Garmestani, S.K., Firouzbakht, M.L., Rack, E.P.: J. Phys. Chem., 83, 2827 (1979).
63. Machulla, H.J., Stöcklin, G.: J. Phys. Chem., 78, 698 (1974).

2.5 Hot Atom Chemistry of Astatine

Klara BEREI and László VASÁROS
Central Research Institute for Physics, Hungarian Academy of Sciences,
H-1525 Budapest P.O.Box 49, Hungary

Astatine is the rarest element[1] since it has no stable isotopes (hence the name: αστατοσ), and only four short-lived At nuclides have been found in nature as descendents of the radioactive decay chains (Ref.2, p.10). Isotopes that can generally be used for chemical studies, i.e. those with a half-life of several hours (^{209}At, ^{210}At, ^{211}At), are produced *via* nuclear reactions in cyclotrons or heavy ion accelerators (Ref.2, p.95). This also offers a good opportunity for studying the properties and reactions of energetic astatine atoms originating as a result of nuclear recoil.

Samson and Aten[3,4] were the first to use recoil astatination to produce astatobenzene by irradiating triphenylbismuth with α-particles in a cyclotron. Recoil astatine produced in ^{209}Bi $(\alpha,2n)^{211}$At nuclear reaction recombines with one of the phenyl groups present, and the organic product can be separated from the target by dissolving it in $CHCl_3$. Shortly afterwards, preliminary results were reported by Norseyev and co-workers on the incorporation of astatine, produced by electron capture from radon, into benzene[5], normal and iso-alkanes[6] as well as into cyclo-alkanes[7]. Later more systematic studies were carried out in the same laboratory on the hot replacement reactions of astatine originating from the ^{211}Rn(EC)^{211}At nuclear transformation[8-16] (and Ref.2, p.234). Advantage was taken of the fact that a mixture of neutron-deficient noble gas isotopes can be obtained as spallation products by bombarding metallic thorium or uranium with 660 MeV protons in a synchrocyclotron[17,18]. Isolation of radon isotopes from this mixture is easily performed by gas chromatography using molecular sieves[19]. The longest lived radon isotope, ^{211}Rn ($T_{1/2}$ = 14.6 hr) purified and filled into ampoules containing organic compounds serves as a source of recoil ^{211}At reacting in situ[8].

Reactions of recoil ^{211}At with benzene and its monosubstituted derivatives in gaseous, liquid and solid phase lead to replacement products with considerable yields[8-11]. The general rules of these interactions do not differ from those observed for hot replacement processes of other recoil halogens.

Hydrogen replacement by recoil ^{211}At results in a nearly statistical isomer distribution of the products regardless describing the electron donor or electron acceptor character of the substituent originally present in the benzene ring[10]. Figure 1 shows an example of isomer distribution if recoil ^{211}At replaces hydrogen atoms in aniline, chloro- or nitrobenzene. The lack of selectivity indicates the energetic reactions of neutral astatine atoms. For comparison the very different isomer distribution observed for thermal astatine reacting under oxidizing conditions is also demonstrated[13,16,20]; in this case the classical orientation rule for electrophilic substitution is obeyed.

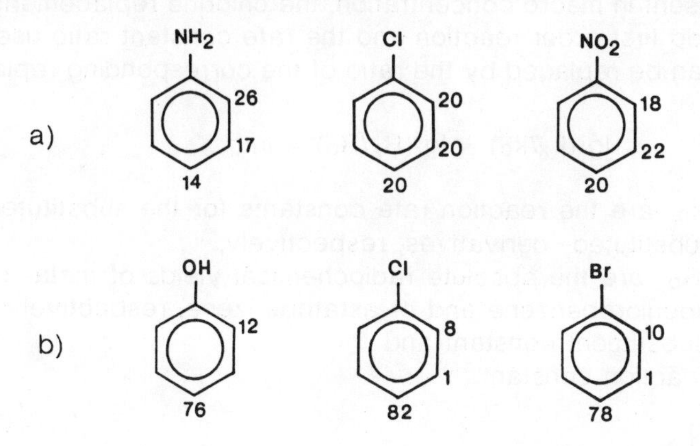

Fig. 1. Isomer distribution of hydrogen replacement in some monosubstituted benzenes (a) by EC produced recoil ^{211}At, (b) by thermal astatine under oxidizing conditions (CH_3COOH + $H_2Cr_2O_7$) [13,16]

Halogen replacement by recoil astatine in monohalobenzenes shows a further resemblance to the analogous reactions of lighter halogens[9,10,15]. The yields increase in the series of fluoro-, chloro-, bromo-, iodobenzene with a reciprocal dependence on bond energy of the halogen to be replaced, as can be seen in Figure 2. The same trend for the gaseous and liquid phase excludes any significant

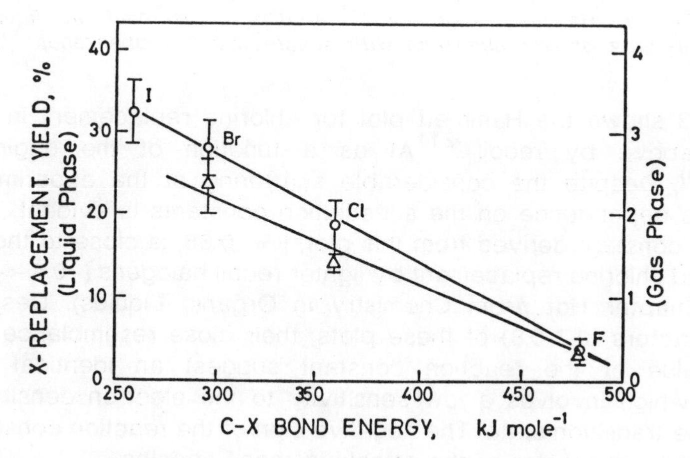

Fig. 2. Dependence of halogen (X) replacement yield on C X bond energy in halobenzenes (o liquid, Δ gas phase)[10,16]

influence of cage processes in the formation of replacement products (see also Chapter: Hot Atom Chemistry in Organic Liquids).

Experiments with liquid mixtures of chlorobenzene and its substituted derivatives[14] have proved that replacement of the chlorine atom by recoil astatine can be treated on the basis of the linear free energy (Hammett) relationship[21,22] commonly used to study the substituent effects in thermal reactions. Since recoil ^{211}At originates in trace amounts, whereas the other components are present in macro concentration, the chlorine replacement can be regarded as a pseudo first order reaction and the rate constant ratio used in the Hammett equation can be replaced by the ratio of the corresponding replacement yields:

$$\lg (k_X/k_O) = \lg (R_X/R_O) = \sigma\rho \qquad (1)$$

where: k_X and k_O are the reaction rate constants for the substituted and non-substituted derivatives, respectively;
R_X and R_O are the absolute radiochemical yields of meta- or para-astatochlorobenzene and of astatobenzene, respectively;
σ is the substituent constant and
ρ is the reaction constant.

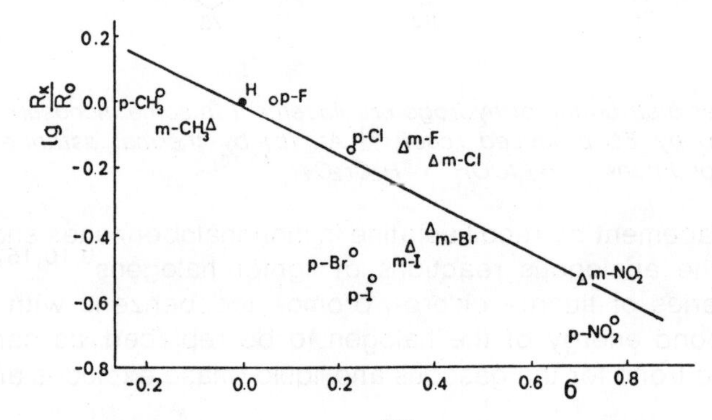

Fig. 3. Hammett plot for ^{211}At→Cl replacement in liquid mixtures of chlorobenzene with substituted chlorobenzenes[14,16]

Figure 3 shows the Hammett plot for chlorine replacement in the systems mentioned above by recoil ^{211}At as a function of the original Hammett σ-constant[23]. Despite the considerable scattering of the experimental points, unambiguous dependence on the substitution constants is evident. The value of the reaction constant derived from this plot, $\rho = -0.66$, is close to those found for hydrogen and chlorine replacement by lighter recoil halogens (−0.4 - −0.7)[14,24-26] (see also Chapter Hot Atom Chemistry in Organic Liquids). Despite the low correlation factors (0.7-0.8) of these plots, their close resemblance and the low absolute value of the reaction constant suggest an identical replacement mechanism which involves a low sensitivity to the electron density distribution change in the transition state. The negative sign of the reaction constant indicates the electrophilic character of the attacking recoil species.

Judging from the results cited above recoil astatine seems to react in aromatic systems as a neutral atom still possessing a certain excess energy. This observation is far from being obvious: The Q-value of the $^{211}Rn(EC)^{211}At$ process is 2.9 MeV which is divided between a γ-cascade of random angle distribution and a neutrino of 0.4 MeV energy. This leaves a fairly low kinetic energy for the recoil astatine[9]. On the other hand, Auger-cascade following the electron capture and the adiabatic electron shell expansion leading to "shake-off" processes[27] may result in high ionization and excitation energies. The main features of the hydrogen and halogen replacement found experimentally for aromatic systems indicate a rapid neutralization of the originally ionized species before the recoil astatine loses all of its excess kinetic or excitation energy.

Some dilution experiments have shown, however, that the reaction of positively charged energetic recoil astatine may also play a role under certain conditions. Vasáros and co-workers[11] have found that both the absolute and relative yields of hydrogen and chlorine replacement by ^{211}At in liquid mixtures vary significantly with the ionization potential (IP) of the solvent. Thus, dilution of chlorobenzene (IP = 9.08 eV) with triethyl amine which has a much lower IP (7.58 eV) than the calculated first IP of the astatine atom (9.6 eV)[28] causes a significant enhancement of chlorine replacement yield with simultaneous decrease of the hydrogen replacement. Dilution with solvents of higher IP values, such as C_6F_6 (IP = 9.88 eV) or CCl_4 (IP = 11.47 eV) result in the opposite effect. Although this phenomenon is not fully understood and needs further investigation, it may be interpreted by the slower neutralization of charged recoil astatine species in a medium with higher IP and thus participation of energetic $^{211}At^+$ -ions in replacement processes.

Summarizing, it can be said that essentially the same rules govern the hot reactions of the recoil ^{211}At as those of the recoil fluorine, chlorine, bromine and iodine. It is reflected in the nearly statistical isomer distribution of the hydrogen replacement products as well as in the influence of the bond strength and of the electron density distribution on the halogen replacement yields. This finding has provided an important evidence for the halogenic nature of astatine, at least if reacting in organic systems.

References

1. Asimov, I.: J. Chem. Educ., **30**, 616 (1953).
2. Gmelin Handbook of Inorganic Chemistry, 8th Ed., Astatine (Kugler, H.K. and Keller, C. Eds.), Springer, Berlin **1985**.
3. Samson, G., Aten A.H.W., Jr., Radiochim. Acta, **13**, 220 (1970).
4. Samson, G., Organic Compounds of Astatine, Thesis, Universitat Amsterdam **1971**.
5. Nefedov, V.D., Toropova, M.A., Khalkin, V.A., Norseyev, Yu.V., Kuzin, V.I., Radiokhimiya, **12**, 194 (1970).
6. Gesheva, M., Kolachkovsky, A., Norseyev, Yu.V., J. Chromatogr., **60**, 414 (1971).
7. Kuzin, V.I., Nefedov, V.D., Norseyev, Yu.V., Toropova, M.A., Khalkin, V.A., Filatov, E.S., Khim. Vys. Energ., **6**, 181 (1972).
8. Berei, K., Vasáros, L., Norseyev, Yu.V., Khalkin, V.A., Radiochem. Radioanal. Letters, **26**, 177 (1976).

9. Meyer, G.-J., Zur Reaktivität und Selektivität anorganischer Formen des Radioelementes Astat bei Substitutionsreaktionen an aromatischen Systemen, Thesis, Jul-1418, KFA-Jülich, **1977**.
10. Vasáros, L., Norseyev, Yu.V., Meyer, G.-J., Berei, K., Khalkin, V.A., Radiochim. Acta, **26**, 171 (1979).
11. Vasáros, L., Norseyev, Yu.V., Berei, K., Khalkin, V.A., Radiochim. Acta, **31**, 75 (1982).
12. Berei, K., Vasáros, L., in The Chemistry of Functional Groups, Suppl. D. (Patai, S. and Rappoport, Z. Eds.), Wiley, New York **1983**, p. 405.
13. Vasáros, L., Berei, K., Kém. Közl., **63**, 64 (1985).
14. Berei, K., Vasáros, L., Norseyev, Yu.V., Sutyor, J., Radiochim. Acta, **42**, 13 (1987).
15. Berei, K., Vasáros, L., Radiochim. Acta, **43**, 61 (1988).
16. Vasáros, L., Berei, K., Norseyev, Yu.V., Radiochim. Acta, **47**, 119 (1989).
17. Belyaev, B.N., Wang, Yun-Yui, Sinotova, E.N., Németh, L., Khalkin, V.A., Radiokhimiya, **2**, 603 (1960).
18. Vachtgel, V.M., Vinel, G.V., Vilov, C., Gromova, I.I., Novgorodov, A.F., Norseyev, Yu.V., Khalkin, V.A., Tsumin, V.G., Isotopenpraxis, **12**, 441 (1976).
19. Kolachkovsky, A., Norseyev, Yu.V., JINR P6-6923, Dubna, USSR (**1969**); Nucl. Sci. Abstr., **27**, 22317.
20. Vasáros, L., Norseyev, Yu.V., Khalkin, V.A., Dokl. Akad. Nauk SSSR, **266**, 120 (1982).
21. Hammett, L.P., Physical Organic Chemistry, McGraw-Hill, New York **1940**, p. 147.
22. Brown, H.C., Okamoto, Y., J. Am. Chem. Soc., **80**, 4979 (1958).
23. Stock, L.M., Brown, H.C., Adv. Phys. Org. Chem., **1**, 35 (1963).
24. Coenen, H.H., Machulla, H.-J., Stöcklin, G., J. Am. Chem. Soc., **99**, 2892 (1977).
25. Coenen, H.H., Machulla, H.-J., Stöcklin, G., Radiochim. Acta, **33**, 21 (1983).
26. Moerlein, S.M., Welch, M.J., Wolf, A.P., J. Am. Chem. Soc. **105**, 5418 (1983).
27. Wexler, S. in Actions Chimiques et Biologiques des Radiations. (Haissinsky, M., Ed.) Masson, Paris **1965**, p. 105.
28. Parsons, R., Handbook of Electrochemical Constants. Butterworth, London **1959**.

2.6 Hot Atom Chemistry of Carbon and Silicon

Peter P. GASPAR
Department of Chemistry, Washington University, Saint Louis, MO 63130
USA

1. Introduction

Carbon and silicon atoms are normally tetravalent in their stable compounds. For atoms of such high valency, the likelihood that the covalence of a recoiling atom will be saturated in a single reactive collision is very small.[1] The most likely primary reactions of polyvalent recoiling atoms are shown in Table I below. While insertion with bond cleavage is capable of forming four new bonds to the recoiling atom, most of the processes depicted lead to the formation of only one or two new bonds.

Table I. Schematic Representation of Some Primary Reactions of Polyvalent Recoiling Atoms M

Abstraction	M + X-Y-Z → M-X + Y-Z
Addition	M + W=Y → M-W-Y + (cyclic M, W—Y triangle)
Displacement	M + X-Y-Z → M-Y-Z + X
Insertion	M + X-Y-Z → X-M-Y-Z
Insertion with bond cleavage	M + X-Y=Z → X-M≡Y + Z

Thus the distinctive flavor of polyvalent hot atom chemistry, including that of carbon and silicon, is due to the circumstance that in contrast to monovalent atoms such as hydrogen and fluorine, the formation of chemically stable products in the primary reactions of carbon and silicon atoms is difficult.[2] The primary reaction products from recoiling carbon and silicon atoms are therefore usually electron-deficient mono-, di-, and trivalent reactive intermediates.[1] Thus one is not merely given the opportunity to study reactive intermediates formed from polyvalent recoiling atoms, one is <u>forced</u> to do so! Indeed there are a number of species such as methyne CH,[3] chloromethyne CCl,[4] silylsilylene SiH_3SiH,[5] and difluorosilylene

SiF_2,[6,7,8] whose gas-phase reaction products were obtained for the first time from recoil experiments.

In the following sections the nuclear transformations employed for the generation of recoiling carbon atoms will be reviewed briefly, and the primary reactions of recoiling carbon atoms will be described, together with the types of experimental evidence that has led to the identification of these reaction processes. The formation of recoiling silicon atoms, their primary reactions, and the nature of the evidence that points to these processes will be described. The gas phase has been employed for most mechanistic studies of the reactions of recoiling carbon and silicon atoms in order to minimize the reactions of recoil species with the debris from the collisions which absorb enough of the initial recoil energy to allow bond-making processes to occur. In the final section of this chapter, future prospects for the study of recoiling carbon and silicon atoms will be presented.

2. Generation of Recoiling Carbon Atoms

The formation of ^{11}C and ^{14}C by nuclear reactions has been reviewed in detail.[9,10,11] Among the nuclear transformations that have been employed for the study of hot atom reactions are: $^{14}N(n,p)^{14}C$,[12] $^{12}C(n,2n)^{11}C$,[13] $^{12}C(\gamma,n)^{11}C$,[14] $^{14}N(p,\alpha)^{11}C$,[15] $^{12}C(p,pn)^{11}C$,[16] $^{10}B(d,n)^{11}C$,[17] and $^{11}B(p,n)^{11}C$.[17] The long half-life of ^{14}C (5730 years) versus that of ^{11}C (20.38 minutes) leads to much larger amounts of radiation damage due to the much longer irradiation times required for the production of detectable quantities of ^{14}C. For that reason ^{11}C has been the isotope of choice in virtually all hot atom chemistry experiments for the study of carbon since the beginning of the 1960's.

There are three low-lying electronic states of atomic carbon, ^3P, ^1D, and ^1S, with heats of formation 171, 201 and 233 kcal/mole, respectively. The high heat of formation of atomic carbon even in its ground electronic state endows carbon atoms with high chemical potential. Thus even thermal energy carbon atoms are highly reactive. The rather small energy difference between the three lowest electronic states leads to the expectation that whatever means are employed to generate recoiling carbon atoms, all three lowest electronic states will be formed together. Calculations by Blint and Newton on the reactions of ^3P, ^1D, and ^1S carbon atoms with H_2 have suggested that the ^1S state might not undergo reaction, while the ^3P and ^1D states should display marked differences in reactivity.[18]

It is clear that the elucidation of the hot atom chemistry of carbon requires experimental differentiation of the effects of excess kinetic energy and electronic state on the high intrinsic reactivity of free carbon atoms. This difficult task has rarely been accomplished.

3. Primary Reactions of Recoiling Carbon Atoms

In the subsections that follow, the primary reactions of recoiling carbon atoms are described together with the experimental evidence for each process. The order of presentation reflects the author's judgment as to how compelling is the argument for a particular process. The reactions are presented in decreasing order of mechanistic clarity.

3.1. Insertion into Carbon-Hydrogen Bonds

Insertion by nucleogenic carbon atoms into carbon-hydrogen bonds, leading to the formation of a carbene:

$$^{11}C + H\text{-}R \rightarrow H\text{-}^{11}C\text{-}R$$

has been suggested to explain the formation of products identical with those derived from the carbene when generated by other means. A carefully studied example is the reaction of recoiling ^{11}C atoms with propane.[19]

Table II below compares the yields of products obtained from the reactions of carbon atoms produced by nuclear recoil with gaseous propane and the yields of products obtained from arc-generated carbon atoms,[20] and carbon atoms generated by decomposition of tetrazoyldiazonium chloride.[21] Product yields from the intramolecular reactions of n-propylmethylene[22] $CH_3(CH_2)_2CH$ and i-propyl-methylene[23] $(CH_3)_2CHCH$, the products of insertion of carbon atoms into the primary and secondary C-H bonds of propane, respectively, are also shown.

The similarity of the product spectrum obtained from ^{11}C atoms and that from the two C_4 carbenes suggests that these carbenes are formed, by C-H insertion, in the reactions of recoiling carbon atoms and propane. The match is inexact, however, and there are indeed considerable differences between the products observed in the reactions of nucleogenic carbon atoms and those produced by striking an electrical arc between graphite electrodes or by decomposition of a chemical precursor. It has also been suggested that double-labeling experiments revealed that some of the C_4 products from reaction of recoiling carbon atoms with propane contain a hydrogen atom from a molecule other than that originally attacked.[24]

Table II. Comparison of Product Yields from the Reactions of Carbon Atoms with Propane and the Yields of Rearrangement and Decomposition Products from n-Propylmethylene and Isopropylmethylene[a]

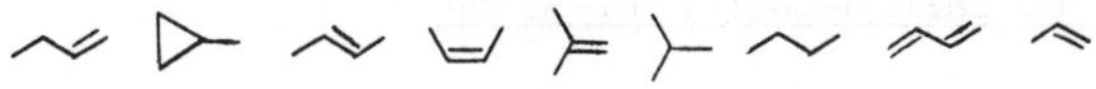

	1-butene	methylcyclopropane	trans-2-butene	cis-2-butene	isobutene	isobutane	n-butane	1,3-butadiene	propene	C_2H_2	C_2H_4	CH_4
nuclear recoil[b] ^{11}C  + propane →	2.4	-	-	-	1.8	1.6	4.0	-	6.2	26.0	14.2	0.5
electric arc[c] C  + propane →	-	10	1	-	35	6	17	27	-	0	-	-
chemical precursor[d] C  + propane →	4.1	4.9	4.1	3.3	12.4	-	-	-	20.7	36.4	-	14.1
chemical precursor[e] $CH_3CH_2CH_2\ddot{C}H$ →	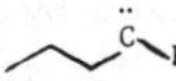 78.2	6:7	1.8		-	-	-	-	5.1	-	8.3	-
chemical precursor[f] $(CH_3)_2CH\ddot{C}\text{-}H$ →	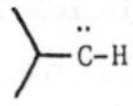 5.1	20	7.4	5.9	59	-	-	-	-	-	-	-

a. Yields are expressed as per cent of total volatile products. b. Reference 19. c. Reference 20. d. Reference 21. e. Reference 22. f. Reference 23.

Degradation of the benzocyclobutene and styrene formed from the gas-phase reactions of recoiling ^{11}C atoms with toluene revealed that the attacking ^{11}C atom was incorporated in the positions predicted by a C-H bond insertion mechanism, rather than in the positions predicted by a pi-addition mechanism.[25] While the effects of xenon (reduction in yield) and oxygen (no effect) additives suggested that styrene results from insertion of singlet ^{11}C atoms into a methyl C-H bond of toluene, similar experiments indicated that benzocyclobutene is formed by insertion of both singlet and triplet ^{11}C atoms into toluene ring C-H bonds.

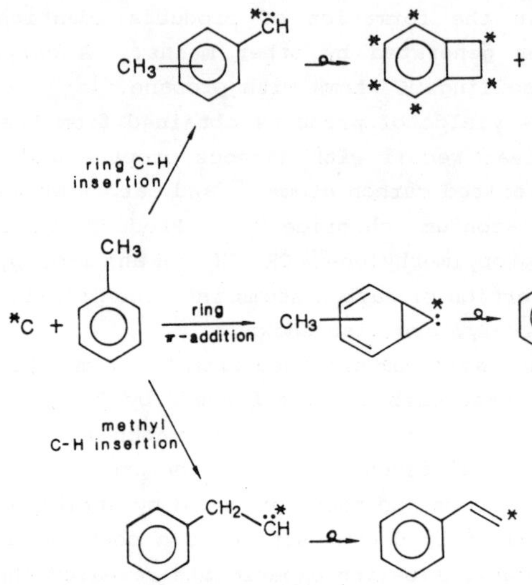

The prediction that random insertion into the <u>ortho</u>-, <u>meta</u>-, and <u>para</u>-C-H bonds of toluene would lead to the distribution of ^{11}C label in the benzocyclobutene product that was found experimentally, 40% CH_2, 60% ring, was based on the mechanism of rearrangement that had been established for the tolylmethylenes formed in the primary insertion step.[26,27]

3.2. Addition to Carbon-Carbon Pi-Bonds

The prototypical addition of a carbon atom to a carbon-carbon <u>pi</u>-bond is the reaction with ethylene forming the cyclic carbene cyclopropylidene. Cyclopropylidenes have been shown to undergo rearrangement to allenes,[28]

$$C + H_2C{=}CH_2 \rightarrow H_2C\overset{C}{\triangle}CH_2 \rightarrow H_2C{=}C{=}CH_2$$

The evidence for the occurrence of this sequence has been summarized by MacKay[24] and Shevlin.[29] Allene was found as a reaction product from ^{11}C atoms and ethylene,[30] and studies with mixtures of C_2H_4 and C_2D_4 indicated that no more than one ethylene molecule was involved in the formation of the allene,[31] while degradation of the allene indicated that 66% was center-labelled.[32] The end-labelled allene was attributed to rearrangement of vinylmethylene, which could arise from C-H insertion:

$$^{11}C + H_2C{=}CH_2 \rightarrow H{-}^{11}C{-}CH{=}CH_2 \rightarrow H_2{}^{11}C{=}C{=}CH_2$$

More recent results of Ferrieri, Wolf and Tang have been interpreted as indicating that direct insertion by ^{11}C atoms into the olefinic double-bond of ethylene occurs, bypassing a cyclopropylidene intermediate.[33,34] It was found that the fraction of center-labelled allene increased from 73.8 ± 4.22 % in pure ethylene to nearly 100% in the presence of 40 mol % oxygen, but decreased to 6% upon the addition of 95 mol % neon moderator.

From the persistence of center-labelled allene in oxygen-scavenged systems and the sharp decrease in the extent of center-labelling with high neon moderation, it was concluded that energetic ^{11}C atoms in the ^1D electronic state insert directly into the double bond of ethylene to yield $H_2C{=}^{11}C{=}CH_2$, while the corresponding insertion by thermal energy ^{11}C atoms will not occur. The diminished yields of both end-labelled and center-labelled allene in highly oxygen-scavenged ethylene samples suggested that ^{11}C atoms in their ^3P electronic state insert both into the C=C bond, yielding $H_2C{=}^{11}C{=}CH_2$, and into a C-H bond of ethylene, yielding $H_2{}^{11}C{=}C{=}CH_2$.

Interestingly, these results imply that if thermal energy ^1D ^{11}C atoms undergo addition to ethylene to produce cyclopropylidene, the cyclopropylidene does not undergo electrocyclic ring opening to center-labelled allene. Semi-empirical molecular orbital calculations by Dewar had predicted a barrier of 50 kcal/mol for this ring-opening,[35] which is surprisingly large considering the facility of this process for a substituted cyclopropylidene.[28]

That thermal energy singlet state carbon atoms undergo addition to olefinic pi-bonds was inferred from study of the reactions of ^{11}C atoms with 1,3-butadiene.[36] One of the products, cyclopentadiene, can be formulated as arising from addition of a ^{11}C atom to a pi-bond:

$$^{11}C + H_2C{=}CH{-}CH{=}CH_2 \rightarrow H_2C\overset{^{11}C}{\triangle}CH{-}CH{=}CH_2 \rightarrow \rightarrow H_2{}^{11}C\text{(cyclopentadiene)}$$

That the carbon atom incorporated in the cyclopentadiene product was at thermal energy was indicated by a doubling of the yield in the presence of 95 mol % neon moderator. A singlet electronic state for the attacking atom was indicated by the small lowering of the yield in the presence of oxygen, an excellent scavenger of ^3P carbon atoms,[37] and by a dramatic decrease in yield due to the addition of xenon, which is known to efficiently convert ^1D to ^3P carbon atoms.[38]

While the pi-addition mechanism written above is an plausible explanation of the formation of cyclopentadiene from the reactions of ^{11}C atoms and butadiene, other primary processes are possible, including a C-H bond insertion mechanism depicted below:

$$^{11}C + H_2C{=}CH{-}CH{=}CH_2 \rightarrow H{-}^{11}C{-}CH{=}CH{-}CH{=}CH_2 \rightarrow \rightarrow H_2{}^{11}C\text{(cyclopentadiene)}$$

Only the ^1D and ^3P electronic states of ^{11}C atoms are usually considered as being involved in the recoil reactions that lead to the formation of covalent bonds. Collisions of ^1S ^{11}C atoms with substrate molecules are believed to lead to no reaction or to dissociation.[34] This belief is based on *ab initio* calculations by Newton on the model system C + H_2.[39] Direct kinetic studies by Husain and Norris on chemically generated ^1S carbon atoms revealed, however, that thermal energy ^1S and ^1D carbon atoms reacted at nearly the same rate, approaching diffusion control, with ethylene, at least 10^6 as rapidly as ^3P carbon atoms.[40]

Evidence has been obtained from the end products of reactions of recoiling carbon atoms with anisole that pi-bonds are attacked as well as C-H bonds.[41,42] This may be inferred from the observation of a product, benzaldehyde, that, as the scheme below indicated can result only from pi-attack.

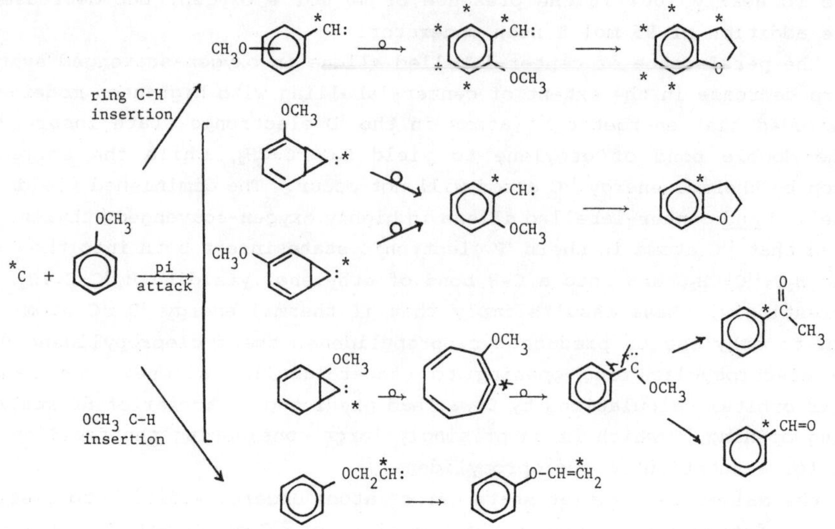

ring C-H insertion

pi attack

OCH_3 C-H insertion

3.3. Insertion With Bond Cleavage

One of the major products from the reactions of recoiling ^{11}C atoms with hydrocarbons is acetylene. The higher yield of acetylene from the reactions of ^{11}C with cyclopropane, compared with other hydrocarbon substrates, has been attributed to the decomposition of cyclopropylmethylene:[43]

$$^{11}C + \text{c-C}_3H_6 \rightarrow [\, H\text{-}^{11}C\text{-c-C}_3H_5 \,] \rightarrow H^{11}C{\equiv}CH + H_2C{=}CH_2$$

Generation of cyclopropylmethylene in the gas-phase from a diazo compound also leads to extensive fragmentation to acetylene and ethylene,[44] and these products are also obtained from reactions of chemically generated carbon atoms with cyclopropane.[45] While insertion into C-H bonds with C-C bond cleavage as a primary reaction of recoiling carbon atoms is strongly indicated by these results, contributions from other pathways is suggested by the finding that some of the acetylene is due to reactions involving more than one cyclopropane molecule.[46] Based on the effects of various moderators in causing a decrease in the acetylene yield from reactions of ^{11}C atoms with ethane (xenon > neon > helium) Taylor, Ache and Wolf proposed that acetylene is formed from high-energy ^3P and low-energy ^1D ^{11}C atoms.[47]

The insertion with bond cleavage mechanism for acetylene formation has received support from theoretical calculations by McKee and Shevlin.[48] Insertion of ^1D carbon atoms into a C-H bond of methane leads to acetylene formation via elimination of two hydrogen atoms from the $^1A''$ excited state of ethylidene $H\text{-}C\text{-}CH_3$.

An insertion-decomposition pathway for the formation of ethylene from the reactions of recoiling ^{11}C atoms with molecules containing methyl groups has been deduced from the isotope effects observed when mixtures of protiated and deuterated molecules were employed as reaction substrates.[49]

$$^{11}C + C_2H_6 + C_2D_6 \rightarrow \rightarrow H_2C{=}CH_2 + H_2C{=}CHD + D_2C{=}CHD + D_2C{=}CD_2$$

The absence of $C_2H_2D_2$ from among the products rendered unlikely the intermediacy of a C_2 species that could be converted to ethylene by hydrogen acquisition. The two mechanisms considered include, as intermediates, vinyl radicals C_2H_3, as suggested by Wolfgang and coworkers,[50] and methyne CH, as proposed by Stöcklin and Wolf:[3]

vinyl radical mechanism:

$$R\text{-}CH_3 + {}^{11}C \rightarrow R\text{-}CH_2\text{-}{}^{11}C\text{-}H \rightarrow R + H_2C{=}{}^{11}CH \xrightarrow{R\text{-}H} H_2C{=}{}^{11}CH_2$$

methyne mechanism:

$$R\text{-}CH_3 + {}^{11}C \rightarrow R\text{-}CH_2\text{-}{}^{11}C\text{-}H \rightarrow R\text{-}CH_2 + {}^{11}C\text{-}H \xrightarrow{R\text{-}CH_3} R\text{-}CH_2\text{-}{}^{11}CH_2 \rightarrow R + H_2C{=}{}^{11}CH_2$$

The vinyl radical mechanism was excluded on the basis of the lack of effect of oxygen additive on the yield of ethylene, and the inverse isotope effect ($k_{R-D} > k_{R-H}$) that would be required to explain the observed distribution of ethylene isotopomers.

Two steps in the methyne mechanism for ethylene formation would be expected to display an isotope effect: the fragmentation of the primary insertion product that produces methyne, and the insertion of methyne into a C-H bond of a methyl group. The observed ethylene product isotopomer distribution agrees well with ratios predicted for an inverse isotope effect of ca. 1.2 in the fragmentation leading to methyne intermediates and a normal isotope effect ($k_{R-H} > k_{R-D}$) of 1.4 for the insertion of a methyne radical into a methyl carbon-hydrogen bond. An inverse isotope effect for the formation of methyne has also been observed by Shevlin and coworkers.[51]

The inverse isotope effect on the fragmentation step can be explained by competition between the cleavage of the C-^{11}C bond and the ^{11}C-H/D bond in R-CH_2-^{11}C-H/D. The stronger C-D bond disfavors carbon-hydrogen bond cleavage and thus favors the competing carbon-carbon bond cleavage that forms methyne.

Thus an elegant series of isotope-effect studies pointed to the operation of an insertion-with-bond-cleavage mechanism for attack of ^{11}C atoms on methyl groups ultimately leading to the formation of ethylene.[49] Ethylene formation by attack of recoiling ^{11}C atoms on alkanes was attributed exclusively to high energy ^{1}D ^{11}C atoms on the basis of the reduction of the ethylene yield to zero in the presence of high concentrations of xenon, an additive capable of efficiently relaxing ^{1}D carbon atoms to their ^{3}P ground electronic state. Neon and helium additives, much more efficient at removing excess kinetic energy but less than a millionth as effective at spin conversion caused a much smaller decrease in the ethylene yield.[47]

3.4. Abstraction

For a polyvalent atom capable of inserting itself into a sigma-bond, the two primary reactions, abstraction, and insertion with bond cleavage, are difficult to distinguish, since their products are often the same. Taylor, Ache and Wolf have proposed that in addition to the insertion-with-bond-cleavage mechanism for methyne formation discussed above, abstraction of hydrogen atoms from C-H bonds by both ^{1}D and ^{3}P carbon atoms can contribute to the formation of methyne.[4] This suggestion was based on the observation of ethylene isotopomer ratios from reactions of recoiling ^{11}C atoms with labelled alkyl chlorides that could be accounted for by a normal hydrogen isotope effect in the fragmentation leading to the formation of the methyne intermediate. The difference in the isotope effects in alkyl chlorides and in alkanes is attributed to the diversion of ^1D ^{11}C atoms to the formation of chloromethyne ^{11}C-Cl by the abstraction reaction:

$$R\text{-}Cl + {}^{11}C \rightarrow R + Cl\text{-}{}^{11}C$$

No products from chloromethyne formed from ^{11}C have been identified, nor have structures been determined for products attributed to fluoromethyne ^{11}C-F intermediates believed to arise from abstraction from fluorocarbons.[52,53,54] The CF formed from CF_4 via abstraction of fluorine atoms by arc-generated carbon atoms undergoes stereospecific addition to olefins, forming cyclopropyl radicals.[55]

The intermediacy of singlet methylene $^{11}CH_2$ in the reactions of recoiling ^{11}C atoms with alkanes was firmly established by studies of Stöcklin and Wolf with propane, in which the same statistical mixture of n-butane and isobutane was obtained as arises from insertion by chemically generated singlet methylene.[19] Jewett and Voigt estimated that 21% of the products arising from reactions of ^{11}C and n-pentane arise from $^{11}CH_2$.[56]

Abstraction of oxygen by arc-generated and chemically produced carbon atoms is a highly favorable process due to the exothermicity of carbon monoxide formation.[29] Since it is difficult to remove the last traces of oxygen from hot atom reaction mixtures, carbon monoxide is an ubiquitous product, and study of the reactions of recoiling ^{11}C atoms with specific oxygenated compounds is technically difficult. The high yield of ^{11}CO observed by MacKay and Wolfgang from reactions of ^{11}C and ethylene oxide were attributed to oxygen abstraction:[57]

$$^{11}C + O\!\lhd \rightarrow {}^{11}C{=}O + H_2C{=}CH_2$$

Of course this process could be regarded as a displacement, a primary reaction of recoiling carbon atoms not otherwise well-documented.

4. Carbon Atom Recoil Chemistry in Nuclear Medicine

^{11}C-labelled compounds have seen wide use in nuclear medicine because the decay characteristics of ^{11}C facilitate imaging and the determination of the in vivo distribution by positron emission tomography. While quite complex molecules have been labelled with ^{11}C, hot atom reactions are generally used to make simple molecules like ^{11}CO, $^{11}CO_2$ and $H^{11}CN$, that are converted into radiopharmaceuticals by rapid biosynthesis or conventional organic chemistry.[58]

5. Generation of Recoiling Silicon Atoms

The study of the hot atom chemistry of silicon is facilitated by the existence of a radioisotope ^{31}Si of convenient halflife, 2.62 h,[59] and decay characteristics, a β-emitter, E_{max} 1.48 mev.[59] ^{31}Si can be made by fast-neutron irradiation of molecules containing ^{31}P (natural abundance 100%), $^{31}P(n,p)^{31}Si$ cross-section ca. 10^2 mbarns,[60] or by thermal-neutron irradiation of molecules containing ^{30}Si (natural abundance 3.1%)[59], $^{30}Si(n,\gamma)^{31}Si$ cross section 110 mbarns.[61]

For study of the gas-phase reactions of recoiling ^{31}Si atoms, convenient precursors have been phosphine PH_3,[62] trifluorophosphine PF_3,[6] and trimethylphosphine PMe_3[63] for fast-neutron irradiations, and SiH_4[64] for thermal-neutron irradiations.

6. Primary Reactions of Recoiling Silicon Atoms

As in the case of carbon, described above, the primary reactions of recoiling silicon atoms are described, together with the experimental evidence for each process, in the subsections that follow. Again, these reactions are described in order of decreasing certainty of the mechanistic conclusions, in the opinion of the present author.

6.1. Insertion into Silicon-Hydrogen Bonds

That recoiling silicon atoms insert into silicon-hydrogen bonds forming α-silylsilylenes:

$$^{31}Si + H\text{-}SiXYZ \rightarrow H\text{-}^{31}Si\text{-}SiXYZ$$

is clear from the trapping of the α-silylsilylene by insertion[5,65] and addition:[66]

$$^{31}Si + SiH_4 \rightarrow [\ H\text{-}^{31}Si\text{-}SiH_3\ ] \xrightarrow{SiH_4} H_3Si^{31}SiH_2SiH_3$$

$$^{31}Si + HSiMe_3 \rightarrow [\ H\text{-}^{31}Si\text{-}SiMe_3\ ] \xrightarrow{HSiMe_3} Me_3Si^{31}SiH_2SiMe_3$$

$$^{31}Si + SiH_4 \rightarrow [\ H\text{-}^{31}Si\text{-}SiH_3\ ] \xrightarrow{H_2C=CH\text{-}CH=CH_2} H_3SiH^{31}Si(\text{cyclopentene ring})$$

The insertion of thermally evaporated ground-state ^3P Si atoms into H-Si bonds and the subsequent insertion and addition reactions of the resulting α-silylsilylenes are known.[67,68,69,70] Isomerization of α-silylsilylenes via intramolecular C-H insertion forming disiliranes that can undergo ring-opening to β-silylsilylenes has also been detected in a hot-atom experiment:[64]

$$H\text{-}^{31}Si\text{-}SiMe_3 \rightarrow H_2{}^{31}Si\overset{CH_2}{\frown}SiMe_2 \rightarrow H\text{-}^{31}Si\text{-}CH_2SiHMe_2 \xrightarrow{Me_3SiH} Me_3Si^{31}SiH_2CH_2SiHMe_2$$

The end-product that arises in this hot-atom reaction sequence had been obtained upon chemical generation of the α-silyl-silylene:[64]

$$Me_3SiSiH_2SiMe_3 \leftarrow Me_3SiH + H\text{-}Si\text{-}SiMe_3 \rightarrow H_2Si\overset{CH_2}{\frown}SiMe_2$$

$$H_2Si\overset{CH_2}{\frown}SiMe_2 \rightarrow H\text{-}Si\text{-}CH_2SiHMe_2 \rightarrow H_2Si(CH_2)_2SiHMe$$

$$H\text{-}Si\text{-}CH_2SiHMe_2 \xrightarrow{Me_3SiH} Me_3SiSiH_2CH_2SiHMe_2$$

When $H\text{-}Si\text{-}CH_2SiHMe_2$ is generated in the high-temperature thermal reaction shown above, there is competition between the intermolecular trapping by Si-H insertion into Me_3SiH found in the hot-atom reaction, and intramolecular trapping by C-H insertion yielding 1-methyl-1,3-disilacyclobutane. This latter process is not observed in a hot-atom reaction, because C-H insertion by a divalent silicon species is an activated process with E_a = 29 kcal/mol,[71] that is quite slow at room temperature. One can therefore deduce that the β-silylsilylene intermediate in the recoil reaction is vibrationally deactivated.

6.2. Addition to Carbon-Carbon Pi-Bonds

In 1974 it was reported that the major product of the reaction of recoiling ^{31}Si atoms and 1,3-butadiene is silole, ^{31}Si-1-silacyclopenta-2,4-diene,[72] a molecule whose formation can be rationalized by invoking the rearrangement of the product of addition of a silicon atom to the butadiene pi-electron system:[73]

^{31}Si + [butadiene] → ^{31}Si[vinylsilirane] → ^{31}Si[silacyclopentene] → → $H_2{}^{31}Si$[silole]

The suggestion that silole was formed as a reasonably stable end product of a hot-atom reaction was quite controversial. Previous attempts at the chemical synthesis of siloles had failed, and a report of the preparation of silole[74] was later retracted.[75] The first C-unsubstituted silole was only synthesized in 1979.[76]

The original identification of ^{31}Si-silole was based on the following observations: 1. The elements present in the molecule were indicated as being C, H, and Si, but not P from its formation by reactions of ^{31}Si with butadiene in reaction mixtures containing no phosphorus [$^{30}Si(n,\gamma)^{31}Si$ on SiH_4] as well as being formed in reaction mixtures containing phosphorus [$^{31}P(n,p)^{31}Si$ on PH_3]. 2. The gas-chromatographic behavior suggested that the molecule contains four carbon atoms but was not identical with any accessible SiC_4H_n compound. 3. An empirical formula $^{31}SiC_4H_6$ was indicated by its formation from reactions of ^{31}Si atoms and butadiene in reaction mixtures without labile hydrogens [$^{31}P(n,p)^{31}Si$ on PF_3]. Acquisition of hydrogen from hydrocarbons by recoiling silicon atoms has never been observed (vide infra).

Evidence for the ^{31}Si-1-silacyclopent-3-en-1-ylidene intermediate depicted in the reaction scheme shown above was the finding of ^{31}Si-5-sila[4.4]nona-2,7-diene. This is a known compound that was also obtained from cocondensation of thermally evaporated silicon with butadiene, and from the addition of chemically generated 1-silacyclopent-3-en-1-ylidene to butadiene.[77]

Si + [butadiene] ⟶ Si[vinylsilirane] → :Si[silacyclopentenylidene]; gas phase → H_2Si[silole]; gas and liquid phases, + butadiene → [5-sila[4.4]nona-2,7-diene]

MeO(Me$_3$Si)Si[silacyclopentene] —Δ, $-MeOSiMe_3$→ :Si[silacyclopentenylidene]

Rearrangement of 1-silacyclopent-3-en-1-ylidene to silole has been demonstrated.[78,79] Chemical generation of this cyclic silylene in the gas-phase led to the isolation of the dimer of silole.[78] Matrix isolation of the pyrolysate of the silaspirononadiene or 1,1-diazido-1-silacyclopent-3-ene allowed direct detection of silole by UV and IR spectroscopy.[79]

Si
MeO, Me_3Si (Si ring) —$-MeOSiMe_3$, Δ→ Si (ring) → → SiH_2 … SiH_2
H, Me_3Si (Si ring) —Δ, $-HSiMe_3$→
Δ, − (butadiene) ↓
Δ or hν, $-3\ N_2$ ↑
N_3, N_3 (Si ring)

Tang and coworkers provided further evidence for the formation of ^{31}Si-silole from the reactions of recoiling ^{31}Si atoms with butadiene.[80] They trapped the carrier-free product and catalytically hydrogenated it to ^{31}Si-1-silacyclopent-3-ene.

$$H_2{}^{31}Si(C_4H_4) + H_2 \xrightarrow{Pd/C} H_2{}^{31}Si(C_4H_6)$$

The Formation of silole in a recoil experiment is of particular significance. Here was a case where a novel molecule that had eluded synthesis for three-quarters of a century was produced in a recoil experiment that served as a prototype for macroscopic chemical synthesis. What clearer example could exist of the remarkable power of hot-atom chemistry in exploring the reactions of free atoms and pointing the way to fruitful new conventional chemical studies?[1,81]

6.3. Abstraction of Hydrogen Atoms

It has been evident from the very first studies of the gas-phase reactions of recoiling silicon atoms in systems containing silicon-hydrogen bonds, that silylene $^{31}SiH_2$ was the major reactive intermediate whose insertion and addition reactions led to the observed, chemically stable products.[62,63,82] When produced by the $^{31}P(n,p)^{31}Si$ nuclear transformation in mixtures of phosphine PH_3 and silane SiH_4, disilane SiH_3SiH_3, and trisilane $SiH_3SiH_2SiH_3$, respectively, the major products were found to be the next higher homologs of the silane substrate, as expected from insertion of $^{31}SiH_2$ into a Si-H bond:

$$^{31}Si + PH_3 + Si_nH_{2n+2} \rightarrow \rightarrow {}^{31}SiH_2$$

$$^{31}SiH_2 + SiH_4 \rightarrow {}^{31}SiH_3SiH_3$$

$$^{31}SiH_2 + SiH_3SiH_3 \rightarrow {}^{31}SiH_3SiH_2SiH_3$$

$$^{31}SiH_2 + SiH_3SiH_2SiH_3 \rightarrow {}^{31}SiH_3(SiH_2)_2SiH_3 + {}^{31}SiH_3SiH(SiH_3)_2$$

Such insertions by singlet ground-state silylene SiH_2 into Si-H bonds, first deduced from the results of hot-atom experiments, have been substantiated in conventional chemical studies.[83] Alternative mechanisms involving free radical intermediates for the formation of these products were rendered unlikely by scavenger experiments.[82]

From the reactions of recoiling ^{31}Si atoms with butadiene, ^{31}Si-1-silacyclopent-3-ene is formed,[72,73,84] in addition to the ^{31}Si-silole already discussed above. This silacyclopentene was also obtained from the addition of chemically generated SiH_2 to butadiene:[72,73]

$$^{31}Si + PH_3 \text{ or } SiH_4 + H_2C{=}CH{-}CH{=}CH_2 \rightarrow \rightarrow {}^{31}SiH_2$$

$$^{31}SiH_2 + H_2C{=}CH{-}CH{=}CH_2 \rightarrow H_2{}^{31}Si\text{(cyclopentene)}$$

That $^{31}SiH_2$ is formed by acquisition of <u>one hydrogen atom at a time</u> is suggested by several different experiments. The major product from the reactions of ^{31}Si atoms in mixtures of phosphine or trimethylphosphine and trimethylsilane is 1,1,1-trimethyldisilane:[65,82,85]

$$^{31}Si + PH_3 \text{ or } PMe_3 + HSiMe_3 \rightarrow \rightarrow {}^{31}SiH_2$$

$$^{31}SiH_2 + HSiMe_3 \rightarrow {}^{31}SiH_3SiMe_3$$

In the reaction mixture PMe_3 + $HSiMe_3$, the only labile hydrogen atom is the one attached to silicon in trimethylsilane, and hence it is likely that formation of $^{31}SiH_2$ proceeds by stepwise acquisition of hydrogens by the recoiling ^{31}Si atom.

The stepwise acquisition of hydrogen <u>and</u> <u>fluorine</u> atoms by recoiling ^{31}Si atoms was clearly demonstrated by Tang and coworkers when they found the products of addition of $^{31}SiH_2$, $^{31}SiHF$, and $^{31}SiF_2$ to butadiene when ^{31}Si atoms were generated by the $^{31}P(n,p)^{31}Si$ nuclear transformation in ternary mixtures of PH_3, PF_3 and butadiene:[86]

$$^{31}Si + PH_3 + PF_3 + \text{(butadiene)} \rightarrow \rightarrow {}^{31}SiH_2 + {}^{31}SiHF + {}^{31}SiF_2$$

$$^{31}SiH_2 + \text{(butadiene)} \rightarrow H_2{}^{31}Si\text{(cyclopentene)}$$

$$^{31}SiHF + \text{(butadiene)} \rightarrow FH^{31}Si\text{(cyclopentene)}$$

$$^{31}SiH_2 + \text{(butadiene)} \rightarrow H_2{}^{31}Si\text{(cyclopentene)}$$

There is still the question of the <u>mechanism</u> of hydrogen (or fluorine) acquisition, since either a direct abstraction or an insertion-dissociation might occur:

direct abstraction:

$$^{31}Si + HSiR_3 \rightarrow {}^{31}SiH + SiR_3$$

$$^{31}SiH + HSiR_3 \rightarrow {}^{31}SiH_2 + SiR_3$$

insertion-dissociation:

$$^{31}Si + HSiR_3 \rightarrow H{-}^{31}Si{-}SiR_3$$

$$H{-}^{31}Si{-}SiR_3 \rightarrow {}^{31}SiH + SiR_3$$

$$^{31}SiH + HSiR_3 \rightarrow H_2{}^{31}SiSiR_3$$

$$H_2{}^{31}SiSiR_3 \rightarrow {}^{31}SiH_2 + SiR_3$$

The mechanism of hydrogen acquisition was indicated by a combination of experiments on the dependence of product yields on total pressure, and their dependence on the concentrations of moderators and scavengers. It was found that the yield of $H_3{}^{31}SiSiMe_3$ from reactions of ^{31}Si atoms in mixtures of PH_3 and $HSiMe_3$

is *not* significantly decreased by an increase in pressure from 1000 to 7000 torr, but *is* decreased by the presence of large amounts of neon moderator.[87] This suggests that removal of excess kinetic energy from the recoiling ^{31}Si atom is more effective at reducing the yield of $^{31}SiH_2$ intermediates than is removal of vibrational energy from silicon atom insertion products.

Furthermore the yield of stable product from the insertion of H-^{31}Si-$SiMe_3$ into the Si-H bond of $HSiMe_3$ is *not* decreased by the presence of nitric oxide, an excellent free-radical scavenger, while the yield of insertion product from $^{31}SiH_2$ *is* decreased by scavenger. Since singlet $^{31}SiH_2$, the electronic state of silylene found to be responsible for product formation (*vide infra*), is *not* efficiently scavenged by NO, the results of scavenger experiments suggest the occurrence of free radical intermediates on the way to $^{31}SiH_2$ but *not* to H-^{31}Si-$SiMe_3$!

Thus the results of scavenger, moderator, and total pressure variation experiments together support direct abstraction as the mechanism for acquisition of hydrogen atoms by recoiling ^{31}Si atoms. The primary abstraction process is indicated by the moderator experiments to occur at high kinetic energies.

A series of competition experiments demonstrated that the silylene $^{31}SiH_2$ formed by consecutive hydrogen-abstraction processes undergoes product-forming insertion and addition reactions at thermal energy and in its ground electronic state.[88] When ^{31}Si was produced by the $^{31}P(n,p)^{31}Si$ transformation in ternary mixtures of phosphine, silane, and methylsilane, the ratio of the products most reasonably attributed to insertion reactions of $^{31}SiH_2$ was identical with the temperature-independent selectivity of thermally generated SiH_2 between these two substrates:

$$^{31}Si + PH_3 + SiH_4 + SiH_3Me \rightarrow \rightarrow X$$

$$X + SiH_3Me \xrightarrow{k_1} H_3{}^{31}SiSiH_2Me$$

$$X + SiH_4 \xrightarrow{k_2} H_3{}^{31}SiSiH_3$$

$$X + \text{(butadiene)} \xrightarrow{k_3} H_2{}^{31}Si\text{(silacyclopentene)}$$

$$H_3SiSiMe_3 \xrightarrow{\Delta} SiH_2 + HSiMe_3$$

$$SiH_2 + SiH_3Me \xrightarrow{k'_1} H_3SiSiH_2Me$$

$$SiH_2 + SiH_4 \xrightarrow{k'_2} H_3SiSiH_3$$

$$SiH_2 + \text{(butadiene)} \xrightarrow{k'_3} H_2Si\text{(silacyclopentene)}$$

It was found that $k_1 : k_2 = 1.32 \pm 0.04$ (independent of temperature, presence of moderators, presence of free radical and ion scavengers) was equal, within experimental error, to $k'_1 : k'_2 = 1.38 \pm 0.05$ (independent of temperature). Hence the product-forming intermediate X in the recoil reaction system may be confidently identified as $^{31}SiH_2$ *in its singlet ground electronic state*.

It could further be established from another competition experiment that nucleogenic $^{31}SiH_2$ is vibrationally relaxed when it undergoes reaction.[88] The ratio of the yield of product obtained from insertion of $^{31}SiH_2$ into an Si-H bond of silane and of the product from addition of $^{31}SiH_2$ to butadiene $k_2 : k_3 = 9 \pm 1$ is equal to the reactivity ratio of thermally generated SiH_2 toward silane and butadiene when extrapolated to room-temperature, $k'_2 : k'_3 = 13 \pm 4$. Since $k'_2 : k'_3$ is temperature dependent, this competition experiment functioned as a 'thermometer' for nucleogenic silylene.

Tang and coworkers had previously employed a combination of moderator and scavenger experiments to establish that the ground electronic state of silylene is a singlet.[89] The absolute yield of the addition product of $^{31}SiH_2$ and butadiene, ^{31}Si-1-silacyclopent-3-ene, was reduced, in the presence of nitric oxide scavenger, by 80% to a plateau value. This reduction was attributed to the presence of 80% triplet and 20% singlet $^{31}SiH_2$. That silylene has a singlet ground state was concluded from the observation that the shape and slope of the silacyclopentene yield versus moderator-concentration curve was not altered by the presence of scavenger. It was argued that if silylene possessed a triplet ground state, collision-induced intersystem crossing due to the moderator would lead to increased scavenging of triplet $^{31}SiH_2$ and hence enhance the moderator effect in a well-scavenged reaction system.

The lack of a scavenger effect on the relative reactivity of $^{31}SiH_2$ toward SiH_4 and SiH_3Me suggests that only one electronic state of $^{31}SiH_2$ contributes to product formation, and comparison of its selectivity with that of thermally generated SiH_2 revealed that $^{31}SiH_2$ reacts entirely as a ground-state singlet.[88] The reduction by 80% of the yields of products from the reactions of $^{31}SiH_2$ in the presence of nitric oxide can be explained by a scavenger effect on steps in the recoil reaction sequence leading to the formation of the product-forming singlet $^{31}SiH_2$ intermediates.

6.4. Ionic Reactions of Recoiling Silicon Atoms

The low ionization potential of atomic silicon, 8.12 ev (^3P) and 7.37 ev (^1D),[90] raises the possibility that silicon ions may participate in the primary reactions of recoiling ^{31}Si, despite predictions according to the classical 'resonance rule'[91,92] that collisions leading to the neutralization of Si^+ should reach maximum cross-sections at energies significantly lower than those at which cross-sections for ionization of neutral Si are at their maxima.[63,93]

By the use of tetramethylsilane Me_4Si as a reaction substrate specific for the capture of silicon ions, it has become probable that reactions of $^{31}Si^+$ ions contribute significantly to the formation of products in recoil systems.[94,95]

When ^{31}Si is produced by the $^{31}P(n,p)^{31}Si$ nuclear transformation in ternary PH_3-SiH_4-Me_4Si mixtures, a product of methyl-abstraction $Me^{31}SiH_2SiH_3$ is found, in addition to the products obtained from binary PH_3-SiH_4 mixtures which were discussed above. The following mechanism, initiated by an ionic reaction, methyl anion transfer to $^{31}Si^+$, is believed to operate:

$$^{31}Si^+ + Me_4Si \rightarrow {}^{31}SiMe + Me_3Si^+$$
$$^{31}SiMe + PH_3, SiH_4 \rightarrow H\text{-}^{31}Si\text{-}Me$$
$$H\text{-}^{31}Si\text{-}Me + SiH_4 \rightarrow Me^{31}SiH_2SiH_3$$

The suggestion that methyl-abstraction was due to a silicon ion is based on the observation of methyl radical and methyl anion transfer to cations by Lampe and coworkers in mass spectrometric experiments:[96,97]

$$Si^+ + MeSiH_3 \rightarrow SiMe^+ + SiH_3$$
$$Me_3C^+ + Me_4Si \rightarrow Me_4C + Me_3Si^+$$

Had a methyl radical been transferred instead of a methyl anion in the recoil experiment, a second methyl radical transfer might have been expected. This would have given rise to $^{31}SiMe_2$, whose product of insertion into SiH_4, $Me_2{}^{31}SiHSiH_3$, was not observed.

While methyl abstraction by high energy neutral silicon atoms remains an alternative mechanistic possibility, alkyl group abstraction by a neutral silicon atom has not been observed in experiments with thermal energy atoms.

Experiments with neon moderator revealed that the yield of the product attributed to ionic reactions of $^{31}Si^+$ suffered a much smaller decrease than the products attributed to the reactions of neutral silicon atoms.

The contribution of ionic processes to the primary reactions of silicon atoms recoiling from the $^{31}P(n,p)^{31}Si$ nuclear transformation may be higher than the maximum absolute yield of 11% observed for the 'ionic product' $Me^{31}SiH_2SiH_3$ from PH_3-SiH_4-Me_4Si mixtures. Other experiments have corroborated the dominant role of neutral ^{31}Si atoms in the primary reactions of recoiling silicon atoms. The presence of H_2 in ternary PH_3-SiH_4-H_2 mixtures leads to an increase in the yield of disilane. Since H_2 has been found to be unreactive toward thermal energy Si^+ ions,[98] but ^1D Si atoms react efficiently with H_2,[99] the increase in the disilane yield can be attributed to efficient conversion of neutral recoiling ^{31}Si atoms in their lowest ^1D electronic state into silylene:

$$^{31}Si\ (^1D) + H_2 \rightarrow {}^{31}SiH_2$$
$$^{31}SiH_2 + SiH_4 \rightarrow {}^{31}SiH_3SiH_3$$

7. Future Prospects for the Study of Recoiling Carbon and Silicon Atoms

We have seen that a distinctive feature of carbon and silicon atom recoil chemistry, shared with other polyvalent atoms, is the formation of reactive intermediates in the primary reaction processes. Some of these reactive intermediates, such as CH, CCl, and CF are very difficult to generate by means other than hot atom chemistry. An analogous species SiH is implicated in the primary steps of ^{31}Si recoil reactions. The opportunity should be grasped to employ the convenient recoil technique to survey the reactions of these interesting methynes C-Z and silylidenes Si-Z.

Another fruitful area is the exploration of the reactions of specific states of recoiling carbon and silicon atoms. The work of Wolf and coworkers on the reactions of ^{11}C with ethylene and butadiene has indicated that different electronic states of recoiling carbon atoms differ dramatically in their reactivity. This was of course suspected from the kinetic studies of Husain and coworkers on ^1D and ^3P carbon atoms, but the kinetic studies probed only the rate of disappearance of the free atoms, without revealing the products of their reactions. In hot atom experiments the products of bond-forming processes are detected and thus the chemistry of free atoms can be efficiently delineated. The state-specific chemistry of recoiling silicon atoms has also only begun to be explored.

The contribution of ionic processes to the primary reactions of recoiling silicon atoms has been mentioned. A promising area for future work is the production of recoiling carbon and silicon ions by x-ray photolysis employing a synchrotron light source.

It is well-known that inner-shell photoionization of any atom contained in a molecule initiates an Auger cascade that culminates in a molecular explosion liberating kinetically excited multiply charged cations.[100] With the availability of high intensity x-rays from synchrotron light sources, it should be feasible to optimize the selectivity of K-shell photoionization and thus selectively ionize particular molecules in reaction mixtures, thus permitting the utilization of the fragment ions such as C^+ or Si^+ in reaction studies.

This method for generating recoiling ions has several advantages over its 'natural' counterparts, K-capture and β-decay: 1. No radioactivity is involved. 2. It can be pulsed, thus lending itself to time-resolved kinetic studies by spectroscopic means. 3. It can be scaled up to the actual production of molecules in isolable quantities.

In conclusion it can be stated that the study of the recoil reactions of carbon and silicon atoms has been fruitful in revealing elementary bond-making processes and their dependence on kinetic energy and electronic state.

Acknowledgment. This chapter is dedicated to the small group of fertile investigators who have illuminated the chemistry of free carbon and silicon atoms: Hans Ache, Richard Ferrieri, David Husain, Colin MacKay, Philip Shevlin, Gerhard Stöcklin, Philip Skell, Yi-Noo Tang, Adolf Voigt, Alfred Wolf, and Richard Wolfgang. I am grateful to my coworkers David Berowitz, Allan Bock, Bong Hyun Boo, Stephen Chiarello, Bruce Cohen, William Eckelman, Jim Frost, Kayhan Garmestani, Adam Helfer, Dewey Holten, Rong-juh Hwang, Carl Levy, Peter Markusch, Siu-Hong Mo, Daniel Strongin, Eric Suchanek, Daniel Svoboda, Matthew Tuchler, and Roger Woods, who contributed so much to the study of recoiling carbon and silicon atoms.

References

1. P.P. Gaspar, "Recoil Chemistry and Mechanistic Studies with Polyvalent Atoms," Advances in Chemistry Series, No. 197, Short-Lived Radionuclides in Chemistry and Biology, J.W. Root and K.A. Krohn, eds., American Chemical Society, Washington, 1981, p. 3.

2. P.P. Gaspar and J.W. Root, Radiochimica Acta, **1981**, 28, 191.

3. G. Stöcklin and A.P. Wolf, "Competitive Gas-Phase Reactions of C^{11} in Binary Oxygen-Alkane Systems," Chemical Effects of Nuclear Transformations, IAEA, Vienna, 1965, Vol. 1, p. 121.

4. K.K. Taylor, H.J. Ache, A.P. Wolf, J.Phys.Chem., **1978**, 82, 2385.

5. P.P. Gaspar and P. Markusch, J.Chem.Soc.,Chem.Commun., **1970**, 1331.

6. Y.-N. Tang, G.P. Gennaro, Y.Y. Su, J.Am.Chem.Soc., **1972**, 94, 4355.

7. O.F. Zeck, Y.Y. Su, Y.-N. Tang, J.Chem.Soc.,Chem.Comm., **1975**, 156.

8. O.F. Zeck, Y.Y. Su, Y.-N. Tang, J.Am.Chem.Soc., **1976**, 98, 3474.

9. A.P. Wolf, Adv.Phys.Org.Chem., **1964**, 2, 201.

10. R. Wolfgang, Progr.Reaction Kinetics, **1965**, 3, 97.

11. R.F. Peterson and R. Wolfgang, Adv.High Temperature Chemistry, **1971**, 4, 43.

12. A.P. Wolf and R.C. Anderson, J.Am.Chem.Soc., **1955**, 77, 1608.

13. B. Suryanarayana and A.P. Wolf, J.Phys.Chem., **1958**, 62, 1369.

14. J. Dubrin, C. MacKay, M.L. Pandow, and R. Wolfgang, J.Inorg.Nucl.Chem., **1964**, 26, 2113.

15. H.J. Ache and A.P. Wolf, Radiochim.Acta, **1966**, 6, 33.

16. G. Stöcklin, H. Stangl, D.R. Christman, J.B. Cumming, and A.P. Wolf, J.Phys.Chem., **1963**, 67, 1735.

17. A.P. Wolf and C.S. Redvanly, Int.J.Appl.Radiat.Isotopes, **1977**, 28, 29.

18. R.J. Blint and M.D. Newton, Chem.Phys.Lett., **1975**, 32, 178.

19. G. Stöcklin and A.P. Wolf, J.Am.Chem.Soc., **1963**, 85, 229.

20. P.S. Skell and R.R. Engel, J.Am.Chem.Soc., **1966**, 88, 4883.

21. P.B. Shevlin and S. Kammula, J.Am.Chem.Soc., **1977**, 99, 2627.

22. J.M. Figuera, J.M. Perez, and A.P. Wolf, J.Chem.Soc.Farad.Trans.I, **1975**, 71, 1905.

23. T. Migita, C.A. Redvanly, and A.P. Wolf, 155th National Meeting of the American Chemical Society, San Francisco, California, March 1968, Abstract No. P226.

24. C. MacKay, "Some Primary Reactions of Free Carbon Atoms and Related Chemistry of C_2, C_3, and C_2O," Carbenes, R.A. Moss and M. Jones, Jr., Eds., Wiley, New York, 1975, p. 1.

25. P.P. Gaspar, D.M. Berowitz, D.R. Strongin, D.L. Svoboda, M.B. Tuchler, R.A. Ferrieri, and A.P. Wolf, J.Phys.Chem., **1986**, 90, 4691.

26. W.J. Baron, M. Jones, Jr., and P.P. Gaspar, J.Am.Chem.Soc., **1970, 92, 4739.**

27. P.P. Gaspar, J.-P. Hsu, S. Chari, and M. Jones, Jr., Tetrahedron, **1985**, 41, 1479.

28. W.M. Jones and J.M. Walbrick, J.Org.Chem., **1969**, 34, 2217.

29. P.B. Shevlin, "The Preparation and Reactions of Atomic Carbon," Reactive Intermediates (Wiley), **1980**, 1, 1.

30. C. MacKay, P. Polak, H.E. Rosenberg, and R. Wolfgang, J.Am.Chem.Soc., **1962**, 84, 308.

31. J. Dubrin, C. MacKay, and R. Wolfgang, J.Am.Chem.Soc., **1964**, 86, 959.

32. M. Marshall, C. MacKay, and R. Wolfgang, J.Am.Chem.Soc., **1964**, 86, 4741.

33. R.A. Ferrieri, A.P. Wolf, and Y.-N. Tang, J.Chem.Soc.,Chem.Commun., **1982**, 124.

34. R.A. Ferrieri, A.P. Wolf, and Y.-N. Tang, J.Am.Chem.Soc., **1983**, 105, 5428.

35. M.J.S. Dewar, E. Haselbach, and M. Shanshal, J.Am.Chem.Soc., **1970**, 92, 3505.

36. R.A. Ferrieri, A.P. Wolf, D.A. Baktuskonis, and Y.-N. Tang, J.Chem.Soc.,Chem.Commun., **1982**, 1321.

37. D. Husain and A.N. Young, J.Chem.Soc.,Farad.Trans.I, **1975**, 71, 525.

38. D. Husain and L.J. Kirsch, Trans.Farad.Soc., **1971**, 67, 2886.

39. M.D. Newton, "Impact of theoretical chemistry on elucidation of hot atom reaction mechanisms," Hot Atom Chemistry Status Report, International Atomic Energy Agency, Vienna, 1975, p. 107.

40. D. Husain and P.E. Norris, Farad.Soc.Disc., **1979**, 67, 273.

41. P.P. Gaspar. Radiochim.Acta, **1988**, 43, 89.

42. D.M. Berowitz, R.A. Ferrieri, P.P. Gaspar, D. Kolinsky, M.B. Tuchler, and A.P. Wolf, to be published.

43. C. MacKay and R. Wolfgang, J.Am.Chem.Soc., **1961**, 83, 2399.

44. P.B. Shevlin and A.P. Wolf, J.Am.Chem.Soc., **1966**, 88, 4735.

45. S. Kammula and P.B. Shevlin, J.Am.Chem.Soc., **1973**, 95, 4441.

46. R.M. Lambrecht, N. Furukawa, and A.P. Wolf, J.Phys.Chem., **1970**, 74, 4605.

47. K.K. Taylor, H.J. Ache, and A.P. Wolf, J.Am.Chem.Soc., **1976**, 98, 7176.

48. M.L. McKee and P.B. Shevlin, J.Am.Chem.Soc., **1985**, 107, 5191.

49. K.K. Taylor H.J. Ache, and A.P. Wolf, J.Am.Chem.Soc., **1975**, 97, 5970.

50. C. MacKay, M. Pandow, P. Polak, and R. Wolfgang, Chemical Effects of Nuclear Transformations, Vol. II, International Atomic Energy Agency, Vienna, 1961, p. 17.

51. G.H. Jeong, K.J. Klabunde, O.-G. Pan, G.C. Paul, and P.B. Shevlin, J.Am.Chem.Soc., **1989**, 111, 8784.

52. D. Blaxell, C. MacKay, and R. Wolfgang, J.Am.Chem.Soc., **1969**, 92, 50.

53. D. Blaxell, C. MacKay, and R. Wolfgang, J.Am.Chem.Soc., **1970**, 92, 50.

54. R.D. Finn, H.J. Ache, and A.P. Wolf, J.Phys.Chem., **1970**, 74, 3194.

55. M. Rehman, M.L. McKee, and P.B. Shevlin, J.Am.Chem.Soc., **1986**, 108, 6296.

56. G.L. Jewett and A.F. Voigt, J.Phys.Chem., **1971**, 75, 3201.

57. C. MacKay and R. Wolfgang, Radiochim.Acta, **1962**, 1, 42.

58. J. Fowler and A.P. Wolf, The Synthesis of Carbon-11, Fluorine-18, and Nitrogen-13 Labelled Radiotracers for Biomedical Applications, NTIS, Springfield, VA, 1983.

59. C.M. Lederer, J.M. Hollander, and I. Perlman, Table of Isotopes, 6th ed., Wiley, N.Y., 1967, p. 10.

60. J.R. Stehn, M.D. Goldberg, B.A. Magurno, and R. Wiener-Chasman, Neutron Cross Sections, Brookhaven National Laboratory, Upton, NY, 1964, P. 15-0-5.

61. G. Friedlander, J.W. Kennedy, and J.M. Miller, Nuclear and Radiochemistry, 2nd ed., Wiley, N.Y., 1964, p. 525.

62. P.P. Gaspar, B.D. Pate, and W. Eckelman, J.Am.Chem.Soc., **1966**, 88, 3878.

63. P.P. Gaspar, S.A. Bock, and W.C. Eckelman, J.Am.Chem.Soc., **1968**, 90, 6914.

64. P.P. Gaspar, S.A. Bock, and C.A. Levy, J.Chem.Soc.,Chem.Commun., **1968**, 1317.

65. S.H. Mo, J.D. Holten III, S. Konieczny, E.C.-l. Ma, and P.P. Gaspar, J.Am.Chem.Soc., **1982**, 104, 1424.

66. P.P. Gaspar, B.H. Boo, and D.L. Svoboda, J.Phys.Chem., **1987**, 91, 5011.

67. P.S. Skell and P.W. Owen, J.Am.Chem.Soc., **1967**, 89, 3933.

68. P.W. Owen and P.S. Skell, tetrahedron Lett., **1972**, 1807.

69. P.S. Skell and P.W. Owen, J.Am.Chem.Soc., **1972**, 94, 5434.

70. R.L. Jenkins, R.A. Kedrowski, L.E. Elliott, D.C. Tappen, D.J. Schlyer, and M.A. Ring, J.Organometal.Chem., **1975**, 86, 347.

71. B.H. Boo and P.P. Gaspar, Organometallics, **1986**, 5, 698.

72. P.P. Gaspar, R.-J. Hwang, and W.C. Eckelman, J.Chem.Soc.,Chem.Commun., **1974**, 242.

73. R.-J. Hwang and P.P. Gaspar, J.Am.Chem.Soc., **1978**, 100, 6626.

74. R.A. Benkeser, R.F. Grossman and G.M. Stenton, J.Am.Chem.Soc., **1962**, 84, 4723.

75. R.A. Benkeser, Y. Nagai, J.L. Noe, R.F. Cunico, and P.H. Gund, J.Am.Chem.Soc., **1964**, 86, 2446.

76. T.J. Barton and G.T. Burns, J.Organometal.Chem., **1979**, 179, C17.

77. P.P. Gaspar, Y.-s. Chen, A.P. Helfer, S. Konieczny, E.C.-L. Ma, and S.-H. Mo, J.Am.Chem.Soc., **1981**, 103, 7344.

78. D. Lei, Y.-S. Chen, B.H. Boo, J. Frueh, D.L. Svoboda, and P.P. Gaspar, Organometallics, submitted for publication.

79. V.N. Khabashesku, V. Balaji, S.E. Boganov, S.A. Bashkirova, P.M. Matveichev, E.A. Chernyshev, O.M. Nefedov, and J. Michl, submitted for publication.

80. E.E. Siefert, K.-L. Loh, R.A. Ferrieri, and Y.-N. Tang, J.Am.Chem.Soc., **1980**, 102, 2285.

81. Y.-N. Tang, "Unusual Compounds Synthesized via Nuclear Recoil Methods," Advances in Chemistry Series, No. 197, Short-Lived Radionuclides in Chemistry and Biology, J.W. Root and K.A. Krohn, eds., American Chemical Society, Washington, 1981, p. 53.

82. P.P. Gaspar, P. Markusch, J.D. Holten, III, and J.J. Frost, J.Phys.Chem., **1972**, 76, 1352.

83. P.P. Gaspar, "Advances in Silylene Chemistry," Reactive Intermediates, M. Jones, Jr. and R.A. Moss, eds, Wiley, New York, **1978**, 1, 229; **1981**, 2, 335; **1985**, 3, 333.

84. G.P. Gennaro, Y.-Y. Su, O.F. Zeck, S.H. Daniel, and Y.-N. Tang, J.Chem.Soc.,Chem.Comm., **1973**, 637.

85. P.P. Gaspar, "The Hot Atom Chemistry of Polyvalent Atoms," 7th International Hot-Atom Chemistry Symposium, Juelich, Germany, September 11, 1973, AEC Technical Report No. COO-1713-44.

86. E.E. Siefert, S.D. Witt, K.-L. Loh, and Y.-N. Tang, J.Organometal.Chem., **1982**, 239, 293.

87. Unpublished work of J.D. Holten III and P.P. Gaspar, "Reaction Studies of Hot Silicon and Germanium Radicals," Progress Report, August 31, 1973, Atomic Energy Commission Technical Report No. COO-1713-43, pp. 6,7.

88. P.P. Gaspar, S. Konieczny, and S.H. Mo, J.Am.Chem.Soc., **1984**, 106, 424.

89. O.F. Zeck, Y.Y. Su, G.P. Gennaro, and Y.-N. Tang, J.Am,Chem.Soc., **1974**, 96, 5967.

90. G. Herzberg, Atomic Spectra and Atomic Structure, Prentice-Hall, Englewood Cliffs, NJ, 1937, p. 140.

91. H.S. Massey and E.H. Burhop, Electronic and Ionic Impact Phenomena, Clarendon Press, Oxford, 1952, p. 441.

92. J.B. Hasted, Physics of Atomic Collisions, Butterworth, London, 1964, p. 420.

93. For examples of large charge-transfer cross-sections at velocities low compared to maxima predicted by the resonance rule, see G.K. Lavrovskaya, M.L. Markin, and V.L. Tal'roze, Kinetics Catalysis (USSR), **1961**, 2, 21.

94. K. Garmestani, S. Chiarello, and P.P. Gaspar, "Reactions of Recoiling Silicon Atoms in Gaseous Mixtures of Phosphine, Silane and Tetramethylsilane," Eighth International Symposium on Organosilicon Chemistry Abstracts, St. Louis, MO, June 7-12, 1987, p. 262.

95. K. Garmestani and P.P. Gaspar, "Alkyl Group Abstraction by Recoiling Silicon Atoms," manuscript in preparation.

96. T.M. Mayer and F.W. Lampe, J.Phys.Chem., **1974**, 78, 2422.

97. G.W. Goodloe and F.W. Lampe, J.Am.Chem.Soc., **1979**, 101, 6028.

98. V.G. Ancich and W.T. Huntress, Jr., Astrophys.J.Suppl.Ser., **1986**, 62, 553.

99. D. Husain and P.E. Norris, J.Chem.Soc.Farad.Trans.II, **1978**, 74, 1483.

100. T.A. Carlson and R.M. White, "'Explosion' of Multicharged Molecular Ions: Chemical Consequences of Inner-Shell Vacancies in Atoms," Chemical Effects of Nuclear Transformations, IAEA, Vienna, 1965, Vol. 1, p. 23.

2.7 Hot Atom Chemistry of Nitrogen

Yoshihiro SENSUI* and Michael John WELCH+
*Faculty of General Education, Rikkyo University, 3-34-1, Nishi-Ikebukuro, Toshima-ku, Tokyo, 171 Japan
+Division of Radiation Sciences, Washington University School of Medicine, 510 South Kingshighway, St. Louis, Missouri 63110 U.S.A.

1. INTRODUCTION

Nitrogen-13 is a positron emitter with a half life of 10 min. Hot atom effects associated with its production have been studied because of the radiopharmaceutical value of its labelled compounds. To produce Nitrogen-13, nuclear reactions such as $^{12}C(d,n,)^{13}N$, $^{14}N(n,2n)^{13}N$, $^{16}O(p,\alpha)^{13}N$, $^{13}C(p,n)^{13}N$, and $^{14}N(\gamma,n)^{13}N$ are employed. The Hot Atom Chemistry (HAC) of ^{16}N (β^-, 7.14sec) in gaseous and liquid water is also of interest in relation to the corrosion of the cooling lines in Boiling-Water-Reactors.

2. INORGANIC SYSTEMS

Many studies on the HAC of nitrogen in inorganic materials have been reported; e.g. graphites [1], carbides [2], carbonates [1], azides [3,4], nitrides [5], nitrates and nitrites [6,7], sulphate [8], cyanide and thiocyanide [7], NH_xF_y [4], LiH/Al_2O_3 [9], water [10-17], CO_x and other gas mixtures [18-20], $C/O_2/He$ [21] and C/NO [22]. Representative cases will briefly be summarized in the next section.

2.1. Solid and Liquid Inorganic Systems

According to Aten, Jr. [6,7], in ^{13}N/nitrate and nitrite systems, highly oxidized ^{13}N-compounds such as $^{13}NO_3^-$ were formed. Thus in $LiNO_3$ and $NaNO_3$ targets, the ratio of the yields between $^{13}NO_3^-$(39-51%) and $^{13}NO_2^-$(39-47%) was approximately unity and there was no thermal annealing effect at 240°C. In $NaNO_2$, only ^{13}NN and /or ^{13}NNO (58-61%) and $^{13}NO_2^-$ (32-45%) were formed.

In frozen ammonia, NH_4F, $NH_4F\cdot HF$ and $N_2H_4\cdot 2HF$ targets at -196°C, the yield of $^{13}NH_3$ was proportional to the (H/N)-ratio in the target molecule over the range 3 to 5, and the inverse relationship was found between the yield of ^{13}NN and the same ratio[4].

In ^{13}N-implantation into LiH in (Al_2O_3/LiH) powder mixtures irradiated by 13 MeV protons, Rössler [8] showed that main products were $^{13}NH_3$ (35%) together with ^{13}NH (or $^{13}NH_2$) radicals (65%). He further confirmed the formation of N-H bonds at low temperature, by optical absorption spectroscopy in the visible and IR region, as a result of the implantation of $^{14}N^+$ ions into LiH single crystal plates at 6°K.

There are interesting works on the HAC of ^{13}N or ^{16}N originating from oxygen in frozen and liquid water, and in steam [11-17]. In frozen water bombarded by 20 MeV protons, the yield of $^{13}NH_3$, one of the main products (others are; $^{13}NH_4^+$, $^{13}NO_2^-$ and $^{13}NO_3^-$, rises to a max of ca 95% with rising dose. An increase of $^{13}NH_3$ at higher doses ($>10^{-1}$ eV/molecule) is caused by the formation of H radicals and their high mobility even at T=77°K. At higher doses, NH_4^+ is oxidized to nitrate, although primarily formed N-O compounds are protected from reduction [10]. In liquid water, ^{13}N produced by the $^{16}O(p,\alpha)^{13}N$ reaction shows different chemical behavior from that produced by the $^{12}C(d,n)^{13}N$ reaction:i.e. the distribution of ^{13}N being NH_4^+ (7%) and NO_3^- (93%) in the former and NH_4^+ (71%), NO_3^-(24%) and NO_2^- (4%) in the latter, even though it is usually considered that the chemical effects of highly energetic recoiling atoms such as ^{13}N are scarcely influenced by which nuclear reaction produces the nuclide.

In a He-purged water target [18], the oxidation of $^{13}NH_4^+$ to $^{13}NO_3^-$ was enhanced by increased dose. That can be explained by postulating the initial production of $^{13}NH_3$ by successive abstraction of H atoms by the ^{13}N atom, followed by the oxidation of $^{13}NH_3$ to $^{13}NO_2^-$ and $^{13}NO_3^-$ by oxidizing species in the water. In water vapor irradiated by protons, ^{13}NO is the main product at the lowest doses with yields exceeding 45% and oxidization to $^{13}NO_2$ increases with radiolytic dose. At high doses ^{13}NN becomes the main product, although the formation of ^{13}NN and ^{13}NNO is due to traces of nitrogen impurity in the water vapor [18].

In the BWR, most of the ^{13}N is found as NO_2^- and NO_3^- in the coolant and/or NH_4^+ in the steam condensate under normal-water-chemistry conditions, although all the ^{13}N is found as NH_4^+ in both the reactor water and the steam condensate under hydrogen-water-chemistry conditions[15]. Most of the ^{13}N released into the main steam line in the BWR is found in NO form, and but little as NH_3 or N_2[18]. In this system, ^{13}NO is formed by the reduction of $^{13}NO_3^-$ and $^{13}NO_2^-$ [16,17].

2.2 Inorganic System in the Gaseous State.

Several inorganic gases, CO, CO_2 and their mixtures with N_2, NO, N_2O, O_2 and C_2H_4, have been examined [18-22]. In these systems, most of the ^{13}N is found as N_2 and N_2O. The formation of ^{13}NN in CO and CO_2 targets is attributed to recombination between ^{13}N and impurity N_2 in the medium and/or on the walls of the chamber. The formation of ^{13}NN with added N_2 is due to an exchange reaction involving translationally excited nitrogen atoms with nitrogen molecules [18]. The formation of ^{13}NNO is explained by the reaction between excited nitrogen molecules $^{13}NN^*$ and oxygen.

In CO_2/N_2 mixture, the distribution of ^{13}N is approximately independent of nitrogen concentration. In $CO/N_2/O_2$, all ^{13}N is found as N_2. For these systems, reaction mechanisms include the abstraction of an oxygen atom by ^{13}N from CO_2, by an excited

^{13}NN from CO_2, and the reaction of energetic ^{13}N with N_2 [19-20]. In the reaction of ^{13}N with pure NO, only ^{13}NN (79%) and ^{13}NO (21%) can be formed by reactions with $\Delta H \leq 0$ [22].

3. ORGANIC SYSTEMS

3.1. Organic Systems in the Condensed State

The HAC of ^{13}N in many sorts of organic media such as liquid and frozen hydrocarbons [20,27], alcohols, ethers, ketones, aldehydes [11,28,30], carboxylic acids[31-34], aromatic hydrocarbons [24] and organic salts [11,25] have been studied. Normal and deuterated benzene and cyclohexane have been studied [26,27], and the yields of relatively simple ^{13}N-compounds as $HC^{13}N$ and $^{13}NH_3$ increase remarkably with the change of phase from solid to liquid, while the yields of $C_6H_xC^{13}N$ and $C_6H_x{}^{13}NH_2$ significantly decrease with this change. The decrease in the yield of $C_6H_xC^{13}N$ with the phase change is balanced by an increase in the yields of the other relatively simple $C^{13}N$-compounds (Fig. 1a), and of the amine compounds (Fig. 1b). Almost all products formed in benzene and cyclohexane show an (H/D)-isotope effect: i.e., (1) the degree of the phase effect is always larger in the protiated than in the deuterated media (the ratio of the difference in the yields between the two phases, $\Delta Y_H/\Delta Y_D$, is always larger than unity) and (2) the degree of isotope effect in HCN in benzene is as high as 2.2, although (3) there is no isotope effect in the respective gross yields of total nitrile and of total amine compounds. The latter facts suggest that either a $C^{13}N$ or ^{13}NH radical is formed in the primary abstraction reaction by the ^{13}N atom.

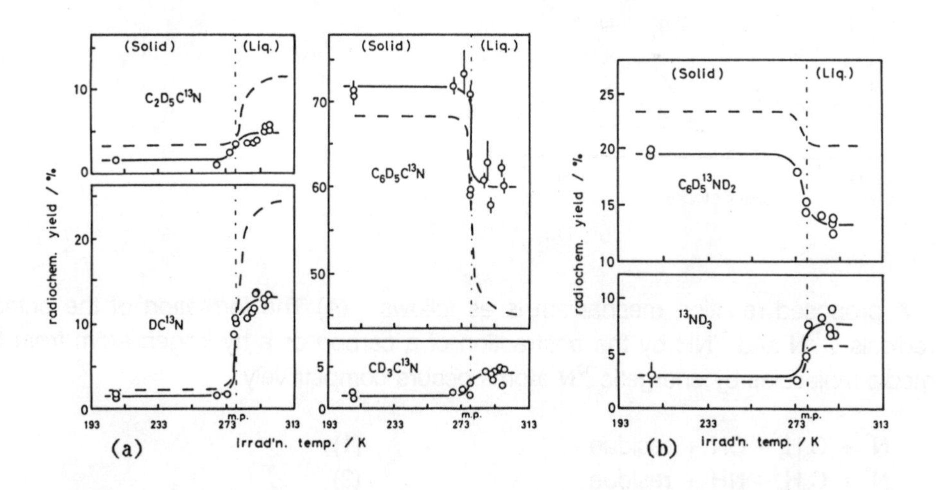

Fig.1 Temperature dependence of the yields of ^{13}N-compounds formed in pile-irradiated benzene-d_6. (a) [^{13}N]CN-compounds, (b) [^{13}N]ND_x-compounds. Dashed curve represents the smmothed yields of the corresponding compounds in protiated benzene.

The large phase effect can be interpreted by a reaction model postulating the schematic concentration profile of fragments in and around the reaction cage of the $C^{13}N$ and ^{13}NH radicals as shown in Fig. 2. In the earlier stages the fragmentation of the bulk molecules (eq. (1)) occurs by virtue of the energy deposition by the recoiling ^{13}N atom or the hot primary radicals ($C^{13}N$ or ^{13}NH). The local concentration of heavy fragments such as phenyl radicals, can be much higher than that of the light fragments, such as hydrogen atoms, in the cage, because of the light fragments being thrown far from the center of the cage [26].

This approach which connects the phase effect with the diffusion of some precursor is supported by the phase effect in the G-values of products in pile irradiation radiolysis of benzene and cyclohexane [25]; i.e., the magnitude of the phase effect for H_2 in the pile irradiation radiolysis of cyclohexane correlates with the portion of H_2 that can be scavenged in the gamma radiolysis [28].

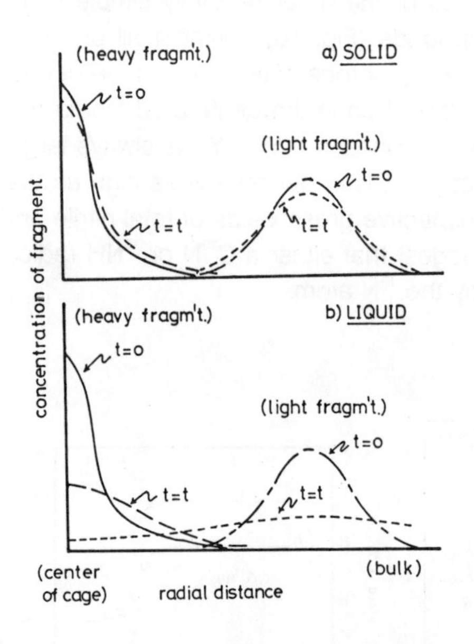

Fig.2 Schematic concentration profile of fragments in and around the reaction cage of $C^{13}N$ or ^{13}NH radicals in solid (a) and liquid (b) media.

A proposed reaction mechanism is as follows. (A) The formation of the primary radicals $C^{13}N$ and ^{13}NH by the abstraction of a carbon or a hydrogen atom from the media molecules by energetic ^{13}N atoms occurs competitively.

$$N^* + C_6H_x \rightarrow CN + residue \quad (1)$$
$$N^* + C_6H_x \rightarrow NH + residue \quad (2)$$

where x is 6 or 12. (B) Radical reactions between $C^{13}N$ or ^{13}NH and radicals such as H and the residual formed in the radiolysis of the medium, take place competitively in the cage around the thermalized ^{13}N-containing radicals.

$$CN + H \rightarrow HCN \qquad (3)$$
$$CN + C_6H_{x-1} \rightarrow C_6H_{x-1}CN \qquad (4)$$
$$NH + H \twoheadrightarrow NH_3 \qquad (5)$$
$$NH + C_6H_{x-1} \twoheadrightarrow C_6H_{x-1}NH_2 \qquad (6)$$

In acetone and diethylether in a pile, the slope of a logarithmic plots of the yield of $^{13}NH_3$ against 1/T parallels that of a plot of the log of the viscosity of the media against 1/T [29]. That is in agreement with a process controlled by the diffusion of some precursor.

On the other hand, a diffusion-controlled process is excluded in the formation of the final ^{13}N-compounds in more chemically reactive media such as nitrobenzene [23] and in protiated and deuterated methanols [30]. These differ from the results in benzene, cyclohexane, acetone and ethyl ether.

The formation of $^{13}NH_4^+$ and $C^{13}N^-$ depends on the atomic ratios of H/N and C/N in a target molecule in several media such as diphenylamine, diphenylhydrazine, benzidine, 2-aminodiphenylamine, azobenzene, chrysoidine, hexamethylenetetramine, purine and guanidiniumthiocyanate [24] (Fig. 3).

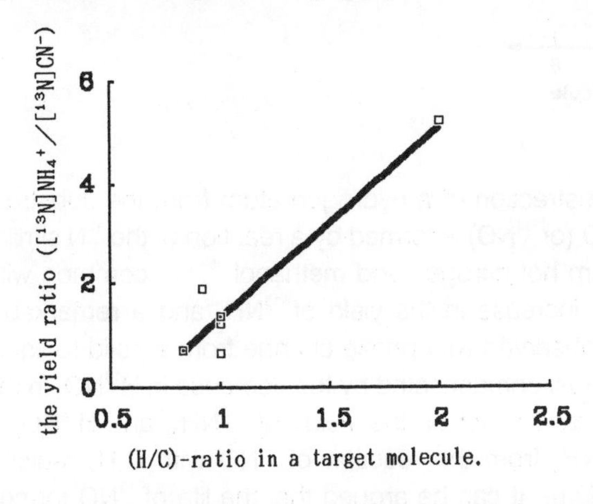

Fig.3 Plots of the yield of ratio ([^{13}N] NH_4^+ / [^{13}N] CN^-) against (H/C)-ratio in a target molecule.

In several deuterated carboxylic acids such as fluoroacetic acid-d, acetic acid-d_4, propionic acid-d_2, propionic acid-d_6 and butyric acid-d_7, a remarkable phase effect is also observed in the formation of $^{13}NH_4^+$ and $^{13}NO_2^-$, while the yield of $^{13}NH_3$ is proportional and that of $H^{13}NO_2$ inversely proportional to the number of hydrogen atoms in a molecule of the carboxylic acid (Fig. 4).

Following reaction mechanism is proposed to explain the results below:

$$^{13}N + CH_3COOH \rightarrow {}^{13}NH \qquad (7)$$
$$^{13}N + CH_3COOH \rightarrow [CH_3COO(^{13}N)H] \rightarrow {}^{13}NO \text{ or } H^{13}NO \qquad (8)$$

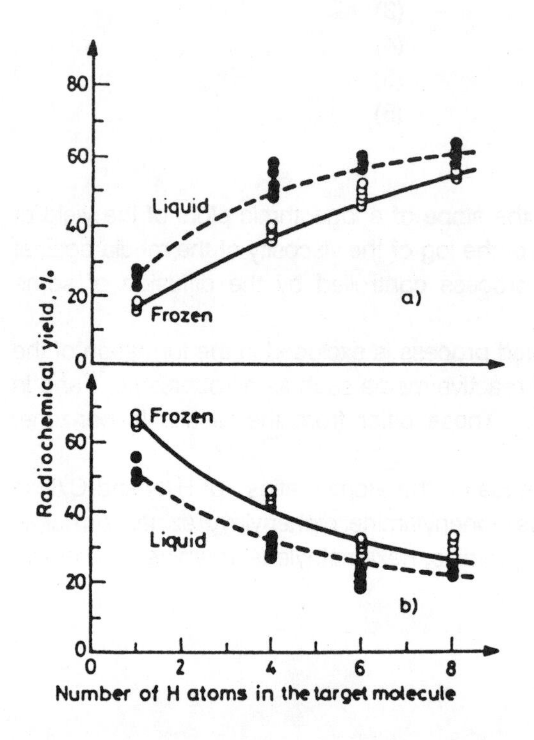

Fig.4 Plots of the yield of ^{13}N-compounds in pile-irradiated carboxylic acid-d_x against the number of hydrogen in the target molecule; (a) [^{13}N] ammonia, (b) [^{13}N] HNO_x ; ○ for frozen and ● for liquid media.

The ^{13}NH radical is formed by the abstraction of a hydrogen atom from the substrate molecule by energetic ^{13}N, and $H^{13}NO$ (or ^{13}NO) is formed by a reaction of the ^{13}N similar to the formation of HNO radicals from hot nitrogen and methanol [35]. In common with the carboxylic acids, a pronounced increase in the yield of $^{13}NH_3$ and a remarkable decrease in the yield of $H^{13}NO_2$ are observed with phase change from a solid to liquid medium. The increase in $^{13}NH_3$ is almost compensated by the decrease in $H^{13}NO_2$ in the acids except butyric-d_7 acid. The phase effect on the yields of $^{13}NH_3$, and $H^{13}NO_2$ is connected with the formation of $^{13}NH_3$ from the reaction of ^{13}NO with C_xH_y radicals formed by the radiolysis of the medium. It can be argued that the life of ^{13}NO formed by Reaction(8) is long enough for it to participate in radical-radical reactions (9) [16,17],

$$^{13}NO + \cdot CH_3 \rightarrow [CH_3{}^{13}NO] \rightarrow {}^{13}NH_3 \quad (9)$$
$$^{13}NO \text{ (or } H^{13}NO) \rightarrow H^{13}NO_2 \quad (10)$$
$$^{13}NH + H \rightarrow {}^{13}NH_x \rightarrow {}^{13}NH_3 \quad (11)$$
$$^{13}NH_x + R\cdot COOH \rightarrow [R\cdot COOH\cdots{}^{13}NH_x] \rightarrow R\cdot CO^{13}NH_2 \quad (12)$$

where suffix x=1 or 2. In butyric-d_7 acid, a pronounced increase in the yield of $^{13}NH_3$ when the phase change is balanced by the sum of a small decrease in the yield ofH$^{13}NO_2$ and a notable decrease in that of [^{13}N] butyramide. The phase effect in the ^{13}N-compounds arises from the diffusion-controlled reactions of the precursors and correlates with the scavenger effects on the formation of $^{13}NH_3$, $H^{13}NO_2$ and [^{13}N] amide examined in acetic acid-d_4 and butyric-d_7 acid. Eq.(7) occurs more easily than Eq.(8) in butyric-d_7 acid as compared with acetic acid-d_4. Hence it is argued that the contribution of the conversion of ^{13}NO to $^{13}NH_3$ by Eq.(9) to the total yield of $^{13}NH_3$ decreases in butyric-d_7 acid as compared with acetic acid-d_4. On the contrary, it may be argued that the contribution of Reaction(11) to the total yield of $^{13}NH_3$ increases in liquid butyric-d_7 acid in comparison with the other acids. The competition between Reactions (11) and (12) is connected to the competition between $^{13}NH_3$ and [^{13}N]-butyramide in the phase effect.

3.2. Gaseous Organic Systems.

There are many investigations on the reaction of ^{13}N in gaseous organic targets such as methane and ethylene [18,22,30,37], benzene [38,39], alcohols [37,40] and halomethanes[30,38,41].

In frozen methane at 77°K, $^{13}NH_3$ and $CH_3{}^{13}NH_2$ which are the main ^{13}N-products are formed by the abstraction of hydrogen atom and by the insertion of ^{13}NH radical into the C-H bond of methane, respectively [30]. In methane and ethylene targets under 1 Torr, only a few tenths percent NO added remarkably enhances the formation of (^{13}NN + ^{13}NO) and conversely depresses the formation of $HC^{13}N$, where the reacting species are $^{13}N(^2D)$ and $^{13}N(^4S)$ [22].

According to Koski, increasing the partial pressure of benzene from 15 to 60 Torr gives an increasing yield of $HC^{13}N$ and slightly decreasing yield of $C_6H_5C^{13}N$. $HC^{13}N$ and $C_6H_5C^{13}N$ are considered to arise as a result of hydrogen abstraction and replacement, respectively. No [^{13}N]aniline nor [^{13}N]pyridine are produced in Koski's system. This is in contrast with the results in the reaction between active nitrogen produced by electrical discharge and gaseous benzene [39].

In halomethane targets, the main products are $HC^{13}N$ in CH_3X and $XC^{13}N$ in CX_4 targets. The free energy change for nitrogen atoms reacting with an alkyl halide favors the formation of cyanide over ammonia or D amine. The formation of $HC^{13}N$, ^{13}NN, ^{13}NO and $^{13}NO_2$ is accounted as follows:

$$^{13}N + N_2 \rightarrow {}^{13}NN + N$$
$$^{13}N + O_2 \rightarrow {}^{13}NO + O$$
$$^{13}N + O_2 + M \rightarrow {}^{13}NO_2 + M$$
$$^{13}N + CH_3Cl \rightarrow HC^{13}N$$

In the reaction of N^+ ions with CF_4 examined in a tandem mass spectrometer, the only radioactive product detected is $FC^{13}N$.

References

1. Süe, P.: Compt. Rend., 229 878(1949).
2. Welch, M.J., Lifton, J.F.: J. Amer. Chem., 93 3385(1971)

3. Reitzner, B., Harbottle, G.: Radiochem. Acta, 2 132-138(1964)
4. Schats, J.J.C., Aten, A.H.W. Jr.: Radiochem. Acta, 15 46-51(1971)
5. Kuhry, J.G.: Radiochem. Acta, 14 122-126(1970)
6. Smith, R.D., Aten, A.H.W.: J. Inorg. Nucl. Chem., 1 298(1955)
7. Aten, A.H.W. Jr., Kapteyn, J.C.: Radiochem. Acta, 17 59-60(1972)
8. Aten, A.H.W. Jr., Michielsen, J.C.F.: J. Inorg. Nucl. Chem., 40 1700(1978)
9. Rössler, K., Batista, M.C., Izquierdo-falquina, A., Uelhoff, W., Vogt, M.: Radiat. Eff., 99 133-142(1986)
10. Rössler, K.,Schurwanz, K.: Ber. Kernforschugsanlage Juelich, JUEL-1990 60(1985)
11. Welch, M.J., Straatmann, M.G.:Raidochem. Acta, 20 124-129(1973)
12. Tilbury, R.S., Dahl, J.R.: Rad. Res., 79 22(1979)
13. Schmitz, G., Nebeling, Rösslr, K.: Ber. Kernforschungsanlage Juelich, JUEL-2119 88(1987)
14. Ohno, S.: Analyst, 95 396-398(1970)
15. Lin, C.C.: J. Radioanal. Nucl. Chem., 130 129-130(1989)
16. Schleiffer, P.J.J., Adloff, J.P.: Radiochim. Acta, 3 145(1964)
17. Ibe, E., Karasawa, H., Endo, M., Suzuke, K., Etoh, Y.: FAIF Int. Conf. on Water Chem. in Nucl. Power Plants, Proc. Vol.2, Tokyo, Apr. 19-22 523-527(1988)
18. Stewart, G.W., Kymerski, P.P., Hower, C.O.: J. Chem. Phys., 61 483(1974)
19. Welch, M.J.: Chem. Comm., 1968 1354-1355(1968)
20. Welch, M.J. Ter-Pogossian, M.M.: private communication
21. Statnick, R.M., Kashihira, N., Schmidt-Bleek, F.: J. Inorg. Nucl. Chem., 31 878-881(1969)
22. Dubrin, J., Mackay, C., Wolfgang, R.: J. Chem. Phys., 44 2208(1966)
23. Kliment, V., Sandrik, R.: Radiochem. Acta, 30 21-24(1982)
24. Aten, A.H.W. Jr.,Kapteyn, J.C.: Radiochem. Radioanal. Lett., 41 257(1979)
25. Krohn, K.A., parks, N.J.: J. Lab. Comp. Radiopharm.: 16 87(1979)
26. Sensui, Y., Tomura, K., Fukuda, Y., Iwai, H.:Radiochim. Acta, 23 12-14(1976);Sensui, Y., Tomura, T., Shima, M., Matsuura, T.: ibid, 26 147-152(1979)
27. Sensui, Y., Tomura, K., Matsuura, T.: Radiochim. Acta, 35 37-42(1984)
28. Sensui, Y., Nakano, K., Tadano, H., Tsukagoshi, K.: Int. J. Appl. Radiat. Isot., 35 135(1984);Cramer, W.A.: In "Aspect of Hydrocarbon Radiolysis" (eds T. Gaumann and J. Hoigne) pp153-211.(Academic Press, London, 1968)
29. Sensui, Y., Tomura,K., Matsuura, T.: Radiochem. Radioanal. Lett., 41 233-244(1979)
30. Sensui, Y., Tomura, K., Matsuura, T.: Radiochem. Radioanal. Lett., 55 39-48(1982)
31. Sensui, Y., Tomura, K., Nakakuki, I., Suzuki, H.: J. Radioanal. Nucl. Chem., Letters. 118 23-31(1987)
32. Sensui, Y., Tomura, K.: J. Radioanal. Nucl. Chem., Art., 132 305-314(1989)
33. Sensui, Y., Tomura, K.: J. Radioanal. Nucl. Chem., Lett., 128 359-366(1988)
34. Sensui, Y., Tomura, K.: J. Radioanal. Nucl. Chem., Article, (in press)
35. Rendall, W.A., Roscoe, J.M.: J. Chem. Soc. Faraday I, 76 1757(1980)

36. Fiergolla, J. Nebeling, B., Rössler, K.: Ber. Kernforschungsanlage Juelich, JUEL-2156 50pp(1987)
37. Perkins, W.C., Koski, W.S.: J. Phys. Chem., 66 474-477(1962)
38. Koski, W.S., Malinin, D., Berta, M., "Chemical Effects of Nuclear Transformations" (IAEA) Vienna, 1 177(1985)
39. Aronovich, P.M., Mikhailov,B.M.: Izv. Akad. Nauk. SSSR.Otdel him, Nauk 544(1956); Aronovich P.M., Bel'skii, N.K., Mikhailov, B.M.: ibid, 696(1956)
40. Koski, W.S., Schmied, H., Perkins. W.O., "Chemical Effects of Nuclear Transformations" (IAEA) Vienna, 2 217(1961)
41. Schmied, H., Koski, W.S.: J. Amer. Chem. Soc., 82 4766(1960)
42. Aten, A.H.W. Jr., Kapteyn, J.C.: Radiochem. Radioanal. Lett., 32 83(1978)

2.8 Hot Atom Chemistry of Oxygen

Richard A. FERRIERI
Department of Chemistry, Brookhaven National Laboratory
Upton, New York, USA 11973-5000

1. Introduction

In recent years, hot oxygen atom chemistry has received increased recognition for its fundamental importance to understanding many of the complex chemical and physical processes involved in photochemistry,[1] combustion,[2] stratospheric chemistry[3] and even in space erosion.[4-7] Unfortunately, it would be impossible to do justice to all of these disciplines within the confines of such a short article. Therefore, the focus of this work will be to enlighten readers on what is known about the basic chemistry of these species when reacted in non-thermal environments with organic molecules, and to point out how this chemistry may or may not be different from that seen from thermal reactions.

Hot oxygen atom chemistry is a poorly understood area owing to the difficulty in using nucleogenic methods for generating these atoms and carrying out fundamental mechanistic studies on their reactions.[8] This difficulty arises from the extremely short half-lives of the atom's radioactive isotopes, oxygen-14 (72 sec), oxygen-15 (122 sec) and oxygen-19 (27 sec), which places constraints on the time needed for the requisite analysis of labelled products. In addition, non-nucleogenic methods for generating hot oxygen atoms are either not well characterized for use in chemical studies, or else are limited by the kinetic energy they can impart. The former is especially true of certain high energy sources (> 1 eV) recently developed for aerospace research to investigate hot atomic oxygen erosion of surfaces.[4] Supersonic expansion of seeded atomic beams of oxygen,[9] and to a lesser extent, laser photodissociation of ozone,[10] have proven to be invaluable in reaction dynamics research as sources for generating quasi-hot atoms. When crossed with a beam of reactant molecules, detailed information about the dynamics of reaction can be obtained either from the scattering profiles of products or from the spectroscopic measurement of their nascent internal energy states. Unfortunately, these techniques are limited to probing reactions at kinetic energies of less than 1 eV, and so this leaves us with just a vague notion of how these species might react as "true" hot atoms.

2. Chemistry at Thermal and Epithermal Energies

Depending on the electronic spin state of the atom, and the nature of the co-reactant, reactions involving atomic oxygen may occur by one of several pathways which could involve abstraction, addition or insertion. Generally, abstraction of hydrogen occurs in reactions involving alkanes, aldehydes, alcohols and ethers, although very few of these reactions have been studied in detail. Even so, the state of the atom can have a strong influence on the nature of the reaction. For example, singlet excited oxygen will insert into C-H bonds of alkanes by choice, and abstract hydrogen only by chance.[11] The insertion adduct can then either decompose yielding a hydroxyl radical that is indistinguishable from that generated through abstraction, or it can stabilize as the alcohol product depending on the surrounding environment. On the other hand, triplet ground-state oxygen will only abstract hydrogen.

Triplet oxygen atoms will also react with the unsaturated bonds of alkenes, alkynes and aromatic compounds primarily through electrophilic addition. The reactions of singlet oxygen with these classes of compounds are not so clear owing to the lack of detailed studies, but presumably they too will add to the unsaturated bond amongst other reactions. However, the triplet oxygen-alkene reactions are perhaps one of the most thoroughly investigated classes of atomic oxygen reactions. Because of the early work carried out by Cventanovic and co-workers[12,13], a strong foundation exists for understanding the general features of the kinetics and the mechanisms of these reactions.

Generally, triplet oxygen will add non-stereospecifically to the unsaturated bonds of alkenes and yield an excited triplet biradical intermediate. This intermediate will either decompose or, in the presence of collisions which serve to promote triplet-singlet conversions, yield hot epoxide and carbonyl products through ring closure and internal rearrangements. Actually, there is some contention now that intersystem crossings of this nature might be facile in certain systems even in the absence of secondary collisions.[14,15] Regardless of this, the absence of sufficient stabilizing collisions generally results in unimolecular decomposition of these vibrationally hot species, and so, one will see a complex mixture of carbonaceous oxygenated products ranging in size from those containing the intact skeleton of the co-reactant down to carbon monoxide. This mechanism is supported not only by the extensive early product studies of Cventanovic, but also by mass spectrometry sampling experiments carried out at somewhat lower gas pressures.[16,17]

Even so, single collision scattering experiments carried out by Lee and co-workers[18-19] utilizing crossed molecular beams of atomic oxygen and co-reactant have been intrumental within the last decade in bringing to light a second primary reaction pathway that involves direct displacement. In the simplest case, reaction between triplet oxygen and ethylene by this mechanism would yield CH_2CHO+H. Of course, this mechanism dispelled earlier interpretations of data which suggested that π-addition followed by biradical decompositin to yield HCO + CH_3 was the sole reaction pathway.[16,20,21] However, it did agree with results from Cventanovic's bulk experiments, where a portion of the chemistry was always observed to pass through a pressure independent fragmentation pathway.[12,13] Such a pathway may be the result of direct displacement in the primary reaction.

Besides addition and displacement, it has long been assumed that hydrogen atom abstraction from alkyl substituted unsaturated hydrocarbons can also become an important reaction of triplet oxygen at higher kinetic energies. There is some early evidence in support of this statement. For example, a nonlinear Arrhenius temperature dependence in the thermal rate constants of triplet oxygen reaction with 1-butene has been interpreted in terms of simultaneous addition and abstraction.[22] Mass spectrometric detection of hydroxyl radicals at elevated temperatures has also confirmed this.[17] More recently, Kleinermanns and Luntz[23] employed atomic oxygen beam studies coupled with laser induced fluorescence to assess the chemical dynamics of the abstraction process with several alkene co-reactants by measuring the nascent internal state distribution of the hydroxyl radicals formed. While they were not able to measure absolute cross sections, these authors did find a general trend of increasing relative cross section for abstraction as a function of collision energy up to approximately 0.7 eV. They also noted that reactive signals measured for hydroxyl radicals were comparable in intensity to those obtained with saturated hydrocarbons at high kinetic energies. This implied that the preexponential factors in the Arrhenius rate expression were comparable in magnitude at high energy for saturated and unsaturated hydrocarbons, suggesting that abstraction might even dominate over the addition mechanism with certain alkenes at even higher kinetic energies.

3. Chemistry in Non-Thermal Environments

While a strong foundation exists that allows us, in many instances, to predict the nature, yield and rate of final product formation from thermal oxygen atom reactions, our perception of these features become somewhat cloudy as these species are allowed to react at higher kinetic energies. This is especially true of early classical recoil hot atom studies carried out by Ruiz and Wolf[24] using oxygen-15, where reactions with simple alkanes gave rise to substantial yields of labelled alcohol products. The mere nature of these products would seem to suggest that insertion into the alkane C-H bonds was an important mechanism for these recoil atoms. However, further investigations using inert bath gasses and scavengers suggested that the predominant reactive species was triplet oxygen-15. This contradicts our understanding of how these species should behave when at thermal energy. Of course, this kind of behavior is quite typical of many classical recoil hot atom studies where reactions which might never be observed at thermal or epithermal energies could, in fact, become the predominant pathway at higher kinetic energies.

Although we cannot neglect the findings from these early recoil hot oxygen studies, we must not forget that studies of this nature have the ability not only to cover an extremely broad band of energy stretching beyond the outer fringes of the chemical reaction range, but also to reflect the cumulative chemistry of various states of the atom, and so, one must proceed cautiously when trying to unravel this complex web in order to identify and assess the relative importance of certain primary reaction pathways of a particular state of the atom.

It was for these reasons that Ferrieri and co-workers[25,26] developed an alternate source for generating and studying the chemistry of hot oxygen atoms. Their method relied on ion beam sputtering of metal oxide targets for its source of hot atoms. Sputtering on Ta_2O_5 with 40 KeV argon ions was shown to proceed by a collision cascade mechanism, where the sputtered atoms were not only predominantly neutral, but also were comprised of only those species residing in their triplet ground state. In addition, a peak energy of 6 eV was obtained for these atoms out of a distribution that extended up to approximately 20 eV.

Recently, this sputtering atom source was utilized to study the low pressure gas-phase reactions of hot triplet oxygen atoms with cis- and trans-2-butene.[27,28] Studies were carried out over a 3000-fold range of pressure extending from $1x10^{-5}$ to $3x10^{-2}$ Torr. Information obtained through gas chromatographic separation coupled with mass spectrometric detection of stabilized products, and through on-line mass spectrometric detection of primary products lead to the reconstruction of the complex scheme of reaction pathways shown in Figure 1.

It was concluded that hot triplet oxygen interacted with these co-reactants through addition, displacement and abstraction mechanisms to yield a mixture of carbonaceous oxygenated products comprising epoxide, carbonyl and alcohol compounds of assorted complexity, and carbon monoxide as the final decomposition product. A non-oxygenated hydrocarbon product spectrum was also observed to consist of diacetylene, benzene, toluene and styrene in decreasing order of importance. These products were presumed to arise from several secondary sources of chemistry within the system, the most obvious being that due to alkyl radical formation from primary oxygenated product fragmentation. Of course, the distribution of all these products was highly dependent on the pressure at which the reaction was carried out.

One of the most striking features of this work was the extremely high hydroxyl radical yields that were measured as water and alcohol products. It was presumed that alcohol formation was the result of secondary radical addition to the butene substrate. This is consistent with previous studies carried out by Cventanovic which showed evidence of alcohol formation in reactions involving triplet oxygen and alkenes, but only at very high temperatures.[12,13]

Figure 2 shows the energy dependence of the hydroxyl radical forming pathways from the above butene studies when plotted as a function of neon moderator concentration. At high moderator concentration, or low kinetic energy, the hydroxyl radical yields from both 2-butene isomers were less than 4%, and in agreement with thermal bulk studies.[13] However, these yields were seen to rise significantly as the kinetic energy increased. It is interesting to note that the high energy yield from trans butene was 2.2 times higher than that from cis butene. Two sources were proposed for hydroxyl radical formation to account for this behavior; one involving direct hydrogen atom abstraction, and another involving intramolecular rearrangement followed by decomposition of the addition biradical. Of course, the viability of such a pathway depends heavily on whether sufficient internal energy exists within the intermediate to

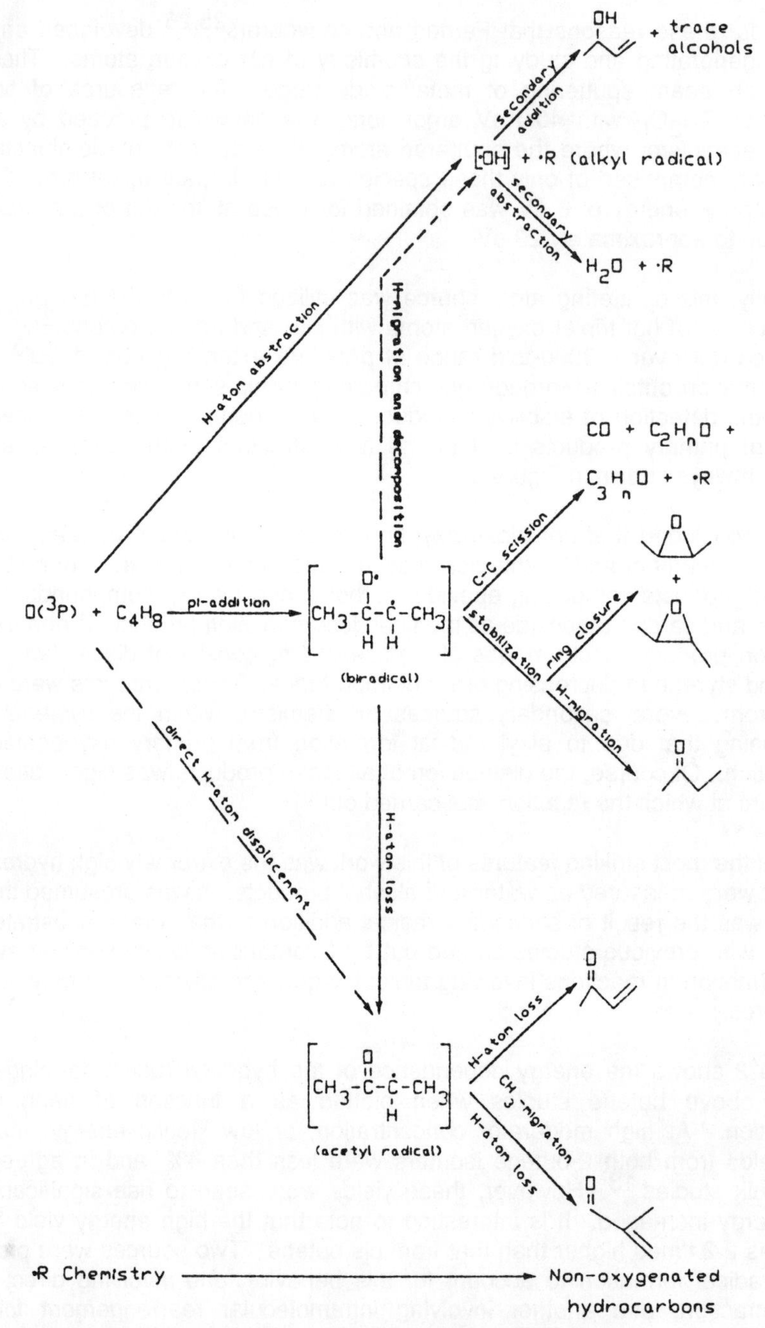

Fig. 1 Reaction pathways involving hot triplet oxygen and 2-butene.

satisfy the energy constraints of the barrier for a 1,2-hydrogen shift. Theoretical calculations suggest that migrations of this nature tend to have exceptionally high activation energies on the triplet manifold, although substantially lower on the singlet.[29] Values as high as 50 kcal/mol have been predicted in some instances. Even so, such a pathway may be possible given the excess kinetic energy available in these experiments.

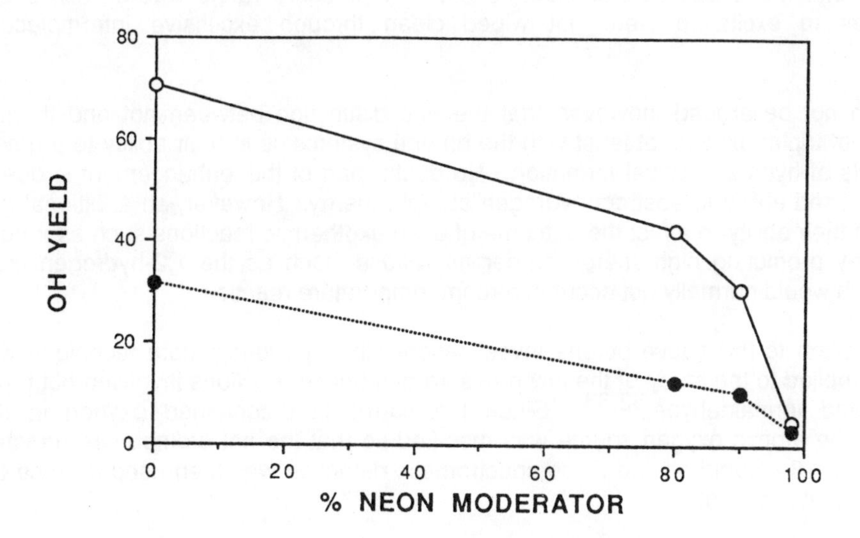

Fig. 2 Energy dependence of the hydroxyl radical forming pathways in triplet oxygen reactions with 2-butene: O,trans-2-butene system; ●,cis-2-butene system. All studies were carried out at $5.6x10^{-3}$ Torr pressure using dilutions of reactant in the neon moderator gas.

While the final outcome of these two pathways would be indistinguishable in a study of this nature, one might expect the yields from the latter to differ, if the nature and degree of internal excitation of the addition biradicals were different. Other observations made in these studies support this view. For example, the yields of carbonaceous oxygenated products requiring either spatial rearrangements, intramolecular migrations or fragmentation of the butene skeleton were always systematically higher in the high energy reactions involving trans butene. All of these observations point to the conclusion that the biradical formed in the trans butene system was more highly excited.

Subtle differences in the impact parameters describing the atom-molecule collisions in the two systems could account for such variations in internal excitation.[30] A number of factors might contribute to this distinction. On the one hand, hyperconjugative electron interactions involving the out-of-plane methyl hydrogens and the π-system of the butene substrate could distort the π-electron cloud through delocalization.[31] Underlying this basic phenomenon, however, are certain spatial constraints imposed on the methyl groups when in the cis geometry. Such constraints are caused by steric repulsions and conformational interactions between the groups which could enhance the hyperconjugative nature of the methyl hydrogens in cis butene over those in trans butene. Of course, these forces should be at play here regardless of whether oxygen reacts as a hot atom or thermal atom. In fact, the moderator studies described above did show evidence for the persistence of such systematic variation in yields of the rearrangement oxygenated products down into the thermal energy range. It may be fortuitous that these studies were carried out in a pressure range where such subtle differences in excitation were not wiped clean through excessive intermolecular collisions.

It can not be argued, however, that the one distinction between hot and thermal reactions of triplet oxygen, at least with the butene systems, is in their ability to promote high levels of hydroxyl radical formation. No doubt, part of this enhancement is due to their increased ability to abstract hydrogen at high energy. However, an additional part is seen in their ability to affect the outcome of even exothermic reactions such as π-bond addition by promoting high-energy barrier migrations, such as the 1,2-hydrogen atom shift, which would normally not occur in a room temperature reaction.

In addition to the above butene investigations, this sputtering atom technique was recently applied to the study of the low pressure gas-phase reactions involving hot triplet oxygen and formaldehyde.[32,33] Since the co-reactant contained oxygen in this instance, the atomic oxygen source was modified so that the hot atoms were enriched with oxygen-18. Rapid on-line mass spectrometic detection was then used to trace the fate of these hot atoms.

Past investigations concerned with the mechanistic and kinetic aspects of this sytem led to the conclusion that the predominant reaction at thermal energy was abstraction of the weak aldehydic hydrogen atom.[34-42] Even spectroscopic measurements of the internal state distributions of the hydroxyl radical product support this finding.[43] However, there is no reason to exclude the possibility that atom addition to the carbonyl bond is also an important reaction pathway. Unlike the butene experiments previously described, both the abstraction and addition reactions are exothermic in this instance. The energy requirements for these various pathways are illustrated in the following energy correlation diagram (Figure 3).

Although not shown, the addition pathway may possess a slightly activated barrier of a few kcal/mol.[44] Even so, if we assume addition can occur, and that oxygen attaches to the carbon atom, we can expect very little chemistry from the triplet dioxymethylene biradical. Ab initio calculations carried out by Dupuis and Lester[45] predict that a 1,2-hydrogen shift yielding excited triplet formic acid would require at least 30 kcal/mol. It is highly unlikely that this sort of rearrangement can occur in a thermal reaction. One can only assume that the only options available to the triplet dioxymethylene biradical are dissociation back to the starting reactants, or stepwise elimination of hydrogen leaving carbon dioxide as a product. In fact, Chang and Barker[44] observed what they thought was carbon dioxide product in the thermal flow-tube reaction involving triplet oxygen and formaldehyde. On the other hand, if reaction by hot triplet oxygen can promote such a shift, then the pathways available to the biradical increase. The reactions listed below illustrate how the oxygen-18 label is incorporated into the various products through hot

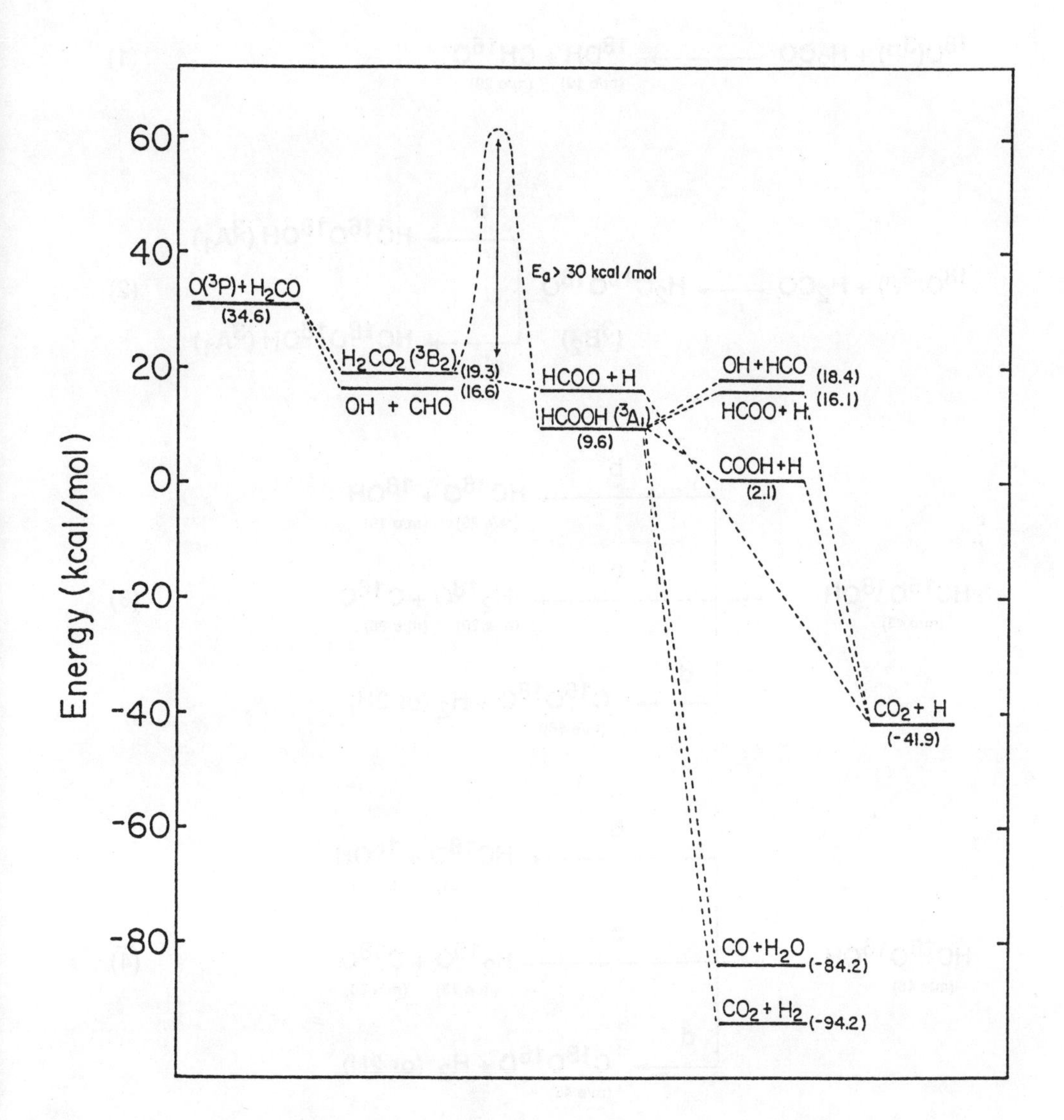

Fig. 3. Energy correlation diagram for the various reaction pathways involving triplet oxygen and formaldehyde.

$$^{18}O(^3P) + H_2CO \longrightarrow \underset{(m/e\ 19)}{^{18}OH} + \underset{(m/e\ 29)}{CH^{16}O} \tag{1}$$

$$^{18}O(^3P) + H_2CO \longrightarrow \underset{(^3B_2)}{H_2C^{16}O^{18}O} \begin{cases} \xrightarrow{a} HC^{16}O^{18}OH\ (^3A_1) \\ \xrightarrow{a'} HC^{18}O^{16}OH\ (^3A_1) \end{cases} \tag{2}$$

$$\underset{(m/e\ 48)}{HC^{16}O^{18}OH} \begin{cases} \xrightarrow{b} \underset{(m/e\ 29)}{HC^{16}O} + \underset{(m/e\ 19)}{^{18}OH} \\ \xrightarrow{c} \underset{(m/e\ 20)}{H_2{}^{18}O} + \underset{(m/e\ 28)}{C^{16}O} \\ \xrightarrow{d} \underset{(m/e\ 46)}{C^{16}O^{18}O} + H_2\ (\text{or } 2H) \end{cases} \tag{3}$$

$$\underset{(m/e\ 48)}{HC^{18}O^{16}OH} \begin{cases} \xrightarrow{b} \underset{(m/e\ 31)}{HC^{18}O} + \underset{(m/e\ 17)}{^{16}OH} \\ \xrightarrow{c} \underset{(m/e\ 18)}{H_2{}^{16}O} + \underset{(m/e\ 30)}{C^{18}O} \\ \xrightarrow{d} \underset{(m/e\ 46)}{C^{18}O^{16}O} + H_2\ (\text{or } 2H) \end{cases} \tag{4}$$

atom reaction. Reactions 1 and 2 depict the abstraction and addition primary reactions, respectively, where pathways 2a and 2a' differ only in the direction of the hydrogen shift along the two possible carbon-oxygen bonds of the biradical. Excited triplet formic acid will decompose by one of three pathways illustrated by 3b-3d, or 4b-4d depending on the position of the label. This decomposition will occur even at atmospheric pressure. However, pathway b is endothermic by 8.6 kcal/mol, and has not been observed when the excited acid was generated at thermal energy.[46-48]

In preliminary studies carried out at 1×10^{-5} Torr pressure, reactive signals were monitored from $HC^{18}O$ and $C^{16}O^{18}O$ products in a time scan mode through cycles where the hot oxygen-18 atom source was modulated on and off. Figure 4 displays the ion signal intensity versus time plot from these products measured through two such cycles. It was not possible to accurately track other products in these studies because of the high backgrounds exerted on the detector by water contaminant in the formaldehyde source, and formaldehyde itself which overwhelmed any reactive signals. Fortunately, the $HC^{18}O$ and $C^{16}O^{18}O$ signals at m/e 31 and 46 were not part of this background.

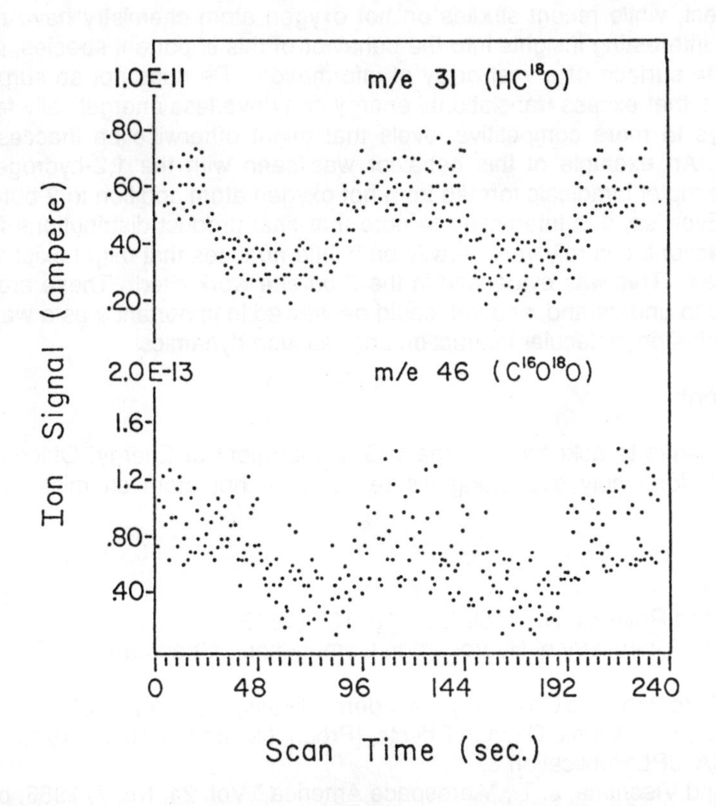

Fig. 4. Reactive ion signals from $HC^{18}O$ (m/e 31) and $C^{16}O^{18}O$ (m/e 46) plotted in a time scan mode through two on/off cycles of the hot oxygen-18 atom source.

Several features of reaction were evident from even these few observations. On the one hand, hot triplet oxygen did attack the carbonyl bond of formaldehyde, as evidenced by the formation of these two products. Of course, it remains to be seen whether or not this reaction is actually more prevalent than hydrogen abstraction. Even so, carbonyl bond attack may not be unique to the hot atom reaction. What seems unique to this species, however, is the fact that once the triplet biradical is formed, it has the ability to pass through a series of high-energy pathways that are normally not accessible at thermal energy: in the first stage, 1,2-hydrogen migration can occur yielding excited triplet formic acid; and in the second stage, endothermic decomposition of the acid to HCO+OH can occur. Differences measured in the reactive signal intensities between $HC^{18}O$ and $C^{16}O^{18}O$ suggest that this endothermic decomposition pathway is, in fact, significant.

SUMMARY

In retrospect, while recent studies on hot oxygen atom chemistry have revealed several new and interesting insights into the behavior of this important species, we have only scratched the surface of a vast array of information. Perhaps not so surprisingly, we have observed that excess translational energy can drive less energetically favorable reaction pathways to more competitive levels that might otherwise be inaccessible at thermal energy. An example of this behavior was seen with the 1,2-hydrogen atom migrations on the triplet biradicals formed from hot oxygen atom addition to 2-butene and formaldehyde. Even so, it is interesting to note that final product distributions from hot atom initiated reactions can rely very heavily on subtle nuances that might exist between reactant molecules. This was evidenced in the 2-butene work cited. These are indeed complex systems to understand, and yet, could be viewed in importance as a way to test present-day theories on molecular interaction and reaction dynamics.

Acknowledgement

The author wishes to acknowledge the U.S. Department of Energy, Office of Basic Energy Sciences, for kindly supporting his research in hot atom chemistry over the years.

References

1. Arnold, S. J. and Rojeska, H., Appl. Opt., 12, 169 (1973).
2. Hucknall, D. J., "Chemistry of Hydrocarbon Combustion," Chapman and Hall, New York 1985.
3. Heicklen, J., "Atmospheric Chemistry", Academic Press, New York, 1976.
4. NASA Workshop on Atomic Oxygen Effects, [Proc.], November 10-11, 1986, Pasadena, CA, JPL Publication 87-4.
5. Leger, L. J. and Visentine, J. T., "Aerospace America," Vol. 24, No. 7, 1986, pp. 32-35.
6. Visentine, J. T., "Atomic Oxygen Effects Measurement for Shuttle Missions STS-8 and 41-G," NASA Technical Memorandum 100459, Vol. 1 and 2 National Technical Information Service, 1988.
7. Hunton, D. E., Scientific Amer., pp. 92-98 (Nov. 1989).
8. Ferrieri, R. A. and Wolf, A. P., Radiochim. Acta, 34, 69 (1983).
9. Sibener, S. J., Buss, R. J., Cheuk, Y. N. and Lee, Y. T., Rev. Sci. Instru., 51(2), 167 (1980).
10. Moore, D. S., Bomse, D. S. and Valentini, J. J., J. Chem. Phys., 79(4), 1745 (1983).
11. Yamazaki, H. and Cventanovic, R., J. Chem. Phys., 41, 3703 (1964).

12. Cvetanovic, R. J., "Advances in Photochemistry," Interscience Publishers, John Wiley and Sons, New York, 1963, (Noyer, W. A., Jr., Hammond, G. S. and Pitts, J. N., Jr., Eds.) pp. 117-149.
13. Cvetanovic, R. J. and Singleton, D. L., "Reviews of Chemical Intermediates," 5, 183 (1984).
14. Yamaguchi, K., Yabushita, S., Fueno, T., Kato, S. and Morokuma, K., Chem. Phys. Lett., 70, 27 (1980).
15. Lee, Y. T., DOE Combustion Research Contractors Meeting, June 1-3, 1988, Lake Geneva, WI, USA.
16. Kanofsky, J. R. and Gutman, D., Chem. Phys. Lett., 15, 236 (1972).
17. Blumenberg, B., Hoyerman, K. and Sievert, R., (Int.) Combust. Proc. 16, 841 (1977).
18. Sibener, S. J., Buss, R. J., Casavecchia, P., Hirooka, T. and Lee, Y. T., J. Chem. Phys., 72, 4341 (1980).
19. Buss, R. J., Baseman, R., He, G., and Lee, Y. T., J. Photochem., 17, 389 (1981).
20. Brown, J. M. and Thrush, B. A., Trans. Faraday Soc., 63, 630 (1967).
21. Kanofsky, J. R., Lucas, D. and Gutman, D., 14th International Symposium on Combustion, The Combustion Institute, Pittsburgh, PA, 1971, 285.
22. Huie, R. E., Herron, J. T. and Davis, D. D., J. Phys. Chem., 76, 3311 (1972).
23. Kleinermanns, K. and Luntz, A. C., J. Chem. Phys., 77(7), 3533 (1982).
24. Ruiz, J. V. and Wolf, A. P., 9th Int. Hot Atom Chem. Symposium, Virginia Poly. Inst., Blacksberg, VA, USA, 1977, Abstract, p. 13.
25. Ferrieri, R. A., Chu, Y.-Y. and Wolf, A. P., NASA Workshop on Atomic Oxygen Effects [Proc.], November 10, 1986, 119, Pasadena, CA, JPL Publication 87-4.
26. Ferrieri, R. A. and Chu, Y.-Y., Rev. Sci. Instru., 59(10), 2177 (1988).
27. Ferrieri, R. A., Chu, Y.-Y. and Wolf, A. P., 13th Int. Hot Atom Chem. Symp. [Proc.], Radiochim. Acta, 43, 95 (1988).
28. Ferrieri, R. A. and Wolf, A. P., J. Phys. Chem., manuscript submitted.
29. Dupuis, M. and Lester, W. A., J. Chem. Phys., 80(9), 4193 (1984).
30. Levine, R. D. and Bernstein, R. B., "Molecular Reaction Dynamics," Oxford University Press, New York, 1974, p. 30 and 141.
31. Bach, R. D., Wolber, G. J. and Pross, A., Israel J. Chem., 23, 97 (1983).
32. Ferrieri, R. A. and Wolf, A. P., DOE Combustion Research Contractors Meeting, June 1-3, 1988, Lake Geneva, WI, USA.
33. Ferrieri, R. A. and Wolf, A. P., J. Phys. Chem., manuscript in preparation.
34. Cvetanovic, R. J., Can. J. Chem., 34, 775 (1956).
35. Niki, H., J. Chem. Phys., 43, 3468 (1965).
36. Niki, H., Daby, E. E. and Weinstock, B., 12th Int. Symp. Combust. [Proc.], 277 (1968).
37. Herron, J. T. and Penzhorn, R. D., J. Phys. Chem., 73, 19 (1969).
38. Mack, G. R. P. and Thrush, B. A., J. Chem. Soc. Faraday Trans (1), 69, 208 (1973).
39. Herron, J. T. and Huie, R. E., J. Phys. Chem. Ref. Data, 2, 467 (1973).
40. Huie, R. E. and Herron, J. T., Prog. React. Kinet., 8, 1 (1978).
41. Klemm, R. B., J. Chem. Phys., 71, 1987 (1979).
42. Klemm, R. B., Skolnik, E. G. and Michael, J. V., J. Chem. Phys., 72, 1256 (1980).
43. Kleinermanns, K. and Luntz, A. C., J. Chem. Phys., 77, 3774 (1982).
44. Chang, J. S. and Barker, J. R., J. Phys. Chem., 83, 3059 (1979).
45. Dupuis, M. and Lester, W. A., J. Chem. Phys., 80(9), 4193 (1984).
46. Kebarle, P. and Lossing, F. P., Can. J. Chem., 37, 389 (1959).
47. Herron, J. T. and Huie, R. E., J. Am. Chem. Soc., 99(16), 5430 (1977).
48. Herron, J. T. and Huie, R. E., Int. J. Chem. Kinetics, 10, 1019 (1978).

2.9 Hot Atom Chemistry of Sulphur

Kazuhiro NIISAWA* and Ko TAKI
School of Hygienic Sciences, Faculty of Industrial Hygiene, Kitasato University, 1-15-1, Kitasato, Sagamihara, Kanagawa, 228, Japan
*: Tanaka Kikinzoku Kogyo K.K., 2-6-6, Kayabacho Chuo-ku NIhonbashi, Tokyo, 103, Japan

The hot atom chemistry of sulphur atom has not been studied extensively. The species ^{35}S, half life 87.9 d., and ^{38}S, half life 2.87 h., both suffering β^- decay, are suitable for study, but the ^{38}Cl activity with the latter species causes some difficulties. The recoils following $^{35}Cl(n,p)^{35}S$ and $^{40}Ar(n,3p)$ is much smaller, although still large for radiative capture(750 eV). The combination of cross sections and half life is such that the dose of ionising radiation accompanying production is always substantial.

The radiochemical work has been reviewed,[1-3] the reactions with -C=C- more recently by Brinkman.[4] Work with photochemically produced hot sulphur is also conveniently collected.[5]

It must be remembered that, like oxygen, atomic sulphur has a number of low lying electronically excited states which may differ in chemical reactivity(Table I).[6] Although the splitting of the J states is greater than kT at 300 K relaxation to an equilibrium distribution is fast in most systems.

Table I. Low lying electronic states of sulphur atom.

Electronic states	$^1S_0$	$^1D_0$	$^3P_0$	$^3P_1$	$^3P_2$
Energy(kJ/mol)	263.3	110.5	6.9	4.8	0.0

The following hot sulphur reactions are known: Hot sulphur denoted by ·S·

Exchange reaction:	·S + R-S- → -C-·S- (R= C, P)	eq. 1
Replacement reaction	·S + R-X- → R-·S- (X = O, CH_2)	eq. 2
Addition reaction:	·S + R-X- → R-X-·S (R = C, X = O)	eq. 3-1
	·S + -C = C- → -C - C- (bridged by ·S)	eq. 3-2
Insertion reactions:	·S + -C-H → -C-·S-H	eq. 4-1
	·S + -C-C- → -C-·S-C-	eq. 4-2

Fragmentation reaction: $\cdot S + R\text{-}H \rightarrow \cdot S\text{-fragments}$ eq. 5

In many cases it is not established whether hot reactions are actually involved. The nascent sulphur is very susceptible to oxidation by air and, possibly, by water.[7,8] With oragnic systems a substantial yield of polymeric compounds is often obtained[9,10,11] and complications from concurrent radiolysis are common.[7]

1.1 Reactions in the condensed phase.

^{35}S formed by the $^{34}S(n,\gamma)^{35}S$ in carbon disulfide gave a high retention (>50%) and its formation was supposed to take place via an ionic process.[12] CCl_4 has been reported to give $CSCl_2$ and sulphur chlorides on neutron irradiation.[13] More complex compounds, benzothiazole derivatives, I and II, shown, have been studied by Taki.[14]

S(1), N, S(8)-H [I]   S(1), N, S(8)-CH_3 [II]

Generating the ^{35}S activity by the (n,γ) reaction, for compound I the total retention was 27.5% and the ratio of S(8) to S(1) activities was 6.9. For compound II the corresponding values were 29.7% and 4.8. Generating the ^{35}S activity by the (n,p) reaction, using an intimate mixture of the compound with p-dichlorobenzene or 1,2,4 trichlorobenzene for compound I the total retention was 4.8% and the S(8)/S(1) ratio was 17.5. For compounds II the retention was 2.1% and the ratio 8.5. Clearly the S(8) is more easily replaced than the S(1). Attempts at direct labelling of biologically useful compounds, cysteine, thiourea etc. have been successful,[15,16] but see Ref. 17,18,19 and 20.

1.2. Gas phase systems.

Both (n,γ) and (n,p) generated ^{35}S exchange with the sulphur in CS_2. The exchange takes place mainly with the ^1D atoms.[7] In H_2S it has been suggested that exchange occurs by formation and dissociation of an excited $H_2S^{35}S$.[8] Kremer and Spicer have shown that ^3P atoms play an important role by studying the Ar/H_2S system producing the ^{38}S by the reaction $^{40}Ar(p,3p)^{38}S$.[21] Lee, Tang and Rowland have found that thermalised atoms predominate in the addition to CO to give COS, but hot atoms are needed for the replacement in CO_2 to give the same product.[22]

2. Insertion Reactions

Insertion reactions into C-H and C-C bonds have been observed. The yield of the insertion products are smaller than for the exchange reactions described above(<10%).[17,23]

2.1. In the condensed phase.

Insertion into C-H and C-C has been investigated in solutions of benzothiazole and of 2-methylbenzothiazole. Using aqueous solutions of the hydrochloride of benzothiazole, ^{35}S from the (n,γ) reaction gave tiny yields of labelled I by insertion into the C-H bond and with 2-methylbenzothiazole labelled II by insertion into the C-C bond. Scavenging by O_2 or NO reduced the yield in the former system but not the C-C insertion yield. The 2-methylbenzothiazole also gave some labelled I. The C-C insertion yields were independent of the concentration. It was proposed that the C-H insertion involves thermalised ^3P sulphur and the C-C insertion hot or ^1D sulphur.(24) The C-C insertion has been confirmed by finding methionine on irradiating norvaline hydrochloride.(17) Church and Rowland have explored the $COCl_2/C_3H_8$/Ar system and compared the behaviour of (n,p) sulphur with that of photogenic hot sulphur. Isopropyl mercaptan is the main product. Its formation did not appear to involve ^1D sulphur, nor was a hot S reaction involved.(25) Smaller amounts of propyl mercaptan were formed. In the ^{38}S/alkane/Ar system ^1D atoms are important for C-H insertion; in the absence of H_2S practically all the ^{38}S was found on the walls of the reaction vessel.(26) Reaction with ethane with CCl_2F_2 to provide chlorine for the (n,p) reaction. In this system insertion into the C-C bond is easier than into the C-H bond. Fig. 1 shows the effect of a radical scavenger on the formation of ethanethiol. The anomalous increase on addition of small concentration of scavenger is attributed to the scavenger protecting the atomic sulphur from reaction with radicals arising from concurrent radiolysis.(27)

3. Fragmentation reactions In many sulphur compounds the reactions are small and the product distributions complex.(9,10) Radical recombination reactions of $CH_3{}^{35}S\cdot$ or $C_2H_5{}^{35}S\cdot$ formed from CH_3Cl and C_2H_5Cl have been studied by Panek and Mudra.(23) Thioethers are the main products. But in the $^{35}S/C_2H_6$/Ar system a vibrationally excited primary product formed mildly hot ^3P sulphur decomposed to give $H_2{}^{35}S$. The effects of the argon concentration is shown in Fig.2.(28)

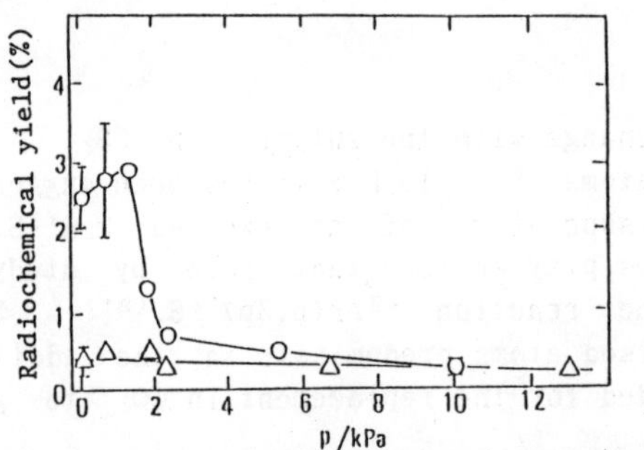

Fig.1. Effect of NO scavenger on ethanethiol (-o-) and dimethy sulfide (-Δ-) formation.

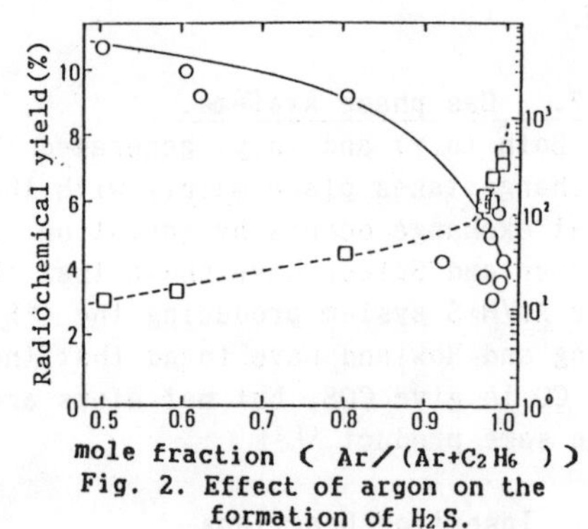

Fig. 2. Effect of argon on the formation of H_2S.

4. Inorganic targets.

Most recent work relates to ^{35}S produced in metal chlorides. It is now clear that at least four ^{35}S species are formed in these systems and several analytical procedures, all using aqueous solution before analysis, have been described.(29-34) But the actual identity of the species in the irradiated crystals is still uncertain. Work using non-aqueous analysis, as done for ^{32}P seems very desirable.(35) Aluminum trichloride may be a suitable target for such a study.(36) The subject has been reviewed by Cifka(37) and more recently by Das.(38)

A very significant discovery is the great importance of very small concentrations(p.p.m.) of OH^- in the target material.[39,40] O_2^- may also be important. Both lead to an increase in the $SO_4^=$ forming species. Thesulphate forming fraction also increases on high temperature irradiation.[41,42] Solid state scavenging using mixed crystals of NaCN/NaCl have shown that the sulphur does not diffuse readily in the matrix.[43] Work continues on the effect of post neutron irradiation treatments of the crystals, but very few mechanisms are certainly established.[44,45,46] These systems have been simulated by doping alkali chloride crystals with traces of ^{35}S introduced from sulphur vapour,[47] or by ion implantation.[48]

It may be significant that four species, S, $S^=$, $SO_3^=$ and $SO_4^=$, found in the alkali chloride systems are also found, using aqueous analysis, in neutron irradiated ammonium sulphate and sodium sulphite[49]; carbon tetrachloride[13] and solutions of lithium chloride in methyl alcohol[50].

References.

1. Urch, D., in "Inorganic Chemistry Reviews" 8 "Radiochemistry" Pub. Butterworths, London. 1975
2. Tominaga, T., Tachikawa, E., "Modern Hot Atom Chemistry" Pub. Springer-Verlag, Berlin, 1981
3. Matsuura, T., Ed. "Hot Atom Chemistry" Pub. Kodansha-Elsevier,Tokyo,1984
4. Brinkman, G.A.,Chem. Rev., 82, 245 (1982).
5. Schofield, K., J. Phys. Chem., Ref. Data, 8, 781 (1979).
6. Gunning , H.E., Strausz, O.P., Adv. Photochem., 4, 143 (1966).
7. Kremer, L.N., Thesis, Univ.of Utah, 1974
8. Hyder, M.L.,Markowitz, S.S., J. Inorg. Nucl. Chem., 26, 318 (1964).
9. Kronard, L., Radiochim. Acta, 8, 89 (1967).
10. Panek, K., Sloma, L., I.A.E.A. Conf. " Chemical Effects of Nuclear Transformations" Prague, 1960 (Pub.1961) 2, 209.
11. Dzantiev, B.G., Steekan, R.A., Shvedchikov, A.P., Shishkov, A.V., I.A.E.A. Conf. " Chemical Effects of Nuclear Transformations" Vienna, 1964 (Pub. 1965) 1, 399.
12. Edwards, R.R., Nesbett, F.B., Solamon, A.K., J. Amer. Chem. Soc., 70, 1670 (1948).
13. (a) Petryaev, E.P., Soloveva, G.D., Mironov, V.P., Radiokhimiya, 12 , 626,,(1970). (b) idem., Radiats, Khim., 2, 82,,(1972).
14. Taki, K., Bull. Chem. Soc. Jpn., 43, 2626, (1970).
15. Arrington, C.C., Kieaser, R.W., J. Phys., Chem., 69, 2302 (1965).
16. Wheeler, O.H., Gonzalez, C.L., Facetti, J.F., Radiochim. Acta, 12, 79, (1969).
17. Dzantiev, B.G., Shishkov, A.V., I.A.E.A. Conf. " Chemical Effects of Nuclear Transformations" Vienna, 1964 (Pub. 1965) 1, 209
18. Dzantiev, B.G., Shishkov, A.V., I.A.E.A. Conf. " Radioisotopes in the Physical Sciences and Industry" Vienna, 1962, 3, 27
19. Dzantiev, B.G., Shishkov, A.V., Kizan, C.K., Radiokhimiya, 10, 389 (1968).
20. Wagner, G., Munze, R., Isotopenpraxis, 11, 58 (1975).
21. Kremer, L.N., Spicer, L.D., J. Amer. Chem. Soc., 97, 5021 (1975).
22. Lee, E.K.C., Tang, Y.N., Rowland, F.S., J. Phys. Chem., 68, 318, (1964).

23. Panek, K., Mudra, K., I.A.E.A., Conf. Vienna 1964. "Chemical Effect of Nuclear Transformations", (Pub. 1965), 1 195
24. Niisawa, K., Taki, K., Bull Chem. Soc. Jpn., 50, 57 (1977).
25. Church, L.B., Rowland, F.S., Radiochim. Acta, 16, 55 (19719).
26. Lindner, L.L., Brinkman, G.A., Veenboer, J. Th., Radiochim. Acta, 27, 95, (1980).
27. Niisawa, K., Taki, K., Bull Chem., Soc. Jpn., 52, 3271, (1979).
28. idem., Radiochim. Acta, 33, 3 (1983).
29. Yoshihara, K., Ting-Chia, Ebihara, H. Shibata, N., Radiochim. Acta, 3, 185, (1964).
30. Meyer, M., Adloff, J.P., Radiochim. Acta, 6, 217, (1966).
31. (a) Abdel-Rassoul, A.A., Abdel-Aziz, A., Aly, H.F., J. Inorg. Nucl. Chem., 31, 3043 (1969). (b) idem. Radiochim. Acta, 14, 113 (1970).
32. Kasrai, M., Maddock, A.G., J. Chem. Soc., A. 1105 (1970).
33. Guilianelli, J.L., Willard, J.E., J. Phys. Chem., 78, 372, (1974).
34. Mukherji, S., Radiat. Eff. 82, 47 (1984).
35. Mahmood, A.J Maddock, A.G., Radiochim. Radioanal. Letts., 25, 293 (1976).
36. Todorovski, D., Maddock,A.G., Kostadinov, K., Radiochim. Acta, 34, 181, (1983).
37. Cifka, J., in " Chemical Effects of Nuclear Transformations in Inorganic Systems" Eds. Harbottle, G. Maddock, A.G., Pub., N. Holland, 1979
38. Das, N.R., Chattopadhyay, P., J. Radioanal. Nucl. Chem., 84, 185 (1984).
39. Baptista, J.L., Newton, G.W.A., Robinson, V.J., Trans. Faraday Soc., 64, 456 (1968).
40. Baptista, J.L., Marques, N.S., J. Inorg. Nucl. Chem., 36, 1638 (1974).
41. Ianovici.E., Taube, M., J. Inorg. Nucl. Chem., 37, 2561 (1975).
42. Furrer, M., J. Inorg. Nucl. Chem., 39, 1085 (1977).
43. Kasrai, M., Bashir, R., Razieh, M., J. Chem. Soc., Faraday Trans. I, 74, 2452 (1978).
44. Bracokova, V., Cifka, J., J. Inorg. Nucl. Chem., 32, 361 (1970).
45. Cifka, J., Bracokova, V., ibid., 32, 365 (1970).
46. D'yakovich, V., Todorovsky, D. Kostadinova, Z., Radiochem. Radioanal. Letts 59, 275 (1983).
47. Todorovsky, D., Maddock, A.G., Radiochim. Acta, 32, 191 (1983).
48. Kasrai, M., Maddock, A.G., Freeman, J.H., Trans. Faraday Soc., 67, 2108 (1971).
49. Kunz, G., Lieser, K.H., Radiochim. Acta, 11, 72 (1969).
50. Meyer, J.P., Radiochim. Acta, 14, 154, (1970).

Chapter 3

Fundamentals of Hot Atom Chemistry

3.1 Molecular Beam Studies and Hot Atom Chemistry

Robert E. CONTINETTI and Yuan T. LEE
Department of Chemistry, University of California, Berkeley and Materials and Chemical Sciences Division, Lawrence Berkeley Laboratory, Berkeley CA 94720 USA

1. Introduction

1.1. Molecular Beam Approaches to Hot Atom Chemistry

Molecular beam techniques play an important role in the elucidation of the detailed dynamics of hot atom chemical reactions. A great deal has been learned about the kinetics of hot atom reactions using traditional techniques in which reactant atoms generated by either radioactive decay or the photodissociation of an appropriate precursor molecule are allowed to react in a bulk, multi-collision environment with subsequent product yield analysis. Recent advances in time-resolved laser-based detection schemes have produced more detailed information on state-to-state rate constants for energy transfer and reactive processes in a variety of chemical systems.[1] However, for the direct measurement of product velocity and angular distributions, identification of the primary products of chemical reactions, and the overall partitioning of energy in chemical reactions, a crossed molecular beams experiment using electron-impact ionization mass-spectrometric detection is the most versatile technique available for acquiring dynamical information.

Experimental measurements of the dynamical attributes of chemical reactions can help us answer not only the question of how fast a reaction proceeds, but what type of collisions lead to reaction. For example, observation of forward-backward symmetry in the center-of-mass (CM) angular distribution about the relative velocity vector reveals the presence of an intermediate collision complex that is long-lived compared to the typical 10^{-12} sec rotational period of the complex.[2] If a long-lived complex is formed, the exact shape of the angular distribution can even reveal the degree of correlation between reactant and product angular momenta.[3] In the case of a direct elementary reaction which does not proceed through a long-lived complex, the form of the CM angular distribution reveals which reactant geometries favor reaction, providing insights into the angular dependence of the potential energy surface. Measurements of product velocity distributions reveal the extent to which energy is shared within the collision complex, or, for an elementary reaction, can provide state-resolved data on the CM angular distribution.

To demonstrate the application of molecular beam techniques to hot atom chemical reactions, two recently studied systems will be discussed here; (1) a study of the influence of translational energy in the 0.6 to 1.5 eV range on the endoergic reactions

$$Br + R\text{-}Cl \rightarrow R\text{-}Br + Cl \qquad (1)$$

where R = o-,m- and p-chlorotoluene (CT) [4] and 1,1- and 1,2-trans-$C_2H_2Cl_2$ (DCE) [5] and (2) an experimental study of the detailed dynamics of the elementary reaction

$$D + H_2 \rightarrow DH + H \qquad (2)$$

at translational energies of 0.53 and 1.01 eV.[6] The first example illustrates the contributions molecular beam experiments can make in the understanding of endoergic substitution reactions. The second example illustrates the role such studies can play in evaluating 'exact' three-dimensional (3-d) quantum scattering calculations and *ab initio* potential energy surfaces for chemical reactions. Other examples of the application of molecular beam techniques to HAC may be found in two earlier articles.[7,8]

2. Experimental Techniques

The crossed beams technique involves crossing two well-defined atomic or molecular beams in a vacuum chamber under single-collision conditions, with subsequent analysis of the distributions of the velocity and laboratory (LAB) scattering angle of the reaction products. Although significant progress has been made in laser-based state-selective detection schemes for reaction products in recent years, the application of such techniques to the measurement of product velocity and angular distributions has been limited.[9] The most useful technique for such measurements is still mass-spectrometric detection using electron-impact ionization of the scattered products in a crossed beams experiment. The principles of a successful crossed molecular beams scattering apparatus have been previously discussed in detail[10,11], but the important points will be reviewed here.

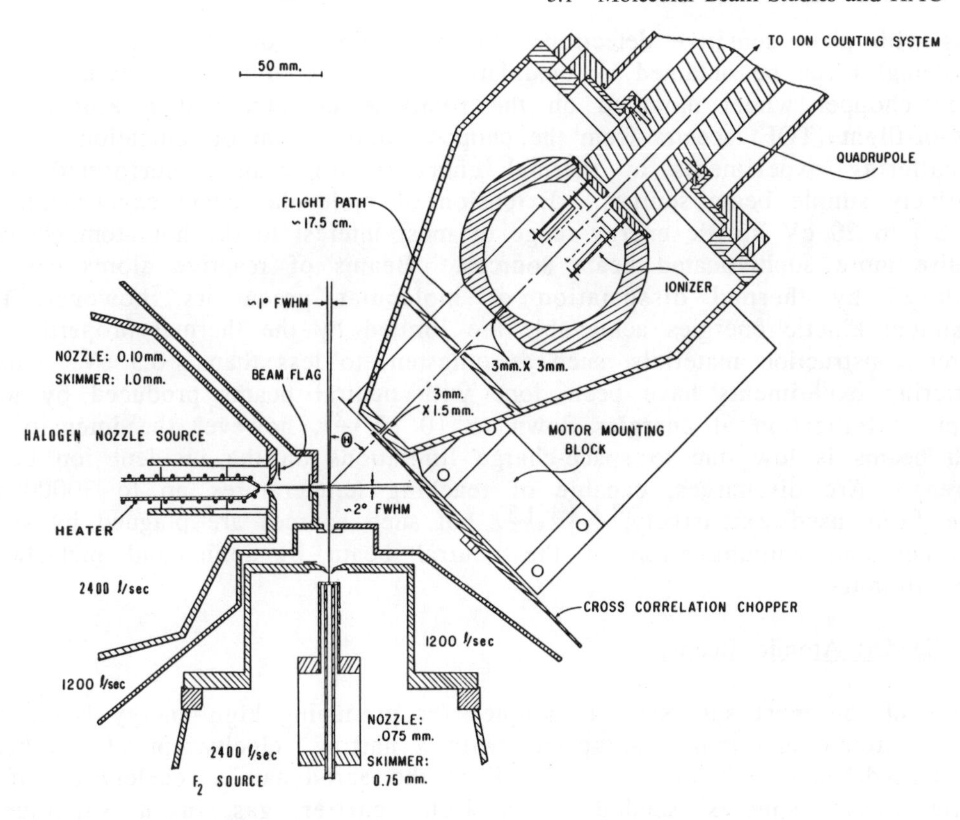

Fig. 1. Scale drawing of a continuous atomic-molecular beam reactive scattering apparatus, showing the high temperature halogen atom beam source and the rotatable mass spectrometer detector.

An experimental setup crossing a molecular beam with a high-energy halogen atomic beam is shown in Fig. 1. Energetic atoms are produced in a high-temperature oven and collimated as they pass through two regions of differential pumping into the main scattering chamber, which is maintained at a pressure of 1 x 10^{-7} torr. Molecular beams of stable species are conveniently produced by supersonic expansion through a small aperture (dia. ≈ 100 μm), with subsequent collimation by skimmers and defining apertures. Products scattered from the beam interaction region at a specific LAB angle then enter the detector, are ionized by electron impact, mass selected in a quadrupole mass spectrometer, and then counted as ions with a rotatable mass spectrometer detector. In the ionizer region, the steady state density of products is as low as 10 to 1000 molecules per cubic centimeter. For this reason, sophisticated differential pumping for both the molecular-beam sources and the ultra-high vacuum mass spectrometric detector is required to reduce the background, allowing detection of the scattered products. Angular distribution measurements are typically made by modulating one of the beams with a tuning-fork chopper and measuring the signal at the product mass with phase-sensitive detection. Product velocity distributions at specific LAB angles can be obtained by modulating the scattered products with a high-speed chopper wheel mounted on the rotatable detector and measuring the time-of-flight (TOF) spectra from the chopper to the point of ionization.

Scattering experiments at thermal energies are readily performed with relatively simple beam sources. Extension of molecular beam experiments to the 0.5 to 20 eV kinetic energy range of most interest to the hot atom chemist require more sophisticated beam sources. Beams of reactive atoms can be produced by thermal dissociation of molecular precursors, however, the maximum kinetic energies achievable are limited by the thermal properties of source construction materials, such as tungsten, to less than ≈ 0.5 eV. Some scattering experiments have been done with neutral beams produced by ion-beam neutralization at energies down to 10 eV[12], however the intensity of such beams is low due to space-charge limitations on the incident ion beam current. Arc discharges, capable of reaching temperatures up to 30000 K, have been used extensively,[13,14,15] but such sources are plagued by short lifetimes and contamination of the neutral beam by ionic and metastable contaminants.

2.1. Seeded Atomic Beams

One of the most successful techniques for producing high energy beams of heavier atomic and molecular species with a narrow velocity spread has been the seeded-beam technique, which utilizes the aerodynamic acceleration of a dilute heavy species seeded in a light carrier gas in a supersonic expansion.[16,17] The average velocity of a dilute seeded beam using an inert carrier gas under extreme expansion conditions is given by

$$v_{seed} = \sqrt{\frac{5kT}{\overline{m}}} \tag{3}$$

where $\overline{m} = x_1m_1 + x_2m_2$ is the mean molecular weight of the gas mixture made from components of molecular weight m_1 and m_2 with mole fractions x_1 and x_2. For the heavy component, 2, the laboratory kinetic energy is given by

$$E_2 = \frac{1}{2}m_2v_{seed}^2 = \frac{1}{2}\frac{m_2}{\overline{m}}5kT \tag{4}$$

Thus, for large mass ratios $m_2/\overline{m}$, considerable acceleration can be achieved. Table 1 shows the upper limit to the kinetic energies achievable using this technique for halogen atoms in the limit of a hard expansion using He as a carrier gas with no velocity slip between the light and heavy atoms. Intense beams of I, Br and Cl can be conveniently generated by thermal dissociation of I_2, Br_2 and Cl_2 in a graphite oven.[18] F atoms are very reactive, however, so Ni ovens must be used at temperatures less than ≈ 1000K. The seeded beam technique allows nearly continuous tuning of the collision energy over a wide range for heavy particles, by merely changing the average molecular weight of the carrier gas by mixing a heavier rare gas with He.

Table 1 Seeded Atomic Beams

Beam	T (°K)	$m_2/\overline{m}$	E_2 (eV)
F/He[a]	1000	4.6	1.0
Cl/He[b]	1500	8.1	2.6
Br/He[b]	1800	16.8	6.5
I/He[b]	3000	24.3	15.7

[a] Thermal dissociation of 0.5% F_2/He in a Nickel oven
[b] Thermal dissociation of 0.5% X_2/He in Graphite ovens, where $X_2 = Cl_2, Br_2, I_2$

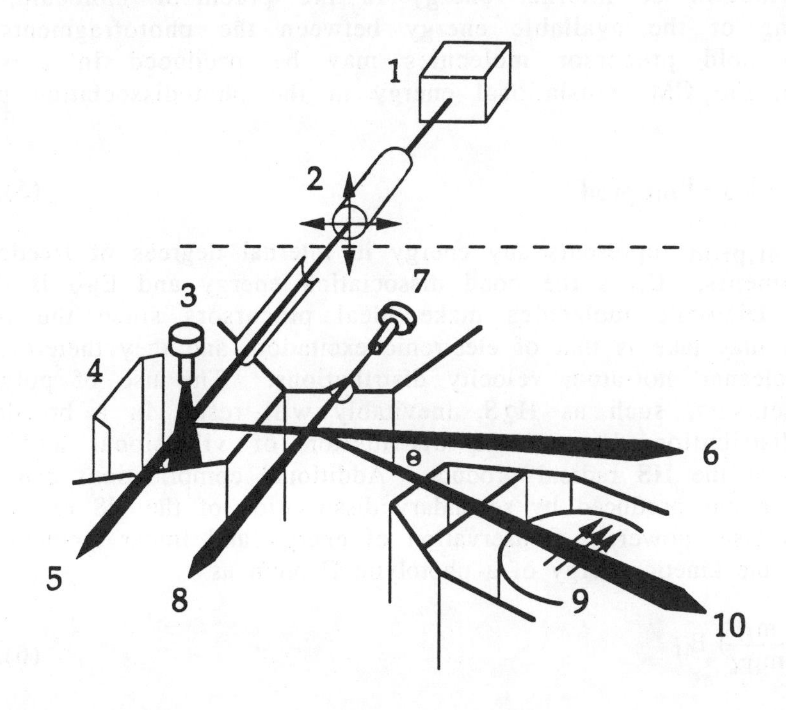

Fig. 2. Schematic view of a photolytic atomic beams experiment. The output of an excimer laser , 1, was polarized with a transmission polarizer, 2. The laser beam then entered the molecular beam machine, crossing a pulsed beam of DI, 3. The DI/laser interaction region is in a differentially pumped chamber, with cryo-panels, 4, assisting in the evacuation. The recoiling D atoms were collimated, forming the D-atom beam, 6, which crossed the H_2 molecular beam, 8, produced in a separate differential pumping chamber by the pulsed valve, 7. DH products, 10, scattered into the mass-spectrometric detector, and were ionized in the electron-impact ionizer, 9.

2.2 Photolytic Atomic Beams

For hydrogen atoms, the seeded-beam technique cannot be used since no lighter carrier gases are available. With the advent of high-power UV pulsed lasers, the classic hot-atom technique of H atom production by photolysis of hydride precursors[19] has become applicable to the study of reactions of H and D atoms at high collision energies. Numerous time-resolved bulk experiments on energy transfer and reaction dynamics have made use of this approach[1], however, only recently have such techniques been used to generate high-intensity 'monoenergetic' atomic beams for scattering studies.[6,20] Fig. 2 shows a schematic diagram of the $D + H_2 \rightarrow DH + H$ scattering experiment using a pulsed photolytic D-atom beam.

The kinetic energy distribution of a photolytic atomic beam is determined by the laser photon energy, the bond-dissociation energy of the precursor, any distribution of internal energy in the precursor molecule, and the partitioning of the available energy between the photofragments. Since internally cold precursor molecules may be produced in a supersonic expansion, the CM translational energy in the photodissociation process is given by

$$E_{tr} = E_{h\nu} - D_0 - E_{int,prod} \quad (5),$$

where $E_{int,prod}$ represents any energy in internal degrees of freedom of the photofragments, D_0 is the bond dissociation energy and $E_{h\nu}$ is the photon energy. Diatomic molecules make ideal precursors since the only form $E_{int,prod}$ may take is that of electronic excitation, and they therefore typically provide 'cleaner' hot-atom velocity distributions. The use of polyatomic H atom precursors, such as H_2S, inevitably will result in a broader kinetic energy distribution due to the distribution of vibrational and rotational excitation of the HS radical product. Additional complications can also arise due to H atoms produced by secondary dissociation of the HS radicals at high photolysis laser powers. Conservation of energy and linear momentum in the CM gives the kinetic energy of a photolytic H atom as

$$E_H = \left(1 - \frac{m_H}{m_{HX}}\right) E_{tr} \quad (6),$$

so, for disparate photofragment masses, nearly all of the translational energy will end up in H atom translation. By using HI, HBr, or H_2S as precursors at the powerful excimer wavelengths of 193 and 248 nm, H atoms can be generated with translational energies from 0.95 to 3.3 eV.[1]

Photodissociation of the hydrogen halides in the ultraviolet can produce both ground $X(^2P_{3/2})$ and spin-orbit excited $X(^2P_{1/2})$ halogen atoms. The branching ratio for the production of these atoms is wavelength dependent, a factor which can complicate bulk experiments in which the photodissociation laser wavelength is tuned to change the kinetic energy. For the production of an atomic beam, however, use may be made of the fact that the electronic transitions associated with the two spin-orbit states have different symmetries with respect to the diatom bond. For the $X(^2P_{1/2})$ channel the transition moment is parallel to the bond, while for the $X(^2P_{3/2})$ channel, the transition moment is perpendicular to the bond. The angular distribution of photofragments produced with a polarized dissociation laser is given by

$$I(\theta) = \frac{1}{4\pi}\,(1 + \beta \cdot P_2(\cos\theta)) \qquad (7).$$

In this equation[21], θ is the angle between the fragment recoil in the CM and the electric vector of the linearly polarized dissociation laser. $P_2(\cos\theta)$ is an associated Legendre polynomial, and β is a form factor which ranges from 2 for a pure parallel transition ($I \approx \cos^2\theta$) to -1 for a purely perpendicular transition ($I \approx \sin^2\theta$). Fig. 3 shows the degree of separation which may be achieved under single collision conditions for the photodissociation of DI at 248 nm. In practice, the discrimination between the two channels is reduced by incomplete polarization of the laser, collisions in the photodissociation source volume and any curve crossing processes in the dissociation event.

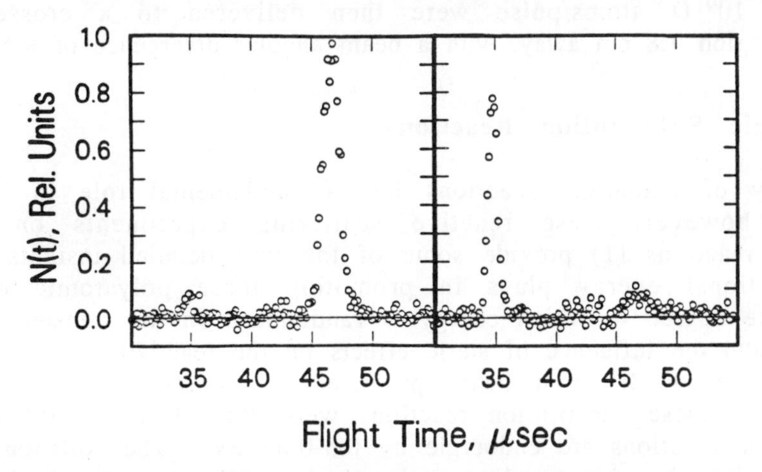

Fig. 3. D atom (m/e=2) TOF spectra. Left frame: E parallel to the direction of detection in the top frame, discriminating against the fast atoms. Right Frame: E perpendicular to the direction of detection.

The atomic beam must also be well collimated in a scattering experiment. This constraint, however, is always in conflict with the desire to produce high intensity beams. To increase the intensity of a photolytic atomic beam, it is desirable to irradiate as many precursor molecules as possible, i.e., either irradiate a small volume with a high precursor number density or increase the size of the photolysis volume. Since the atomic beam crosses a secondary beam in a finite interaction volume (on the order of 0.03 cm^3), several centimeters away from the atomic beam source, the finite size of the photodissociation source volume can cause a significant broadening of the atomic beam angular divergence. In principle, this problem can be solved by moving the photolysis volume arbitrarily far away from the cross beam, but, the decrease in beam intensity due to the smaller solid angle subtended at larger distances makes this impractical.

By using pulsed molecular beam techniques[22], high precursor number densities may be established, allowing generation of high intensity atom beams from small source volumes. Under such conditions, however, some collisions may occur in the source volume, causing the beam velocity distribution to broaden, and producing possible beam contaminants by chemical reactions in the source volume. In the reactive scattering experiments we have performed on the $D + H_2 \rightarrow DH + H$ reaction, beam intensity requirements dictated that the D atom beam had to be formed under such conditions, leading to a broadening of the velocity distribution.[6] Chemical reactions such as $D + DI \rightarrow D_2 + I$ and $D + HI \rightarrow DH + I$ in the source also produced fast D_2 and DH impurities in the atomic beam. Under the conditions of the experiments done on the $D + H_2 \rightarrow DH + H$ reaction, a number density of DI of $\approx 1 \times 10^{14}$ molec/cm^3 in a photolysis volume of ≈ 0.03 cm^3 was achieved. Dissociation of 75% of these molecules produced 1×10^{12} D atoms, of which 1×10^9 D atoms/pulse were then delivered to a crossed beam interaction region 4.8 cm away, with a beam angular divergence of $\approx 6°$.

3. Endoergic Substitution Reactions

The study of endoergic reactions has a fundamental role in hot atom chemistry, however, these reactive scattering experiments on the Br substitution reactions (1) provide some of the first detailed insights into the role translational energy plays in promoting these polyatomic endoergic reactions, the degree to which energy is randomized in the transient collision complexes, and the influence of steric effects on the reactivity.

Using a seeded Br atom beam produced by thermal dissociation in a graphite oven, these substitution reactions were studied in the 0.65-1.50 eV range. These reactions are endoergic by 0.5-0.65 eV. The collision energies were tuned by changing seeding ratios and carrier gases and the source temperatures of both reactant beams. The measured cross sections at the different collision energies were normalized by measuring the elastic scattering of the reactants. A typical set of product LAB angular distributions for the Br + o-CT reaction are shown in Fig. 4. Product TOF spectra were also measured at several angles. The angular distributions and TOF spectra were simultaneously fit with an algorithm which convoluted input CM energy and angular distributions over the apparatus function. The collision energy resolution in these experiments was typically $\Delta E/E \approx 30\%$, chiefly determined by the spread in reactant beam velocity and angular distributions. To fit the data, the CM energy and angular distributions are iteratively varied until a good fit was achieved. The product translational energy distributions $P(E_T)$ were fit using a functional form;

$$P(E) = (E' - B)^p (E_{avl} - E')^q \qquad (8)$$

in which B is related to any barrier in the exit channel, which would force the $P(E_T)$ to peak away from the statistical limit of zero, and E_{avl} is the total energy available to the products. The parameters p, q, and B were optimized to give the best fit to the data. The product CM angular distributions were parameterized with Legendre polynomials.

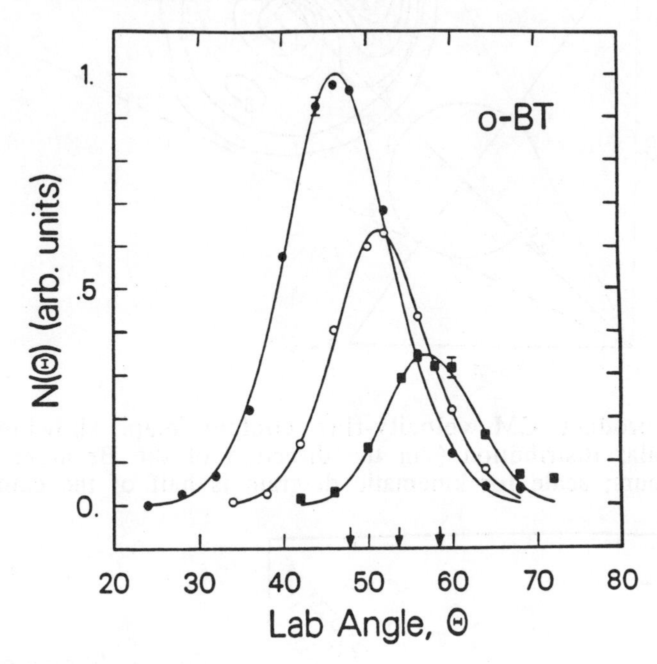

Fig. 4. LAB angular distribution for the o-BT product of the Br + o-CT reaction at energies of 1.34 eV (●), 1.08 eV (○) and 0.91 eV (■). Solid lines are fits to the data (see text).

3.1. Br + o-,m-,p-CT

A direct visualization of the results in a crossed-beams experiment is given by the CM product velocity-flux contour map, as shown in Fig. 5 for the para-bromotoluene (p-BT) products. The strong forward scattering observed indicates that the transient collision complex survives for less than one rotational period. The CM product angular distributions for both the o-BT and p-BT products were found to be forward-peaked. The product CM translational energy distributions for these reactions are peaked near zero translational energy, with approximately 30% of the available energy appearing in product translation. The o-BT translational energy distributions were peaked at a slightly smaller translational energy than the p-BT products.

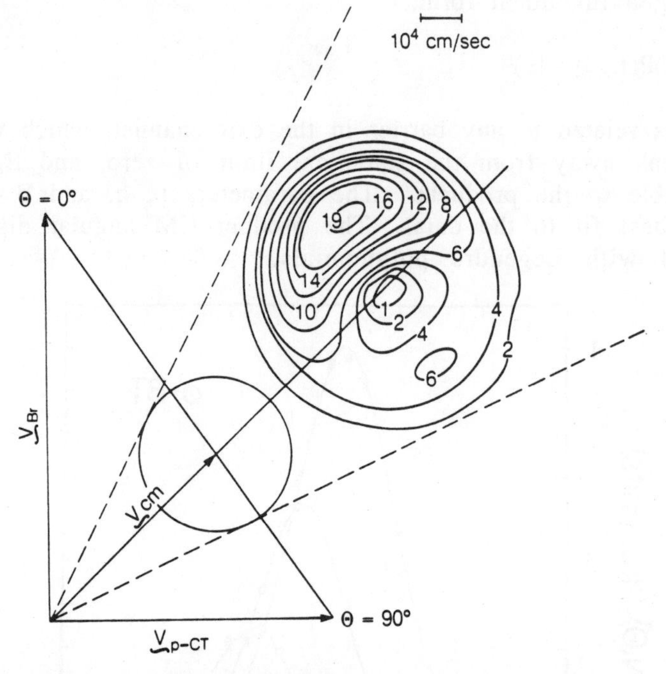

Fig. 5. p-BT product CM velocity-flux contour map, showing a forward peaking CM angular distribution (in the direction of the Br atom in the CM). Scale is for contours; scale for kinematic diagram is half of the contour scale.

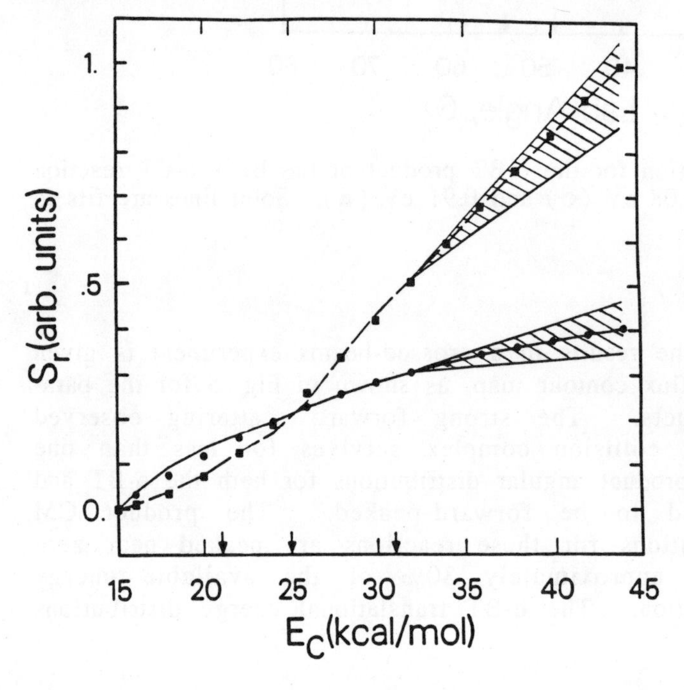

Fig. 6. Excitation Functions, $S_r(E)$, for the p-BT (—) and o-BT (– –) products. Arrows indicate the most probable experimental collision energies. Shaded regions indicate uncertainty in S_r at high energies. The points represent predicted excitation functions using a reduced-mode model of energy sharing in the collision complexes.

The excitation functions, $S_r(E)$, found for these reactions are shown in Fig. 6. $S_r(E)$ for the o-BT products rises sharply with energy, while for p-BT, $S_r(E)$ is flatter. The p-BT cross section is larger at the lower collision energies, however. The higher cross section for p-BT at the lower collision energies may be due to the fact that the methyl group ortho to the Cl position in o-CT sterically hinders the Br attack. The excitation functions and $P(E_T)$'s observed indicate that more modes are active in the Br-o-CT collision complex. The larger reaction cross section for Br + o-CT may be due to the larger number of active modes in the transient collision complex, which may serve to dissipate the translational energy of the collision better, allowing Br to add more readily to o-CT than to p-CT and subsequently react.

One of the most striking observations in this study, however, was that no reaction was observed for Br + m-CT at collision energies up to 1.26 eV. This negative result indicates that the substitution cross section for m-CT is at least a factor of ten lower than for o-CT. This o,p directing behavior of CH_3 substituents is well documented in condensed-phase organic chemistry, and is usually explained in terms of the electron donating capability of the methyl group, which stabilizes the o- and p- adducts by either increasing the o- and p- frontier electron populations in the reactant molecule or by lowering the total π electron energy of the o- and p- adducts relative to the m- adduct. Although no rigorous quantum mechanical calculation of the heats of formation of the isomeric radical intermediates through which these reactions proceed have been done, the energy associated with removing an electron from conjugation with the π cloud of the ring and localizing it at the o-, m- and p- positions of various aromatic molecules has been calculated.[23)] For toluene, only 0.03 eV difference was found between the o- and m- localization energies, a number which we may associate with the stability of the radical adduct intermediate. Such a small energetic difference cannot explain the differences in the dynamics of these reactions.

These gas-phase results may indicate that the reactivities of the isomers of CT in the gas phase are governed by the shape, especially the slope of the entrance channel, of the Br-CT potential energy surface (PES) along the reaction coordinate. The increased electron populations o- and p- to the methyl group in CT could enhance the attraction between Br and these sites during the approach. Such an effect would make the PES rise more gradually in the entrance valley, allowing translational energy to couple more readily with the reaction coordinate and promote the reaction. Effects of this sort have been seen in classical trajectory studies of atom-diatom systems by Polanyi and coworkers[24)], and may well explain the striking differences in reactivity between the isomers of CT.

3.2. Br + 1,1- and 1,2-trans-DCE

The product translational energy distributions found for the Br + DCE reactions were very similar to those for the Br + CT reactions. Once again, approximately 30% of the available energy appears in product translation. The product CM angular distributions, however, are indicative of a much longer-lived collision complex in these reactions compared with the Br + CT reactions. This is shown by the near forward-backward symmetry in the CM-frame velocity-flux contour maps for the Br + chloro-olefin reactions, as shown for the Br + 1,2-trans-DCE reaction in Fig. 7, which implies that the lifetime of the collision complexes in these reactions is longer than a rotational period. This is due to the fact that formation of the bromodichloroethyl radical adduct is exoergic by approximately 0.35 eV, resulting in a longer adduct lifetime when compared with the Br + CT adducts, which are endoergic by ≈ 0.09 eV.[5)]

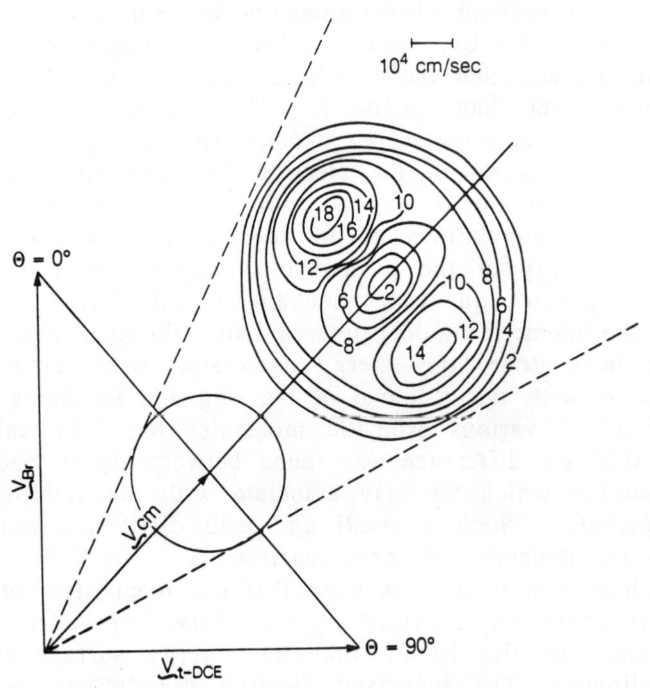

Fig. 7. Product CM velocity-flux contour map for the Br + t-DCE reaction, showing a more nearly forward-backward symmetric product t-BCE CM angular distribution. See caption for Fig. 5.

The shape of the excitation functions for the Br + DCE reactions were also found to be consistent with a mechanism in which vibrational energy in the complex is shared in few of the available modes. The excitation functions for the Br + DCE reactions also showed striking differences in reactivity for the two isomers studied. The cross section for the Br + 1,2-trans-DCE reaction is significantly larger than that for 1,1-DCE reaction. This result is consistent with the traditional theory of anti-Markovnikov addition, which predicts that radical attack at the least-substituted carbon will be favored due to resonance stabilization of the resulting radical adduct.[25)] However, the simplest explanation for these results, as well as a large body of gas-phase radical-alkene addition reactions, is that for Br + 1,1-DCE, the Cl substituents hinder the approach of the attacking atom, reducing the probability of addition and subsequent reaction.

3.3. Conclusions about Endoergic Reactions

Several unifying features were observed in these studies of the dynamics of endoergic Br substitution reactions. In both the aromatic and alkene reactions, endoergic substitution occurs in a quasi-direct fashion as shown by measurement of the $P(E_T)$'s and excitation functions for the reactions. In fact, the number of active modes remains approximately the same for both the Br + DCE and Br + CT reactions. This offers the intriguing possibility that the dynamics of endoergic aromatic substitution reactions can be modeled by the simpler analogous atom-alkene reactions. Steric effects were also shown to play a significant role. Earlier studies of the exoergic reactions of F atoms with similar compounds[26)] indicated that the F atom addition reactions are not very site-selective, which is not surprising in light of their exoergicity. In the case of Br addition, which is much less exoergic and therefore proceeds with less long-range attractive forces, subtle differences between isomeric potential energy surfaces can manifest themselves much more strongly in the reaction cross sections.

4. Dynamics of the Elementary Reaction $D+H_2 \rightarrow DH+H$

High resolution scattering experiments on atom-diatom systems can play a critical role in the evaluation of theoretical chemical dynamics calculations and *ab initio* PES's for chemical reactions. For example, work done on the F + H_2, HD, and D_2 systems provided some of the first experimental evidence for the role that quasi-bound states due to quantum mechanical resonances play in otherwise 'direct' chemical reactions.[27)] The F + H_2 system is, however, several years away from being treated exactly with quantum scattering calculations, although the PES for this system has been improved significantly in recent years.[28)] The three-electron, three-proton hydrogen exchange reaction, on the other hand, can now be treated exactly quantum mechanically over a wide energy range. Although measurements of product angular distributions in this system are difficult because of the substantial potential energy barrier, the recent advances in the production of high kinetic energy photolytic atomic beams have now made such measurements possible.

4.1 *Ab Initio* Reaction Dynamics

Fundamental to the prediction of the dynamics of a chemical reaction is the quantitative calculation of the forces which determine the outcome of a collision. Due to the simplicity of the H_3 system, the PES for this system is known with greater accuracy than for any other reactive system. It has long been known that the hydrogen exchange reaction proceeds via a collinear minimum energy path. Sophisticated *ab initio* calculations of the energy of H_3 in several hundred configurations have been done. An analytic fit, based on calculations by Liu and Siegbahn[29] was done by Truhlar and Horowitz[30] in 1978. This surface has been used in many dynamics calculations, and is referred to as the LSTH surface. The LSTH surface heavily weights collinear H_3 geometries, and gives a barrier in the minimum-energy collinear configuration of 0.425 eV. The more recent Double-Many-Body Expansion, or DMBE representation of the PES includes more non-collinear configurations and has a collinear barrier of 0.419 eV[31], in accordance with the most recent *ab initio* [32] and quantum Monte Carlo calculations[33,34].

The H_3 system was the first reaction for which detailed dynamical predictions were possible using quasi-classical trajectory calculations.[35] These early studies showed that the DH products for the D + H_2 reaction, for example, were directly backward-scattered at low collision energies, with progressively more forward scattering occurring as the collision energy increases, allowing more non-linear configurations to react. QCT calculations are economical to perform, and still play an important role in the evaluation of experimental results.[36]

Schatz and Kuppermann performed the first fully converged three-dimensional quantum scattering calculations on the H + H_2 reaction in 1975 up to collision energies of 0.5 eV.[37] Extension of such calculations to other isotopic combinations and to the higher energies of more significance to experimentalists did not become possible until 1988, however, with the work of Zhang and Miller[38] and Manolopolous and Wyatt.[39] Recently, Zhang and Miller (ZM) [40], and subsequently Zhao, Truhlar, Schwenke and Kouri (ZTSK) [41] have calculated differential cross sections (DCS's) for the D + H_2 reaction on both the LSTH and DMBE surfaces, respectively. These extensive calculations provide the first accurate detailed picture of the reaction dynamics for any chemical reaction.

4.2. Critical Experimental Tests

Considerable effort has been made to obtain experimental results to test the extensive theoretical predictions available for the H_3 system. In the 1960's, bulk photochemical hot atom techniques were first applied to the D + H_2 reaction to measure the total reactive cross section by White and Kuppermann.[42] Crossed molecular beams studies, using thermal dissociation of D_2 or H_2 to make the atomic beams, were also initiated by Datz and Taylor[43] and Fite and coworkers.[44] Kwei and coworkers used radiochemical techniques to obtain the TH product angular distribution of the T + H_2 reaction.[45] These early scattering experiments verified that the products were backward scattered in the CM at low collision energies, as dynamics calculations had predicted.

In recent years significant progress has been made in detailed measurements on the H_3 reaction. Advances in both the production of energetic H or D atoms by photodissociation and laser-based spectroscopic detection techniques have enabled the product vibration-rotation state distributions to be measured for several isotopic variants of the hydrogen exchange reaction using both Coherent Anti-Stokes Raman Scattering (CARS) by Valentini and coworkers[46] and Resonance Enhanced Multiphoton Ionization (REMPI) by Zare and coworkers.[47] In these studies, pulsed UV lasers are used to generate energetic H atoms, with subsequent time-resolved probing of the products allowing product-state distributions to be effectively recorded under single collision conditions. At the level of product-state distributions, good agreement between theory and experiment has now been observed for the D + H_2 reaction.[48] Total cross section measurements using vacuum ultraviolet laser induced fluorescence measurements of the H and D atom products have been made by Bersohn's group, also using photolytic methods of atomic beam generation.[49]

The first crossed beams scattering experiments in which the DH product velocity distributions were measured were reported by Toennies and coworkers for both D + $H_2(v=0)$ and D + $H_2(v=1)$.[50,51] For the $H_2(v=0)$ reaction, energetic D atoms were produced with a high-temperature arc discharge, with a very broad D atom velocity distribution, which precluded resolution of the DH vibrational states in the experiment.

4.3 Vibrational State-Resolved Differential Cross Sections

By application of the photolytic atomic beam technique, Gentry and coworkers first reported product vibrational state-resolved DCS measurements for the D + H_2 reaction.[20] By photolyzing D_2S at 193 nm and making use of rotatable beam sources to tune the collision energy by changing the beam intersection angle, product velocity distributions were measured at single LAB angles as a function of collision energy from 0.85 to 1.05 eV with an energy resolution of $\approx$20%. The LAB angles were chosen to allow measurement of the backward scattered DH(v=0) and DH(v=1) as a function of collision energy.

In our laboratory, measurements of state-resolved DCS's as a function of LAB scattering angle have been made on the D + H_2 reaction at energies of 0.53 and 1.01 eV with an energy resolution of $\approx$10%. As Fig. 2 shows, these experiments were done by photolyzing DI at 248 nm, making use of a polarized laser to allow spatial separation of the D atoms to change the collision energy. The pulsed D-atom beam crossed a pulsed H_2 beam, with product velocity distributions measured as a function of LAB scattering angle. A typical raw DH TOF spectrum is shown in Fig. 8. As shown in the figure, the raw TOF spectra had to be corrected for modulated background inherent in the pulsed beams technique. Careful measurement of the background signals associated with the D-atom and H_2 beams allowed the TOF spectra to be corrected, yielding the spectra shown in Fig. 9.

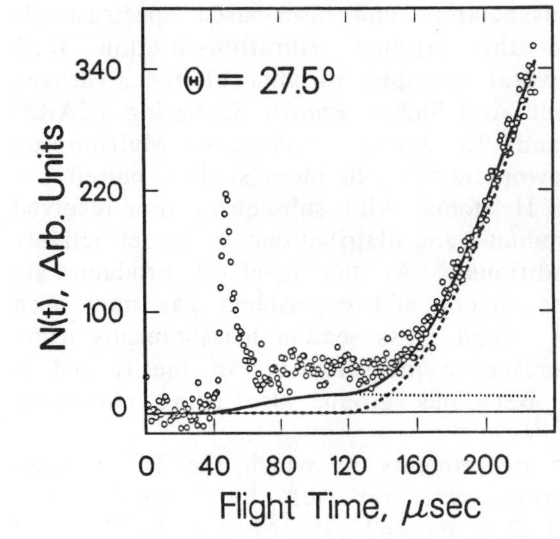

Fig. 8. Raw TOF spectrum (m/e = 3) for the E_c = 1.01 eV D + H_2 reaction at a LAB angle of 27.5°. The curves fit to the data represent the modulated background contributions to the signal: —— ; total modulated background: ········ ; D-atom-beam modulated background: - - - -; H_2-beam modulated background.

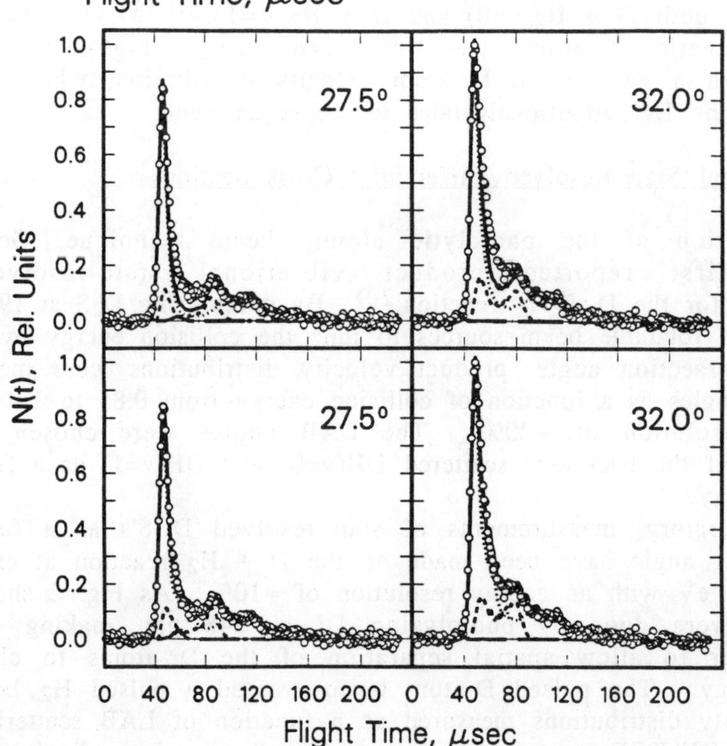

Fig. 9. Comparison of representative DH TOF spectra with the theoretical predictions of Zhang and Miller (top frames) at 27.5° and 32°. The bottom frames show the comparison using the best-fit DCS. The circles represent the TOF data, the solid line is the results of the Monte Carlo simulation summed over all DH(v,j) states. The ····· line is for DH(v=0,j) products; the - - - - line is for DH(v=1,j) products. A small contribution from DH(v=2,j) is seen near 60 μsec in the 27.5° spectra

Consideration of the kinematic diagram in Fig. 10 shows that at a LAB angle of 27.5°, for example, four peaks might be observed in the TOF spectrum in the limit of no rotational excitation; fast, forward scatted DH(v=0) and DH(v=1) and slower, backward scattered DH(v=1) and DH(v=0). In the spectra shown in Fig. 9, the backward scattered DH(v) states are resolved. Once the corrected product TOF spectra and LAB angular distributions were obtained, a direct comparison of the experimental results with the dynamical predictions of ZM and ZTSK was possible using a Monte Carlo simulation code to perform the CM to LAB transformation of the theoretical DCS's to the LAB frame for comparison with the experimental results.

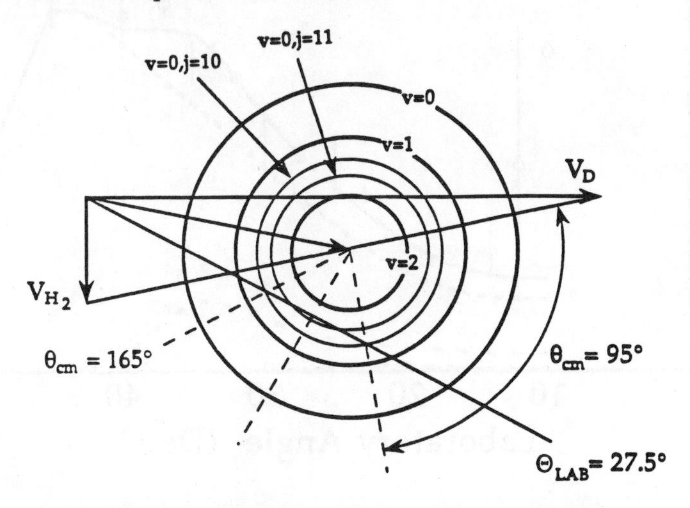

Fig. 10. Kinematic diagram for the D + H_2 → DH + H reaction at 1.0 eV, showing the relationship between the CM and LAB reference frames. The concentric circles centered at the origin of the CM frame represents the maximum CM recoil velocities for DH products in v = 0 , 1 and 2. The CM recoil velocities for DH(v=0,j=10 and 11) products are also shown.

Representative results of the Monte Carlo simulation of the TOF spectra for D + para-H_2 → DH + H at a collision energy of 1.01 eV are shown in the top frames of Fig. 9. The theoretical DCS's used in these simulations were the D + H_2(j=0) DCS calculations of ZM. Little difference was observed between the calculations of ZM and ZTSK for the D + H_2(j=0) reaction. A significant discrepancy is seen between theory and experiment at flight times from 50 to 80 μsec corresponding to DH products with small CM velocities. Qualitatively, though, the agreement between theory and experiment is quite good. Integration of the normalized TOF spectra obtained gives the LAB angular distribution shown in Fig. 11 at a collision energy of 1.01 eV. At this level of comparison, no major discrepancies are seen between theory and experiment. ZTSK have also done calculations for H_2(j=1) reagents, which show a more significant difference than that between the two separate calculations for H_2(j=0) on the two PES's. Scattering experiments with D + normal-H_2 did not show a significant difference from the D + para-H_2 results, however, so mere inclusion of more reactant H_2 rotor states probably does not account for the observed differences between theory and experiment.

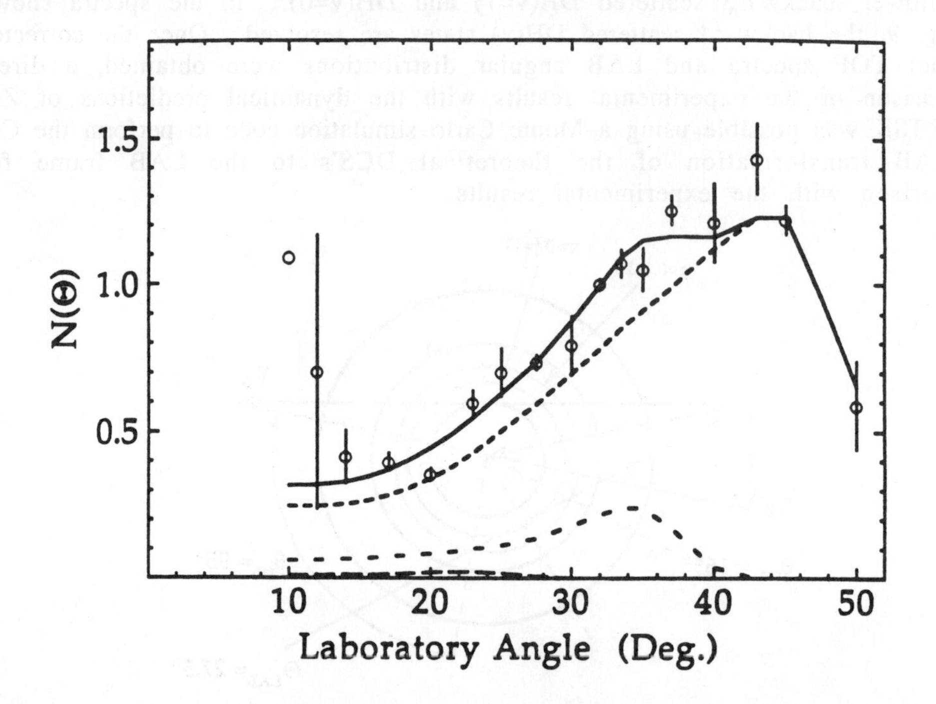

Fig. 11. LAB angular distribution at E_c = 1.01 eV generated by integrating the corrected TOF's. The solid line shows the results of the Monte Carlo simulation of the experiment using the theoretical predictions summed over vibrational states. The contributions from the DH vibrational states are shown as; DH(v=0) - - - - - ; DH(v=1) - - - - ; DH(v=2) – – – –.

To ascertain the magnitude of the discrepancies between theory and experiment, the Monte Carlo simulation was used to iteratively adjust the theoretical DCS's until the simulation fit both the LAB angular distribution and TOF spectra simultaneously.[52] The fits to the TOF spectra in the lower frames of Fig. 9 show the level of agreement obtained between simulation and experiment. The final best-fit state-to-state DH(v,j) DCS's are by no means unique, but they do provide a qualitative view of the region in which discrepances are observed between theory and experiment. The most significant discrepancies were observed for the lesser-populated rotationally excited DH products at both collision energies. Cartesian CM velocity-flux contour maps showing the differences between theory and experiment are shown in Fig. 12 at both collision energies. The contour maps at 0.53 eV show that although the products were observed to be backward scattered in the CM, significant broadening of the DCS in the backward hemisphere was observed compared to the theoretical results. At 1.01 eV, the peak of the DCS is still seen to be ≈125° in the CM as predicted theoretically, but the DCS's are significantly broadened in the

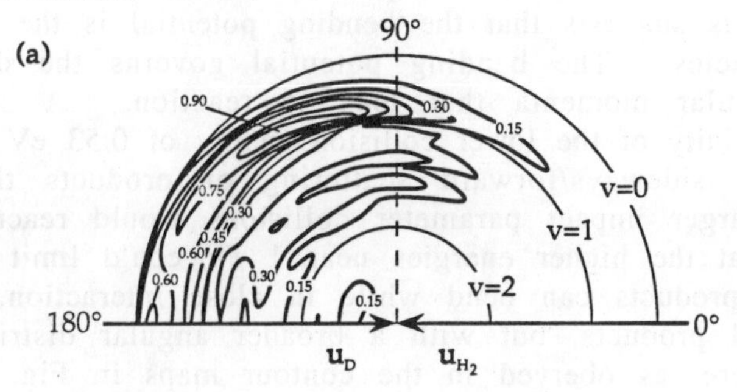

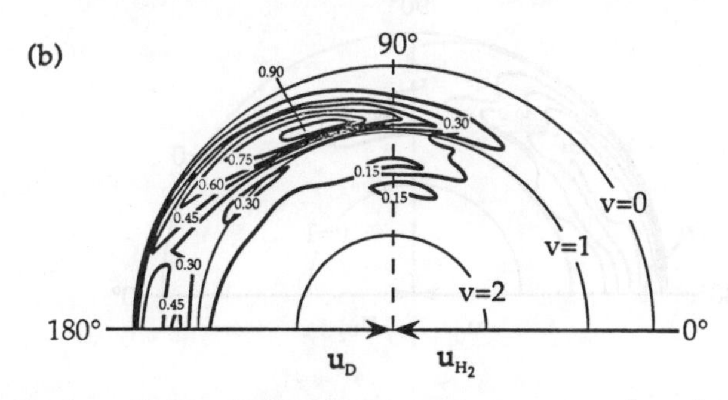

Fig. 12a). Cartesian CM velocity-flux contour maps for the $D+H_2 \rightarrow DH + H$ reaction at $E_c = 0.98$ eV. The top frame shows the best-fit DCS, while the bottom shows the contour map obtained from the theoretical predictions of ZM.

backward hemisphere, with more rotationally excited products observed in the experiment. Gentry's group has observed similar discrepancies. At a collision energy of 0.85 eV, they have also seen a significant discrepancy in the ratio of forward/backward scattered products.[53] Thus, the available high-resolution molecular beam experiments indicate that the theoretical predictions are not yet perfect.

4.4 Implications for the H_3 PES

Since two different groups have now done fully converged quantum scattering calculations on the $D + H_2$ reaction that qualitatively agree[40,41]), the discrepancies between the DCS measurements and the dynamics calculations must reflect deficiencies in the PES's on which the calculations have been done. The PES's are fits to nearly the same set of *ab initio* calculations, with the greatest emphasis placed on collinear arrangements of the three atoms. High energy bent configurations of the H_3 complex have recieved little attention until recently[54]. The fact that the largest discrepancies between theory and experiment were seen for rotationally excited DH products suggests that the bending potential is the source of the observed discrepancies. The bending potential governs the distribution of initial orbital angular momenta that lead to reaction. A softer bending potential in the vicinity of the lower collision energy of 0.53 eV could lead to substantially more sideways/forward scattering of products than predicted theoretically, as larger impact parameter collisions would react. A steeper bending potential at the higher energies near 1 eV could limit the extent to which the D-H_2 products can bend while in close interaction, giving more rotationally excited products, but with a broader angular distribution in the backward hemisphere, as oberved in the contour maps in Fig. 11. At this stage, to get quantitative accord between theory and experiment, a more detailed, systematic study of the H_3 PES appears to be in order.

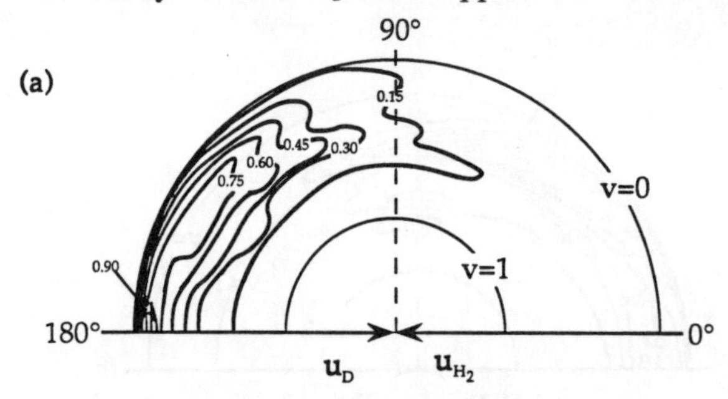

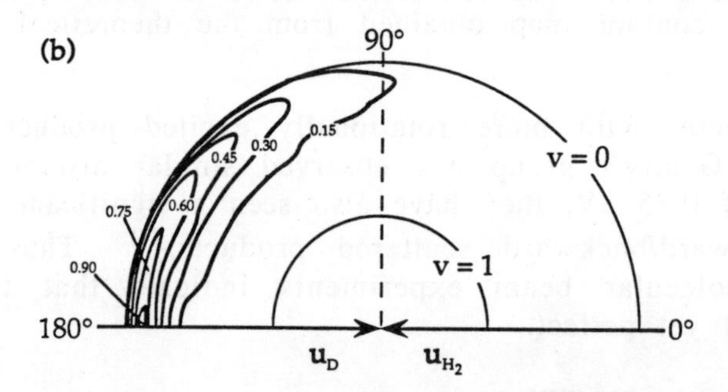

Fig. 12b). Cartesian CM velocity-flux contour maps for the $D+H_2 \rightarrow DH + H$ reaction at $E_c = 0.51$ eV. The top frame shows the best-fit DCS, while the bottom shows the contour map obtained from the theoretical predictions of ZM.

5. Conclusions

As illustrated by the examples in this chapter, crossed molecular beams experiments can probe the detailed dynamics of chemical reactions. In the case of elementary atom-diatom reactions these experiments provide critical tests of dynamical calculations and the PES's on which they are done. This is an important step in the verification of our *ab initio* understanding of chemical reaction dynamics. Once quantitative agreement between theory and experiment has been reached for the simplest chemical reaction, efforts to extend dynamics calculations to more complex systems and to develop approximate, yet accurate, dynamical theories will be able to proceed with confidence.

In the area of polyatomic hot atom chemical reactions, such as the endoergic Br substitution reactions, crossed beams scattering with electron-impact ionization mass spectrometric detection will remain the most versatile technique for acquiring dynamical information, due to the difficulties associated with thorough spectroscopic probing of complicated polyatomic species. The molecular beam technique can be applied to virtually any material which can be introduced into a molecular beam, with the universal mass-spectrometric detection scheme providing information on the distribution of energy in the products and the lifetime of transient collision complexes.

In the area of elementary chemical reactions, the future holds great promise for obtaining more detailed experimental results on the dynamics of elementary reactions. The work on vibrational state-resolved DCS's for the hydrogen exchange reaction does not test the theoretical results to the limit of their predictions. Rotationally resolved DCS's willl have to be measured to provide the final answers for this elementary reaction. Welge and coworkers have developed a technique which allows TOF spectra of H atoms to be measured, allowing better resolution of final product states due to the larger H atom recoil velocities.[55] This technique should be able to achieve rotational state resolution if the reactant beams can be sufficiently collimated. In addition, the application of state-specific spectroscopic techniques, such as REMPI, to measuring DCS's for individual product quantum states should become more feasible in the near future for the hydrogen exchange reaction.

Acknowledgements

The work described in this chapter as examples were carried out together with Dr. G.N. Robinson and B.A. Balko in recent years. Their contributions are gratefully acknowledged. This work was supported by the Director, Office of Basic Energy Sciences, Chemical Sciences Division of the U.S. Department of Energy under contract No. DE-AC03-76SF00098.

References

1. Flynn, G.W., and Weston, R.E., Jr.: Ann. Rev. Phys. Chem., 37, 551 (1986).
2. Miller, W.B., Safron, S.A., and Herschbach D.R.: Disc. Farad. Soc. 44, 108 (1967).
3. McClelland, G.M., and Herschbach, D.R.: J. Phys. Chem., 83, 1445 (1979).
4. Robinson, G.N., Continetti, R.E., and Lee, Y.T.: J. Chem. Phys., 89, 6226 (1988).
5. Robinson, G.N., Continetti, R.E., and Lee, Y.T.: J. Chem. Phys., 89, 6238 (1988).
6. Continetti, R.E., Balko, B.A., and Lee, Y.T.: J. Chem. Phys., 93, 5719 (1990).
7. Lee, Y.T.,: "Hot Atom Chemistry Status Report"; International Atomic Energy Agency, Vienna 1975, p.123.
8. Yoshihara, K. and Lee, Y.T.: "Hot Atom Chemistry" (T. Matsuura, Ed.) Kodansha, Tokyo (and Elsevier, Amsterdam), 1984, p. 63.
9. Murphy, E.J., Brophy, J.H., and Kinsey, J.L.: J. Chem. Phys., 74, 331 (1981).
10. Lee, Y.T., McDonald, J.D., LeBreton, P.R., and Herschbach, D.R., Rev. Sci. Inst., 40, 1402 (1968).
11. Lee, Y.T.: Chemica Scripta, 27, 215 (1987); Lee, Y.T.: in "Atomic and Molecular Beam Methods", Vol. 1, (G. Scoles, ed.), Oxford Univ. Press, London (1988), Ch. 22, p. 553.
12. Van Zyl B., Utterback, N.G., and Amme, R.C.: Rev. Sci. Inst., 47, 814 (1976).
13. Young, W.S., Rodgers, W.E., and Knuth, E.L.: Rev. Sci. Inst., 40, 1346 (1969).
14. Way, K.R., Yang, S-C., and Stwalley, W.C.: Rev. Sci. Inst., 47, 1049 (1976).
15. Garvey, J.F. and Kuppermann, A.: Rev. Sci. Inst., 57, 1061 (1986).
16. Becker, E.W., and Henkes, W.: Z. Physik 146, 320 (1956).
17. Miller, D.R.: in "Atomic and Molecular Beam Methods", Vol. 1, (G. Scoles, ed.), Oxford Univ. Press, London (1988), Ch. 2, p.18.
18. Valentini, J.J., Coggiola, M.J., and Lee, Y.T.: Rev. Sci. Inst., 48, 58 (1977).
19. Williams, R.R., and Ogg, R.A., Jr.: J. Chem. Phys., 15, 691 (1947).
20. Buntin, S.A., Giese, C.F., and Gentry, W.R.: J. Chem. Phys., 87, 1443 (1987).
21. Zare, R.N., Mol. Photochem., 4, 1 (1972).
22. Gentry, W.R.: "Atomic and Molecular Beam Methods" (G. Scoles, Ed.), Oxford University Press, Oxford 1988, Ch. 3, p.54.
23. Wheland, G.W.: J. Am. Chem. Soc., 64, 900 (1942).
24. Polanyi, J.C., Sathyamurthy, N. : Chemical Physics, 33, 287 (1978).
25. Mayo, F.R., and Walling, C.: Chem. Rev. 27, 351 (1940).
26. Shobatake, K., Lee, Y.T., and Rice, S.A.: J. Chem. Phys., 59, 6104 (1973).
27. Neumark, D.M., Wodtke, A.M., Robinson, G.N., Hayden, C.C., and Lee, Y.T.: Phys. Rev. Lett., 53, 2226 (1984).
28. Bauschlicher, C.W., Walch, S.P., Langhoff, S.R., Taylor, P.R., and Jaffe, R.L., J. Chem. Phys., 88, 1743 (1988).
29. Liu, B., and Siegbahn, P.: J. Chem. Phys., 68, 2457 (1978).
30. Truhlar, D.G., and Horowitz, C.J.: J. Chem. Phys., 68, 2466 (1978).
31. Varandas, A.J.C., Brown, F.B., Mead, C.A., Truhlar, D.G., and Blais, N.C.: J. Chem. Phys., 86, 6258 (1987).
32. Liu, B.: J. Chem. Phys., 80, 581 (1984).
33. Ceperley, D.M., and Alder, B.J.: J. Chem. Phys., 81, 5833 (1984).
34. Barnett, R.N., Reynolds, P.J., and Lester, W.A., Jr.: J. Chem. Phys., 82, 2700 (1985).
35. Brumer, P., and Karplus, M.: J. Chem. Phys., 54, 4955 (1971).

36. For example, Aoiz, F.J., Herrero, V.J., and Saez, V.: Chem. Phys. Lett., 161, 270 (1989).
37. Schatz, G.C., and Kuppermann, A.: J. Chem. Phys., 65, 4668 (1975).
38. Zhang, J.Z.H., and Miller, W.H., Chem. Phys. Lett., 153, 465 (1988).
39. Manolopoulos, D.E., and Wyatt, R.E., Chem. Phys. Lett., 159, 123 (1989).
40. Zhang, J.Z.H., and Miller, W.H., J. Chem. Phys., 91, 1528 (1989).
41. Zhao M., Truhlar, D.G., Schwenke, D.W., and Kouri, D.J.: J. Phys. Chem., 94, 7074 (1990).
42. Kuppermann, A., and White, J.M.: J. Chem. Phys., 44, 4352 (1966).
43. Datz, S., and Taylor, E.H.: J. Chem. Phys., 39, 1896 (1963).
44. Geddes, J., Krause, H.F., and Fite, W.L.: J. Chem. Phys., 56, 3298 (1972).
45. Kwei, G.H., and Lo, V.W.S.: J. Chem. Phys., 72, 6265 (1980).
46. Gerrity, D.P., and Valentini, J.J.: J. Chem. Phys., 81, 1290 (1984).
47. Marinero, E.E., Rettner, C.T., and Zare, R.N.: J. Chem. Phys., 80, 4146 (1984).
48. Kliner, D.A.V., Rinnen, K.-D., and Zare, R.N.: Chem. Phys. Lett., 166, 107 (1990).
49. Johnston, G.W., Katz, B., Tsukiyama, K., and Bersohn, R.: J. Phys. Chem., 91, 5445 (1987).
50. Goetting, R., Mayne, H.R., and Toennies, J.P.: J. Chem. Phys., 85, 6396 (1986).
51. Goetting, R., Herrero, V., Toennies, J.P., and Vodegel, M.: Chem. Phys. Lett., 137, 524 (1987).
52. Continetti, R.E.: Ph.D. thesis, Univ. of Calif., Berkeley, 1989, LBL-28126.
53. Buntin, S.A., Giese, C.F., and Gentry, W.R.: Chem. Phys. Lett., 168, 513 (1990).
54. Bauschlicher, C.W., Jr., Langhoff, S.R., and Partridge, H.: Chem. Phys. Lett., 170, 345 (1990).
55. Welge, K.A., XIIth Int. Symp. on Molecular Beams, Abstracts of Invited Talks and Contributed Papers (May 29 - June 2, 1989, Perugia, Italy), p.I.10.

3.2 Energy Transfer Processes and Retention of Hot Atoms

Robert E. JOHNSON, Min LIU, Raul A. BARAGIOLA, John W. BORING
Department of Nuclear Engineering and Engineering Physics
University of Virginia, Charlottesville, VA 22903, USA

1. Introduction

Upon absorbing a slow neutron and emitting an energetic gamma ray (n,γ) a single atom in a large organic molecule receives an impulsive energy. If this energy is small the 'hot' atom may transfer its momentum to neighboring atoms within the molecule or to neighboring molecules. This occurs in such a way that the atom does not travel far from its initial location in the organic molecule and may even be retained in its initial site with, possibly, dissociation occurring somewhere else in the molecule[1]. The process of retention can also occur by geminate recombination: the energized atom having been ejected from its parent molecule dissipates its energy and then returns to that site in a low probability, temperature dependent process discussed elsewhere(4.3). Alternatively, a highly energized atom may travel significant distances, escaping from its own molecule or its initial bonding site, and deposit its energy over some region in the solid. It is these energy transfer processes which we will examine here.

The excitation energies considered here are in the range 10eV to one keV. The lower limit of this range is closely related to kinetic energies achieved in sputtering due to electronic excitation of solids (5. 9), a process of interest in both low-temperature condensed-gas solids and organic solids. The upper end of the range is similar to ion bombardment energies for implantation or sputtering experiments and to fast recoil energies produced by incident ions(4 .1). In the examples of interest we assume the atom is energized from within a molecule in the solid (e.g. Fig. 1), resembling an energetic primary recoil produced in a collision cascade (e.g. 4.1). In this section we examine the fate of the recoil both analytically, by range calculations, and by molecular dynamics calculations carried out using pair potentials to describe the interactions between atoms in the molecule.

The fate of an energized atom in a molecule is determined both by the size and direction of the impulse, by the local atomic geometry, and by the cohesive energy of the material. In almost all experiments the impulse received is randomly oriented(4 .3). Therefore, measurements must eventually be compared to the

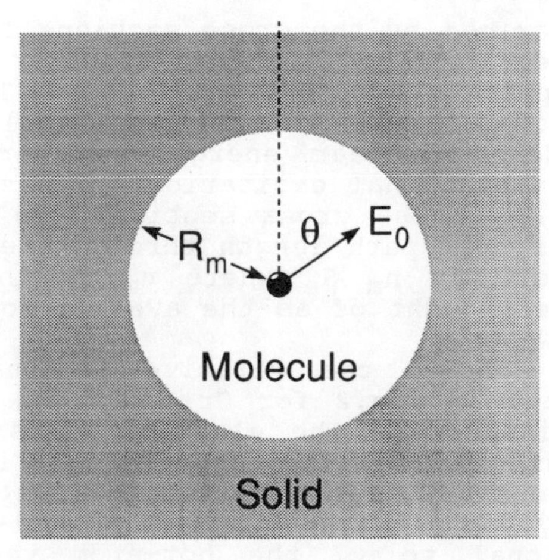

Fig.1 Schematic diagram of hot atom. A Hot atom set in motion with energy E_o in an organic molecule of average radius R_m schematic diagram.

probability of a particular end result averaged over the random orientations for a given impulse size and a given molecular structure. In order to understand the retention process we will also give results before averaging.

A conceptually simple picture for understanding retention is to think of the decay of the excited molecule as a unimolecular reaction. If the energy is greater than that required for loss (dissociation) of the energized species then that reaction occurs in competition with all other possible decay/dissociation modes. This picture is useful when many available modes are allowed and when they can be weighted according to the number of possible reaction paths leading to the same end state. That is, it is useful when dynamic aspects are not important. This occurs for the lower excitation energies and is discussed in 4.3 and 4.4. As the energy is increased the dynamics of the interaction of the excited atom with its neighbors controls energy loss and, therefore, determines retention. The energy of even very energetic atoms inevitably degrades, being shared with other atoms, so the unimolecular decay concept eventually becomes applicable and retention processes are typically temperature dependent(4.3). The process by which the atomic motion is randomized happens by a series of collisions (collision cascade) in which, as time increases, more atoms in the molecule/solid are set in motion until chemical bonding dominates(4.1).

2. Energy Loss Processes

Consider an atom, such as Cr in an organic molecule, in which the atom is surrounded by ligands. If this atom receives an impulsive energy E_o (e.g. 100eV) much greater than the binding energy with its neighbors, U_M, it is then possible to describe the interaction with its neighbors using binary collision cross sections[2]. Energy is transferred to neighbors either by direct momentum transfer (elastic nuclear energy transfer, T) or by electronic excitations (electronic energy transfer, Q) and the collisions are described by the cross sections for energy transfer $d\sigma_T$ and $d\sigma_Q$. Integrating over energy transfer gives the nuclear and electronic stopping cross sections[3)], $S_n = \int T d\sigma_T$ and $S_e = \int Q d\sigma_Q$ often referred to as the elastic and inelastic loss terms respectively. (Note: nuclear energy transfer to or within a molecule leads to vibrational excitation and dissociation, another 'inelastic' effect.) These cross sections are used to determine the energy loss per unit path length through the material $(dE/dx)_n = n_m S_n$ and $(dE/dx)_e = n_m S_e$ where n_m is the number density. (dE/dx) can also be thought of as the average force exerted on the hot atom as it slows down.

In order to compare the relative importance, these cross sections are plotted in Fig.2 for Cr and H on S, O and H in the energy region of interest. The elastic collision cross sections are obtained using a so-called 'universal interaction' cross section[4)] (see also IV.1). The electronic (inelastic) interaction can be very roughly approximated by the Lindhard-Scharff expression which is proportional to v, the hot-atom velocity[4,5)]. This applies where the center of mass energy of the colliding species is much higher than the threshold energy. (Note: when possible, accurate potentials between pairs should be used, e.g. ref. (6).) It is seen in Fig.2 that the nuclear energy loss is the dominant process for heavy atoms in the energy region of interest. At these energies the elastic stopping cross section is often written $S_n \propto E_o^{2m}$ due to a repulsive potential which varies with separation, r, as r^{-m},[2)]. In Fig.2, $m \approx 0.3$ for Cr on O. The elastic nuclear energy loss is also important because it leads to deflection of the energized atom, enhancing the possibility of retention. An important related quantity is the so-called diffusion cross section (or momentum transfer cross section), σ_d,[3)]; i.e $\sigma_d = S_n/(\gamma E_o)$ where γE_o is the maximum energy transfer to a 'stationary' atom of mass M $[\gamma = 4M_oM/(M_o+M)^2]$, A the energized atom having energy E_o and mass M_o. This quantity is the cross section for loss of forward momentum and is also shown in Fig.2, where E_o is the energy of the hot atom.

It is seen in Fig.2 that, even at the lowest energies, σ_d is always of the order of the atomic size, therefore, 'binary' collisions can only crudely describe the interaction of the energized atom with its neighbors. The binary collision concept, of course, has a long history (e.g. 4.1) in describing the dynamics of atomic and molecular encounters since 'large' energy transfers, which require close collisions, are often most important. The concept of closeness is generally described by the impact parameter, b, the projection of the distance between the colliding species perpendicular to the motion of the incident atom. Fig.3 shows the energy transfer T vs b for 200 eV Cr and H atoms incident on S, O and H. It is seen that the larger energy transfers correspond to impact parameters smaller than the mean distance between atoms in a large organic molecule, so that binary collision cross sections can be used effectively for considering energy degradation and hot-atom retention. We will subsequently consider a more complete description via a molecular dynamics calculation.

It is also seen from Figs. 3a and 3b that a large mismatch in mass results in small energy transfers, i.e. $\gamma \ll 1$. Further, the deflection θ_o of the moving atom is given by

$$\cos\theta_o = \{1-[(1+\mu)/2](T/E_o)\}/[1-(T/E_o)]^{\frac{1}{2}}, \qquad (1)$$

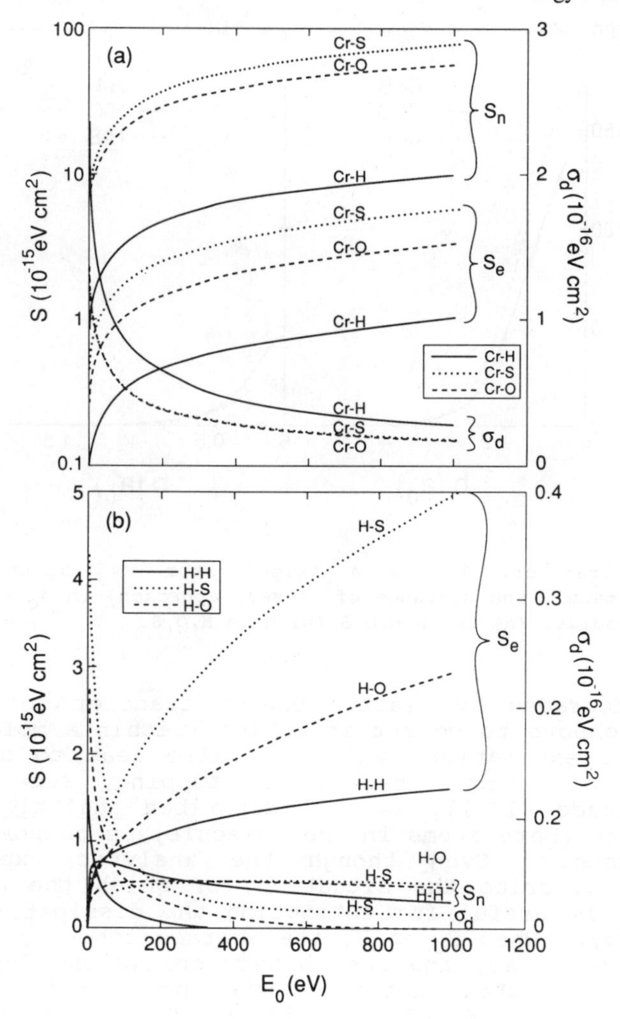

Fig.2 **Left hand axis stopping power, S_n or S_e as indicated vs E_o. Right hand axis σ_d the diffusion cross section.** (a) Cr on H, O, S. (b) H on H,O,S.

where $\mu = M/M_o$ 3). For an energized Cr atom in an organic molecular environment μ<<1, (T/E_o) << 1, so that the deflection $\theta_o \approx (T/E_o)^{\frac{1}{2}}$ is also small. Therefore, even though the elastic collision energy loss, S_n, is large for this case, the deflections are small and stopping can be looked on, roughly, as a drag force, as has been assumed by Matsuura and co-workers (see e.g. 4 .3). That is, the average force on a Cr atom for such a case, is roughly, $(dE/dx)_n \propto v$, which is close to what is seen in Fig. 2. On the other hand, for a light species (e.g. H on S in Fig. 3), for which is μ >> 1, large deflections can occur based on Eq. 1, even though γ << 1 and (T/E_o) << 1. Therefore, a proton below one keV scatters significantly while slowing down.

The energy of the atom receiving the initial impulse may, as

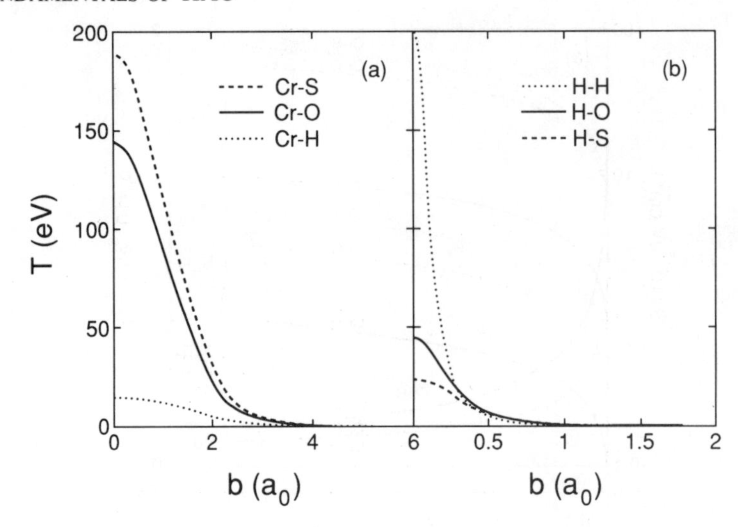

Fig.3 Energy transfer, T, to a target atom vs impact parameter, b, (approximately the distance of closest approach) in $a_o = 0.529 \times 10^{-8}$ cm a Bohr radius. (a) Cr on H,O,S (b) H on H,O,S.

we saw, be degraded by elastic energy transfer collisions which cause its neighbors to be set in motion (within a molecule this is a 'vibrational excitation' which can also lead to dissociation). The sequence of events leading to stopping, referred to as a collision cascade (IV.1), is well described <u>analytically</u>[2,3] when the environment (here atoms in the molecule) is composed of roughly identical atoms. Even though the analytic expression only approximately describe the situation for which the atoms are not identical, it is useful for estimating the dissipation of E_o, the hot atom energy. When $E_o >> U$, the average cohesive energy of the atoms in the material, <u>and</u> when binary collisions dominate, it is straightforward to show that the number of struck atoms (recoils) having energy between E and E +dE is $[(\beta\nu(E_o)/E^2)\ dE]$[2,3] (see also IV.1). Here β is roughly a constant ($\beta \approx 6/\pi^2$ for an exponential interaction[2]) and $\nu(E_o)$ is the energy lost collisionally (for Cr at these energies, $\nu(E_o) \approx E_o$). Recent molecular dynamics calculations show these expressions roughly apply even <u>when the collisions are not binary</u>[7]. This expression is then helpful in estimating damage to the molecular environment.

Before calculating retention of the energized atom, <u>the loss of material</u> from an isolated molecule containing the Cr is first described. Fig.4 shows the yield (number of atoms ejected from the 'surface' per energized atom) multiplied by U from an amorphous or crystalline atomic solid vs. depth of the energized atom into the sample, Y(z), given as Y_{ave} (an average value). Molecular calculations were carried out for atomic and molecular samples using van der Waals interactions for the pair potentials. The integrated yield, $\Delta\bar{z} = \int Y(z)dz$ [3,8], is an effective length which can be written as $\Delta\bar{z} \approx c\ [\ell\ (E_o - U)/U]$ for $E_o >> U$ where ℓ is the mean spacing between atoms and c is a number (~0.15) which can be obtained from the recoil spectra above or from molecular dynamics simulations [7,8,9]. It is also observed in performing such

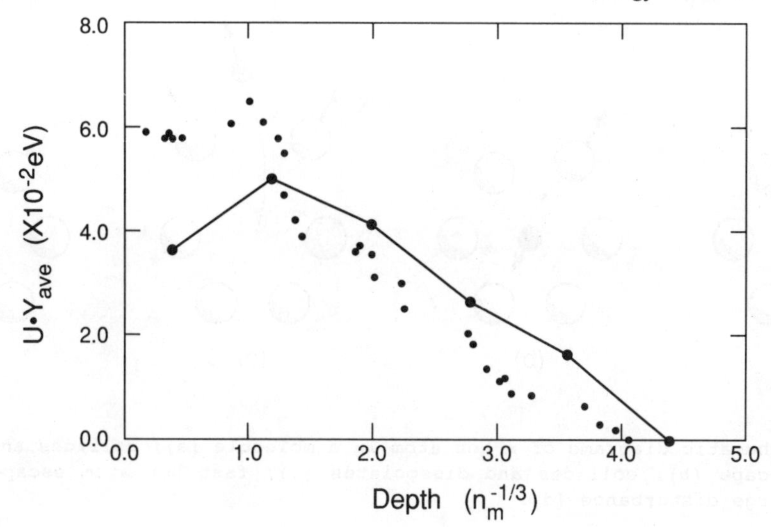

Fig.4 Average sputtering yield times the cohesive energy, U, in amorphous solid argon (dots) and crystalline solid Ar (line) for a hot argon atom produced with energy ($E_o/U \approx 13$) at a depth in number of monolayers ($n_m^{-1/3}$) $\approx 3.3 \times 10^{-8}$ cm. (from ref. 7).

simulations that if the net molecular cohesive energy is small compared to E_o then, even if ejection does not occur, 'the' hot sample can decay by 'boiling' atoms off the 'surface' at later times: i.e., $E_o > NU$ where N is the number of atoms in the molecule and U is the average cohesive energy per atom (i.e. the enthalpy for dissociation). It is found, therefore, that for the low energies retention is high, although molecular dissociation may eventually occur. When large molecules, with energized metal atoms, <u>are imbedded in a solid</u> then the late loss of species due to sputtering and thermal decay is reduced enormously due to energy transfer (cooling) to neighboring molecules. This transfer can be roughly described using energy diffusion with a diffusivity $\kappa \approx \sigma_d \bar{v}^{3)}$, where the mean local energy per atom $E \approx m\bar{v}^2/2$, and m is the atomic mass.

3. Escape (Non-retention)

Of greater interest for retention is the dissipation of forward momentum (IV.3). If an atom is energized on the 'surface' of the solid, or of a large molecule, and its momentum is directed 'outward' it may be deflected by neighbors when it tries to exit, but it needs only overcome its binding energy to the solid in order to escape. However, from the interior of a large molecule (e.g. Fig. 5) it can only escape if it retains its forward momentum as in Fig. 5c and d. This can occur if it interacts very weakly with the outer (surface) atoms, Fig. 5d, as is the case for very small σ_d at high E_o. It can <u>also</u> escape if it collides in such a way that it ejects these outer atoms <u>and</u> retains sufficient momentum to escape as in Fig. 5c (e.g. large metal atom in an molecule). Finally, a hot atom produced below the 'surface' can be efficient

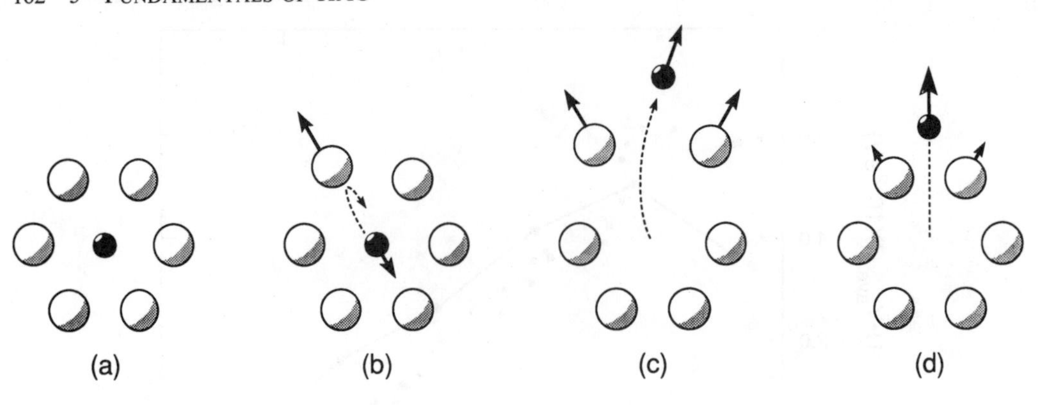

Fig.5 Schematic diagrams of a hot atom in a molecule (a); collides and does not escape (b); collides and dissociates (c); fast hot atom escapes without large disturbance (d).

at ejecting 'surface' atoms as in Fig. 5b, losing its momentum. In such a case the molecule may either dissociate completely, as discussed, 'releasing' the initially hot atom, or remaining vibrationally hot. Ignoring these possibilities, we deal with only 'primary retention' (e.g. 4 .3) and, therefore, will determine the probability of escape (non-retention). (Note: since neighboring molecules can produce a 'cage-effect' (4 .3) we assume escape means it travels sufficiently far away that recombination is unlikely.)

The projected ranges shown in Fig. 6 (i.e., the mean distance traveled, projected along the initial direction, $\bar{R}_p$) can be used to estimate retention. These are given for energized Cr and H atoms stopping in condensed H_2O. However, these distances roughly scale with the density of the material, $\rho = mn_m$, with m the average atomic mass and n_m the atomic density, and are, of course, seen to increase with increasing energy. An important related quantity is the range straggling [4], the spread in the probability of the penetration distance, which is seen in Fig. 6 to be comparable to the projected range at the lower energies. For low energy particles and large deflections the mean range for particles of roughly equal mass is $\bar{R}_p \approx 3.2/(n_m \sigma_d)$ [2]. That is, the energized particle comes to rest close to its point of origin but 'rattles around' a lot before stopping.

The mean range and the range straggling can be used to estimate retention. If we define the probability of having a projected range between R_p and $R_p + dR_p$ as (dP/dR_p), then the retention probability in a roughly spherical molecule of average radius R_m can be defined as

$$P_r(R_m) \approx \int^{R_m} (dP/dR_p)\, dR_p \quad . \tag{2}$$

Using only two parameters (i.e. mean projected range, $\bar{R}_p$, and straggling $\Delta\bar{R}_p$) one can approximate

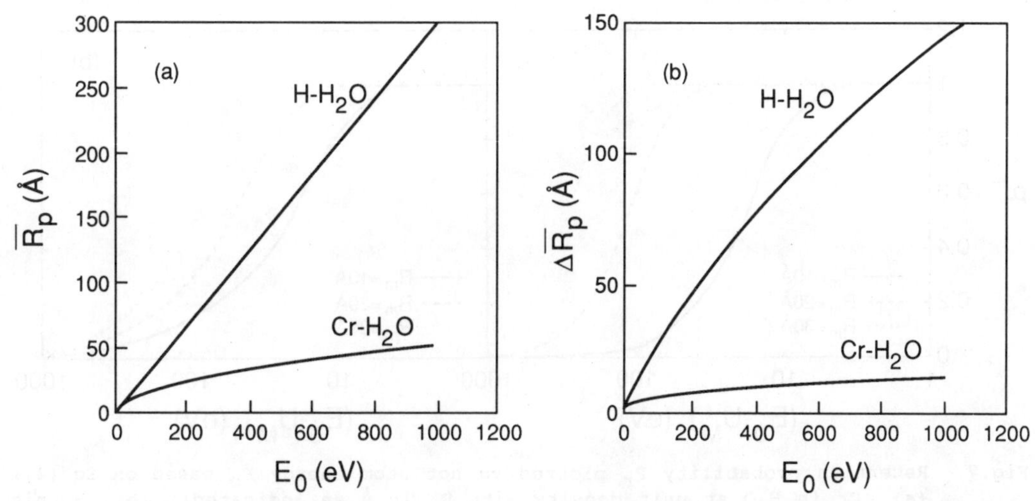

Fig.6 (a) Mean projected range $\bar{R}_p$ vs E_o, hot atom energy; (b) range straggling, $\overline{\Delta R}_p$ vs E_o.

$$(dP/dR_p) \approx \exp\left[-(R_p - \bar{R}_p)^2 / 2\Delta\bar{R}_p^2\right] / (2\pi\Delta\bar{R}_p^2)^{1/2} \tag{3}$$

if $\bar{R}_p >> \overline{\Delta R}_p$. [This integrates to one if we extend R_p to negative values which implies that particles can backscatter.] Assuming Eq.3 holds (and extending the integral in Eq. 2 to negative values) then

$$P_r \approx \{\mathrm{erf}\left[(R_m - \bar{R}_p)/(2\Delta\bar{R}_p^2)^{1/2}\right] + \mathrm{erf}\left[(R_m + \bar{R}_p)/(2\Delta\bar{R}_p^2)^{1/2}\right]\}/2 \tag{4}$$

where erf is the error function

$$\mathrm{erf}(x) \equiv \left[2\int_o^x \exp(-y^2)\, dy/\pi^{1/2}\right] .$$

P_r, calculated as in Eq. 4, is plotted versus (E_o-U_M) in Fig. 7 for hot atoms Cr and H imbedded in a large molecule made up of many H_2O molecules. This is done for three values of the average molecular radius R_m, where U_M is the average attachment energy of the hot atom to the molecule. Since the relative size of the straggling for Cr is somewhat smaller than that for H, the transition from retention to non-retention is somewhat sharper. For a hot Cr atom a simplified estimate can be made assuming that both $\overline{\Delta R}_p$ and the deflections are small: i.e., $(dE/dx) \approx c\,\rho E^{1/2}$. That is, stopping is related to the mass density of the material, so that $R_p \approx 2E_o^{1/2}/c\rho$. For such a case Eq.3 is sharply peaked so that P_r is approximated by a step function, $P_r \approx \theta(R_m-\bar{R}_p)$, where $\theta(x) = 1$, $x>o$, $\theta(x) = o$, $x<o$. This is one form used by Matsuura and Sasaki[10]. That is, Eq. 4 is replaced by θ. This function depends on the quantity

$$\bar{R}_p/R_m \approx 2\, E_o^{1/2} / (c\rho R_m). \tag{5}$$

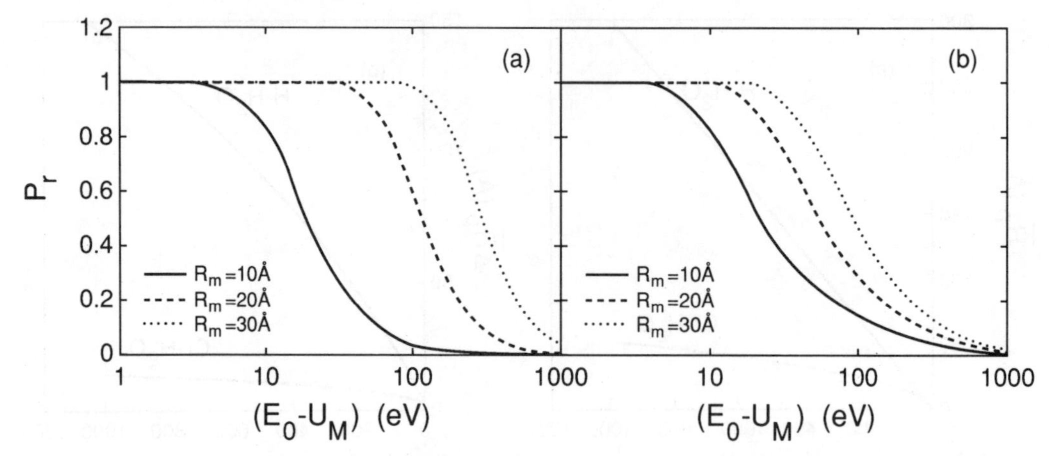

Fig.7 Retention probability P_r plotted vs hot atom energy E_o based on Eq (4): (a) Cr in H_2O at unit density with R_m in Å as indicated; (b) H unit density with R_m in Å as indicated.

where $(R_m\rho)$ is the mass per unit area along a path through the molecule. We plot in Fig. 8 the results shown in Fig. 7a for Cr in H_2O vs the quantity $[(E_o-U_M)^{1/2}/(\rho R_m)]$ where U_M is the attachment energy of the energized (hot) atom to the molecule. It is seen that the curves are now roughly the same. Inelastic effects are included implicitly as both S_e and S_n are used to obtain $\bar{R}_p$ and the kinetic energy of interest is the amount above U_M, the binding energy of Cr to the molecule. However, binding among the other atoms in the molecule is ignored in such a calculation.

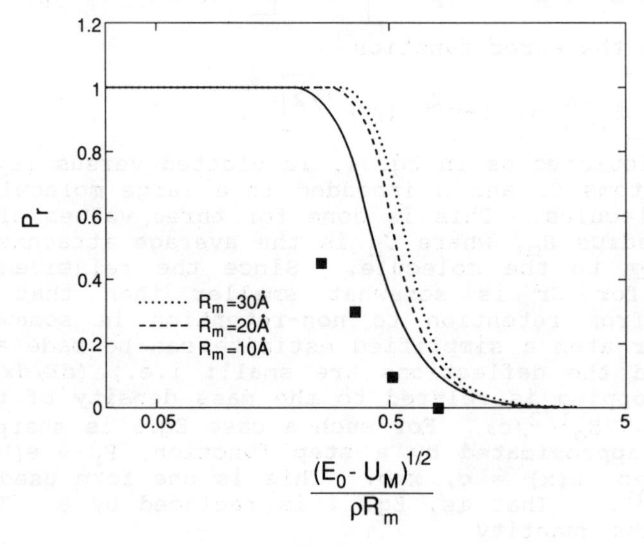

Fig.8 Average retention probability from Fig. 7a plotted vs $[(E_o-U_M(^{1/2}/\rho R_m]$ with ρ = 1 gm/cm^3. Squares: results from molecular dynamics calculations (see text).

As a comparison to the above we have carried out a molecular dynamics (MD) calculation for the retention of Cr in a roughly spherical sample of $R_m \approx 6.5Å$, made up of 31 diatomic molecules bound to each other by Lennard-Jones pair potentials. We used, for convenience, O_2 molecules which we had used in earlier calculations[9], giving $\rho R_m \approx 9 \times 10^{-8}$ gm/cm^2 for the surrounding material. The atom is given a velocity corresponding to E_o in random directions. Twenty directions are chosen for each energy and the position and direction of motion of the energized Cr atom are noted after 1 ps. We found that for $(E_o - U_M) = 5$eV, $P_r = 0.45$; for 10 eV, $P_r = 0.3$ for 20 eV, $P_r = 0.1$; and for 50 eV, $P_r = 0$. The pair interactions in the MD program are van der Waals with a narrower repulsive wall than that used in the analytic expression for S_n. This accounts for part of the shift to lower values for the MD result in Fig. 8. In addition, in the small amorphous cluster created there are paths of escape without much blockage by the O_2 reducing P_r somewhat. Finally, using R_p to calculate P_r allows a particle to 'escape' (i.e. achieve $R > R_p$) and return by a collision with an atom on a neighboring molecule, increasing P_r slightly. For the molecular dynamics calculation using a finite sample this can not occur. In spite of these differences, the sense of the effect is the same. Increasing the intermolecular binding in the molecular dynamics calculation would also shift the effect to lower values of $[(E_o - U_M)^{\frac{1}{2}}/\rho R_m]$. In this way the drop in P_r is indicative of the binding forces and, therefore, of the interaction potentials.

For a molecule which is close to planar, escape occurs easily if the Cr has a significant velocity component perpendicular to the plane. As a rough estimate, we assume escape occurs by penetration of the ligands for angles between θ_M and $\pi/2$, where θ is measured from the normal to the plane. For $\theta < \theta_M$ we assume escape always occurs. A rough value for P_r in this case is obtained by multiplying the expression in Eq. 4 by $\cos\theta_M$. In the above examples the effect of neighboring molecules in the solid or liquid, which helps increase retention, is either ignored or treated very roughly, as discussed.

4. Conclusions

Many of the well known energy transfer expressions used in the study of particle penetration and sputtering (5. 9) can be applied to aspects of energy transfer in the retention of hot atoms in a molecule. Here we have considered the energy transfer from a hot atom to atoms of the ligands of a large organic molecule. We used a simple analytic model along with calculated projected ranges to describe retention. These results are compared to results obtained from a molecular dynamics calculation of a Cr in a small cluster of O_2 molecules. The general trend is seen in Fig. 8 to be the same, with the molecular dynamics results for the case chosen yielding slightly smaller values of P_r at the same scaled initial velocity, as discussed. In this, the role of the material binding occurs primarily in the energy required to remove the metal atom (U_M) with, as is the case also for sputtering, the binding between other species in the sample having a small effect except at very low energies (i.e. near the 'threshold' for escape). Molecular dynamics calculations present an attractive means of calculating expectations for hot-atom retention. This procedure lends itself well to having a molecule containing a hot atom surrounded by other molecules.

Acknowledgement

This work is supported by grants from the Astronomy Division and the Division of Materials of the U.S. National Science Foundation.

References

1. e.g. Matsuura. T., "Hot Atom Chemistry" (Kodansha, Tokyo, and Elsevir, Amsterdam) (1984).
2. e.g. Sigmund, P. in "Sputtering by Particle Bombardment I" (ed. H. Berisch) (Springer-Verlag, Berlin) 9-72 (1981).
3. e.g. Johnson, R.E. "Introduction to Atomic Collisions" (Plenum, N.Y.) (1982); "Energetic Charged-Particle Interactions with Atmospheres and Surfaces" (Springer-Verlag, Berlin) (1990).
4. Zeigler, J.F., Biersack, J.P., Littmark, U. "The Stopping and Range of Ions in Solids" (Pergamon Press, N.Y.) (1985).
5. Lindhard, J. Scharff, M., Phys. Rev 124, 128 (1961).
6. Torrens, I.M., Interatomic Potentials (Academic Press, N.Y.) (1972).
7. Cui, S.T., Johnson, R.E., Cummings, P.T., Surf. Sci 20, 186 (1985); 222, 491 (1984).
8. Johnson, R.E., Brown, W.L., Nucl. Instr. Meth 198, 103 (1982).
9. Banerjee, S., Liu, M., Johnson, R.E., Surf. Sci. Lett. 255, L504 (1991).
10. Matsuura, T., Takenawa, H., Suzuki, T., Hirota, R., Sasaki, K.: J. Radioanal. Nucl. Chem. Lett., 146, 223 (1990).

3.3 Collisional De-excitation of Excited Rare Gas Atoms in the Metastable and Resonant States

Yoshihiko HATANO
Department of Chemistry, Tokyo Institute of Technology, Meguro-ku, Tokyo 152, Japan

1. Introduction

There have been remarkable advances in recent investigations of the collisional de-excitation of excited rare gas atoms both in the metastable and resonant states.[1-8] This process is of great importance in fundamental and applied chemical physics, and has been studied experimentally using W-value methods, static afterglow methods, flowing afterglow methods, beam methods, and pulse radiolysis methods. Comparative discussions of the methods, as shown in Table 1, have indicated that the pulse radiolysis method is superior,[2,4,5,6,8] as was first demonstrated by Ueno and Hatano,[9] for determining absolute rate constants or cross sections. Recent advances in the experimental investigation, in particular by means of pulse radiolysis methods, will be discussed and compared with theoretical ones.

2. De-excitation of $He(2^3S)$ and $Ne(^3P_0, {}^3P_1$, and $^3P_2)$

The de-excitation rate constants of $He(2^3S)$ and $Ne(^3P_0$, $^3P_1$, and $^3P_2)$ by various atoms and molecules were obtained at room temperature using a pulse radiolysis method combined with nanosecond time-resolved spectroscopy.[9-12] An attempt has been made to correlate the obtained rate constant values with various molecular parameters such as ionization potentials and polarizabilities. A relatively good correlation has been obtained[10] for $He(2^3S)$, as shown in Fig.1, between the de-excitation probability $P(=k_M/k_C)$ and the excess energy ΔE $[=E(He^*)-IP_M]$, where $k_M, k_C, E(He^*)$, and IP_M are the experimental rate constant, the calculated gas kinetic collision rate constant, the excitation energy of $He(2^3S)$, and the ionization potential of the target atom or molecule M, respectively. However, the reason for the correlation is not yet well understood.

A similar experiment has been made for the de-excitation of Ne($^3P_0$, $^3P_1$, and $^3P_2$) by atoms and molecules.[11,12] Two new features of the results obtained have been demonstrated in this experiment. One is the J-dependent de-excitation cross sections, the other is a comparison between a theory of the de-excitation of the optically allowed resonant state and the experimental result for Ne($^3P_1$) which is partly allowed because of a weak spin-orbit coupling.

Table 1. Comparison of the Experimental Methods[6]

Method	Advantages	Disadvantages
Static afterglow	Suitable for determining absolute rate constants	Effects of metastable species Effects of diffusion processes Low time resolution
Flowing afterglow	Suitable for determining absolute rate constants Easy to study spectroscopy	Assumptions of various parameters in gas fluid dynamics Disturbance of flow by the addition of quenchers
Beam	Direct observation of the reaction Energy dependence and angular correlation of the reaction, leading to interaction potentials	Difficulty in determining absolute cross sections Difficulty in measuring low energy collisions Difficulty in measuring collisions of short lifetime species
Pulse radiolysis	Suitable for determining absolute rate constants Energy dependence of cross section obtained from the temp. dep. of rate const. High time resolution Easy data analysis	Care needed in specifying the reaction Care needed in choosing experimental conditions Operation and maintenance of accelerators Radiation safety control

A pulse radiolysis method has the great advantage of obtaining not only absolute de-excitation rate constants or cross sections but also their collisional energy dependence. A velocity averaged absolute cross section, σ_M, is obtained as a function of mean collisional energy, E, from the temperature dependence of an absolute rate constant. Recently, the temperature dependence of the rate constants for the de-excitation of He(2^3S) by atoms and molecules has been measured from 133 to 300 K.[13] According to the theory of Penning ionization,[1] the collisional energy dependence of its cross section is given, if the interaction potential $V^*(R)$ for $He(2^3S)-M$ and the autoionization rate $\Gamma(R)/h$ from $He(2^3S)-M$ to $He-(M^++e^-)$ are available, by the following simple equation:

$$\sigma_T \propto E^{\alpha/\beta-1/2} \quad \text{or} \quad k(T) \propto T^{\alpha/\beta} \qquad (1)$$

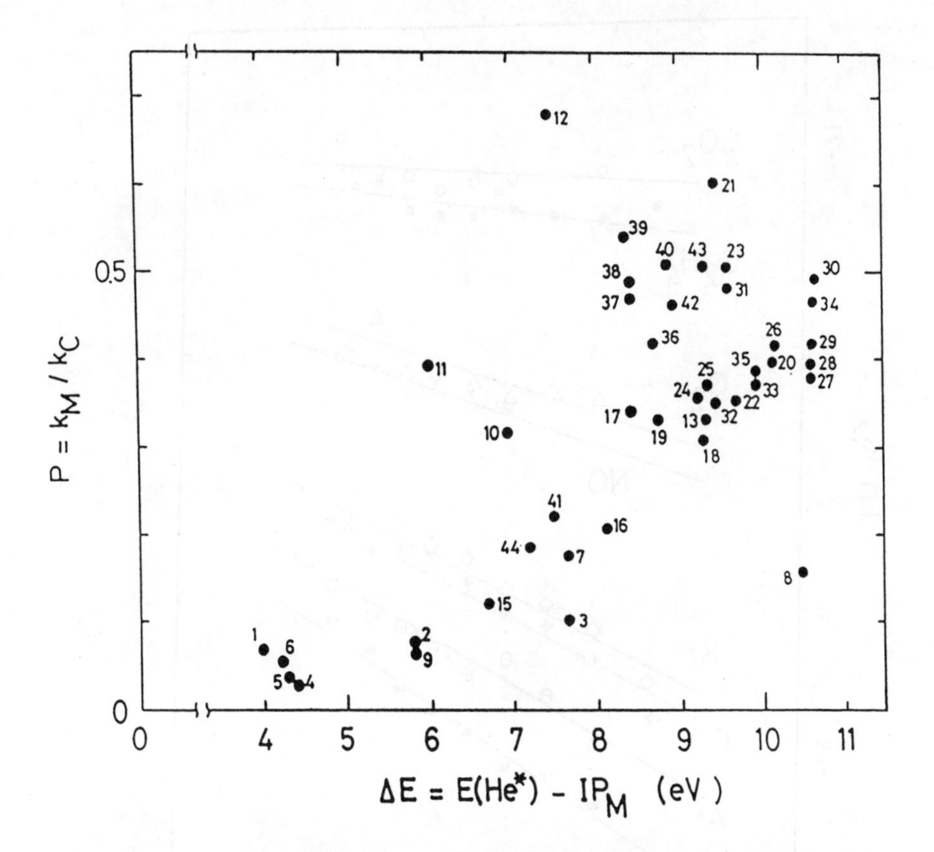

Fig.1 Correlation between the de-excitation probability, P, and the energy difference, Δ E, between the excitation energy of $He(2^3S)$ and the first ionization potentials of M.[10]
The numbers in the figure refer to atoms or molecules M as follows.
(1) Ar, (2) Kr, (3) Xe, (4) H_2, (5) D_2, (6) N_2, (7) O_2, (8) NO, (9) CO, (10) N_2O, (11) CO_2, (12) SO_2, (13) NH_3, (14) SF_6, (15) CH_4, (16) C_2H_6, (17) C_2H_2, (18) C_2H_4, (19) C_3H_8, (20) C_3H_6, (21) $CH_3C{\equiv}CH$, (22) cyclo-C_3H_6, (23) $H_2C{=}C{=}CH_2$, (24) n-C_4H_{10}, (25) iso-C_4H_{10}, (26) C_4H_8-1, (27) iso-C_4H_8, (28) trans-C_4H_8-2, (29) cis-C_4H_8-2, (30) $H_2C{=}CH{-}CH{=}CH_2$, (31) $C_2H_5C{\equiv}CH$, (32) neo-C_5H_{12}, (33) cyclo-C_6H_{12}, (34) C_6H_6, (35) n-C_7H_{16}, (36) CH_3Cl, (37) CH_2Cl_2, (38) $CHCl_3$, (39) CCl_4, (40) C_2H_5Cl, (41) CCl_2F_2, (42) CH_3OH, (43) C_2H_5OH, (44) H_2O, (45) D_2O.

where σ_T and k(T) are the total Penning ionization cross section and the corresponding rate constant, respectively, and Γ (R) and V*(R) are empirically represented as

$$\Gamma(R) = A\exp(-\alpha R), \tag{2}$$
$$V^*(R) = B\exp(-\beta R), \tag{3}$$

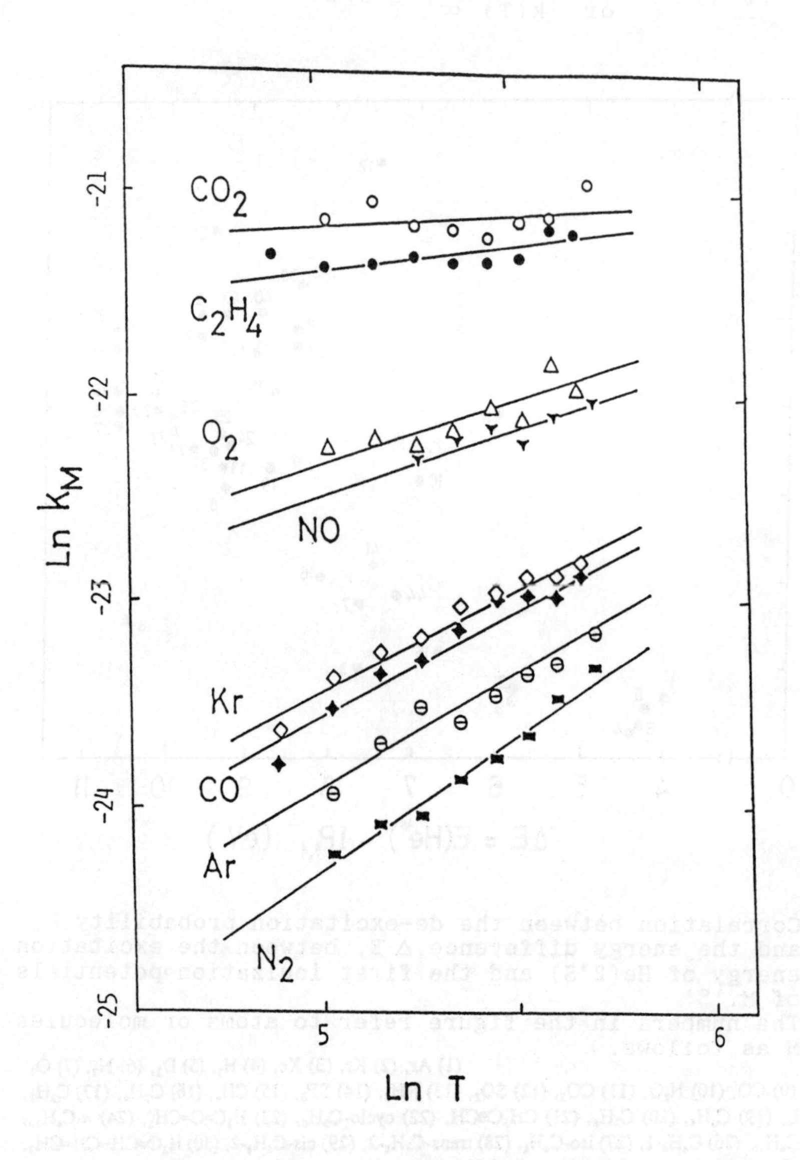

Fig.2 Log-log plot of the de-excitation rate constants vs. temperature.[13]

where A, B, α, and β are constants and R is an intermolecular distance between $He(2^3S)$ and M. According to Eq.(1), the slope of log-log plots of k(T) vs T gives, as shown in Fig.2, the values of α/β.[13] For all the molecules M listed in Table 2 the α/β value increases with decreasing P. Since β is about the same for all M, Table 2 shows clearly that the larger α, i.e., the shorter range the interaction between $He(2^3S)$ and M, the smaller P, i.e., the less efficient energy transfer from $He(2^3S)$ to M.[13] This conclusion is compatible with the exterior electron density model of Ohno et al.[14]

In conclusion the measurement of absolute de-excitation rate constants as a function of temperature using pulse radiolysis methods has clarified the detailed microscopic mechanism of the de-excitation process and led to an interpretation of the difference in the magnitude of observed rate constants with target molecules M and temperature.

Table 2. Values of α/β and P [13]

	α/β	P
N_2	1.4	0.05
CO	1.1	0.07
Ar	1.0	0.07
Kr	1.0	0.07
NO	0.6	0.16
O_2	0.6	0.18
C_2H_4	0.3	0.31
CO_2	0.1	0.39

3. De-excitation of $He(2^1P)$, $Ar(^1P_1)$, and $Ar(^3P_1)$

The de-excitation of the resonant state of rare gas atoms has been less studied than that of the metastable state because of experimental difficulties owing to the short lifetime of the resonant state.[15-20] There have been reported, however, several theoretical formulations based on a long-range dipole-dipole interaction for the de-excitation cross section of the radiative atoms.[21,22] It has been, therefore, necessary to compare the theory with the experimental results of the resonant or lowest radiative state atoms. It has been reported recently[15,16,18] that the collisional energy dependence of the de-excitation cross sections of $He(2^1P)$, $Ar(^1P_1)$, and $Ar(^3P_1)$ by atoms and molecules by using a pulse radiolysis method which has the great advantage of obtaining the absolute values of the de-excitation cross sections of the resonant atoms as well as the metastable states. The experimental technique is almost the same as for the metastable states

A comparison,[18] shown in Fig.3, between the experimental result of the collisional energy dependence of the de-excitation cross section of $He(2^1P)$ by Ar and the theoretical ones calculated from the W-K theory[21] and the K-W theory[22] makes it clearly possible for the first time to compare in detail the experimental results with the theoretical ones. Previous comparisons between experiments and theories have been made only for one value of the rate

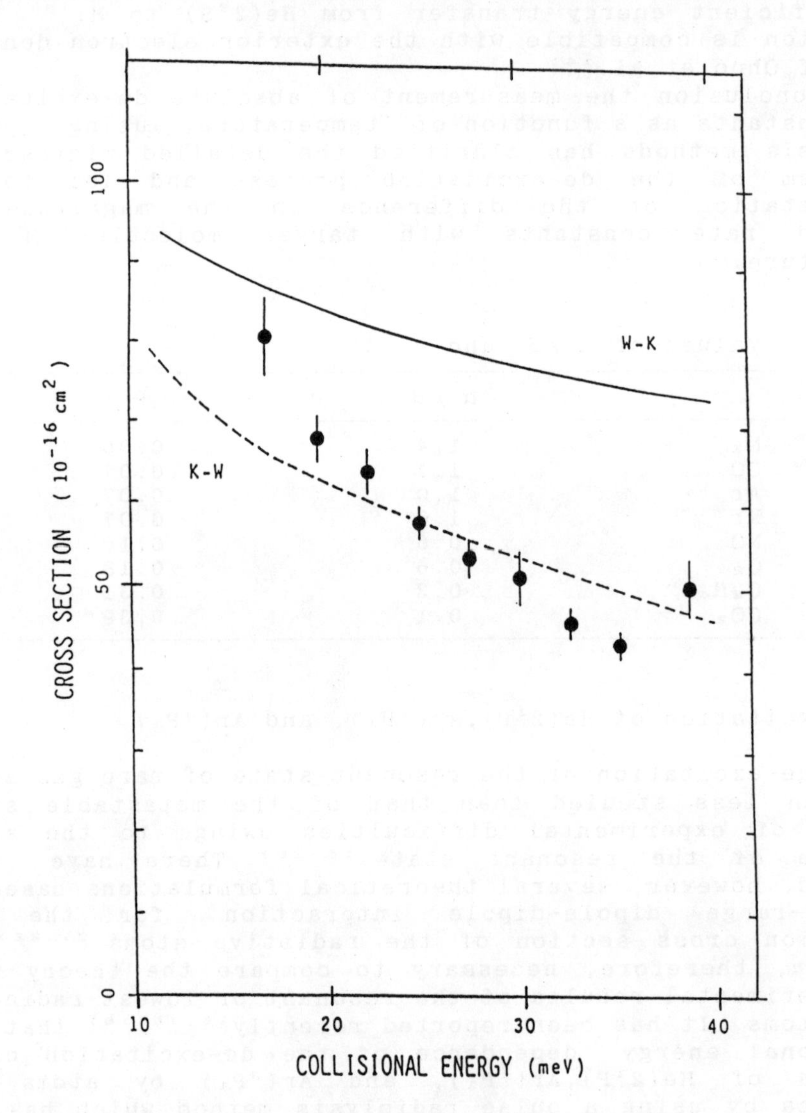

Fig.3 Collisional energy dependence of the de-excitation cross section of $He(2^1P)$ by Ar; (●) experiment; (—) W-K theory; (--) K-W theory.[18]

constant or the cross section, at a particular temperature, usually room temperature, or collisional energy, respectively. The present experimental results can discriminate between different theories and supports a modified new theory, the K-W theory, in which a bent trajectory, instead of the straight trajectory simply assumed in the W-K theory, is taken into consideration.

The collisional energy dependence of the de-excitation cross sections by Kr and Xe has also been obtained using a pulse radiolysis method.[18] The experimental results for Ar, Kr and Xe have been systematically compared in detail with theoretical calculations. The de-excitation cross sections of $He(2^1P)$ by other atoms and molecules have also been obtained and compared with Penning ionization cross sections calculated by the theory of a long-range dipole-dipole interaction.[17] It is concluded that an electron exchange process makes an important contribution to the total de-excitation mechanism even in the case of a resonant atom of $He(2^1P)$. Instead of the simple theories of W-K and K-W, a new theoretical calculation has been presented[19] to explain the experimental cross sections obtained and their collisional energy dependence. The new theory is based mainly on a long range dipole-dipole interaction between $He(2^1P)$ and M but partly on electron exchange between them. The calculation uses an impact parameter method including an anisotropic effect in the trajectory and a reported real interaction potential between $He(2^1P)$ and M dependent on M at its repulsive part, in addition to a dipole-dipole interaction potential at its longer interaction ranges.

It is also a fact that very few studies have been reported on simple excitation transfer, in which Penning ionization is energetically impossible, from resonant rare gas atoms to the atoms and molecules. The temperature dependence of the de-excitation rate constants of the resonant states of Ar, $^1P_1$ and $^3P_1$, by SF6 and N_2 has been measured in the temperature range from 133 to 300 K using a pulse radiolysis method, thus obtaining the collisional energy dependence of the de-excitation cross sections.[15] The results of the cross sections for SF6 are compared with the W-K theory and good agreement is obtained. The results for N_2 agree with predictions of the cross sections for a nonresonant case. Even in the case of the de-excitation of the resonant state, such as $Ar(^1P_1)$ or $Ar(^3P_1)$, the cross section value and its collisional energy dependence are very similar to those for the metastable state, i.e., $Ar(^3P_0)$ or $Ar(^3P_2)$. This result is again compatible with the W-K theory because N_2 has almost no optical absorption in the energy region corresponding to the excitation energy of $Ar(^1P_1)$ and $Ar(^3P_1)$. It is concluded, therefore, that a long-range dipole-dipole interaction is important in the de-excitation processes of $Ar(^1P_1)$ and $Ar(^3P_1)$ by SF_6, but that a short-range interaction with curve crossing dominates in the de-excitation of $Ar(^1P_1)$ and $Ar(^3P_1)$ by N_2.

4. De-excitation of He(2^3S,2^1S, and 2^1P) and Ar($^3P_0$,$^3P_1$,$^3P_2$, and $^1P_1$) by Group-IV Hydride Molecules

The de-excitation of excited rare-gas atoms by group-IV hydrides is of particular importance in both basic and applied chemical physics studies. In basic studies, a systematic comparison of the de-excitation cross sections for different group-IV hydride compounds is greatly needed to understand the de-excitation mechanism, while in applied studies, the need for the absolute cross-section values has become pressing in order to model the reactive plasmas of group-IV compounds.

A pulse radiolysis method has been recently applied [20,23] to the measurement of the cross sections for the de-excitation of He(2^3S), He(2^1S) and He(2^1P) by CH_4, SiH_4 and GeH_4 and also of Ar($^3P_0$),Ar($^3P_2$),Ar($^3P_1$), and Ar($^1P_1$) by CH_4,SiH_4, and GeH_4. The cross section values obtained which are largely dependent on both the electronic states of rare gas atoms and the target molecules have been compared with the above-mentioned theories for the de-excitation of metastable and resonant states to obtain some regularities of cross section values correlating with some fundamental parameters of the target molecules, such as ionization potential and polarizability. The de-excitation cross section values obtained have been compared also with reported cross sections for product formation which are mainly obtained by optical emission or LIF spectroscopy. The former cross section values are found to be much larger than the latter ones, indicating that most of the products still remain unobserved.

Such comparison has clarified the de-excitation mechanism for each He*(or Ar*)-M system.

References

1. Niehaus,A.: Adv.Chem.Phys.,45,399(1981);"Physics of Electronic and Atomic collisions",(S.Datz, Ed.) North Holland(1982),p.237.
2. Hatano,Y.: "Current status of destruction rate constant measurements involving electronically excited species", in 3rd Int.Symp.Dynamics Mol. Collsions,Kaiserslautern, 1983, (unpublished).
3. Yencha,A.J.: "Electron Spectroscopy-Theory,Techniques, and Applications-," Vol.5,(C.R.Brundle and A.D.Baker, Ed.) Academic(1984),p.197.
4. Hatano,Y.: "Proceedings of 19th Int.Conf.on Phenomena in Ionized Gases, Invited Papers,Belgrade,1989," (V.J.Zigman, Ed.) Univ.Belgrade Press(1989),p.242.
5. Hatano,Y.: Radiat.Phys.Chem.,34,675(1989).
6. Hatano,Y.: "Pulse Radiolysis,"(Y,Tabata,Ed.) CRS Press (1991),p.199.
7. Hitachi,A., Ukai,M., Hatano,Y.: "Handbook of Radiation Chemistry" (Y.Tabata,Y.Ito, and S.Tagawa, Ed.) CRC Press(1991),P.223.

8. Ukai,M., Hatano,Y.: "Gaseous Electronics and Its Applications,"(M.Hayashi, R.Crompton, T.Makabe, and D.Boyd, Ed.) Kruwer Academy,in press.
9. Ueno,T., Hatano,Y.: Chem.Phys.Lett.,40,283(1976).
10. Ueno,T., Yokoyama,A., Takao,S., Hatano,Y.: Chem.Phys., 45,261(1980).
11. Yokoyama,A., Takao,S., Ueno,T., Hatano,Y.: Chem.Phys., 45,439(1980).
12. Yokoyama,A., Hatano,Y.: Chem.Phys.,63,59(1981).
13. Koizumi,H.,Ukai,M.,Tanaka,Y.,Shinsaka,K.,Hatano,Y.: J.Chem.Phys.,85,1931(1986).
14. Ohno,K., Matsumoto,S., Harada,Y.: J.Chem.Phys.,81,4447 (1984).
15. Ukai,M., Koizumi,H., Shinsaka,K., Hatano,Y.: J.Chem. Phys.,84,3199(1986).
16. Ukai,M., Koizumi,H., Shinsaka,K., Hatano,Y.: J.Chem. Phys.,84,5575(1986).
17. Ukai,M., Nakazawa,H., Shinsaka,K., Hatano,Y.: J.Chem. Phys.,88,3263(1988).
18. Ukai,M., Yoshida,H., Morishima,Y., Nakazawa,H., Shinsaka,K., Hatano,Y.: J.Chem.Phys.,90,4865(1989).
19. Morishima,Y., Yoshida,H., Ukai,M., Shinsaka,K., Kouchi,N., Hatano,Y.: J.Chem.Phys.,94,2564(1991).
20. Yoshida,H., Morishima,Y., Ukai,M., Shinsaka,K., Kouchi,N., Hatano,Y.: Chem.Phys Lett.,176,173(1991).
21. Watanabe,T., Katsuura,K.: J.Chem.Phys.,47,800(1967).
22. Kohmoto,M., Watanabe,T.: J.Phys.Soc.Jpn.,42,246(1977).
23. Yoshida,H., Kawamura,H., Ukai,M., Kouchi,N., Hatano,Y: J.Chem.Phys., to be published.

3.4 Stereo Organic Hot Atom Chemistry

Richard A. FERRIERI and Alfred P. WOLF
Department of Chemistry, Brookhaven National Laboratory, Upton, New York 11973, U.S.A.

and

Edward P. RACK
Department of Chemistry, University of Nebraska-Lincoln, Lincoln, Nebraska 68588-0304 and Medical Research, Department of Veterans Affairs Medical Center, Omaha, Nebraska 68105, U.S.A.

1. Introduction

The mainstay of organic hot atom chemistry since its early beginnings has involved a technique of irradiating incapsulated reaction systems containing the recoil atom precursor, target compound, and any additional substances such as radical scavengers and kinetic energy moderators which could alter the state of the reactive species. While extrinsic properties such as organic and individual product yields have been readily measured, intrinsic properties inferred and new reaction channels (both exo- and endoergic) observed and characterized by this technique, no definitive answer may be given to the mechanistically important question in recoil atom chemistry; that is, retention versus inversion of configuration in homolytic substitution ($S_{HH}2$)

$$X_i^* + RX_j \xrightarrow{X_i \ for \ X_j} RX_i^* + X_j$$

by recoil atoms at sp^3-hybridized carbon. However, stereoorganic hot atom chemistry can provide insight into the dynamics of hot-atom substitution reactions.

1.1. Stereochemical Consequences of Hot Atom Substitution Reactions in the Gas-Phase: Mechanistic Considerations

Numerous studies can be found in the literature which address the stereochemical consequences of gas-phase homolytic substitution ($S_{HH}2$) involving recoil atoms and target molecules possessing either multiple or single asymmetric carbon centers. This has been a popular subject for hot atom chemists to investigate over the years because resolving the finer details of what affects reaction stereochemistry can provide insight towards understanding the mechanistic aspects of these rather simple hot atom processes. In Table 1 a summary is presented of the results[1-4] from gas-phase studies on recoil tritium-for-hydrogen and recoil halogen-for-halogen[5-14] reactions.

Table 1. Previous Gas-Phase Recoil Tritium-for-Hydrogen and Halogen-for-Halogen Substitution Studies at Chiral Carbon Atoms

Reaction	Target Molecule	% Retention of Configuration	Ref.
T-for-H	p-2-butanol	90	1
T-for-H	L-2-butanol	95	1
T-for-H	*dl*-2,3-dichlorobutane	93	2
T-for-H	*meso*-2,3-dichlorobutane	80	2
T-for-H	*dl*-1,2-dichloro-1,2-difluoroethane	98	3
T-for-H	*meso*-1,2-dichloro-1,2-difluoroethane	99	3
T-for-H	*dl*-1,2-dichloro-1,2-difluoroethane	96	4
T-for-H	*meso*-1,2-dichloro-1,2-difluoroethane	96	4
^{18}F-for-F	*dl*-2,3-difluorobutane	80	5
^{18}F-for-F	*meso*-2,3-difluorobutane	81	5
^{18}F-for-F	*dl*-(2S,3R)-chlorofluorobutane	85	5
^{18}F-for-F	*dl*-(2S,3S)-chlorofluorobutane	81	5
^{18}F-for-F	*dl*-(2S,3R)-bromofluorobutane	76	5
^{18}F-for-F	*dl*-(2S,3S)-bromofluorobutane	78	5
^{18}F-for-F	2(S)-fluoropropionyl fluoride	71	6
18F-for-F	2(R)-fluoropropionyl fluoride	73	6
^{18}F-for-Cl	*dl*-1,2-dichloro-1,2-difluoroethane	90	7
^{18}F-for-Cl	*meso*-1,2-dichloro-1,2-difluoroethane	90	7
^{18}F-for-Cl	*dl*-(2S,3R)-chlorofluorobutane	79	5
^{18}F-for-Cl	*dl*-(2S,3S)-chlorofluorobutane	80	5
^{18}F-for-Cl	*dl*-2,3-dichlorobutane	77	5
^{18}F-for-Cl	*meso*-2,3-dichlorobutane	75	5
^{18}F-for-Cl	2(S)-chloropropionyl chloride	65	6
^{18}F-for-Br	2(S)-bromopropionyl bromide	61	6
^{18}F-for-Br	*dl*-(2S,3R)-bromofluorobutane	65	5
^{18}F-for-Br	*dl*-(2S,3S)-bromofluorobutane	78	5
^{38}Cl-for-F	*dl*-2,3-difluorobutane	91	9
^{38}Cl-for-F	*meso*-2,3-difluorobutane	93	9

^{38}Cl-for-F	*dl*-(2S,3R)-chlorofluorobutane	85	9
^{38}Cl-for-F	*dl*-(2S,3S)-chlorofluorobutane	75	9
^{34m}Cl-for-F	2(S)-fluoropropionyl fluoride	29	6
^{34m}Cl-for-F	2(S)-fluoropropionyl chloride	27	6
^{38}Cl-for-Cl	*dl*-1,2-dichloro-1,2-difluorobutane	91	4
^{38}Cl-for-Cl	*meso*-1,2-dichloro-1,2-difluorobutane	92	4
^{38}Cl-for-Cl	*dl*-2,3-dichlorobutane	93,79	9,10,11
^{38}Cl-for-Cl	*meso*-2,3-dichlorobutane	95,89	9,11
^{38}Cl-for-Cl	*dl*-(2S,3R)-chlorofluorobutane	85	9
^{38}Cl-for-Cl	*dl*-(2S,3S)-chlorofluorobutane	81	9
^{34m}Cl-for-Cl	2(S)-chloropropionyl fluoride	23	6
^{34m}Cl-for-Cl	2(S)-chloropropionyl chloride	19	8
^{34m}Cl-for-Cl	2(R)-chloropropionyl chloride	21	8
^{34m}Cl-for-Cl	2(R)-chloro-1-propanol	20	12
^{34m}Cl-for-Cl	2(S)-chloro-1-propanol	21	12
^{34m}Cl-for-Cl	2(S)-chloro-4-methylvaleryl chloride	59	12
^{75}Br-for-F	2(S)-fluoropropionyl fluoride	63	13
^{75}Br-for-F	2(R)-fluoropropionyl fluoride	67	13
^{75}Br-for-Cl	2(S)-chloropropionyl chloride	71	13
^{75}Br-for-Cl	2(R)-chloropropionyl chloride	75	13
^{80m}Br-for-Cl	*dl*-2,3-dichlorobutane	90	2
^{80}Br(IT)-for-Cl	*dl*-2,3-dichlorobutane	70	14
^{80}Br(IT)-for-Cl	*meso*-2,3-dichlorobutane	78	14
^{75}Br-for-Br	2(S)-bromopropionyl bromide	81	13
^{75}Br-for-Br	2(R)-bromopropionyl bromide	84	13
^{125}I(EC)-for-Cl	*dl*-2,3-dichlorobutane	64	14

The early tritium studies clearly showed that regardless of the nature of the target molecule, substitution always occured with predominant, if not exclusive, retention of configuration. These results seemed to correlate well with a direct impact model formulated to describe hot atom reactions. Accordingly, hot atom substitutions should be fast, direct and occur from the front-side of the target molecule.

Similiar behavior was observed in early work on halogen-for-halogen substitution in systems containing multiple asymmetric carbon sites. Noteworthy are the studies of Rowland and co-workers[7,10,11)] in *meso*- and *dl*-1,2-dichloro-1,2-difluoroethanes and in *meso*- and *dl*-

2,3-dichlorobutanes where similiar conclusions were drawn relative to the tritium experiments. However, these authors did point out that small yields of inversion products were always detected in these systems in amounts larger than could be accounted for simply through radiation effects, and that a genuine mechanism involving energetic substitution with inversion of configuration must be operative.

Additional studies carried out by Stöcklin and co-workers[4)] on ^{38}-Cl-for-Cl substitution in the diastereomeric dichlorodifluoroethanes led to a consideration of two possible models describing halogen atom substitutions: one involving direct replacement with retention of configuration, in accord with the earlier impact model proposed for tritium substitution; and an inertial model involving formation of a highly excited complex with a lifetime sufficient to allow for motion of the bound atoms or groups to permit inversion of configuration. The interesting dichotomy with this latter model is that while the internuclear motions within such a complex would most likely have activation barriers that could certainly be satisfied in a hot atom experiment of this nature, the lifetime of the complex in the gas phase would not be long enough to allow such motions to occur. In fact, this contention was consistent with Stöcklin's findings that while the yields of retention products were subject to changes in target pressure, the yields of inversion products were not. Of course, complex formation might be a viable pathway in liquid-phase experiments if solvent-cage effects could stabilize such a species.

A series of gas-phase studies carried out by Wolf, Rack, and co-workers[6,8,12,13)] on halogen-for-halogen substitution in molecules with single chiral centers were instrumental in changing researcher's attitudes regarding a distinct mechanism for inversion product formation. The striking feature in all of these latter studies was that not only were substantial amounts of inversion products observed but, in many instances, the inversion product yields were actually *greater* than that of the retention products. Noteworthy in this series, are the studies on ^{38}Cl and ^{34m}Cl-for-Cl substitution on 2(R) and 2(S)-chloropropionylchloride where 80% of the substitution products had inverted configurations. The authors noted that back-side approach to the chiral carbon site in 2-chloropropionyl chloride was far less sterically hindered than that for any of the rotational conformers of the 1,2-dichloro-1,2-difluoroethane diastereomers, and that this could account for the substantially higher degree of inversion here if different pathways for substitution, distinguished only by the approach of the displacing atom, were operative. The hypothesis that the degree of retention (or inversion) was strongly affected by steric factors was further tested by these authors using 2(S)-chloro-4-methylvaleryl chloride as the substrate, where the increased alkyl group size increased steric hindrance to back-side attack. The percent inversion dropped to 40% in this instance.

These authors also noted that stereochemistry was affected by the nature of the hot atom which was perhaps related to mass, size or polarizability of that atom. Figure 1 shows an example of this dependence for substitutions involving recoil ^{18}F, ^{34m}Cl and ^{75}Br atoms on 2(S)-chloropropionylchloride. By the same token, stereochemistry was affected by the nature of the leaving group. An example of this dependence is shown in Figure 2 for ^{75}Br-for-X (X=F,Cl,Br) substitutions in 2(S)-halopropionylhalide.

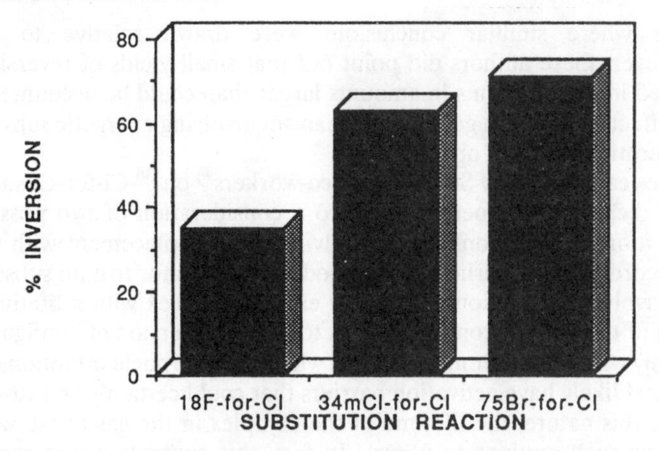

Fig. 1. Effect of hot atom nature on configuration interchange for substitutions on 2(S)-chloropropionyl chloride.

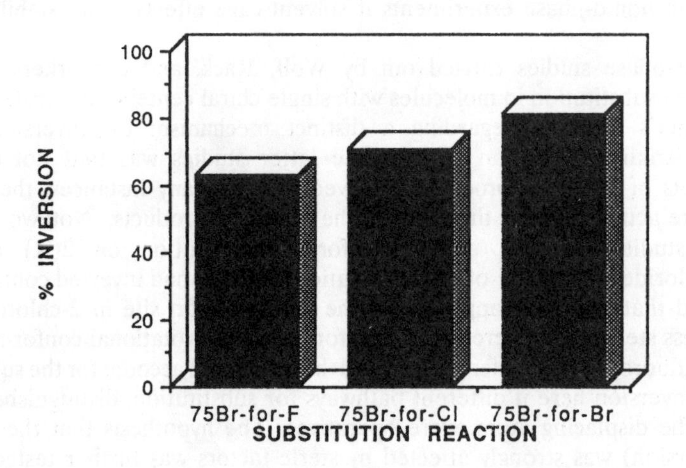

Fig. 2. Effect of displaced atom nature on configuration interchange for ^{75}Br atom substitutions on 2(S)-halopropionyl halides.

Of course, one might argue that such behavior, as noted above, could be due to a combination of effects that are not exclusively dependent on steric factors, namely point and direction of impact. Specifically, the decrease in inversion with increase in alkyl group size in 2(S)-chloro-4-methylvaleryl chloride could be due to inertial restrictions, where the ability of the target molecule to invert rapidly during the reactive collision is hampered because of these larger groups, and therefore, its ability to yield an inverted product are reduced. By the same token, changes in the nature of the atoms mutually involved in the bond making bond breaking process could have a similiar effect. The general obvious implications from all these results is that both the impact and inertial models, as they were described in the earlier works, do not have general validity in halogen hot atom chemistry. That is, not all hot atom substitutions are fast and direct involving front-side attack, but can be from the

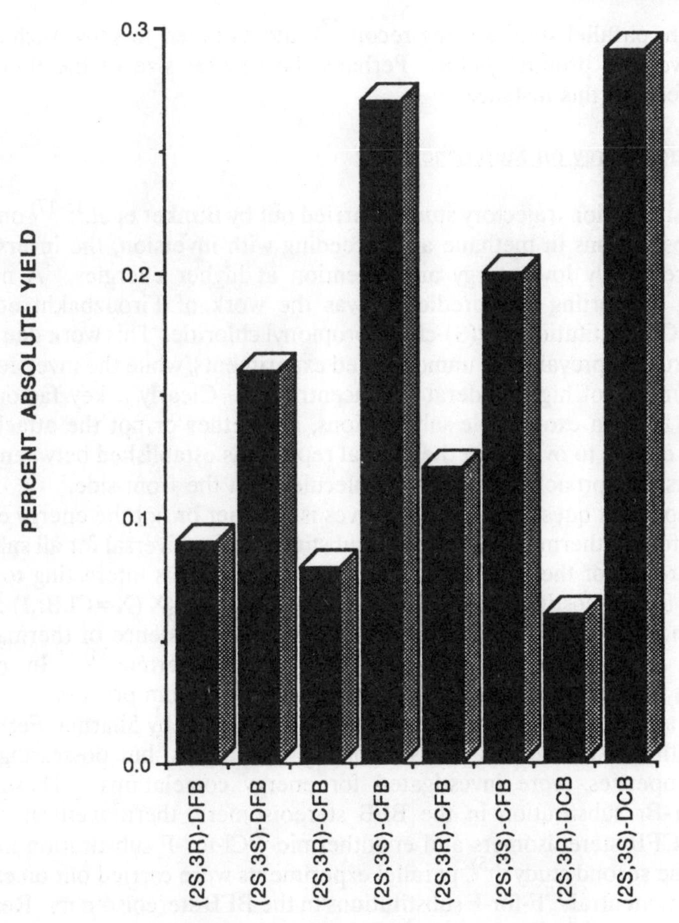

Fig. 3. Absolute yields for inversion products arising from ^{38}Cl-for-X (F,Cl) substitutions on diastereomeric dihalobutanes.

back-side of the molecule, colinear with the bond being broken, perhaps by an inelastic reactive collision.

Very recent work carried out by the same group on ^{38}Cl and ^{34m}Cl-for-X (X=F,Cl) substitutions in (2S,3R)-*meso*- and (2S,3S)-*dl*-difluorbutanes (DFB's), (2S,3R)-*dl*- and (2S,3S)-*dl*-dichlorofluorobutanes (CFB's), and (2S,3R)-*meso*- and (2S,3S)-*dl*-dichlorobutanes (DCB's) provided addtional evidence in support of a direct substitution pathway leading to inversion products that involved back-side attack.[13] This conclusion was revealed by the observation that the inverted product yields were always systematically smaller with the (S,R) configuration of each target molecule than with the (S,S) configuration, as seen in Figure 3. There is little doubt here that this systematic variation was due to steric factors, since the target molecules within each set were identical in every way except for the spatial orientation of their groups. Therefore, inertial effects could not be considered an important factor affecting stereochemistry. Of course, the degree of hindrance to the incoming atom would be subject to differences in the rotational conformer populations within each configuration.

Interestingly enough, parallel studies using recoil ^{18}F atoms failed to show such systematic variation in the inversion product yields. Perhaps the smaller size of the fluorine atom minimized such effects in this instance.

1.2. Effect of Kinetic Energy on Stereochemistry

Early computer simulation trajectory studies carried out by Bunker et al.[15-17] on T + CH_4 predicted some substitutions in methane as proceeding with inversion, the inversion mode predominating at relatively low energy and retention at higher energies. A noteworthy experimental study supporting this prediction was the work of Firouzbakht et al.[18] on exothermic ^{18}F-for-Cl substitution in 2(S)-chloropropionyl chloride. This work demonstrated that the retention product prevailed in unmoderated experiments, while the inversion product prevailed in experiments of high moderator concentration. Clearly a key factor affecting stereochemistry, at least in exothermic substitutions, is whether or not the attacking atom possesses sufficient energy to overcome the mutual repulsions established between itself and the leaving group as it approaches the target molecule from the front-side.

Of course, an important question to ask ourselves is whether or not the energy effect seen on stereochemistry for exothermic halogen atom substitutions is universal for all substitutions of this nature, regardless of their thermochemical properties. It is interesting to note that while exothermic F-for-X substitutions have been reported for CH_3X (X=Cl,Br,I) at thermal energy[19] no evidence has ever been obtained to support the existence of thermal halogen atom substitutions that are either thermoneutral or endothermic.[20] In retrospect, substitutions of this nature are only likely to occur as true hot atom processes.

Two key studies addressing this issue were recently carried out by Sharma, Ferrieri, Wolf and Rack.[21,5] In the first, three reactions involving ^{38}Cl atoms, but possessing different thermochemical properties, were investigated for energy correlations. These included exothermic ^{38}Cl-for-Br substitution in the BFB stereoisomers, thermoneutral ^{38}Cl-for-Cl substitution in the CFB stereoisomers and endothermic ^{38}Cl-for-F substitution in the CFB stereoisomers. In the second study[21,5], parallel experiments were carried out on exothermic ^{18}F-for-Br and thermoneutral ^{18}F-for-F substitutions in the BFB stereoisomers. Results from these studies are presented in Figures 4 and 5 for the (S,R) configuration of each target molecule. Similiar behavior is observed within each case for the corresponding (S,S) configuration.

The general trends observed from these studies are outlined as follows: (i) all exothermic substitutions proceed with increasing levels of inversion as the kinetic energy is lowered; (ii) contrary to this, all thermoneutral and endothermic substitutions proceed with the same level of inversion, regardless of the kinetic energy. These trends may be explained by the hypothesis that exothermic substitutions will persist into the thermal energy range, and therefore, show dependences on moderator concentration that reflect the subtle differences between the energy requirements for front-side and back-side attack at the asymmetric carbon. On the other hand, thermoneutral and endothermic substitutions will proceed only as hot atom reactions, and therefore, may not exhibit moderator dependences if both channels possess similiar energy dependences. Of course, absolute product yields for these latter reactions should fall-off to zero at, or below, some threshold energy.

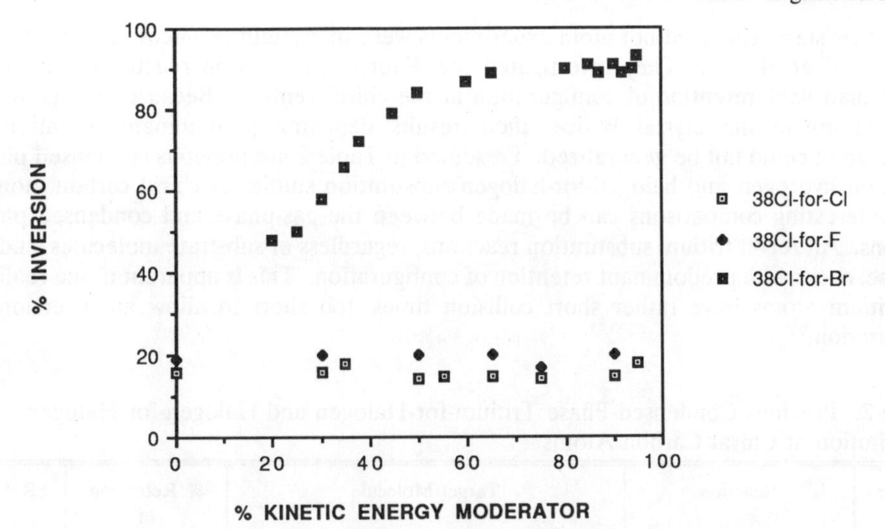

Fig. 4. Effect of kinetic energy on 38Cl-for-X (F,Cl,Br) substitutions on (2S,3R)-*dl*-chlorofluorobutane and (2S,3R)-*dl*-fluorobromobutane.

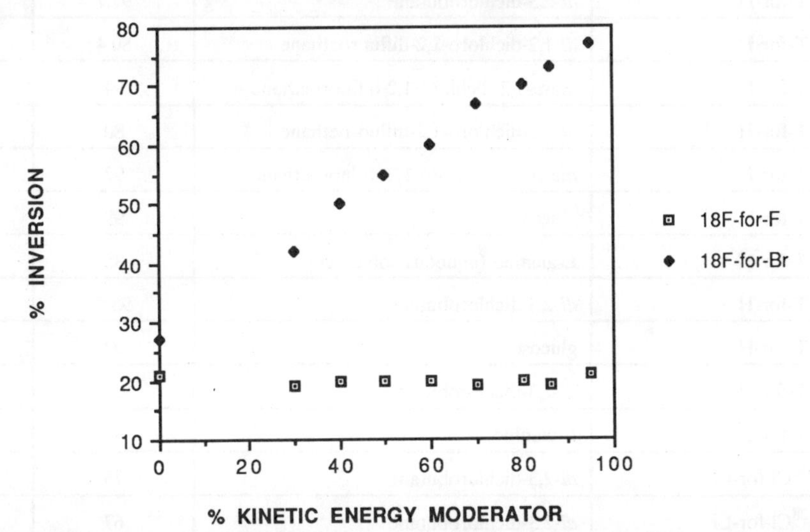

Fig. 5. Effect of kinetic energy on 18F-for-X (F,Br) substitutions on (2S,3R)-*dl*-bromofluorobutane.

2. Stereochemical Consequences of Hot Atom Substitution Reactions in the Condensed Phase

Hot atom reactions in the condensed phase are generally different than their counterparts in the gas phase. Those differences are mainly the result of collisional stabilization of excited products in the condensed phase, density and cage effects where thermalized hot atoms are trapped in solvent cages with radical debris produced in hot atom collisions. This may lead to one difficulty in the interpretation of data in condensed phase systems. Results can be due to racemization and/or equal rates of retention and inversion reaction channels.

The first stereochemical hot atom experiments were in crystalline glucose and L-alanine by Rowland et al.[22,23] They investigated the T-for-H substitution reactions and found greater than 95% retention of configuration at the chiral centers. Because of cage effect complications in the crystal lattice, their results depicting predominant retention of configuration could not be generalized. Presented in Table 2 are previous condensed phase tritium-for-hydrogen and halogen-for-halogen substitution studies at chiral carbon atoms. Some interesting comparisons can be made between the gas-phase and condensed phase reactions. All recoil tritium substitution reactions, regardless of substrate molecules studied or phase, occur with predominant retention of configuration. This is apparent if one realizes that tritium atoms have rather short collision times, too short to allow an inversion of configuration.[6]

Table 2. Previous Condensed-Phase Tritium-for-Halogen and Halogen-for-Halogen Substitution at Chiral Carbon Atoms

Phase	Reaction	Target Molecule	% Retention of Configuration	Ref.
liquid	T-for-H	*dl*-2,3-dichlorobutane	97.7	2
	T-for-H	*dl*-1,2-dichloro-1,2-difluoroethane	80.4	3
	T-for-H	*meso*-1,2-dichloro-1,2-difluoroethane	94	3
	T-for-H	*dl*-1,2-dichloro-1,2-difluoroethane	80	4
	T-for-H	*meso*-1,2-dichloro-1,2-difluoroethane	92	4
	T-for-H	glucose	99	23
	T-for-H	L-alanine (aqueous solution)	85	22
	T-for-H	*dl*-2,3-dichlorobutane	95.5	2
solid	T-for-H	glucose	99	22
	T-for-H	*dl*-2,3-dichlorobutane	95.5	24
	T-for-H	L-alanine	95	23
liquid	^{38}Cl-for-Cl	*dl*-2,3-dichlorobutane	75	25
	^{38}Cl-for-Cl	*dl*-2,3-dichlorobutane	67	26
	^{38}Cl-for-Cl	*meso*-2,3-dichlorobutane	60	26
	^{38}Cl-for-Cl	*dl*-1,2-dichloro-1,2-difluorobutane	65	27
	^{80m}Br (or ^{80}Br)-for-Br	*meso*-2,3-dichlorobutane	60	28
	^{80m}Br (or ^{80}Br)-for-Br	*dl*-2,3-dichlorobutane	50	28
	^{38}Cl-for-Cl	2(R)-chloropropionyl chloride	55	29
	^{38}Cl-for-Cl	2(S)-chloro-1-propanol	53	30
	^{38}Cl-for-Cl	2(R)-chloro-1-propanol	57	30

solid	^{38}Cl-for-Cl	*dl*-2,3-dichlorobutane	50	2
	^{38}Cl-for-Cl	*meso*-2,3-dichlorobutane	60	2
	^{38}Cl-for-Cl	*dl*-2,3-dichlorobutane	71	26
	^{38}Cl-for-Cl	*meso*-2,3-dichlorobutane	71	26
	^{80m}Br-for-Br	*dl*-2,3-dichlorobutane	58	25
	^{126}I-for-I	*dl*-2,3-dichlorobutane	54	25

Rowland[2,10,21] and Stöcklin[4,25] investigated the stereochemical course of halogen-for-halogen substitution reactions in halocarbon molecules with multiple asymmetric centers. These studies were restricted to diastereomeric compounds such as *dl*- and *meso*-$(CHFCl)_2$ and *dl*- and *meso*-2,3-dichlorobutane because of experimental difficulties in resolving chiral molecules with a single chiral center. In their stereochemical studies, Rowland and co-workers found racemization occurring in the liquid and solid phases, unlike greater than 93% retention of configuration at the asymmetric centers in gas phase reactions.

In an important innovative approach, Stöcklin and his group[25] studied the effects of several solvents on the stereochemistry of recoil chlorine-38 in liquid 2,3-dichlorobutane. Stöcklin concluded that the solvents influenced the rotational conformation population and, therefore, the retention to inversion ratio. Stöcklin suggested that these results could only be interpreted by assuming two channels for hot substitution: (1) direct replacement without a change in configuration leaving the product molecule with little excitation energy and (2) a backside attack with inversion giving rise to a highly excited product molecule. However, Ache and his co-workers[26-28] found no conformational effects in the stereochemical course of chlorine-38-for-chlorine substitution in various dichloroalkanes and $(CHFCl)_2$. These data suggested to the authors that the stereochemical cause of the substitution process is controlled by the properties of the solvent molecules, most likely intermolecular interactions between reactants and solvents. In addition, their results suggested that the excited complex is formed by both direct and backside attack in the chlorine substitution reactions in $(CHFCl)_2$.

In the first section, the interesting and important Machulla and Stöcklin stereochemical study[4] of the diastereomers of $(CHFCl)_2$ employing the effects of a collapsing molecular environment on the ^{38}Cl-for-Cl substitution was discussed from the viewpoint of a gas phase system. They suggested that the hot substitution in the liquid phase could not be satisfactorily explained by the "impact model", nor by radical combination, but rather by a nondirect process such as the formation of a caged electronically excited intermediate whose lifetime was prolonged by the liquid cage wall. While it is now known from the subsequent studies by Wolf et al.[5-9] that an excited complex is not necessary for an inversion channel, it was important in that it suggested two distinct channels leading to retention of configuration and inversion of configuration in halogen-for-halogen substitution reactions at chiral centers.

In the first stereochemical study using optical enantiomers for halogen-for-halogen substitution in the condensed phase[30], Ache and his co-workers determined the solvent dependence on the ratio of retention to inversion following ^{38}Cl-for-Cl substitution in 2(R)-chloro-1-propanol and 2(S)-chloro-1-propanol. This was an important step in the study of the liquid phase as the use of optical enantiomers, which possess only one asymmetric center, not only minimizes the possible steric influence on initial attack which could be present in diastereomeric compounds, but also removes the obvious influence or the difference in the thermodynamic properties of the resulting products in the course of the substitution process. For the next 2(S)-chloro-1-propanol and 2(R)-chloro-1-propanol, the percent retentions of configurations for ^{38}Cl-for-Cl substitutions are 53% and 57% respectively. In good agreement with the author's previous studies in diastereomeric haloalkanes,[26-28] the addition of methanol, a solvent of high dielectric constant resulted in higher retention-inversion ratios than hydrocarbon solvents of low dielectric constant. The authors concluded that their results were more consistent with a radical-radical recombination than with a one-step hot replacement mechanism.

In their gas-phase studies of 2-chloro-1-propanol, Wolf et al. found from an infrared spectroscopy study that 2-chloro-1-propanol forms molecular aggregates via hydrogen bonding at system processes greater than 340 Torr. Therefore, in the liquid state, 2-chloro-1-propanol does not behave as a single chiral compound, vitiating any conclusions regarding the stereochemistry or mechanism of the substitution process.[30] The molecule 2-chloropropionyl chloride does not form dimers and behaves as a single chiral compound in the liquid state. Rack and his co-workers[29] determined the ^{38}Cl-labelled products by virtue of (n,γ) activation in neat 2(R)-chloropropionyl chloride and the effects of solvents on the course of the ^{38}Cl-for-Cl substitution. As expected the major ^{38}Cl-labelled product was HCl (66±8), followed by CH_3Cl (8.2±0.1), 2(R)-chloropropionyl chloride (2.6±0.1), 2(S)-chloropropionyl chloride (3.2±0.1) and higher alkyl chlorides. The major product is $H^{38}Cl$ by hydrogen abstraction from substrate molecules. For the ^{38}Cl-for-Cl substitution reaction, the observed percent inversion is 55%. Regardless as to whether in the liquid state, the mechanism involves a one-step reaction mechanism or one involving an intermediate caged radical-radical recombination, the formation of the inversion product is preferred in contrast to the predominant formation of retention products found in the previous studies involving diastereomers.[2-4,25-28] The inversion to retention ratio for the ^{38}Cl-for-Cl substitution at the chiral center of 2(S)-chloropropionyl chloride was studied as a function of mole-fraction additives. The addition of solvents of high dielectric constant such as acetonitrile and cyclohexanone resulted in higher inversion/retention rates than hydrocarbon solvents which reduced the inversion/retention rates below the value observed in the neat substrate. This behavior for the chiral substrate was unlike that found for the diastereomers previously studied. These results suggested that the stereochemical cause of the substitution reaction is controlled by the properties of the solvent molecules, most likely by factors which affect the magnitude of intermolecular interaction between reactants and solvents.

Without question, it can be said that the stereochemistry of hot atom reactions in the condensed phase are far from understood. While addressed by various authors important questions regarding caging, complex formation, one-step substitution and conformational effects have yet to be answered. Perhaps what is needed are more studies in the gas phase, similiar to those reported in the earlier section and gas to condensed phase transition studies with both enantiomer and diastereomers.

References

1. Henchman, M., Wolfgang, R.: J. Am. Chem. Soc., 81, 2991 (1961).
2. Wai, C.M., Ting, C.T., Rowland, F.S.: J. Am. Chem. Soc., 86, 2525 (1964).
3. Palino, G.F., Rowland, F.S.: J. Phys. Chem., 75, 1299 (1971).
4. Machulla, H.-J., Stöcklin, G.: J. Phys. Chem., 78, 658 (1974).

5. Ferrieri, R.A., Sharma, R.B., Rack, E.P., Wolf, A.P.: manuscript to be submitted to J. Phys. Chem.
6. To, K.-C., Wolf, A.P., Rack, E.P.: J. Phys. Chem., 87, 4929 (1983).
7. Palino, G.F., Rowland, F.S.: Radiochim. Acta, 15, 57 (1971).
8. Wolf, A.P., Schueler, P., Pettijohn, R.P., To, K.-C., Rack, E.P.: J. Phys. Chem., 83, 1237 (1979).
9. Sharma, R.B., Ferrieri, R.A., Meyer, R.J., Rack, E.P., Wolf, A.P.: J. Phys. Chem., 94, 2316 (1990).
10. Rowland, F.S., Wai, C.M., Ting, C.T., Miller, G.: "Chemical Effects of Nuclear Transformations", IAEA, Vienna, 1965, 1, p. 333.
11. Wai, C.M., Rowland, F.S.: J. Phys. Chem., 71, 2752 (1967).
12. To, K.-C., Rack, E.P., Wolf, A.P.: J. Phys. Chem., 74, 1499 (1981).
13. Firouzbakht, M.L., Ferrieri, R.A., Wolf, A.P., Rack, E.P.: J. Phys. Chem., 90, 5339 (1986).
14. Daniel, S.M., Ache, H.J., Stöcklin, G.: J. Chem. Phys., 78, 1043 (1974).
15. Bunker, D.L., Pattengill, M.D.: J. Chem. Phys., 53, 3041 (1970).
16. Valencich, T., Bunker, D.L.: Chem. Phys. Lett., 20, 50 (1973).
17. Bunker, D.L.: Acc. Chem. Res., 7, 195 (1974).
18. Firouzbakht, M.L., Ferrieri, R.A., Wolf, A.P., Rack, E.P.: J. Am. Chem. Soc., 109, 2213 (1987).
19. Subramania, I., Rowland, F.S.: J. Phys. Chem., 85, 2488 (1981).
20. Ingold, K.U., Roberts, B.P.: "Free Radical Substitution Reactions", Wiley, New York, 1971.
21. Sharma, R.B., Ferrieri, R.A., Rack, E.P., Wolf, A.P.: Radiochim. Acta, 50, 91 (1990).
22. Kay, J.G., Malsan, R.P., Rowland, F.S.: J. Am. Chem. Soc., 81, 5050 (1959).
23. Keller, H., Rowland, F.S.: J. Phys. Chem., 62, 1373 (1958).
24. Tang, Y.N., Ting, C.T., Rowland, F.S.: J. Phys. Chem., 74, 675 (1976).
25. Vasaros, L., Machulla, H.-J., Stöcklin, G.: J. Phys. Chem., 76, 501 (1972).
26. Wu, J., Ache, H.J.: J. Am. Chem. Soc., 99, 6021 (1977).
27. Acciani, T.R., Su, Y.Y., Ache, H.J., Rack, E.P.: J. Phys. Chem., 82, 975 (1978).
28. Su, Y.Y., Ache, H.J.: J. Phys. Chem., 80, 659 (1976).
29. Borkar, N., Latifi, A.A., Rack, E.P.: J. Chem. Phys., 85, 3125 (1986).
30. Wu, J., Boothe, T.E., Ache, H.J.: J. Chem. Phys., 68, 5285 (1978).
31. Wai, C.M., Rowland, F.S.: J. Phys. Chem., 74, 434 (1970).

3.5 Theoretical Approaches to the Hot Atom Chemistry of Hydrogen

Trina VALENCICH
Department of Chemistry and Biochemistry, California State University, 5151 State University Dr., Los Angeles, CA 90032

1. INTRODUCTION

The distinguishing reagent in classical "hot atom" chemistry is hot in at least two ways. It is translationally energized and radioactive.[1] Radioactivity made analysis of its chemical fate convenient and this feature of the chemistry was a consequence of the experimental method used to energize the element. The acceleration process first used was the conversion of matter into energy which accompanies nuclear transmutations, and the initial event produces bare nuclear projectiles.

Historically, theoretical treatments have partitioned the problem into two energy domains. In discussing the "stopping power" of the medium[2] high energy physics covers collisional slowing of the high speed species;[3] and charge and electronic energy exchange.[2] Classical hot atom chemistry claims: chemical reactions; collisional stabilization or decomposition of internally excited products; and the translation to internal energy exchange processes typical of more conventional chemistry.[4] Methods used in the latter domain can be further categorized by the information used for integral terms involving the probability of elementary reactive and non-reactive processes (experimental yields, models, or trajectory calculations). If radioactivity is not essential to the topic, then combustion reactions, plasmas and explosions can be included as hot atom chemistry.[5] If we limit our region of interest to where "chemistry" is possible, then photochemically initiated reactions [6] and crossed molecular beam experiments[7] fall into the domain of hot atom chemistry. This also means that quasiclassical trajectory calculations will be the most likely source of the single collision probability functions.

Like death and taxes there are only two certainties here, the hot atom ultimately ends up bound in some stable molecule, and the value of the relative energy of the very first collision is known. Theoretical predictions depend upon two generally unknown functions: the distribution of collisional energies actually experienced by the hot atom (the collision spectrum), and the probability of all possible events as a function of energy (expressed as cross section functions). Specification of the energy borders which delineate these two regimes must be somewhat arbitrary. Considering the width of the total energy range involved and the variety of fundamental processes sampled, it would be surprising if any theoretical treatment were completely successful in predicting all of the measured quantities.

To evaluate the theoretical status of this field, we shall focus then on best case comparisons. This choice will limit our coverage to systems which are relatively simple, neglecting for example treatments of condensed phases.[8] Nuclear recoil tritium systems are our topic then, as they are expected to avoid the complications due to the involvement of multiple or excited electronic states. We will compare two more recent investigations[9,10] with the results of five studies discussed in the last review. Therefore we will begin with a review of the mathematical methods involved, a comparison of the most thoroughly examined systems to date will follow, and we will finish with a summary of the status of theoretical contributions to hot atom chemistry.

2. BACKGROUND

The Estrup-Wolfgang Kinetic Theory (KT) of hot atom reactions derived a procedure to relate the "average logarithmic energy loss" parameter, called α, to changes in measured product yields as a function of the total pressure and the concentration of inert moderators.[11] Approximate total collision diameters and a hard sphere model for non-reactive scattering were employed. This treatment assumes that the entity of interest becomes a neutral, ground electronic state atom while its translational energy is still above regions where any chemistry takes place. Therefore exact specification of this energy is not important. The Kinetic Theory of hot atom reactions was thoroughly reviewed in the previous edition of this series,[12] and a complete discussion here would be redundant. However, owing to its importance to the evolution of terms and concepts in the field, we will refer to these terms where relevant.

Hot atom product yields have been predicted by statistical[13-23] or stochastic manipulation[9,10,24,25] of single collision reaction probabilities. These calculations focus on the collision spectrum and competition between various channels for the reactive element as a function of energy. Here then can be included the influence of added thermal radical scavengers. The computational procedure is generally broken into two parts.

2.1. Mathematical Methods

2.1.1. Single Collision Probabilities

First, the single collision probabilities for reactive and energy exchange processes are generated. These probabilities have been collected from single collision trajectory simulations subject to potential energy force fields;[26-30] modeled by hard sphere calculations;[31,32] and approximated by model functions.[9,19] Hard sphere treatments assume no deflection of the hot atom until it makes contact with a partner treated as a rigid sphere or collection of spheres. The scattering angle and distribution of energy in the products are based essentially on random number tosses at the point of contact. The attractive simplicity of the approach derives from ignoring the internal motion of the target and forces before and after the collision. This method is conceptually appropriate for short interaction times. As will be discussed below, reaction probabilities computed by the hard sphere method can compare remarkably well with those predicted by trajectory methods.

The availability of standardized trajectory software, makes it relatively easy to sample internal states and include directional influence from the of the target.[33] The quasiclassical trajectory method for generating statistics on single collision events has been recently reviewed, we will simply state the basics here.[34] Hamilton's equations of motion derive from Newtonian mechanics and are based upon the conservation of energy, mass and momentum. Once a potential function can be described mathematically, the appropriate derivatives are integrated numerically in time from a selected set of initial coordinates and momenta to calculate the outcome for one collision event. The process is repeated, sampling starting conditions appropriate to the experimental conditions being simulated, until the uncertainty in the quantities of interest; such as reaction probabilities (see Fig. 1 and 2), distribution of energy in the products of the reaction (see Fig. 3) and the angles at which they are scattered are comparable to measured data.

Trajectory calculations ignore interference phenomenon, tunneling and the quantization of vibrational and rotational energy. However, methods exist for sampling starting conditions appropriate to quantal distributions, and binning the time average values of product internal energy to mimic quantization in the products. The average values of ordinary applications of these calculations are expected to be valid. Since the classical description is the high energy, heavy particle limit of quantum mechanical behavior, the hot atom experiment, more so than any other system, is the situation where the trajectory technique should be most appropriate.

Depending upon the complexity of the system being examined, additional secondary probability information is needed and can be provided by trajectory computations. Types of secondary probability functions are: P(E, E'), P(E, E*) and P(E, χ). P(E, E') is the probability that the hot atom's laboratory energy is E' after a nonreactive collision with a target at energy E. Fig. 3 shows examples of moderator functions, P(E, E'), including model forms and versions which have been taken from trajectory calculations.[27] The probability that TR is formed with internal energy E* after reaction of T with HR at laboratory energy E is given by P(E, E*). P(E, χ) is the probability that the collision products are scattered at a center of mass angle, χ.

A series of such curves generated over a wide range of collision energies, together with parameters for collisional stabilization and unimolecular decomposition of reaction products, form the input for the second stage of the calculation.

2.1.2. Product Yield Calculations

If Boltzmann conditions were being simulated, the sum of the integral product of the probability of reaction as a function of energy times the familiar [35] distribution of energy transformation would then finish the calculation. However, since the actual distribution of energy is not known, the second part of the computation must fold into the integrals the probabilities of energy exchange or generate the distribution stochastically along with the product yields. Energy exchange probabilities have also been approached with the same methods used to generate the reactive part of the problem.[31,36-38]

Porter's integral reaction probability (IRP) theory is typical of Boltzmann based approaches.[13-21,23] The method allows direct calculation of reaction yields, $A_{ci}(E)$, when the total collisional cross sections, $S_k(E_r)$, and reactive cross sections, $\sigma_k(E_r)$, are known. $A_{ci}(E)$ is the probability that reaction i will occur upon collision with component c subsequent to introduction of the hot atom into the system at initial laboratory energy E. The laboratory energy is denoted by E and the relative collisional energy is E_r. Each p_{ci} term is the probability that a collision with component c at energy E will produce product i and is determined by the collisional cross sections for all processes possible at energy. The value of $A_{ci}(E)$ is calculated by numerical integration of the following Volterra integral:

$$A_{ci}(E) = [p_{ci}(E)\, X_c S_c(E_r) / (\Sigma_k X_k S_k(E_r))]$$

$$+ \int_0^{\infty} \Sigma_k [X_k S_k(E_r) / (\Sigma_j X_j S_j(E_r))]\, [1 - \Sigma_j p_{kj}(E)]\, P(E, E')\, dE \qquad (1)$$

The equivalent stochastic simulation method[9,10,22,23] also requires the total and reactive cross section functions. A typical example is executed as follows. A tritium is assigned a large kinetic energy, the value having been shown by trial to be insensitive to the exact choice. One of the reaction channels is selected by random methods appropriately weighted with the $\sigma(E_r)$. If it is not reactive, a new translational energy is calculated by interpolation of P(E, E') followed by weighted random selection, using the cumulative distribution method:

$$R = \int_0^{E'} P(E,x)\, dx \qquad 0<R<1 \qquad (2)$$

in which R is a random number and E' is found by trapezoidal numerical integration.

The channel selection process is repeated now at the new energy. If a reactive channel is selected, a similar calculation yields the internal energy of the newly formed product. If decomposition of the product is not energetically possible, the outcome is merely recorded at that energy and a new tritium is initiated. If sufficient internal energy is deposited in the tritium containing product, the rate of bimolecular stabilization and the rates of all distinct decomposition processes are computed by Bunker's[40] rotationally corrected RRKM theory. If the relative rates of T loss and the other channels are all less than successively selected random numbers, stabilization is identified as the result at this energy and another T is initiated. Likewise, if the decomposed fragment contains the tritium, this result is added to the count and a new cycle is started. If T loss occurs, its resulting laboratory energy must be chosen, including the correction for the differences between the laboratory frame and the center-of-mass system. A new channel is now selected at this energy.

Information on radiation damage is also predicted by a similar calculation for the target when non-reactive events leave it sufficiently energized. The collisional history of individual hot atoms is accumulated in this manner. In Fig. 4 the stochastic histograms, reproduced here from Ref. 10, each multiplied by 0.18 for ease in comparison, are superimposed upon the $\sigma(E_r)$ curve for $T + CH_4$. As a computational bonus, the collision spectrum, f(E), and energy loss, average values of α, statistics for the system are also generated directly at the same time, Fig. 5.

The accuracy of both the IRP and stochastic techniques has been demonstrated by comparing their calculations on model problems which make the integrals soluble in closed form. An experimental uncertainty of 5% in the yield of individual products predicts an 11% uncertalnty in a ratio of two yields when each has only one reaction source. When one of the yields has two sources, the yield ratio uncertainty increases to 17%. The first item of concern then begins with the potential energy description in the trajectory calculation; or the appropriateness of any model function used. Given that most of the potentials used in trajectory calculations of reactive and nonreactive probabilities are "empirical" to some degree, we are essentially comparing model calculations to measured product yields in this chapter.[41]

3. Best Case Systems

3.1 $T + H_2$ (D_2, and HD)

Experimentally difficult and theoretically accessible, H_3 and its isotopic variations continue to be the benchmark for chemical reactions. Its potential energy surface has been determined by quantum mechanical methods more accurately and over more coordinate space than any other system.[41-46] For reviews of recent experimental and theoretical results see Ref. 45 and 46. Approximate dynamical simulations,[47-51] quasi-classical trajectory computations,[52-57] quantum scattering calculations,[58-63] and tunneling treatments have been applied to various analytical fits to the *ab initio* surface Siegbahn and Liu (SL) and the well studied surface of Porter, Karplus, and Sharma (PKS).[51,64-68]

3.1.1. Potential Energy Surfaces

Single collision probability data suitable for the calculation of hot tritium atom reaction yields with H_2, D_2, and HD have been computed by trajectory simulations on the PKS surface[29,30], on an extended Huckel surface,[26] and by hard sphere treatments.[31,32] The barrier on PKS surface is thinner and approximately 2 kJ/mole lower than the SL surface.[65] The thinness causes a factor of two increase in the rate of reaction at 300 K for H + $H_2(\upsilon=1)$ due to tunneling.[65] However, the zero angular momentum, three dimensional (3D) quantal reaction probabilities on PKS and SL look very similar except for the 5 kJ/m shift in threshold energy.[58] The extended Huckel formulation by Malcolme-Lawes (EM) results in a barrier that is 0.3 kJ/mole lower than PKS and a barrier width more like the SL surface.[26] The minimum energy reaction path on the EM surface is displaced outward toward the reactants region by about 8 pm, relative to *ab initio* calculations and the PKS path is displaced inward by about 3 pm.

Thermal rate measurements suggest that the barrier to reaction on the *ab initio* SL surface is less than 1 kJ/mole too high and that this is not the source of the factor of 4 difference at 300 K for the first excited vibrational state ($\upsilon=1$).[64-70] Information on internal state distributions of the hydrogen products has only recently been possible through advances in nonlinear spectroscopy.[71-73] Lee and coauthors have reported the most complete comparison between the highest quality molecular beam experiments with fully converged three dimensional quantum scattering calculations performed on the most accurately known *ab initio* surface representation.[45] In general, the agreement between these more direct measurements and theory is quite impressive. The differences are interpreted as evidence that the bend aspect of the *ab initio* potential representation is too steep near the barrier and the curvature of the bend potential at higher energies should be steeper.[45] Some information is available on the effects on product state distributions of the bend characteristics of the potential.[64-66,74,75] Blais, Truhlar and Garrett found more rotational excitation in the product without a change in the center-of-mass scattering angle upon using a modification of the Liu-Siegbahn-Truhlar-Horowitz (LSTH) fit which only softened the bend character of the representation.[74]

3.1.2 Single Collision Probabilities

The reaction cross sections, $\sigma(E_r)$, reported for two potential surfaces and the hard sphere treatments of Malcolm-Lawes (HM) and Suplinskas (HS) are plotted versus energy in Fig. 1 and 2. Porter, Karplus and Sharma (PKS) applied standard

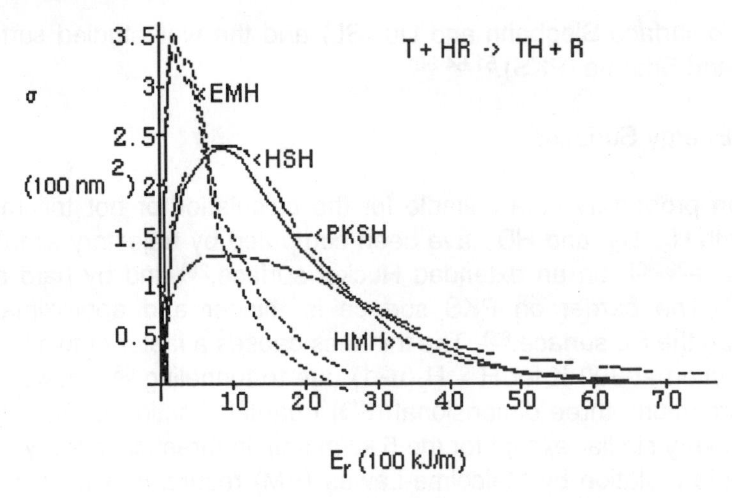

Fig. 1. Cross section functions for abstraction of H: T + HR -> TH + R. PKSH is from the trajectory calculations of Ref. 30; EMH is from the trajectory calculations of Ref. 26; HSH and HMH are hard sphere calculations from Ref. 32 and 31 respectively. To facilitate comparison, the Porter, Karplus, and Sharma curve marked PKSH, for the abstraction of H from molecular hydrogen will be shown in the next figure as well.

quasiclassical trajectory sampling techniques in their simulations on this well known surface. The trajectory calculations on the (EM) surface were run with phase sampled zero point vibrational energy (υ=0) and without rotational energy (j=0).

Several questions immediately present themselves with the information in Fig. 1 and 2. Firstly, are the differences between the details of the PKS and EM surfaces, which produce quite different $\sigma(E_r)$ curves, significant for the hot atom situation? The details of the minimum energy reaction path (MEP) across a potential energy surface may well be unimportant for reactions taking place at much higher energies. If the radial distance at which the potential matches the kinetic energy is the only important factor for high energy encounters, then hard sphere calculations should do as well as trajectory simulations in providing the input to compute hot yields. Secondly, would a cross section curve like HMH, which is reduced relative to PKSH by a factor of 0.42, show a simple reduction in total yield, all else the same? This is an issue determined by the collision spectrum, but it could have implications for scaling up reduced dimensionality calculations. Also, are hot atom yields sensitive to a threshold shift of 5 kJ/m as reported between the 3D quantal predictions on the PKS and SL surfaces? Finally, the cross section data tempts an evaluation of the extent of collisional dissociation of the target, a type of radiation damage. We examine the computation of hot atom yields with an eye to these issues as well as to their comparison with experimental results.

3.1.3. Hot Atom Yields

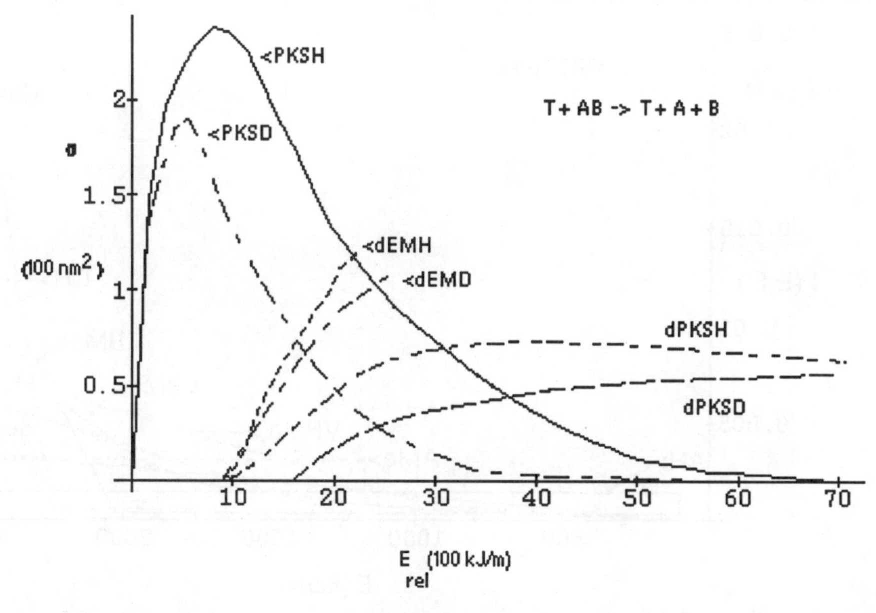

Fig. 2. Cross section curves for decomposition of the target: T + AB -> T + A + B. The curves marked dPKSH and dPKSD are for collisional dissociation of H_2 and D_2 respectively (predicted by Porter-Karplus, and Sharma, Ref. 30). The corresponding functions, dEMH and dEMD, are predicted by the trajectory calculations of Malcolme-Lawes, Ref. 26, using an extended Huckel surface. Also shown are the abstraction curves for H_2 and D_2 calculated by Porter, Karplus, and Sharma, PKSH and PKSD.

Porter and Kunt (PK) applied the IRP approach to calculate hot T atom yields from the trajectory results of Porter, Karplus and Sharma on PKS.[19] Their simplest experimental situation, see Table 1, with one reactive component, predicted an IRP yield of HT of 30.52 % in self-moderated H_2 and a 22.02 % yield of DT in D_2, using hard sphere non-reactive scattering, version A. These values increased to 69.92% HT and 57.30% DT, when anisotropic non-reactive scattering, type C, was used. In addition, the per collision values of α were 0.8659 and 0.9189 in H_2 and D_2 respectively with model A, and dropped to 0.2270 and 0.2388 with version C.

The moderator function of model A, marked in Fig. 3 as AH and AMe for hydrogen and methane respectively, defines isotropic hard sphere scattering with large collisional energy losses. Version A originates from neutron scattering theory where high speed collisions with structureless targets at small (nuclear) impact parameters are the dominant interaction. Models B (indicated as BH and BMe) and C describe anisotropic scattering and are more realistic for the longer range interactions between atoms and molecules at slower speeds. Model C (marked as CH and CMe) is based on quantum scattering calculations of Tang and Karplus on H + H_2 and the oscillations in the curve have been suppressed. Energy transfer with version C is dominated by forward scattered grazing collisions where energy

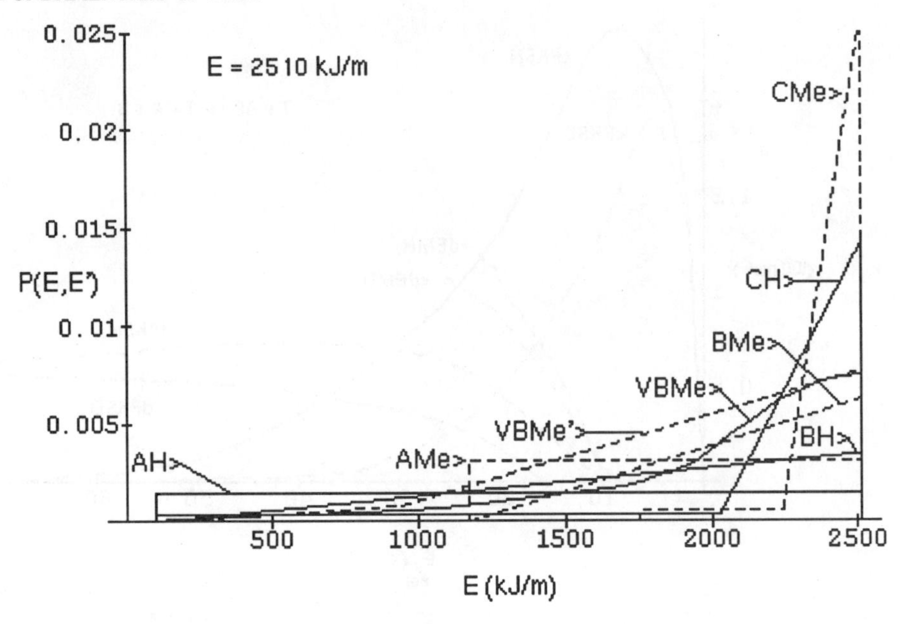

Fig. 3. Moderator functions, P(E,E'), describe the probability that the laboratory energy of the hot atom is E' after a nonreactive collision with a target at laboratory energy E, here E=2510 kJ/m. The straight line segments are models. The solid lines are for non reactive collisions between tritium and hydrogen, the dashed lines are for collisions with methane. These energy loss models are independent of energy, and the difference between the Me (for methane) or H (for hydrogen) designation is determined by mass. Also shown is a P(E,E') function from the trajectory calculations of Valencich and Bunker, VBMe, see Ref. 10.

losses are small.

The predictions[16] of yield ratios in mixtures of H_2, D_2 and He consistently agreed better with the experimental ratios[76,77] when model C was used (rather than A) for non-reactive scattering. The experimental specific activity ratio, however, is less variable and has an average value of 1.5 in the absence scavengers.[78] The total yields are computed to be more than 50% smaller with the hard sphere, type A, scattering. The computed HT/DT ratio is also within the advertised uncertainty of the experiment.

Helium may not be as effective as the heavier inert gases in charge transfer processes with tritium because its ionization potential is high. It is possible that the consistently higher yields of HT in He moderated systems, relative to Ar, arise from reactions involving tritium ions. Seewald and Wolfgang showed that the addition of 30% Xe to inert gas moderated mixtures markedly reduced the HT yield only in the He systems.[77] Hard sphere calculations by Malcolme-Lawes have suggested that the higher yields in helium moderated systems arise because vibrationally excited products are less likely to dissociate upon collision with the lighter He than with the other, heavier inert gases.[31] However, Blais and Truhlar (BT) have shown that hard sphere calculations over estimate the amount of collisional dissociation.

Simlations by BT indicated that highly excited H_2 is approximately twice as likely, on the average, to lose energy in a collision with Ar as to dissociate.[37] In addition, the rate of collisional relaxation of diatomic species which were vibrationally excited to levels near the dissociation limit was recently measured.[78] Rates of collisional relaxation were enhanced by factors of from 50 to 250 compared to rates of vibrational energy loss for the same situation but with υ=1 or 2.

The computed yield ratios for H_2/D_2 mixtures as a function of Ar mole fraction agree less well with the experimental results. The ratio is predicted to be 1.503 (37.41%/24.89%) for the lowest mole fraction (0.3) of Ar considered, the measured value is 1.35 with Ar. The calculated value extrapolates to a moderated limit of 1.37 with Ar (and He), at X_{Ar} =1, compared to the measured limit of 1.15 in Ar. Although the change is definitely in the correct direction, a best case limit of 5% in the experimental uncertainty in the yield of each product puts the calculation just outside the 1.28 high end limit. The yields calculated by Porter and Kunt depend upon the cross sections used for the inert moderator as well as the energy loss model. They tested the effect of cutting the total collisional cross sections, assumed to be energy independent, by a factor of 3.55 for all three components, while leaving the reactive part unchanged. This change more than doubled the individual yields with model A and increased the yield ratio by an insignificant factor of 1.05. A description for non-reactive energy exchange which is better than model C may be required to resolve this discrepancy.

The other three calculations report a ratio of reactivity integrals, I_{HT}/I_{DT}, rather than IRP yields as discussed for Porter and Kunt.[24,30,31]

$$I_{HT}/I_{DT} = \left(\int_0^E \sigma_{HT} d \ln E\right) / \left(\int_0^E \sigma_{DT}\, d \ln E\right) \qquad (3)$$

These values can be compared to HT/DT yield ratios for equimolar (H_2/D_2 =1) mixtures at the moderated limit only and fold in a Maxwell-Boltzmann collisional distribution function. Malcolme-Lawes and Suplinskas both quote hard sphere values of 1.15 for this ratio, and the EM trajectory study reports a ratio of 1.18. As noted above, these numbers agree with the experimental yield ratio better than the value of Porter and Kunt.

The different assumptions applied in the PK calculations can be tested one at a time, and they predict different total yields. Therefore, these computations make a clear statement. Equation (3) does not contain composition variables, allow for alternative non-reactive models, or include scavengers. Application of the same kind of yield calculation to each data set is of interest. As part of the calibration testing for the stochastic simulation studies on tritium with methane by Valencich, some of the systems treated by Porter and Kunt[19] were also examined and are tabulated in Table 1.[10,80]

Table 1 demonstrates the equivalence between the IRP and stochastic simulation techniques. Although incomplete at this time, it gives preliminary results of applying the same treatment to some relevant data. The HT yields predicted from

TABLE 1. HOT TRITIUM PRODUCT YIELDS WITH MOLECULAR HYDROGEN,[a] T + HR

id.#	σ, Scat., Dec..	Abstrac.	Decompo.	Scaven.	α	Ref.
		T + H_2				
1	PKS, C, none:	355=71%	X	X	.24	10
1'	*PKS, C, none:*	*70%*	*X*	*X*	*.23*	*19*
194	PKS/2, C, none:	265=53%	X	X	.24	80
202	EM, C, none:	1384=69%	X	X	.24	80
2	PKS, A, none:	30%	X	X	.81	20
2'	*PKS, A, none:*	*30%*	*X*	*X*	*.87*	*16*
193	PKS/2, A, none:	87=17%	X	X	.86	80
200	EM, A, none:	699=35%	X	X	.85	80
3	PKS, C, cut:	1487=59%	432=17%	X	.25	80
153	PKS, A, cut:	345=34%	67= 7%	X	.82	80
5	PKS, C, ext	55%	35%	X	.24	10
4	PKS+Br_2, C, none:	366=73%	X	36=7%	.24	80
152	PKS+Br_2,, C, cut:	353=71%	90=18%	35=7%	.24	80
145	EMH+Br_2, C, cut:	666=67%	140=14%	59=6%	.26	80
7	PKS/2+Br_2, C, cut:	369=46%	80=10%	69=9%	.25	80
138	PKS+Br_2,, A, cut:	164=33%	23= 5%	32=6%	.91	80
132	EMH+Br_2, A, cut:	192=38%	21= 4%	19=4%	.83	80
		T + D_2				
6	PKS, C, none:	60%	X	X	.27	10
6'	*PKS,C, none:*	*60%*	*X*	*X*	*.24*	*19*
7'	*PKS, A, none:*	*22%*	*X*	*X*	*.92*	*19*
173	PKS/2, C, none:	368=76%	X	X	.28	80
170	EM, C, none:	683=68%	X	X	.27	80

T + (H_2/D_2=1)

id.#	σ, Scat., Dec.	Abstrac.	Decomp.	Scav.	α	Ref.	HT/DT
15	PKS,C,none	H: 1207=39%	X	X	.24	80	1.40±.14
		D: 862=28%	X				
15'	*PKS,C, none*	*H: 39%*	*X*	*X*		*19*	*1.51*
		D: 26%	*X*				
192	EM, C, none	H: 181=36%	X	X	.23	80	.90
		D: 177=35%	X	X			
148	PKS+Br_2, C, cut	H: 194=39%	44=9%	20=4%	.25	80	1.55±.28
		D: 125=25%	44=9%				
134	PKS/2+Br_2, C, cut	H: 128=26%	26=5%	24=5%	.27	80	1.38±.29
		D: 93=19%	21=4%				
19	PKS/2 →+Br_2, C, cut	H: 130=32%	35=9%	14=4%	.26	80	1.51±.16
		D: 86=22%	25=6%				

[a]PKS indicates the cross section data was taken from Ref. 30., "/2" means the values were divided by 2, " →" runs had the abscissa shifted lower by 5 kJ/m. When bromine was included, "+Br_2", it was 2% of the initial mixture by moles and the cross section data came from Ref. 28. EM

identifies Ref. 26 as the cross section source. The non-reactive scattering model is identified under "Scat." as A or C. If decomposition was included its cross section function was either truncated at the highest energy at which trajectories were run, "cut" under Dec., or extrapolated, "ext", to some reasonable intersection with the abscissa. Product yields were determined by stochastic simulation, SS, unless IRP theory was used in which case the line is italicized. The value of the average logarithmic energy loss is indicated under α.

the PKS and EM cross section curves for H_2 with either model for self-moderation are basically the same. With D_2, the EM calculation yields about 10% more DT than PKS with both models for self-moderation. Product yields are cut roughly in half in equimolar mixtures from their corresponding single component yields. However, the yield ratios are more sensitive to a 5-10% variation in individual terms so the ratios from the one component systems are not the same as the ratios of the yields from the equimolar systems. Individual experimental yield values for HT and DT rather than ratios are needed to clarify the description of self-moderation. However, the fact that product yields remain constant as the amount of bromine is increased, above a few percent, argues against much trapping by this route. It is well known that thermal hydrogen and its isotopes react with HBr and DBr, formed from Br_2 scavenging, more readily than with H_2 or D_2.[28] In addition, if transitions to excited electronic states of H_2 and D_2 were important at higher energies, collisional decomposition of ground state hydrogen could be insignificant.[82]

3.2 T + CH_4 (CD_4)

Methane is the prototypical reagent for alkane chemistry, with more degrees of freedom and more complex reaction possibilities than molecular hydrogen. Like H_3, it is difficult to acquire direct experimental evidence for some issues with CH_5 because the threshold energies for all of its reactive processes are relatively high. Isotope effects should be important here and the system is simple enough that accurate *ab initio* information is available. Trajectory treatments of the reactions of tritium with methane include triatomic approximations[83] and several six atom simulations.[23,27,84,85]

3.2.1. Potential Energy Surfaces

Steckler *et al.*[86] recently applied their reaction path analysis to the (reversed) abstraction portion of the potential surfaces used in trajectory studies by Raff,[26] and Chapman and Bunker.[35] The objective here was to determine the features of the surface necessary to agree with measured thermal rate constants for abstraction of H from H_2 by CH_3. The rate constants were calculated by improved canonical variational transition state theory with small-curvature semi-classical adiabatic ground-state transmission coefficients (ICVT-SCSAG). This investigation illustrates the power of the combination of experimental and theoretical approaches to a problem and demonstrates the considerable constraints on the details of the reaction path swath required to reproduce the measurements over a range of temperatures and isotopic combinations.

Both of the potentials examined had mathematical forms which complicated the search for the minimum energy reaction path, the computation of the normal mode frequencies and resultant zero point energy along the reaction path. To perform the comparison, it was therefore necessary to modify these potentials slightly to remove these problems while generating minimal changes in their descriptions. We shall use MR, and MVCR to refer to these fits to the potentials developed by Raff, and Valencich, Chapman and Bunker respectively. Later we shall use R, and VB to refer to the surfaces and data from the surfaces of Raff, and Valencich and Bunker respectively. These results and their comparison with the *ab initio* path calculated by Walch[87] with a polarization configuration interaction wavefunction allowing all single and double excitation configurations with the restriction that only one electron be allowed outside the valence bond space POL-CI(SOGVB) have led to an improved model potential of abstraction for this system.[88]

Comparison[86] of the reactant and product descriptions with experimental values and CI computations, indicates that MR does better in describing the zero point energies. However, a large error in the MR endoergicity results in a prediction for the equilibrium constant, K_e, for the reaction at 1340 K which is low by a factor of 10. The MVCB description does better with the endoergicity but less well with the zero point energies, resulting in a K_e which is a factor of 4 low at the same temperature. The saddle point geometries for abstraction on the MR and MVCB surfaces do not agree with the POL-CI calculations, but both are generally late. The barrier height for abstraction is the most relevant item here and this value is low by 14 kJ/m on MVCB and low by 24 kJ/m on MR compared to the value of 56 KJ/m estimated by Walch. The most serious difficulty with the MVCB description is that the barrier is too narrow and would lead to too much tunneling.

The behavior of a harmonic description of the normal mode frequencies as the system moves along the abstraction reaction coordinate on MVCB and MR was also compared[86] with the *ab initio* calculations of Yamashita and Yamabe, which used a 4-31G split valence basis set.[89] This comparison indicates that the transition state geometry persists too long on the MVCB surface. However, plots of these frequencies in Fig. 2 and 3 of Ref. 86 show an unexpected amount of similarity in general.

Recent *ab initio* calculations on the substitution process have focused on the D_{3h} reaction mechanism, partly because more phase space is involved in less symmetric pathways.[87] Also, earlier work indicated that the D_{3h} trigonal bipyriamid (TBP) was an energetically preferred reaction intermediate relative to several possible alternative structures.[90] Both unmodified (R and CB) empirical potentials have TBP saddle point geometries similar to the results of Walch. The CB version is closer, barrier height 23 kJ/m higher than the best estimate extrapolated by Walch, than Raff's model, axial distance 10 pm small and barrier height 63 kJ/m too high. However, for this process, the substitution barrier is much narrower on the R surface than on the CB surface.[86]

The saddle point normal mode analysis and the resulting transition state theory thermal rate of substitution calculated by Schatz *et al.*,[91] for the R surface is incomplete since none of the trajectories examined in detail proceeded by this mechanism. The actual trajectory path for substitution on the R surface is not known.[23] An examination of less symmetric motion to products on R indicated the presence of more than one connection to the abstraction reaction from the TBP transition state.[10] In each of these surfaces, the barrier to abstraction is considerably lower than that for substitution.[23,27] The contribution to the thermal rate of abstraction by such mechanisms is unclear, with or without tunneling. However, the single collision trajectory probabilities for substitution can still be used to predict hot atom product yields regardless of microscopic mechanism that led to their values.

3.2.2. Product Yields

Abstraction and substitution resulting from hot tritium reactions with methane (and deuteromethane) have been computed by the IRP[23] and stochastic methods from cross sections generated by trajectories run on the VB and R surfaces.[9,10] Raff reports,[23] see Table 2, IRP hot atom yield ratios for HT/CH_3T of 0.79 (with hard sphere self moderation and Br_2 scavenging), and photochemical (272 kJ/m T from TBr) ratios of 0.053 for CD_3T/DT and 8.70 for HT/CH_3T with type C moderation (1-12% differences mentioned between type A and C moderation). Mixtures of CH_4, CD_4, and Br_2 were also simulated and led to the conclusion that the substitution cross sections with CH_4 were low by a factor of 2-3 below 272 kJ/m. Included in the IRP set was a calculation of a hot T yield ratio of 3.78 for HT/CH_3T using limited VB trajectory results,[85] hard sphere moderation, and no analysis of the CH_3T product for decomposition.[23]

A subsequent stochastic simulation implemented the complete trajectory results of VB and included the decomposition of methane and the substitution products, see Table 2.[10] The absolute yields are reported, where available, as well as the pertinent ratios. Firstly, the nuclear recoil product yields in self moderated methane are of the right order of magnitude on both surfaces. Secondly, both trajectory studies produce stochastic nuclear recoil yield ratios of HT/CH_3T that agree with the experimental value, within the expected uncertainty. The yields are on the low side of the measured values, an average stochastic product yield tends to be low by 3.4%. The stochastic yields for the R surface were low by 5 and 8% for abstraction and substitution respectively, on the VB surface only the substitution value was low, by 4%. While these differences are not great, it is clear that individual yields are more discriminating than ratios. Inverting substitution makes a significant contribution to the yield of CH_3T only in the VB simulation. However,

TABLE 2. HOT TRITIUM PRODUCT YIELDS WITH METHANES,[b] T + CX_4

X	σ; Ref.: E range	Abstrac.	Subst.	Inv.	α	HT/CH_3T	LPD/RD
H	VB; 10: II	19.8±3%	21.0±6%	28%	.50	.94±.32	20.5/20.8
H	VB; 9: I + II	16 ± 3%	18 ±6%	18%		.89±..5	24–3%
H	*VB; 23: III*					*3.78*	
H	*R; 23: III*					*.79*	
H	R; 10: II	13.6±3%	17.4±3%	0%	.07	.78±.08	49±2%
H	Nuc. Rec. Exp.: I	20 ±5%	25 ±5%			.80±.18	5±5%
D	VB; 10: I	15.9±3%	21.1±6%	24%	.40	.75±.11	5/1
D	R; 10: I	24.0±3%	24.0±3%	0%		1.0±.30	
D	Nuc. Rec. Exp.: I	18 ±5%	22 ±5%			.80±.18	
H	VB; 10: IV	10.4±3%	4.1±3%	100%	.07	2.5±4.0	
H	*Raff; 23: IV*					*8.7*	
H	R; 10: IV	29±3%	3.0±3%	0%		10±	
H	Photo. Exp.: IV	(12 to 17% total yield of products)					3-4
D	VB; 10: IV	11.3±3%	1.2±3%	100%	.08	9.4±5.0	
D	*R; 23: IV*					*19*	
D	R;10: IV	31 ±3%	2.4%±3%	0%		13±	
D	Photo. Exp.: IV	(12 to 17% total yield of products)					15-19
H	VB+Br_2, Ar(C): II	13.8 ± 3%	12.6 ± 6%	24%	.074	1.1±0.5	
H	VB+Br_2, Ar(A): II	9.5 ± 3%	4.0 ± 6%	25%	.07	2.4±0.5	
H	VB+Br_2, Ar(A): I	11 ± 3%	12 ± 6%	19%		.91	
H	Nuc. Rec. Exp., Ar	7 ± 5%	12 ± 5%			.58±.13	2±2%
			CH_4/CD_4=1				
	VB; 10: IV	5.8±3%,H	2.4±3%,H	100%		2.4±.3,H	
		5.5±3%,D	0.3±3%,D	100%		18 ± 4,D	
	R; 23: III					*2.4 /1*	
						[HT][CD4]/[DT][CH4] = 1.18	
						[CH3T/CH4]/[CD3T/CD4]=6.9	
	Photo. Exp.: IV					HT/DT=1.4	
						CH3T/CD3T=6.9	

[b]Energy region IV covers the region from initiation at 272 kJ/m down to thermal energies, III represents the limits covered in the IRP calculations, II was used in Ref. 10 and usually went up to 25 MJ/m, and I includes the region up to the actual initiation energy.

processes which retain the ordering of the non-reactive hydrogens dominate the hot yield of substitution products in both treatments.

The nuclear recoil VB simulations with CD_4 compare even more favorably with the experimental values, at the ratio level and at the individual yield level. Abstraction and substitution product yields are found to increase for CD_4 on R, whereas the measurements indicate both product yields decrease.[77] Here then, an acceptable ratio arises from numbers which are changing in the wrong direction. Abstraction and substitution cross sections on R both peak at energies which are lower with CD_4 than with CH_4, suggesting a dominant role for the lower energy end of the curve.

The self moderating properties, P(E, E'), of the two surfaces were determined differently. Raff used one impact parameter to generate reaction probabilities and a much larger value to compute the values for P(E, E'). This computed moderator function is very similar to model C tested by Porter and Kunt, and in fact the same resulted in an extremely inefficient moderator model for methane, see Table 2. The resultant average value for α on R was 0.07,[10] this is less efficient than H_2, where α= 0.24, or D_2, α= 0.27, and is comparable to model C for Ar.

The entire collection of data for single collision events, including the moderator function, was generated from the same set of trajectories by Valencich and Bunker.[10] The average stochastic α value generated by the VB trajectory data for CH_4 is 0.50, giving $\alpha(CH_4)$=6.7 α(Ar) which compares well with the value which was extracted by Seewald and Wolfgang from experimental data, $\alpha(CH_4)$=(6.±1) α(Ar).[77]

Trajectory studies of reactive systems generally sample impact parameters, from a squared distribution, out to the point where reaction probabilities become unprofitably small.[33] The larger the impact parameter, the smaller the amount of energy transferred in scattering events. This extrapolates to zero energy being transferred by an infinite number of grazing collisions. It is well understood that the effective collision radius increases in general as the relative collisional energy decreases.[32] All three models used for energy transfer by Porter and Kunt, and the one form used by Raff, were independent of the collision energy and A and C represent the opposite ends of limiting behavior. Stochastic predictions were unchanged with a type B moderator function because while more collisions occurred, fewer of them were reactive. This result and the test performed by PK suggest that a more effective model for moderation combined with the reactive probabilities of Raff would increase predicted product yields, which are already high, without changing the ratios.

It is interesting that, as with hydrogen, self moderated nuclear recoil systems predict large amounts of scavenged products for both surfaces, (20.5% CH_2TBr and 20.8% CH_3Br on VB; and 49% total decomposition on R). Root observed similar absolute yields of decomposition products when nuclear recoil T systems used I_2 as the scavenger.[25] Inclusion of the decomposition channels indicates that "energy shadowing" is not operative with methane. Low energy processes are not depleted by removal of hot atoms, instead the products which are formed at high energies

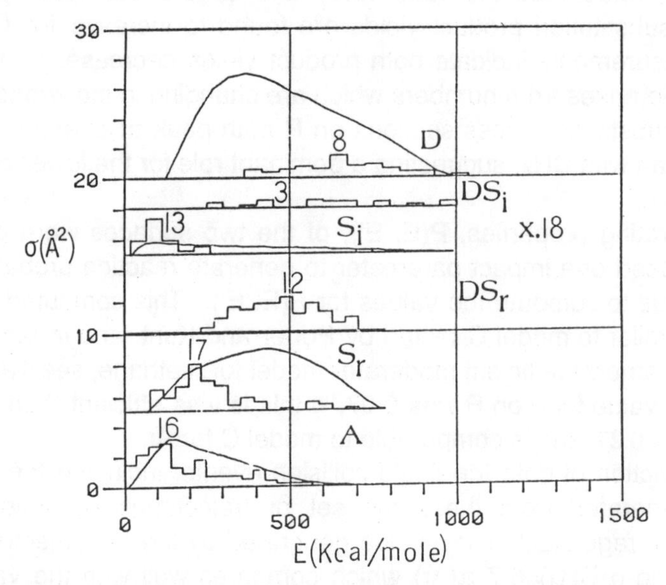

Fig. 4. Stochastic simulation histograms, Ref. 10, superimposed (x 0.18) upon the reaction cross section curves, $\sigma(E_r)$, this figure is reproduced with permission from Ref. 10. The smoothed curves are the reaction cross sections (square angstroms) for A=abstraction, S_r=substitution which retained the ordering of the non-reacting hydrogen ligands, S_i=inverting substitution, and decomposition of the substituted products, DS_r and DS_i respectively as well as D=decomposition of the methane target. The integer next to each histogram peak gives the number of events in that peak.

tend to be depleted by decomposition. When decomposition releases the originally "hot" atom, it is reintroduced into the mixture with drastically reduced kinetic energy.

Decomposition derives from the large amount of energy deposited upon substitution and is quite insensitive to the details of the critical configuration, including the degree of relaxation of the methyl group, the frequency of the critical coordinate and the threshold energy for decomposition with the VB description. The sensitivity of stochastic results to the trajectory input was also tested by redrawing all the $\sigma(E_r)$, P(E,E*), P(E,E') and P(E,χ) curves to be as different as possible yet within their error bars, where available. The noise level of the trajectory data is within the uncertainty of the stochastic simulation.

This type of examination could not be performed for Raff's description of CH_5 because secondary probability data were not reported. As discussed earlier for hydrogen targets, the significance of the prediction of large amounts of radiation damage is difficult to assess. Either decomposition fragments react further in the laboratory, and/or the high energy predictions from these approximations to the ground state surface are unreliable. It is clear that the yield of stable products here is adequate, and methane has channels available at high energies which could completely circumvent the decomposition path. However, additional calculations involving transitions to excited state surfaces would be necessary and the fate of products formed from these routes would be another issue.

Systems where the tritium is introduced at much lower energies, for example by the photochemical rupture of the bond in TBr, examine the surface descriptions in regions where decomposition is not an issue. The VB surface predictions agree well with the experiments as the data were used to coarsely determine surface parameters. Raff's treatment, however used no experimental data for calibration purposes. The individual laboratory yields are not known because the T scavenged by Br_2 gets recycled by the photolysis process. However the total yield of products has been estimated. Examination of the calculated individual product yields indicates that a high yield of abstraction (2-3 times the estimated total yield) with CH_4 on R causes the ratio of abstraction to substitution to be too high, which is not surprising considering the barrier size. It must be remembered that tunneling corrections were not included in these calculations. Tunneling would improve the photochemical ratio of abstraction to substitution from Raff's surface, however this would also further increase the total stochastic yield of products on this surface.

Simulations including an inert moderator were also performed, although the hydrogen system already puts the simple models examined for energy transfer in doubt. When a hard sphere inert moderator was added to the system, X_{Ar}=0.90, the thermalization properties did not change much but nearly twice as many collisions were sampled before reaction took place. When type C moderation was used for argon, 2.5 times more collisions were necessary for thermalization and the number of collision sampled before the target was removed from tracking was four times larger. The total yields are all reduced, the yield ratio is unchanged, and the individual error bars are relatively larger, because fewer collisions occur between tritium and methane.[20] The greatest percent difference between the self and inert moderated collision spectra occurs in the counting bin at the very lowest energy, below 210 kJ/m, where cross section curves have the greatest relative uncertainty and are changing rapidly. Considering the level of treatment of the inert moderator and the validity of a classical description near the threshold region, the agreement between the stochastic predictions of Valencich and Bunker and the experimental values is acceptable. Further investigation of this situation awaits trajectory input from an improved surface.[88]

4. Ionic Energy Loss Processes

It is appropriate, at this point, to return to consideration of the scheme according to which energy was partitioned in discussing the hot atom experiment. It is true that the IRP and stochastic product yield demonstrate an insensitivity to the exact energy at which tracking of the hot atom begins. However, the good agreement between experiment and theory could be fortuitous if the distribution of collisions, f(E), actually sampled in the reactive region is greatly different than predicted.

A qualitative investigation of this possibility was performed by initiating the simulation at 17 GJ/m and including the following ionic processes for M= CH_4, and, in some cases, Ar:[9,10]

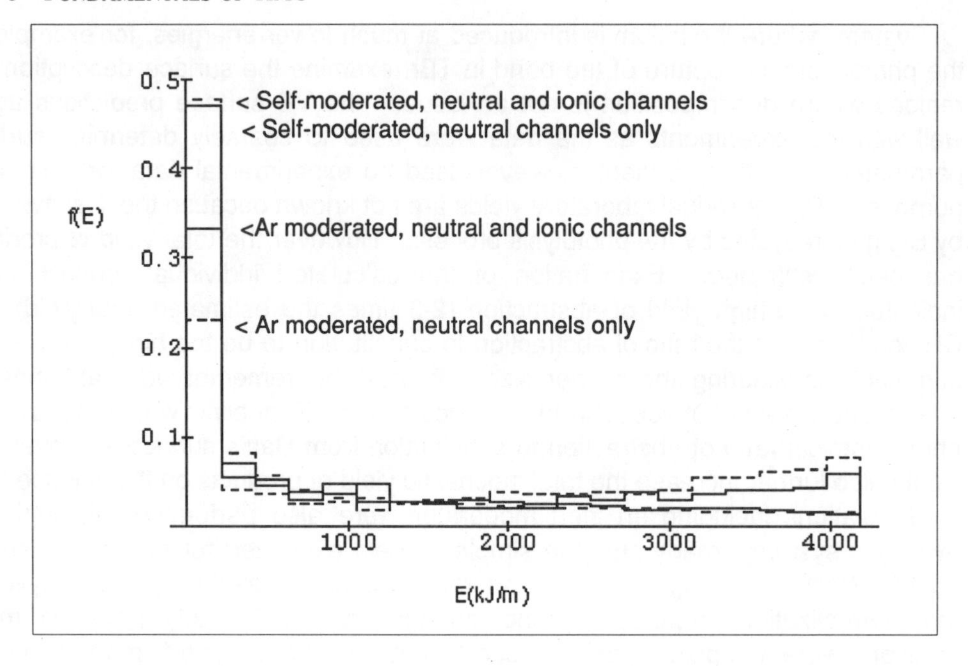

Figure 5 The collision spectrum, f(E) in the reactive region generated by initiating each tritium with 17 GJ/m of energy, including processes (4) through (6) with the other possibilities predicted by VB trajectories in self moderated and type C Ar moderated methane.

$$T^+ + M \rightarrow T^+ + M^+ + e^- \quad (4)$$
$$T^+ + M \rightarrow T + M^+ \quad (5)$$
$$T + M \rightarrow T^+ + M + e^- \quad (6)$$

Fig. 5 shows the collision spectrum predicted in the reactive region. When Ar was included model A was used for non-reactive scattering. More than a million collisions were simulated in generating each curve marked with a dot in this figure, square root uncertainties were demonstrated for each counting bin. Included in Fig. 5 are the distributions from paper III,[9] generated at lower initial tritium energies without the ionic processes. This figure shows that the model for non-reactive energy transfer makes a larger difference in f(E) than including, or not including processes (4) through (6). The predicted yields are smaller and the relative uncertainties are larger because the sample size is smaller, nearly 300 total tritiums were tracked, but the yield of individual products and the ratio of abstraction to substitution are within the uncertainties of the measured values. The predictions of radiation damage are also unchanged. This limited theoretical investigation supports the long standing hot atom assumption, that hot atom yields arise from reactions in the energy range appropriate for formation of stable chemical products.

5. Hot Atom Bond Energy Effect

The yield of TH, or TD, abstracted by hot tritium atoms from RH, or RD, increases as the bond dissciation energy of RH, or RD, decreases. The source of this effect has been experimentally investigated by nuclear recoil and photochemically initiated tritium reactions with several hydrocarbons. The situation has been simulated theoretically by Chapman and Suplinskas[92] and by Valencich, Chapman and Bunker (CVB).[93] Chapman and Suplinskas approximated the various hydrocarbons as triatomic RH molecules and described the TRH interactions with a LEPS potential energy function. The variables in the simulation were with mass of R and the dissociation energy of the RH bond. In this calculation, the yield of abstraction increases as the RH bond dissociation energy decreases. However, the mathematical form of the LEPS potential necessarily ties the reaction barrier height to the value of the reaction exoergicity.[94] It was noted that the yield of abstraction could as well be said to increase with reaction exothermicity. Valencich, Chapman and Bunker repeated the simulation using the potential form evolved by Bunker and coworkers because its form allowed for independent variation of reaction exothermicity and the barrier height. This simulation clarifies this feature of hot atom chemistry. The yield of abstraction increases as the barrier height for reaction decreases, regardless of whether or not the reaction is exothermic.[93]

6. Summary

In conclusion, this chapter could also have been titled "Hot Atom Contributions to Theory" because the results of this type of experiment has been invaluable to the development of theoretical descriptions of some fundamental chemistry. Theoretical treatments have been initiated because the experimental data itself elicits interesting questions. The full set of experimental data has challenged alternative models for the interactions in the system. Individual product yields rather than ratios of yields are shown to be the discriminating information. The yield of stable products formed by the reaction of hot tritium atoms with H_2 and CH_4, and their isotopic analogs, can be considered adequately described. Hot atom abstraction yields are understood to be determined by the value of the barrier height for abstraction, which may or may not be determined by the reaction exothermicity. The collision spectrum in the region of chemical importance has been demonstrated to be independent of the exact value of the initiating energy, validating a basic assumption of hot atom chemistry. Effective thermal scavengers have been included with a fairly constant effect. Three issues of interest invite additional inquiry: trajectory predictions for the surface representation developed by Truhlar and colleagues[88] which improves the descriptions of abstraction; improved energy transfer models, and the decomposition of collisionally excited target molecules (H_2[34] and CH_4[95]) and internally excited reaction products (HT and CH_3T).

References

1. Friedlander,G., Kennedy,J.W., Miller, J.M.: "Nuclear and Radiochemistry",.Wiley, New York, 1964.
2. Gilbody,H.B.: Adv. in Atomic and Molec. Physics **22**, 143 (1986).
3. Wilson, W.E.: Radiation Research **49**, 36 (1972).
4. Wolfgang, R.: Progress in Reaction Kinetics **3**, 97 (1965).
5. Kaplan, I.G., and Miterev, A.M.: Adv. Chem. Phys. **68**, 255 (1987).
6. Betts, J.: Ph.D. Thesis, California Institute of Technology, 1972.
7. Gonzalez Urena, A.: Adv. Chem. Phys. **66**, 213 (1987).
8. Rossler, K., Pross, L.: Radiation Effects **48**, 207 (1980).
9. Valencich, T.: Chem. Phys. Lett. **104**, 620 (1984).
10. Valencich, T.: J. Chem. Phys., **79**, 671 (1983).
11. P.J. Estrup and R. Wolfgang, J. Am. Chem. Soc. **82**, 2661 (1960).
12. Malcolme-Lawes, D.J.: "Hot Atom Chemistry" (T. Matsuura, Ed.) Kodansha, Tokyo (and Elsevier, Amsterdam), 1984, p. 39,.
13. Adams, J.T., Porter,R.N.: J. Chem. Phys. **59**, 4105 (1973).
14. Malerich, C.J.,Spicer, L.D.: J. Chem. Phys. **59**, 1577 (1973).
15. Wotzak,G.P.: J. Chem. Phys. **59**, 899 (1973).
16. Kiezer, J.: J. Chem. Phys. **58**,4524 (1973).
17. Malerich, C.J. Spicer,L.D.: Chem. Phys. Lett. **18**, 405 (1973).
18. Keizer, J.: J. Chem. Phys. **56**, 5958 (1972).
19. Porter, R.N., Kunt,S.: J. Chem. Phys. **52**, 3240 (1970).
20. Chapin, D.M., Kostin, M.D.: J. Chem. Phys. **46**, 2506 (1967).
21. Porter,R.N.: J. Chem. Phys. **45**, 2284 (1966).
22. Malcolme-Lawes, D.J.: J. Chem. Phys. **57**, 2481 (1972).
23. Raff, L.M., J. Chem. Phys., **60**, 2220 (1974).
24. Rowland, F.S., Coulter, P.: Radiochim. Acta **2**, 163 (1964).
25. Root,J., Ph.D. Thesis, University of Kansas, Kansas, 1964 (University Microfilms, Ann Arbor, Michigan).
26. Malcolme-Lawes, D.J.: J. Chem. Soc. Faraday II **71**, 1183 (1975).
27. Valencich, T., and Bunker, D.L., J. Chem. Phys. **61**,21 (1974).
28. White, J.M., J. Chem. Phys. **58**, 4482 (1973).
29. Karplus, M., Porter, R.N., Sharma, R.D.: J. Chem. Phys. **45**, 3871 (1966).
30. Karplus, M., Porter, R.N., Sharma, R.D.: J. Chem. Phys. **43**, 3259 (1965).
31. Malcolme-Lawes, D.J., J. Chem. Phys. **57**, 5522 (1972).
32. Suplinskas, R., J. Chem. Phys. **49**, 5046 (1966).
33. Hase, W.L., VENUS (1988), Quantum Chemistry Program Exchange, University of Illinois, Bloomington, Illinois.
34. Truhlar, D.G., Garrett, B.C.: Ann. Rev. Phys. Chem. **35**, 159 (1984).
35. Steinfeld, J.I., Francisco, J.S., Hase, W.L., "Chemical Kinetics and Dynamics." Prentice Hall, Englewood Cliffs, New Jersey, 1989.
36. Green, S.: J. Chem. Phys. **93**, 1496 (1990).
37. Blais, N.C., Truhlar, D.G.: J. Chem. Phys. **65**, 5335 (1976).
38. Chapman, S., Bunker, D.L.: J. Chem. Phys. **62**, 2890 (1975).
39. Saythyamurthy, N.: Comp. Phys. **3**, 120 (1981).
40. Bunker, D.L.: J. Chem. Phys. **57**, 332 (1972).
41. Hase, W.L.: "Aspects of the Kinetics and Dynamics of Surface Reactions," (U. Landman, Ed.) AIP Conference Proceedings, New York, 1980, Vol., p. 109.
42. Mentch, F., Anderson, J.B.: J. Chem. Phys. **80**, 2675 (1984).
43. Liu, B.: J. Chem. Phys. **80**, 581 (1984).
44. Siegbahn, P., Liu, B.: J. Chem. Phys. **68**, 2457 (1978).
45. Continetti, R.E., Balko, R.A., Lee, Y.T.: J. Chem. Phys. **93**, 5719 (1990).
46. Valentini, J.J., Phillips, D.L.: "Advances in Gas Phase Photochemistry and Kinetics", (M.N.R. Ashfold and J.E. Baggot, Ed.) Royal Soc. of Chem., London, **2**, 1 (1989).
47. Bowman, J.M., Lee, K.T., Walker, R.B.: J. Chem. Phys. **79**, 3742 (1983).

48. AbuSalbi, N., Kouri, D.J., Baer, M.: Chem. Phys. Let. **105**, 472 (1984).
49. Sun, J.C., Choi, B.H., Poe, R.T., Tang, K.T.: Phys. Rev. Lett. **44**, 1211 (1983).
50. Walker, R.B., Hayes, E.F.: J. Phys. Chem. **87**, 1255 (1983).
51. Pollak, E., Wyatt, R.E.: J. Chem. Phys, **78**, 4464 (1983).
52. Blais, N.C., and Truhlar, D.G.: "Potential Energy Surfaces and Dynamics Calculations" (D.G. Truhlar, Ed.) Plenum, New York, 1981, p. 431.
53. Mayne. J.R., and Toennies, J.P.: J. Chem. Phys. **75**, 1794 (1981).
54. Sathymurthy, N., Toennies, J.P.: Chem. Phys. Lett **143**, 323 (1988).
55. Blais. N.C., Truhlar, D.G.: J. Chem. Phys. **88**, 5457 (1988).
56. Aoiz, F.J., Herrero, V.J., Saez, V.: Chem. Phys. Lett.. **161**, 220 (1989).
57. Brumer, P., Karplus, M.: J. Chem. Phys. **54**, 4955 (1971).
58. Walker, R.B., Stechel, E.B., Light, J.C.: J. Chem. Phys. **69**, 2922 (1978).
59. Schatz, G.C., Kuppermann, A.: J. Chem. Phys. **65**, 4668 (1976).
60. Zhang, J.Z.H., Miller, W.H.: Chem. Phys. Lett. **153**, 465 (1988).
61. Manolopoulous, D.E., Wyatt, R.E. : Chem. Phys. Lett. **159**, 123 (1989).
62. Zhang, J.Z.H., Miller, W.H.: J. Chem. Phys. **91**, 1528 (1989).
63. Zhao, M., Truhlar, D.G., Schwenke, D.W., Kouri, D.J. : J. Phys. Chem., (in press).
64. Varandas, A.K.C.: Chem. Phys. Lett. **69**, 295 (1982).
65. Garrett, B.C., Truhlar, D.G.: J. Phys. Chem. **89**, 2205 (1985).
66. Truhlar, D.G., Horowitz, C.J.: J. Chem. Phys. **68**, 2466 (1978).
67. Schatz, G.C.: "Potential Energy Surfaces and Dynamics Calculations" (D.G. Truhlar, Ed.) Plenum, New York, 1981, p. 287.
68. Truhlar, D.G., Wyatt, R.E.: Ann. Rev. Phys. Chem. **27**, 1 (1976).
69. Rozenshtein, V.B., Gershenzon, Y.M., Ivanov, A.V., Kucheryavil, S.I.: Chem. Phys. Let., **105**, 423(1984).
70. Bowman, J.M., Lee, K.T.: Chem. Phys. Lett. **94**, 363 (1983).
71. Gerritz, P.P., Valentini, J.J.: J. Chem. Phys. **81**, 1290 (1984).
72. Marinero, E.E., Rettner, C.T., Zare, R.N.: J. Chem. Phys. **80**, 4146 (1984).
73. Nick, J.C., Valentini, J.J., J. Chem. Phys. **92**, 1083 (1990).
74. Blais, N.C., Truhlar, D.G., Garrett, B.C.: J. Chem. Phys. **82**, 2300 (1985).
75. Auerbach, S.M., Zhang., J.Z.H., Miller, W.M.: J. Chem. Soc. Faraday Trans. **86**, 1707 (1990).
76. Lee, J.K., Musgrave, B., Rowland, F.S.: J. Chem. Phys. **32**, 1266 (1960).
77. Seewald, D., Wolfgang,R.: J. Chem. Phys. **47**, 1297 and 143 (1967).
78. Sappey, A.D., Copeland, R.A.: J. Chem. Phys. **93**, 5741 (1990).
79. Chou, C.C., Rowland, F.S.: J. Chem. Phys. **46**, 812 (1967).
80. Valencich, T., Arcia, E., Abboud, N.: calculations in progress using a modified version of QCPE Program #434, HotAtom, by Valencich, T., 1982 which will be resubmitted to the QCPE.
81. Urch, D.S., Welch, M.J.: Chem. Com. **1965**, 126.
82. Stine, J.R., and J.T. Muckerman, J. Chem. Phys. **68**, 185 (1978).
83. Kuntz, P., Nemeth, E., Polanyi, J., Wong, W.: J. Chem. Phys. **52**, 4654 (1970).
84. Bunker, D.L., Pattengill, M.D.: J. Chem. Phys. **53**, 304 (1970).
85. Valencich,T., and D.L. Bunker, Chem. Phys. Lett. **20**, 50 (1973).
86. Steckler, R., Dykema, K.J., Brown, F.B., Hancock, G.C., Truhlar, D.G., Valencich, T.: J. Chem. Phys. **87**, 7024 (1987).
87. Walch, S.P.: J. Chem. Phys. **72**, 4932 (1980).
88. Joseph, T., Steckler, R., Truhlar, D.G. : J. Chem. Phys. **87**, 7036 (1987).
89. Yamashita, K., and Yamabe, T.: Int. J. Quantum Chem. Symp. **17**, 177 (1983).
90. Ehrenson, S, Newton, M.D.: Chem. Phys. Lett. **13**, 24 (1972).
91. Schatz, G.C., Walch, S.P., Wagner, A.F.: J. Chem. Phys. **73**, 4536 (1980).
92. Chapman, S., Suplinskas, R.J., J. Chem. Phys. **60**,248 (1974).
93. Chapman, S., Valencich, T., Bunker, D.L.: J. Chem. Phys. **60**, 329 (1974).
94. Parr, C.A. and Truhlar, D.G.: J. Phys. Chem. **75**, 1844 (1971).
95. Hase, W.L., Date, N., Bhuiyan, L.B., Buckowski, D.G.: J. Phys. Chem. **89**, 2502 (1985).

3.6 Nonequilibrium Time Dependent Theory of Hot Atom Reactions

Katsuhisa KOURA
Aerodynamics Division, National Aerospace Laboratory, 7-44-1 Jindaijihigashi, Chofu, Tokyo 182, Japan

Bernie SHIZGAL
Department of Chemistry, University of British Columbia, 2036 Main Mall, Vancouver, British Columbia, V6T 1Y6 Canada

1. Introduction

One of the main objectives of the study of chemical reaction kinetics is the elucidation of the details of the reaction dynamics given in terms of the collision cross sections leading to reaction. The hot atom experiment and theory can offer information with regard to the high energy portion of the cross sections above the threshold energy. In a gas phase hot atom experiment, a translationally highly energetic atomic species, often the product of a nuclear transformation, is introduced into a multicomponent system of gas moderators, reactants, and scavengers. The hot atom loses energy via collisions with the moderators until it reaches the energy range over which a reaction occurs. The atom is then able to react with a reactant until its energy falls below the threshold for reaction or it is removed by reaction with a scavenger at thermal energies.

The steady state (time independent) approach initiated by the kinetic theory of Estrup and Wolfgang[1] has been developed by many authors with the concepts of the collision density and the integral reaction probability.[2] They were primarily interested in providing a method to interpret experimental data which give the fraction of atoms that end up as products of the reaction with the different reactants in the system, or the yield of reaction.

On the other hand, the dynamical features of hot atoms such as the reaction rate constant, the hot atom temperature (mean energy), and the mean reaction lifetime and distance can be studied by the time dependent approach based on the chemical kinetic Boltzmann equation. The need for a time dependent description of the hot atom reaction was first suggested by Keizer.[3] This is physically reasonable because the process of moderation and reaction of a hot atom is intrinsically time dependent. Keizer[4] indicated that the dynamical (quasi-) steady state may possibly exist in the process of hot atom reaction because of the dynamical balancing between the cooling and heating effects due to nonreactive and reactive collisions, respectively, and the hot atom reaction may be treated using the (quasi-) steady state reaction rate constant, a standard concept of chemical reaction kinetics. The dynamical steady state theory was pursued by Keizer and Root and their co-workers for several years[4-9] and also discussed recently by Robson.[10] The basis for the time dependent approach is presented in Section 2 and the dynamical steady state theory is discussed in Section 3.1.

A more rigorous analysis of the time dependent approach based on solutions of the Boltzmann equation was considered by Koura[11-14] with a Monte Carlo simulation (Section 3.4), by Shizgal[15,16] and Fitzpatrick,[17] and Knierim et al.[18] with a moment method (Section 3.2), and by Shizgal[19] with a discrete ordinate method (Section 3.3). One of the main results of these works is that the dynamical steady state is not realized for most physically realistic situations and, therefore, the time dependent approach requires nonequilibrium time dependent solutions of the Boltzmann equation.

2. Time Dependent Formulation

In the time dependent approach, a large number of hot atoms generated instantaneously or during a lapse of time are taken as initial hot atoms and the time evolution of the velocity distribution function of the hot atoms is investigated. Because the hot atoms are considered to be dilutely dispersed in reservoir molecules and mutually non-interacting and the collision between a hot atom and reservoir molecules may be assumed to be binary except in dense gases, the hot atom velocity distribution function is governed by the linear Boltzmann equation.

The velocity distribution function $f_A(\mathbf{v},t)$ of hot atoms A at time t represents the number of hot atoms $[f_A(\mathbf{v},t)d\mathbf{v}]$ with velocity in the range $\mathbf{v}$ to $\mathbf{v}+d\mathbf{v}$; $f_A(\mathbf{v},t)$ is normalized so that the total number of hot atoms, $N_A(t)$, is given by $N_A(t)=\int f_A(\mathbf{v},t)d\mathbf{v}$. The velocity distribution function of hot atoms may also be considered as the probability distribution of the hot atom velocity defined by $p_A(\mathbf{v},t)=f_A(\mathbf{v},t)/N_A(t)$. On the other hand, the velocity distribution function $f_R(\mathbf{w})$ of reservoir molecules R represents the number of reservoir molecules R $[f_R(\mathbf{w})d\mathbf{w}]$ with velocity in the range $\mathbf{w}$ to $\mathbf{w}+d\mathbf{w}$ per unit volume and is assumed to be the time independent Maxwellian distribution

$$f_R(\mathbf{w}) = n_R(m_R/2\pi kT_R)^{3/2}\exp(-m_R w^2/2kT_R) \quad (1)$$

normalized as $n_R=\int f_R(\mathbf{w})d\mathbf{w}$, where n_R, m_R, T_R, and w are the number density, mass, temperature, and speed of reservoir molecules R, respectively, and k is the Boltzmann constant; n_R and T_R are assumed to be constant. The time evolution of $f_A(\mathbf{v},t)$ is described by the linear Boltzmann equation

$$\partial f_A/\partial t = J(f_A), \quad (2)$$

where $J(f_A)$ denotes the hot atom collision terms that describe the change in f_A due to elastic, inelastic, and reactive collisions with reservoir molecules. The form of each collision term is similar and, here, the collision terms are explicitly written for a non-moderated system where reservoir molecules consist of a single species R without internal degrees of freedom and hot atoms undergo multichannel reactions specified as α

$$A + R \xrightarrow{\alpha} \text{products}, \tag{3}$$

where the backward reaction is neglected because of the small concentration of products; i.e.,

$$J(f_A) = \int [f_A(\mathbf{v}',t) f_R(\mathbf{w}') - f_A(\mathbf{v},t) f_R(\mathbf{w})] g \sigma_{eR}(g,\Omega) d\Omega d\mathbf{w} - \Sigma_\alpha \int f_A(\mathbf{v},t) f_R(\mathbf{w}) g \sigma_{r\alpha}(g) d\mathbf{w}, \tag{4}$$

where $\mathbf{v}'$ and $\mathbf{w}'$ are, respectively, the velocities after collision betweeen a hot atom with velocity $\mathbf{v}$ and a reservoir molecule with velocity $\mathbf{w}$, $g=|\mathbf{v}-\mathbf{w}|$ is the relative speed, $\sigma_{eR}(g,\Omega)$ is the differential cross section for the elastic scattering into a solid angle Ω, and $\sigma_{r\alpha}(g)$ is the total cross section for the α reaction channel. The reactive cross section is finite over a certain energy range $E_1<E<E_2$ and zero elsewhere, because above E_2 a hot atom is too energetic to result in reaction while E_1 is the minimum (threshold) energy required for reaction[1]; realistic cross sections are provided by trajectory calculations.[2,6] In model calculations, the simple step function

$$\sigma_{r\alpha}(g) = \sigma_r, \quad E_1<E<E_2, \qquad = 0, \quad \text{elsewhere}, \tag{5}$$

is often employed, where σ_r is constant, $E=\mu g^2/2$ is the relative energy, $\mu = m_A m_R/(m_A+m_R)$ is the reduced mass, and m_A is the hot atom mass.

Integrating Eq.(2) over the velocity $\mathbf{v}$ yields the usual reaction rate equation

$$dN_A(t)/dt = -\kappa(t) N_A(t), \tag{6}$$

where $\kappa(t)$ is the overall rate constant given by

$$\kappa(t) = \Sigma_\alpha \kappa_\alpha(t), \tag{7}$$

in which $\kappa_\alpha(t)$ is the rate constant for the α channel defined by

$$\kappa_\alpha(t) = \int g \sigma_{r\alpha}(g) p_A(\mathbf{v},t) f_R(\mathbf{w}) d\mathbf{v} d\mathbf{w}. \tag{8}$$

The reaction rate equation for the number of product molecules, $N_\alpha(t)$, generated through the α channel is written as

$$dN_\alpha(t)/dt = \kappa_\alpha(t) N_A(t). \tag{9}$$

Although Eq.(6) or (9) takes the standard form of a reaction rate equation, the rate constant $\kappa(t)$ or $\kappa_\alpha(t)$ is time dependent through the probability distribution $p_A(\mathbf{v},t)$ and, therefore, Eqs.(6) and (9) cannot be solved without the knowledge of $p_A(\mathbf{v},t)$. If $p_A(\mathbf{v},t)$ is obtained from the Boltzmann equation, then time dependent properties of hot atoms can be calculated; e.g., the product yield Y_α through the α reaction channel is given by $Y_\alpha = N_\alpha(t)/N_A(0)$, where $N_A(0)$ is the initial number of hot atoms; the mean energy of hot atoms, $\langle E_A \rangle$, is given by $\langle E_A \rangle = \int (m_A v^2/2) p_A(\mathbf{v},t) d\mathbf{v}$, and the hot atom temperature T_A is given by $T_A = (2/3k)\langle E_A \rangle$, where v is the hot atom speed; the mean reaction lifetime $\langle \tau_r \rangle$ is given by $\langle \tau_r \rangle = \int_0^t t(-dN_A/dt)dt \,/ \int_0^t (-dN_A/dt)dt$.

3. Methods of Solution

In order to solve the Boltzmann equation, a set of cross sections for nonreactive (elastic or inelastic) and reactive collisions should be known or assumed over the wide energy range from extraordinarily high to thermal energies. Accurate and efficient solutions of the Boltzmann equation are required to test the reliability of (assumed) cross sections and suggest modifications through quantitative comparisons with experimental results such as yields of reaction; the method of solution should be applicable to realistic and complex systems where hot atoms interact with multicomponent reservoir molecules (with internal degrees of freedom) through multichannel nonreactive and reactive collisions.

There exist various methods for solving the linear Boltzmann equation and, here, some methods of solution which have been employed in the time dependent approach are briefly described and discussed for the simple system where reservoir molecules consist of a single species R without internal degrees of freedom and hot atoms undergo the single reaction

$$A + R \rightarrow \text{products}. \tag{10}$$

It is noted that this simple system can be used to study the cooling effect of moderators by decreasing the ratio of the reactive to elastic cross sections in proportion to the fractional concentration of reactive molecules R.

3.1. Local Maxwellian Approach and Dynamical Steady State Theory

The local Maxwellian approach[4,7-9] is based on the assumption that the velocity distribution attains the local Maxwellian distribution at a hot atom (time dependent) temperature $T_A(t)$

$$p_A[\mathbf{v},T_A(t)] = [m_A/2\pi kT_A(t)]^{3/2} \exp[-m_A v^2/2kT_A(t)] \tag{11}$$

before hot atoms are appreciably depleted by the hot atom reaction because of the smallness of the reactive cross section relative to the elastic cross section. This approach offers significant advantages in terms of conceptual and computational simplicity, because a single physically meaningful parameter $T_A(t)$ is assumed to determine all of the dynamical features of the hot atoms. The equation that determines $T_A(t)$ is obtained from Eq.(2) by multiplying both sides by $m_A v^2/2$ and integrating over $\mathbf{v}$ by the use of Eq.(6) as

$$dT_A/dt = (2/3k) [\xi_e(T_A) + \xi_r(T_A) + (3k/2)T_A \kappa(T_A)] \equiv F(T_A), \quad (12)$$

where

$$\xi_e(T_A) = \int (m_A v^2/2) [p_A(\mathbf{v}',T_A) f_R(\mathbf{w}') - p_A(\mathbf{v},T_A) f_R(\mathbf{w})] g \sigma_{eR}(g,\Omega) d\Omega\, d\mathbf{w} d\mathbf{v}, \quad (13)$$

$$\xi_r(T_A) = -\Sigma_a \int (m_A v^2/2)\ p_A(\mathbf{v},T_A) f_R(\mathbf{w}) g \sigma_r(g)\ d\mathbf{w} d\mathbf{v}, \quad (14)$$

are, respectively, the hot atom energy change rates due to elastic and reactive collisions with reservoir molecules R, $\sigma_r(g)$ being the total reactive cross section, and $\kappa(T_A)$ is the rate constant obtained from Eqs.(8) and (11). Equation (12) is integrated as

$$t = \int_{T_A(0)}^{T_A} 1/F(T_A)\ dT_A, \quad (15)$$

where $T_A(0)$ is the initial hot atom temperature.

The local Maxwellian approach is simplified further if the hot atom reaction is assumed to have attained a steady state [$dT_A/dt=0$ in Eq.(12)] where the hot atom temperature T_A remains constant at the value T_A^* determined by

$$\xi_e(T_A^*)/\kappa^* + \xi_r(T_A^*)/\kappa^* + (3k/2)T_A^* = 0 \quad (16)$$

before hot atoms are appreciably depleted. In Eq.(16), κ^* is the value of $\kappa(T_A)$ at $T_A=T_A^*$. It is of interest to note that the first term of Eq.(16) represents the cooling rate due to elastic collisions and the second and third terms represent the heating rate due to reactive collisions and, therefore, Eq.(16) shows a dynamical balancing between the cooling and heating in the reacting system. This dynamical steady state theory was developed by Keizer.[4] It is shown that two solutions of Eq.(16) are dynamically stable; a high temperature (quasi-) steady state (HTSS) with $T_A^*>T_R$ is possible for a highly reactive system and a low temperature steady state (LTSS) with $T_A^*<T_R$ is possible for any reactive system. The dynamical steady state theory is quite attractive because Eqs.(6) and (9), respectively, have simple solutions

$$Y_A = \exp(-\kappa^* t), \quad (17)$$

$$Y_a = \kappa_a^*/\kappa^* [1 - \exp(-\kappa^* t)], \quad (18)$$

where $Y_A=N_A(t)/N_A(0)$ and κ_a^* is the value of $\kappa_a(T_A)$ at $T_A=T_A^*$. The dynamical steady state theory as well as the local Maxwellian approach can be applied to realistic complex systems. The steady state rate constant treatment was, in fact, employed and discussed in the analysis of nuclear recoil experiments.[5,6]

The time dependent local Maxwellian approach was studied by Root et al.[7-8] by solving Eq.(12) or (15) and various aspects of the local Maxwellian approach were elucidated. The HTSS was not realized in their model calculations.

By contrast, a steady state non-Maxwellian velocity distribution was suggested by Robson[20, 21] with a variational principle from the Boltzmann equation. The variational principle, whose physical interpretation may be given in terms of the entropy production theorems of nonequilibrium thermodynamics, is outlined. In the dynamical steady state where the velocity probability distribution is time independent, assuming the velocity and time variables separate as

$$f_A(\mathbf{v},t) = N(t)h(\mathbf{v}), \tag{19}$$

it follows that Eq.(2) yields

$$N(t) = N_0 \exp(-Kt), \tag{20}$$

$$-J(h) = Kh, \tag{21}$$

where N_0 is a constant of integration and the separation constant is written as K; the eigenvalues of $-J(h)$ and the corresponding eigenfunctions are denoted as K_i and $h_i(\mathbf{v})$, respectively. If the lowest eigenvalue K_1 is distinct from all the others, then in the long-time limit $f_A(\mathbf{v},t)$ $\sim h_1(\mathbf{v})\exp(-K_1 t)$ and $N_A(t) \sim \exp(-K_1 t)$, which is a solution of Eq.(6) provided that the rate constant κ is identified with the lowest eigenvalue K_1. Substituting

$$h(\mathbf{v}) = p(\mathbf{v}, \beta)\,\phi(\mathbf{v}) \tag{22}$$

in Eq.(21) yields

$$H(\phi) = K\, p(\mathbf{v}, \beta)\,\phi, \tag{23}$$

where $p(\mathbf{v}, \beta) = (\beta^2/2\pi)^{3/2}\exp(-\beta^2 v^2/2)$ is the Maxwellian distribution with $\beta^2 = m_A/kT_R$ and $H(\phi)$ is a self-adjoint operator derived from $-J(h)$. The variational principle is proved as that the minimum value of the quantity

$$K = \int \phi H(\phi)\, d\mathbf{v} \;/\; \int p(\mathbf{v}, \beta)\,\phi^2\, d\mathbf{v} \tag{24}$$

is the required lowest eigenvalue K_1 and the minimizing function ϕ is the corresponding eigenfunction, which may represent the deviation from the Maxwellian distribution. A trial function $\phi = \exp(-\theta v^2)$ with one parameter θ, which is found by setting $dK/d\theta = 0$, gives, in fact, the HTSS or LTSS for simple model cross sections. More elaborate trial functions with several parameters might be employed, depending upon the degree of sophistication required. The real value of the variational method lies in its ability to handle complex collision models in a relatively straightforward way but intuition for the choice of an appropriate trial variational function is an important ingredient in its successful application. Here, it is pointed out that the steady state non-Maxwellian velocity distribution at the HTSS or LTSS was also obtained by Koura[22] using the BGK (Bhatnagar, Gross, and Krook) model equation.

3.2. Moment Method

A traditional method of solution of the linear Boltzmann equation is the moment method which involves the expansion of the velocity distribution function in a complete set of orthogonal functions, i.e., an expansion in a basis set. The choice of basis functions has often been the Sonine polynomials, $S^{(i)}(y^2)$, (or eqivalently the Laguerre polynomials), where $y=v[m_A/2kT_A(t)]^{1/2}$ is the reduced hot atom speed. In the application to the evolution of the hot atom distribution function, the expansion of the distribution function is about a Maxwellian parametrized with the hot atom temperature, $f_A^{(0)}[T_A(t)]$, i.e.,

$$f_A(y,t) = f_A^{(0)}[T_A(t)]\ [1 + \phi(y,t)], \tag{25}$$

where the perturbation of the distribution function, $\phi(y,t)$, is given by

$$\phi(y,t) = \Sigma^{\infty}_{i=2}\ b_i(t)S^{(i)}(y^2). \tag{26}$$

The expansion coefficients $b_i(t)$ are referred to as the moments of the distribution function and satisfy the set of moment equations

$$(1/N_i)(db_i/dt) = \alpha_i - \beta_i + \Sigma^{\infty}_{j=2}\ B_{ij}b_j, \quad i=2,\ 3,\ 4,\ \ldots,\ \infty, \tag{27}$$

where $N_i=(\sqrt{\pi}/2)\Gamma(i+1)(i+3/2)$ and α_i and β_i result from the moments of the collision operator that results from the term in unity in Eq.(25). The matrix B involves the matrix elements of the collision operator and is characterized by the moderator temperature and the time varying hot atom temperature. Consequently, Eq.(27) is a linear equation with non-constant coefficients and integrated numerically coupled with the equation that determines the time evolution of the hot atom temperature as well as the number density. The coefficients b_0 and b_1 vanish owing to the definition of the number density and temperature through $f_A^{(0)}$. The details of this calculation are in the paper of Shizgal and Fitzpatrick.[17] This method of solution is rather cumbersome, because it involves the calculation of the two-temperature matrix elements of the collision operator that is a technical calculation especially if applied to realistic systems.

This approach was applied to a variety of model systems in order to determine the extent of the departure from the local Maxwellian distribution. The results of numerical calculations[15-17] demonstrate that the departure from the local Maxwellian is large and therefore the local Maxwellian approach is not valid for the quantitative description of hot atom reactions. The moment method, which was also used by Knierim et al.,[18] however, suffers from some difficulties. It does require a numerical integration of the moment equations and may be time consuming if a large number of expansion terms have to be retained. Also, for mass ratios near unity, the expansion proves to be asymptotic and it is difficult to obtain useful results for situations far removed from equilibrium. This difficulty may somewhat be removed by a bimodal expansion[18] that includes a Maxwellian component $f_A^{(0)}(T_R)$ at the reservoir temperature as well as an expansion about $f_A^{(0)}[T_A(t)]$.

3.3. Discrete Ordinate Method

The Boltzmann equation, Eq.(2), can be written explicitly as an integral operator in the form

$$\partial f_A(y)/\partial t = \int K(y,y')f_A(y')y'^2dy', \quad (28)$$

where the kernel K(y,y') contains the elastic and reactive collision terms of Eq.(4). The equation is reduced to a set of ordinary differential equations by the use of the quadrature procedure

$$\int_0^\infty \exp(-y^2)y^2 f(y)dy = \sum^N_{i=1} w_i f(y_i), \quad (29)$$

where y_i and w_i are the quadrature points and weights, respectively, as discussed elsewhere by Shizgal.[23] If this algorithm is used to evaluate the integral on the right hand side of Eq.(28) for all $y=y_i$, then Eq.(28) can be written in the matrix form

$$\partial \mathbf{f}_A/\partial t = A\cdot\mathbf{f}_A + \mathbf{g}_A, \quad (30)$$

where A is a matrix which contains both elastic and reactive collision cross sections, $\mathbf{f}_A$ is a vector with components $f_i=f_A(y_i)$, and $\mathbf{g}_A$ is an arbitrary steady vector source of hot atoms with components $g_i=g_A(y_i)$. The reduction of the Boltzmann equation to a set of ordinary differential equations with the discrete ordinate method is much more direct than with the moment method. The determination of the matrix representative of the collision operator requires function evaluations rather than the calculation of matrix elements and is easier to implement, even for realistic cross sections, and more accurate especially for situations far removed from thermal equilibrium. Also, the expansion in this case is not about a local Maxwellian distribution so that the coefficient matrix is time independent.

Equation (30) is a linear equation with a constant coefficient that should be compared with the moment equations, Eq.(27). Its solution is a standard textbook problem and does not require a numerical integration in time as does Eq.(27). If U is the matrix of eigenvectors of A, i.e., $A\cdot U=-\lambda\cdot U$, λ being the diagonal eigenvalue matrix whose components are the eigenvalues of A, the solution of Eq.(30) is then given by

$$f_A(y_i,t) = \sum^N_{j=1} U_{ij}\{F_j(0)\exp(-\lambda_j t) - G_j[\exp(-\lambda_j t) - 1]/\lambda_j\}, \quad (31)$$

where

$$F_j(0) = \sum^N_{k=1}(U^{-1})_{jk}f_k(0), \quad (32)$$

$$G_j = \sum^N_{k=1}(U^{-1})_{jk}g_k, \quad (33)$$

and $f_k(0)$ is the initial value of the vector component f_k. The eigenvalue spectrum of A determines the nature of the time evolution of the system. The velocity distribution function is expressed as an eigenfunction expansion with eigenvalues and their separation, if any, provides for a useful physical interpretation of the results. This aspect of the formalism is another advantage of this approach. It is shown[19] that the dynamical steady state approach requires that there be a separation of different portions of the eigenvalue spectrum as in the Chapman-Enskog method of solution of the Boltzmann equation in the treatment of transport phenomena.

This discrete ordinate method was applied[19] to a three component system consisting of the hot atom A, a single reactant (denoted by R) with the number density n_R, and an inert moderator (denoted by M) with the number density n_M. The elastic collisions between the hot atom and the two components R and M are modeled with the hard sphere cross sections σ_{eR} and σ_{eM}, respectively, and the reactive cross section is taken as the step function given by Eq.(5). An initial Gaussian speed distribution function of the form

$$f_A(y,0) = C\exp[-\delta(y^2 - y_0{}^2)^2] \tag{34}$$

was employed with $\delta=2\times10^{-4}$ and the initial hot atom temperature $T_A(0)=600T_R$, i.e., $y_0=(1.5T_A(0)/T_R)^{1/2}=30$, where the factor C is the normalization constant. The time evolution of the hot atom speed distribution function $f_A(y,\hat{t})/f_A{}^{(0)}(y)$ is shown in Fig.1 for the mass ratios $m_R/m_A=10$ and $m_M/m_A=5$, the cross section ratios $n_R\sigma_{eR}/n_M\sigma_{eM}=1.0$ and $\sigma_r/\sigma_{eR}=0.5$, and the reduced threshold energies $E_1/kT_R=40$ and $E_2/kT_R=80$, where $\hat{t}$ is the reduced time defined by $\hat{t}=[n_R\sigma_{eR}(2kT_R/\pi m_A)^{1/2}]t$.

The time dependent hot yield Y(t) is given from Eqs.(6) and (9) as

$$Y(t) = 1 - \exp[-\int_0^t \kappa(t)dt], \tag{35}$$

and the hot yield after some sufficiently long time t_∞ is given by

$$Y_\infty = 1 - \exp[-\int_0^{t_\infty} \kappa(t)dt]. \tag{36}$$

The time variation of the hot atom temperature $T_A(\hat{t})/T_R$, the reaction rate constant $k(\hat{t})=\kappa(\hat{t})/[n_R\sigma_{eR}(2kT_R/\pi m_A)^{1/2}]$, and the yield $Y(\hat{t})$ is shown in Fig.2. The rapid decrease of the hot atom temperature is accompanied by the an initial increase of the rate constant to a maximum and then a decrease as the hot atom cools further. The time dependent yield increases monotonically to a steady value at a long time. This yield at a long time is an experimentally determined quantity that is used to interpret the dynamics of hot atom reactions. It can also be written in terms of the time integrated distribution function $\bar{f}_A(x)$ with $x=y^2$ defined by

$$\bar{f}_A(x) = \int_0^\infty f_A(y,t)/N_A(t)dt \tag{37}$$

as

$$Y_\infty = 1 - \exp[-\int_0^\infty R(x)\bar{f}_A(x)dx], \tag{38}$$

where

$$R(x) = \int f_R(w) g \sigma_r(g)\, dw. \tag{39}$$

The yield of reaction therefore does not require an explicit time dependent approach. The time integrated distribution $\hat{\alpha}\sqrt{\pi}\, y^3 \bar{f}_A(y^2)$ corresponding to the time dependent distribution function presented in Fig.1 is shown in Fig.3, where $\hat{\alpha} = \hat{f}\alpha_R + (1-\hat{f})\alpha_M$, $\hat{f} = n_R\sigma_{eR}/(n_R\sigma_{eR} + n_M\sigma_{eM})$, $\alpha_s = 1 + \beta_s \ln\beta_s/(1-\beta_s)$, $\beta_s = [(1-m_s/m_A)/(1+m_s/m_A)]^2$, and m_s is the molecular mass of the component $s(=R,M)$. The distribution function can be calculated directly from a time integrated Boltzmann equation with the initial distribution function as the inhomogeneous term, i.e.,

$$\int_0^\infty K(y',y)\bar{f}_A(y'^2)y'^2 dy' = f_A(y,t_\infty) - f_A(y,0). \tag{40}$$

In Eq.(40), the distribution function $f_A(y,t_\infty)$ is essentially the Maxwellian and different from zero only in a small energy range near thermal. Hence, this can be neglected. The ordinate in Fig.3 is chosen by an asymptotic analysis of Eq.(40). With the asymptotic form of the kernel in the Boltzmann equation, Shizgal[19] showed that this time integrated distribution function can be directly related to the time independent probability density function assumed by Wolfgang and Estrup[1] with the slowing down form of the collision density in the neutron thermalization.

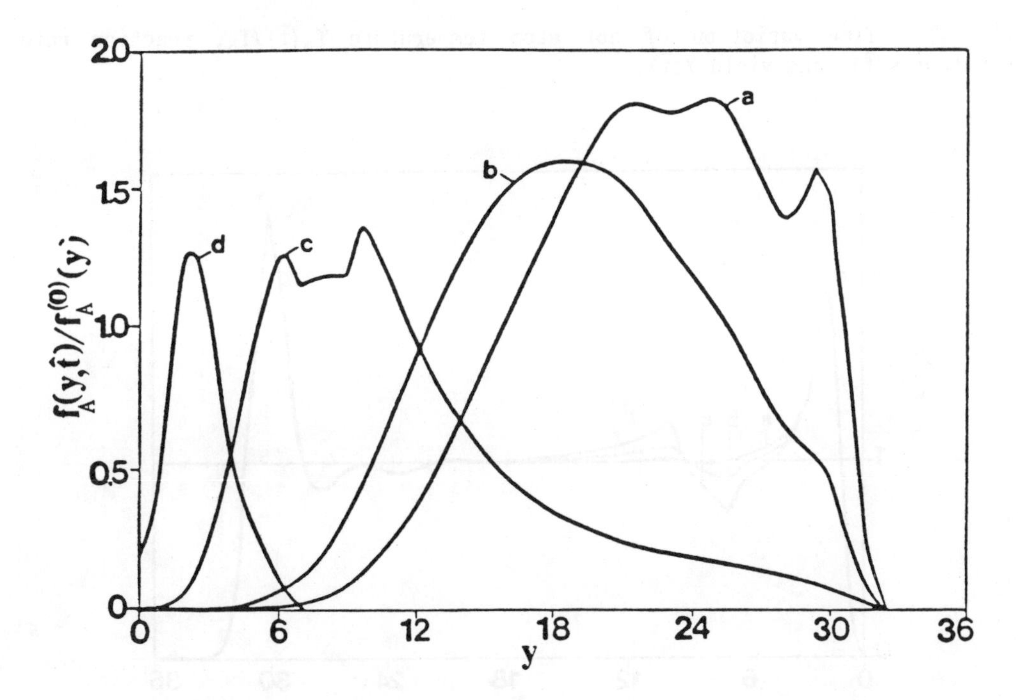

Fig. 1. Time evolution of speed distribution function. The reduced time $\hat{t}$ is equal to (a) 0.03, (b) 0.05, (c) 0.2, and (d) 1.0.

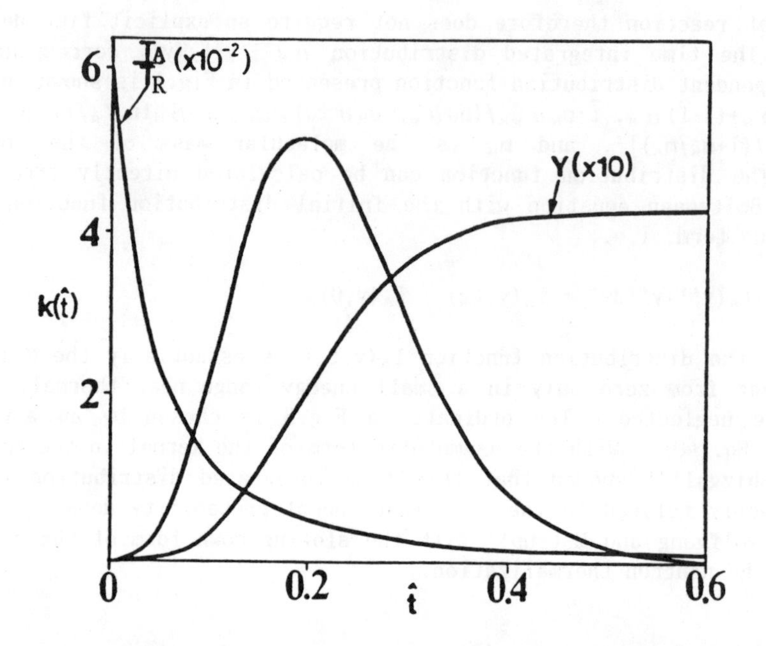

Fig. 2. Time variation of hot atom temperature $T_A(\hat{t})/T_R$, reaction rate constant $k(\hat{t})$, and yield $Y(\hat{t})$.

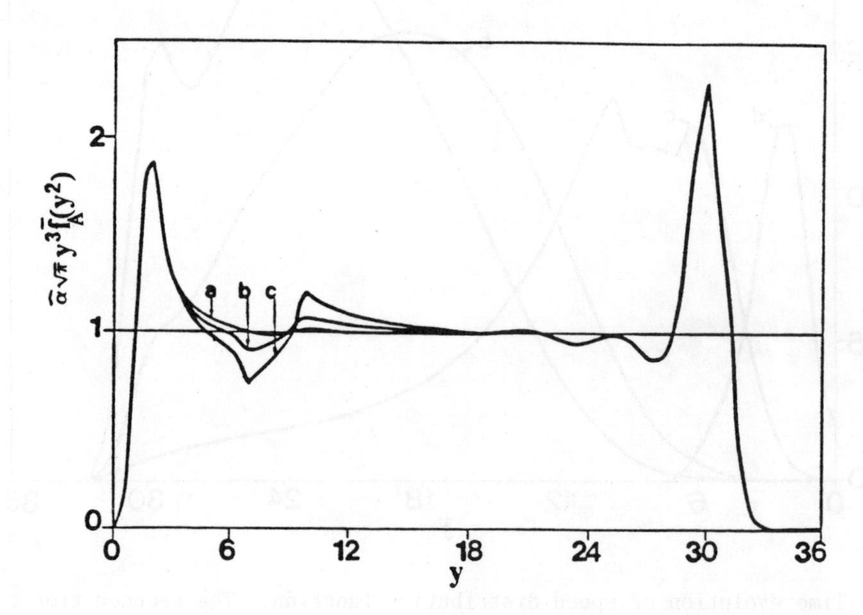

Fig. 3. Time integrated speed distribution function corresponding to Fig.1 for the cross section ratio σ_r/σ_{eR} equal to (a) 0.2, (b) 0.5, and (c) 1.0.

3.4. Monte Carlo Simulation

The time evolution of the velocity distribution of hot atoms can also be studied by the Monte Carlo simulation, where a large number of hot atoms are followed through the Monte Carlo procedures constructed using some assumptions such as the molecular chaos on which the Boltzmann equation is based. The Monte Carlo method employed by Koura in Refs.11-14 becomes more efficient by introducing the null-collision technique,[24-26] where the hot atom collision frequency is made to be constant or independent of the relative speed g by counting null (hypothetical) collisions that do not change the hot atom velocity. The Monte Carlo simulation is able to handle the time evolution of the position distribution of hot atoms as well as the velocity distribution. The Monte Carlo procedures for the simulation of the time evolution of hot atom velocities and positions from time t to $t+\Delta t$ are described as follows.

(1) At initial time (t=0), a velocity $\mathbf{v}$ and a position $\mathbf{r}$ are assigned to each of hot atoms A of the number $N_A(0)$ by initial velocity and position distributions.

(2) All the hot atoms of the number $N_A(t)$ at time t are followed individually in the subsequent procedures i)-iv), which are repeated during the time step Δt:

i) A time interval Δt_c between successive collisions of the hot atom with reservoir molecules R is assigned by the probability density function

$$p(\Delta t_c) = \nu_c \exp(-\nu_c \Delta t_c), \qquad (41)$$

where ν_c is the constant (between successive collisions) collision frequency given by $\nu_c=n_R S_{max}$, in which S_{max} is the maximum value of $S(g) =g[\sigma_{eR}(g)+\sigma_r(g)]$ at $g\leq g_{max}$, $\sigma_{eR}(g)=\int\sigma_{eR}(g,\Omega)d\Omega$ is the total elastic cross section, g_{max} is the effective maximum value of the relative speed g between successive collisions and evaluated as $g_{max}=v+w_{max}$, v is the hot atom speed, and w_{max} is the effective maximum speed of reservoir molecules taken to be a sufficiently large value of about $5(2kT_R/m_R)^{1/2}$. The null-collision cross section $\sigma_{null}(g)$ for which no (real) collision occurs is defined by $S_{max} =g\sigma_{null}(g) + S(g)$.

ii) When the summation of Δt_c is less than Δt ($\Sigma\Delta t_c\leq\Delta t$), the position $\mathbf{r}$ of the hot atom with velocity $\mathbf{v}$ is changed into the new position $\mathbf{r}'=\mathbf{r}+\mathbf{v}\Delta t_m$ corresponding to the free motion during the time interval $\Delta t_m=\Delta t_c$. When $\Sigma\Delta t_c>\Delta t$, $\mathbf{r}$ is changed into $\mathbf{r}'=\mathbf{r}+\mathbf{v}\Delta t_m$ corresponding to the remaining time interval $\Delta t_m=\Delta t_c-(\Sigma\Delta t_c-\Delta t)$ and the simulation procedure for the hot atom comes to an end.

iii) At the time ($t+\Sigma\Delta t_c$) when the collision occurs, the velocity $\mathbf{w}$ of a collision partner of reservoir molecules is assigned by the probability distribution

$$p_R(\mathbf{w}) = f_R(\mathbf{w})/n_R. \qquad (42)$$

iv) A collision kind χ [= null, elastic (eR), or reactive (r)] is assigned by the probability density

$$p_\chi = g\sigma_\chi(g)/S_{max}. \quad (43)$$

If χ=null, then the hot atom velocity **v** is not changed. If χ=elastic, then the hot atom velocity **v**' after collision is calculated from the collision dynamics (momentum and energy conservation) by assigning a scattering solid angle Ω by the probability density function

$$p(\Omega) = \sigma_{eR}(g,\Omega)/\sigma_{eR}(g). \quad (44)$$

If χ=reactive, then the hot atom disappears and the simulation procedure for the hot atom comes to an end. The hot atom number N_A is reduced by 1; if N_A becomes zero, then the simulation procedure is stopped. The collision time $t+\Sigma\Delta t_c$ is stored as a reaction lifetime τ_r and the distance $|\mathbf{r}'|$ is stored as a reaction distance d_r. The product molecular number N_p, which is initially zero, is added by 1.

(3) At a convenient time, the time dependent properties of hot atoms are calculated according to their definitions from the hot atom velocities **v** and positions **r**, the hot atom number N_A and product molecular number N_p, and the reaction lifetime τ_r and distance d_r.

In order to demonstrate the time dependent features of hot atoms, the Monte Carlo simulation is carried out for the simple model system: The elastic cross section is taken as the hard sphere model with the constant cross section σ_{Re} and the isotropic scattering $[\sigma_{eR}(g,\Omega)=\sigma_{eR}/4\pi]$ and the reactive cross section is taken as the step function given by Eq.(5). The initial hot atom velocity and position distributions are taken as delta functions: All the hot atoms have the same speed $v_0=[2E_A(0)/m_A]^{1/2}$ but isotropic velocity directions and exist at the origin of coordinates, **r**=0, where $E_A(0)$ is the initial hot atom energy. The velocity **v**, position **r**, and time t are normalized by the thermal most probable speed $v_m=(2kT_R/m_A)^{1/2}$, the (elastic) free path $\lambda_e=(n_R\sigma_{eR})^{-1}$, and the (elastic) thermal collision time $t_c=\lambda_e/v_m$, respectively. Typical results are presented in Figs. 4-6 for the mass ratio m_A/m_R=1, the cross section ratio σ_r/σ_{eR}=1, the reduced threshold energies E_1/kT_R=10 and $E_2/kT_R=10^3$, and the reduced initial energy $E_A(0)/kT_R=10^5$, where the values of E_1, E_2, and $E_A(0)$ correspond to a typical hot atom reaction with $E_1\sim0.1$ eV, $E_2\sim10$ eV, and $E_A(0)\sim1$ KeV at the reservoir temperature $T_R\sim300$ K.

Figure 4 shows the time evolution of the product yield $Y(t)\,[=N_p/N_A(0)=1-N_A/N_A(0)]$, the hot atom temperature $T_A(t)/T_A(0)\,[=\langle E_A\rangle/E_A(0)]$, and the reaction rate constant $\kappa(t)/v_m\sigma_{eR}$. The time dependent yield indicates that the hot atom reaction almost finishes at $t/t_c\lesssim0.5$ and the steady yield is about 0.9. The hot atom temperature decreases monotonically to the reservoir temperature and the HTSS is not realized in this case. [The (quasi-) HTSS appears in more highly reactive case.] The rate constant increases to a peak followed by the decrease to zero and does not indicate a steady value. It is noted that the hot atom velocity distribution attains the Maxwellian distribution at $t/t_c\gtrsim1$ after the hot atom reaction finishes.

Figure 5 shows the time evolution of the mean reaction lifetime $\langle\tau_r\rangle/t_c$ and distance $\langle d_r\rangle/\lambda_e$, which are calculated from the summation of all the reaction lifetimes and distances as $\langle\tau_r\rangle=\Sigma\tau_r/[N_A(0)-N_A]$ and

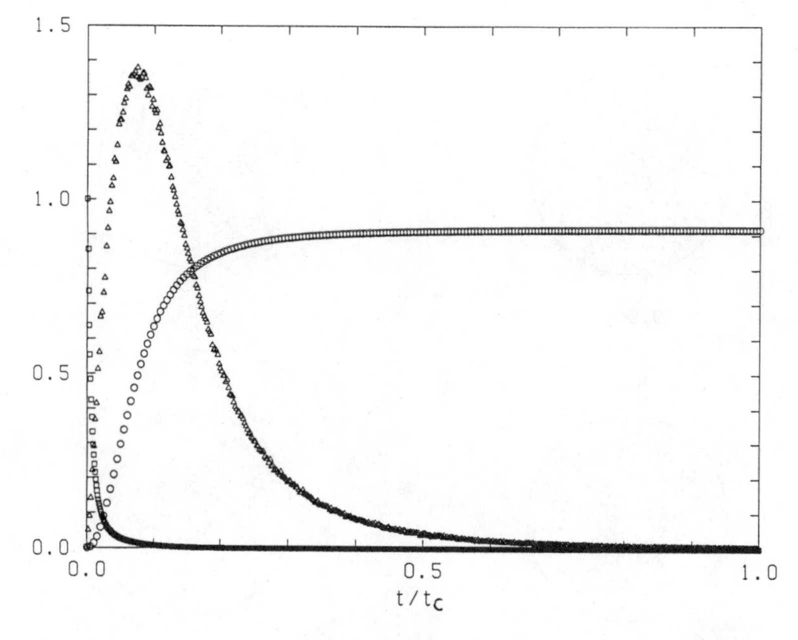

Fig. 4. Time evolution of yield $Y(t)$ (○), hot atom temperature $T_A(t)/T_A(0)$ (□), and reaction rate constant $\kappa(t)/v_m\sigma_{eR}\times10^{-1}$ (△).

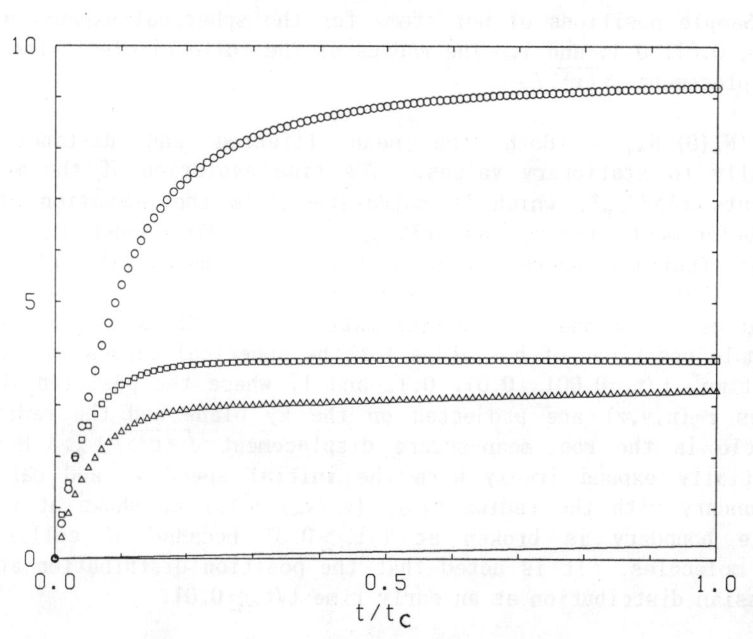

Fig. 5. Time evolution of mean reaction lifetime $\langle\tau_r\rangle/t_c\times10^2$ (○), distance $\langle d_r\rangle/\lambda_e$ (□), and mean square displacement $\langle r^2\rangle/\lambda_e^2\times10^{-1}$ (△) as compared with the gradient of the thermal diffusion coefficient $6D_{th}/v_m\lambda_e\times10^{-1}$ (—).

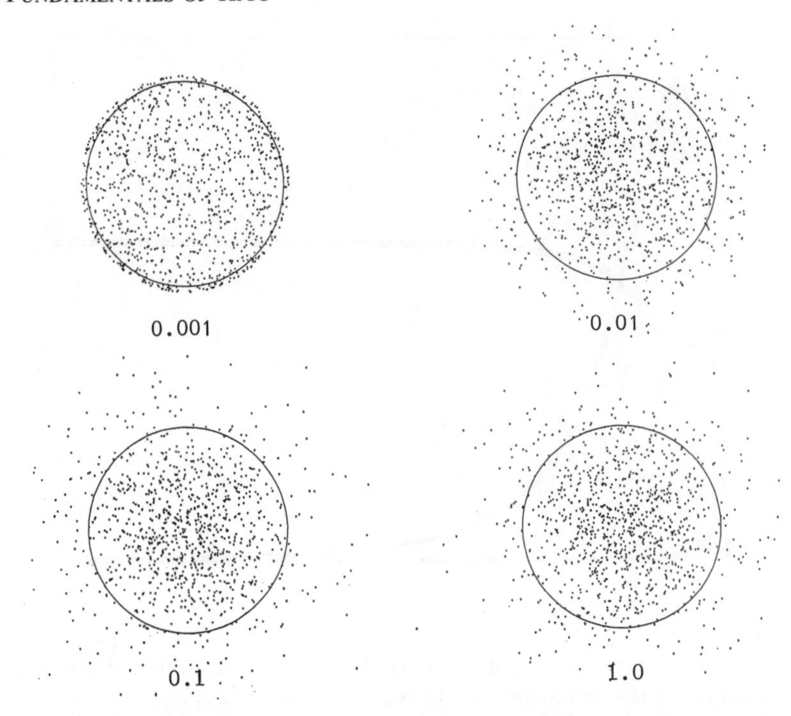

Fig. 6. Sample positions of hot atoms for the spherical expansion at time t/t_c=0.001, 0.01, 0.1, and 1. The radius of the solid circle is the root-mean-square displacement $\sqrt{\langle r^2\rangle}/\lambda_e$.

$\langle d_r\rangle=\Sigma d_r/[N_A(0)-N_A]$. Both the mean lifetime and distance increase monotonically to stationary values. The time evolution of the mean square displacement $\langle r^2\rangle/\lambda_e^2$, which is calculated from the summation of all the square displacements $r^2=|\mathbf{r}|^2$ as $\langle r^2\rangle=\Sigma r^2/N_A$, is also shown in Fig.5. The gradient monotonically decreases to the thermal diffusion value of $6D_{th}/v_m\lambda_e$, where $D_{th}=(59/58)(3\pi/8n_R\sigma_{eR})(kT_R/2\pi\mu)^{1/2}$ is the thermal diffusion coefficient of the second order approximation of the Chapman-Enskog solution.

The sample positions of hot atoms for the spherical expansion are shown in Fig.6 at time t/t_c=0.001, 0.01, 0.1, and 1, where the position (Cartesian) coordinates $\mathbf{r}$=(x,y,z) are projected on the xy plane and the radius of the solid circle is the root-mean-square displacement $\sqrt{\langle r^2\rangle}/\lambda_e$. Most of hot atoms initially expand freely with the initial speed v_0 and make a clear circle boundary with the radius $r/\lambda_e=(v_0/v_m)(t/t_c)$ as shown at t/t_c=0.001. The circle boundary is broken at $t/t_c\gtrsim 0.01$ because of collisions with reservoir molecules. It is noted that the position distribution attains the quasi-Gaussian distribution at an early time $t/t_c\gtrsim 0.01$.

4. Concluding Remarks

The nonequilibrium time dependent approach to hot atom chemistry has the potential to elucidate the dynamical features of hot atom reactions, which are not amenable to analysis by conventional steady state considerations. One of the main results of comparative calculations for various time dependent aspects of hot atom reactions is the demonstration that the local Maxwellian approach or the dynamical steady state theory is not justified for most physically realistic situations. The hot atom reaction kinetics is intimately coupled to the relaxation behavior and requires nonequilibrium time dependent solutions of the Boltzmann equation. There is a need to extend current efforts to include more realistic and complex reactive systems. Moreover, to fully utilize the nonequilibrium time dependent theory for the determination of details of hot atom dynamics there may be a need to develop and refine experimental techniques so as to extract useful information from time dependent approaches.

References

1. Estrup, P.J. and Wolfgang, R.: J. Am. Chem. Soc. 82, 2665 (1960).
2. See, for example, Malcolmes-Lawes, D.J.: "Hot Atom Chemistry" (T. Matsuura ed.) Kodansha, Tokyo, (and Elsevier, Amsterdam), 1984, p.39.
3. Keizer, J.: J. Chem. Phys., 56, 5958 (1972).
4. Keizer, J.: J. Chem. Phys., 58, 4524 (1973).
5. Grant, E.R. and Root, J.W.: J. Chem. Phys., 64, 417 (1976).
6. Feng, D.-F., Grant, E.R., and Root, J.W.: J. Chem. Phys., 64, 3450 (1976).
7. Knierim, K.D. and Root, J.W.: Radiochimica Acta, 24, 103 (1977).
8. Grant, E.R., Feng, D.-F., Keizer, J., Knierim, K.D., and Root, J.W.: "Fluorine-Containing Free Radicals: Kinetics and Dynamics of Reactions", (J.W. Root, ed.) ACS Symposium Series No.66, Am. Chem. Soc., Washington, D.C., 1978, p.314.
9. Grant, E.R., Knierim, K.D., and Root, J.W.: Chem. Phys. Lett., 53, 588 (1978).
10. Robson, R.E.: J. Chem. Phys. 85, 4486 (1886); 88, 198 (1988).
11. Koura, K.: J. Chem. Phys., 65, 3883 (1976).
12. Koura, K.: J. Chem. Phys., 66, 4078 (1977).
13. Koura, K.: Prog. Astronaut. Aeronaut., 51, 949 (1977).
14. Koura, K.: "Hot Atom Chemistry" (T. Matsuura ed.) Kodansha, Tokyo, (and Elsevier, Amsterdam), 1984, p.180.
15. Shizgal, B.: J. Chem. Phys., 69, 5355 (1978).
16. Shizgal, B.: J. Chem. Phys., 72, 3156 (1980).
17. Shizgal, B. and Fitzpatrick, J.M.: J. Chem. Phys., 72, 3143 (1980).
18. Knierim, K.D., Lin, S.L., and Mason, E.A.: J. Chem. Phys., 75, 1159 (1981).
19. Shizgal, B.: J. Chem. Phys., 74, 1401 (1981).
20. Robson, R.E., Mason, E.A., and Lin, S.L.: J.C.U.N.Q. Nat. Phil. Res. Rept. No.57, 1978.
21. Robson, R.E.: Chem. Phys. Lett., 66, 535 (1979).
22. Koura, K.: J. Chem. Phys., 72, 1756 (1980).
23. Shizgal, B.: J. Computat. Phys. 41, 309 (1981).
24. Koura, K.: Phys. Fluids, 29, 3509 (1986).
25. Koura, K.: Prog. Astronaut. Aeronaut., 117, 25 (1989).
26. Koura, K.: Phys. Fluids A, 2, 1287 (1990).

3.7 Bimolecular Hot Chemistry Reaction Rates in Gas Phases

Michael HEYL and Kurt ROESSLER

Institut für Radioastronomie der Universität Bonn, D-5300 Bonn and
Institut für Nuklearchemie des Forschungszentrums Jülich, D-5170 Jülich, Germany

The earliest method for determination of product yields of hot chemical reactions is based upon the kinetic theory developed by *Estrup and Wolfgang.*[1] It is valid only for a statistically well-defined energy distribution, i.e. hot atoms have to undergo a sufficiently high number of collisions before reaction. This assumption is fulfilled in general for hot atoms produced by nuclear recoil, but fails for photodissociation products with initial energies of typically a few eV.[2] The kinetic theory only describes an average energy loss. A correct description of the amount of hot reaction at low energies would provide a detailed knowledge of the true energy distribution. The rate constant R is an integral folding of the energy dependent reaction cross section $\sigma(E)$ with the velocity distributions of the reactants. The rate constant for two species A and B is given by the sixfold integral:[3]

$$R = \iint f_A(\vec{v}_A,t)\cdot f_B(\vec{v}_B,t)\cdot\sigma(E)\ |\vec{v}_A-\vec{v}_B|\,d\vec{v}_A d\vec{v}_B \qquad (1)$$

f_A and f_B are the time-dependent distributions for the velocities $\vec{v}_A$ and $\vec{v}_B$ and $d\vec{v}_A$ and $d\vec{v}_B$ symbolize the differential cartesian components of velocity. With knowledge of R the product yield for an irreversible reaction can be easily developed for thermal as well as for hot processes. The velocity distribution necessary for determining the rate constant (1) can be calculated e.g. by Monte-Carlo simulation.[4] However, the major problem is the unknown $\sigma(E)$. Eq. (1) depends on the area of potential overlap but in general not on the exact shape of the cross section curve.

However, in all cases where neither theoretically calculated nor experimentally determined energy dependent cross sections are available, a very simple procedure may be used to find values which can be expected to be valid at least in the range of the threshold energy.[5] This method is based upon the fact that reactands in thermal equilibrium have Maxwell-Boltzmann velocity distributions leading to the following thermal reaction rate:

$$R(T) = (\pi\mu)^{-1/2}\,(2/kT)^{3/2}\int_0^\infty E\cdot\sigma(E)\cdot e^{-E/kT}dE \tag{2}$$

Here μ is the reduced mass $m_A m_B/(m_A + m_B)$ and

$$E = \frac{\mu}{2}\,|\vec{v}_A-\vec{v}_B|^2 \tag{3}$$

Eq. (2) is the Laplace Transforms of the product $E\cdot\sigma(E)$. Assuming a cross-section with the simple form:[6,7]

$$\sigma(E) = C\cdot\frac{(E-E_o)^n}{E} \tag{4}$$

where E_o is the threshold energy, C a constant and n a real number, eq. (4) leads to:

$$R(T) = C\cdot 2^{3/2}\cdot(\pi\cdot\mu)^{-1/2}\cdot(kT)^{n-1/2}\cdot\Gamma(n+1)\cdot e^{-E_o/kT} \tag{5}$$

Here $\Gamma(n+1)$ is the Gamma function. With the preexponential factor **A**:

$$A = C\cdot 2^{3/2}\cdot(\pi\cdot\mu)^{-1/2}\cdot(k)^{n-1/2}\cdot\Gamma(n+1) \tag{6}$$

one finds:

$$R(T) = A\cdot T^{n-1/2}\cdot e^{-E_o/kT} \tag{7}$$

The rate constant of a large number of thermal chemical reactions, in particular atom-molecule reactions, are tabulated in the form given in eq. (7). To obtain energy dependent cross sections from given reaction rates the procedure of inverse Laplace transformation can be used, due to the uniqueness of the Laplacian formalism:

$$n = \frac{1}{2}:\quad R(T) = A_1\cdot e^{-E_o/kT} \quad\Leftrightarrow\quad \sigma(E) = C_1\cdot\frac{(E-E_o)^{1/2}}{E} \tag{8}$$

$$n = 1:\quad R(T) = A_2\cdot T^{1/2}\cdot e^{-E_o/kT} \quad\Leftrightarrow\quad \sigma(E) = C_2\cdot\frac{(E-E_o)}{E} \tag{9}$$

$$n = \frac{3}{2}:\quad R(T) = A_3\cdot T\cdot e^{-E_o/kT} \quad\Leftrightarrow\quad \sigma(E) = C_3\cdot\frac{(E-E_o)^{3/2}}{E} \tag{10}$$

This procedure makes use of the fact that those atoms in the Maxwell-Boltzmann equation which react possess kinetic energies at or slightly beyond the threshold value. Thus, they resemble very much the hot atoms from photodissociation processes, the primary energies of which amount to a few eV only. The inverse Laplacian treatment extracts from the experimentally determined thermal reaction rates that which is not dependent on the Maxwell-Boltzmann distribution, i.e. the underlying energy dependent cross sections. Even if it is true that the threshold region is the most sensitive for the choise of assumptions, the above described procedure is the most exact for this energy region. The major uncertainties may arise from experimental errors, in particular in the activation energy values.

It is important to note that the correlation between the rate constant R(T) and the cross section $\sigma(E)$ in (8) - (10) must be modified, using the experimental activation energy E_{exp}. It is defined in general as the slope of the logarithmic plot of R(T) vs. 1/T:[8]

$$E_{exp} = -k\cdot\frac{d\ \ln(R(T))}{d(1/T)} = kT^2\cdot\frac{d\ \ln(R(T))}{dT} \tag{11}$$

The correlation between the experimentally determined activation energy E_{exp} and the threshold energy E_o of the cross-section can be easily found. Insertion of eq. (2) in eq. (11) leads to:[9]

$$E_{exp} = E_O + (n - \frac{1}{2})\cdot kT \tag{12}$$

Since the experiments are usually carried out over a temperature range the activation energy represents an average value $<E_{exp}>$ at an average temperature $<T>$ with $<T> \in [T_{min}, T_{max}]$:

$$E_O = <E_{exp}> - (n - \frac{1}{2})\cdot k\cdot <T> \tag{13}$$

Only the parameter n = 1/2 yields identical values for $<E_{exp}>$ and E_o.

In case E_{exp} is not determined exactly by several individual approaches, it is recommended to consider the cross sections and related hot reaction rate constants as approximate values only. The goal of the present work is the evaluation of the order of magnitude of hot rates and comparison with data from atom-molecule or ion-molecule reactions in ground or excited states, in order to predict whether hot reactions may compete at all.[10] There are many approaches in the literature to reaction kinetics and mechanisms, in particular of hot hydrogen atoms,[11-15] some of theoretical work using the trajectory method. There is however no direct comparison of thermal and hot reaction rate constants, which are so much needed to introduce hot atom chemistry into astrophysics and theoretical cosmochemistry.[10]

There are two conditions for the validity of the application of the inverse Laplace transformation: 1. The threshold energy E_o determined from the experimental activation energy E_{exp} via eq. (13), should lie very close to threshold energies found by theoretical investigations. 2. Only one chemical reaction should be possible within the energy range considered. This means that processes which are in competition with the hot reaction investigated must have much higher threshold energies.

Both arguments will be demonstrated by an example: The most important hot reaction in the coma of a comet is the destruction of water molecules by hot hydrogen from photodissociation of water itself.[5] The energy distribution of the hot H-atoms peaks at 1.8 eV and the preferred reaction is H-abstraction:

$$\vec{H} + H_2O \Rightarrow OH + H_2 \tag{14}$$

where "→" denotes the symbol for "hot". The theoretical value of the activation energy is $E_{th} = 0.923$ eV [17]. Two thermal rate constants are available for reaction (14) from the literature:

$$R(T) = 1.5\cdot10^{-10}\cdot e^{-10250K/T} \quad [cm^3s^{-1}] \quad ^{18)} \tag{15}$$

$$R(T) = 2.0\cdot10^{-10}\cdot e^{-10580K/T} \quad [cm^3s^{-1}] \quad ^{17)} \tag{16}$$

The activation energies are $E_{o/1} = 0.883$ eV and $E_{o/2} = 0.912$ eV, resp. Thus the cross sections, are for n = 1/2:

$$\sigma(E) = 1.5\cdot10^{-10}cm^3s^{-1}\cdot(\mu/2)^{1/2}\cdot\frac{(E - E_{o/1})^{1/2}}{E} \tag{17}$$

and

$$\sigma(E) = 2.0\cdot10^{-10}cm^3s^{-1}\cdot(\mu/2)^{1/2}\cdot\frac{(E - E_{o/2})^{1/2}}{E} \tag{18}$$

The energy dependence of both cross sections is shown in Fig. 1. The deviation of their threshold energies from the exact value of 0.923 eV is small. Two processes compete with H-abstraction, i.e. H-substitution:

$$\vec{H}' + H_2O \Rightarrow H'HO + \vec{H} \tag{19}$$

and impact dissociation:

$$\vec{H} + H_2O \Rightarrow OH + H + H \tag{20}$$

H-substitution is not an important process. Experiments [19] with hot Tritium-atoms (activation energy $E_o = 0.8$ eV) are reported to show, that the reaction enthalpy is zero. Hot H-atoms should exhibit the same behaviour. To break the OH-bonds an energy of 5.11 eV is necessary, a value which is much higher than the 1.8 eV imparted by photodissociation. Thus, impact dissociation is not possible.

The cross section in eq. (17) is now used to calculate the hot rate constant R(E) for the reaction in eq. (14) via eq. (21):

$$R(E) = \sigma(E)\cdot(\frac{2\cdot E}{\mu})^{1/2} \tag{21}$$

Fig. 2 shows a comparison of reaction constants obtained from eq. (21) with the thermal ones from eq. (15). The two abscissae are not congruent, the curves are only displayed together for better comparison. Thermal hydrogen shows rate constants steadily increasing with temperature, whereas those for hot hydrogen rise steeply beyond the reaction threshold reaching a plateau value. The striking fact is, that the hot rate constants are by many orders of magnitude higher

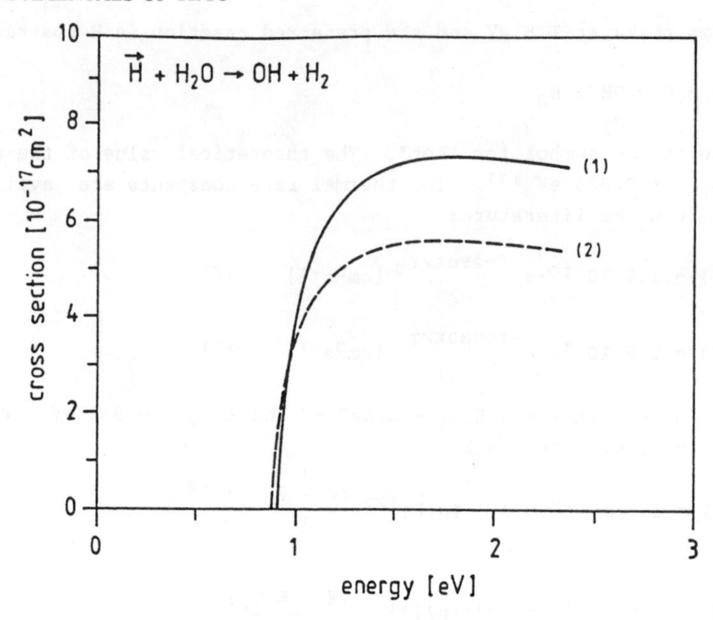

Fig. 1: Energy dependent reaction cross sections for hot hydrogen abstraction in gaseous H_2O as calculated from thermal reaction rates (1) from [18] and (2) from [17].

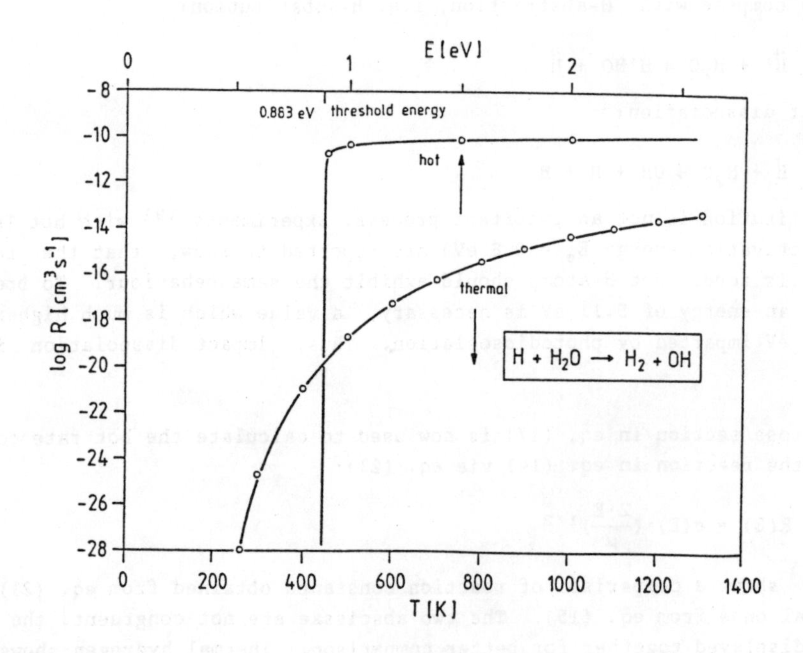

Fig. 2: Hot and thermal reaction rates constants for hydrogen abstraction in gaseous H_2O. (The scales of the two abscissae are not congruent.)

than the thermal ones. The factor amounts to almost 10^{18} for room temperature. Recently a comparison of rate constants of hot and thermal oxygen in gas phase has also yielded differences of several orders of magnitude.[10] The fact that the cross section evaluated for the H/H_2O system by the trajectory method [16] range in the same order of some 10^{-17} cm^2 as those obtained in this work is an additional proof for the validity of this classical inverse Laplacian approach for an easy estimation of bimolecular hot atom reaction rate constants.

References

1. Estrup, P.J., Wolfgang, R.: J.Am.Chem.Soc. 82, 2665 (1960).
2. Wolfgang, R.: J.Chem.Phys. 39, 2983 (1963).
3. Eliason, M.A., Hirschfelder, J.O.: J.Chem.Phys. 30, 1426 (1959).
4. Kuora, K.: "Hot Atom Chemistry" (T.Matsuura, Ed.) Kodansha, Tokyo, 1984, p.181.
5. Heyl, M.: Report-Jul-2409 (1990).
6. Stiller, W.: "Nichtthermisch aktivierte Chemie", Birkhauser, Basel, 1987.
7. Stiller, W.: Arrhenius Equation and Non-Equilibrium Kinetics", Teubner, Leipzig, 1989.
8. Benson, S.W.: "The Foundation of Chemical Kinetics", McGraw-Hill, New York, 1960.
9. Tolman, R.C.: J.Am.Chem.Soc. 42, 2506 (1920).
10. Roessler, K.: "Solid State Astrophysics" (E. Bussoletti, G. Strazzulla, Eds.), North Holland, Amsterdam, 1991, p. 197.
11. Hatano, Y.: "Hot Atom Chemistry" (T. Matsuura, Ed.) Kodansha, Tokyo, 1984, p.98.
12. Malcolme-Lawes, D.J.: "Hot Atom Chemistry" (T. Matsuura, Ed.) Kodansha, Tokyo, 1984, p.39.
13. Valentini, J.J.: Radiochim.Acta 43, 105(1988).
14. Cousins, L.M., Leone, R.: Radiochim.Acta 43, 107(1988).
15. Wolfrum, J.: Radiochim.Acta 43, 114(1988).
16. Kleinermanns, K.: Radiochim.Acta 43, 118(1988).
17. Schatz, G.C., Colton, M.C., Grant, J.L.: J.Phys.Chem. 88, 2971 (1984).
18. Duley, W.W., Williams, D.A.: "Interstellar Chemistry", Academic, London, 1984.
19. Rowland, F.S., Hathaway, L., Kambara, T.: "Chemical Effects of Nuclear Transformations", IAEA, Wien, 1961, Vol.2, p. 255.

3.8 Muonium Hot Atom Chemistry

Masayoshi Senba, Donald J. Arseneau, and Donald G. Fleming
TRIUMF and Department of Chemistry, University of British Columbia
4004 Wesbrook Mall
Vancouver, B. C. Canada, V6T 2A3

1 Introduction

The positive muon (μ^+) has a mass about 1/9 of the proton but still 200 times heavier than the electron. Thus Muonium (Mu= μ^+e^-), the bound state of the positive muon and electron, has almost identical chemical properties as hydrogen, in particular its ionization potential (13.6 eV). Because of its light mass and convenient life time of its μ^+ "nucleus" (2.2 μs), muonium provides a unique opportunity to investigate isotopic mass effects in chemical reaction dynamics with an unprecedented mass ratio (Mu:T=1:27). The muon spin rotation (μSR) technique, which relies on the fact that the positive muon produced in pion decay ($\pi^+ \rightarrow \mu^+ + \nu_\mu$) is highly spin polarized, has proven to be a valuable tool in the fields of (gas phase) chemical reaction dynamics, both for thermal reactions,[1-5] including spin exchange,[6,7] and hot atom (Mu*) reaction processes.[8-13] The technique measures the muon spin polarization retained in various chemical species containing the positive muon; in particular as muonium ($P_{\rm Mu}$), and diamagnetic species ($P_{\rm D}$). This article deals only with the interpretation of (primarily μSR) data for epithermal (hot atom) reactions rather than thermal muonium kinetics. There can be several possible contributing mechanisms[8,9] which need to be understood. For example, there is often a "missing" or "lost" polarization $P_{\rm L}$, such that

$$P_{\rm Mu} + P_{\rm D} + P_{\rm L} = 1 . \qquad (1)$$

where the initial muon polarization is taken to be unity. The distribution of muon polarization depends markedly on density; for most molecular gases near 1 atm $P_{\rm Mu} \approx 0.8$,[10,11,14] in contrast to results in most liquids, where $P_{\rm Mu} \approx 0.2$ is observed.[12] These differing density dependences of the muon polarizations have fostered two distinct models: charge exchange/hot atom[8-16] and spur.[8,17-19] Similar interpretations can be found in the fields of positronium[20,21,18] and hot atom[22-24] chemistry.

The charge exchange/hot atom model is a natural extension of early work in the field of hot atom (tritium) chemistry[22-28] and is supported by μSR results in low pressure gases. It contends that the process of a muon slowing down in such gases can be roughly divided into three stages or energy regions:[16,29–34] Bethe-Bloch ionization, cyclic charge exchange, and thermalization. The Bethe-Bloch regime takes place above roughly 100 keV depending on the moderator[35] and is characterized by the loss of the muon's kinetic energy through the ionization and inelastic excitation of moderator atoms. Somewhere between 100 keV and the threshold energy for the charge exchange process, the μ^+ undergoes a series of charge changing collisions. At the end of the cyclic charge transfer regime, the muon emerges as either muonium or a positive muon, depending on the electron loss and capture cross sections as well as on the energy moderation cross sections for a specific gas.[30–32] If muonium is produced below the electron loss threshold of muonium (13.6 eV), no further electron loss is possible (final muonium formation). The energy at which this final muonium is formed (E_{max}), is generally different from the energy at which the last electron loss takes place. For Ar it has been calculated to be about $E_{max} = 9$ eV,[32] with higher values for He and Ne. Since "stable" muonium is produced at E_{max} with substantial kinetic energies (on the chemical bond scale), as it thermalizes in the moderator there is a finite possibility that this muonium (Mu*) atom will undergo a hot atom reaction, placing muon in a diamagnetic chemical environment. As is shown in the following, the μSR technique is sensitive to these reactions.

While the effect of pressure, or time between collisions, upon the muon polarization is negligible for Bethe-Bloch ionization, it is of considerable importance in the charge exchange regime. Since electrons in the moderator are unpolarized, whereas the μ^+ is effectively 100 % spin polarized, muonium is initially formed equally in two spin states, $|\alpha_\mu\alpha_e\rangle$ and $|\alpha_\mu\beta_e\rangle$. The $|\alpha_\mu\alpha_e\rangle$ state is an eigenstate of the μ^+e^- hyperfine interaction, but the $|\alpha_\mu\beta_e\rangle$ state is a superposition of the singlet and $M = 0$ triplet eigenstates and hence is not a stationary state. In this case then, the muon polarization oscillates between $|\alpha_\mu\beta_e\rangle$ and $|\beta_\mu\alpha_e\rangle$ on a time scale given by the inverse of the hyperfine frequency, $1/\nu_0 =$ 0.22 ns. Consequently, there will be a significant lost polarization if the period of cyclic charge exchange cycles is comparable to 0.22 ns. In most molecular gases, $P_{\rm L} \to 0$ for pressures above 1 atm,[14,30–32,34] although there are notable exceptions in heavy gases with low ionization potentials.[14,36]

Hot atom reactions, at least as conventionally viewed, can only occur in a molecular gas (e.g., $\mathrm{Mu^* + C_2H_6 \rightarrow MuH + C_2H_5}$), thereby depleting $P_{\rm Mu}$ and correspondingly enhancing $P_{\rm D}$.[8,10,11] Abstraction reactions of this nature are expected to be independent of moderator pressure, while substitution reactions (e.g., forming $\mathrm{C_2H_5Mu^*}$) are expected to exhibit a pressure dependence due to the necessity of third body collisions to give a stable product.[8,10,14] Hot ion reactions, forming muon molecular ions (e.g., $C_2H_6{}^+$), could also contribute to an enhanced diamagnetic yield, but to date, these are established with certainty only for the lighter noble gases: He, Ne, and Ar.[37] It is noted also, in the field of hot tritium chemistry, that conventional wisdom holds that hot ion reactions are not able to compete during the slowing down process with charge neutralization and T* reactivity,[11,22,26,28] though there does not appear to be any direct experimental evidence for this.

The spur model of muonium formation, an alternative explanation for the distribution of muon polarization, is based on ideas advanced by Mögensen to explain positronium ($\mathrm{Ps} = e^+e^-$) formation in dense media[17–19,38] and starts from a fundamentally different premise. Rather than ascribing the observed distribution of muon polarization to processes occurring *during* the thermalization process, it invokes radiation-induced "spur" processes that occur essentially *after* thermalization. It is largely predicated on μSR studies in condensed media[12,17–19,39] but has also recently found favor in studies of high density gases as well.[8,9,40] A charged particle, in this case a positive muon, leaves a "track" of paramagnetic species, such as ions, electrons, and free radicals, as it thermalizes. Muonium and diamagnetic muon species are postulated to form in this track by charge neutralization and ion–molecule reactions during the last few picoseconds of the slowing down process. The lost fraction is ascribed to spin exchange between muonium and the paramagnetic species on a time scale longer than that for muonium or diamagnetic muon formation but less than typical (μs) observation times.[18,19]

The introduction of these two models has led to considerable debate in the μSR community as to the correct interpretation of initial muon yields.[11,12,14,17,18] Until recently, arguments in the field in favor of each model were predominately based on results from markedly different media: liquids and low density gases. Recent attempts to bridge this gap have inc luded studies of the inert gases Ar and Xe at pressures up to 60 atm,[40] for N_2 up to 200 atm and C_2H_6 up to 250 atm[8] and for CH_4 up to 200 atm.[9]

At the lower pressures, below about 10 atm, the distributions of muon polarization in the rare gases and in N2 into P_D and P_{Mu} are qualitatively consistent with expectations from charge exchange during the slowing down process. In particular Xe, with a low IP (12.1 eV), compared to that of Mu (13.6 eV) exhibits only Mu formation, though a significant lost fraction P_L remains at all pressures probably indicating that Xe is an inefficient moderator for Mu,[36] though this could also indicate the formation of a MuXe complex.[40] At higher pressures in the cases of Ar and N_2, the data are more consistent with an interpretation based on the spur model.[8] It is noted that hot atom (Mu*) reactions are not possible in the noble gases and in N_2 its unusually strong triple bond (10.5 eV) mitigates against any hot atom reactivity.

In contrast to N_2, which also has a large IP (15.6 eV), most molecular gases have IP's below the 13.5 eV value for muonium and correspondingly Mu formation is exothermic right down to thermal energies. Thus, as seen in the case of Xe, all muons should thermalize as the neutral species; ie, 100% Mu formation is expected. However, in *all* molecular gases studied to date,[10,11,14] notably here in the alkanes[8–10] and in H_2,D_2,[13] there is a significant diamagnetic component of polarization seen over a wide range of pressures. At the lower pressures, below about 10 atm, these diamagnetic "yields" are indicative of hot atom reactivity and it is the mandate of this paper to explore such reactions. Comparison with the corresponding epithermal reactions of H* and T* reveal some interesting isotope effects. At the higher pressures, radiation-induced spur processes may be of some importance.[8,9]

2 Muon Spin Rotation Technique

The μSR technique is well documented,[12,15,41–44] so only its main features will be described here. Spin-polarized muons are stopped in a target vessel filled with the gas of interest (H_2, CH_4, etc.) A complete description of the apparatus and gas-target vessels used over the years at TRIUMF may be found in Refs. 8,9,14. The target cell was located in a magnetic field applied perpendicular to the initial muon spin direction. Muonium was detected in a weak transverse field ($\sim$ 7 G) where the ensemble of muon spins precesses at 9.8 MHz whereas muons in diamagnetic environments were detected in fields of about 200 G (or $\sim$ 2.7 MHz), so that these different muon environments could easily be distinguished. It should be noted that the difference in the values of the applied field does not significantly affect the polarization of either muon state[32] in this field range. In fields on the order of 200 G, the precession of the spin of the muonium atom is not observed due to the limited time resolution ($\approx$ 2 ns) of detectors and electronics used. The muon environment has no effect upon the mean lifetime of the muon (2.2 μs) which decays via the emission of a positron preferentially along its instantaneous spin direction. In an experiment, a set of scintillation counters are positioned around the vessel to detect the incoming muon and outgoing positron. The raw data takes the form of a histogram of the number of positrons detected along a given direction as a function of the time interval between detection of the muon and positron. A typical histogram includes several million events and is described by

$$N(t) = N_0\, e^{-t/\tau_\mu}\,[1 + S(t)] + b\,, \tag{2}$$

where N_0 is a normalization factor, τ_μ is the muon lifetime (2.2 μs), and b is a time-independent background. The term $S(t)$ is the muon spin rotation signal of interest; for the transverse-field experiments, it is expressed by

$$S(t) = A_{\mathrm{Mu}} e^{-\lambda_{\mathrm{Mu}} t} \cos(\omega_{\mathrm{Mu}} t + \phi_{\mathrm{Mu}}) + A_{\mathrm{D}} e^{-\lambda_{\mathrm{D}} t} \cos(-\omega_{\mathrm{D}} t + \phi_{\mathrm{D}}) \tag{3}$$

where A_i, λ_i, ω_i, and ϕ_i are the initial amplitude, relaxation rate, angular frequency, and phase with the subscript referring to the relevant environment: 'Mu' for muonium and 'D' for diamagnetic muon. Frequently, one is interested in λ since this contains information concerning the thermal reaction rate.[1-6] However, the present studies are concerned with epithermal processes which are reflected in the amplitudes A_{Mu} and A_{D}.

Since the amplitudes are dependent upon the detector geometry and other details of the experiment, it is convenient to define the polarization for each state of the muon in the gas in the following way.

$$P_{\mathrm{Mu}} = \frac{2A_{\mathrm{Mu}}}{A_{\mathrm{ref}}} \tag{4}$$

$$P_{\mathrm{D}} = \frac{A_{\mathrm{D}}}{A_{\mathrm{ref}}} \tag{5}$$

where P_{Mu} and P_{D} are the muonium and diamagnetic polarizations, respectively. The quantity A_{ref} is the measured initial muon amplitude for the particular detector geometry. The factor of two in Eqn. 4 is valid only in the low fields used in this study and results from the fact that muonium is observed in the spin state $|\alpha_\mu \alpha_e\rangle$ but not $|\alpha_\mu \beta_e\rangle$. Past μSR studies[14,16,30-33] have shown that P_{L} in low pressure gases is due to cyclic charge exchange, affecting P_{Mu} and P_{D}in slightly different ways.[32,33] Nevertheless, the quantities f_D and f_{Mu} defined by

$$f_{\mathrm{D}} = 1 - f_{\mathrm{Mu}} = \frac{P_{\mathrm{D}}}{P_{\mathrm{Mu}} + P_{\mathrm{D}}}\,, \tag{6}$$

can be used as a reproducible measure of the *relative* amounts of diamagnetic muons and muonium in the gas as long as the pressure is not too low (say above 1 atm).[32,33]

The quantity f_D is plotted in Fig. 1 for CH_4 over a range of densities corresponding to pressures up to 200 atm and in Fig. 2 for CH_4, C_2H_6 and C_3H_8 over a much lower density range (the propane pressure extended up to only $\sim$ 5 atm). It is less clear how to properly account for P_L at the higher densities where the period of charge exchange cycles becomes much less than the period of the hyperfine oscillation, so that there is no associated depolarization.[8,9] The present paper focuses attention on the low density region covered by Fig. 2, where the diamagnetic fraction f_D can be interpreted in terms of hot atom reactivity.

3 Hot Muonium Chemistry

In the hot atom world, muonium is expected to undergo epithermal substitution and/or abstraction reactions with RH, where, for example, R = CH_3 here, or thermalize via collisions with the moderator, as represented by the reaction scheme

$$
\begin{array}{llll}
(i) & \mathrm{Mu}^* + \mathrm{RH} \xrightarrow{k_{\mathrm{abs}}} \mathrm{MuH} + \mathrm{R} & & \\
(ii) & \xrightarrow{k_{\mathrm{sub}}} \mathrm{RMu}^* + \mathrm{H} & \xrightarrow[\mathrm{M}]{k_{\mathrm{st}}} \mathrm{RMu} + \mathrm{H} & \\
(iii) & & \xrightarrow{k_{\mathrm{dis}}} \mathrm{R} + \mathrm{Mu} + \mathrm{H} & \mathrm{(R1)} \\
(iv) & \xrightarrow{k_{\mathrm{th}}} \mathrm{Mu} + \mathrm{RH} & &
\end{array}
$$

where k_{abs} and k_{sub} are the rate constants for abstraction and substitution reactions, respectively, while k_{th} is for thermalization of Mu through collisions with the moderator gas. In substitution reactions, the product RMu^* is expected to have an internal excitation energy of approximately 5 eV, estimated from hot tritium studies,[10,11,23,25] and thus ultimately requires a third body 'M' (RH for a pure gas) for stabilization, with rate constant k_{st}; otherwise, it may undergo unimolecular dissociation, with rate constant k_{dis}. The assumptions in this model, which is essentially a thermal kinetics one, are that the ratios of the rate constants are averaged over the epithermal energy range of interest ($\sim$ 1- 10 eV) and that there is no depolarization of the muon in this energy range.[11,14] From reaction scheme R1, the appropriate kinetics differential equations can be formulated and solved to yield the diamagnetic fraction

$$
f_{\mathrm{D}} = \frac{k_{\mathrm{abs}}}{k_{\mathrm{abs}} + k_{\mathrm{sub}} + k_{\mathrm{th}}} + \frac{k_{\mathrm{sub}} k_{\mathrm{st}}[\mathrm{M}]}{(k_{\mathrm{dis}} + k_{\mathrm{st}}[\mathrm{M}])(k_{\mathrm{abs}} + k_{\mathrm{sub}} + k_{\mathrm{th}})} . \tag{7}
$$

A fit of this equation to the μSR data for CH_4 up to a density of $\approx 2.2\,\mathrm{mol\,l^{-1}}$ is shown in Figs. 1 and 2, taken from Ref.[9] Also shown in Fig. 2 is a fit to f_{D} for C_2H_6,[8] as well as a fit to data obtained in C_3H_8 over a smaller range of densities.[9] All three gases show the curvature in f_{D} characteristic of contributions from substitution reactions, along with sizeable low pressure intercepts indicative of abstraction reactions. The results of the fits are listed in Table 1 in terms of the zero and infinite density fractions $f_{\mathrm{D0}} = k_{\mathrm{abs}}/(k_{\mathrm{abs}} + k_{\mathrm{sub}} + k_{\mathrm{th}})$ and $f_{\mathrm{D\infty}} = f_{\mathrm{D0}} + k_{\mathrm{sub}}/(k_{\mathrm{abs}} + k_{\mathrm{sub}} + k_{\mathrm{th}})$, as well as the relative stabilization efficiency $k_{\mathrm{st}}/k_{\mathrm{dis}}$. Similar behavior was also observed in the heavier alkanes (c-C_6H_{12} and n-C_6H_{14}), but for a pressure range of 0–2 atm.[14] Table 1 also gives results for fitted values of f_{D} obtained in

Table 1: Results of fitting f_D to the hot atom model.

Molecule	f_{D0}[a]	$f_{D\infty}$[b]	k_{st}/k_{dis}[c]
H_2	0.43 ± 0.02	≈ 0.43	$\approx 0.$
D_2	0.42 ± 0.02	≈ 0.42	$\approx 0.$
N_2	0.17 ± 0.03	≈ 0.17	$\approx 0.$
CH_4	0.12 ± 0.02	0.19 ± 0.02	1.8 ± 1.5
C_2H_6[d]	0.17 ± 0.01	0.26 ± 0.01	1.3 ± 0.5
C_3H_8	0.15 ± 0.03	0.23 ± 0.04	15 ± 20
C_6H_{14}[e]	0.0	0.31 ± 0.04	150 ± 70
C_6H_{12}[e]	0.0	0.35 ± 0.03	130 ± 40

[a] Diamagnetic fraction in the limit of zero density; $f_{D0}=k_{abs}/(k_{abs}+k_{sub}+k_{th})$ in Eqn. 7.
[b] Total diamagnetic fraction extrapolated to infinite density; $f_{D,infinity}=f_{D0}+k_{sub}/(k_{abs}+k_{sub}+k_{th})$ in Eqn. 7.
[c] Stabilization efficiency relative to dissociation, in units of l mol^{-1}.
[d] Data from Ref. 8.
[e] Data from Refs. 10, 14.

Table 2: Hot Atom Yields for Mu*, H*, and T* Reactivity in the Alkanes.

Molecule	BE[a]	$Y(T^*)$[b]	$Y_a(H^*)$[c]	$Y_a(Mu^*)$[d]	$Y(Mu^*)$[e]	$I(T^*)$[f]	$I(Mu^*)$[g]
CH_4	104	0.50	—	0.12 ± 0.02	0.19 ± 0.02	0.70	0.15
C_2H_6	98	0.65	0.12 ± 0.02	0.17 ± 0.01	0.26 ± 0.01	1.5	0.36
C_3H_8	97	0.66	0.28 ± 0.04	0.15 ± 0.03	0.23 ± 0.04	2.1	0.47
C_6H_{14}	—	0.72	—	0.0	0.31 ± 0.04	2.5	0.74
C_6H_{12}	96	1.2	—	0.0	0.35 ± 0.03	—	—

[a] C-H Bond Energy in kcal mol^{-1}, taken from Ref. 45. The value quoted for C_3H_8 is an average of the values for the 1 and 2 positions.
[b] Total hot tritium yield, from sources described in Ref. 10, taken from Table 2 in that paper. That the yield for cyclohexane exceeds unity by 20% may be taken as a measure of error for all the T * yield quoted.
[d] Integral Reaction Probability for abstraction reactions from photochemically produced H* from Ref. 50, at an energy of 1.5 eV.
[e] Mu* hot atom yields at zero pressure, f_{D0}, from intercepts of fits of Eqn. 7 to data in Fig. 2, from Table 1.
[f] Reactivity Integral I for hot tritium reactivity calculated from the WE formalism[26] and taken from Table 2. Ref. 10.
[g] Reactivity Integral I for Mu* reactivity (re)calculated from the WE formalism, as described in Ref. 10.

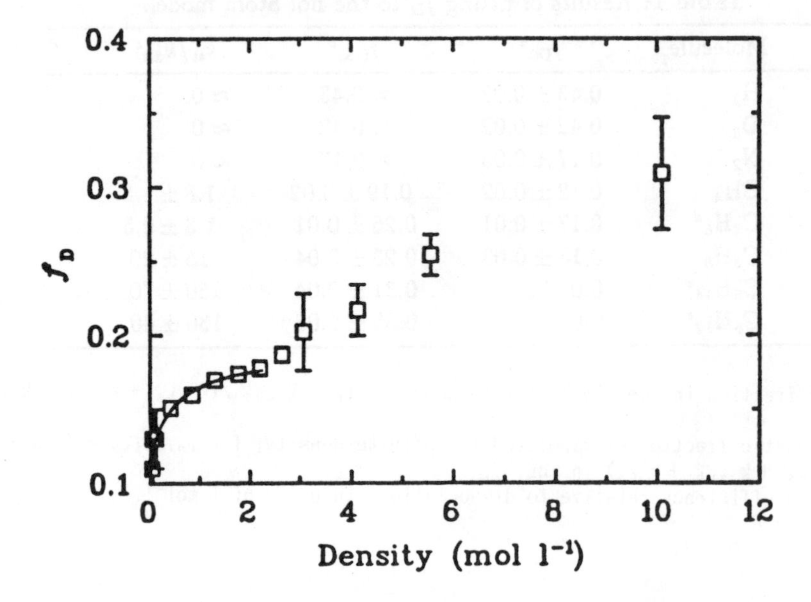

Figure 1. Diamagnetic fraction f_D as defined by Eqn. 6, as a function of density in CH_4. The solid line is a fit to the data up to 2.2 mol l^{-1} using Eqn. 7. The error bars are due to counting statistics only.

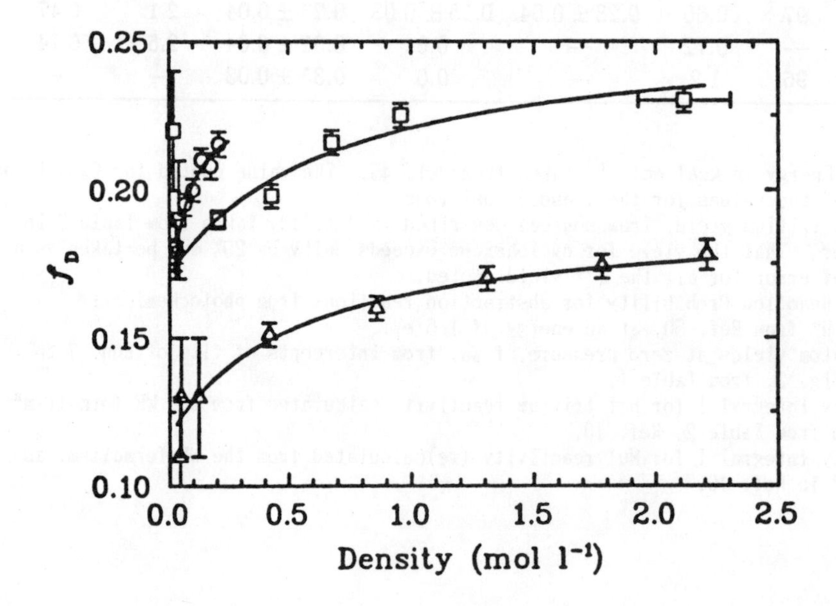

Figure 2. Diamagnetic fraction f_D for CH_4 (triangles), C_2H_6 (squares) and C_3H_8 (circles), as a function of (low) density in the gas. See also caption to Fig. 1.

H_2 and D_2 gas measured in the range $\sim$ 1-5 atm,[13] which were independent of pressure in this range.

Comparing the three sets of data for the alkanes in Fig. 2 with one another and with previous work,[10,14] two trends are clear. First, the hot atom yield f_D tends to increase with molecular size, approaching a constant value ($f_{D\infty} \approx 0.35$) in the heavier alkanes. The decrease from C_2H_6 to C_3H_8 seems anomalous in this regard, but it should be noted that the value for propane is less reliable since, as shown in Fig. 2, the yield is still increasing at the highest density measured, 0.21 mol l^{-1} (4.7 atm). The overall increase in yield is reasonable since the cross section for hot atom reactions can be expected to be proportional to the size of the molecule. Secondly, since so-vibrationally excited molecules with a large number of vibrational modes (C_3H_7Mu) are not as likely to dissociate as those with a small number of modes (CH_3Mu), the ratio k_{st}/k_{dis} increases as the molecular size is increased, leading to less Mu and a predominance of substitution reactions. *All* the diamagnetic yield in C_6H_{14} and C_6H_{12} appears to be provided by substitution reactions, and $f_D \rightarrow f_{D\infty}$ at much lower density than in the lighter alkanes..

As is clear from Eqn. 7, the discussion above and the fits in Fig. 2., as given in Table 1, the muon yields approach a constant "plateau" value, $f_{D\infty}$, as $M \rightarrow \infty$. Such a plateau is indeed seen in the data of Fig. 2; eg., at densities $\sim$ 2.5 mol l^{-1} in CH_4 but it is difficult to account for the subsequent further increase seen in f_D at the higher densities (Fig. 1) on this basis. While it is possible that additional light (fragmentation) products could be formed, such as MuH^*, requiring correspondingly higher densities for stabilization, this does not seem likely since the amounts of such fragments detected in hot tritium studies are small.[24] Moreover, a simple extension of the hot atom model represented by Eqn. 7 *cannot* account for the upward trend in the data seen in Fig. 1 (nor for the similar trend seen in the C_2H_6 data[8]), regardless of the amount of light fragments which might be formed, since the second derivative of Eqn. 7 is always negative. A more realistic, non-homogeneous, energy-dependent formulation of the same mechanism might fit the high density behavior, as might more complex mechanisms. Cluster formation around the energetic intermediates may be important at high density, but it is hard to say how this differs in effect from collisional stabilization. It is also possible that more complex density dependences of thermalization and charge exchange processes could affect the amount of Mu formed.[8] It is known that the stopping power of charged particles, notably protons, is dependent upon density[46] and that less charge neutralization occurs for protons in large alkane molecules.[47] Both effects could contribute to an increasing diamagnetic yield with increasing density,[8,10] but it is not known how substantial these effects could be; proton stopping powers, for example, differ by only about 20% between the gas phase and condensed media.[46] We conclude that additional mechanisms must be playing a role in discriminating between the amount of muonium and diamagnetic muon states seen at the higher densities in Fig. 1. The spur model is briefly explained here. See also discussion in Ref.[8]

As mentioned previously, the spur model, based on ideas advanced by Mögensen for positronium chemistry studies[18] has been successful in explaining μSR results in the liquid phase.[17,19] Studies of Ps formation by Jacobsen[38] on moderately dense gases of N_2, C_2H_6, CO, and SF_6 show that the yield of Ps increases with pressure and that this trend can be well described by the spur model as well. Very similar results have been seen in μSR

studies in N_2, where the muonium fraction f_{Mu}also increased markedly with density up to pressures $\sim$ 250 atm. From the muon polarizations at high density in CH_4 (Fig. 1) and in C_2H_6 (Ref.[8]) though, it would appear that such a model has little validity, because f_{Mu} *decreases* (f_D increases) with increasing density. However, in the alkanes, and in contrast to N_2, proton transfer reactions from $RHMu^+$ molecular ions in the spur, forming RMu and thus contributing to f_D are in strict competition with molecular ion neutralization forming Mu, on a time scale that is likely much shorter than that for both Mu spin exchange and any charge neutralization of bare muons.[8] If so, an increase in f_D with increasing density in the alkanes may well be expected, consistent with observation (Fig. 1, Ref.[8]). Indeed, a simple linear extrapolation of the data in Fig. 1 to $\sim$ 25 mol l^{-1} (approximate liquid density[49]) yields a value of 0.5, in relatively good agreement with with μSR studies in liquid methane.[48] From this result and similar studies[8] of C_2H_6, the diamagnetic muon yield in the alkanes at densities above 2–3 mol l^{-1} appears to be largely independent of temperature but rather simply proportional to density, a result that seems to be more consistent with a spur model than a hot model of Mu formation. It is noted, however, that related studies of hot tritium chemistry in the alkanes (cited in Ref.[11]) do not appear to reveal a similar density dependence in the tritium yields.

3.1 Isotope Effects in Hot Atom Reactivity

It is of interest to compare the hot muonium (Mu*) yields obtained from the fits of Eqn. 7 to f_D in the alkanes (Fig. 2) with the corresponding values from hot tritium[24] and hot hydrogen atom[50] chemistry, obtained from their respective integral reaction probabilities. These values are compared (as "Yield" Y) in Table 2, which includes values for n-hexane and c-hexane from an earlier study[14] as well. The earlier values[10] of f_D for the lighter alkanes were measured at moderate pressures and did not correspond to $f_{D\infty}$. Both the abstraction yields Y_a from the low pressure intercepts in the fits of Eqn. 7 to the data (f_{D0}) and the total high ("infinite") pressure yields Y from the asymptotes of these fits ($f_{D\infty}$) are shown in Table 2. Also given are the C–H Bond Energies (BE)[45] and the T* and Mu* "Reactivity Integrals" (I) from the Wolfgang-Estrup (WE) theory,[26] discussed below.

A general formalism[30-33] that has been developed to describe μ^+ charge exchange and Mu formation in gases can easily be extended to describe Mu hot atom reactivity.[13] According to this formalism, the probability that the a hot atom produced at energy E_{max} does *not* undergo any reactive collision down to E_{min}; i.e., its survival probability is given by

$$S(E_{max}, E_{min}) = \exp\left(-\int_{E_{min}}^{E_{max}} \frac{\sigma_{\rm rxn}(E)\,dE}{\alpha(m,M,E)\,\sigma_{\rm tot}(E)\,E}\right), \tag{8}$$

It is worth remarking that E_{max} is the energy at which muonium is produced after cyclic charge exchange, expected to be on the order of 10- 20 eV.[10] Assuming that the products of the hot atom reaction are stable, the hot atom yield per incident atom at thermal energy $E_{kT} = 3kT/2$, related to the value of f_D observed at thermal energy by the μSR technique, is given by

$$Y(E_{max}, E_{kT}) = 1 - \exp\left(-\int_{E_{kT}}^{E_{max}} \frac{\sigma_{\rm rxn}(E)\,dE}{\alpha(m,M,E)\,\sigma_{\rm tot}(E)\,E}\right), \tag{9}$$

where $\sigma_{\rm rxn}(E)$ and $\sigma_{\rm tot}(E)$ are respectively the energy-dependent reactive (hot atom) and total non-reactive cross-sections (i.e., *excluding* the reactive cross-section itself). The quantity $\alpha(m, M, E)$ represents a kinematic mass- and energy-dependent energy loss parameter which can be expressed by

$$\alpha(m, M, E) = -\ln f(E)\left[1 + \frac{J(E)/E}{1 - f(E)}\right] \tag{10}$$

where $f(E)$ and $J(E)$ are the elastic and inelastic energy loss parameters which can be calculated directly from fundamental physical quantities in question such as the mass of the hot atom (m) and that of the moderator (M) as well as the angular differential cross sections of atomic processes contributing to the slowing down of the hot atom. Details for calculating $\alpha(m, M, E)$ are given elsewhere for the case where elastic, ionization and excitation processes contribute to the slowing down.[30] It should be emphasized that $\sigma_{tot}(E)$ *does not* include $\sigma_{rxn}(E)$. This is because the reactive process, which causes a change in chemical species, does not contribute to the slowing down of the hot atom. Also it is noted that the denominator of the integrand in Eqn.9 (or Eqn.8) is the stopping power (dE/dx) per moderator atom (molecule).

For most cases, unfortunately, cross sections over a wide energy interval are generally poorly known, so simpler models[27] are often invoked to interpret experimental hot atom yields. Explicit time-dependent solutions of the Boltzmann equation have also been considered,[51,52] but these are not easily amenable to the analysis of experimental data (see further discussion in Ref. 11). In a simple case where the moderation is due to energy-independent isotropic elastic scattering (J(E)=0), $\alpha(m, M, E)$ is given by[10,30]

$$\alpha(m, M, E) = -\ln f(E) = -\ln\frac{M^2 + m^2}{(M+m)^2} \approx \frac{2mM}{(m+M)^2} \approx 2m/M \tag{11}$$

where it is assumed that the hot atom is much lighter than the moderator ($M \gg m$). In this special case, Eqn. 9 reduces to the familiar Wolfgang-Estrup result,[26]

$$\begin{aligned} Y(E_{max}, E_{kT}) &= 1 - \exp(-I(E_{max}, E_{kT})/\alpha) \\ &= 1 - \exp(-I(E_{max}, E_{kT})M/2m) \end{aligned} \tag{12}$$

with the reactivity integral

$$I(E_{max}, E_{kT}) = \int_{E_{kT}}^{E_{max}} \frac{\sigma_{\rm rxn}(E)\, dE}{\sigma_{\rm tot}(E)\, E}. \tag{13}$$

The reactivity integrals I given in Table 2 have been obtained from this formalism (those for T* taken from Table 2 in Ref. 10).

From Eqns. 9 and 13, it can be seen that the hot atom yield is determined essentially by a competition between reactive ($\sigma_{\rm rxn}$) and non-reactive ($\sigma_{\rm tot}$) processes, the latter serving simply to moderate the hot atom, in conjunction with the kinematic parameter $\alpha(m, M, E)$. If α is large, moderation is very efficient (e.g., T* in the presence of He), and the yield is then expected to be small, particularly if $\sigma_{\rm tot}$ is also large. Conversely, inefficient moderation and large reactive cross-sections are requirements for large yields. It is of interest in this regard to compare the μSR yields (f_D) for H_2 and D_2 in Table 1, which are the same within the accuracy of the experiment, even though the elastic moderation effect in H_2 should be twice as efficient as in D_2 Energy moderation in Mu* reactivity has correspondingly been interpreted as being primarily due to *inelastic* scattering,[10,11,13] consistent with other studies of epithermal (H*, T*) reactivity[24,53,54] as well as with recent muon slowing down time measurements[35] in H_2 and D_2 at TRIUMF.

It is important to realize that, as the kinetic energy of the hot atom approaches thermal energy ($3kT/2$), the hot atom will spend a long time in the energy region just above thermal energy. Therefore, it is important to know accurately the relevant cross sections in the near thermal regime, even though the reaction cross section perse' may be quite small there. Currently, work is in progress to calculate isotope effects in the hot atom yields for Mu*+H_2 and T*+H_2 from Eqn. 9, where the cross sections for both elastic and inelastic scattering as well as those for the reaction processes have been found from Classical Trajectory (CT) calculations,[55] and the slowing down of the thermalization rate in the near-thermal region referred to above is explicitly taken into account.[56]

From studies of μ^+ charge exchange,[11,30–34] we expect the energy regime for Mu* reactivity to lie in the interval $E_1 \sim 1$ eV to $E_2 = E_{max} \sim 10-20$ eV determined by the energy of the last charge exchange cycle. While the values of E_2 after charge exchange for T* and H* are likely much larger than for Mu*,[11,22,26,28] the cross sections for both abstraction and substitution in the alkanes fall essentially to zero for kinetic energies much above 20 eV, with that for substitution being more sharply peaked, and with threshold energies ~ 0.5 eV and 1.5 eV, respectively.[50,27,57] Thus it is reasonable to expect much the *same* energy interval for *all* H* atom isotopes, with mass effects becoming important only in the cross sections and kinematic factor $\alpha(m, M, E)$ of Eqn. 9. Unfortunately, the H* work[50] quoted in Table 2 is derived from photodissociation of HI with an upper energy limit for hot atom reactivity, E_2, of 2.5 eV (the two values in Table 2 are from data reported at 1.5 eV). In this energy regime, only abstraction reactions are likely to be important.[22,27,57] On the other hand, since both Mu* and T* originate from nuclear sources, their yields can be directly compared, revealing pronounced isotope effects.

The trends for both the T* and Mu* total yields in Table 2 are similar through the series of alkanes: they are lowest in CH_4 and increase with the size of the molecule, and both yields are larger for cyclohexane than hexane. The latter result reflects an enhanced substitution reaction[10] as there is no abstraction yield for Mu* in the larger alkanes (Tables 1, 2). The trend linking reactivity with molecular size is primarily due to increasing substitution yields, related to the longer dissociation lifetimes of larger excited molecules (recall Eqn. 7). The most dramatic difference between molecules is seen in comparing the muon yields in CH_4 and C_2H_6 – the total yield Y and even the abstraction yield Y_a are considerably higher for C_2H_6. This may be a reflection of decreased C–H bond energies facilitating abstraction, as advocated some years ago by Rowland and coworkers,[22,25,57] and seen also in a comparison of of the muon yields for H_2 and N_2[11,13] in table 1. However, the C–H bond energy continues to decrease somewhat through propane to the hexanes, but the abstraction yield is actually less for propane than ethane (though the error bars should be kept in mind) and it goes to zero for the hexanes. Of relevance here also is the considerably enhanced H* (1.5 eV) abstraction yield seen in C_3H_8 vs. C_2H_6. This enhancement is reflected in neither the total yields for high energy T* or Mu* nor the abstraction yields for the latter, but is observed in the ratio of TH/RT yields from photochemically generated T*.[57,58] This clear distinction between energy regimes, indicates the importance of substitution reactions at higher (above 1.5 eV) energies, consistent taken with the excitation functions reported in Refs. 50 and 27.

The isotopic effects seen in the total yields themselves as well as in the reactivity integrals (I) for Mu^* and T^* reactivity in Table 2 are quite dramatic: on average, the experimental hot T yields are about three times as large as those for Mu. Since energy moderation in the alkanes seems to be dominated by *inelastic* scattering, α_{Mu} and α_T should be comparable — an assumption which has been incorporated in arriving at the (WE) reactivity integrals I in Table 2 (see also discussion in Ref. 10), yielding a factor of four enhancement in T^* over Mu^* reactivity. These values derive from the assumption that the same energy interval E_1 to E_2, applies to both hot muonium and hot tritium, which, from Eqn. 13, implies a similar enhancement in reactive cross sections $\sigma_{rxn}(E)$, assuming as well that the non-reactive cross sections $\sigma_{tot}(E)$ are the same in both cases.

The WE approximation[28] to the exact result defined by Eqn. 9 has been called into question,[27,51,52] but it does provide a reasonable and easily adaptable theoretical framework for the interpretation of experimental yields in the absence of detailed knowledge of the cross sections, e.g., via classical trajectory (CT) calculations. Indeed, a factor of four enhancement in $\sigma_{rxn}(E)$ for T^* vs. Mu^* reactivity in the alkanes is consistent with a simple mass scaling of CT calculations[27,51,59] (see also discussion in Refs. 10 and 11) but specific calculations are required to substantiate this. The principal problem with the calculations of reaction dynamics in general, though, is that the potential energy surfaces (PES's) are poorly known, even in the threshold region (see, e.g., Ref. 3), let alone globally. An exception to this statement is the (Liu-Siegbahn) PES for H_3.[60,61] Trajectory calculations are in progress on this surface to compare the Mu^* and T^* yields seen in H_2 and D_2[55] where a recent treatment of hot atom slowing down is also included. It is noted that studies reported earlier[2] of the *thermal* Mu reaction rates for these reactions gave exemplary agreement between theory and experiment.

Unfortunately it is not possible to directly compare the Mu^* and H^* yields in Table 2 because of the different energy regimes involved. Nevertheless, an isotope effect is indicated because the H^* (abstraction only) values are still substantial, though the energy regime is a factor of 10 lower. Perhaps there is a greater isotope effect in hot (H) atom abstraction than in substitution reactions.

It would be of considerable interest now to have the results of CT calculations for hot atom (Mu^*, H^*, and T^*) reactivity on the alkanes. Though early results for T^* in CH_4 do not appear encouraging in this regard,[10,59] there are now newer PES's available.[62] Work along these lines is also in progress in the halogens[63] and, as noted, in H_2 and D_2.[55] It is hoped that the comparisons presented in Table 2 will motivate similar calculations in the alkanes and on related molecules, where there is much data on hot atom reactivity available.[11,22,50]

4 Conclusions

The hot atom Mu^* yields have been compared with the results of hot tritium (T^*)[24] and H^* reactivity[50] in the alkanes, with the expectation that their mass differences (up to a factor of 27!) would reveal some important isotope effects. The yields themselves indeed differ appreciably (Table 2) with those for T* typically a factor of three larger than the Mu* yields. Since both these probes originate from nuclear sources, their respective hot atom yields can be assumed due to abstraction and substitution reactions and energy moderation over comparable energy intervals. The yields cited for epithermal (1.5 eV) H* reactivity,[50] on the other hand, are exclusively due to abstraction reactions, but they are comparable to the Mu* yields (Table 2), which result from reaction over a much wider energy interval, suggesting a considerable isotope effect in abstraction reactions. The hot atom yields for Mu* and T* have been interpreted within the Wolfgang-Estrup formalism,[26] and the resulting reactivity integrals I differ by a factor of four, likely due to a corresponding difference in reactive cross sections σ_{rxn}. Such a difference is consistent with isotope effects found in classical trajectory calculations in the alkanes[27] and in other molecules,[51,63] but detailed calculations of this nature over a wide enough energy interval comparing Mu* and T* reactivity have not yet been reported. Work along these lines is in progress in the halogens[63] and in H_2 and D_2,[55] but are now urgently needed in the alkanes. As well, such calculations could help to understand the "global nature" of the underlying potential energy surfaces.

5 Acknowlegements

We would like to thank other members of the TRIUMF gas-phase μSR group who have participated in the experiments referred to herein, Alicia Gonzalez (now at USC), James Pan and particularly Jim Kempton (now at Computer Associates, Wash. DC). The financial support of NSERC(Canada) is also gratefully acknowledged.

References

1. Baer, S, Fleming, D. G., Arseneau, D. J., Senba, M., Gonzalez, A. C.: ACS Advances in Chemistry Series, 1991 (in press).
2. Reid, I. D., Garner, D. M., Lee, L. Y., Senba, M., Arseneau, D. J., Fleming, D. G.: J. Chem. Phys., 86, 5578 (1987).
3. Gonzalez, A. C., Reid, I. D., Garner, D. M., Senba, M., Fleming, D. G., Arseneau, D. J., Kempton, J. R.: J. Chem. Phys., 91, 6164 (1989).
4. Garner, D. M., Fleming, D. G., Arseneau, D. J., Senba, M., Reid, I. D., Mikula, R. J.: J. Chem. Phys., 93, 1732 (1990).
5. Roduner, E., Lourier, P. W. F., Brinkman, G. A., Garner, D. M., Reid, I. D., Arseneau, D. J., Senba, M., Fleming, D. G.: Ber. Bunzenges. Phys. Chem., 94, 1224 (1990).
6. Senba, M., Fleming, D. G., Arseneau, D. J., Garner, D. M., Reid, I. D.: Phys. Rev. A, 39, 3871 (1989).
7. Turner, R. E., Snider, R. F., Fleming, D. G.: Phys. Rev. A, 41, 1565 (1990).
8. Kempton, J. R., Senba, M., Arseneau, D. J., Gonzalez, A. C., Garner, D. M., Pan, J. J., Fleming, D. G.,Percival, P. W., Brodovitch, J. C., Leung, S. K.: J. Chem. Phys., 94, 1046 (1991).
9. Kempton, J. R., Arseneau, D. J., Fleming, D. G., Senba, M., Gonzalez, A. C., Pan, J. J., Templemann, A., Garner, D. M.: J. Phys. Chem., 95, 7338 (1991).
10. Fleming, D. G., Senba, M., Arseneau, D. J., Reid, I. D., Garner, D. M.: Can. J. Chem., 64, 57 (1986).
11. Fleming, D. G.: Radiat. Phys. Chem., 28, 115 (1986).
12. Walker, D. C.: Acc. Chem. Res., 18, 167 (1985); Walker, D. C.: in "Muon and Muonium

Chemistry", Cambridge University, Cambridge, 1983; Walker, D. C., Jean, Y. C., Fleming, D. G.: J. Chem. Phys., 70, 4534 (1979); 72, 2902 (1980).
13. Fleming, D. G., Lee, L. Y., Senba, M., Arseneau, D. J., Reid, I. D., Garner, D. M.: Radiochimica Acta, 43, 98 (1988).
14. Arseneau, D. J., Garner, D. M., Senba, M., Fleming, D. G.: J. Phys. Chem., 88, 3688 (1984); Arseneau, D. J.: M. Sc. Thesis, University of British Columbia, 1984; Fleming, D. G., Arseneau, D. J., Garner, D. M., Senba, M., Mikula, R. J.: Hyperfine Interact., 17-19, 655 (1984).
15. Fleming, D. G., Garner, D. M., Vaz, L. C., Walker, D. C., Brewer, J. H., Crowe, K. M.: in "Positronium and Muonium Chemistry", Ache, H. J., Ed., Advances in Chemistry 175, American Chemical Society, Washington, DC, 1979, p. 279.
16. Fleming, D. G., Mikula, R. J., Garner, D. M.: Phys. Rev. A, 26, 2527 (1982); Mukla, R. J.: Ph. D. Dissertation, University of British Columbia, 1981.
17. Percival, P. W.: J. Chem. Phys., 72, 2901 (1980); Percival, P. W.: Radiochimica Acta, 26, 1 (1979); Percival, P. W., Roduner, E., Fischer, H: Chem. Phys., 32, 353 (1978).
18. Moegensen, O. E., Percival, P. W.: Radiat. Phys. Chem., 28, 85 (1986); Moegensen, O. E.: J. Chem. Phys., 60, 998 (1974).
19. Leung, S. K., Brodovitch, J. C., Percival, P. W., Yu, D.: Can. J. Phys., 68, 949 (1990); Leung, S. K. et al.: Chem. Phys., 121, 393 (1988); Percival, P. W., Adamson-Sharpe, K. M., Brodovitch, J. C., Leung, S. K., Newman, K. E.: Chem. Phys., 95, 321 (1985).
20. Tabata, Y., Ito, Y.: Hyperfine Interact., 17-19, 641 (1984).
21. Ache, H. J.: in "Positronium and Muonium Chemistry", Ache, H. J., Ed., Advances in Chemistry 175, American Chemical Society, Washington, DC, 1979, p. 1.
22. Rowland, F. S.: in "Molecular Beams and Reaction Kinetics", Schlier, Ch., Ed., Academic, New York, 1970, p. 108, p. 127.
23. Ferro, L. J., Spicer, L. D.: J. Chem. Phys., 69, 4335 (1978).
24. Baker, R. T., Silbert, M., Wolfgang, R.: J. Chem. Phys., 52, 1120 (1970); Seewald, D., Wolfgang, R.: J. Chem. Phys., 47, 143 (1967).
25. Lee, E. K. C., Rowland, F. S.: J. Am. Chem. Soc., 85, 897 (1963).
26. Estrup, P. J., Wolfgang, R.: J. Am. Chem. Soc., 82, 2661 (1960); Wolfgang, R.: Ann. Rev. Phys. Chem., 16, 15 (1965).
27. Malcolme-Lawes, D. J.: in "Hot Atom Chemistry, recent trends and applications in the physical and life sciences and technology", Matsuura, T., Ed., Kodansha (Elsevier), Tokyo, 1984, p. 39; Malcolme-Lawes, D. J.: J. Chem. Soc. Far. Trans. II, 73, 1222 (1977); Malcolme-Lawes, D. J.: J. Chem. Phys., 56, 3442 (1972).
28. Wolfgang, R.: J. Phys. Chem., 74, 4601 (1970); Rowland, F. S.: J. Phys. Chem., 74, 4603 (1970).
29. Turner, R. E.: Phys. Rev. A, 28, 3300 (1983); Turner, R. E., Senba, M.: Phys. Rev. A, 29, 2541 (1984).
30. Senba, M.: J. Phys. B, 21, 3093 (1988).
31. Senba, M.: J. Phys. B, 22, 2027 (1989).
32. Senba, M.: J. Phys. B, 23, 1545 (1990).
33. Senba, M.: Hyperfine Interact., 65, 779 (1990).
34. Fleming, D. G., Senba, M.: in "Atomic Physics with Positrons", Hunberston, J. W., Armour, E. A. G., Eds, Plenum, New York, 1987, p. 343.
35. Senba, M., Arseneau, D. J., Fleming, D. G. et al: work in progress.
36. Senba, M., Turner, R. E., Arseneau, D. J., Garner, D. M., Lee, L. Y., Reid, I. D., Fleming, D. G.: Hyperfine Interact., 32, 795 (1986).
37. Arseneau, D. J., Fleming, D. G., Senba, M., Reid, I. D., Garner, D. M.: Can J. Chem., 66, 2018 (1988).
38. Jacobsen, F. M.: Chem. Phys., 109, 455 (1986).
39. Roduner, E., Brinkman, G. A., Lourier, P. W. F.: Chem. Phys., 88, 143 (1984); Roduner, E.: Hyperfine Interact., 17-19, 785 (1984).
40. Kempton, J. R., Senba, M., Arseneau, D. J., Gonzalez, A. C., Pan, J. J., Templemann, A., Garner, D. M., Fleming, D. G.: Hyperfine Interact., 63, 801 (1990).
41. Heffner, R. H., Fleming, D. G.: Phys. Today, Dec. 1984, p. 38.
42. Schenck, A.: in "Muon Spin Rotation Spectrometry. Principles and Applications in Solid State Physics", Adam Hilger, Bristol, 1985.
43. Roduner, E.: "Lecture Notes in Chemistry 49: The Positive Muon as a Probe in Free

Radical Chemistry: Potential and Limitations of the μSR Techniques", Springer-Verlag, Berlin, 1988.
44. Cox, S. F. J.: J. Phys. C, 20, 3187 (1987).
45. "CRC Handbook of Chemistry and Physics", 59th ed., Weast, R. C., Ed., CRC, West Palm Beach, 1978.
46. Woods, C. J., Sofield, C. J., Cowern, N. E. B., Murrell, M., Draper, J.: J. Phys. B, 17, 867 (1984).
47. Bissinger, G., Joyce, J. M., Lapicki, G., Laubert, R., Varghese, S. L.: Phys. Rev. Lett., 49, 318 (1982).
48. Jean, Y. C., Ganti, R., Stadbauer, J.: J. Phys. Chem., 91, 1270 (1987).
49. Medard, L.: "Gas Encyclopaedia", Elsevier, Amsterdam, 1976.
50. Nicolas, J. E., Vaghjiani, G.: J. Chem. Soc. Far. Trans. II, 83, 607 (1987); 82, 1945 (1986).
51. Porter, R. N., Kunt, S.: J. Chem. Phys., 52, 3240 (1970); Malcolme-Lawes, D. J.: J. Chem. Soc. Far. Trans. II, 71, 1183 (1975).
52. Shizgal, B.: J. Chem. Phys., 74, 1401 (1981); Knierim, K. D., Lin, S. L., Mason, E. A.: J. Chem. Phys., 75, 1159 (1981).
53. Oldershaw, G. A., Smith, A.: J. Chem. Soc. Far. Trans. I, 74, 1687 (1978); Vidaud, P., Fink, R. D., Nicholas, J. E.: J. Chem. Soc. Far. Trans. I, 75, 1619 (1979).
54. Baker, T. K., Malcolme-Lawes, D. J.: J. Chem. Soc. Far. Trans. I, 69, 928, 1858 (1973); Hall, R. B., Malcolme-Lawes, D. J.: J. Chem. Soc. Far. Trans. I, 70, 648 (1974).
55. Senba, M., Fleming, D. G., Mayne, H.: work in progress.
56. Senba, M.: work in progress.
57. Tachikawa, E., Rowland, F. S.: J. Am. Chem. Soc., 90, 4767 (1968); Lee, E. K. C., Rowland, F. S.: J. Am. Chem. Soc., 84, 3085 (1962); Root, J. W., Breckenbridge, W., Rowland, F. S.: J. Chem. Phys., 43, 3694 (1965).
58. Chou, C. C., Smail, T., Rowland, F. S.: J. Am. Chem. Soc. Comm., 91, 3104 (1969); Chou, C. C., Rowland, F. S.: J. Am. Chem. Soc. Comm., 88, 2612 (1966).
59. Raff, R. M.: J. Chem. Phys., 60, 2220 (1974); Bunker, D. L., Pattengill, M. D.: J. Chem. Phys., 53, 3041 (1970).
60. Blomberg, M. R. A., Liu, B.: J. Chem. Phys., 82, 1050 (1985); Truhlar, D. G., Horowitz, C. J.: J. Chem. Phys., 68, 2466 (1978).
61. Valentini, J. J., Phillips, D. L.: in "Bimolecular Collisions", Ashfold, M. N. R., Baggott, J. E., Eds., Royal Socity of Chemistry, London, 1989, Vol 2.
62. Gordon, M. S., Truhlar, D. G., J. Am. Chem. Soc., 108, 5412 (1986).
63. Connor, J. N. L., Edge, C. J., Lagana, A.: Mol. Phys., 46, 1231 (1982); Connor, J. N. L., Whitehead, J. C.: private communication.

3.9 Random Walk Theory and Hot Atom Chemistry

Koichi FUNABASHI
Kawai Institute for Culture and Education, 2-1-10, Imaike, Chikusa-ku, Nagoya, 464, Japan

1. Introduction

A number of problems in condensed-phase physics and chemistry can be analyzed in terms of random walks[1] in periodic space lattices. These include exciton trapping[2,3], charge transport in amorphous media[4], electron scavenging in glasses[5,6], and chemical reactions [7]. Hot atom chemistry (HAC) is no exception. Various aspects of solid-state HAC could be directly related to random walks. The phase effect in HAC, for example, is attributed to the cage effect [8], which is related to the probability of repeated visits at a given site in the random-walk theory. Diffusion-controlled chemical reactions[9] are important in HAC. The random-walk theory is a model for the diffusion-controlled reactions. Although the theory of diffusion-controlled reactions gives the correct long-time asymptotic rate constant, it does not yield the proper transient rate. The random-walk theory is designed to give the correct rate constant at any time, so that it could be useful in studying the transient behavior of HAC reactions.

Although many systems of our interest are not perfect crystals, the random-walk theory could still be relevant, since Scher and Lax [4] have shown that the ensemble average of random walks in random media is equivalent to random walks on a simple lattice.

The random walker in the random-walk theory is a particle. Electrons and excitons in condensed phases could become wave-like and delocalized under certain conditions. The random-walk theory can not handle chemical reactions involving these delocalized species. Long-range tunneling is also beyond the scope of the random-walk theory.

In the following sections, the basic equations for the random-walk theory of Montroll and Weiss [1] are summarized. These basic equations are then applied to simple chemical reactions.

2. Random-Walk Theory

In this section, basic equations for discrete and continuous-time-random-walks on infinite lattices (i.e., lattices with infinite number of lattice points) are summarized. For lattices with a finite number of lattice points with periodic boundary conditions, the reader is referred to the work by Montroll and Weiss[1].

2.1. Discrete Random Walk

Let $P_n(s)$ be the probability that the random walker is at a point s after the nth step. When the walkers are neither created nor destroyed in the walk (i.e., walkers are conserved).

$$\sum_s P_n(s) = 1 \tag{1}$$

We restrict ourselves to the initial condition

$$P_0(s) = \delta_{s,o} \tag{2}$$

which corresponds to walks which start from the origin s=o. The random-walk generating function is defined by

$$P(s, z) = \sum_0^{\infty} z^n P_n(s) \tag{3}$$

Using (1) and (3),

$$\sum_s P(s, z) = (1-z)^{-1} \tag{4}$$

where we assume $|z| \leq 1$.

Let $F_n(s)$ be the probability that a random walker reaches the point s for the first time at step n. If the random walker is at s at step n, he must have reached there at some step j and then returned to s in n-j steps. Therefore, $P_n(s)$ and $F_n(s)$ are related by

$$P_n(s) = \delta_{n,o}\,\delta_{s,o} + \sum_{j=1}^{n} F_j(s)\, P_{n-j}(o) \tag{5}$$

with the initial condition (2).

Multiplying z^n on both sides of (5) and summing over n, we obtain

$$F(s, z) = [P(s, z) - \delta_{s,o}] / P(o, z) \tag{6}$$

where the generating function of $F_n(s)$ is defined by

$$F(s, z) = \sum_{n=1}^{\infty} F_n(s)\, z^n \tag{7}$$

Let $F_n(s)$ be the probability that the random walker reaches s for the rth time at step n. This function satisfies the recurrence formula,

$$F_n^{(r)}(s) = \sum F_{n-j}^{(r-1)}(s)\, F_j(o) \tag{8}$$

Its generating function is given by

$$F^{(r)}(s, z) = [F(o, z)]^{r-1} F(s, z) = \sum_{n=1}^{\infty} F_n^{(r)}(s)\, z^n \tag{9}$$

Let us now consider the statistics of the number of distinct lattice points visited during an n-step walk. Let S_n be the average number of lattice points visited in an n-step walk. Then,

$$S_n = 1 + \sum_s' \{F_1(s) + F_2(s) + \dots F_n(s)\} \tag{10}$$

where the primed summation proceeds over all lattice points except the origin. The summand of (10) represents the probability that the point s has been occupied at least once in the first n steps.

It is convenient to define a quantity Δ_k by

$$\Delta_k = S_k - S_{k-1}, \qquad k = 1, 2, \dots \tag{11}$$

Since $S_0 = 1$ and $S_1 = 2$, we find $\Delta_1 = 1$. Then

$$\Delta_n = \sum_s' F_n(s) = -F_n(o) + \sum_s F_n(s) \tag{12}$$

Hence the generating function for Δ_k is

$$\Delta(z) = \sum_1^{\infty} z^n \Delta_n = -\sum_1^{\infty} z^n F_n(o) + \sum_s \sum_{n=1}^{\infty} z^n F_n(s) \tag{13}$$

so that

$$\Delta(z) = -F(o, z) + \sum_s F(s, z). \tag{14}$$

Substitution of (6) into (14) gives

$$\Delta(z) = -1 + \sum_s \frac{P(s, z)}{P(o, z)} \tag{15}$$

From (4),

$$\Delta(z) = -1 + \{(1-z)P(o, z)\}^{-1} \tag{16}$$

The generating function S(z) for S_n is defined as

$$S(z) = \sum_{n=0}^{\infty} z^n S_n \tag{17}$$

Using the relationships,

$S_0 = 1$, $S_1 = 1 + \Delta_1$, ..., $S_n = 1 + \Delta_1 + \Delta_2 + \dots \Delta_n$, etc

We find

$$S(z) = \frac{1}{1-z} + \frac{z\Delta_1}{1-z} + \frac{z^2\Delta_2}{1-z} + \dots = \frac{1}{1-z} + \frac{\Delta(z)}{1-z}$$

Using (16),

$$S(z) = \{(1-z)^2 P(o, z)\}^{-1} \tag{18}$$

As $z \to 1$, the asymptotic behavior of P (o, z) in one, two, three dimensions is as follows[10].

$$\text{1D} \qquad P(o, z) = (1-z^2)^{1/2} \tag{19}$$

$$\text{2D} \qquad P(o, z) \sim -\pi \log (1-z) \tag{20}$$

$$\text{3D} \qquad P(o, z) \sim P(o, 1) + a(1-z)^{1/2} + \ldots \tag{21}$$

where a is a constant which depends on the lattice.

2.2. Continuous-Time-Random-Walks

The preceding results for discrete random walks can be used as a basis for continuous-time-random-walks on discrete lattices.

Let $\psi(\tau)$ be the probability density for the occurrence of the nth step at time t and $\psi(\tau)$ be the jump-time distribution function which is the probability density for the occurrence of a jump at time τ following the last jump. These functions satisfy

$$\phi_n(t) = \int_0^t \phi(\tau)\, \phi_{n-1}(t-\tau)\, d\tau, \qquad n = 1, 2, \ldots \tag{22}$$

$$\phi_o(t) = \delta(t) \tag{23}$$

The Laplace transform of the convolution integral (22) is given by

$$\int_0^\infty e^{-ut} \phi_n(t)\, dt = [\phi(u)]^n \tag{24}$$

where

$$\phi(u) = \int_0^\infty e^{-ut} \phi(t)\, dt \tag{25}$$

The probability density for reaching s starting from the origin for the first time at time t is given by

$$\bar{F}(s, t) = \sum_{n=0}^\infty F_n(s)\, \phi_n(t) \tag{26}$$

The Laplace transform of (26) is

$$\bar{F}^*(s, u) = \int_0^\infty \bar{F}(s, t)\, e^{-ut}\, dt = \sum_{n=0}^\infty F_n(s)\, [\phi(u)]^n = F[s, \phi(u)] \tag{27}$$

where F (s, z) is the generating function (7).

3. Simple Chemical Kinetics

3.1. Scavenging Reaction

We consider a simple cubic lattice in which the origin is a sink and every other lattice site may initially be occupied by a scavenger molecule. In order to calculate the scavenging rate, we calculate the number of scavengers arriving at the origin for the first time as a function of time. This function, the flux of scavenging, will be proportional to the initial probability that a site is occupied by a scavenger, that is to the concentration of scavenger. Although the walker in this model is a scavenger molecule, the sink may be more mobile than the scavengers in some system. The dynamics of the walker is governed by the relative motion of the sink and the scavenger. It is simply a matter of mathematical convenience to fix the position of the sink, because we are interested only in the case where the scavenger concentration is far in excess of the sink concentration in this application. The effect of exchanging the role of the walker on the rate constant will further be discussed in the last section.

For this application of random-walk theory, it is necessary to consider the summation of (26) over site s as defined by

$$\overline{F}(t) = a^k \sum_{s \neq 0} \overline{F}(s, t) \tag{28}$$

where a is the lattice constant and k is the dimension of the system. The function (28) is the number of scavengers arriving at the origin for the first time per unit time per unit concentration of scavengers and therefore the rate constant of the diffusion-controlled reaction between the sink at the origin and the scavengers. Although $F_n(s)$ in (26) and (28) was defined as the probability that a random walker reaches the point s for the first time at step n starting from the origin, the same function $F_n(s)$ in (28) must be understood as the probability that a scavenger reaches the origin for the first time at step n starting from site s. These two functions are clearly equivalent.

The Laplace transform of (28) is defined as

$$\overline{F}^*(u) = \int_0^\infty e^{-ut}\, \overline{F}(t)\, dt \tag{29}$$

Using (4) and (6),

$$F^*(u) = a^k \left[\frac{1}{[1-\phi(u)]\, P[o, \phi(u)]} - 1 \right] \tag{30}$$

Up to this point, we have assumed that the walker reacts with the sink with unit probability, i.e., the diffusion-controlled reaction. Let us now consider a more general case in which the reacting site (origin) has probability f for reaction and probability (1-f) for survival to jump away from the reacting site. Then, the number of scavengers reacting at the origin per unit time per unit concentration of scavengers is given by

$$\overline{F}(t) = a^k \sum_{s \neq 0} [f \overline{F}(s, t) + f(1-f) \overline{F}^{(2)}(s, t) + f(1-f)^2 \overline{F}^{(3)}(s, t) \ldots] \tag{31}$$

where

$$\overline{F}^{(n)}(s, t) = \sum_r F_n^{(r)}(s)\, \phi_n(t) \tag{32}$$

and $F_n^{(r)}(s)$ is the probability that the walker reaches s for the r-th time at step n as in (8). Using (9), (24) and (32), the Laplace transform of (31) can be expressed as

$$\overline{F}^*(u) = \int_0^\infty e^{-ut}\,\overline{F}(t)\,dt = a^k \left[\frac{1}{[1-\phi(u)]\,P[o, \phi(u)]} - 1 \right] L(u) \quad (33)$$

where

$$L(u) = f / \left\{ f + \frac{1-f}{P[o, \phi(u)]} \right\} \quad (34)$$

In order to understand the relationship between (31) and the usual diffusion kinetics, we consider the exponential jump-time distribution

$$\phi(t) = w e^{-wt} \quad (35)$$

where w is the transition rate between the nearest neighbor sites and is equivalent to the jump frequency in the diffusion kinetics. The Laplace transform of (35) is given by

$$\phi(u) = w/(u+w) \quad (36)$$

The asymptotic ($t \to \infty$) form of (31) can be found from the Laplace transform[11] of (33) as $u \to 0$. Using (21), (33) and (36) for 3-D systems,

$$\overline{F}(t) \to \frac{a^3 w f}{1 + [P(o, 1) - 1] f}, \qquad t \to \infty \quad (37)$$

where P (o, 1) depends upon the lattice structure and is equal to W=1.516... for a simple cubic lattice[10]. With f=1, (37) can be written as

$$\overline{F}(t) \to a^3 w / W \quad (38)$$

The usual diffusion kinetics of the same problem gives the well-known asymptotic expression for the rate constant k for the diffusion-controlled reaction[8]

$$k = \overline{F}(t) \sim 4\pi DR\,[1 + R/(\pi R t)^{1/2}] \quad (39)$$

where R is the reaction radius and D is the diffusion constant which is in a simple cubic lattice,

$$D = wa^2/6 \quad (40)$$

Since the reaction radius R is an unknown parameter, (38) is formally identical with 4πDR in (39). If (38) is equated with 4πDR, radius R is

$$R = 6a/4\pi W \sim a/\pi \quad (41)$$

While (39) shows divergence at t=0, numerical calculation[5] of (31) shows that it remains finite as $t \to 0$.

In the case of 1-D systems and the exponential distribution (35), (31) and (32) lead to the result

$$\overline{F}(t) = awe^{-wt}[I_0(wt) + I_1(wt)] \tag{42}$$

where w is the transition rate between the nearest neighbors as before, and I_0 and I_1 are modified Bessel functions[12]. With the long-time asymptotic forms for I_0 and I_1, (42) takes the form

$$\overline{F}(t) \sim 2a(w/2\pi t)^{1/2}(1 - 1/8wt \cdots) \tag{43}$$

which can be compared with the result of the simple diffusion equation

$$\overline{F}(t) = 2(D/\pi t)^{1/2} = 2a(w/2\pi t)^{1/2} \qquad (D = wa^2/2) \tag{44}$$

These results for three- and one-dimensional systems are to show that the simple diffusion equation gives agreement only with the long-time asymptotic value of the random-walk theory.

$\overline{F}(t)$ is shown in Fig. 1 and compared to the corresponding flux obtained from the diffusion equation with the identification of the diffusion constant D as

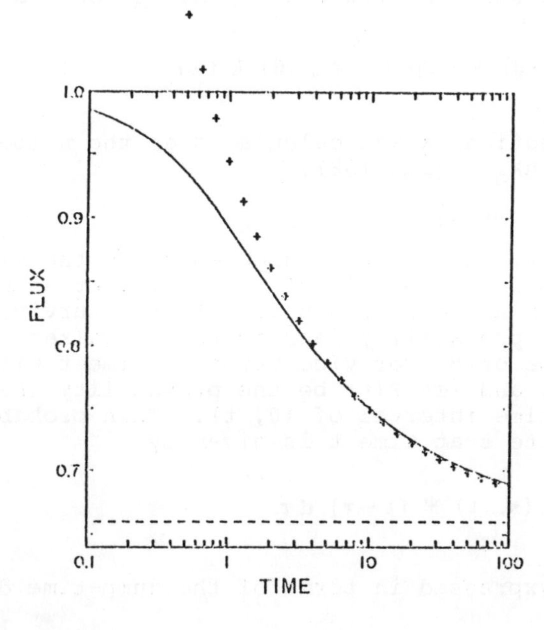

FIG. 1. The relative flux of scavenging reactions vs time, log scale. —— CTRW with exponential time distribution. ---- Smoluchowski equation without transient. ++++ Smoluchowski equation with transient showing divergence for t=0. For CTRW the flux is $\overline{F}(t)$ which is unity for t=0. The units of time are natural for CTRW, that is, w=1.

$D = a^3 w/(\text{number of nearest neighbors})$,

where a is the lattice constant, w is the jump frequency from (35), and the reaction radius is taken to be about 0.3a.

3.2. Survival Fraction

In the theory of diffusion-controlled reaction involving two species, A and B, the time evolution of the reacting species is generally governed by the first order differential equation of the form

$$dN_A(t)/dt = kN_A(t)\,N_B(t) \tag{45}$$

where N_A and N_B are concentrations of species A and B, the constant k has the physical meaning of a rate constant. When the initial concentration of B is much greater than that of A, it is good approximation to assume that $N_B(t) \sim N_B(0)$ at all times, so that (45) may be written in the form of the pseudo-first-order reaction

$$dN_A(t)/dt = kN_B(0)\,N_A(t) \tag{46}$$

In the Smoluchowski treatment[5] of this problem in a three dimensional space, the rate constant k has the well-known asymptotic form[3] $k = 4\pi DR$.

Using (46), the survival fraction of A, f_A, can be expressed as

$$f_A = N_A(t)/N_A(0) = \exp\left(-\int_0^t N_B(0)\,k\,dt\right) \tag{47}$$

In the previous section, k was calculated as the number of B's arriving at the sink. Using (38),

$$f_A = \exp\left[-N_B(0)\,a^3\,wt/W\right] \tag{48}$$

Up to this point, the minority species A are the sinks and the majority species B have the role of walkers. Let us now exchange these roles between A and B, and calculate the survival fractions. Let Q(s, t) be the probability density that a walker reaches site s starting from the origin or vice versa at time t without being trapped at a sink, and let $\Psi(t)$ be the probability that a walker remains fixed in time interval of (0, t). Then probability of a walker being at site s at time t is given by

$$\overline{P}(s, t) = \int_0^t Q(s, t)\,\Psi(t-\tau)\,d\tau \tag{49}$$

But, $\Psi(t)$ can be expressed in terms of the jump-time distribution function $\phi(t)$ as

$$\Psi(t) = \int_t^\infty \phi(x)\,dx \tag{50}$$

The Laplace transform of (49), $\overline{P}(s, u)$, is given by

$$\overline{P}(s, u) = Q(s, u)\,[1-\phi(u)]/u, \tag{51}$$

where Q(s, u) is the Laplace transform of Q(s, t) and $\phi(u)$ is given by (25). Q(s, t) can be written as

$$Q(s, t) = \sum_{n=0}^{\infty} U_n P_n(s)\,\phi_n(t) \tag{52}$$

where U_n is the probability that a walker survives an n-step walk without being trapped, and $\phi_n(t)$ is given in (22). The Laplace transform of $\phi_n(t)$ is given as in (24). Using (24) and (52), (51) can be expressed as

$$\overline{P}(s, u) = \sum_{n=0}^{\infty} U_n P_n(s)\,[\phi(u)]^n\,[1-\phi(u)]/u \tag{53}$$

Since the survival fraction can also be written as

$$f_A = \sum_s \overline{P}(s, t) \tag{54}$$

the Laplace transform of f_A, $L\{f_A\}$, takes the form

$$L\{f_A\} = \sum_s \sum_{n=0}^{\infty} U_n P_n(s)\,[\phi(u)]^n\,[1-\phi(u)]/u$$

$$= \sum U_n\,[\phi(u)]^n\,[1-\phi(u)]/u \tag{55}$$

because of the identity (1).

Since the starting point of the walker, which is chosen to be the origin of the coordinate system in the above derivation, is not a special site, (55) can be regarded as an equation which converts the survival fraction in terms of step numbers to the Laplace transform of survival fraction as a function of time. If the sinks (B's) are distributed randomly, U_n can be expressed approximately as

$$U_n \sim (1-c)^{S_n - 1} \tag{56}$$

where S_n is the average number of lattice sites visited during an n-step walk as in (10) and c is the probability that a lattice site is a sink, i.e., $c=a^3N_B(0)$ for a simple cubic lattice, for example. A more rigorous formulation of U_n requires a cumulant function instead of S_n. We assume that (56) is a good approximation for $c \ll 1$.

If we are interested only in the long-time asymptotic value of f_A, we might approximate S_n in (56) by its asymptotic (i.e., large n) form [1],

$$S_n \sim n/W \tag{57}$$

Use of (57) in (56), together with (55), leads to

$$L\{f_A\} \rightarrow (u + cw/W)^{-1} \tag{58}$$

and

$$f_A \rightarrow \exp(-cwt/W) = \exp(-N_B(0)\, a^3\, wt/W) \tag{59}$$

which is identical with (48). We conclude that, in the case of exponential jump-time distribution function in three dimensional space, the long-time asymptotic form for the survival fraction of the minority member A, f_A, is independent of whether the minority member is the sink or the walker.

References

1. Montroll, E. W.: J. Math. Phys. 6, 167 (1965).
2. Montroll, E. W.: J. Phys. Soc. Jpn. Suppl. 26, 6 (1969).
3. Klafter, J., Silbey, R.: J. Chem. Phys. 72, 843 (1980).
4. Scher, H., Lax, M.: Phys. Rev. B7, 4491 (1973).
5. Helman, W. P., Funabashi, K.: J. Chem. Phys. 66, 5790 (1977).
6. Hamill, W. H., Funabashi, K.: Phys. Rev. B16, 5523 (1977).
7. Helman, W. P., Funabashi, K.: J. Phys. Chem. 71, 2458 (1979).
8. Matsuura, T.: "Hot Atom Chemistry" (T. Matsuura, Ed) Kodansha, Tokyo (and Elsevier, Amsterdam), 1984, p. 303.
9. Noyes, R. M.: "Progress in Reaction Kinetics", (G. Porter, Ed), Pergamon, New York, 1961, 1, p. 129.
10. Montroll, E. W.: Proc. Symp. Appl. Math. Am. Soc. 10, 193 (1963).
11. Erdelyi, A., Magnus, W., Oberhettiuger, F., Tricomi, F. G.: "Tables of Integral Transforms", McGraw-Hill, 1954.
12. Whittaker, E. T., Watson, G. N.: "A Course of Modern Analysis", Cambridge, 1958.

3.10 RRKM- and Non-RRKM Behavior in Gas-Phase Reactions

Yoichi SAKAI
Department of Chemistry, Daido Institute of Technology,
40 Hakusui-cho, Minami-ku, Nagoya 457, Japan

1. Basic concepts of the RRKM theory

It is well-known that Rice-Ramsperger-Kassel-Marcus (RRKM) theory is a very powerful tool in studies of chemical kinetics. RRKM theory has been established as a model for unimolecular processes such as decomposition and isomerization of excited species in the gas phase. This model enables us to predict rate constants and branching ratios of different reaction paths. Excited or energized species A^* are produced through molecular collision in a thermal system, photoactivation, chemical activation, and so on, as follows:

$A + M \longrightarrow A^* + M$ (1-T)

$A + h\nu \longrightarrow A^*$ (1-P)

$B + C \longrightarrow A^*$ (1-C).

In any case, the first step is formation of energized species. The energized species A^* react in one of the ways;

$A^* + M \longrightarrow A + M$ (2)

$A^* \longrightarrow A^{\neq}$ (3)

where M in Reaction (2) is acting as a bath gas molecule or a moderator molecule which is chemically inert and gains the excitation energy of A^* through thermal collision, stabilizing A^* to A. Here, one supposes that bath gas molecules exist in the systems of (1-P) and (1-C) as well as in (1-T). $A^{\neq}$ is an activated complex in the absolute rate theory for chemical reaction, which subsequently decomposes or isomerizes yielding products;

$A^{\neq} \longrightarrow$ Products (4).

The overall rate constant k_{uni} of Reactions (1) to (4) for a thermally energized system is formulated as;

$$k_{uni} = \int_{E_0}^{\infty} \frac{k_3 dk_1/k_2}{(1 + k_3/k_2[M])}, \text{ where } dk_1/k_2 = \frac{N^*(E^*)\exp(-E^*/kT)dE^*}{\int_0^{\infty} N^*(E^*)\exp(-E^*/kT)dE^*} \quad (5).$$

in which E^* is the energy of the energized molecule A^*, E_0 the energy required for A to be activated to $A^{\neq}$, $N^*(E^*)$ the number of quantum states for energized species A^* per unit energy at the energy E^*, and k the Boltzmann constant. The first version of the expressions for k_{uni} was proposed by Lindemann in 1919, and has been modified to reproduce experimental results, leading eventually to the RRKM version. Detail explanations or derivations of the expressions are beyond the scope of the present review, and we can find them in the excellent books on this theory[1,2] or textbooks on chemical kinetics.[3,4] It should, however, be mentioned that the essential principles in RRKM theory are the followings. Firstly, the rate constant k_1 of energization is evaluated as a function of E^* by a quantum-statistical-mechanical treatment, while k_2 is independent of energy and $k_2[M]$ can be replaced by k_2P in a first approximation where P is a total pressure of the system. The second is that the absolute rate theory is applied to an evaluation of $k_3(E^*)$ dependent on energy, which demands a distinction between the energized species A^* and the activated complex $A^{\neq}$. These treatments lead to the following expression for $K_3(E^*)$:

$$k_3(E^*) = L^{\neq} \Sigma P(E^{\neq})/hFN^*(E^*) \quad (6)$$

where $L^{\neq}$ is the reaction path degeneracy, $\Sigma P(E^{\neq})$ the sum of the number of quantum vibrational-rotational states accessible to the activated complex $A^{\neq}$ with energy $E^{\neq}$, $E^{\neq}=E^*-E_0$, h the Plank constant, and F a correction factor for a centrifugal effect.

In evaluating Equation (6), an important assumption is made: the internal energy is statistically distributed among all the vibrational modes in the energized species. In other words, rapid intramolecular energy randomization could occur on a time scale short relative to the mean lifetime of the unimolecularly-reacting species. It might be very helpful for understanding the above feature to look back on the expression for $K_3(E^*)$ in the RRK version preceding RRKM theory, which is not exactly the same but is not very different:

$$k_3(E^*) = k^{\neq}[(E^*-E_0)/E^*]^{s-1} \quad (7)$$

where $k^{\neq}$ is the rate constant corresponding to the free passage and s is a vibrational degree of freedom for A^* molecule.

This expression was derived by considering the following analogy: Suppose that n balls are statistically distributed over s boxes. What is the probability for a particular box to contain more than m balls? Here, "n balls" and "m balls" correspond to "n- and m energy quanta", $n=E^*/kT$ and $m=E_0/kT$, "s boxes" to "s vibrational degrees of freedom, and "a particular box" to "a particular vibrational oscillator". When energy of more than E_0 is deposited in the particular oscillator, a reaction occurs. It is an essential point in RRK theory that $k_3(E^*)$ should be proportional to this probability. This implies that the higher s is, the lower the $k_3(E^*)$ is. This basic feature is still present in RRKM theory.

2. Application of RRKM theory

RRKM theory has been successful in interpreting the experimental results for unimolecular reactions. Many examples can be found in a review paper by Holbrook.[5] A typical and famous example was demonstrated by Rabinovitch and co-workers.[6] They measured rate constants k_3 for the decomposition of the energized 2-

alkyl radical produced in thermal H-atom addition to 1-olefins, that is, $R\text{-}CH_2CH{=}CH_2 + H$ (where R= $-CH_3$ (C_4) to $-C_{13}H_{27}$ (C_{16})) $\rightarrow$ $R\text{-}CH_2CH\text{-}CH_3^*$ $\rightarrow$ R + $CH_2{=}CHCH_3$, showing that the experimental values for k_3 agree well with those calculated according to RRKM theory; the rate constants decrease with an increase in the number of carbon atoms corresponding to an increasing number of vibrational degrees of freedom s; e.g., 2.0×10^7 and 3.1×10^2 s^{-1} for C_4^* and C_{16}^* radical, respectively, or approximately a decrease of a factor of 2.6 for each additional CH_2 added to the radical.

We can find in major journals many other examples of the successful prediction of rate constants using RRKM theory. One of the latest reports is one by Rakestraw and Holmes.[7] They measured and calculated the rate constants for three types of unimolecular decompositions: eliminations of HF and HCl and release of a Cl atom, of chemically energized CF_3CH_2Cl through the radical combination CF_3 + CH_2Cl, determining the values of the threshold energy for each decomposition by comparing the measured rate constants to predictions from RRKM theory.

3. non-RRKM behavior

As described above, a RRKM treatment has allowed unimolecular rate constants to be predicted agreeing with experimental values in many systems. However, a question about the treatment has existed since the early stage of development of this theory. The question is defined in the title of the review paper by Oref and Rabinovitch in 1979;[8] that is, "Do highly excited reactive polyatomic molecules behave ergodically?" In their ambitious review paper, many experimental results were cited and the appropriateness of the statistical (ergodic) assumptions in the RRKM theory was discussed, leading to their answer of "YES" to the above question.

Recently, several experimental results have been reported which suggest the presence of nonstastical or non-RRKM behavior, slow intramolecular vibrational relaxation relative to unimolecular reaction. They were found mainly in systems produced through chemical activation methods for energizing a part of a molecule initially.

Rowland and co-workers have investigated chemical reactions in the gas phase and applied RRK- or RRKM treatments to analysing the chemical kinetics. Outlines of studies at the earlier stage can be seen in the review papers of Rowland.[9,10] In the last decade his group has found a few excellent examples of non-RRKM energized-species in their research using radioactive atoms produced initially as hot atoms.[11-13] The procedure to get energized species is a kind of chemical activation, using thermal atomic fluorine- or chlorine-addition to olefin compounds, for example, as

$$RCH{=}CH_2 + X \rightarrow RCH\text{-}CH_2X^* \quad (X{=}F \text{ or Cl atom}).$$

As is well known, hot ^{18}F and ^{38}Cl atoms are created with high kinetic recoil energy through $^{19}F(n, 2n)^{18}F$ and $^{37}Cl(n,\gamma)^{38}Cl$ nuclear reactions. Suppose that the hot atoms are produced from a moderator molecule, $CClF_3$ or SF_6, which is a chemically inactive major-component in the gaseous system. The hot atoms should make many collisions with the moderator molecules, relaxing to thermal energy. In such systems, 98% and 95% of the hot ^{18}F and ^{38}Cl atoms, respectively, were found to be eventually thermalized in an atomic state.[14,15] It should be noted that SF_6 and CCl_3F are moderators for energized species as well as for hot atoms. Thermalized radioactive atoms have been used in a series of investigations for chemical reactions of F or Cl atoms with various gaseous compounds of interest in seeking non-RRKM species or in atmospheric chemistry.

To mention the actual experimental methods briefly in the case of Ref.[11] as a typical example, gaseous mixtures of tetraallyltin (0.1 Torr) and SF_6 (500 to 4000 Torr) were irradiated with fast neutrons. The irradiated gas sample was submitted to radiogas-chromatography to obtain the radiochemical yield of the ^{18}F-labeled species $CH_2=CH^{18}F$

The first example of a non-RRKM molecule found by Rowland and co-workers is an energized radical $SnC_{12}H_{20}{}^{18}F^*$ from thermal atomic ^{18}F addition to tetraallyltin[11]:

$$Sn(CH_2CH=CH_2)_4 + {}^{18}F \rightarrow (CH_2CH=CH_2)_3SnCH_2CH^{18}FCH_2{}^* \quad (8).$$

The energized radical decomposes unimolecularly as

$$(CH_2CH=CH_2)_3SnCH_2CH^{18}FCH_2{}^* \rightarrow CH_2=CH^{18}F + (CH_2CH=CH_2)_3SnCH_2 \quad (9)$$

The rate constant for the unimolecular decomposition(9) was compared to those corresponding to the decomposition (9) for radicals with less complexity, which were also determined experimentally in a similar way. Surprisingly, it was proved that the unimolecular decomposition rate constant k_3 (or k_9 here) fell between those for $CH_3CH^{18}FCH_2$ and $C_2H_5CH^{18}FCH_2$. Since the number of vibrational degrees of freedom for $SnC_{12}H_{20}{}^{18}F^*$ radical is much higher than that of $C_2H_5CH^{18}FCH_2$, the rate constant k_9 should be much smaller if $SnC_{12}H_{20}{}^{18}F^*$ behaves in the unimolecular decomposition as a RRKM molecule.

Accordingly, this finding should imply that the excitation energy of the newly formed C-F bond was not fully randomized over all of the vibrational degrees of freedom in $SnC_{12}H_{20}{}^{18}F^*$. It was concluded that such non-RRKM behavior could be due to the lack of energy transfer beyond the central C-Sn-C bonding on the time scale of the decomposition, "heavy-atom blocking" of intramolecular energy transfer.

Subsequently, Rowland and co-workers[12] carried out a similar experiment for tetraallylgermanium and illustrated that the energized radical formed by ^{18}F addition also shows non-RRKM behavior. These experiment results stimulated Marcus and co-workers,[15-19] who have done a number of theoretical investigations that gave support for the presence of a heavy-atom blocking effect. Rabinovitch and co-workers,[20,21] who also were stimulated by the work of the Rowland and Marcus groups, carried out experiments in the related chemical systems, but no non-RRKM behavior was found in the decompositions of the energized radicals $(CH_2CH=CH_2)_3SnCH_2CHCH_3{}^*$ and $(CH_3)_3SnCH_2CH_2CHCH_2{}^*$ from H-atom addition to corresponding olefins. The causes for the apparent disagreement between experiments on the addition of H atoms and ^{18}F atoms have not yet been resolved, and are still under investigation.

Recently, a third example demonstrating non-RRKM behavior has come from Rowland's laboratory.[13] It is an energized radical $SnC_8H_{12}{}^{38}Cl^*$ from thermal ^{38}Cl-atom addition to tetravinyltin;

$$Sn(CH{=}CH_2)_4 + {}^{38}Cl \rightarrow (CH_2{=}CH)_3SnCHCH^{38}Cl^* \qquad (10).$$

This radical was found to decompose unimolecularly by releasing the ^{38}Cl atom again, i.e., the reverse reaction of (10). The half stabilization pressure $P_{1/2}$ was determined to be 650 ± 150 Torr for the energized radical, where $P_{1/2}$ means the pressure at which the rate of collisional stabilization equals that of the unimolecular decomposition, i.e., $k_3=k_2[M]$ at $P=P_{1/2}$ or $k_3=k_2P_{1/2}$ in the above general reactions (2) and (3). The $P_{1/2}$ values for $SnC_8H_{12}{}^{38}Cl^*$ was compared to those of $CH_2CH_2{}^{38}Cl^*$ (800 ± 120 Torr) and $CH_3CHCH_2{}^{38}Cl^*$ (150 ± 50 Torr) from ^{38}Cl-addition to ethylene[22] and propene[23], respectively, which are $RCH{=}CH_2$ molecules with R=-H and R=-CH_3 while R=-$Sn(CH{=}CH_2)_3$ in tetravinyltin. Since k_2 did not vary greatly for stabilization of these three radicals here, $P_{1/2}$ is considered as an approximate measure of the unimolecular decomposition rate constant k_3.

The $P_{1/2}$ values for both $CH_2CH_2{}^{38}Cl^*$ and $CH_3CHCH_2{}^{38}Cl^*$ are consistent with RRKM theory. The vibrational degree of freedom is 60 for $SnC_8H_{12}{}^{38}Cl^*$, while those for $CH_2CH_2{}^{38}Cl^*$ and $CH_3CHCH_2{}^{38}Cl^*$ are 15 and 24, respectively. If the excitation energy is distributed statistically over all of the degrees of freedom of $SnC_8H_{12}{}^{38}Cl^*$, the $P_{1/2}$ is anticipated to be much smaller than that (150 Torr) of $CH_3CHCH_2{}^{38}Cl^*$. Observations, however, show that the $P_{1/2}$ is higher, close to that of $CH_2CH_2{}^{38}Cl^*$, implying that the region for energy randomization is restricted to just the one chain to which ^{38}Cl adds while the other three vinyl chains are not coupled to it vibrationally during the decomposition. It should be mentioned that tin atom can block intramolecular energy transfer in $SnC_8H_{12}{}^{38}Cl^*$ as well as in $SnC_{12}H_{20}{}^{18}F^*$.

References

1. Robinson, P. J.: Holbrook, K. A.: "Unimolecular Reactions", Wiley, New York, (1972).
2. Forst, W.: "Theory of Unimolecular Reactions", Academic Press, New York, (1973).
3. Laidler, K. J.: "Theories of Chemical Reaction Rates", MacGraw-Hill Book Company, New York (1969).
4. Laidler, K. J.: "Chemical Kinetics", 3rd Ed. Happer & Row, Publishers, New York (1987).
5. Holbrook, K. A.: Chem. Soc. Rev., **12**, 163 (1983).
6. Hardwidge, E. A.: Rabinovitch, B. S.: Ireton, R. C.:J. Chem. Phys., **56**, 340 (1973).
7. Rakestraw, D. J.: Holmes, B. E.: J. Phys. Chem., **95**, 3968 (1991).
8. Oref, I.: Rabinovitch, B. S.: Acc. Chem. Res., **12**, 166 (1979)
9. Rowland, F. S.: "Molecular Beams and Reaction Kinetics" (Ed. by Schlier, Ch.), Academic Press, New York, 127 (1970).
10. Rowland, F. S.: Radiochim. Acta, **43**, 87 (1988).
11. Rogers, P. J.: Montague, D. C.: Frank, J. P.: Tyler, S. C.: Rowland, F. S.: Chem. Phys. Lett., **89**, 9 (1982).
12. Rogers, P. J.: Selco, J. I.: Rowland, F. S.: Chem. Phys. Lett., **97**, 313 (1983).
13. Sakai, Y.: Iyer, R. S.: Rowland, F. S.: J. Phys. Chem., **94**, 3368 (1990).
14. Rowland, F. S.: Rust, F: Frank, J. P.: ACS Symp. Ser. **66**, 26 (1978).

15. Lee, F. S. C.: Rowland, F. S.: J. Phys. Chem., **81**, 1229 (1977)
16. Lopez, V.: Marcus, R. A.: Chem. Phys. Lett., **93**, 232 (1982).
17. Lopez, V.: Fairen, V.: Lederman, S. M.: Marcus, R. A.: J. Chem. Phys., **84**, 5494 (1986).
18. Lederman, S. M.: Lopez, V: Voth, G. A.: Marcus, R. A.: Chem. Phys. Lett., **124**, 93 (1986).
19. Lederman, S. M.: Lopez, V: Fairen, V.: Voth, G. A.: Marcus, R. A.: Chem. Phys., **139**, 171 (1989).
20. Wrigley, S. P.: Rabinovitch, B. S.: Chem. Phys. Lett., **98**, 386 (1983).
21. Wrigley, S. P.: Oswald, D. A.: Rabinovitch, B. S.: Chem. Phys. Lett., **98**, 386 (1983).
22. Lee, F. S. C.: Rowland, F. S.: J. Phys. Chem., **81**, 1235 (1977).
23. Lee, F. S. C.: Rowland, F. S.: J. Phys. Chem., **81**, 1222 (1977).

Chapter 4

Hot Atom Chemical Processes in Condensed Phase

4.1 Computer Simulation of Collision Cascades in Solids

Kurt ROESSLER
Institut für Nuklearchemie, Forschungszentrum Jülich, Postfach 1913, D-5170 Jülich, Germany

1. Introduction

Computer simulation of reactive collisions was introduced to hot atom chemistry in the sixties. The first model applied was the trajectory method[1-4]. The individual encounters of projectile and target molecules were simulated by solving numerically the equations of motion of point masses over a potential energy hypersurface. Projectiles studied were T, F, and O in simple gases: H_2, HF, Br_2, O_2, CH_4, etc.; for a review cf.[5]. The molecular dynamic approach used in these systems was inherent to physico-chemical kinetics.

It took somewhat longer to apply computational techniques to solid state hot atom chemistry. Computer simulation of the slowing down of energetic atoms by a series of elastic and inelastic collisions, thereby displacing the target atoms (secondaries) and creating a collision cascade, was a domain of theoretical solid state physics[6]. The processes included erosion of the target (sputtering), changes in its physical properties (radiation damage) or chemical composition (hot atom chemistry). The theory of displacement cascades and their analytical treatment[7,8] were however for quite a time devoted to metallic substrates only. Computer simulation techniques were first introduced into studies of low energy radiation damage events by Vineyard et al.[9-11] who studied small crystallites of a few hundred atoms bound together by e.g. Lennard-Jones potentials, with boundary restraints to represent imbedding in a larger lattice. This model has been applied to bcc- and fcc-metals[9-12], to sputtering[13] and in one case even to alkali halides[14].

The alternative procedure was to construct the trajectory of a moving particle as a series of isolated binary collisions[15-20], an approximation which is useful in particular at high energies. The more elaborate models included electronic excitation. Since isolation of the collisions was difficult to obtain at low energies, a more developed program was presented 1972 by M.T. Robinson and I.M. Torrens: MARLOWE[21-23]. This code follows the primary and secondary projectiles through a series of binary atomic collisions, where always the currently fastest particle is calculated. The fact that individual cascades can be displayed as well as statistical information can be obtained makes it very valuable for chemical problems. A first paper on hot atom chemistry in alkali hexahalometallates A_2MX_6 appeared in 1974[24]. Besides MARLOWE there are many other codes for computer simulation of collision cascades, such as QDYN (quick dynamics), a multiple interaction cascade simulation program with interesting implications for insulators and molecular targets by D.E. Harrison[25,26] and TRIM by J.P. Biersack[27-31]. The latter program is based on the binary collision approach but treats molecular arrangement and lattice structure in a rather analytical way. It is quite fast, consumes only little computing time, and thus is popular among solid state physicists. It should be mentioned that otherwise data on stopping powers, ranges, and straggling are only available from tables on elemental targets and have to be extrapolated for chemical compounds[32-34]. However, it yields much less detailed information on chemistry than e.g. MARLOWE.

One inherent drawback of many codes is the fact that the interaction potentials for nuclear and electronic stopping (Sn,Se) were developed primarily for metallic targets. The discussion of the right potentials for low and high energy cases continues through all computer simulation approaches[23,26,35]. Most of hot atom chemical studies use insulators as targets. The collisional conditions should be somewhat different for ionic or molecular solids with covalent bonds and their stronger localization of electrons, than for metals[36]. J.P. Biersack has made a comparison of the potentials in the two cases[31,37]. He concludes that in ionic insulators, Coulomb forces between projectile and target ions act over a large distance due to the lack of any effective screening. Nuclear stopping might be drastically enhanced in ionic crystals at low energies, if the projectile maintains its charged states. This cannot always be excluded. Some di-atomic potentials[38] describe the stopping of light ions better than the Thomas-Fermi or Molière potentials used e.g. in MARLOWE, since in the absence of Coulomb forces their stopping power is lower. Electronic stopping powers determined for elementary targets appear to be well applicable also for insulators. Recently, a series of new programs have been presented on the basis of TRIM, including electronic collisions by δ-electrons in tracks and molecular dynamics for chemical interactions[39].

Another difficulty was pointed out by M.T. Robinson and I.M. Torrens[23]: At low energies, in particular below 5 eV, particles may no longer collide with individual atoms of the medium but interact with the crystal as a whole. Critical energies at which manybody effects might supervene can be estimated from the comparison of the velocity of the moving atom with that of longitudinal sound waves in the solid. The critical energies for metals range from about 5 eV (Al) to 28 eV (W). These values will however be somewhat lower for the insulators, and the binary collision approach seems to be valid down to a few eV.

2. The MARLOWE program

The best code for application to chemical problems is hitherto the program MARLOWE by M.T. Robinson et al.[22-24,40-43]. It includes a proper lattice structure by formulating the neighbourhood of each characteristic atom or ion. However, it can also introduce defects, a kind of polycrystallinity, amorphous or statistical arrangement of lattice constituents, surface of every kind, and by random (Monte-Carlo) displacement of atoms also thermal vibration. The program stores the data of each individual collision of the cascade. Thus, it is rather slow and time consuming compared to more analytical programs such as TRIM. However, it yields so many details for extrapolation of chemical processes following the "physical" events, that it is really worth its money.

Table 1: Potentials used in standard MARLOWE.

ELASTIC INTERACTIONS: THOMAS-FERMI-MOLIERE-POTENTIAL

$$V(R) = \frac{Z_1 Z_2 \cdot e^2}{R} \left(0.35\, e^{-0.30R/a_{12}} + 0.55\, e^{-1.2R/a_{12}} + 0.10\, e^{-6.0R/a_{12}}\right)$$

R: apsis of collision

a_{12}: screening length $= \left(\frac{9}{128}\pi^2\right)^{1/3} a_H \left(Z_1^{1/2} + Z_2^{1/2}\right)^{-2/3}$

a_H: Bohr radius

INELASTIC INTERACTIONS (COLLISION BY COLLISION)

$$Q(R,E) = \frac{0.045}{\pi} \frac{S_e}{a_{12}^2} e^{-0.3R/a_{12}}$$

$S_e(E)$: electronic stopping cross section

LINDHARD, SCHARFF, SCHIOTT: $S_e = 7.51\,(3\pi^2 e^2 a_H/32) \cdot (Z_1 + Z_2) \cdot V/V_o$

FIRSOV: $S_e = (8e^2 a_H) \cdot Z_1^{7/6}\, Z_2 (Z_1^{2/3} + Z_2^{2/3})^{-3/2} \cdot V/V_o$

A random number generator program for the angle of incidence onto the surface and the space distribution of projectiles induced by nuclear processes or knock-ons inside a solid, allows to calculate different cascades and to obtain good statistics over a large number of events. The individual binary collisions are computed for S_n by Thomas-Fermi-Mollière potentials and S_e by LSS and Firsov equations. cf. Table 1. For special applications it is possible to modify the interaction potentials. Atoms can be moved when a threshold energy is delivered by a collision; they are stopped when the energy falls below a cut-off value indicating thermalization, in general at a few eV. It is possible to obtain information on range, straggling, site and potential pairing or clustering of defects, sputtering, backscattering, replacement events, formation of secondary atoms by knock on, their number and energy distribution, and many other parameters. The fastest particle is followed first, thus, simulating a kind of temporal development of the cascade. Very important for chemistry is the fact that displaced lattice atoms or defects can be targets for further collisions.

For most of the Jülich work the program was used in its version 11 (1 June 1978). There are new versions (MARLOWE 12 from July 1984, MARLOWE 13 to appear in January 1992).

The program is available e.g. from Mr. L. Garcia de Viedma, NEA-Data Bank, F-91590 Gif-sur-Yvette. It is suggested to consult M.T. Robinson to get the newest information. Potential users in Europe should contact Dr. Marc Hou, Physique de Solides Irradiés, Université Libre de Bruxelles, Belgium.

3. Chemical implications

The potentials used in the program do not contain attractive forces, thus, a direct calculation of chemical interactions is impossible. Epithermal motions or diffusion processes at the end of the cascade cannot be computed. For this a proper molecular dynamics program would be necessary. As a consequence, MARLOWE extrapolations for chemistry can never give exact values for specific processes but orders of magnitude. It constitutes rather a collision dynamical assistance for mechanistic discussion.

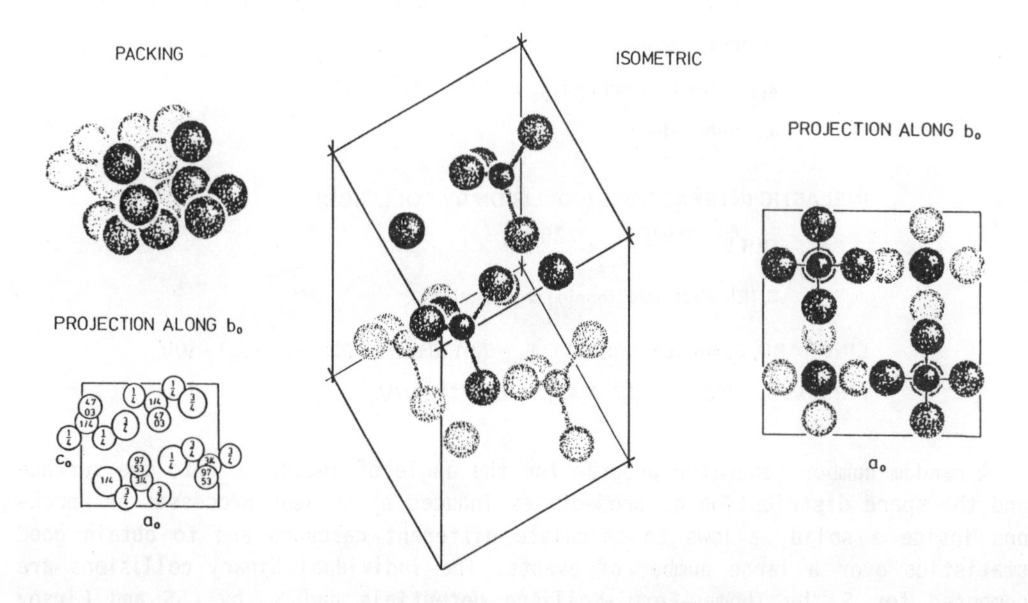

Fig. 1. Original, mononoclinic lattice of $KMnO_4$ (left) and cubic model lattice for MARLOWE calculations (middle and right).

When applying the program to chemical problems, quite complex lattices have to be formulated. In principle this is no obstacle, since the subprogram LATTIC[44] searches neighbours of individual atoms and creates a closed shell, from that the projectile cannot escape without colliding. It is, however, the interpretation of the data which becomes tedious and erroneous in a too complicated lattice. In many cases a somewhat simpler arrangement, the so called "model lattice", is constructed based on classical symmetries. The overall arrangement should be similar, the symmetry of the ligands in chemical compounds and the density have to be conserved. Fig. 1 shows a typical example for this type of symmetrification. Calculations with both types of lattices did not show large discrepancies.

Another implication for chemistry is that the program does not consider chemical bonds. Each atom is positioned in the lattice without interaction with its neighbours. Isotropic bond energies can be introduced by an intelligent choice of displacement threshold energies. This is done by an empirical balance of the different forces: lattice energies, directed covalent bond energies, angles of incidence of projectile, Coulomb interaction, thermal vibrations, etc.. Selecting the right displacement threshold, binding energies (which are substracted from transferred energy) and cutoff (thermalization) energy is a piece of art of the chemical operator of MARLOWE. In general, not only one value is chosen, but case studies are made with several values in order the estimate their influenec on the results.

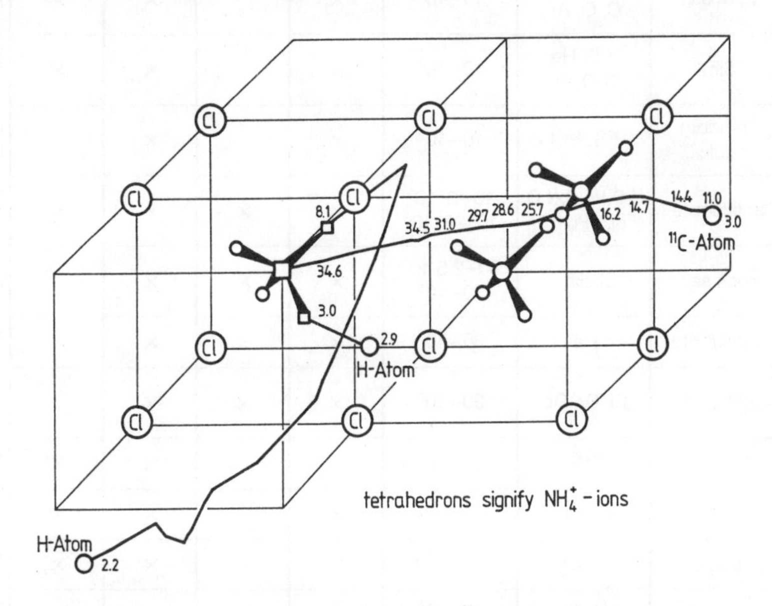

Fig. 2. Cascade of 50 eV ^{11}C atom in NH_4Cl. The numbers signify the current energies of primary and secondary particles.

Solid state physical applications of the program demands good statistics by averaging over a series of cascades (10^3-10^5). This is also true for chemical problems. But, the information which can be obtained from an analysis of individual cascades is equally valuable here. Fig. 2 presents a small collision cascade of ^{11}C from a nuclear process in NH_4Cl. The original recoil energy is about 2 MeV. The 50 eV in this case are only chosen to demonstrate processes in a concise picture. The hot carbon and secondary hydrogen atoms could interact chemically with NH_4^+-ions by insertion or H-abstraction. The endpoints of the physical calculation do not necessarily represent the real endpoints when

Table 2: Solid compounds studied in Jülich by MARLOWE for collision dynamics.

target	lattice* structure	projectile	kinetic energy, eV	range determination	inelastic loss	defects, recombination	secondaries, energy distrib.	references
Al	fcc	O	5–20	×		×		[45]
C	diamond graphite	H, D, He C, O, Ar	$10–10^5$	×		×	×	[46–48]
C_4H	"anti-SiF_4"	H, D, He C, O, Ar	$10–10^5$	×		×	×	[45]
C_2H	"antifluorite"	H, D, He C, O, Ar	$10–10^5$	×		×	×	[45, 48]
CH	"rock salt"	H, D, He C, O, Ar	$10–10^5$	×		×	×	[45]
CH_4	"SiF_4"	H, D, He C, O, Ar	$10–10^5$	×		×	×	[45, 47–52]
"DNA"	"random cubic"	^{32}S, ^{38}Cl	$10–10^2$	×		×		unpublished
H_2O-ice	"antifluorite"	H, D, He, C, N, O ^{207}Bi, ^{207}Pb, ^{234}Th	$10–3\cdot10^5$ $10^4–3\cdot10^5$	×	×	×	×	[49, 53–56, 67]
KX (X = Cl, Br, I)	rock salt	Cl, Br, I	$30–2.5\cdot10^5$ $30–10^6$	×	×	×		[45, 57, 58]
K_2SnCl_6	antifluorite	Re	$30–10^5$	×	×	×		[54–62]
K_2ReX_6 (X = Cl, Br)	antifluorite	Cl, Br, Re	$30–10^5$	×	×	×		[24, 60]
KIO_3	original	^{128}I	$30–10^3$			×	×	[45]
$KMnO_4$	"cubic"	O, Mn	$10–10^5$	×		×	×	[45]
$KClO_4$	"cubic"	O, Cl	$10–10^5$	×		×	×	[45]
MgO	cubic	U, Th ^{207}Pb, ^{207}Bi	$30–10^5$ $10^4–3\cdot10^5$	×	×	×		[63–67]
NH_4X (x = Cl, Br, I)	cubic	He, C	$30–2\cdot10^6$	×		×		[53]
SiC	diamond	C, O	$10–10^5$	×	×			[45]
SiO_2	"antifluorite"	H, D, He, C, N, O ^{207}Pb, ^{207}Bi	$10–3\cdot10^5$ $10^4–3\cdot10^5$	×	×	×	×	[53, 55, 56, 64]
ThF_4	"SiF_4"	^{192}Tl, ^{233}Ac	$10^5–5\cdot10^6$	×	×			[44]
UO_2	fluorite	U, Th ^{207}Pb, ^{207}Bi	$30–10^5$ $10^4–3\cdot10^5$	×	×	×	×	[63–68]

* The structures in citation marks are model lattices.

chemical interaction are involved. The differences may, however, not exceed a few Å.

Last but not least, MARLOWE computer calculation forces the hot atom chemist to look into the details of the lattice structure (free space, structured voids, blocked passages, typical neighbours for reaction, etc.). In solid state hot atom chemistry this is not selfunderstanding. Table 2 lists the systems studied in Jülich.

4. Examples of chemical interpretation of MARLOWE results

4.1. Range calculation

The calculation of the various kinds of ranges of the projectiles (vector, penetration or projected, total range) and the longitudinal and transversal straggling belong to the basic tasks of every cascade simulation program and can be carried out much faster with analytical programs such as TRIM. Even if it seems at the first glance that ranges are physical data, they have an important meaning for chemistry. It is the question wether the projectile can leave its original neighbourhood, where it would recombine, or whether it is transported into regions of the lattice which are further away.

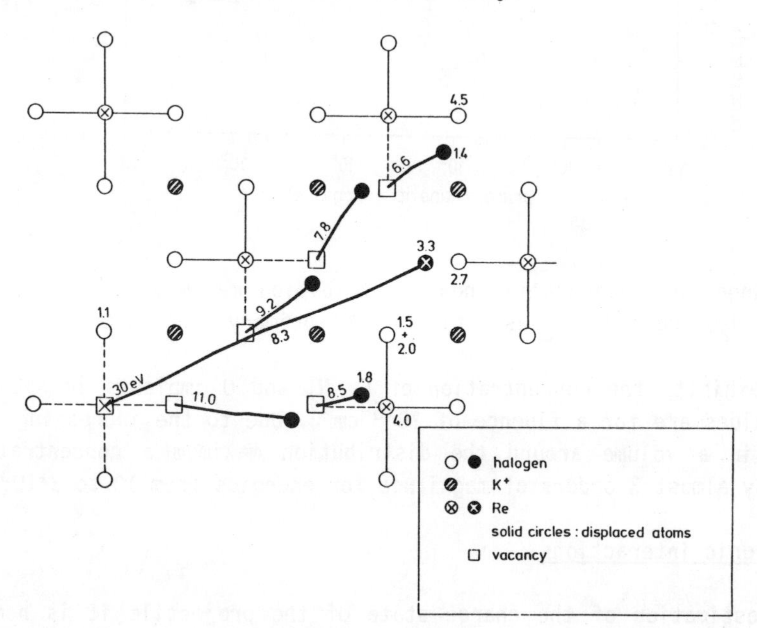

Fig. 3. Projection onto (100)-plane of a cascade by a 50 eV Re in K_2ReCl_6, [59].

Fig. 3 shows this for a 30 eV Re projectile in a hexachlororhenate(IV) lattice. It can leave its original complex site and reach another lattice unit, where it can combine with the ligands (in mixed crystals different ones) from the neighbouring complexes[59-62]. Furthermore, the range distribution and in particular the longitudinal straggling govern the concentration of the implants and their possibility to recombine, e.g. to C_2^- in carbon implanted alkali halides [58].

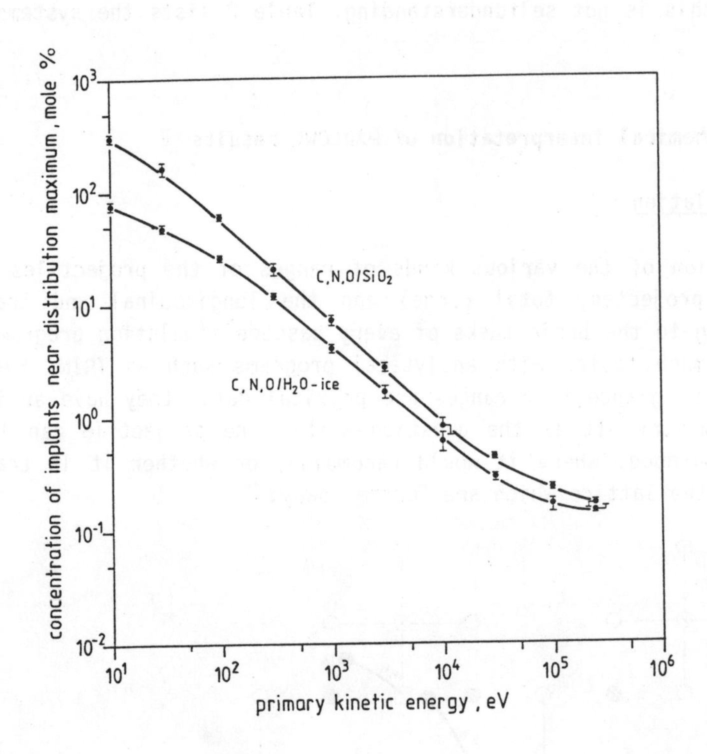

Fig. 4. Change in concentration near distribution maximum (±σ) of C, N, and O implants in H_2O ice and SiO_2 as a function of primary kinetic energy, from [56].

Fig. 4 exhibits the concentration of C, N, and O implants in SiO_2 and H_2O-ice. The values are for a fluence of 10^{15} cm^{-2}. Due to the increasing straggling one finds in a volume around the distribution maximum a concentration which decreases by almost 3 orders of magnitude for energies from 10 to $3*10^5$ eV[56].

4.2. Electronic interactions

For an estimation of the charge state of the projectile it is necessary to know its S_e, since the inelastic transfer is devided among excitation and ionization of projectile and target atoms, cf. the discussion in[64]. Fig. 5 exhibits the total inelastic loss of C, N, and O projectiles in frozen H_2O as a function of primary energy. The figure illustrates the rule of thumb, that $S_e \sim S_n$ when the energy of the projectile in keV is similar to its mass in a.m.u.. For hydrogen that is the case $\leq$ 1 keV, for C at about 12 keV.

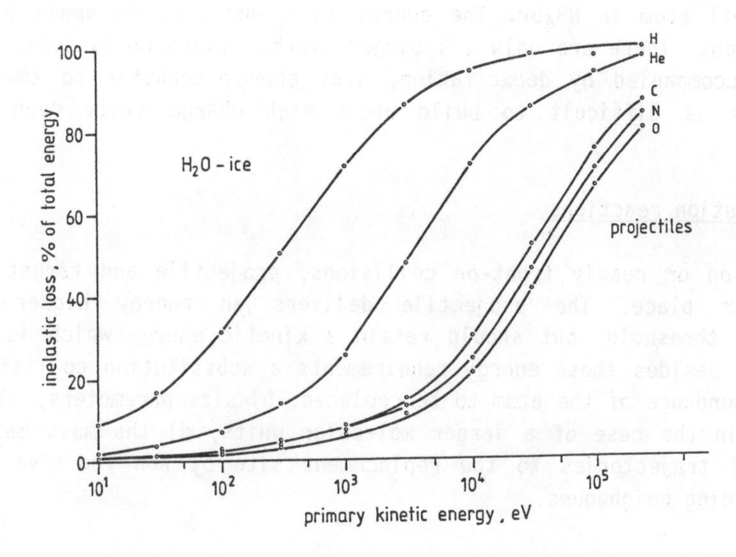

Fig. 5. Electronic excitation (S_e) by H, He, C, N, and O projectiles in H_2O ice as depending on the primary kinetic energy [56].

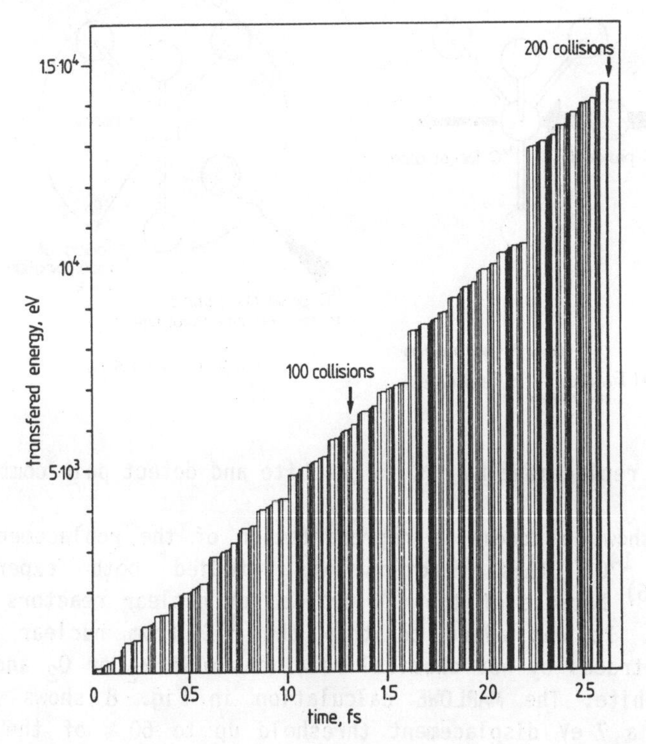

Fig. 6. S_e increments at the beginning of the cascade of a 2 MeV C in NH_4Br.

Fig. 6 shows the integrated S_e for the first 200 collisions of a 2 MeV ^{11}C

nuclear recoil atom in NH_4Br. The energy is transferred in small packages by many collisions. There are only 1 % bigger events. Since collisional excitation is always accompanied by deexcitation, i.e. energy transfer to the collision partners, it is difficult to build up a high charge state even in a MeV particle.

4.3. Substitution reactions

By front-on or nearly front-on collisions, projectile and target atoms can change their place. The projectile delivers an energy higher than the displacement threshold, but should retain a kinetic energy which is below the bond energy. Besides these energy requirements a substitution collision depends on a) the abundance of the atom to be replaced, b) size parameters, c) screening by ligands in the case of a larger molecular units, d) the mass match and e) focussing of trajectories to the replacement site by non reactive collisions with surrounding neighbours.

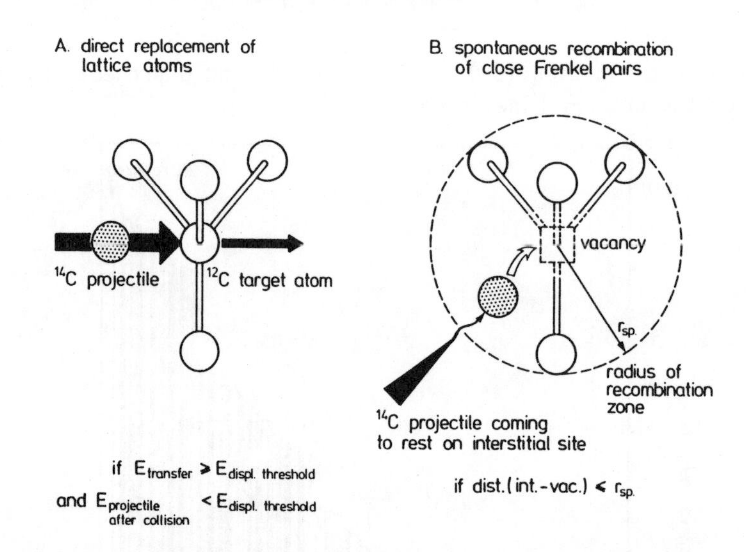

Fig. 7. Direct replacement by ^{14}C in graphite and defect pair combination, [46].

Fig. 7 A. shows a schematic representation of the replacement collision in graphite by ^{14}C. This reaction was studied both experimentally and theoretically[46] because of the ^{14}C problem of nuclear reactors with graphitic fuel elements. It was aimed to trap the ^{14}C from nuclear reactions with unavoidable N traces by hot chemical reactions with H_2 or O_2 and to extract it from the graphite. The MARLOWE calculation in Fig. 8 shows that under the assumption of a 7 eV displacement threshold up to 60 % of the eV ^{14}C end on lattice sites by replacement. Fig. 7 B shows the recombination of interstitial carbon atoms with nearby vacancies within a certain distance, the spontaneous recombination radius. The reentry of ^{14}C amounts to $\geq$ 90 % before any further chemical rection could take place. Similar behaviour has been observed for Th or U α-recoils in UO_2[63,64]. Most of the experiments demonstrate, that at least the same type of atom is easily bound to the new site. This may not be the case for different types of projectiles and target.

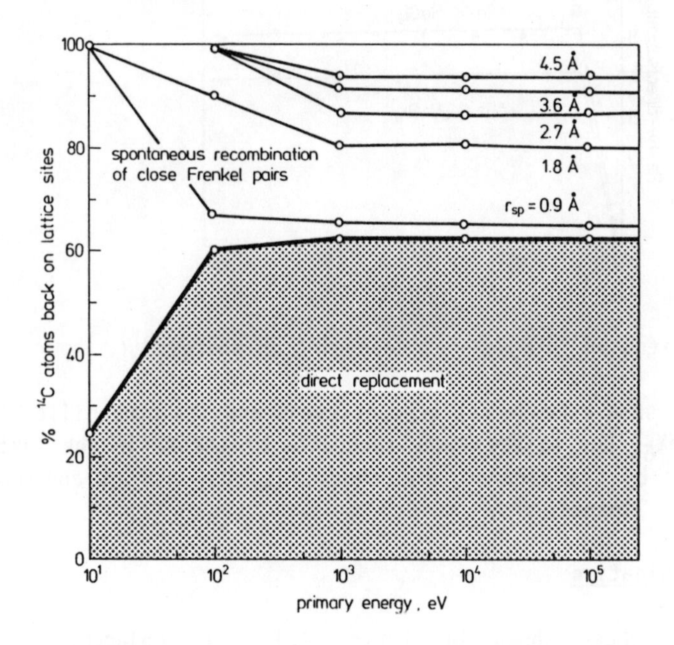

Fig. 8. Direct replacement and defect pair combination of ^{14}C in graphite, [46].

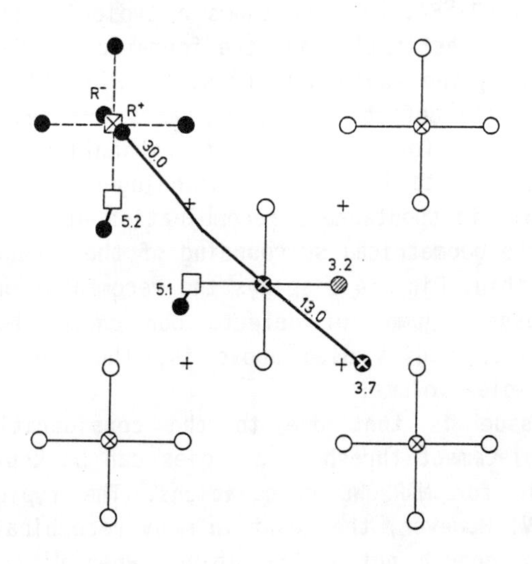

Fig. 9. 30 eV Re recoil in K_2ReCl_6 leading to replacement; projection onto (100)-plane. Symbols are as in Fig. 3. From [61].

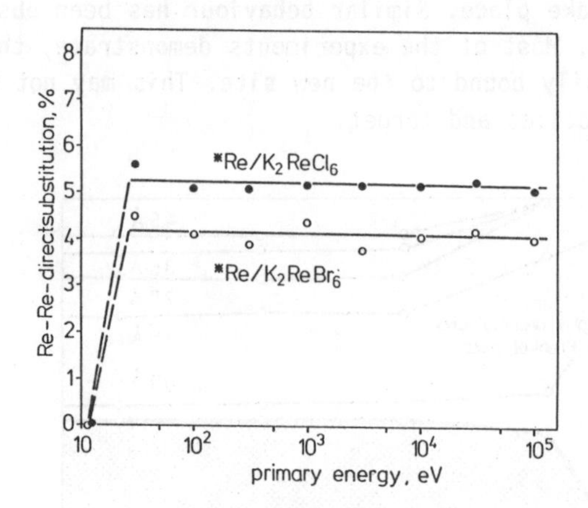

Fig. 10. Re-substitution in K_2ReX_6 as depending on energy [61].

Figs. 9 and 10 show a Re-Re replacement event and its probability for a 30 eV Re recoil in K_2ReX_6. Due to the lower abundance of the Re in the lattice (11 %) and the shielding by the ligands, the chance is only 4-5 % and lower in the case of heavier Br ligands.

4.4. Defect recombination

It has already been shown in chapter 4.3 that replacement events were followed by recombination steps. An almost quantitative agreement between theoretical calculation and experiment was found in the case of ligand recoil in hexahalometallates (IV) [24,60]. Fig. 11 shows a typical cascade leading to the 50 % halogen for halogen substitution and the formation of halogen interstitials and vacancies. When analysing their distances, in Fig. 12, it becomes obvious that the majority of these defects (Frenkel) pairs are separated by less than 0.8 a_0, a reasonable radius for spontaneous recombination. Fig. 13 lists these results from calculation: up to 95 % reentry of halogens into the ligand state.

A very important role in spontaneous recombination at the end of the cascade within 10^{-12} s plays the geometrical surrounding of the vacancy and the position of the interstitial within. Fig. 14 displays the recombination zone in an alkali halide crystal. Successive jumps of defects can cause the zone to be even larger. The recombination radius used above is, thus, only an average value representing a more complex volume.

Another important issue is that due to the consideration of spontaneous recombination the displacement threshold energies can be kept considerably low. This is characteristic for MARLOWE calculations. The typical Wigner-energies range from 15 to 40 eV. However, they contain many recombination steps and only one pair which is far enough not to recombine. When distributing the energy necessary to produce one stable Frenkel pair over all the (recombination) events, the low MARLOWE thresholds of a few eV would result.

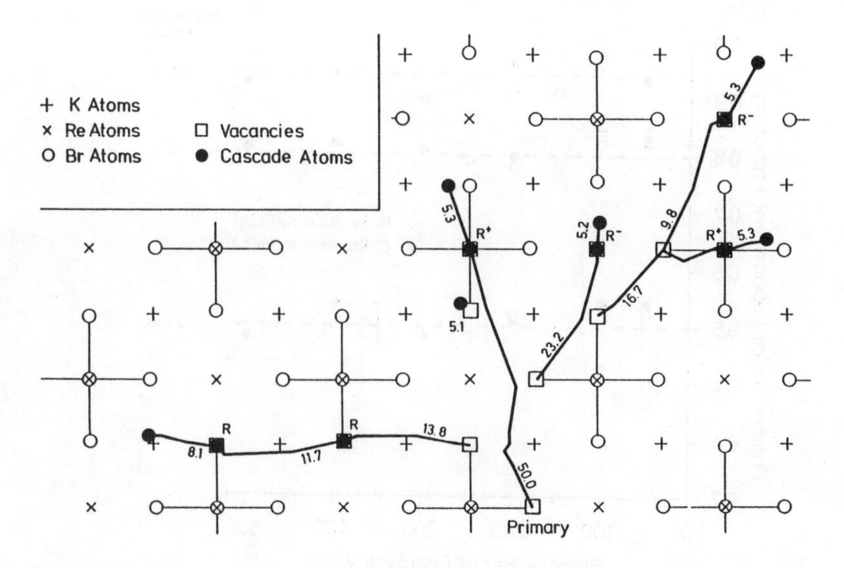

Fig. 11. Projection of the collision cascade of a 50 eV Br in K_2ReBr_6 onto the (100)-plane, from [24].

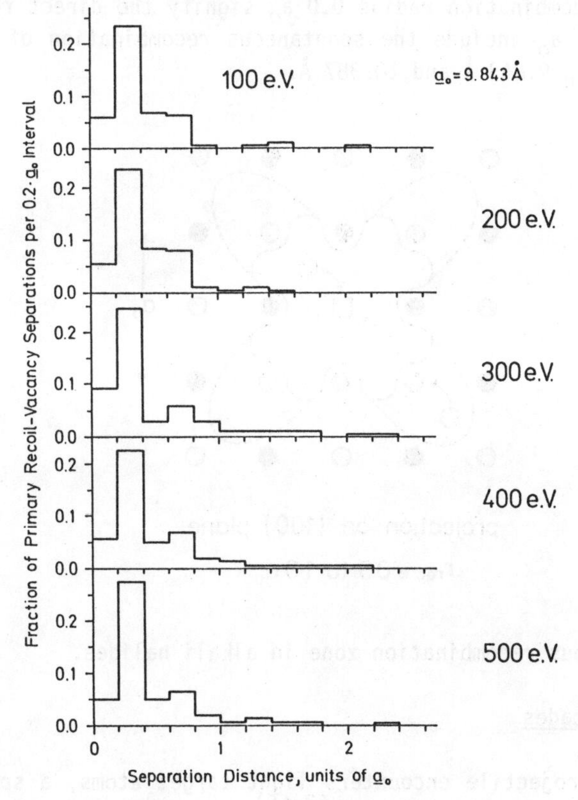

Fig. 12. Separation of interstitials and vacancies in K_2ReCl_6, from [24].

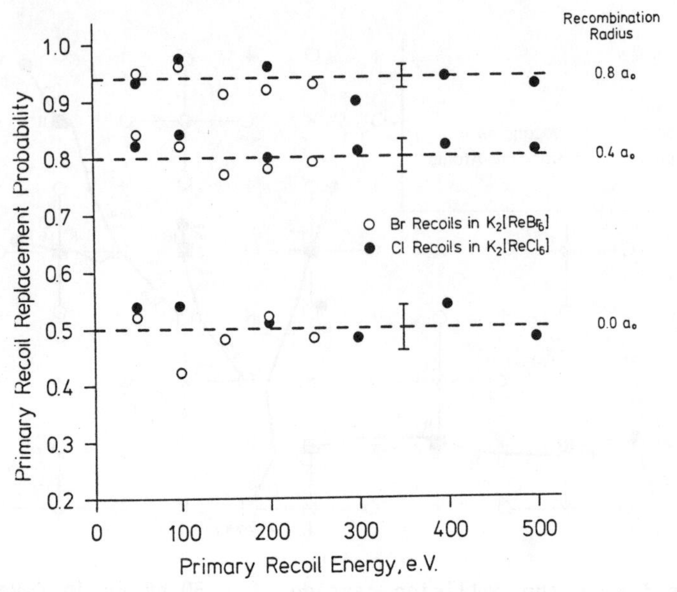

Fig. 13. Probability of reentry of recoil halogen into the complex, from [24]. The values for recombination radius 0.0 a_0 signify the direct replacement, those for 0.4 a_0 or 0.8 a_0 include the spontaneous recombination of Frenkel pairs in these distances. a_0=9.843 Å and 10.387 Å.

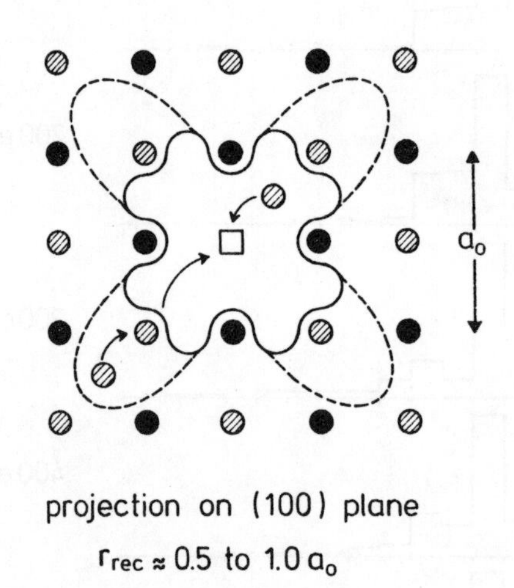

Fig. 14. Spontaneous recombination zone in alkali halides.

4.5. Aligned cascades

When a heavy projectile encounters light target atoms, a special collisional behaviour occurs: aligned cascades[63-65]. Fig. 15 shows schematically the typical collisions of atoms of equal mass, leading to deflection of trajectories, and of unequal mass, causing aligned cascades. Eqs. 1 and 2 show for the case of a heavy collision partner, that the angles of deflection would approach to zero.

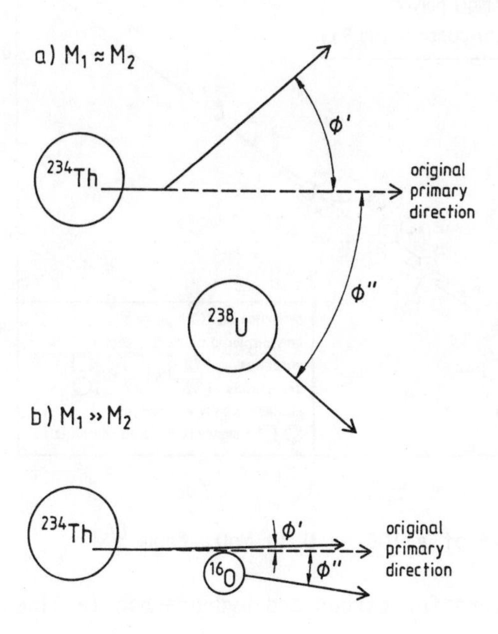

Fig. 15. Schematic representation of collisions between two partners of nearly equal mass a) and very unequal masses b), from [64,65].

(1) $\cos\phi' = (1-T/E)^{\frac{1}{2}} + \frac{1}{2}(1-M_2/M_1)(T/E)(1-T/E)^{-\frac{1}{2}}$ and

(2) $\cos\phi'' = [T(M_1 + M_2)^2/4EM_1M_2]^{\frac{1}{2}}$,

with T : energy transferred in the collision,
E : primary energy before collision,
M_1 : mass of primary atom,
M_2 : mass of secondary atoms.

Computer simulation of single cascades by low energy Th or U atoms in MgO[63-66] show that light oxygen atoms are coming to rest near to or in front of the primary, Fig. 16. At high energies a swarm of light particles will move in front of the heavy and result at the end in a lake of the lighter before or around the heavy. This is a very important effect which may change the stochiometry and the reactivity of the cascade region where chemical reaction occur. In the case of Th or U, the oxygens can induce oxidation and formation of uranyl ions, important for $^{234/238}$U disequilibrium in nature and radwaste storage[63-66,68].

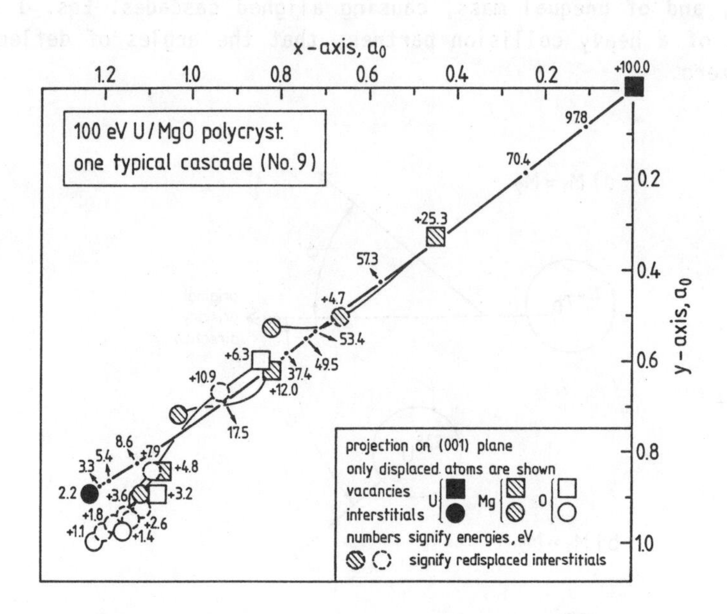

Fig. 16. Aligned cascade of a 100 eV U in MgO, from 64).

Table 3. Set of parameters for carbon and hydrocarbon lattices.

system	H/C ratio	lattice type	a_o Å	ρ $g \cdot cm^{-3}$	minimum C–C dist., Å	$E_{disp.}$ (C) eV	$E_{disp.}$ (H) eV	$E_{bind.}$ (C) eV	$E_{bind.}$ (H) eV	$E_{cut\ off}$ eV
carbon	0	diamond (8)	4.50	1.75	1.95	8	–	6	–	2
C_4H	0.25	anti-SiF_4* (2)	3.63	1.70	2.20	7	4	5	2	2
C_2H	0.5	anti-fluorite (4)	4.65	1.65	2.33	7	4	5	2	2
CH	1.0	rock-salt (4)	3.85	1.51	2.72	6	4	4	2	2
CH_4 (s)	4.0	SiF_4 (2)	4.69	0.52**	4.06	6	4	4	2	2

* with slighty changed lattice positions of C in order to adjust C–C distances of 2.2 Å (ΔX = 0.43 a_o)
** density at 90 K

4.6. Multicenter reactions in collision cascades

The example is given here for solid hydrocarbons, in particular frozen CH_4, where every kind of projectile creates hot carbon and hydrogen secondaries which can interact within the cascade to new complex hydrocarbons. The mechanism of multicenter reactions will be valid, however, for many other systems likewise[49,52]. Starting point was the observation of a-C:H (amorphous hydrogenated carbon), polycyclic hydrocarbons and even amorphous carbon in discharge deposition of organic vapours and the MeV ion irradiation of frozen CH_4 [47-52,70].

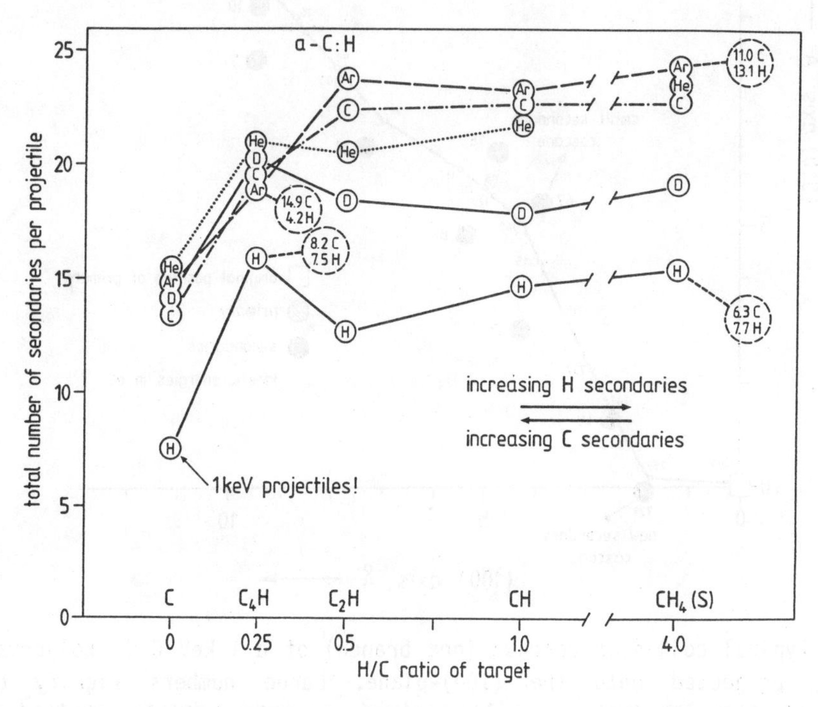

Fig. 17. Secondaries formed by 1 keV primaries in carbon and hydrocarbons.

Fig. 17 shows the secondary atom production by some 1 keV particles in a series of carbon and hydrocarbon original and model lattices. The conditions are given in Table 3. Even for 1 keV light projectiles a very high number of secondaries is formed with energies sufficiently high to create tertiaries, etc., i.e. a full side branch of the cascade[47,48]. Fig. 18 shows that the hot carbon atoms in graphite are situated within a few Å to each other. Fig. 19 displays a projection of a cascade of a 1 keV C in frozen CH_4 with the end points of the secondaries around the primary. Fifteen hot carbons and a number of hot hydrogens inside an activated zone with a radius of about 10 Å containing furthermore CH_3 and CH_2 radicals can result in a concerted multicenter reaction, which could explain the strong H-elimination and the formation of cyclic and polycyclic structures found in the experiments[49-52,70].

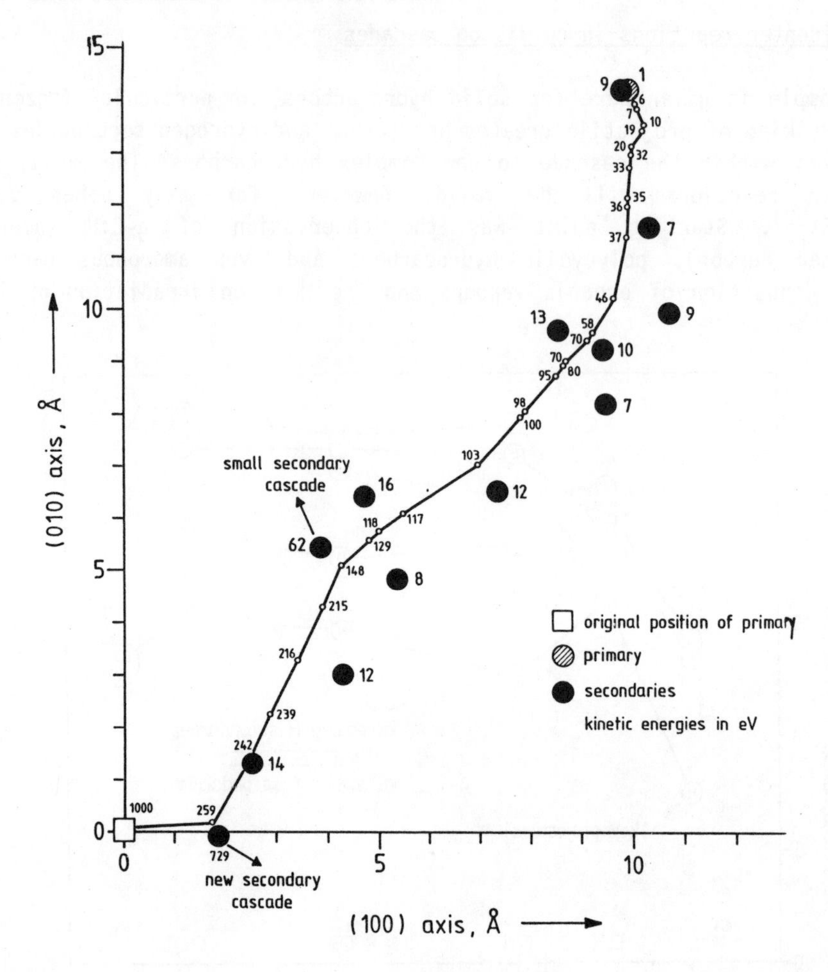

Fig. 18. Typical collision cascade (one branch) of a 1 keV C in polycrystalline graphite, projected onto the (100)-plane. Large numbers signify energies transferred to secondaries, small numbers energies still retained by the primary, from [47].

4.7. Effects of collision dynamics on suprathermal reactivity

It has been shown recently that suprathermal, i.e. hot reactions in gas phase are extremely fast when compared to thermal ones [49,71,72]. In the solid they will have a chance of interaction at energies < 10-20 eV when moving long enough through the lattice with some low energy collisions. Fig. 20 shows that a 1 keV C projectile in NH_4Br transfers the energy at the end of the cascade rather slowly and in small packages. This is an ideal condition for a hot solid state interaction such as an insertion in NH_4^+ to form $[H_3N\text{-}CH]^{*+}$. The information of the speed of hot reaction obtained from gas phase studies can, thus, be applied to solid state systems with a certain confidence.

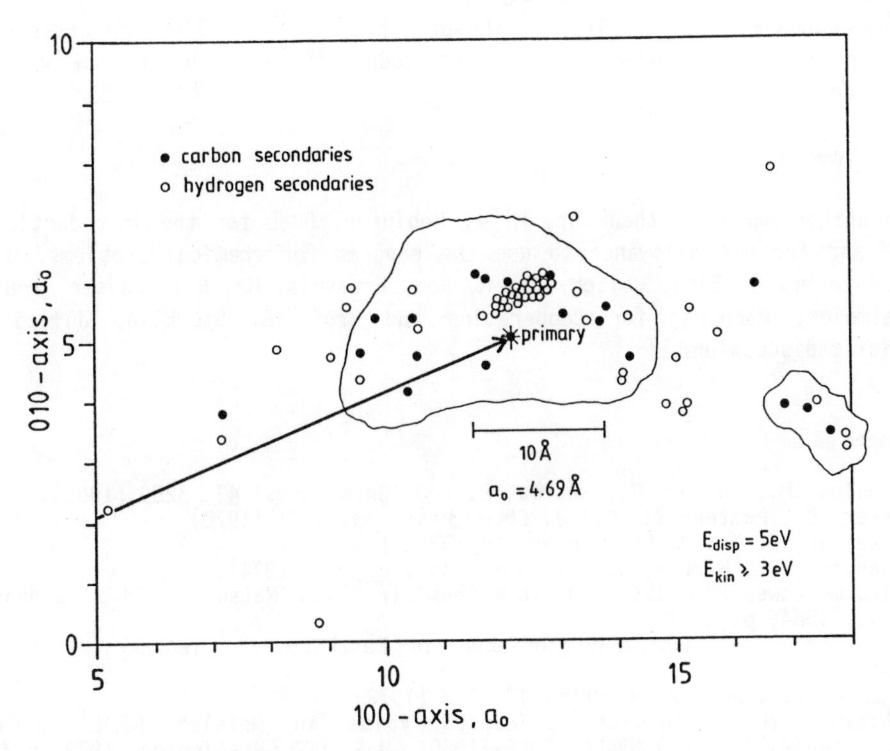

Fig. 19. Endpoints of hydrogen and carbon secondaries in a cascade of 1 keV C in frozen CH_4. Projection onto the (100)-plane [52].

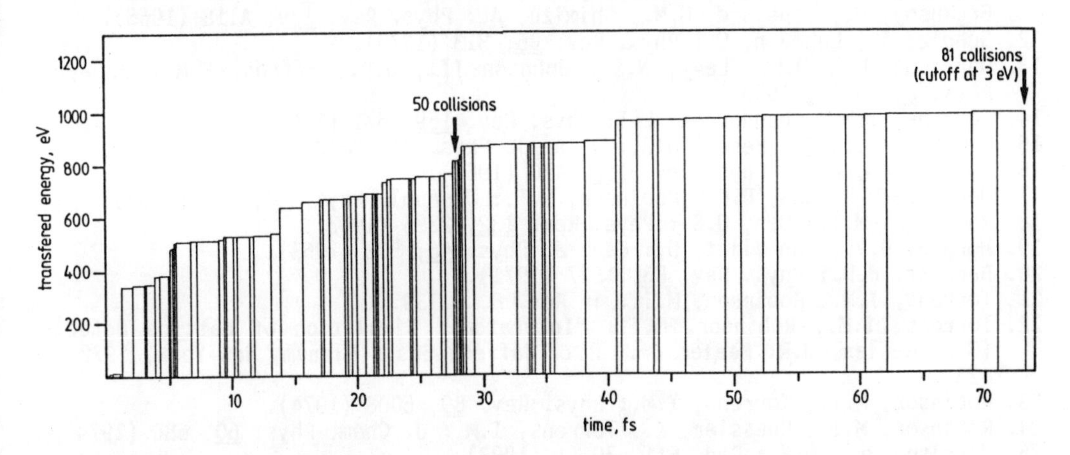

Fig. 20. End of a cascade of a 1 keV C in NH_4Br.

5. Conclusion

Computer simulation of collision cascades has helped and will assist furtheron to derive mechanisms for hot solid state chemistry. It may contribute to transfer new kinetic models from the gas phase to the solid. The crossing of MARLOWE results with molecular dynamics codes [39] will bring new valuable information.

Acknowledgments

The author wants to thank Dr. M. T. Robinson, ORNL for the introduction to MARLOWE and for his allowance to use the program for chemical problems. He is indebted to Mr. G. Eich, Jülich, Dr. M. Hou, Brussels, Mr. R.I. Kaiser, and Dr. G. Westmeier, Marburg, for cooperation and Prof. G. Stöcklin, Jülich for mechanistic discussion.

References

1. Karpulus, M., Porter, R., Sharma, R. : J. Chem. Phys. 43, 3259 (1965).
2. Bunker, D., Pattengill, M.: J. Chem. Phys. 53, 3041 (1970).
3. Muckerman, J. T.: J. Chem. Phys. 57, 3388 (1972).
4. Valencich, T., Bunker, D.: J. Chem. Phys. 61, 21 (1974).
5. Malcolme-Lawes, D. J.: "Hot Atom Chemistry" (T. Matsuura, Ed.), Kodansha, Tokyo, 1984, p. 39.
6. Leibfried, G.: "Bestrahlungseffekte in Festkörpern", Teubner, Stuttgart, 1965.
7. Sigmund, P. : Rev. Roum. Phys. 17, 823 (1972).
8. Robinson, M.T.: "Radiation Induced Voids in Metals" (J.W. Corbett, L.C. Ianniello, Eds.) USAEC, CONF-710601, U.S. GPO, Washington, 1972, p.397.
9. Gibson, J.B., Goland, A.N., Milgan, M., Vineyard, G.M.: Phys. Rev. 120, 1229 (1960).
10. Erginsoy, C., Vineyard, G.M., Englert, A.: Phys. Rev. 133, A595 (1964).
11. Erginsoy, C., Vineyard, G.M., Shimizu, A.: Phys. Rev. 139, A118 (1965).
12. Scholz, A., Lehmann, C.: Phys. Rev. B6, 813 (1972).
13. Harrison Jr., D.E., Levy, N.S., Johnson III, J.P., Effron, H.M.: J. Appl. Phys. 39, 3742 (1968).
14. Torrens, I.M., Chadderton, L.T: Phys. Rev. 159, 671 (1967).
15. Beeler Jr., J.R., Besco, D.G.: J. Appl. Phys. 34, 2873 (1963).
16. Beeler Jr., J.R.: Phys. Rev. 150, 470 (1966).
17. Oen, O.S., Holmes, D.K., Robinson, M.T.: J. Appl. Phys. 34, 302 (1963).
18. Robinson, M.T., Oen, O.S.: Phys. Rev. 132, 2385 (1963).
19. Morgan, D.V., Van Vliet, D.: Can. J. Phys. 46, 503 (1963).
20. Barrett, J.H.: Phys. Rev. B3, 1527 (1971).
21. Torrens, I.M., Robinson, M.T.: in Ref. 8, p.739.
22. Torrens, I.M., Robinson, M.T.: "Interatomic Simulation of Lattice Defects" (P.C. Gehlen, J.R. Beeler Jr., R.I. Jaffee, Eds.) Plenum, New-York, 1972, p. 423.
23. Robinson, M.T., Torrens, I.M.: Phys. Rev. B9, 5008 (1974).
24. Robinson, M.T., Roessler, K., Torrens, I.M.: J. Chem. Phys. 60, 680 (1974).
25. Harrison Jr., D.E.: Rad. Eff. 70, 1 (1983).
26. Harrison Jr., D.E.: Rad. Eff. 99, 153 (1986).
27. Biersack, J.P., Haggmark, L.G.: Nucl. Inst. Meth. 174, 257 (1980).
28. Biersack, J.P., Eckstein, W.G.: Appl. Phys. 34, 73 (1984).
29. Eckstein, W.G., Biersack, J.P.: Z. Phys, B63, 471 (1986).
30. Biersack, J.P., "Ion Beam Modification of Insulators" (P. Mazzoldi, G.W. Arnold, Eds.) Elsevier, Amsterdam, 1987, p.1.
31. Biersack, J.P.: in ref. 30, p. 648.

32. Northcliffe, L.C., Schilling, R.F.: Nuclear Data Tables A7, 233 (1970).
33. Ziegler, J.F.: "Handbook of Stopping Cross-Section for Energetic Ions in All Elements", Pergamon, New-York, 1980.
34. Littmark, U., Ziegler, J.F.: "Handbook of Range Distributions for Energetic Ions in All Elements", Pergamon, New-York, 1980.
35. Torrens, I.M.: "Interatomic Potentials", Academic, New-York 1972.
36. Littmark, U. Roessler, K.: Rad. Eff. 64, 49 (1982).
37. Biersack, J.P., Städele, M.: Rad. Eff. 64, 51 (1982).
38. Biersack, J.P., Ziegler, J.F.: Nucl. Instr. Meth. 194, 93 (1982)
39. Biersack, J.P., Nucl. Inst. Meth. Phys. Res (1992) in press.
40. Hou, M., Robinson, M.T.: Nucl. Instr. Meth. 132, 641 (1976).
41. Oen, O.S., Robinson, M.T.: Nucl. Instr. Meth. 132, 647 (1976).
42. Robinson, M.T.: "Sputtering by Particle Bombardment" Vol.1 (R. Behrisch. Ed.) Springer, Berlin, 1981, p. 73.
43. Eckstein, W.: "Computer Simulation of Ion Solid Interaction" Springer, Berlin, 1991.
44. Westmeier, W., Roessler, K.: Report- Jül-1563 (1978).
45. Roessler, K., Eich, G.: in preparation.
46. Schmitt, A., Roessler, K.: unpublished results (1979).
47. Roessler, K., Eich, G.: "Polycyclic Hydrocarbons and Astrophysics" (A. Legér et al., Eds.) Reidel, Dordrecht, 1987, p.173.
48. Roessler, K., Eich, G.: "Amorphous Hydrogenated Carbon Films", E-MRS Meeting June 1987, Vol. XVII, Les Editions de Physique, Paris, 1987, p. 167.
49. Roessler, K.: "Solid State Astrophysics" (E. Bussoletti, G. Strazzulla, Eds.) North Holland, Amsterdam, 1991, p. 197.
50. Patnaik, A. Roessler, K., Zador, E.: Radiochim. Acta 50, 757, (1990).
51. Roessler, K., Eich, G., Patnaik, A., Zador, E.: XXI Lunar Planet. Sci. Conf., 1990, p. 1035.
52. Roessler, K.: Nucl. Instr. Meth. Phys. Res. (1992) in press.
53. Roessler, K., Eich, G.: "Properties and Interactions of Interplanetary Dust" (R. H. Giese, P. Lamy, Eds.) Reidel, Dordrecht, 1985, p. 351.
54. Roessler, K.: ibidem, p. 357.
55. Roessler, K.: Rad. Eff. 99, 21 (1986).
56. Roessler, K., Eich, G.: Nucl. Instr. Meth. Phys. Res. B32, 446 (1988).
57. Roessler, K.: J. Physique (Paris) 37, C7-279 (1976).
58. Roessler, K., Manzanares, A.R.: Report-Jül-1924 (1984).
59. Roessler, K., Pross, L.: Radiochem. Radioanal. Lett. 18, 291 (1974).
60. Roessler, K., Robinson, M. T.: "Atomic Collisions in Solids" (S. Datz, B.R. Appleton, C.D. Moak, Eds.) Plenum, New-York, 1975, p. 237.
61. Pross, L.: Report-Jül-1511 (1978).
62. Roessler, K., Pross, L.: Rad. Eff. 48, 207 (1980).
63. Ordonez-Regil, E., Schleiffer, J.J., Adloff, J.-P., Roessler, K.: Radiochim. Acta 47, 177 (1989).
64. Roessler, K.: "Gmelin Handbook of Inorganic Chemistry" 8th Edition, Thorium, Suppl. A4, Springer, Berlin, 1983, p. 189.
65. Adloff, J-P., Roessler, K.: Radiochim. Acta 52/53, 269 (1991).
66. Adloff J-P., Roessler, K.: this issue.
67. Roessler, K., Eich, G.: Radiochim. Acta 47, 87 (1989).
68. Roessler, K.: "Gmelin Handbook of Inorganic Chemistry" 8th Edition, Uranium, Suppl. A6, Springer, Berlin, 1983, p. 135.
69. Roessler, K., Otterbach, J., Stöcklin, G.: J.Phys.Chem. 76, 2499 (1972).
70. Kaiser, R.I.: Report-Jül-2492 (1991).
71. Heyl, M.: Report-Jül-2409 (1990).
72. Heyl, M., Roessler, K.: this issue.

4.2 Hot Atom Chemistry of Organic Liquids

Klara BEREI
Central Research Institute for Physics, Hungarian Academy of Sciences,
H-1525 Budapest P.O.Box 49, Hungary

1. INTRODUCTION

The chemical effects of nuclear transformations were first observed by irradiating liquid ethyl iodide[1], and most investigations on recoil atom reactions in the following years were carried out using liquid systems (for reviews see[2-5]). Nonetheless, the general rules governing hot reactions in the liquid phase are still much less understood than those valid for the gas phase[6,7].

Difficulties in interpreting hot atom reactions in liquid systems stem mainly from the variety of processes: bond rupture, energy and charge transfer, radical formation and ultimate bond formation, occurring in close proximity. Furthermore, theoretical considerations concerning the energy loss, charge transfer, and the kinetics of high energy processes are hardly utilizable in the liquid phase[8]. An early attempt by Milman[9] to apply the Estrup-Wolfgang kinetic theory[10,11] to the reactions of recoil bromine atoms in liquid binary mixtures was not followed by many others.

Due to the overlap of competing processes occurring in a small volume, it is hard to distinguish the results of genuine hot reactions from those of thermalized recoil atoms. In gas phase experiments noble gases can be used as moderators which, by virtue of collisions, decrease the kinetic energy of the hot atoms without chemical interaction. No such completely inert substances that are conveniently miscible with organic liquids are known. Neither does the scavenger technique offer a clear-cut differentiation for liquid phase systems: scavengers present in low concentration can readily compete with the diffusion controlled processes of thermalized recoil atoms which have made many collisions before forming new chemical bond. Reactions of thermalized atoms occuring in the liquid cage, called by Milman[12] "immediate radical recombination" or more precisely specified as geminate radical recombinations[13-16] are, however, not necessarily influenced by the small amounts of reactive species present in the irradiated system.

On the other hand, there is a much greater variety of systems that can be irradiated in the liquid than in the gas phase, among them are quite a few substances of biological interest. This allows the utilization of recoil atom reactions to directly produce compounds labelled with radioactive atoms. This possibility was demonstrated by Gluekauf and Fay[17] very soon after the discovery of the Szilard-Chalmers effect[1] and it has developed into a sovereign field of recoil or direct labelling, mainly as a first step for the production of radiopharmaceuticals[18-20].

Reactions of hot atoms often result in highly excited product molecules which decompose to a great part in the gas phase. In closely packed liquids the probability of survival for such molecules is greatly increased due to the fast energy transfer to the adjacent solvent molecules.

The stereochemical course of the hot reactions in liquids may differ significantly from that observed in the gas phase leading to important conclusions on the mechanism of such reactions.

2. ROLE OF THERMAL PROCESSES

As Willard expressed it first in 1964 the main problem of this field is to determine the "...relative roles of displacement and radical formation mechanisms for those combination events which are not sensitive to low concentrations of scavengers..."[4], or taking Stöcklin's shorter formulation ten years later: "How important is caging?"[8].

2.1 Cage effect or geminate radical recombination

The cage effect was postulated by Franck and Rabinowitsch[21,22] to explain the decrease of the photolytic quantum yield in solutions. The recombination of a radical pair generated in the same event (photolysis, radiolysis, nuclear recoil, high energy collision, etc.) is greatly enhanced in the liquid phase. This is the result of interactions with the solvent molecules which hinder the escape of the fragments (R and X) from each other's vicinity:

$$RX \longrightarrow [R\cdot + X\cdot]_{\text{liquid cage}} \longrightarrow R\cdot + X\cdot \quad (1)$$

$$RX \longrightarrow [R\cdot + X\cdot]_{\text{liquid cage}} \longrightarrow RX \quad (2)$$

The probability of re-encounter (α') of the two fragments if their distance of separation is λ and their molecular diameter is d (assuming equal size as a first approximation), can be described as follows:

$$\alpha' = \Pi \cdot d^2 / 4\Pi\lambda^2 = (d/2\lambda)^2 \quad (3)$$

In the gas phase at the 100 Pa pressure $\lambda \sim 10^{-5}$ cm, and, if we take the mean molecule diameter to be 3×10^{-8} cm, the value of α' is $\sim 2.5 \times 10^{-6}$. Since at normal pressures only one of every thousand is a triple collision, the probability of recombination of the two fragments is negligible: $\sim 2.5 \times 10^{-9}$. In liquids the mean free path does not differ significantly from the diameter of the particles: $\lambda \sim d$, thus $\alpha' \sim 1/4$. Since here all encounters are triple collisions the probability of recombination is assumed to be of the order of magnitude 10^{-1} [21]. Luther and Troe[23] were able to prove experimentally that the increased probability of recombination in liquids is caused mainly by the change in the collision frequency. They observed essentially equal recombination of photodissociated iodine atoms in liquid and gaseous ethane at equal pressure.

Noyes[15] introduced *geminate radical recombination* as a more precise term for this phenomenon also suggesting that a distinction be made between two different types of these processes.

In *primary geminate recombination* the fragments remain in close proximity — almost within bonding distance of one another — until they lose enough energy to recombine. This takes place in a period of 10^{-13} - 10^{-12} s, not much longer than the time scale of vibration.

Secondary geminate recombination is diffusive in nature: the initial separation of the fragments is greater than the molecular diameter and they do interact with the solvent molecules before they re-encounter and finally recombine with the original partner. The time scale for this process was assumed to be of the order 10-100 ps. Indeed, it was later found by Eisenthal and colleagues[24] — using the picosecond laser technique — to be of about 70 and 140 ps for I_2 recombination in hexadecane and carbon tetrachloride, respectively.

Radicals which survive over a period of about 10^{-9} s almost certainly diffuse so far apart ("escape the cage") that there is only a negligible chance for them to re-encounter. They will react at random with other radicals or molecules of the bulk substance and can, therefore, be trapped effectively by the small amounts of reactive species (scavengers) present. This offers a good chance to distinguish between reactions of kinetically free radicals and cage processes.

On the other hand, it has proved difficult if not impossible to distinguish experimentally between the results of primary and secondary geminate recombinations despite the conceptual distinction suggested by Noyes[15]. According to this, primary recombination occurs too rapidly for surrounding molecules to compete with it, except in a medium consisting almost entirely of a very reactive scavenger. In contrast, secondary processes are likely to be influenced by the reactivity of the medium since they involve interaction of the fragments with the solvent molecules.

In the best known model for geminate recombination developed by Noyes[25,25] radicals represented by spheres react in a liquid treated as a continuum characterized by its viscosity. Making use of the Stokes-Einstein equation a linear relationship can be derived between geminate recombination and the reciprocal viscosity of the solvent. Deviations of experimental results from the predictions of this model are due to its simplifications: neglecting long range forces between reactants, treating the solvent as a structureless continuum and some other approximations[26].

A more sophisticated picture of cage processes has been revealed by models derived from trajectory studies — by making use of computer simulations (for example[27]) — which also account for the intermolecular interactions of the solvent molecules with the radical pair and with each other, considering the solution to be composed of discrete particles instead of being a structureless continuum. The validity of these considerations was reinforced by experimental results[23,28] showing the influence of the chemical nature and structure of the medium on the cage effect.

2.2 Cage effect in recoil processes

The problem we face in liquid phase hot atom chemistry is to distinguish between reactions which lead to similar products though they are different in nature, i.e between genuine hot processes (Eq.4) and reactions of thermalized recoil atoms (A·) with the nearby radicals (R·). These radicals may originate in the previous attack of the hot recoil atom (A*) (Eq.5) or in the nuclear transformation itself (Eq.6) if the energy gained thereby is too small to provide for the escape of the recoil atom from the parent cage.

$$A^* + RX \longrightarrow RA + X\cdot \qquad (4)$$

$$A^* + RX \longrightarrow [R\cdot + X\cdot + A\cdot]_{cage} \longrightarrow RA + X \qquad (5)$$

$$RA \xrightarrow{IT\ or\ (n,\gamma)} [R\cdot + A^*] \longrightarrow [R\cdot + A\cdot]_{cage} \longrightarrow RA \qquad (6)$$

2.2.1 Density variation technique

At first sight the most straightforward approach to this problem is to study the influence of continuously increasing density on the products of recoil atoms.

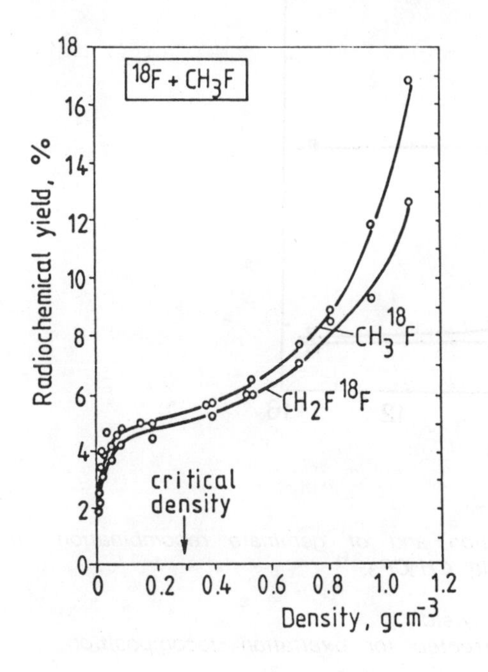

Fig. 1. Yields of replacement as a function of density for ^{18}F reacting in CH_3F-I_2 systems[29]

Richardson and Wolfgang[29)] were able to show that if recoil ^{18}F atoms react with methyl fluoride, a considerable part of the ^{18}F-labelled molecules is produced by radical recombinations in the liquid cage. Figure 1 shows the absolute yields of the two products varying with the density of CH_3F from gas to condensed phase. The first sharp rise in the yields levelling off at about 0.2 $g.cm^{-3}$ density can be ascribed to the effect of increasing collisional stabilization of highly excited primary products of fluorine (Eq.7) and hydrogen (Eq.8) replacement:

$$^{18}F^{*} + CH_3F \longrightarrow CH_3{}^{18}F + F\cdot \qquad (7)$$

$$^{18}F^{*} + CH_3F \longrightarrow CH_2F^{18}F + H\cdot \qquad (8)$$

The second rise above the critical density was interpreted as the onset of cage recombination in the formation of $CH_3{}^{18}F$ and $CH_2F^{18}F$.

Similar dependence has been established by a number of research groups[30-40)] for several recoil halogens reacting with volatile hydrocarbons and with some of their substituted derivatives.

Manning and Root[30 32)] have found that the extent of collisional stabilization of internally excited hot products changes over the same range as that of cage recombination. Therefore, as they pointed out, reliable establishment of cage reactions can be performed by density variation experiments only if combined

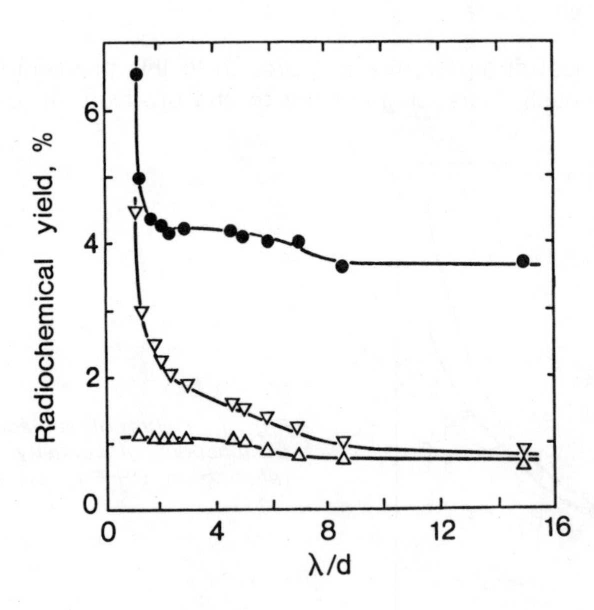

Fig. 2. Effect of excitation decomposition and of geminate recombination on the formation of ^{18}F replacement products in CH_3CF_3.[31)]

∇ - *apparent $^{18}F \rightarrow F$ replacement yield*
• - *$^{18}F \rightarrow F$ replacement yield corrected for excitation decomposition*
Δ - *$^{18}F \rightarrow CH_3$ replacement yield*

with a total yield analysis for every particular hot reaction channel. Applying this method they were able to show that some products are formed to a significant extent in cage processes whereas others are not. An example for ^{18}F atoms reacting in the CH_3CF_3 system[31)] is shown in Figure 2. Here the yields of fluorine and methyl group replacement are given as a function of the reduced length parameter, i.e. the ratio of mean intermolecular distance (λ) to molecular diameter (d). It can be seen that with decréasing λ/d ratio ,i.e. with increasing density, the apparent fluorine replacement yield continually increases whereas that corrected for excitation decomposition channels shows a plateau over a wide range down to λ/d values smaller than 2. The sharp rise at this point is attributed to the onset of cage processes. On the other hand, the corrected yield for CH_3 replacement does not show any increase even at low λ/d values,thereby indicating the absence of cage reactions. The total organic yields due to cage processes (4-6%) have been found to be comparable in extent to the true hot yields (8-9%) in these systems. Bearing in mind that efficient hydrogen abstraction by thermal fluorine atoms from the parent molecules successfully competes with the secondary processes, these yields are attrributed to primary geminate recombination.

Rack and co-workers obtained plots of similar nature for recoil Br and I reacting in methyl halogenides, ethane and some unsaturated hydrocarbons[34-40)].

2.2.2 Variation of medium reactivity

Another method suitable for studying the role of cage processes is by altering the reactivity of the medium towards the thermalized recoil atom. By means of dilution experiments applying solvents of different reactivities the competition between secondary cage recombinations of recoil atoms with original fragments and their reactions with the solvent molecules of the cage wall can be changed.

A systematic study was carried out to establish the role of cage reactions for recoil chlorine atoms in mono- and disubstituted benzenes[41,42)]. The effect of different solvents present at high concentrations was compared with the effect of a very efficient scavenger (I_2) present at small concentration.

The data summarized in Table 1 show a drastic decrease in replacement yields if the parent aromatic molecules in the cage are replaced by molecules highly reactive towards thermalized recoil atoms. This is due to the easy hydrogen abstraction by chlorine from the aliphatic hydrocarbons or alcohols. The addition of I_2 scavenger has no effect in these mixtures.

Dilution with benzene — where hydrogen abstraction by chlorine atoms is an endothermic process — has a much less dramatic effect. The addition of I_2 scavenger, however, decreases the yield to approximately the same value as the aliphatic species. This phenomenon can be explained by the formation of a charge transfer (Π-) complex between Cl atoms and benzene[43-45)] thereby promoting the "escape" of ^{38}Cl atoms from the cage, thus competing with the geminate recombination. (This interpretation was later supported by the experimental results of Eisenthal and co-workers[46)]. Applying picosecond laser photolysis they observed competition between charge transfer complex formation and secondary geminate recombination for iodine atoms reacting in CCl_4 — C_6H_6 mixtures.) The Π-complex is not stable enough to prevent the ^{38}Cl atoms from reacting with the surrounding radicals resulting in higher yields than expected for dilution. The addition of I_2 scavenger prevents these uncorrelated recombinations.

Table 1. Effect of reactive diluents on the replacement yields by recoil ^{38}Cl [41,42]

System	Diluent mole %	Without I_2	0.5 mole % I_2	Currected for dilution
		Radiochemical yield (%)		
		$^{38}Cl \rightarrow Cl$		
o-$C_6H_4Cl_2$	0	30.5	15.7	15.7
+ c-C_6H_{12}	90	1.3	1.3	13
+ CH_3OH	90	1.9	—	19
+ C_2H_5OH	90	1.2	—	12
+ C_6H_6	90	15.2	2.0	20
o-C_6H_4ClF	0	24.4	8.7	8.7
+ CH_3OH	50	—	4.4	8.8
m-C_6H_4ClF	0	22.5	6.0	6.0
+ CH_3OH	50	—	3.5	7.0
p-C_6H_4ClF	0	23.4	10.5	10.5
+ CH_3OH	50	—	4.5	9.0
o-$C_6H_4ClNO_2$	0	4.3	1.4	1.4
+ CH_3OH	50	—	0.8	1.6
		$^{38}Cl \rightarrow NO_2$		
o-$C_6H_4ClNO_2$	0	15.5	9.1	9.1
+ CH_3OH	50	—	4.3	8.6

Comparison of the yields corrected for dilution (last column of Table 1) shows that the addition of an efficient scavenger in the usually applied small amounts has essentially the same effect as does a reactive cage wall around ^{38}Cl atoms. It means that in a system providing fast reactions of thermalized recoil atoms or promoting their escape from the cage the role of secondary recombination cannot be significant.

In contrast, in systems highly diluted with perfluorinated hydrocarbons the yields of $^{38}Cl \rightarrow Cl$ replacement do not decrease and remain high even in the presence of I_2 scavenger, as can be seen from the data in Table 2. Figure 3 shows that the enhancement of the yields occurs only for the chlorine replacement by recoil ^{38}Cl, whereas the fluorine replacement by the same recoil atom does not show any change with the composition of the medium, thus indicating a genuine hot process. The increasing chlorine replacement yields seem to be connected with replacing dichlorobenzene by hexafluorobenzene in the solvent cage, i.e. with the surrounding of the recoil ^{38}Cl by molecules highly inert towards chlorine atoms[47], thereby hindering its escape and consequently increasing the probability of its recombination with the chlorophenyl radical that originated in a previous attack of hot ^{38}Cl on the dichlorobenzene molecule.

Table 2. Effect of non-reactive diluents on the $^{38}Cl \rightarrow Cl$ replacement yields[41]

System		Diluent mole %	Without I_2	0.5 mole % I_2	Corrected for dilution
			Radiochemical yield (%)		
C_6H_5Cl		0	26.4	5.9	5.9
	+ C_6F_6	90	43.2	4.0	40
o-$C_6H_4Cl_2$		0	30.5	15.7	15.7
	+ C_6F_6	50	36.5	13.9	27.8
	+ C_6F_6	90	40.7	8.2	82
	+ C_6HF_5	90	33.2	7.1	71
	+ 1,2-$C_3F_6Cl_2$	90	29.0	11.2	(112)
m-$C_6H_4Cl_2$		0	28.6	7.4	7.4
	+ C_6F_6	90	23.8	2.3	23
p-$C_6H_4Cl_2$		0	38.2	20.4	20.4
	+ C_6F_6	90	—	9.9	99

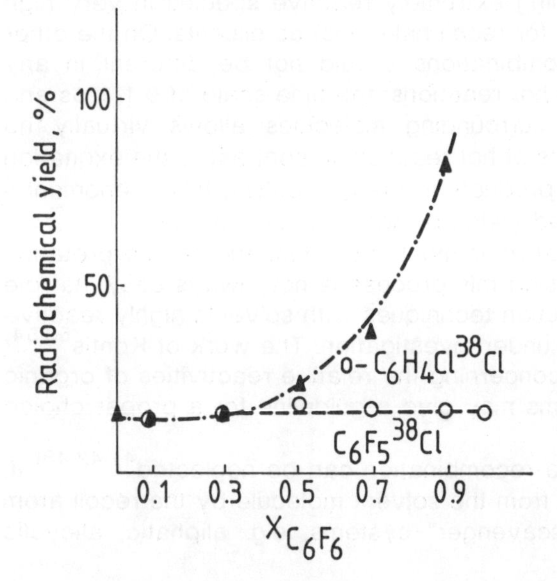

Fig. 3. Radiochemical yield corrected for dilution for $^{38}Cl \rightarrow Cl$ and $^{38}Cl \rightarrow F$ replacement in o-$C_6H_4Cl_2$-C_6F_6-I_2 mixtures[41]

Similar conclusions were drawn from investigations on the validity of conventional reaction kinetics in the formation of labelled organic products by recoil atoms in liquid binary mixtures[48]. Its rules should prevail only if the reactants were homogeneously distributed, i.e. if cage processes could be neglected. Using some reasonable approximations it was shown that conventional reaction kinetics can be applied to the formation of labelled compounds from benzene derivatives and from dichloroethane but not to formation of ^{38}Cl labelled carbon tetrachloride.This may indicate the role of the cage effect in the last case and is well in line with the results of Brinkman and co-workers[49-52] who carried out a comprehensive study on recoil Cl atoms reacting in a series of halocarbons diluted with solvents of different reactivities. Comparing the results with those of radiolytic studies they came to the conclusion that in polychlorinated methanes and ethane only a small part (3-5%) of the total activity can be attributed to hot products and much higher yields (20-30%) to the products of cage reactions.

2.2.3 Conclusions

The following thermal processes may possibly interfere with the hot reactions of recoil atoms in liquids:

Diffusion controlled reactions of kinetically free thermal recoil atoms with radicals and molecules in the bulk which can be successfully eliminated by efficient scavengers present in small amounts (0.5-1 mole %).

Primary geminate recombination of recoil atom with the molecule fragment produced by energetic collision or by the recoil itself. This process is determined by the energy of dissociation and by the properties of the radical pair and its extent can only be established by the density variation technique combined with the total product yield analysis[30-32]. To eliminate or suppress this process would be possible only in systems containing extremely reactive species in very high concentration (e.g. ≥ 99 mole % Br_2 for recoil halogens) as diluents. On the other hand, the products of primary recombinations should not be different in any chemical aspect from those of initial hot reactions: the time scale of 0.1-1 ps and the lack of interactions with the surrounding molecules allows virtually no rearrangement of the original products of hot reaction. In contrast to the excitation decomposition of newly formed hot products in the gas phase, this phenomenon may be responsible for the increased yields of hot reactions in liquids.

Secondary geminate recombination in most cases hinders the interpretation of hot reactions. Tracing or suppressing this process is not always easy. Its role can best be established by using dilution techniques with solvents highly reactive towards the thermalized recoil atom under investigation. The work of Kontis[53,54] and Rao[55-58] and their colleagues concerning the relative reactivities of organic solvents towards recoil chlorine atoms may give a guideline for a proper choice of such substances.

The role of secondary geminate recombination can be neglected[41,42,48] if:

a) hydrogen can be abstracted from the solvent molecule by the recoil atom with low activation energy ("self-scavenger" systems, e.g. aliphatic, alicyclic hydrocarbons, alcohols);

b) the recoil atom can form a charge transfer complex with the solvent molecules and thus escape from the vicinity of the geminate radical (e.g. aromatic substances).

Accordingly, reliable conclusions can be drawn on the course of hot reactions of recoil atoms with aliphatic, alicyclic, aromatic hydrocarbons and with their mono- or disubstituted derivatives if we use classical scavenger techniques to suppress the diffusion controlled thermal processes.

3. HOT REACTIONS

Monovalent recoil atoms have most often been used for investigations in organic liquids because they are able to react as neutral atoms building stable organic bonds in one-step processes. Thus, conclusions can be drawn on the primary high energy processes from the amount and ratio of final products labelled with radioactive atoms. Reactions of polyvalent atoms are more difficult to interpret since the labelled products originate in several steps only the first of which occurs in the high energy range.

Most of the valuable information on the mechanism of hot processes has been gained from studying replacement reactions. Abstraction products of tritium and halogens are often diatomic inorganic species susceptible to isotope exchange thereby altering the primary results of hot reactions. Addition reactions can be studied mainly by means of unsaturated hydrocarbons. In aromatic systems hot addition leads to immediate polymerization of the products formed; analysis of the polymer fraction is a tedious procedure rarely giving valuable information[59-61] on the genuine hot process.

3.1 Stereochemical course

Stereospecificity of hot reactions in molecules containing asymmetric carbon atoms is able to provide insight into the dynamics of interaction. Practically absolute retention of the original configuration for the replacement reactions of recoil tritium[62-65] was interpreted on the basis of Wolfgang's Impact Model which postulates a direct interaction of the hot atom with the reactant molecule on a time scale of 10^{-14}-10^{-13} s excluding Walden inversion. For a long period this Golden Rule[7] was considered to be generally valid since recoil halogens also exhibit a prevalent stereospecificity in their replacement processes, especially in the gas phase[64,66-69]. A somewhat higher extent of inverted products observed for the liquid systems was first explained by the contribution of radical recombinations allowing racemization of the intermediate radicals in the liquid cage[66,70].

Trajectory studies of Bunker and Pattengill[71,72] showed, however, that Walden inversion cannot be excluded even for hot replacement of hydrogen by tritium in methane. This view was supported by the experimental results of Vasáros et al.[73] who found that the extent of inverted products for $^{38}Cl \rightarrow Cl$ replacement in liquid dichlorobutane diastereomers is not affected by temperature, viscosity or mass ratio though these usually alter the conditions for radical recombination. The inversion/retention ratio varies substantially, however, on changing the nature of the solvent, thereby altering the conformer ratio and thus the conditions for the hot atom attack on the dichlorobutane molecule. Machulla and Stöcklin[64] concluded from studies with $(CHClF)_2$ diastereomers that $^{38}Cl \rightarrow Cl$ replacement in the liquid phase occurs partly by direct replacement in accordance with the Impact Model and partly via an electronically unstable intermediate held together by the nearby solvent molecules ("caged complex") for a time sufficient for Walden inversion to take place. Highly convincing evidence for the possibility of Walden inversion in the course of hot processes has been provided by Wolf et al.[74-77]. They have found inversion of configuration to be prevalent when recoil ^{38}Cl replaces chlorine in gaseous 2-chloropropionyl chloride. (See Chapter "Stereo Organic Hot Atom Chemistry").

3.2 Bond energy effect

Early studies with alkanes and alkylhalogenides indicated that the product yields of hot atom reactions are inversely dependent on the bond strength of the atom or group to be replaced or abstracted, both in gaseous and liquid systems[78-82]. Wolfgang interpreted the bond energy effect for hydrogen abstraction by hot tritium atoms on the basis of the Impact Model assuming a stripping mode of abstraction ("glancing collision"[7]). According to this model, if the tritium atom approaches the C-H bond axis at approximately right angles, only a small fraction of its kinetic energy will be effective along the line of T-C-H centres resulting in the sensitivity to the value of bond dissociation energy. Rowland and co-workers[79] assumed a concerted mechanism of collision between hot atom and the reacting molecule implying bond excitation during the interaction.

More information could be gained from investigations on the aromatic replacement by monovalent hot atoms (Eqs. 9,10). In this case the impact parameters tend to remain nearly the same whereas the chemical properties of the reactant molecule and the bond energy of the atom or group to be replaced vary considerably if one uses a series of monosubstituted benzene derivatives or of disubstituted benzene derivatives where only one substituent is changed:

$$A^* + C_6H_5X \longrightarrow C_6H_5A + X\cdot \qquad (9)$$

$$A^* + C_6H_4XY \longrightarrow C_6H_4YA + X\cdot \qquad (10)$$

where A^*: monovalent hot atom
X, Y: monovalent atom or functional group

Dependence of the yields on the bond energy of the substituted atom or group was established by White and Rowland[83] for hot replacement by recoil tritium atoms in crystalline substituted benzoic acids. The same trend was found by Pozdeyev and colleagues[84] for halogen replacement by tritium in liquid halobenzenes. The phenomenon was interpreted by the formation of an excited intermediate between tritium and the aromatic molecule in the course of the hot reaction.

Extensive work carried out to determine the main factors governing the hot replacement by recoil halogen atoms in aromatic systems led, however, to different opinions concerning the mechanism of these reactions[42,59,85-103]. Thus,

Miller and Dodson[85], the pioneers of the field, considered the hydrogen replacement by recoil ^{38}Cl in liquid benzene to take place *via* an atom-molecule collision in an epithermal energy range, forming a short-lived complex which subsequently decomposes into the labelled products. Nesmeyanov and coworkers[86], on the other hand, studying aromatic halogen replacement by ^{82}Br suggested that the yields depend on the mass ratio of the reacting atoms rather than on the bond strength and hence supported the billiard-ball mechanism involving atom-atom collisions. Stocklin and Tornau[89] assumed the validity of the Impact Model[6,7] for hot replacement of heavy atoms or groups by ^{38}Cl in monosubstituted benzenes.

Recent systematic studies in several laboratories[42,87,88,93,96,99,100] have shown that models based on atom-atom collisions cannot be valid for hot aromatic replacement processes. Hot halogen replacement observed in the four halobenzenes with recoil halogens originating from different nuclear processes (Eq.(9), $A^* =$ ^{18}F, ^{34m}Cl, ^{38}Cl, ^{76}Br, ^{82}Br, ^{125}I, ^{128}I, ^{211}At) seems to depend mainly on the nature of the reacting halogen and on the bond strength in the benzene ring of the halogen to be replaced (X=F, Cl, Br, I). Somewhat unexpectedly this has been found to be true not only for halogens formed in (n,2n) and (n,γ) nuclear reactions with high initial kinetic energy[91,93] but also for those originating *via* EC with relatively low kinetic and high ionization and excitation energy[96,99,100]. This indicates fast neutralization of originally ionized recoil species[99,100] followed by their reactions as neutral atoms that still possess definite excess energy.

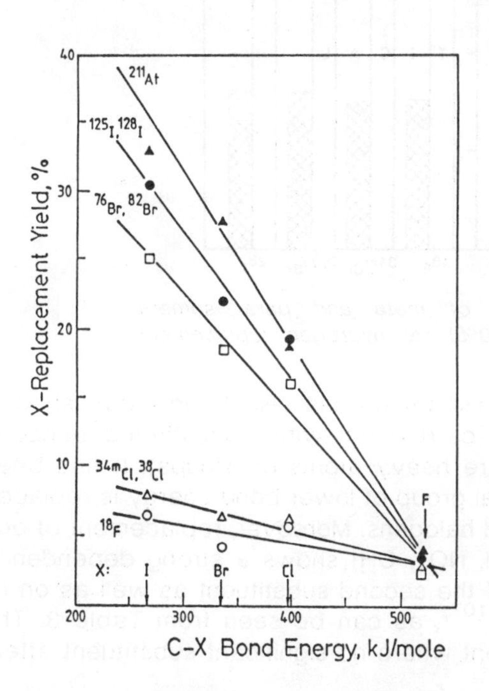

Fig. 4. Dependence of the halogen-for-halogen replacement yields on the bond energy of the leaving halogen[91,93,96,99,100]

A linear dependence of the halogen replacement yields on the reciprocal C-X bond energy value of the leaving halogen has been established for each hot halogen — as is demonstrated in Figure 4. Based on this dependence it has been assumed[93,96,103] that the replacement reactions of hot halogens with benzene derivatives in liquid systems occur in the energy range comparable to the bond energies (a few eV-s) *via* an identical reaction mechanism which involves atom-molecule collision with the formation of a short lived excited intermediate.*

* Note that this dependence is least significant for ^{18}F.

3.3 Effect of electron density distribution

Hydrogen substitution by hot halogens in monosubstituted benzenes (Eq.(10) where X=H) results in a nearly statistical isomer distribution[89,91-96,99,100] substantially differing from those characteristic of thermal electrophilic (e.g. [104]) or homolytic (e.g. [105]) halogenations. However, the deviation from exactly statistical distribution shows a definite trend: the yields of para isomers are somewhat higher at the expense of those for meta isomers as can be seen from Figure 5. (The yields of ortho substituted products correspond to the statistical values.) The observed — albeit low — selectivity of different sites in the benzene ring implies that the orientation rule for electrophilic halogenation manifests itself to some degree in these reactions.

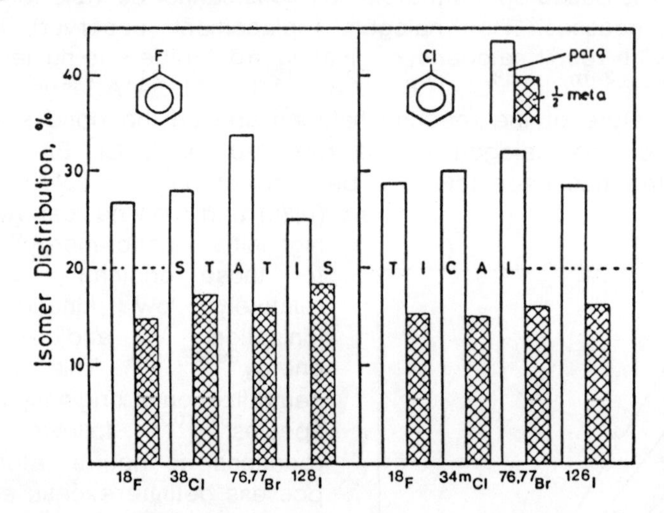

Fig. 5. Relative abundance of meta and para isomers (ortho + meta + para = 100%) for hydrogen replacement by hot halogens[91,93,99]

The influence of electron density distribution has also been established in intramolecular competition experiments carried out with disubstituted benzene derivatives (Eq. (10), where X and Y are heavy atoms or groups). It has been found[42,61,106] that the atom or functional group of lower bond energy is replaced with higher probability by hot tritium and halogens. Moreover, replacement of one and the same heavy atom or group (Cl, NO_2, OH) shows a strong dependence on the presence and chemical nature of the second substituent as well as on its relative position in the benzene ring[42,107], as can be seen from Table 3. The only exception is the $^{38}Cl \rightarrow F$ replacement where no significant substituent effect could be detected.

More quantitative information has been obtained by applying the linear free energy (Hammett) relationship[108] commonly used to study the substituent effects in thermal reactions:

$$\lg(k_X/k_O) = \sigma \cdot \rho \tag{11}$$

where k_X: reaction rate constant for the substituted derivative
k_O: reaction rate constant for the unsubstituted derivative
σ: substituent constant
ρ: reaction constant

Table 3. Effect of the chemical nature and relative position of the second substituent on the replacement by hot ^{38}Cl[42)]

System		Radiochemical yield (%)*	
		$^{38}Cl \longrightarrow Cl$	$^{38}Cl \longrightarrow X$ (X=F,NO_2,OH)
C_6H_5Cl		5.9	—
$C_6H_4Cl_2$	ortho	5.3	---
	meta	3.7	---
	para	10.2	—
C_6H_5F		—	3.1
$C_6H_4F_2$	ortho	—	4.1
	meta	—	3.2
	para	—	3.3
C_6H_4ClF	ortho	8.7	2.7
	meta	5.4	2.9
	para	10.6	3.4
$C_6H_5NO_2$		—	5.4
$C_6H_4ClNO_2$	ortho	1.4	9.1
	meta	0.5	3.9
	para	2.0	4.2
C_6H_5OH		---	2.3
C_6H_4ClOH	ortho	—	1.3

*Values per atom or group are given

The Hammett equation, which correlates the reaction rates of related systems with the empirical constants characteristic of the nature and relative position of the substituents, reflects the influence of the electron density distribution on the transition state of the reaction. The time of interaction for hot atoms must be much shorter than in the case of thermal reactions. (Just how much shorter, still belongs to the mysteries of hot atom chemistry.) The first question, therefore, was whether the data obtained for replacement processes by recoil atoms could be correlated by the Hammett equation at all. If such correlation can be found, some judgement on the reaction mechanism from the value of the reaction constant ρ can be made.

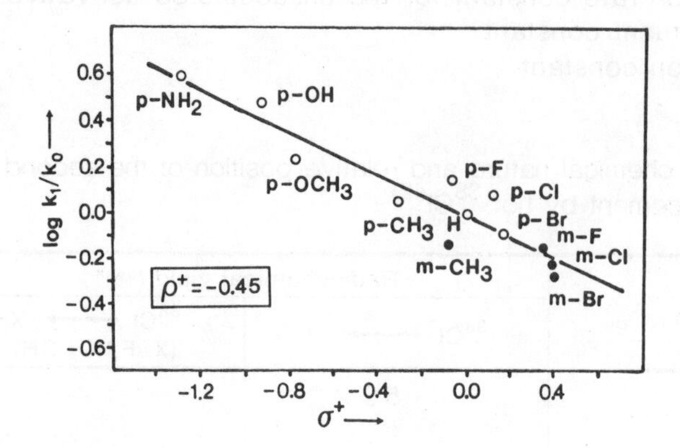

Fig. 6. Relative rates of radiobromination via the $^{76,77}Kr(\beta^+,EC)^{76,77}Br$ decay in monosubstituted benzene derivatives plotted versus Brown's constants σ^+.[99]

Coenen and coworkers[94,99], when studying the hydrogen substitution by recoil halogens in liquid monosubstituted benzene derivatives (Eq. (10), $A^* = {}^{38}Cl$, ^{76}Br, ^{77}Br; X=H), found a linear dependence of hot chlorination and bromination (see Figure 6) yields on Brown's σ^+ substituent constant[109]. Similar results were reported by Moerlein and coworkers[100] on recoil bromination of monosubstituted benzenes with ^{76}Br and ^{77}Br formed *via* nuclear decay from the corresponding krypton isotopes. Intermolecular competition experiments performed with some recoil halogens in equimolar mixtures of chlorobenzene with substituted chlorobenzenes (Figure 7) have also shown limited but definite dependence of

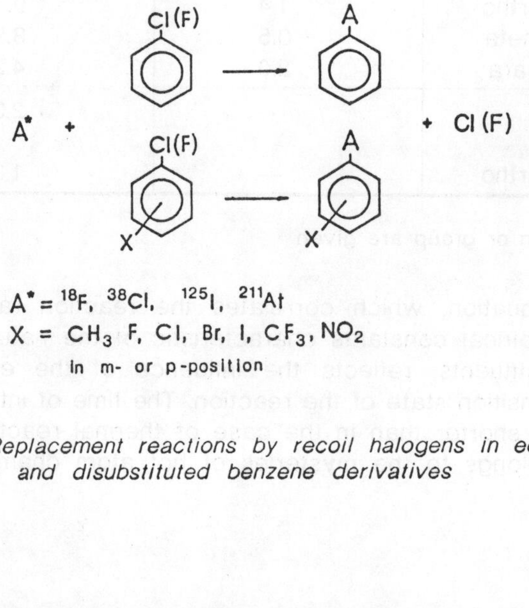

Cl(F) → A

A^* +   + Cl (F)

Cl(F) (X) → A (X)

$A^* = {}^{18}F, {}^{38}Cl, {}^{125}I, {}^{211}At$

$X = CH_3, F, Cl, Br, I, CF_3, NO_2$

in m- or p-position

Fig. 7. Replacement reactions by recoil halogens in equimolar mixtures of mono- and disubstituted benzene derivatives

the replacement ratios on the Hammett substituent constant σ [102]. As can be seen from Table 4, the reaction constant values (ρ) are practically the same for different nucleogenic halogens and they differ substantially from those observed for thermal halogenation reactions[110,111].

Table 4. Reaction constants (ρ) for some replacement reactions by halogens

Replacement	ρ	Ref.
Thermal aromatic halogenation		
Fluorination	−2.45	[111]
Chlorination	−10.0	[110]
Bromination	−12.1	[110]
Replacement by recoil halogens		
^{38}Cl-for-H	−0.56	[94]
^{76,77}Br-for-H	−0.45	[99]
^{76}Br-for-H	−0.7	[100]
^{77}Br-for-H	−0.6	[100]
^{38}Cl-for-Cl	−0.48	[102]
^{125}I-for-Cl	−0.46	[102]
^{211}At-for-Cl	−0.66	[102]
^{18}F-for-Cl	−0.04	[102]
^{38}Cl-for-F	+0.03	[102]

These results can be explained by assuming that the recoil halogens take part in the reaction as neutral species still possessing excess energy originating from the nuclear process. An identical high energy reaction mechanism seems to be responsible for the replacement including the formation of a short-lived intermediate as a result of recoil atoms — unsolvated energetic halogens with electrophilic character — interacting with the aromatic molecule. It is reasonable to assume that the energy range where all these recoil atoms would participate in the same neutral chemical state cannot be higher than 1-2 eV [102,103].

On the other hand, no dependence on the substituent constants could be detected for ^{18}F replacing chlorine nor for ^{38}Cl replacing fluorine in analogous systems as can also be seen from the ρ-values (−0.04 and +0.03) in Table 4. This phenomenon can be interpreted by a different reaction mechanism taking place in a higher energy range where the time of interaction may be so short that no intermediate can be formed and thus the electron density distribution within the aromatic molecule would not play any role. This is in line with the fact that ^{18}F — due to its smaller mass — possesses higher velocity than the bulkier halogen atoms in the same energy region[7]. The behaviour of ^{38}Cl replacing fluorine is harder to explain and needs further investigation.

3.4 Summary

Tritium and halogens take part in liquid phase hot reactions as unsolvated neutral atoms.

Hot replacement by recoil halogens occurs in an energy range which is comparable to the bond energy in organic compounds (a few eV-s) *via* atom molecule collisions possibly involving a short lived excited intermediate product of the colliding partners. This may be the reason why Walden inversion can take place in the course of hot replacement, and furthermore why the bond strength and the electron density distribution have an influence on the yields of such reactions.

In some cases (e.g. ^{38}Cl for F and ^{18}F for Cl replacement in the benzene ring) no influence of the chemical properties of the reacting molecule could be observed. This might indicate direct replacement in a higher energy range.

References

1. Szilard, L., Chalmers, T.A., Nature, **134**, 462 (1934).
2. Willard, J.E., Ann. Rev. Nucl. Sci. **3**, 193 (1953).
3. Willard, J.E., in Chemical Effects of Nuclear Transformations, IAEA, Vienna **1961**, **I**, p. 215.
4. Willard, J.E., in Chemical Effects of Nuclear Transformations, IAEA, Vienna **1965**, **I**, p. 221.
5. Stöcklin, G., Chemie heisser Atome, Verlag Chemie, **1969**.
6. Wolfgang, R., Ann. Rev. Phys. Chem. **16**, 15 (1965).
7. Wolfgang, R., Progr. React. Kinetics **3**, 97 (1965)
8. Stöcklin, G., in Hot Atom Chemistry Status Report, IAEA, Vienna **1975**, p. 161.
9. Milman, M., Radiochim. Acta **2**, 180 (1964).
10. Estrup, P.J. Wolfgang, R., J. Am. Chem. Soc., **82**, 2665 (1960).
11. Wolfgang, R., J. Chem. Phys. **39**, 2983 (1963).
12. Milman, M., Radiochim. Acta, **1**, 15 (1962).
13. Noyes, R.M., J. Chem. Phys., **18**, 999 (1950).
14. Noyes, R.M., J. Chem. Phys., **22**, 1349 (1954).
15. Noyes, R.M., J. Am. Chem. Soc., **77**, 2042 (1955).
16. Roy, J.C., Hamill, W.H., Williams, R.R., Jr., J. Am. Chem. Soc., **77**, 2953 (1955).
17. Glückauf, E., Fay, J.W.J., J. Chem. Soc., **1936**, 390.
18. Sylvester, D.J., in Radiopharmaceuticals and Labelled Compounds, IAEA, Vienna **1973**, **I**, p. 197.
19. Fowler, J.S., Wolf, A.P., Nucl. Sci. Ser., Nucl. Med., NAS-NS-3201, **1982**.
20. Stöcklin, G., in Handbuch der medizinischen Radiologie (Ed. Diethelm, L. et al.) Springer Verlag, Berlin **1988**, Band XV/1B, pp. 31-117.
21. Franck, J., Rabinowitsch, E., Trans. Faraday Soc., **30**, 120 (1934).
22. Rabinowitch, E., Wood, W.C., Trans. Faraday Soc., **32**, 138 (1936).
23. Luther, K., Troe, J., Chem. Phys. Letters, **24**, 85 (1974).
24. Chuang, T.J., Hoffman, G.W., Eisenthal, K.B., Chem. Phys. Letters, **25**, 201 (1974).
25. Noyes, R.M., Z. Elektrochem., **64**, 55 (1960).
26. Noyes, R.M., Progr. React. Kinetics, **1**, 131 (1961).
27. Bunker, D.L., Jacobson, B.S., J. Am. Chem. Soc., **94**, 1843 (1972).
28. Zellweger, J.M., van den Bergh, H., J. Chem. Phys., **72**, 177 (1980).
29. Richardson, A.E., Wolfgang, R., J. Am. Chem. Soc., **92**, 3480 (1970).
30. Manning, R.G., Root, J.W., J. Phys. Chem., **79**, 1478 (1975).

31. Manning, R.G., Root, J.W., J. Chem. Phys., **64**, 4926 (1976).
32. Manning, R.G., Mo, S.-H., Root, J.W., J. Chem. Phys., **67**, 636 (1977).
33. Loberg, M.D., Krohn, K.A., Welch, M.J., J. Am. Chem. Soc., **95**, 5496 (1973).
34. Helton, R.W., Grauer, W.M., Rack, E.P., Radiochim. Acta, **19**, 44 (1973).
35. Berg, M.E., Grauer, W.M., Helton, R.W., Rack, E.P., J. Phys. Chem., **79**, 1327 (1975).
36. Berg, M.E., Loventhal, A., Adelman, D.J., Grauer, W.M., Rack, E.D., J. Phys. Chem., **80**, 837 (1976).
37. To, K.-C., Berg, M.E., Grauer, W.M., Rack, E.P., J. Phys. Chem., **80**, 1411 (1976).
38. Loventhal, A., Berg, M.E., Rack, E.P., Radiochim. Acta, **24**, 91 (1977).
39. Garmestani, S.K., Rack, E.P., J. Phys. Chem., **83**, 2316 (1979).
40. Garmestani, S.K., Firouzbakht, M.L., Rack, E.P., J. Phys. Chem., **83**, 2827 (1979).
41. Berei, K., Ache, H.J., J. Phys. Chem., **84**, 687 (1980).
42. Berei, K., Kardos, Zs., Vasáros, L., Radiochim. Acta, **38**, 83 (1985).
43. Miller, B., Walling, C., J. Am. Chem. Soc., **79**, 4187 (1957).
44. Bűhler, R.E., Ebert, M., Nature, **214**, 1220 (1967).
45. Kontis, S.S., Urch, D.S., Radiochim. Acta, **15**, 21 (1971).
46. Langhoff, C.A., Gnädig, K., Eisenthal, K.B., Chem. Phys., **46**, 117 (1980).
47. Kobrina, L.S., Fluorine Chem. Rev., **7**, 1 (1974).
48. Vasáros, L., Berei, K., in Proc. 4th Symp. Radiat. Chem., Akadémiai Kiadó, Budapest **1977**, p. 39.
49. Brinkman, G.A., Gerritsen, G.A.V., Visser, J., Radiochim. Acta, **26**, 153, (1979).
50. Brinkman, G.A., Gerritsen, G.A.V., Visser, J., Radiochem. Radioanal. Letters, **42**, 319 (1980).
51. Brinkman, G.A., Gerritsen, G.A.V., Visser, J., Radiochim. Acta, **27**, 203 (1980).
52. Brinkman, G.A., Chem. Rev., **81**, 267 (1981).
53. Kontis, S.S., Urch, D.S., Radiochim. Acta, **20**, 39 (1973).
54. Kontis, S.S., Malcolme-Lawes, D.J., Urch, D.S., Radiochim. Acta, **24**, 87 (1977).
55. Bhave, R.N., Rao, B.S.M., Radiochim. Acta, **27**, 143 (1980).
56. Bhave, R.N., Rao, B.S.M., Radiochim. Acta, **30**, 189 (1982).
57. Chandrasekhar, N., Bhave, R.N., Rao, B.S.M., Radiochim. Acta, **36**, 163 (1984).
58. Chandrasekhar, N., Bhave, R.N., Rao, B.S.M., Radiochim. Acta, **39**, 5 (1985).
59. Brinkman, G.A., Visser, J., Lindner, L., Radiochim. Acta, **26**, 77 (1979).
60. Brinkman, G.A., Kaspersen, F.M., Veenboer, J.Th., Radiochim. Acta, **28**, 61 (1981).
61. Bhave, R.N., Brinkman, G.A., Rao, B.S.M., van Halteren, B.W., Radiochim. Acta, **31**, 185 (1982).
62. Henchman, M., Wolfgang, R., J. Am. Chem. Soc., **81**, 2991 (1961).
63. Palino, G.F., Rowland F.S., J. Phys. Chem., **75**, 1299 (1971).
64. Machulla, H. J. Stöcklin, G., J. Phys. Chem., **78**, 658 (1974)
65. Tang, Y.N., Ting, C.T., Rowland, F.S., J. Phys. Chem., **74**, 675 (1976).
66. Wai, C.M., Ting, C.T., Rowland, F.S., J. Am. Chem. Soc., **86**, 2525 (1964).
67. Palino, G.F., Rowland, F.S., Radiochim. Acta, **15**, 57 (1971).
68. Wai, C.M., Rowland, F.S., J. Phys. Chem., **71**, 2752 (1967).
69. Daniel, S.M., Ache, H.J., Stöcklin, G., J. Phys. Chem., **78**, 1043 (1974).
70. Wai, C.M., Rowland, F.S., J. Phys. Chem., **74**, 434 (1970).
71. Bunker, D.L., Pattengill, M., Chem. Phys. Letters, **4**, 315 (1969).
72. Bunker, D.L., Pattengill, M.D., J. Chem. Phys., **53**, 3041 (1970).
73. Vasáros, L., Machulla, H.-J., Stöcklin, G., J. Phys. Chem., **76**, 501 (1972).
74. Wolf, A.P., Schueler, P., Pettijohn, R.P., To, K.-C., Rack, E.P., J. Phys. Chem., **83**, 1236 (1979).
75. To, K.-C., Rack, E.P., Wolf, A.P., J. Chem. Phys., **74**, 1499 (1981).
76. To, K.-C., Rack, E.P., Wolf, A.P., J. Phys. Chem., **87**, 4929 (1983).

77. Firouzbakht, M.L., Ferrieri, R.A., Wolf, A.P., J. Am. Chem. Soc., **109**, 2213 (1987).
78. Root, J.W., Breckenridge, W., Rowland, F.S., J. Chem. Phys., **43**, 3694 (1965).
79. Tachikawa, E., Rowland, F.S., J. Am. Chem. Soc., **90**, 4767 (1968).
80. Root, J.W., J. Phys. Chem., **73**, 3174 (1969).
81. Tang, Y.-N., Lee, E.K.C., Tachikawa, E., Rowland, F.S., J. Phys. Chem., **75**, 1290 (1971).
82. Smail, T., Iyer R.S., Rowland, F.S., J. Phys. Chem., **75**, 1324 (1971).
83. White, R.M., Rowland, F.S., J. Am. Chem. Soc., **82**, 4713 (1960).
84. Pozdeyev, V.V., Nesmeyanov, An.D., Dzantiev, B.G., Radiokhimiya, **5**, 395 (1963).
85. Miller, J.M., Dodson, R.W., J. Chem. Phys., **18**, 865 (1950).
86. Nesmeyanov, An.N., Filatov, E.S., Mansfeld, A., Radiokhimiya, **3**, 610 (1961).
87. Halpern, A., J. Inorg. Nucl. Chem. **25**, 619 (1963).
88. Stamouli, M.I., Katsanos, N.A., Z. Phys. Chem. Neue Folge, **47**, 306 (1965).
89. Stöcklin, G., Tornau, W., Radiochim. Acta, **9**, 95 (1968).
90. Nefedov, V.D., Toropova, M.A., Khalkin, V.A., Norseyev, Yu.V., Kuzin, V.I., Radiokhimiya, **12**, 194 (1970).
91. Berei, K., Stöcklin, G., Radiochim. Acta, **15**, 39 (1971).
92. Vernois, J., Abdel-Ghani, A.H., Muxart, R.: Radiochem. Radioanal. Letters, **12**, 7 (1972).
93. Berei, K., Vasáros L., Radiochim. Acta, **21**, 75 (1974).
94. Coenen, H.H., Machulla, H.-J., Stöcklin, G., J. Am. Chem. Soc., **99**, 2892 (1977).
95. Brinkman, G.A., Veenboer, J. Th., Visser, J., Lindner, L., Radiochim. Acta, **24**, 161 (1977).
96. Vasáros, L., Norseyev, Yu.V., Meyer, G.-J., Berei, K., Khalkin, V.A., Radiochim. Acta, **26**, 171 (1979).
97. Halteren, B.W., Veenboer, J.Th., Brinkman, G.A., Radiochem. Radioanal. Letters **51**, 373 (1982).
98. Bhave, R.N., Rao, B.S.M., Radiochim. Acta, **30**, 189 (1982).
99. Coenen, H.H., Machulla, H.-J., Stöcklin, G., Radiochim. Acta, **33**, 21 (1983).
100. Moerlein, S.M., Welch, M.J., Wolf, A.P., J. Am. Chem. Soc., **105**, 5418 (1983).
101. Kontis, S.S., Gasparakis, E., Radiochim. Acta, **36**, 103 (1984).
102. Berei, K., Vasáros, L., Norseyev, Yu.V., Sutyor, J., Radiochim. Acta, **42**, 13 (1987).
103. Berei, K., Vasáros, L., Radiochim. Acta, **43**, 61 (1988).
104. Olah, G.A., Kuhn, S.J., Hardie, B.A., J. Am. Chem. Soc., **86**, 1055 (1964).
105. Engelsma, J.W., Kooyman, E.C., van der Bij, J.R., Rec. Trav. Chim., **76**, 325 (1957).
106. Sato, T., Radiochem. Radioanal. Lett., **16**, 249 (1974).
107. Kardos, Zs., Berei, K., Vasáros, L., Radiochem. Radioanal. Letters, **17**, 233 (1974).
108. Hammett, L.P., Physical Organic Chemistry, McGraw-Hill, New York **1940**, p. 147.
109. Brown, H.C., Okamoto, Y., J. Am. Chem. Soc., **80**, 4979 (1958).
110. Stock, L.M., Brown, H.C., Adv. Phys. Org. Chem., **1**, 35 (1963).
111. Cacace, F., Giacomello, P., Wolf, A.P., J. Am. Chem. Soc., **102**, 3511 (1980).

4.3 Primary Retention, Recoil Energy Spectra and Appearance Energy

Tatsuo MATSUURA and Ken-ichi SASAKI*
Institute for Atomic Energy, Rikkyo University, 2-5-1, Yokusuka, 240-01 Japan
*Faculty of General Education, Rikkyo University, 3-34-1, Nishi-Ikebukuro, Toshima-ku, Tokyo, 171 Japan

1. Introduction

Significant experimental information on the behavior of (n, γ) activated radionuclides in the condensed phase is provided by the retention, i.e the fraction of radioactive atoms found in the chemical form of the target compound. It is well known that the retention is highly dependent on conditions such as temperature and gamma dose during neutron irradiation, as well as on various stimuli such as heating, crushing and exposure to electromagnetic radiations following neutron irradiation. It is customary to distinguish between the initial retention, R, which is the value corresponding to the end of the neutron irradiation, and the long-term retention which includes the additional effects of subsequent spontaneous or stimulated processes[1] .

If suitable experimental conditions are found for which secondary recombination and hot reaction producing the parent species are suppressed or their contribution decreased to a negligible extent, the measured initial retention usually becomes very low (1% or less), and is called "primary retention". It reflects the percentage of the nuclear reactions in which none of the original bonds in the molecule is ruptured by the recoil, and/or the percentage of geminate recombinations immediately after the recoil event. What is relevant here, is that the energy of the recoil atoms produced by the (n, γ) reaction in general has a broad spectrum due to the multiple emission of prompt γ-rays in cascade, apart from the possible internal conversion of some gamma rays, and that only those recoil atoms which lie in the lowest energy region of the spectrum are involved in the primary retention. Thus the primary retention depends largely on the recoil energy spectrum, reflecting the initial consequences of the recoil phenomena. We show in this article that a parameter designated as the "appearance energy" of the hot atom[2,3] , which is the minimum recoil energy necessary for producing a free hot atom from the target compound in given circumstances, can be derived from the experimentally determined primary retention and the computed recoil energy spectrum. Factors influencing the primary retention and the appearance energy are also surveyed. Since these two important parameters carry several types of fundamental information, such as the possible nature of the initial recoil species and the mechanisms of inter- and intramolecular energy transfer induced by a relatively low energy recoil atom[4] , we discuss also these fundamental aspects of the initial recoil processes in the condensed phase.

2. The Primary Retention

2.1. Components of the Retention

The initial retention includes various types of reactions related with recoil, and is usually assumed to be the sum of several components[3, 5-11]:

$$R = \Sigma R_i = R_n + R_c + R_h + R_a \ (+R_s). \tag{1}$$

The R_i terms have following signification:

R_n represents the part of the neutron-capture events which do not lead to the rupture of the chemical bonds of the activated atom, because the recoil energy is insufficient. Ignoring internal conversion, this situation results from the fortuitous cancellation of the recoil momenta imparted to the radioactive atom by the successive γ's released in the de-excitation of the compound nucleus.

R_c reflects the geminate or primary recombination of the freed atom with its close lying original fragment in a cage[12] constituted by the surrounding molecules.

R_h results from hot reactions such as a replacement collision between the recoil atom and an isotopic atom in the nearby target molecules.

R_a is the retention arising from thermally activated secondary recombinations between the recoil atom and uncorrelated fragments produced by the recoil atom or by radiolysis[13].

R_s is the contribution to the retention due to the separation procedure. It is difficult to control and for the present discussion it is an irrelevant term. For this reason, it is bracketed in equation (1).

2.2. Features of the Primary Retention

The primary retention comprises only the "nuclear" and "cage" components R_n and R_c (neglecting R_s). R_n reflects the minimum energy required for breaking the chemical bonds of the activated atom. It depends on following parameters: recoil energy spectrum, strength and number of chemical bonds of the atom before the neutron capture, mass of bound partners. The latter parameter is known as the Suess effect[14], which plays a notable role in the case of isolated molecules, such as in the gas phase. The efficiency of bond breaking decreases as the ratio of mass M_1 of the recoil atom to the mass M_2 of the attached atom, increases. This is because the fraction of the recoil energy available for internal excitation, i.e. $[M_2/(M_1 + M_2)]$, decreases as the ratio increases. The rest of the energy, $[M_1/(M_1 + M_2)]$ is used for the translation of the target molecule as a whole. In condensed phases, all the recoil energy is imparted to the recoil atom and its attached atoms.

R_c depends strongly on various parameters, not only on the size and shape of the target molecule, but also on the nature of the surrounding medium, such as type of solvent and temperature. A detailed discussion of these parameters will be given below.

In order to obtain the primary retention, various experimental techniques are employed. These include irradiation of the target in a diluted liquid or solid solution, or at an adsorbed state on a large surface area, or in the existence of scavenger.

2.3. The Temperature Dependence of the Primary Retention[3, 11]

The temperature dependence of the individual components of the retention can be anticipated on the basis of simple arguments. R_n, arising mainly from a nuclear process, should be essentially independent of the temperature. The same holds for R_h, which involves kinetic energies much higher than chemical bond energies. The component

R_a , on the other hand, increases markedly with temperature. Because this term represents the most substantial contribution to the observed retention, frequently masking the temperature trend of the other components, the initial retention usually increases with irradiation temperature. Even at the lowest irradiation temperatures, the contribution of R_a cannot be completely neglected in a solid matrix[15] .

Since the nuclear term R_n is temperature-independent, any change in the primary retention with temperature, if observed, reflects that of the cage component R_c. It is conjectured that the component R_c should have a negative temperature coefficient in contrast to the secondary recombination term R_a , which has a positive temperature coefficient as stated above. The reason for this conjecture is as follows[3] . The recoil atom may be assumed to be temporarily incorporated in an excited multiatomic "recoil species" because of failure of bond rupture or because of fast geminate recombination, which may reconstruct partially the original bonds. Thus the multiatomic activated recoil species, which have a relatively short lifetime may either be the parent species or a "ligand-deficient species". The problem is the fate of this activated species during de-excitation by collisions with the molecules constituting the cage wall. There are two alternative fates. One is the transfer of the excess energy to the surrounding molecules without further chemical decomposition, resulting in the reformation of the original parent species. The second alternative would correspond to a relatively long lifetime of the excited species, and eventually a free recoil atom may be released. In general the first possibility prevails, i.e., upon collision with the inert cage molecules the excited species tends to be de-excited and reconstitute the parent species. However, if the temperature is relatively high, the cage wall becomes less rigid, and the de-excitation efficiency by collision will be decreased, or the excited species will diffuse to a longer distance. This favors the second process, and accordingly the retention will decrease with increasing temperature.

This assumption is consistent with the known temperature dependence of the radiolytic decomposition of many compounds irradiated with X or γ rays, whereby G values of radiolytic decomposition generally increase with temperature. Because the excitation of the recoil species involved in the primary retention is low, the recoil reaction in the present case may be regarded as similar to radiolysis. The pathway from a parent substrate to final products initiated by the action of ionizing radiations or by the reaction of a low-energy recoil atom is illustrated schematically in Fig. 1[3,11] . In both cases it crosses an intermediate activated complex-like state to which two activation energies can be attributed: one (ΔE_f) for the forward reaction to the product formation, and one (ΔE_b) for the return to the initial state. Energy (or heat) must be supplied to the intermediate state in order to open the exit channel towards the products. In other words, the product yield must have a positive temperature dependence.

Experimental support for the negative temperature dependence of the retention has been found for the retention of ^{103}Ru and ^{97}Ru in irradiated [Ru(phen)$_3$] $(ClO_4)_2$ dissolved in a solvent or adsorbed on an ion-exchanger with large surface area[16] . In these systems, the observed retentions are sufficiently low to be confidently considered as primary retentions. The retentions of the two isotopes for the samples irradiated at room temperature are clearly below those observed at dry ice temperature.

A decisive experimental verification of this new concept was made by the present authors, by using Cr(acac)$_3$ dissolved in benzene, to which ferric ion was added as a scavenger to assure the retention to be primary. The experiments were conducted between room temperature and liquid nitrogen temperature[3] . The retention was the lowest at room

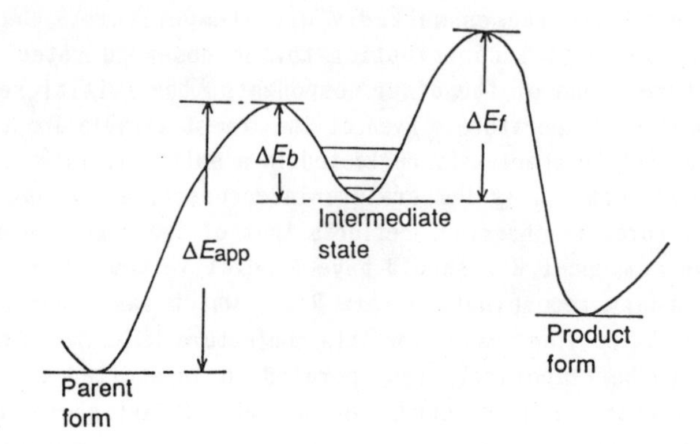

Fig. 1. Schematic energy diagram from the parent compound to the recoil products via the intermediate state. ΔE_{app} , appearance energy of hot atom; ΔE_b , activation energy for the backward reaction, ΔE_f , activation energy for the forward reaction.

temperature. Frozen samples were irradiated at "ice" temperature ca −10 ℃, dry-ice temperature and at liquid nitrogen temperature. The retention was maximum for the sample irradiated at dry-ice temperature[3]. This may be due to the formation of aggregates when the sample mixture containing benzene, ethanol, the chromium complex and scavenger, was first frozen at liquid nitrogen temperature, and next stored for more than one hour at the higher temperatures[17]. Similar observations were made for other β-diketonate chromium complexes[18]

2.4. Isotope Effect in Retention and the Primary Retention

Returning to the various components of the retention, expressed in equation (1), the largest isotope effect must be observed in the "nuclear " term R_n . The recoil energy spectrum reflects the characteristics of the de-excitation cascade of the compound nucleus, i.e. energy, intensity and angular correlations of the emitted gamma rays and the lifetime of intermediate nuclear levels, as will be described in the following section. On the other hand, the components R_c , R_h , and R_a are much less sensitive to isotope effects. An isotope effect in the R_a term may possibly appear, because the recoil atom with higher recoil energy can be projected to a greater distance from the original site, provided recombination occurs between the correlated pairs. However, annealing will very probably occur between uncorrelated pairs, so the contribution of an isotope effect to this term will substantially decrease.

Hence, if the de-excitation schemes of the compound nucleus leading to the isotopes differ notably, the isotope effect in the primary retetention should increase. As a more practical guess, the isotope effect should be more pronounced in cases where the value of the retention is low, i.e. where the terms R_h and R_a are small. Thus a larger isotope effect in the retention can be expected when the measured retention lies closer to the primary retention.

There is much experimental evidence for this expectation are available: for the ruthenium isotopes (^{103}Ru and ^{97}Ru) both in ruthenocene[19] and in ruthenium phenanthroline[16, 20]; for the chromium isotopes (^{51}Cr and ^{55}Cr) in $Cr(acac)_3$[4] and for the copper isotopes (^{64}Cu and ^{66}Cu) in Cu phthalocyanine[21]. It can be safely concluded that the magnitude of the isotope effect in the retention indicates how close the measured value approaches the primary retention.

Another concern of hot atom chemists related to isotope effects in retention has been whether or not the observed differences can be predicted from either the maximum or the average recoil energies of the product nuclei or not, i.e., whether or not retention decreases with increasing (maximum or average) recoil energy. We designate "normal correpondence" for the case where this prediction proves to be true.

A literature survey of the isotope effect on the initial retention including the R_a term has revealed that while this prevision is verified in many cases, such as in Zn and Ru, there are also as many counter-examples, such as for Zr and Sb.[7] The occurrence of an isotope effect in the various components of the retention has been described before: it is the highest in R_n, and small in the other terms. Hence the isotope effect in the initial retention may probably reflect the isotope effect of the primary retention, at least qualitatively.

The isotope effect on the primary retention will now be considered. It is worth mentioning again that each nuclide has its own pattern in the recoil energy spectrum and that the relative population of recoil atoms in the lowest energy region has a decisive effect on the primary retention. Since the pattern in this region is essentially independent of the maximum or average recoil energy, the primary retention, in principle, should correlate with neither energy. Only in cases for which the isotopes have almost similar recoil spectra, the relative populations of recoils up to some energy will be roughly inversely proportional to the maximum (or average) recoil energy. Then the isotope effect on retention will at least appear qualitatively as expected. This may be designated as the "apparent normal correspondence".

The case of chromium (^{51}Cr and ^{55}Cr)[3,22] and probably that of cupper (^{64}Cu and ^{66}Cu)[21] have proved to be the "truly normal correspondence" in the isotope effect on retention. In these systems, the observed retention follows the prediction not only from the maximum (or average) recoil energy, but from the actual recoil energy spectra. The authors believe that the cases of truly nomal correspondence are those in which the charging due to internal conversion is negligible for both isotopes, or at least occurs almost to the same extent. This point will be discussed in a later section (4.2) on the basis of the appearance energy.

2.5. Solvent Effect on the Primary Retention

The primary retention should be affected by the nature of the solvent, since it reflects not only the probability of failure of rupture of the original molecule but also, in a solution, the probability of geminate recombination of the original partners in the solvent cage. Although only a few cases of the effect of solvent on the primary retention in solutions have been investigated, it has been reported that, among many physico-chemical parameters, the molecular weight of the solvent affects the primary retention of $[Ru(phen)_3](ClO_4)_2$ in organic solutions[20]. As shown in Fig. 2, The optical isomer, the Λ isomer, of the complex was irradiated, and the radiochemical yields of the Λ and Δ isomers (denoted as Λ yield and Δ yield, respectively) were obtained. Both yields were regarded as those corresponding to the primary retentions, because there was no dependence of the target complex concentration on the yields. The outstanding feature here is that the heavier the molecular weight, the higher the primary retention, with a linear correlation between them. The wall consisting of heavier molecules more effectively prevents the escape of the recoil atom from the original cage.

Irradiation of an optical isomer provides further information on the disorder at the recoil site and on its relation to the components of the primary retention. The yields of the target form (Λ yield) are remarkably higher than those of the antipode (Δ yield). This finding shows that the original steric configuration is well preserved in the irradiation in solution and suggests that the main part of the primary retention is due to non-rupture of the target molecule.

The Δ yield should account for one half of the racemization yield, and the other half should be included in the Λ yield. Accordingly, the conservation of the original configuration (possibly due to non-rupture) should be given by the difference between the

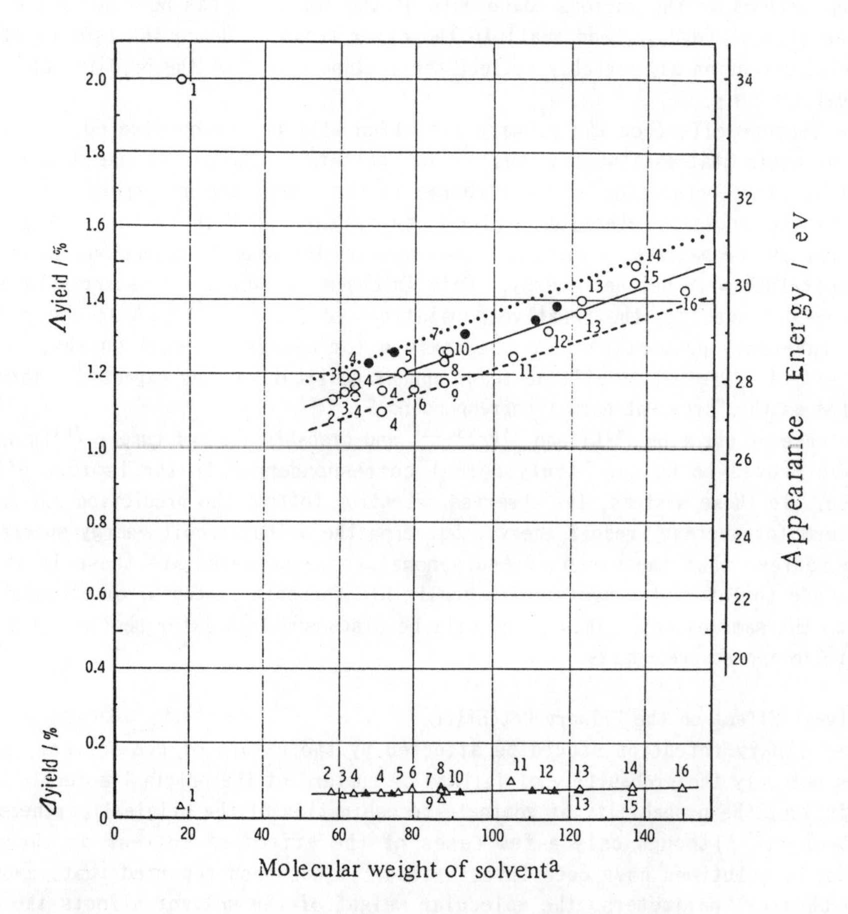

Fig. 2. Primary retention and appearance energy of ^{103}Ru in $[^{103}Ru(open)_3](ClO_4)_2$ in various solvents, plotted against the molecular weight of the solvents. In the case of mixed solvent, the results were plotted against the weighted means of the molecular weights. Solid marks, mixture of nitrobenzene and nitromethane (●, Λ yield; ▲, Δ yield). Open marks (○, Λ yield; △, Δ yield), water (1), acetone (2), nitromethane (3), nitromethane-benzene (4), nitroethane-benzene (5), pyridine (6), 1-nitropropane (7), 2-nitropropane (8), aniline-benzene (9), phenol-benzene (10), benzonitrile-benzene (11), nitrobenzene-benzene (12), nitrobenzene (13), m-nitrotoluene (14), o-nitrotoluene (15), and o-chloronitrobenzene (16). Solid lines, observed Λ and Δ yields. Dotted line, sum of Λ and Δ yields. Dashed line, difference between Λ and Δ yields.

two yields, as shown by the dashed line in Fig. 2. The formation of the labeled racemic form in the solvent cage requires more excitation (via geminate recombination, term R_c) than the genuine conservation of the optical configuration (non-rupture, term R_n); hence the racemization yield corresponds to the upper part of the Λ yield. For the same reason, in Fig. 2, the Δ yield can be placed above the Λ yield, and the addition of the two yields is shown by the dotted lines. The upper lines represents the appearance energy. It is to be noted that the primary retention (and the appearance energy) as well as the component R_n depend on the nature of the solvent.

The finding here also suggests an idea of the nature of the recoil species and its de-excitation process. The most plausible initial recoil species in this case is considered to be an excited "multiatomic" ligand-deficient species, whose molecular weight is larger than that of the various solvents investigated. The efficiency of the de-excitation should increase with the molecular weight of the solvent molecule owing to the higher efficacy of the mutual collisions. As an exception, in an aqueous medium the primary retention is much higher than expected on the basis of the molecular weight of water. Clustering of water molecules[23] seems to be of the origin of this anomaly.

2.6. Effect of the Molecular Size of the Target on the Primary Retention

It is of interest to learn how the size of the target molecule affects the primary retention, keeping both the central metal atom and the type of ligand fixed. The anticipated features of this dependence of the primary retention for the case of chromium β-diketonates are as follows:

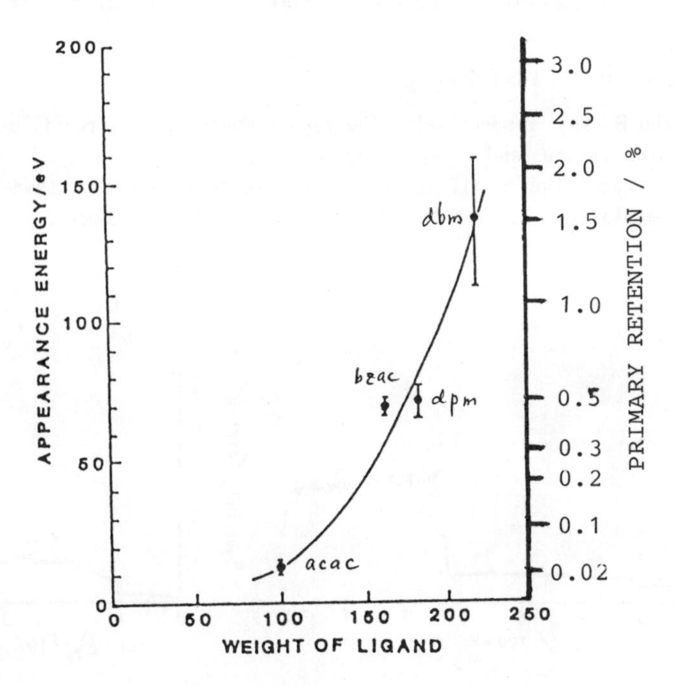

Fig. 3. Primary retention and appearance energy of ^{51}Cr in various β-diketonate chromium complexes, plotted against the molecular weight of ligand.

(1) Provided only the metal-ligand bonds are concerned, the primary retention will be unchanged irrespectively of the size of the various ligands, because the strength of the six Cr--O bonds is almost the same.
(2) It is possible that the recoil energy of the central atom can be dissipated to an extent depending on the number and perhaps on the mass of the atoms in the ligand groups. Effectively this will tend to increase the primary retention.

The present authors investigated this effect on various β-diketonate chromium complexes[24]. The results are shown in Fig. 3, in which the observed retention increases very steeply with the molecular weight of the ligands. Recent findings on further complexes, including fluorine-substituted group in the ligand, have shown that the correlation with the molecular size is not so simple and that not only the weight of ligand but also other factors, such as the total bond energies in the ligand, affect the primary retention[25]. The detailed discussion will be presented in Section 4.

3. Recoil Energy Spectra

3.1 Calculation of Recoil Energy Spectrum

Recoil energy spectra of (n, γ)-produced nuclides can be calculated using a Monte Carlo simulation[3, 26-33]. However, because of the lack of detailed information on the nuclear excited levels, several assumptions are needed. These are : 1) uncorrelated, isotropic emission for all γ's emitted in cascade, 2) no internal conversion, and 3) negligibly short lifetime for intermediate levels, unless data are available. The calculation procedure is as follows[33].

For a single γ-ray emission, the recoil energy is calculated from the simple expression,

$$E_r = p^2 / 2M = E^2 / 1862M \tag{2}$$

where E_r, p, M, and E are, respectively, the recoil energy in eV, recoil momentum, the mass of the recoil atom in amu, and γ-ray energy in keV.

For a γ-ray cascade, the recoil energy is calculated by a vector summation of the successive recoil momenta (p_i), imparted by the γ-rays in a sequence of transitions[34].

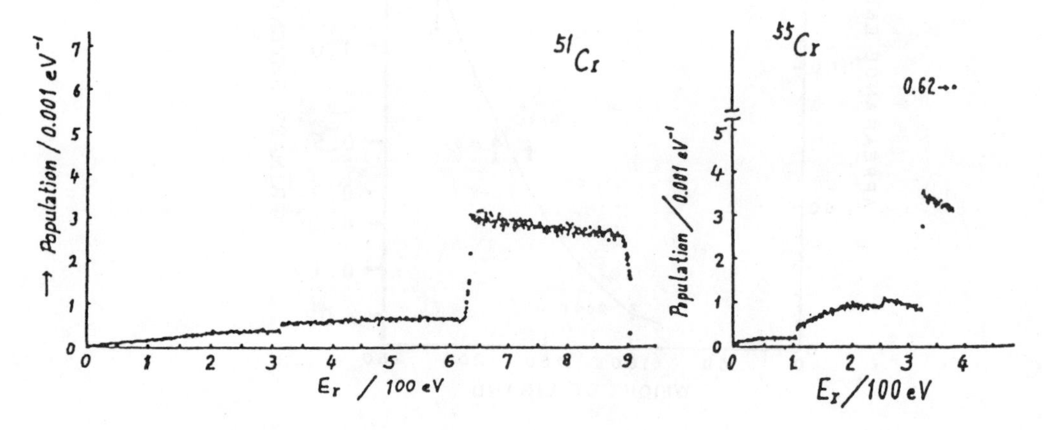

Fig. 4. Computed recoil energy spectra of ^{51}Cr and ^{55}Cr.

$$E_r = |\Sigma p_i|^2 / 2M$$
$$= (1/2M)\{(\Sigma|p_i|^2) - 2\Sigma(|p_i||\Sigma p_j|\cos\theta_{i-1,i})\} \qquad (3)$$

where $\theta_{i-1,i}$ represents the angle between the ith momentum and the vector sum of momenta up to the (i-1)th γ-ray.

Monte Carlo simulation can be applied to obtain E_r for random values of the angle. Detailed calculation procedures with a simple personal computer program are given in ref. 31. If the lifetime of an excited level is long enough to allow for the dissipation of the recoil energy, the subsequent momenta should be accumulated separately. Fig. 4 shows the computed recoil energy spectra of ^{51}Cr and ^{55}Cr[3,24,34]. Kinney[32] calculated the recoil energy spectrum of ^{96}Mo taking into account available data of angular correlations of γ-rays. This spectrum differed only slightly from that obtained with the assumption of isotropic emissions. Up to now, sufficient data on the spins of the excited levels of nuclides of interest have not been available for the accurate calculation of recoil spectra.

3.2 Available Recoil Energy Spectra

The recoil energy spectra so far reported in the literature concern the following (n, γ)-produced nuclides: ^{32}P[30], ^{36}Cl[26], ^{38}Cl[31], ^{51}Cr[4], ^{55}Cr[4], ^{60}Co[33], ^{64}Cu[21], ^{66}Cu[21], and ^{103}Ru[33]. We have recently computed the spectra for the following additional nuclides[35]: ^{45}Ca, ^{47}Ca, ^{49}Ca, ^{52}V, ^{59}Fe, ^{59}Ni, ^{63}Ni, ^{65}Ni, ^{69}Zn, ^{99}Mo, ^{128}I, ^{141}Ce, ^{143}Ce, ^{142}Pr, ^{147}Nd, ^{149}Nd, ^{151}Nd, ^{153}Sm, ^{155}Sm, ^{161}Dy, ^{169}Er, ^{171}Er, ^{167}Yb, ^{175}Yb, ^{177}Yb, and ^{181}Hf. The most up-to-date data on capture γ-rays have been used. However they may be in part inaccurate because of uncertainties in assignment of nuclear levels and intensities of γ-rays.

3.3. Integrated Recoil Energy Spectra and Appearance Energy

The recoil energy spectrum (Fig. 4) is integrated from energy zero up to a given

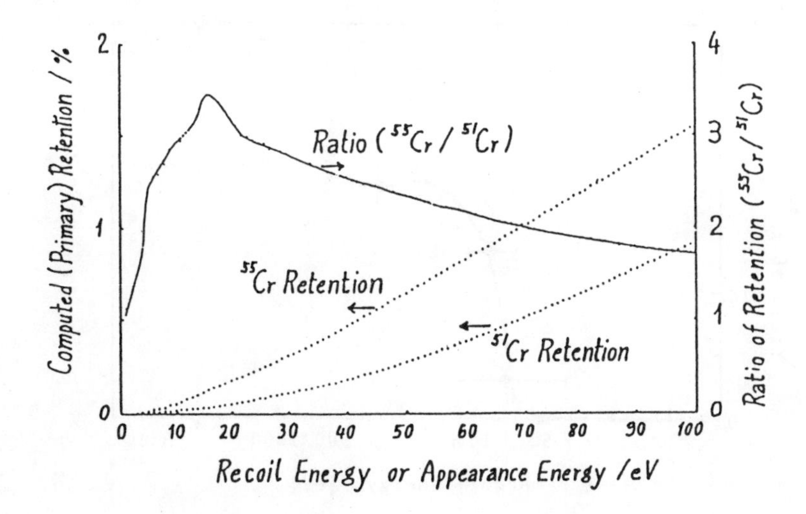

Fig. 5. Computed relationship between the primary retention and the appearance energy of ^{51}Cr and ^{55}Cr, and ratio of the ($^{55}Cr/^{51}Cr$) retentions.

upper limit. Next the area obtained is divided by the total area to yield an integrated spectrum, which represents the probability of the recoil energy being below the selected threshold energy as a function of this energy. A part of this plot is shown in Fig. 5, which shows the relationship between the primary retention and the threshold energy, i.e., the appearance energy. From the experimentally obtained primary retention and the calculated integrated recoil energy spectrum, we can estimate the appearance energy.

4. Appearance Energy

4.1 Historical Background

The name of appearance energy was introduced by Yoshihara and Kudo in their work on the recoil behavior of ^{115m}In produced by the ^{115}In(γ, γ')^{115m}In reaction in NaInY · 3H_2O, (Y = EDTA)[2]. The γ-irradiation of the complex was performed at dry ice temperature by means of an electron linear accelerator using a platinum convertor to produce bremsstrahlung. The yield of free radioindium as a function of the recoil energy of the indium atom is plotted in Fig. 6. It can be seen that the yield is zero until a threshold energy of 60 eV, named "appearance energy", The yield increases until a plateau of about 20%. This behavior has been interpreted as due to "hot zone" reactions, which incorporate a substantial part of the radionuclides into a chemical form other than the free form in the solid target[36].

Similar experiments were performed by the same authors in the indium EDTA complexes, Na · [inY(OH_2)] · 2H_2O, K[InY(OH_2)] · H_2O, and H[InY(OH_2)] : the appearance energies were ca 60 eV for the former two complexes and below 50 eV for the latter[37]. In another experiment, the same authors obtained an appearance energy of about 40 eV for the Lu EDTA complex[38]. It amounts to 45 eV for the In-HEDTA complex, with a plateau as high as 70--80 %[39].

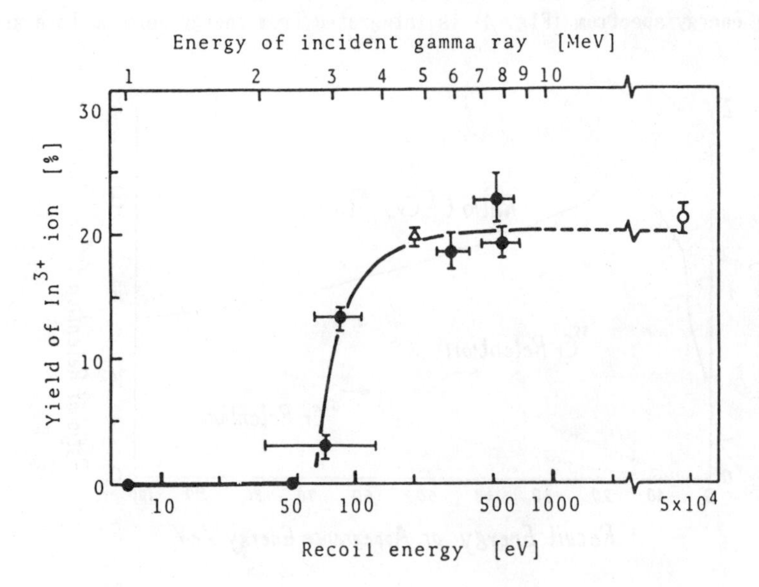

Fig. 6. Energy dependence of recoil product yield ($^{115m}In^{3+}$) from Na [In · edta] . ●:(γ, γ'), △:(n,γ) , and ○:(γ,n).

(γ, γ') reactions have the advantage that the maximum recoil energy can be varied. On the other hand, its application is limited. It can be considered as a first, straightfoward method for the determination of the appearance energy[40). The method utilizing the recoil energy spectrum described in 3.2 may be a second method, which can be applied, in principle, to every (n,γ)-produced radionuclide, when the primary retention and recoil energy spectrum are available. All the following data were obtained by this method.

The appearance energies for ^{103}Ru from [Ru(phen)$_3$] $(ClO_4)_2$ in nitrobenzene and nitromethane are 30 and 28 eV respectively[33]. Yoshihara's group have recently derived 29 eV and 63 eV for ruthenium in Ru(acac)$_3$[41] and in $RuCp_2$[42] respectively, both from the retentions observed in solid state irradiations. The appearance energy of ^{51}Cr from Cr(acac)$_3$ is 14 ~16 eV[3,24], the values obtained for various β-diketonate complexes increase steeply with the molecular weight of the attached ligand (Fig. 3). For example, the values for Cr(dpm)$_3$ and Cr(dbm)$_3$, where dpm and dbm represent dipyvaloylmethanato and dibenzoylmethanato ligands respectively, are 68eV and 136eV, respectively.

The energies for copper in the phthalocyanine complex are 96 and 120 eV for ^{64}Cu and ^{66}Cu respectively[21]. However, the true appearance energies may be lower. The reason is that the lowest retentions were obtained for the sulfuric acid solution in the absence of scavenger, and they probably do not represent the primary retentions. This is sustained by the observation of differences in the retentions for the α and β forms, even in solution[21]. If the compex were monomolecular in solution, the two crystallographic forms should behave similarly.

4.2 Factors Affecting Appearance Energy

In the discussion of the magnitude of appearance energies, reference has usually been made to the value of 25eV, which is a threshold energy generally assumed for the displacement of an atom from its site in an ionic solid[8]. However, the appearance energy of a hot atom may depend on the chemical and physical environments like the primary retention. From a chemical point of view, the bond strength of the transmuted atom may be the most important parameter[40]. The size and shape of a target molecule, as well as the nature of the solvent, may also affect the appearance energy. Furthermore, the direction of the ejected atom probably has a large effect on the threshold energy. For example, if the molecule has a planar structure, the atoms ejected in the direction of open space will escape relatively easily; on the contrary, those ejected in the direction of the chemical bonds will require more energy to escape from the molecule. This aspect is an interesting topic for a theoretical discussion[4]. Hence the threshold value depends on the angle of ejection of the recoil atom with respect to the direction of the chemical bonds. Amongst all possible threshold values, the lowest one would correspond to the appearance energy which is determined in the first method. In the second method, the appearance energy would be slightly higher because it represents an average value over the whole recoil energy spectrum and over all possible angles of ejection[40]. A quantitative discussion of the dependence of appearance energy on temperature is still premature.

The dependence on the size of target molecule has been investigated by the present authors for chromium in various β-diketonate complexes, assuming a constant scavenger efficiency of ferric ions for each type of ligand. It is described in the next section.

It seems worthwhile to investigate the isotope effect on the appearance energies. It is anticipated that the appearance energies for a given compound should be the same for all isotopes. This was approximately found for chromium isotopes (^{51}Cr and ^{55}Cr)[3], giving strong support to the validity of the assumptions used in the calculation of the recoil energy spectra, i.e. the isotropic emission of γ-rays and the negligible role of the Auger effect.

4.3 Dependence of Appearance Energy on the Molecular Size

The model and the assumptions adopted for the theoretical treatment are the following [23]:

(1) A free hot Cr atom with a given initial energy, depending on the recoil energy spectrum, is produced by rupture of Cr-O bonds at the center of a molecule. It is assumed that this atom possesses most of the recoil energy, and transfers a small amount of energy to the original ligand partners.

(2) The hot atom is slowed down on its way through the surrounding molecules, regarded as a uniform medium, with a constant friction coefficient.

(3) The hot atoms which have sufficient energy can easily escape from the surface of the molecule, but the atoms which were born with relatively low energy are stopped and thermalized within a molecule. Whether the thermalized atoms in a molecule contribute to the retention or escape from the surface may depend on the rest position in the molecule, as shown in Fig. 7(a) or (b). For the sake of simplicity, it has been assumed that the probability of the atom to contribute to the retention is 100%, independent of the distance travelled by the hot atom as in Fig. 7(c). If this probability is assumed to

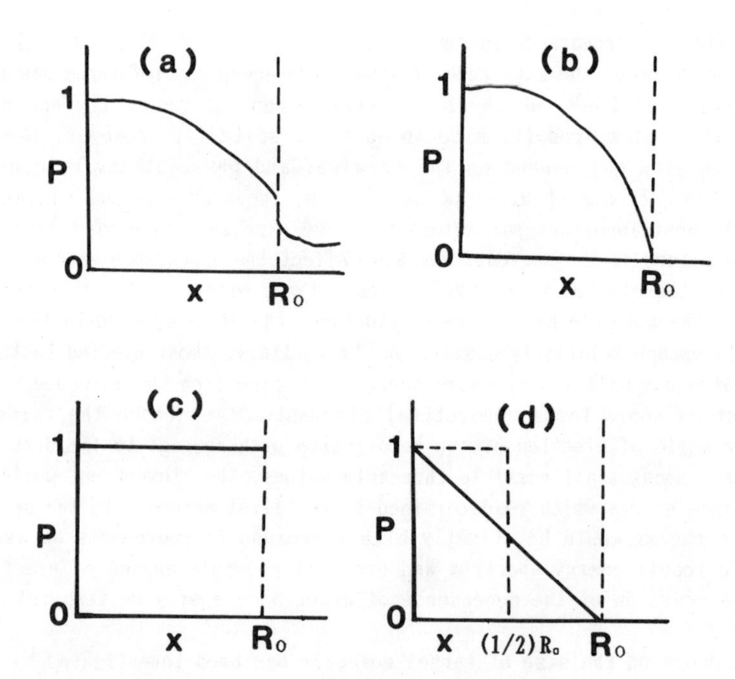

Fig. 7. Estimated probability for a thermalized recoil atom to contribute to the retention as a function of the distance of its rest site from the center of the molecule (x). R_0 = molecular radius.
(a) without scavenger (b) in presence of a scavenger
(c) simplified model 1 (d) a simplified model 2

be a linear function of the radius as in Fig. 7(d), the mathematical treament will lead to the same conclusion as in (c).
(4) The radius of the complex compound is proportional to the cubic root of the molecular weight of the molecule. This means the electron density in the molecule is assumed to be the same whatever the type of ligand.
(5) The friction coefficient of a hot atom moving within a molecule has been tentatively assumed to be proportional to the mass of a free ligand.

A simple mathematical treatment, starting from an equation of motion has led to the conclusion that the appearance energy should be proportional to the 2.67th power of the molecular weight of the ligand[24]. After normalization at 14 eV, the experimental appearance energy for $Cr(acac)_3$, the data for three other complexes agreed well with the mathematical model.

From a microscopic viewpoint, the assumption (5) may suggest that a heavier ligand molecule, upon collision with the hot atom, repels the latter more effectively than a lighter ligand in the direction of some limited region around the origin, where the probability of retention is high, as in Fig. 7(a) or (b).

However, recently obtained retentions for the complexes containing F-substituted ligands, $Cr(tfa)_3$, $Cr(hfa)_3$, and $Cr(fod)_3$, where tfa, hfa, and fod represent trifluoroacetylacetonato, hexafluoroacetylacetonato, and 1,1,1,2,2,3,3-heptafluoro-7,7-dimethyl-4,6-octanedione ligands respectively, are lower than those expected from the 2.27th. power law[25]. This suggests that other factors may influence the retardation or acceleration of the motion of a hot atom in a molecule. These may be the total number of bonds and the total bond energy in a ligand, the type of radical contained in a ligand (such as phenyl radical), or the free volume in a molecule. Because the fluorine atom is smaller than the methyl group - although the weight is almost the same - the molecules containing a F-substituted ligand have more vacant space than those containing no F-substituted ligand. In presence of fluorine atom, the diffusion of a hot atom may be increased and the retention decreased, as has been observed.

4.4 Remarks on the Possible Nature of the Initial Recoil Species and an Energy Transfer Processes

The success of this theoretical interpretation, at least in part, together with recent findings, lead us to a further discussion on the initial recoil phenomenon. it concerns two points: (1) the possible nature of the initial recoil species and (2) the energy transfer process.

(1) A free hot atom may be one possible initial recoil species, although we have hitherto only assumed a multiatomic excited species, such as ligand-deficient species or the excited parent species, as the most probable one. The latter species may be a product of the intramolecular geminate recombination of the free atom in this new model. Concerning the significance of the rest position of the initial free recoil atom on the retention, the dependence of the primary retention on temperature and on the solvent can be interpreted as follows by this model.

Temperature dependence (in section 2.3): As the temperature increases, the thermal motion of the molecules constituting the cage is enhanced, and the cage wall becomes softer. As a consequence the activated recoil species will de-excite more slowly and there will be a greater probability of escaping from the cage and travelling a large distance, leading to a reduced retention.

Solvent dependence (in section 2.5): The new model anticipates that the molecular weight of the solvent cage may become larger than the mass of the free recoil atom. In this case, on a collision with the solvent cage, the probability of back scattering of the lighter recoil atom should increase with the mass of the solvent molecule. Thus the probability of finding the thermalized atom in the vicinity of the original site, where a high concentration of ligand fragments are ready for recombination, increases. As a result, the retention increases with the molecular weight of solvent, as observed in Fig. 2.

(2) Concerning the energy transfer process, an important factor would be the total bond energy of the ligand. When an excited species collides with a nearby molecule, the efficiency of de-excitation increases with the chemical complexity, i.e. with increasing degree of freedom of vibrational and electronic modes of the molecule[43]. A tentative plot of experimental appearance energies for the eight types of β-diketonates complexes vs total bond energy of the ligand, gave a scattered result, but showed the opposite tendency to that of the mass plot like Fig.3. The linear combination (1:1) of the mass plot and bond-energy plot (with the average values of relative mass and relative total bond energy of the ligand as the abscissa) gives a smoother curve, with an exception for $Cr(fod)_3$, which has about three times as large molecular weight as $Cr(acac)_3$. It suggests that a combination of "positional consideration" (mass-plot) and "energy consideration" (bond-energy plot) gives a better picture of the de-excitation process of the initial recoil products.

Other mechanisms which might intervene in the deexcitation process of the recoil species are (1) partial transfer of the initial recoil energy to the originally attached ligands at the instant of bond breaking, and (2) the inelastic collisions of the recoil atom with the surrounding molecules. The fact that the odd behavior of $Cr(fod)_3$ results from the mass effect supports this "inelatic collision model" for the intramolecular energy transfer process.

To elucidate these quite interesting and important processes, much more experimental and theoretical work on the primary retention and on appearance energies is needed.

Acknowledgement: The authors thank Professor J. P. Adloff of Centre de Recherches Nucleaires, Strasbourg, Professor A. G. Maddock of University of Cambridge, Dr. D. S. Urch of University of London, and Professor Kenji Yoshihara of Tohoku University, for their useful discussion on this paper.

References

1. Ackerhalt, R., Harbottle, G.: Radiochim. Acta, 17, 126 (1972).
2. Yoshihara, K., Kudo, H.: J. Chem. Phys., 52, 2950 (1970).
3. Matsuura, T., Sasaki, K.: Radiochim. Acta, 49, 17 (1990).
4. Johnson, R. E., Liu, M., Baragiola, R. A., Boring, J. W.: This book, Chap. II-2 (1992).
5. McCallum, K. J., Maddock, A. G.: Trans. Faraday Soc., 49, 1150 (1953).
6. Maddock, A. G., Wolfgang, R.: in "Nuclear Chemistry", (L. Yaffe, ed.), Academic Press, New York, 1968.
7. Tachikawa, E., Matsuura, T.: Kagaku Sosetsu, 23, 130 (1979).
8. Vargas, J. I., Maddock, A. G.: in "Chemical Effects of Nuclear Transformations in Inorganic Systems", (G. Harbottle and A. G. Maddock, ed.), North-Holland, Amsterdam., 1979, p. 461.
9. Tominaga, T., Tachikawa, E.: in "Modern Hot Atom Chemistry and Its Applications", Springer, Heidelberg, 1981, p. 81.
10. Matsuura, T.: in "Hot Atom Chemistry", (T. Matsuura, ed.), Kodansha, Tokyo (and

Elsevier, Amsterdam) 1984, p. 303.
11. Matsuura, T.: in "Artificial Radioactivity", (K. Narayana and H. J. Arnikar, ed.), Tata McGraw-Hill, New Delhi, 1985, p. 308.
12. Frank, J., Ravinovich, E.: Trans. Faraday Soc., 30, 120 (1934).
13. Matsuura, T., Collins, C. H., Collins, K. E.: in "Hot Atom Chemistry", (T. Matsuura, ed.), Kodansha, Tokyo (and Elsevier, Amsterdam) 1984, p. 238.
14. Suess, H.: Z. Physik. Chem., 45B, 297, 312 (1940).
15. Veljikovic, S. R., Harbottle, G.: J. Inorg. Nucl. Chem., 24, 1517 (1962).
16. Tanaka, M.: Radiochim. Acta, 34, 109 (1983).
17. Sasaki, K., Matsuura, T.: 32th Symp. on Radiochemistry, Tokai, Oct. 1988.
18. Matsuura, T., Takenawa, H., Suzuki, T., Ito, H., Hirota, R., Sasaki, K.: to be published.
19. Harbottle, G., Zahn, U.: in "Chemical Effects of Nuclear Transformations", Vol. II, IAEA, Vienna, 1985, p. 133.
20. Sasaki, K., Furukawa, M., Yamatera, H.: Radiochim. Acta, 31, 121 (1982).
21. Matsuura, T., Sasaki, K., Shoji, H.: J. Radioanal. Nucl. Chem. Articles, 134, 311 (1989).
22. T. Matsuura, H. Kurihara, T. Nagahara, K. Sasaki, J. Radioanal. Nucl. Chem. Lett., 106, 243 (1986).
23. Arsenault, L. J., Blotcky, A. J., Medina, V. A., Rack, E. P.: J. Phys. Chem., 83, 893 (1979).
24, Matsuura, T., Takenawa, H., Suzuki, T., Hirota, R., Sasaki, K.: J. Radioanal. Nucl. Chem. Lett., 146, 223 (1990).
25. Matsuura, T., Ito, H., Hirota, R., Sasaki, K.: 35th Symp. on Radiochemistry, Osaka, Nov. 1991.
26. Cobble, J. W., Boyd, G. E.: J. Am. Chem. Soc., 74, 1282 (1952).
27. Campbell, I.: Nukleonika, II, No. 4, 605 (1957).
28. O'Connor, D.: Acta Physica Polonica, 17, 273 (1958).
29. Hsing, C., Hsing, H., Gordus, A. A.: J. Chem. Soc., 34, 535 (1961).
30. Cifka, J.: Radiochim. Acta, 1, 125 (1963).
31. Ferro, L. J., Spicer, L. D.: J. Chem. Phys., 69, 1320 (1978).
32. Kinney, J. H.: J. Nucl. Mat., 103 & 104, 1331 (1981).
33. Sasaki, K., Matsuura, T.: St. Paul's Rev. Sci., 31, 11 (1991); Proc. Int. Symp. on Near Future Chemistry in Nuclear Energy field, Tokai, 115 (1989).
34. Schweinler, H. C.: in "Chemical Effects of Nuclear Transformations", Vol. 1, IAEA, Vienna, p. 63 (1961).
35. Matsuura, T., Sasaki, K.: IAERU-8902-a (1989).
36. Harbottle, G.: in "Chemical Effects of Nuclear Transformations in Inorganic Systems", (Harbottle and Maddock, ed.), North-Holland, 1979, p. 41.
37. Yoshihara, K., Yang, M. H., Shiokawa, T.: Radiochem. Radioanal. Lett., 4, 143 (1970).
38. Yoshihara, K., Mizusawa, Radiochem. Radioanal. Lett., 9, 263 (1972).
39. Yoshihara, K., Fujita, A., Shiokawa, T.: J. Inorg. Nucl. Chem., 39, 1733 (1977).
40. Yoshihara, K.: Sci. Rep. Tohoku Univ. 1st Ser., LXXII, 1 (1989).
41. Kaneko, I., Sekine, T., Yoshihara, K.: J. Radioanal. Nucl. Chem. Lett., 144, 89 (1990).
42. Matsue, H., Kaneko, I., Sekine, T., Yoshihara, K.: J. Radioanal. Nucl. Chem. Lett., 145, 271 (1990).
43. Urch, D. S.: in "Hot Atom Chemistry", (T. Matsuura, ed.), Kodansha, Tokyo (and Elsevier, Amsterdam) 1984, p. 134.

4.4 Annealing Studies

Carol H. COLLINS[a], Silvia BULBULIAN[b] and Alfred G. MADDOCK[c]

[a] Instituto de Química, Universidade Estadual de Campinas
Caixa Postal 6154, 13081 Campinas, SP, Brasil

[b] Instituto Nacional de Investigaciones Nucleares
Apartado Postal 18-1027, Col. Escandón, Deleg. Miguel Hidalgo
México 11801 DF México

[c] University Chemical Laboratory, Cambridge University
Lensfield Road, Cambridge CB2 1EW, England

Although much has been published on annealing reactions in hot atom chemistry, the sum total of our definitive knowledge is disappointedly small. The following will summarize relevant observations and indicate some hypotheses and conclusions which are suggested by these observations.

As shown in other chapters, the relative values of recoil energy and bond energy are such that it is reasonable to expect the rupture of practically all the chemical bonds of the molecule in which the nuclear transformation occurs, a result supported by experimental results in gases and liquids, as well as by theoretical considerations. In crystalline solids, recoil energies of 30-60 eV are considered necessary to separate the fragments,[1-5] energy levels readily obtainable in most nuclear transformations. However, in solids, significant fractions of the transformed (recoil) atoms are encountered, upon subsequent analysis, in forms indistinguishable from the original ions or molecules. These results suggest that other processes, in addition to failure to rupture the bonds or geminate recombination (experimentally not distinguishable from the former), cause recombination to reform the parent or parent-like species. These processes include the reactions which the recoiling atom suffers during its trajectory and those induced by any one of a variety of agents present at the end of the recoil trajectory. These latter processes are called "annealing reactions" and occur on time scales of microseconds or less up to years. Thus, any discussion of annealing reactions, and the possible means by which these reactions occur, must take into account both the annealing agents present during and immediately after the nuclear transformation and those introduced in posterior annealing processes, since it is hard to imagine that very different mechanisms operate on the same transformed species in the same matrix environment, differing only in time scale. Complicating this picture further are those reactions which occur during the analysis of the crystalline solid. Since most analyses require destruction of the solid matrix, dissolution-induced formation of parent or parent-like molecules may contribute to give results which suggest solid state reactions but are, in reality, induced by the act of dissolution or occur after the species are in solution.

Annealing reactions usually, but not always,[6] produce parent or parent-like species, with kinetics which are strikingly similar from one system to another: isothermal annealing curves almost always show a rapid increase in the quantity of parent, up to a plateau value which depends on the annealing temperature (Figure 1). After this, a very slow increase can occur, if the sample is maintained at the initial temperature, or another rapid rise can be produced, if the temperature is increased. Upon reaching the plateau characteristic of this second temperature, another very slow increase results, with a subsequent change in temperature resulting in a further rapid increment. Isochronal annealing curves also show a series of increases and pseudo-plateaus with the constantly increasing temperature. Isochronal curves taken for different time periods maintain the same general form but show quantitative differences (Figure 2).

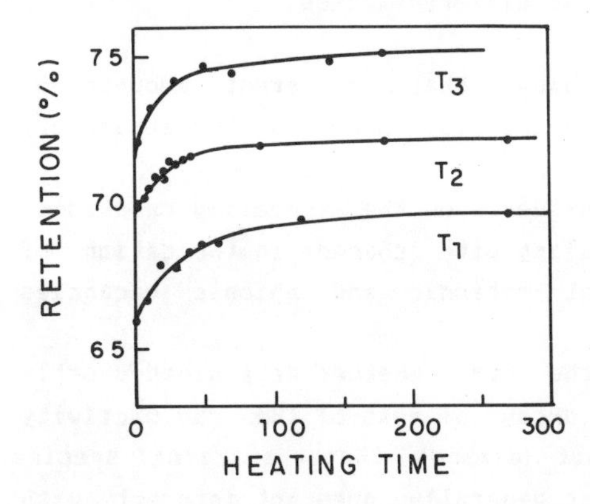

FIGURE 1. Typical isothermal annealing curves at different temperatures

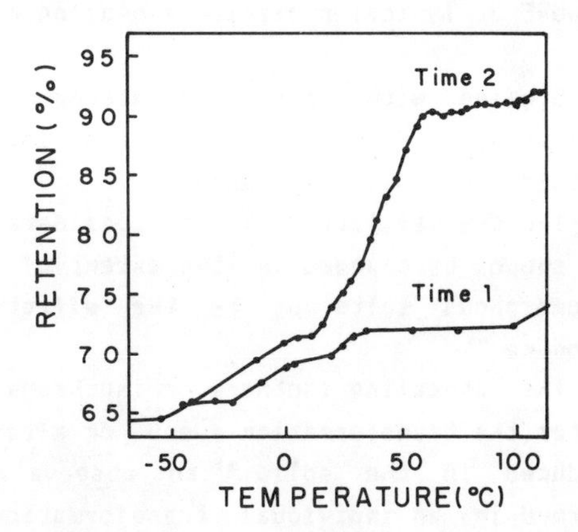

FIGURE 2. Typical isochronal annealing curves at different times

In addition to the increases and plateaus characteristic of the reformation of parent or parent-like species, the annealing process may alter the distribution of non-parent species, without modifying the apparent yield of the parent.[7]

1. Modes of Annealing

Annealing reactions are induced by elevated temperatures and/or species formed by the ionizing radiation present in the environment of the transformed atom during its thermalization. These same agents are those most used to induce annealing after storage (Figures 1-3), although annealing has also been reported after ultraviolet irradiation, after application of pressure, after ultrasound treatment and even after being subjected to shock waves.[8] Annealing may also occur when the structure of the solid is changed, such as when it is hydrated, dehydrated or crushed.[8]

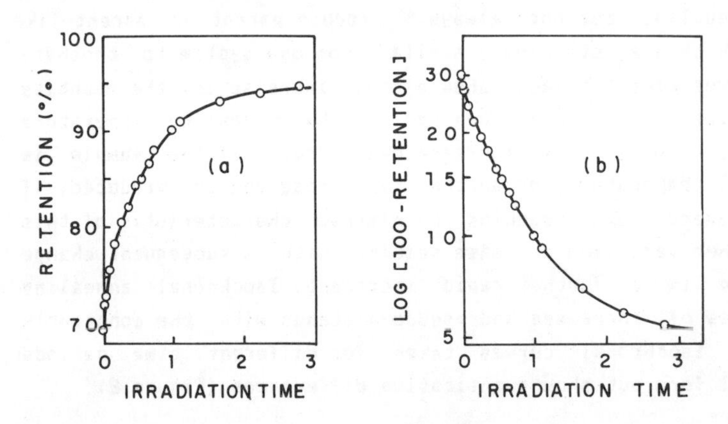

FIGURE 3. Typical radiation annealing curves at different doses

Studies with controlled atmospheres suggest that different amounts of annealing, if not different recombination processes, occur as the atmosphere outside the solid is changed.[8,9]

The crystal lattice has a considerable influence on the annealing reactions, as shown by changes in the extent of annealing with changes in the cation of isomorphous salts or by the effects that cationic and anionic vacancies produce.[9]

The annealing isotherm or isochronal is the same, whether determined shortly after the transformation event or after the decay of most of the radioactivity induced in the solid,[8] an observation that demands that the recoil species formed in an individual transformation event generally does not interact with others produced in similar transformation events. The annealing involves only entities in the immediate vicinity of each transformed atom, as well as whatever fragments are produced by the individual event.

When either geometric isomerism or stereoisomerism is possible, thermal annealing reactions usually reproduce the original target molecule.[10-13]

Radiation-induced annealing also shows a preference for reformation of the parent isomer.[12] Somewhat less template preference is shown in thermal annealing following high energy (γ,p) recoil than after low energy (n,γ) activation.[11]

Two-centered complexes reveal similar behavior, with thermal annealing producing labelled parent at both the cationic and anionic sites.[14,15]

2. Effect of Type of Nuclear Reaction

When more than one radioactive species is possible as a result of the nuclear transformation, the initial retentions may differ,[4,16-19] perhaps due to the difference in recoil energy. However, the thermalized recoil atoms must have similar environments as the annealing reactions are frequently very similar, whether dealing with two different radioactive species produced by the same nuclear reaction (e.g. (n,γ) [20-22]) or the same radionuclide produced by two different nuclear transformations (e.g., (n,γ) and (n,2n) [23]) although this is not always the case.[24] Differences in internal conversion of the capture radiation are also involved.

If the recoil occurs in a crystalline solid in which only a small percentage of the target compound is present, diluted in an isomorphous compound, the radionuclides produced by (n,γ) activation may recombine to reform the original target compound, while those produced by (n,2n) or (γ,n) activations, with longer recoil ranges, generally do not reform the original target.[25]

3. Low Temperature Thermal Annealing

Some annealing processes are detectable at very low temperatures, even in systems that are clearly hard, ionic solids, implying very low activation energies are required for reconstruction, at least for this part of the reformation process. It seems reasonable to suppose that these low temperature processes involve the radioactive species interacting with fragments trapped in the same or adjacent unit cells to the radioactive atom. Data from mixed crystals of the general formula $M'_2[MX_6]$ suggest an appreciable proportion of the (n,γ) reactions lead to such situations[26]. Unfortunately, present analytical procedures do not permit reliable measurements of the kinetics of this low temperature annealing.

As the annealing temperature (or ionizing radiation dose) increases, more annealing is seen, suggesting somewhat higher activation energies and a process that involves a slightly larger reaction region, still containing the fragments caused by the individual recoil event. Reassembly of parent or parent-like products from such sites ought to show first order characteristics, although more than one energy of activation might be involved.

4. Higher Temperature Annealing Processes

At higher temperatures, the annealing processes more closely resemble those that occur in solids which have been doped, by cocrystallization or coprecipitation, with a radioactive atom, initially present in a chemical form different from that of the host.[27-29] Since the doping procedure most certainly has introduced the radioactive species into a different chemical environment than that which surrounds the thermalized recoil atom, even if in the same bulk host solid, these annealing processes are considered to be insensitive to the exact structure of the site containing the radioactive species and instead reflect the properties of the bulk crystal.[27] That this high temperature region depends principally on the gross properties of the solid, rather than on the details of the immediate environment, as is the case in the lower temperature processes, is also supported by the observations from dopant/host studies that chromium-51-labelled Cr(III), cocrystallized or coprecipitated into non-chromate ionic solids, produces, after thermal or radiation annealing, products which are indistinguishable from chromium-51-labelled chromate,[7] while iodine-131-labelled iodide becomes oxidized in non-iodate solids,[30] and trace radio-labelled halides in $M'_2[MX_6]$ become complexes.[31] Undoubtedly some of the annealing is closely related to an exchange reaction as has been demonstrated in the case of Tl_4Cl_6.[32] Thus, at high annealing temperatures, the exact nature of the matrix appears unimportant and bulk properties, such as crystalline defects which could promote atom/ion rearrangements are those affecting the annealing process.[29,33] The rate controlling step governing the kinetics of this process should reflect some kind of diffusive mechanism. However, the precision of the data is seldom sufficient to decide conclusively.

Multiple stage, multizone annealing patterns have been obtained for hard ionic solids, such as potassium chromate [8,27] and in organic solids, such as hexabromoethane.[34,35] In the latter case, five separate thermal annealing stages could be identified, some sensitive to external defects, such as those produced by radiation or impurities (doping-induced defects) and others dependent only on local (intrinsic) defects.

5. Influence of Defects

Intrinsic annealing is also seen in ionic solids, although less frequently.[8] Much more common is the sensitivity which annealing reactions, specially at higher temperatures, show to the presence of defects in the matrix material, whether they be present before, or are introduced by or after the neutron irradiation. Thus, crystal structure dislocations, as well as induced vacancies, affect the extent of annealing in a manner similar to effects seen from post-irradiation crushing.[7]

Although many different kinds of defects affect the progress of the annealing process, their mode of action has not been definitively established. Perhaps defects initiate the reconstruction by provision of space for the diffusion of fragments, or even the diffusion of the transformed atom itself. On the other hand, their action may be due to their provision of electronic defects, or to a combination of both. Because ionizing radiation almost always accompanies the activating irradiation, vacancies can trap electrons and subsequently give rise to mobile electronic species. This poses a number of interesting questions, some of which are susceptible of clarification by suitable experiments. For instance, are the annealing processes defect sensitive in systems where the separable product and the target substance contain the target/radioactive atom in the same oxidation state? At least one study suggests not, or at least that the annealing is not sensitive to radiation-induced defects.[8]

Conversely, although thermal annealing and thermal decomposition often show parallel behavior,[36] annealing of (n,γ) and radiation damage are not the same.[37] Thus the picture with respect to defects is not straightforward and may well be compound specific.

A comparison of the effects of thermal and ultraviolet annealing of irradiated phosphates is also significant. In these systems two different processes can be distinguished: bond rupture converting polyphosphate to orthophosphate and oxidation converting *P(I) and *P(III) species to orthophosphate. At modest temperatures, thermal annealing leads mostly to bond rupture, while at higher temperatures both processes occur. Photoannealing, on the other hand, occurs primarily due to the oxidation process, apparently by a purely electronic mechanism.[38]

There is far less data supporting a purely free space effect of vacancies. Indeed, the very slightly studied pressure-initiated annealing reactions [9] suggest that annealing can arise from a diminution in free space.

The important developments in the study of solid state reactions of trace radioactive-atom-doped crystals[31,32] indicate that dislocations might be expected to affect high temperature annealing reactions, which are essentially identical to the solid state reactions induced in dopant/host solids at similar temperatures. This draws attention to a type of experiment so far not attempted with (n,γ) irradiated solids. Sulphur produced by the (n,p) reaction in single crystals of alkali chlorides showed, after autoradiography, to have migrated, with heating, toward the surface along dislocations.[39] This also happens in periodates doped with trace quantities of radiolabelled iodate.[40] It would be interesting to explore such effects in, for instance, single crystals of potassium chromate. For reasonable spacial resolution, it would be necessary that the radioactive atom emit soft electrons, as is the case with chromium-51, although the photons produced by 10% of the decays would produce a low uniform background during the autoradiography.

6. In Situ Studies

Almost all of the measurements of the amount and distribution of the transformed atoms are realized after destruction of the crystalline solid by dissolution. However, a few attempts have been made to apply physical, in situ, methods such as Mössbauer emission spectroscopy, perturbed angular correlation and analysis of the K_α and K_β X-rays associated with EC decay to identify the state of the transformed atom. Most of these studies provide only limited information due to the very low concentration of the transformed atom and the large background signals resulting from the radiolysis which occurs during activation. The number of possible nuclides susceptible to such studies is also a limiting factor. For these and other reasons, most of the physical studies, whether on recoil-produced, implanted or radionuclide-doped solids, have emphasized only the initial distribution of such species, whether by Mössbauer spectroscopy,[41-43] perturbed angular correlation,[44] ultraviolet spectrophotometry[45] or the K_β/K_α intensity ratio [46] studies. Only a few studies have tried to identify the distribution of the radionuclide after annealing treatments.

In purely physical studies, the annealing of hafnium-181 in several hafnium complexes was investigated by perturbed angular correlation [47] while Mössbauer studies of iron-57-labelled ferric chloride surface doped onto Prussian blue ($KFe^{III}[Fe^{II}(CN)_6]$) show incorporation of the labelled ferric iron, even at room temperature.[48]

Dopant/host studies have compared the <u>in situ</u> values with those after dissolution. Formation of cobalt-57-labelled <u>tris</u>-dipyridylcobalt(III) perchlorate trihydrate from a $^{57}CoCl_2.nH_2O$-doped $[Co(dipy)_3](ClO_4)_3.3H_2O$ solid matrix was characterized both by Mössbauer emission spectroscopy and by chemical analysis.[49] Solution analysis showed essentially 100% formation of the labelled complex after only four hours of heating at 38 °C while only 71% of the labelled complex could be identified from Mössbauer spectra after 54 hours at the same temperature. These results suggest that formation of the final complex within the solid matrix probably involves intermediates which analyze, upon dissolution, as parent, even though they are not identified as such by the <u>in situ</u> study. It may be commented that very few attempts have been made to trap unstable species from the lattice by scavenger reactions during dissolution for analysis.

Comparison of the corresponding K_β/K_α intensity ratios with the Cr(III) and Cr(VI) distributions, after dissolution, for chromium-51-labelled Cr(III) surface-doped onto a thin film of solid potassium chromate indicated a similar result. At both low and high temperatures, the values were quite similar but at intermediate temperatures on the isochronal annealing curve, the quantity of Cr(VI) indicated after dissolution was higher than that suggested by the physical measurement.[50] Interestingly, at lower temperatures, where no annealing to Cr(VI) was observed, the K_β/K_α measurement remained constant, even though the dissolution analysis revealed the typical monomer-dimer "crossover" reaction.[50] The differences observed between the <u>in situ</u> physical analysis and the distribution revealed by chemical analysis suggests that species which do not appear as Cr(VI) to the physical analysis already have a structure/environment which yields the oxidized species upon dissolution. It should be pointed out that the K_β/K_α intensity ratio determination does not reveal the exact oxidation state of the individual atoms, whenever there is a distribution between Cr(III) and Cr(VI). Thus, the K_β/K_α ratio does not reveal the special surroundings of a Cr(III), or even a Cr(IV) or Cr(V) atom in the solid, although these surroundings are fundamental in determining whether, in solution, the atom is Cr(VI) or Cr(III), or even Cr(III)-monomer or Cr(III)-dimer.

7. Kinetics of Annealing

Although the curves obtained for isothermal annealing in solids are qualitatively similar, a number of different kinetic interpretations have been advanced. The most attractive of these considers the isothermal curve as representing groups of first order processes with distributed activation energies (Figure 4) or even with each first order process having a separate characteristic activation energy.[8] However, these, as well as most other annealing studies have reported an insufficient number of reproducible data points to permit reasonable confidence in the results.

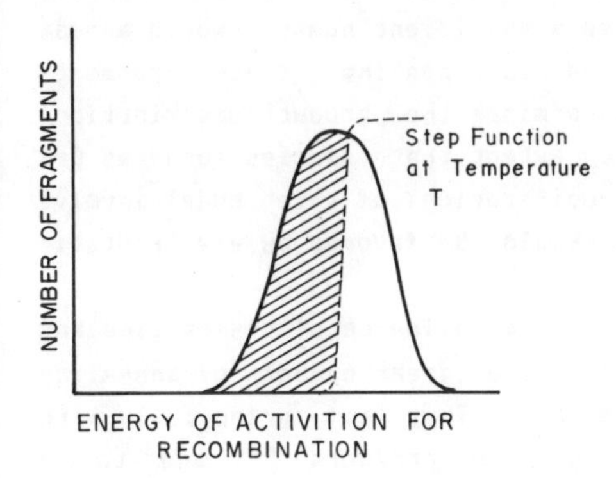

FIGURE 4. Typical distribution of activation energies

Other kinetic analyses have proposed second order processes, reactions whose individual velocities are related to activation energy spectra instead of discrete values or processes involving diffusion-controlled kinetics. Perhaps the most reasonable of these proposals involves annealing as a first order process with distributed energies of activation, the variation in which depend on diffusion.[8]

Radiation annealing has also been considered to be a first order process.[8] The kinetics of annealing initiated by other modes have been too little studied to permit detailed kinetic analysis.

8. Models for Annealing

Having described the principal characteristics of annealing reactions, it remains to describe the annealing process as it occurs within the crystalline solid. However, despite the mass of literature on this subject, it remains essentially terra incognita. The great variety of substrates which show annealing after a nuclear transformation has converted one of its atoms to a radioactive tracer, as well as the great variety of entities considered to enhance such reassemblies, suggest that no single model or mechanism will suffice, although attempts have been made to do so.[51] The other extreme is also possible: each substrate having its own individual annealing mechanism. However, it is to be hoped that some similarities exist amongst similar compound types. As mentioned earlier, there may be more than one annealing process involved, as it is necessary to account for low temperature and intrinsic annealing processes as well as higher temperature processes.

One of the first models,[52] initially proposed for oxyanions and, later, also applied to complexes, supposes that the recoiling central atom loses its ligands, depending on the difference in electronegativity between the central atom and its ligands. If the central atom were a metal (such as chromium in chromates), the ligands are lost as ions and the central atom acquires a positive charge, while, if the central atoms is a non-metal (bromine in bromates) the ligands and the central atom remain as non-ionic, atomic species. Those fragments which have lost a sufficient number of ligands will react, upon dissolution, to give non-parent yield while those fragments which did not loose a sufficient number would appear after dissolution as parent. When subjected to annealing, these fragments recombine and the extent of recombination determines the product distribution. Certainly the model must be modified to the extent that species such as Cr^{6+} could not survive in any host lattice. Other modifications of this model involve the recombination of correlated pairs, which should be favored by electrostatic attraction between each pair.[8,9]

These models, which do not explictly involve the influence of crystalline and induced defects, were applied over the years to a great number of annealing studies in oxyanions and transition metal complexes. They fail principally with respect to the oxidation states of the observed products [53] and to the similarity of results, in some systems, independent of the dissolution solvent.[54]

Another group of models is based on overlapping zones being produced as a result of the nuclear transformation. The first of these, the "hot zone", implied that the transformed atom would come to rest in a very-shorted-lived molten region of great disorder whose restructuring occurs upon appropriate treatments.[55] Such a model implies very low initial retentions, as is often observed, but does not explain why, if such a large amount of damage occurs, relatively high retentions are observed even for low temperature irradiations,[9] nor is it compatible with the mixed crystals data.[26]

The other zone models, "center of disorder" and "three domains", predict much less local damage. In the former [26,56] the transformed atom from the (n,γ) reaction comes to rest no more than a few atomic diameters from its original position, having produced but a small number of fragments. This is possible if, shortly after the transformation, the recoiling atom transfers much of its kinetic energy to the other atoms of the crystalline network which are involved in the collision. The latter atoms dissipate the kinetic energy of recoil away from the transformed atom, leaving it close to its original site and its original partners. The overall crystal damage is small and the transformed atom is held in a metastable configuration of little disorder until submitted to an appropriate treatment which permits reformation of the original molecule.

The three domain model [3] is a more recent version of the disorder model, and allows for higher recoil reactions. It is also related to the path travelled by the recoiling atom. The first domain is that of the original unit cell, the recoil not having been sufficient to remove the transformed atom from its original site. Here it is susceptible to recombination with geminate fragments or closely correlated ones. If the recoil was sufficient to break the bonds and move the atoms beyond a certain distance, its final position will be such that it has no chance of recombining with its original partners. This intermediate domain contains those atoms whose trajectories do not permit geminate recombination but which are susceptible to induced reactions upon subsequent treatment.

These models predict that, in the inner zones, annealing can occur independent of external influences in a manner similar to a recrystallization (without, however, needing to be molten), favoring, as well, the stereospecificity of the reassembly process. This reassembly process may account for the low temperature component of the annealing.

A further group of models for annealing is electronically based, implying the necessity of a "trigger" species to initiate an annealing event. In these, the transformed atom would not need to diffuse; it remains at the end of its track, surrounded by a number of fragments, sufficient, if they were to combine, to produce a parent or parent-like substance upon dissolution of the solid, lacking only the arrival of the trigger species. The trigger species, for their part, may diffuse freely through the solid, being continuously trapped and released, as a function of temperature and trap-defect concentrations, as well as of the depth distribution of the traps, controlling the velocity of the annealing. With this number of variables, almost all possible annealing events can be described!

The trigger species are usually species with high mobility in any crystalline solid, such as electrons, holes, and excitons.[8,9] With such easily diffusable species, the amount of annealing depends on the concentration of defects in the crystal which trap and release these species as a function of the annealing treatment. The velocity and activation energy distribution depend on the different depths of the traps which could be of specific levels or represent a continuous spectrum of energies.[8]

Another possible mobile species is the defect itself (vacancies or other point defects) which, instead of trapping and releasing the lighter particles, interact directly with the transformed atom and its surroundings.[8,9] Since the locus of the transformed atom is, in itself, a type of defect, the diffusion of the nearby defects toward this position may have a favorable potential gradient and, once arrived, they furnish sufficient relaxation energy to cause rearrangement and combinations of the fragments already present. Direct evidence of the role of vacancies has been detailed in the case of Tl_4Cl_6.[3e]

The existence of both types of diffusing species account very well for the typical forms of the isothermal annealing curves. Nearby defects or lightly trapped electronic species move rapidly toward the site of the transformed atom, causing the initial rapid increase in parent or parent-like compound; the plateau then indicating the local exhaustion of these entities. A further, higher temperature pulse, or other treatment such as radiation or crushing, enhances the availability of the mobile entities and permits further annealing.

9. Annealing Reactions in Solids

At the molecular level, one can envision that the annealing of a recoiled ligand species (*X recoiled from MX_6, for example) can occur as a one step direct replacement:[57]

$$*X + MX_6 \rightarrow MX_5{*X} + X$$

or as a multistep post-activation annealing process via a ligand vacancy:[58]

$$MX_6 \rightarrow MX_5\square + X$$
$$MX_5\square + M'X_6 \rightarrow MX_6 + M'X_5\square$$
$$\vdots$$
$$M''X_5\square + *X \rightarrow M''X_5{*X}$$

For the annealing of a central atom (*M recoiled from MX_6, for example), one-step direct replacement [10,51] is possible during the thermalization after a transformation but less likely as an annealing step:

$$*M + MX_6 \rightarrow {*MX_6} + M$$

Multistep ligand addition is more likely in post-activation annealing,[6,28,59] either via simple stepwise addition, in case free ligand species exist in the vicinity:[28]

$$*M + X \rightarrow {*MX}$$
$$*MX + X \rightarrow {*MX_2}$$
$$\vdots$$
$$*MX_5 + X \rightarrow {*MX_6}$$

or as a stepwise addition involving ligand transfer:[28,58]

$$*M + MX_6 \rightarrow {*MX} + MX_5\square$$
$$*MX + MX_6 \rightarrow {*MX_2} + MX_5\square$$
$$\vdots$$
$$*MX_5 + MX_6 \rightarrow {*MX_6} + MX_5\square$$

Most probably the annealing is a combination of simple addition, to the extent that free ligands are available amongst the fragments, and ligand transfer,[60] with the details depending on the exact environment of the transformed atom.

Polynuclear ligand transfer can also occur, since the fragment containing the transformed atom most likely comes to rest in close proximity to unaltered parent units.[61] Hence, the ligand groups may be able to act as bridging groups to produce polynuclear species such as:

```
   X                 X      X
*M   MX4   or   X4M    *M     MX4
   X                 X      X
```

in which the M and *M atoms may, or may not, be in the same oxidation state. The polynuclear species thus formed may be unstable in solution and, therefore, not survive for direct analytical detection. On the other hand, polynuclear species containing the transformed atom, either reduced or with the same oxidation state have been encountered when such species survive under the analytical conditions used. In those cases when the polynuclear species decomposes upon dissolution, differences relating to different dissolution conditions should reflect their presence, as is seen with some cobalt complexes and oxyanions.[8,61]

The polynuclear species should be important to annealing processes, with radiolabelled parent or parent-like species resulting from either internal redox or rearrangement of the ligand species within the polynuclear species, possibily initiated by the appearance of a mobile trigger. The effects of phase changes, such as hydration or dehydration, should also promote the redistribution of ligands within a polynuclear species.

Various possibilities have been considered for provoking an annealing reaction, wherein a transformed recoil atom, probably stripped of its original partners, reassumes its original form, or a form sufficiently similar to appear as such upon dissolution. The true picture, if it be possible one day to know it, will probably indicate that the many different types of solid compounds have different routes of annealing of transformed atoms to arrive at the final species distribution and that the overall mechanism of "annealing" may require more than one "model" for an adequate description.

References

1. Yoshihara, K., Kudo, H.: J. Chem. Phys., 52, 2950 (1970).
2. Yoshihara, K., Mizusawa, T.: Radiochem. Radioanal. Lett., 9, 263 (1972).
3. Yoshihara, K., Fujita, A., Shiokawa, T.: J. Inorg. Nucl. Chem., 39, 1733 (1977).
4. Kaneko, I., Sekine, T., Yoshihara, K.: J. Radioanal. Nucl. Chem. Lett., 144, 89 (1990).
5. Matsuura, T., Sasaki, K.: Radiochim. Acta, 49, 17 (1990).
6. Lanças, F.M., Collins, C.H.: Radiochim. Acta, 35, 77 (1984).
7. Ackerhalt, R.E., Collins, C.H., Collins, K.E.: Trans. Faraday Soc., 65, 1927 (1969).
8. Vargas, J.I., Maddock, A.G.: "Chemical Effects of Nuclear Transformations in Inorganic Systems", (Harbottle, G., Maddock, A.G., ed.) North Holland Publishing Company, Amsterdam, 1979, Chapter 26.
9. Collins, C.H., Collins, K.E.: "Chemical Effects of Nuclear Transformations in Inorganic Systems", (Harbottle, G., Maddock, A.G., ed.) North Holland Publishing Company, Amsterdam, 1979, Chapter 8.
10. Bonte, J.L., Martin, D.S.: J. Inorg. Nucl. Chem., 39, 1481 (1977).
11. Omori, T.M., Akimoto, T., Shiokawa, T.: Radiochim. Acta, 27, 191 (1980).
12. Sasaki, K., Iiyoshi, N., Watanaka, J., Yamatori, H.: Radiochim. Acta, 30, 99 (1982).
13. Sasaki, K., Furukawa, M., Yamatera, H.,: Radiochim. Acta, 36, 123 (1984).
14. DiRisio, C.D., Marques, R.O.: J. Radioanal. Nucl. Chem. Lett., 118, 235 (1987).
15. Abbas, Z.H., Venkateswarlu, K.S.: Radiochim. Acta, 49, 61 (1990).
16. de Mendonça, J.M.A., Bellido, A.F.: J. Radioanal. Nucl. Chem. Art., 98, 75 (1986).
17. Beltran, C., Bulbulian, S., Archundia, C.: J. Radioanal. Nucl. Chem. Lett., 96, 59 (1985).
18. Matsuura, T., Kurihara, H., Nagahara, T., Sasaki, K.: J. Radioanal. Nucl. Chem. Lett. 106, 175 (1986).
19. Matsuura, T., Sasaki, K., Shoji, H.: J. Radioanal. Nucl. Chem. Art., 134, 311

(1989).
20. Groening, H.R., Harbottle, G.: Radiochim. Acta, 14, 109 (1979).
21. Dedgaonkar, V.G., Lokhande, R.S., Chaudhari, M.B.: Radiochim. Acta, 27, 101 (1980).
22. Weber, I., Wiles, D.R.: Radiochim. Acta, 30, 83 (1982).
23. Ackerhalt, R.E., Harbottle, G.: Radiochim. Acta, 17, 126 (1972).
24. Omori, T., Kikuchi, T., Shiokawa, T.: Radiochem. Radioanal. Lett., 37, 233 (1979).
25. Müller, H.: "Chemical Effects of Nuclear Transformations in Inorganic Systems", (Harbottle, G., Maddock, A.G., ed.) North Holland Publishing Company, Amsterdam, 1979, Chapter 25.
26. see section IV.9.
27. Collins, C.H., Ackerhalt, R.E., Collins, K.E.: Radiochim. Acta, 17, 73 (1972).
28. Lanças, F.M., Collins, K.E., Collins, C.H.: Radiochim. Acta, 38, 189 (1985).
29. Collins, K.E., de Andrade, J.C., Collins, C.H.: Radiochim. Acta, 29, 117 (1981).
30. Musić, S., Vekić, B., Vlatković, M.: J. Inorg. Nucl. Chem., 41, 1055 (1979).
31. Duplatre, G.: "Hot Atom Chemistry. Recent Trends and Applications in the Physical and Life Sciences and Technology" (Matsuura, T., ed.) Elsevier, Amsterdam, 1984. Chapter III-B.
32. see section IV.6.
33. Collins, K.E., de Andrade, J.C., Collins, C.H.: Radiochim. Acta, 35, 71 (1984).
34. Collins, K.E., Harbottle, G.: Radiochim. Acta, 3, 21 (1964).
35. Collins, K.E., Harbottle, G.: Radiochim. Acta, 3, 29 (1964).
36. Pinto, C.O.B.M., Fabris, J.B., Duplatre, G., Machado, R.M.: Radiochem. Radioanal. Lett., 38, 269 (1979).
37. Archundia, C.; Albarrán, G., Maddock, A.G.: Radiochim. Acta, 32, 197 (1983).
38. Lindner, L.: "Chemical Effects of Nuclear Transformations in Inorganic Systems", (Harbottle, G., Maddock, A.G., ed.) North Holland Publishing Company, Amsterdam, 1979, Chapter 9.
39. Maddock, A.G., Todorovsky, D.S.: Radiochim. Acta, 32, 197 (1983).
40. Takriti, S., Duplatre, G.: Radiochim. Acta, 42, 179 (1987).
41. Sano, H., Harada, M., Endo, K.: Bull. Chem. Soc. Jpn., 51, 2583 (1978).
42. Kulshreshtha, S.K., Srivastava, S.B., Thomas, V.G., Raj, P.: Radiochim. Acta, 39, 175 (1986).
43. Kulshreshtha, S.K., Thomas, V.G., Srivastava, S.B.: Radiat. Eff., 106, 289 (1988).
44. Boussaha, A., Marques Netto, A., Abbé, J.C., Haessler, A.: Radiochem. Radioanal. Lett., 24, 43 (1976).
45. Rössler, K., Pross, L.: Radiat. Eff., 48, 207 (1980).
46. Yoshihara, K., Hibino, A., Yamoto, I., Kaji, H.: Radiochem. Radioanal. Lett., 48, 303 (1981).
47. Fabris, J.D., Vargas, J.I., Marques Netto, A., Baudry, A.L.: Radiochim. Acta, 25, 85 (1978).
48. Borshagovskii, B.V., Goldanskii, V.I., Seifer, G.B., Stukan, R.A.: Izvest. Akad. Nauk S.S.S.R., ser. khim., 5, 1016 (1971).
49. Collins, C.H., Collins, K.E., de Jesus Filho, M.F., Friedt, J.M.: J. Inorg. Nucl. Chem., 43, 1735 (1981).
50. Collins, K.E., Collins, C.H., Heitz, C.: Radiochim. Acta, 28, 7 (1981).
51. Nath, A.: "Radiochemistry", vol. 2 (Newton, G.W.A., ed.) The Chemical Society, London, 1975, Chapter 2-I.
52. Libby, W.F.: J. Am. Chem. Soc., 62, 1930 (1940).
53 Collins, C.H., Collins, K.E., Ghoss, Y.F., Apers, D.J.: Radiochim. Acta, 4, 211 (1964).
54. Mahieu, B., Prendez, M., Apers, D.J.: Radiochem Radioanal. Lett., 25, 67

(1976).
55. Harbottle, G., Sutin, N.: J. Phys. Chem., 62, 1344 (1958).
56. Müller, H.: Angew. Chem. Int. Ed. Eng., 6, 133 (1967).
57. Müller, H., Obergfell, P., Hagenlocher, I.: J. Phys. Chem., 90, 3418 (1986).
58. Bell, R.; Rössler, K., Stöcklin, G., Upadhyay, S.R.: J. Inorg. Nucl. Chem., 34, 461 (1972).
59. Ramshesh, V.: Radiat. Phys. Chem., 27 185 (1986).
60. Collins, K.E., Collins, C.H.: "Memorias del III Simposio sobre Química Nuclear, Radioquímica y Química de Radiaciones", (Negrón Mendoza, A., Albarrán, G., eds.) Universidad Nacional Autonoma de México, México, D.F., 1980, p. 2.
61. Maddock, A.G., Collins, K.E.: Can. J. Chem., 46, 3924 (1968).

4.5 Exchange Reactions in Solids

Gilles DUPLÂTRE

Laboratoire de Chimie Nucléaire, Centre de Recherches Nucléaires, B.P. 20, 67037 Strasbourg Cédex, France

1. Introduction

In a previous review, a short survey was made of the various theories which have been proposed in the field of solid state exchange reaction chemistry (ERC), and typical data were scrutinized to illustrate the limits of validity of the models.[1)]

The various systems studied were shown to be reducible to 3 main classes of compounds : (i) simple inorganic salts, particularly those containing oxyanions ; (ii) the transition metal chelates ; (iii) the mixed-valence and mixed-bond compounds. In the first and second of these groups, the studies are most often conducted by inserting a labelled dopant ion into the solid matrix. The changes observed in the chemical state of the dopant after applying some physicochemical stimulus, such as heat or radiation, might or might not result from a genuine isotopic exchange reaction, according as the matrix would include or not an isotope of the dopant. In the last group, the labelling can be made directly on one of the constituents of the matrix, ascertaining that any witnessed reaction is ascribable to an isotopic exchange, inasmuch as no electron exchange would take place.

It was also pointed out that the theories advanced could be described by the combination of a few key-words : (i) the ultimate reaction of the process can be a genuine isotopic exchange between the labelled atom and an atom of the matrix, or consists in the binding of the former with neighbouring matrix ligands ; (ii) these reactions can be triggered by the occurrence, at the site of the labelled atom, of either light entities, like electrons, holes and excitons, or lattice defects, such as ion vacancies ; (iii) the rate-determining step can be the release and/or the movement of any of the species just mentioned.

For example, the activated exchange model proposes that heating the doped crystals releases charges from multidepth donors ; these charges migrate and can be captured by the labelled dopants, which become excited, providing enough local energy to trigger either an exchange or a ligand capture reaction.[2,3] Alternatively, the stepwise oxidation model suggests that the incoming of (positive) charges to the dopant suffices to induce the chemical changes.[4] The implication of charges is of course likely when the matrix can easily provide them, such as when it has been subjected to radiation.[4] Specific experiments can be made to check the validity of the models, such as by injecting space charges into the doped matrix[3] or by introducing specific co-dopants, able either to compete with the labelled dopant for charge capture or, on the contrary, to favour the production of charges, thus reducing or enhancing the extent of exchange, accordingly.[4]

Complementarily, the implication of defects in the exchange process is likely when this occurs at high temperatures, particulary when the exchange is found to proceed when some decomposition of the matrix occurs.[5] More specifically, only the presence of lattice defects can be invoked when exchange is observed in a labelled mixed-valence compound.[6,7]

When that review[1] was being written, about a hundred papers had appeared on ERC. Since then, publications have been very sparse, save two series of experiments specifically intended to demonstrate the role of defects in the exchange processes and to attempt some quantitative approach to the data. These series, both carried out at the Strasbourg laboratory, were concerned with two different systems : the labelled mixed-valence compound $Tl(I)_3Tl(III)Cl_6$,[7-13] and the alkali periodates doped with labelled iodate.[14-17] The aim of the present paper is to summarize and examine the contents and conclusions of these works.

2. Exchange in a labelled mixed-valence compound, $Tl(I)_3$ $Tl(III)Cl_6$

Choosing a labelled mixed-valence compound to study isotope exchange offers the advantage of obviating the uncertainties inherent in chemical analysis as encountered in the case of annealing reactions of recoil atoms and also of some doped systems,[1] as the species in the exchange are normal lattice occupants. The specific choice of Tl_4Cl_6 was prompted by the fact that it belongs to a class of compounds[18] which can be prepared and labelled at a specified valence using a wet procedure : no significant exchange occurs either in solution or in the solid state, at moderate temperatures.

Thermally activated exchange is found to occur at a convenient rate in the temperature range from about 450 K to 550 K.[7] In contrast with what is known for some annealing reactions and doped systems, the process is not sensitive to the nature of the atmosphere, nor to the previous action of γ rays even at doses as high as 21 MRad.[7] At a specified time and temperature (T), the extent of exchange is the same whether the labelling is made on the uni or on the trivalent state of thallium. Note that in the latter case, the exchanged fraction is expressed as (neglecting the initial fraction) :

$$E(\%) = 100\ 4p_I/3, \qquad (1)$$

where p_I is the ratio of the activity in the form of Tl(I) to the total activity. These findings strongly suggest that the exchange results from a genuine interchange of the Tl(I) and Tl(III) ions in the lattice, not affected by the presence of radiation induced charged defects.

A hint to the mechanism of the reaction is given by observing that the preparation of the samples has important effects : no reproducible results can be obtained without careful standardization of each of the steps of the synthesis. In particular, the exchange is greater in crushed crystals.[7] This indicates that the physical state of the lattice plays a role in the process, by the presence of specific defects : thus, crushing the crystals may either introduce an extrinsic type of defect whose action would add to that of the intrinsic defects, enhancing the exchange, or create particular regions in the lattice where the latter would diffuse more easily. On the basis of simple first order kinetics, it is found that 3 reaction steps at least, with activation energies of 1.52 eV (9.3%), 1.64 eV (26.7%) and 1.71 eV (64%), are necessary to describe the isochronals ; the proportion of the reaction of lowest activation energy increases after crushing. Several experiments, described in the following, were run thereafter to disclose the nature of these defects or regions.

In neutron irradiated Tl_4Cl_6, the initial proportion of ^{204}Tl(III) after the ^{203}Tl(n, γ)^{204}Tl reaction is $p_{III} \simeq 1/6$.[8] After long heating times, it tends to the statistical value of 1/4 corresponding to E = 100%. The course of the isochronal annealing is found to parallel closely that of the exchange when temperature increases.[8] Therefore, it appears that even though the initial Tl(I)/Tl(III) distribution probably arises from local hot atom reactions, the subsequent annealing reactions are completely independent of these : neither the charge or the point defects created locally along the recoil track or in the bulk, by the neutrons and accompanying γ rays, are important to the process of the exchange.

In ^{208}Tl recoil-implanted Tl_4Cl_6, the initial distribution is such that $p_{III} \simeq 1/6$.[9] The ^{208}Tl atoms are generated from the α decay of ^{212}Bi, in the sequence $^{212}Pb \rightarrow {}^{212}Bi \rightarrow {}^{208}Tl$, while ^{212}Pb is obtained by collecting on a gold foil the daughters of ^{220}Rn produced in the radioactive series of a ^{228}Th source. As the recoil energy of ^{208}Tl is 117 keV, the fact that p_{III} is the same as in the neutron irradiated material, where ^{204}Tl has a maximum recoil energy of about 0.1 eV only, shows that the initial energy and location of the hot atoms have no influence on the final distribution. Again, long heating times lead to $p_{III} \simeq 1/4$, the statistical distribution. However, the exchange isochronal appears to coincide roughly with the reaction step of lowest energy found in the labelled compound and ascribed to the lattice regions of highest disorder.[7] As the implanted ions have a maximum population at about 25 nm from the surface of the crystals, this shows that, by contrast with what is found after the (n, γ) reaction, the nature and/or the density of defects created by implantation modify importantly the exchange process.

Doping the crystals with aliovalent cations which should promote the formation of extrinsic cation vacancies in the lattice, such as Pb^{2+} or In^{3+}, does not lead to significant changes in the exchange isochronals of labelled Tl_4Cl_6.[10] This excludes any important role for these defects in the exchange. On the contrary, coprecipitating Tl_4Cl_6 with such salts as TlCl to give matrices in which anion vacancies are dominant, enhances greatly the exchange, which occurs at much lower temperatures.

Three independent physical techniques were used to study more specifically the formation of defects in Tl_4Cl_6.[11] Positron lifetime spectroscopy (LS) and the Doppler broadening technique (DBARL) both show that there is an easy formation of cation vacancies, with a formation enthalpy of $H_v = H_f/2 = (0.35 \pm 0.01)$ eV, H_f denoting the formation enthalpy of a pair of defects. Conductivity (σ) measurements show the existence of two regions in the plots of log(σT) as a function of 1/T : the intrinsic and extrinsic regions, above and below 450 K, with activation energies $E_\sigma = (0.69 \pm 0.05)$ eV and (0.51 ± 0.04) eV, respectively. The former value is rather low for ionic crystals and shows that Tl_4Cl_6 is a good ionic conductor. Qualitatively, this agrees with the value found for H_V. Quantitatively, E_σ in the intrinsic region should be given by :

$$E_\sigma = H_f/2 + H_m, \tag{2}$$

where H_m is the motional enthalpy of the diffusing defect responsible for conductivity. Identifying this defect with the cation vacancy, as suggested by the LS and DBARL results, leads to $H_m = (0.69 - 0.35)\,eV = 0.34\,eV$; this is lower than $E_\sigma = 0.51\,eV$ in the extrinsic region, which should also represent H_m. It may be noted however, that this region corresponds to very low values of σ, implying a rather large uncertainty in the measurements.

In the ground crystals, the LS results show the formation of extrinsic cation vacancies, which are annealed at about 423 K.[12] Once the crystals have been heated to this temperature, the variations of the positron lifetime in subsequent heating and cooling cycles parallel closely those observed in the untreated material. The energies H_f and E_σ are the same as in the uncrushed crystals.

From this wealth of results, it appears that the exchange mechanism implies the presence of defects : the low formation and migration energies of the cation vacancies, as compared to the high activation energies related to the exchange itself, point out the anion vacancies as the driving defects. In a similar way as previously proposed for halide-doped hexahalorhenates,[19] the following scheme of reactions appears therefore likely :[13]

vacancy formation $\quad Tl(III)Cl_6^{3-} \rightleftharpoons Tl(III)Cl_5\square^{2-} + Cl^-$ (3)

vacancy migration $\quad Tl(III)Cl_5\square^{2-} + Tl(III)'Cl_6^{3-} \rightleftharpoons Tl(III)Cl_6^{3-} + Tl(III)'Cl_5\square^{2-}$ (4)

exchange reaction $\quad Tl(III)''Cl_5\square^{2-} + Tl(I)''' \rightleftharpoons Tl(III)'''Cl_5\square^{2-} + Tl(I)''$ (5)

where the primes are used to distinguish neighbouring Tl atoms. Quantitatively, a new kinetic approach to ERC is applied, based on the random diffusion of a defect towards the reaction site.[20] In the case of a single type of defect, the exchanged fraction is given by :

$$100 - E = 100 \exp[-\textstyle\int_0^t BU(t)dt] \tag{6}$$

The equilibrium concentration of defects is expressed by :

$$B = B_0 S \exp[-H_f/(2k_B T)] \tag{7}$$

where $B_0 = 10.3\ 10^{21} cm^{-3}$ is the maximum concentration of sites for Schottky pairs in Tl_4Cl_6,[13] S is the entropy factor and k_B, the Boltzmann constant. The reaction rate function becomes :

$$U(t) = 4\pi r_0 D[1 + r_0/(\pi D t)^{1/2}] \tag{8}$$

where

$$D = D_0 \exp[-E_D/(k_B T)] \tag{9}$$

is the diffusion coefficient of the mobile defect, E_D is the diffusion activation energy and r_0, the reaction radius. Using Eq. (6) leads to mediocre results : the average deviation, ω, which should be close to the experimental error (1%) in favourable cases, is about 2% and 3% for the untreated and crushed materials, respectively. Furthermore, some values of the parameters are not satisfactory. The fitting parameters in Eqs. (6)–(9) are $X = B_0 S r_0 D_0$, $Y = r_0^2 B_0 S D_0^{1/2}$, E_D and $H_f/2$. Reasonable guesses would be[13] $r_0 = 0.5\,nm$, the average distance between neighbouring Cl^- ions of different anions, $S \simeq 1$ to 3, $H_f/2 = 0.35\,eV$ (or 0.18 eV, from the conductivity data alone). However, the fits are such that either r_0 or B (through S or H_f) are much too high ; this is illustrated in table 1, for a series of equivalent fits (because of the correlation between the parameters), all giving $\omega = 2.1\%$ for the untreated samples. The corresponding calculated curves are shown as solid lines in fig. 1.

Table 1. Typical values of the parameters derived when fitting Eq. (6) to the data (isochronal and isothermals) of exchange in untreated labelled Tl_4Cl_6. In all cases, the quality of fit is such that $\omega = 2.1\%$. ^{a}: fixed values.

$D_0(10^{-3}cm^2s^{-1})$	0.042	0.251	1.53	6.33	20.7	312	0.00265	0.685
E_D (eV)	1.42	1.53	1.65	1.74	1.81	1.99	1.42	1.74
S	1^a	1^a	1^a	1^a	1^a	1^a	1930	29
$H_f/2$ (eV)	0.35^a	0.29^a	0.23^a	0.18^a	0.14^a	0.043	0.35^a	0.18^a
r_0 (nm)	6.2	3.8	2.3	1.55	1.1	0.5^a	0.5^a	0.5^a

It may be seen from table 1 that when B has reasonable values at the highest T (523 K), e.g. when $B/B_0 < 3\%$, which corresponds to $S \simeq 1$ and $H_f/2 > 0.14$ eV, r_0 ranges from 1.1 to 6.2 nm ; conversely when r_0 is fixed at 0.5 nm, the ratio B/B_0 is close to 1. From fig. 1 it appears that the fit is worse at the lowest T, and this is more pronounced for the crushed material. Therefore, extensions of Eq. (6) were tentatively applied,[13] including the possibility of having either 2 different regions in the lattice or 2 types of vacancies, intrinsic and extrinsic. This new approach leads to a much better description of the data, allowing one to fit the whole of the isochronals and isothermals of the untreated and crushed materials with $\omega \simeq 1.5\%$. However, the lower limit to r_0 is again rather high, at about 1.2 nm.

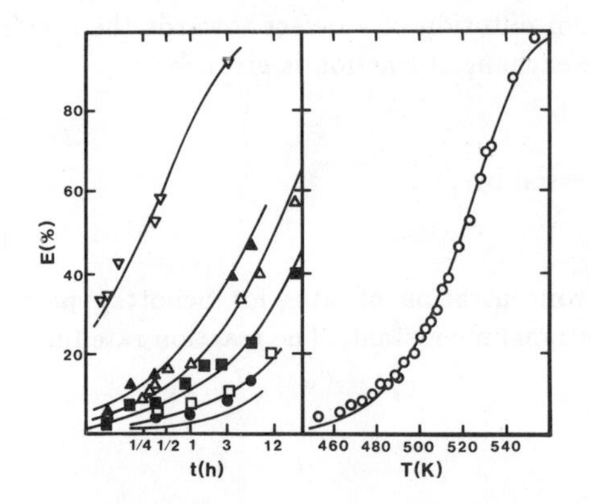

Fig. 1. Variation of the exchanged fraction, E(%), in labelled Tl_4Cl_6.
Left : isothermals at (•) 453 K, (□) 463 K, (■) 473 K, (△) 482 K, (▲) 489 K, and (▽) 523 K.
Right : isochronal. For the solid lines, see text.

3. Exchange in $^{131}IO_3^-$-doped alkali periodates

The choice of the periodates as matrices was mainly prompted by the similarity previously found between exchange isothermals in I^--doped periodates[21] and a decomposition isothermal,[22] suggesting some link between the two processes and the implication of intrinsic defects. Iodate was chosen as a dopant instead of iodide to avoid many of the problems encountered in previous works with the latter, such as the loss of activity due to the evolution of I_2 upon heating.[14]

In a first step, methods to prepare $^{131}IO_3^-$ from $^{131}I^-$ and to analyse the various iodine oxidation states are established, the previously proposed analytical procedures being inadequate.[14] The doped samples are prepared by precipitation from hot solutions, leading to the formation of crystallites all having nearly the same size, at $(50 \pm 4) \mu m$. The distribution of the dopants inside the crystals is found to be satisfactorily random.[14] By contrast with what was observed in the I^--doped compounds,[21] no other forms than labelled iodate and periodate are found, even after heating the samples, so that the exchanged fraction, E, can be defined as the ratio of the activity found in the latter state to the total activity.

In freshly prepared samples the initially exchanged fraction, E_0, has a peculiar behaviour as a function of the dopant concentration, C_d, with a maximum of 19% at $C_d \simeq 25$ (atom) ppm in KIO_4. This maximum also occurs for the positronium intensity measured in LS experiments. These unexpected results are quantitatively explained by supposing that the dopants can aggregate in the matrix during the precipitation. Each dopant ion would introduce a specific defect, most likely an oxygen vacancy, favouring positronium formation and subsequently suppressed upon aggregation.[14]

In Na, K and Rb periodates, the onset of the thermally activated exchange occurs some 100 K below that of decomposition (T_D). This exchange is not correlated with the initial exchange, as the difference between E after 2 h heating at 473 K and E_0 is constant as a function of C_d, even though E_0 passes from 10% ($C_d = 5$ ppm) to 19% (25 ppm), then down to 1% (above 300 ppm). Below T_D, the isothermals show an increase of E to a T-dependent plateau value. When decomposition intervenes, E passes through a maximum before reaching a plateau. There is no influence of the atmosphere.

The occurrence of plateaux in annealing and in exchange isothermals is a rather common phenomenon, which has received no explanation yet.[1] For the first time, a very suggestive clue as to their origin is found in doped KIO_4 when examining the distribution of the activity in the crystals after heating :[15] the activity in the surface region of the crystals increases to a T-dependent plateau value when time increases. This value is close to 100% at 473 K, whereas the exchanged fraction for the total volume of the crystals saturates at 20%. It thus appears that the dopants, initially somewhat randomly distributed, are expelled to the surface of the crystals, where they can no more suffer any exchange reaction. This is confirmed by the spatial distribution of E, which is found to be much lower at the surface than inside the crystals, after heating.[15] Furthermore, at the plateaux for moderate T, the sum of the exchanged fraction and of the fraction of dopants having reached the surface is not 100% ; this shows that the dopants can be classified in 3 categories : those which have irreversibly exchanged in the bulk, those which have reached the surface and are essentially unexchanged, and a third fraction, which is trapped as iodate inside the crystal and is suppressed at high enough T. In $NaIO_4$ however, for which similar exchange isothermals are obtained, the dopants suffer an efficient exodiffusion only when some decomposition occurs.[16] Therefore, the plateaux in the isothermals cannot be explained by the exodiffusion of the dopants proper, but rather by that of some driving defect which must be responsible both for the exchange reactions, which cease once it has left the bulk, and for the exodiffusion of the dopants. A scheme of diffusion based on the oxygen vacancy migration is proposed :[15] the labelled I(V) ion would mostly follow the vacancy, probably by virtue of electrostatic interactions, and migrate at random until it reaches the surface ; when the ion fails to jump towards the next anionic site with the vacancy and remains in its initial position as I(VII), exchange is completed.

That the surface of the crystals possesses peculiar adsorption properties is shown by using a poorly dissolving medium, an acetone-water mixture :[14] after several washings of the doped $NaIO_4$ crystals, 92% of the iodate activity remains retained on their surface, even though they are reduced to 0.1% of their initial weight ; complementarily, 96.5% of dissolved labelled iodate stirred in the presence of undoped $NaIO_4$ crystals is rapidly adsorbed on the latter. These phenomena are not observed in water, probably because of the strong solvation of the ions. It is very likely that the surface of the crystals would have charge properties, explaining why it would represent an efficient trap for some ions and defects.

Quantitatively, kinetics based on the diffusion of the labelled I(V) ions promoted by the vacancy migration, with a sink at the surface and two trapping sites in the bulk where the ions can either exchange to I(VII) or remain as I(V), lead to satisfactory results in the case of KIO_4. However, applying these kinetics would demand the knowledge of the iodate fractions defined above as a function of time and T. To compare the exchange in the various matrices, a convenient trial function is therefore found in a modified form of the Erofeev equation :[16,22]

$$E = E_{\infty} \{1 - \exp[-(kt)^n]\} \tag{10}$$

Here, n represents the dimensionality of the process : if little energy is needed to produce the driving defect, n should range from 1 (linear movement) to 3 (threedimensional development of the reaction) and should be higher by one unit if the defect formation energy is not negligible. As shown in table 2, strong correlations are found between the parameters of the lattices and the ease of exchange : (i) Exchange occurs only in the isomorphous tetragonal periodates, with a rather low decomposition T and therefore, a lower defect formation energy. (ii) At specified T, the ease of exchange such as expressed by E/E_{∞} (see Eq. 10) is in the order Rb > K > Na (hydrated) > Na (anhydrous) : the tighter (R smaller, f_c higher) the lattice is, the more difficult the exchange. (iii) In the less compact lattices (R larger, f_c smaller) exchange is more rapid, but so is the exodiffusion : E_{max} is thus lower.

Table 2. Correlation between lattice parameters [structure, either orthorhombic, O, or tetragonal, TG ; onset of decomposition, T_D ; packing coefficient, f_c ; radius of the largest free space, R] and kinetic parameters of the exchange [maximum exchanged fraction, at T_D, E_{max} ; dimensionality of the exchange reaction, n].

Lattice	Structure	R (nm)	T_D (K)	f_c (%)	E_{max} (%)	n
$CsIO_4$	O		> 823	46.5	0	
$RbIO_4$	TG	0.084	$\simeq$ 473	45.8	15.3	$\simeq 1$
KIO_4	TG	0.077	473	46.8	21.2	$\simeq 1$
$NaIO_4$	TG	0.063	493	50.8	71.6	$\simeq 2$

4. Comparing the decomposition and exchange processes in alkali periodates

The importance of the lattice parameters found for exchange in the periodates provides a clue as to the possible relationship with the decomposition process, studied in detail for KIO_4 and $NaIO_4$ in a next step.[17]

Briefly, most of the features observed in the exchange study are also apparent. If caution is taken to avoid shaking of the crystals during heating, the following facts are observed. (i) In isothermals, the decomposed fraction, D, increases with time up to a T-dependent plateau value. (ii) There is no effect of the atmosphere (whether in air or in vacuo). (iii) At the plateau, the partly decomposed crystals consist in two parts : an outer, fragile powdery layer of pure iodate and an inner, crystalline core of pure periodate. (iv) The dimensions of the core remain unchanged, even though it has lost most of its substance, in such a way that its density decreases in proportion to the decomposed fraction. Its X-ray diffraction patterns are the same as those of the initial pure periodate crystals. (v) When a plateau is reached and the outer layer is removed, the decomposition starts again and proceeds in a similar way to the previous heating. In particular, when the samples are subjected to agitation, which continuously removes this layer, the decomposition proceeds to 100% whatever the temperature.

These findings[17] show that the decomposition process is complex. Like the doped samples, the very efficient exodiffusion of the iodate formed by decomposition is probably promoted by defects. These get trapped at the surface and diffuse further into the accumulating iodate outer layer. The presence of plateaux must arise from some equilibrium between the defect populations of the outer layer, of the interface and of the crystalline core, which are to be considered as parts of a whole, otherwise one cannot understand how the removal of the layer, even though very loosely bound to the core, allows the decomposition to recommence. Continuous rupture of this equilibrium by agitation suppresses the saturation in D.

Quantitatively, the variation of D can be fitted by an expression similar to Eq. (10), with D in lieu of E. The dimensionality n varies roughly from 2 (at 543 K) to 3 (573 K) for KIO_4 and from 3 (510 K) to 4 (548 K) for $NaIO_4$, indicating some continuity between the exchange and decomposition processes. Again, n for the tighter lattice, $NaIO_4$, is higher by one unit than for KIO_4, suggesting that nucleation is not an energetically negligible process in the former case comparatively to the latter. Similar values for n are found under continuous agitation of the samples.[17]

A value of $n = 3$ (or 4) suggests some kind of explosive, autocatalytic process, while $n \simeq 1$ as found in the exchange study indicates the mere diffusion of a defect. At low T, corresponding to the latter case, the driving defects, most likely the oxygen vacancies, would move at random, dragging the iodate dopants out to the surface. When T increases, their presence at a site would induce sufficient changes in the vibrational modes of nearby oxygen ligands to casually result in bond rupture, initiating the decomposition in an autocatalytic way. Although this was not done in the previous works,[14–17] it seems interesting to analyze the exchange data when decomposition occurs and thus compare the kinetic parameters for these two processes at the same T. In the following, only the data for $NaIO_4$ are considered.

Schematically, the reactions can be written as (the asterisk denotes the labelled ions) :

$$^{\star}IO_3^- + IO_4^-(\text{lattice}) \xrightarrow{F} {}^{\star}IO_4^- \xrightarrow{G} \text{decomposition} \tag{11}$$

The integral forms of the formation, F(t), and decomposition, G(t), functions are expressed by Eq. (10) and by its complement to 100%, respectively. The solution for the final exchanged fraction is given by the convoluted function (subscripts E and D refer to exchange and to decomposition, respectively) :

$$\begin{aligned} E &= \int_0^t (dF/dt')H(t')G(t-t')dt' \\ &= \int_0^t At'^{(n_E-1)} \exp[-(k_E t')^{n_E}]\, H(t')\, \{1 - D_\infty + D_\infty \exp[-(k_D(t-t'))^{n_D}]\}\, dt' \qquad (12) \\ A &= E_\infty\, n_E\, k_E^{n_E} \end{aligned}$$

Here, H(t') expresses the probability of a suitable configuration of the local periodate lattice for the exchange to take place : if the lattice is rapidly reorganized in the course of decomposition, as the X-ray diffraction measurements would suggest, then $H(t') \doteq 1$; otherwise, $H(t') = 1 - D(t')/100$. However, because of the low value of k_D as compared to k_E at specified T, taking $H(t') = 1$ or not or, similarly, supposing that the labelled iodate produced from decomposition can or cannot participate in the exchange, does not lead to significant changes in the fits.

The variations with T of the derived parameters are shown in fig. 2 which includes, for comparison, the values obtained for the exchange data[16)] below T_D and for the decomposition data[17)] analyzed independently (note that k_D is in min^{-1}, not in s^{-1} as erroneously given previously[17)]). The corresponding calculated curves, drawn as solid lines in fig. 3, show good agreement with the data, with $\omega = 1.57\%$. The values for k_D give a reasonable Arrhenius plot, with $k_D^\circ = 1.2\ 10^8 min^{-1}$ and $E_D = 1\,eV$, showing that the present treatment is adequate ; n_D is scattered at 4 ± 1, confirming the essentially three-dimensional development of the decomposition ; as for k_D and n_D, the present values for D_∞ fit well in an analysis based solely on the decomposition data.

The most striking finding is that the exchange parameters show a marked break at about T_D (475 K) : n_E decreases suddenly from 1.6 ± 0.1 to 0.7 ± 0.2, and the Arrhenius plot for k_E gives two regions, below T_D, where $k_E^\circ = 2.2\,min^{-1}$ and $E_E = 0.16\,eV$, and above T_D, where $k_E^\circ = 5.7\ 10^8 min^{-1}$ and $E_E = 0.96\,eV$, close to E_D. Thus, in spite of the continuity between the two processes, the exchange is modified by the decomposition. The phenomenological approach used does not allow one to discover the nature of the defects involved and several possibilities are open. Thus, taking the oxygen vacancies as responsible for the exchange, their autocatalytic production upon decomposition may result in their association, like in bivacancies, more efficient to promote further decomposition ; the presence of these new defects would modify both the concentration and the diffusion properties of the monovacancies.

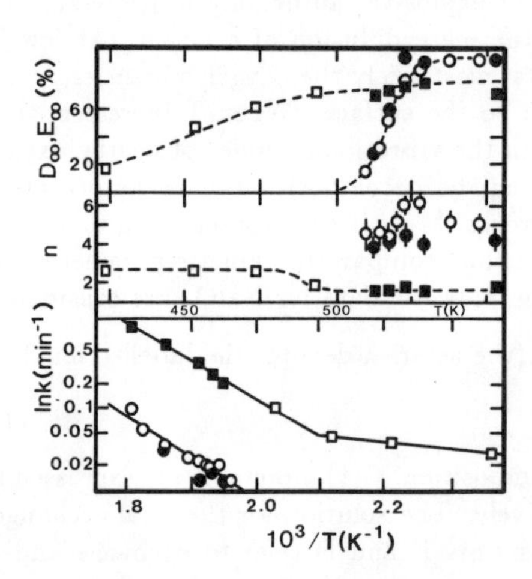

Fig. 2. Temperature variations of the fitting parameters from Eqs. (10), open symbols, and (12), full symbols, in iodate-doped $NaIO_4$. The circles and squares are for the exchange and the decomposition processes, respectively. The dashed lines are guidelines.

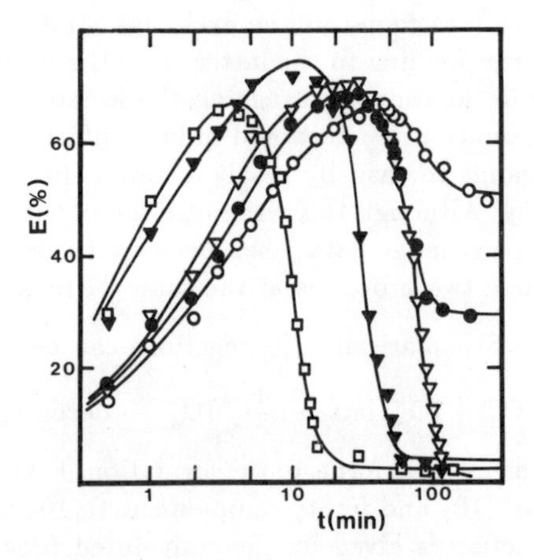

Fig. 3. Variation of the exchanged fraction, E(%), with time, t(min), in iodate-doped $NaIO_4$ above T_D, at : (○), 513 K ; (•), 518 K ; (▽), 523 K ; (▼), 538 K ; (□), 553 K. The solid lines are calculated by using Eq. (12) and the parameters shown in fig. 2.

5. Conclusion

The present summary of two long-lasting experiments on different ERC systems shows that useful information can be obtained by combining other, physical, techniques to the usual chemical analyses. The process of exchange can be complex and the characterization of the species involved requires numerous and precise experiments ; the choice of well defined systems is obviously an important prerequisite. Even though they may be rather approximate, the use of mathematical expressions specific to solid state chemistry proves to be useful, at least to delineate the gross features of the exchange and to allow comparison between different systems. Still, more efforts should be undertaken towards more appropriate kinetic equations whenever possible.

The initial goal of understanding the annealing reactions via ERC is not yet within reach and more systems should be studied. In particular, it would be rewarding to assess whether the plateaux observed in many other doped systems would arise, as found here, from the exodiffusion of the driving defects.

Acknowledgement The author expresses his gratitude to S.M. Fernandez-Valverde (Mexico) and S. Takriti (Syria) for their very fruitful collaboration.

References

1. Duplâtre, G.: "Hot Atom Chemistry" (T. Matsuura, Ed.) Kodansha, Tokyo (and Elsevier, Amsterdam), 1984, p.200.
2. Nath, A., Khorana, S., Mathur, P.K., Sarup, S.: Indian J. Chem., 4, 51 (1966).
3. Kalliat, M., Nath, A.: J. Inorg. Nucl. Chem., 43, 271 (1981).
4. Khorana, S., Wiles, D.R.: J. Inorg. Nucl. Chem., 33, 1589 (1971).
5. Lazzarini, E., Fantola-Lazzarini, A.L.: J. Inorg. Nucl. Chem., 38, 657 (1976).
6. Lazzarini, E., Fantola-Lazzarini, A.L.: J. Inorg. Nucl. Chem., 37, 407 (1975).
7. Fernandez-Valverde, S.M., Duplâtre, G., Maddock, A.G.: J. Inorg. Nucl. Chem., 40, 999 (1978).
8. Fernandez-Valverde, S.M., Duplâtre, G.: Radiochim. Acta, 24, 121 (1977).
9. Fernandez-Valverde, S.M., Duplâtre, G., Paulus, J.M.: Radiochim. Acta, 31, 131 (1982).
10. Fernandez-Valverde, S.M., Olguin-Gutierrez, M.T., Duplâtre, G.: Radiochim. Acta, 40, 209 (1986).
11. Fernandez-Valverde, S.M., Duplâtre, G.: J. Chem. Soc. Faraday Trans. 1, 82, 2825 (1986).
12. Fernandez-Valverde, S.M., Duplâtre, G.: J. Radioanal. Nucl. Chem. Lett., 107, 307 (1986).
13. Fernandez-Valverde, S.M., Duplâtre, G.: Radiochim. Acta, 46, 79 (1989).
14. Takriti, S., Duplâtre, G.: Radiochim. Acta, 42, 179 (1987).
15. Takriti, S., Duplâtre, G.: Radiochim. Acta, 43, 45 (1988).
16. Takriti, S., Duplâtre, G.: Radiochim. Acta, 43, 205 (1988).
17. Takriti, S., Duplâtre, G.: J. Chem. Soc. Faraday Trans. 1, 84, 2831 (1988).
18. Day, P.: "Mixed Valence Compounds", Endeavour, 29, 45 (1970).
19. Bell, R., Roessler, K., Upadhyay, S.R.: J. Inorg. Nucl. Chem., 34, 461 (1972).
20. Waite, T.R.: Phys. Rev., 107, 471 (1957).
21. Boyd, G.E., Larson, Q.V.: J. Am. Chem. Soc., 91, 4639 (1969).
22. Patnaik, S.K., Mahrana, P.K.: Radiochem. Radional. Lett., 53, 367 (1982).

4.6 Chemical Reaction Induced by Recoil Implanted Atoms

Kenji YOSHIHARA and Tsutomu SEKINE
Department of Chemistry, Faculty of Science, Tohoku University, Sendai, JAPAN 980

1. Introduction

The chemistry of implanted atoms has developed recently by recoil rather than ion implantation. The latter technique is not very convenient for implantations at low temperature and the radiation damage induced by nonradioactive components may become excessive. On the other hand, recoil implantation has similarities with hot atom chemistry in solids; irradiations are easily performed at low temperature in conditions where the radiation damage is minimum. The merit of recoil implantation is to be practicable in an ordinary radiochemistry laboratory even if no sophisticated and costly equipments are available. Wherever an accelerator or a nuclear reactor is accessible, the technique is easily applicable to various inorganic or organometallic solid systems.

The practice of recoil implantation is characterized by a wide choice of recoil source and catcher combinations. Energetic recoil atom reactions with molecules can be systematically investigated by changing the types of nuclear reaction and the nature of the catcher compounds in which the recoil atoms are implanted. The specific chemical reactions, as well as competing reactions, of recoil implanted atoms can be elucidated in this way. Another interesting feature of the chemistry of implanted atoms has been recently recognized by the Tohoku University group. The parent type chemical yield of the implanted atoms is much higher (about one order of magnitude) than that of the same hot atoms produced inside the catcher compound under the same irradiation conditions. This remarkable enhancement of the parent yield suggests the participation of quite reactive modes - much more reactive than those involved in the hot-zone created around the "normal" hot atom.

2. Mechanism of implantation reaction

Rössler and Pross[1] have investigated the implantation of radioactive recoil atom *M (*M = radioactive atoms of Re, Os, Ir and Pt) in K_2MX_6 type compounds such as potassium hexachlororhenate:

$$^{*}M + K_2MX_6 \rightarrow {}^{*}MX_6^{2-} + M \qquad (1)$$

The compounds chosen were the hexachloro-derivatives of M = Re, Pt, Ir, Os and Sn. The authors observed that the yield of the parent form $^*MX_6^{2-}$ increases linearly with increase of the force constant ratio F(*M-X)/F(M-X). According to their argument, the reaction takes place through abstraction of six chlorine ligands by the atom implanted in an interstitial position. Their argument is different from that in their first paper[2] which stressed the direct substitution reaction of M by *M in a similar reaction system. The present authors performed a systematic study of recoil implantation reactions in various complexes of tris(β-diketonato)metal(III). The relative importance of the substitution and abstraction reactions has been determined using mixed ligand complexes of chromium in *Cr-for-Cr implantation[3]:

$$^{51}V(p,n)^{51}Cr + Cr(acac)_x(dbm)_{3-x} \rightarrow {}^{51}Cr(acac)_y(dbm)_{3-y} \tag{2}$$

where acac = acetylacetone, dbm = dibenzoylmethane, x=1 or 2, and y=1 or 2. The experimental results could not be explained by statistical abstraction of the ligands (ligand pickup) by the recoil implanted atom, and a displacement type reaction was concluded to be more important than the abstraction reaction. Though the nature and size of the ligands used in the experiments were different from those in the reaction system $^*M + MX_6^{2-}$, this seems to show an interesting tendency in the implantation reactions in the cage in which the recoil atom comes to rest.

Following the relation between the force constant ratio and the parent chemical yield in the paper of Rössler and Pross[1], recent recoil implantation study of the system

$$^*M + M(acac)_3 \rightarrow {}^*M(acac)_3 + M \tag{3}$$

has revealed some specific features[4]. In Fig.1 the parent type yield $^*M(acac)_3$ is plotted against the force constant ratio F(*M-O)/F(M-O) where *M = *Cr, *Tc and *Ru and M = Al, Co, Cr and Fe. The yield increases linearly with increase in the force constant ratio. The linear relation is believed to show competition between *M and M in the reaction cage. However there is a notable exception for the case of chromium implantation in $Co(acac)_3$. A possible explanation for this exception is the following:

$$^*Cr(0) + Co^{III}(acac)_3 \rightarrow {}^*Cr(I) + Co^{II}(acac)_2 + acac^- \tag{4}$$
$$^*Cr(I) + Co^{II}(acac)_2 \rightarrow {}^*Cr(acac)_2 \tag{5}$$
$$^*Cr(acac)_2 + acac^- \rightarrow {}^*Cr(acac)_3 \tag{6}$$

These processes include ligand loss, exchange and ligand pickup. A redox reaction is assumed in Eq.(4). Meinhold et al.[5] studied fission recoil implantation of ^{103}Ru in various metal acetylacetonates. When their parent yield of fissiogenic ruthenium is plotted against the force constant ratio in recoil implantation in $M(acac)_3$ type compounds, one can obtain a similar linear relation together with an exception in the case of the $Co(acac)_3$ catcher. Probably fissiogenic ruthenium with a positive charge $^*Ru^+$ is more reactive to $Co(acac)_3$ than the (γ, n) produced *Ru atom (possibly no positive charge) implanted in the catcher. A generalized scheme for the implantation reaction mechanism in β-diketonates is shown in Fig.2. It involves somewhat complex reaction routes induced by recoil implanted atoms. Cage reactions with competition between two metal atoms are sometimes obscured by interference of other types of reactions. Though one has to be cautious because of this complexity, implantation reactions can be described in successive steps by reasonable procedures.

Isomerization mechanisms have been studied in geometrical and optical isomers of tris-(benzoylacetonato)metal(III) $M(ba)_3$ and tris(acetylacetonato)metal(III) $M(acac)_3$ using recoil

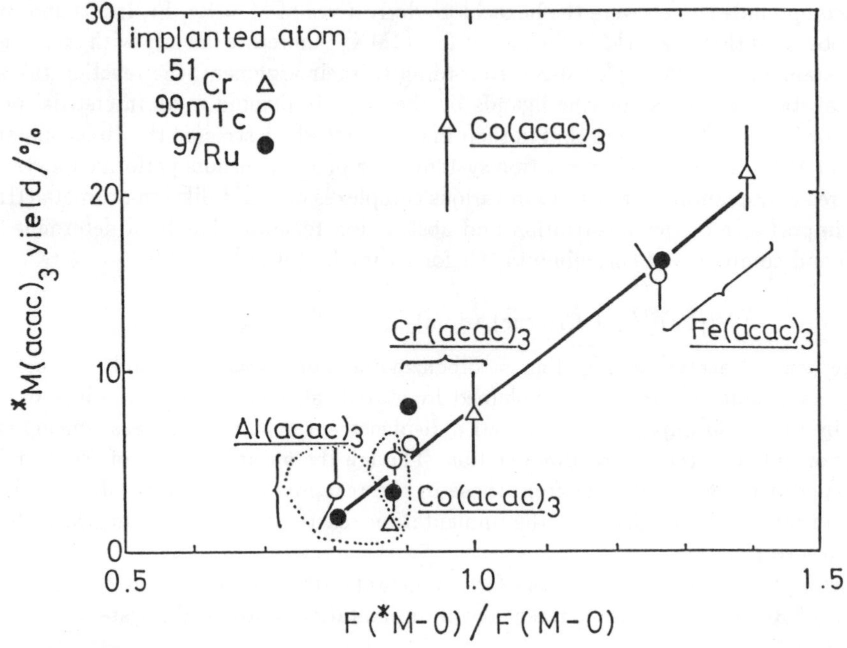

Fig. 1. The *M(acac)$_3$ yield against the force constant ratio. Implanted atoms are shown by the symbols while catcher molecules are indicated by the underlined formulae.

implantation and ordinary hot atom reaction[6]. Implantation and (n,γ) or (γ,n) reactions gave nearly the same fac/mer isomer ratios in Cr(ba)$_3$. Similarly, nearly the same Δ/Λ ratios were obtained for optical isomerization in Cr(acac)$_3$. However, the ratio Δ/Λ in Ru(acac)$_3$ with low recoil energy ^{103}Ru was small. The isomerization mechanisms have been explained on the basis of (a) a directed bond rupture model and/or (b) a caged twist model for low energy recoil atoms from the (n,γ) reaction. Similar models can be elaborated for recoil atoms with higher energy from the (n,γ) reaction, (γ,n) reaction and implantation taking into account the type of attack of the recoil atom. Fig.3 shows the scheme of isomerization mechanisms for the implantation reaction. It involves (a) an attack-induced bond rupture and (b) an attack-induced caged twist models. The both models lead to the 5/1 mer/fac ratio for mer-Cr(ba)$_3$ and the 1/1 mer/fac ratio for fac-Cr(ba)$_3$ in isomerization when the energy is sufficient. However, it should be noted that almost all the atoms undergo to a simple recombination as shown in (c) when the energy of the reacting atom is not sufficient at the lower tailing part of its energy distribution.

3. Energy dependence of implantation reaction

In addition to enhancement of the parent type yield mentioned earlier, implantation reactions are also peculiar because the yield increases with energy up to a plateau value. The saturation energy of the yield is approximately three orders of magnitude larger than in an ordinary hot atom reaction. A thin film technique was used to control the energy of the atom implanted in the catcher film. Both the source and the catcher are deposited in a film, but

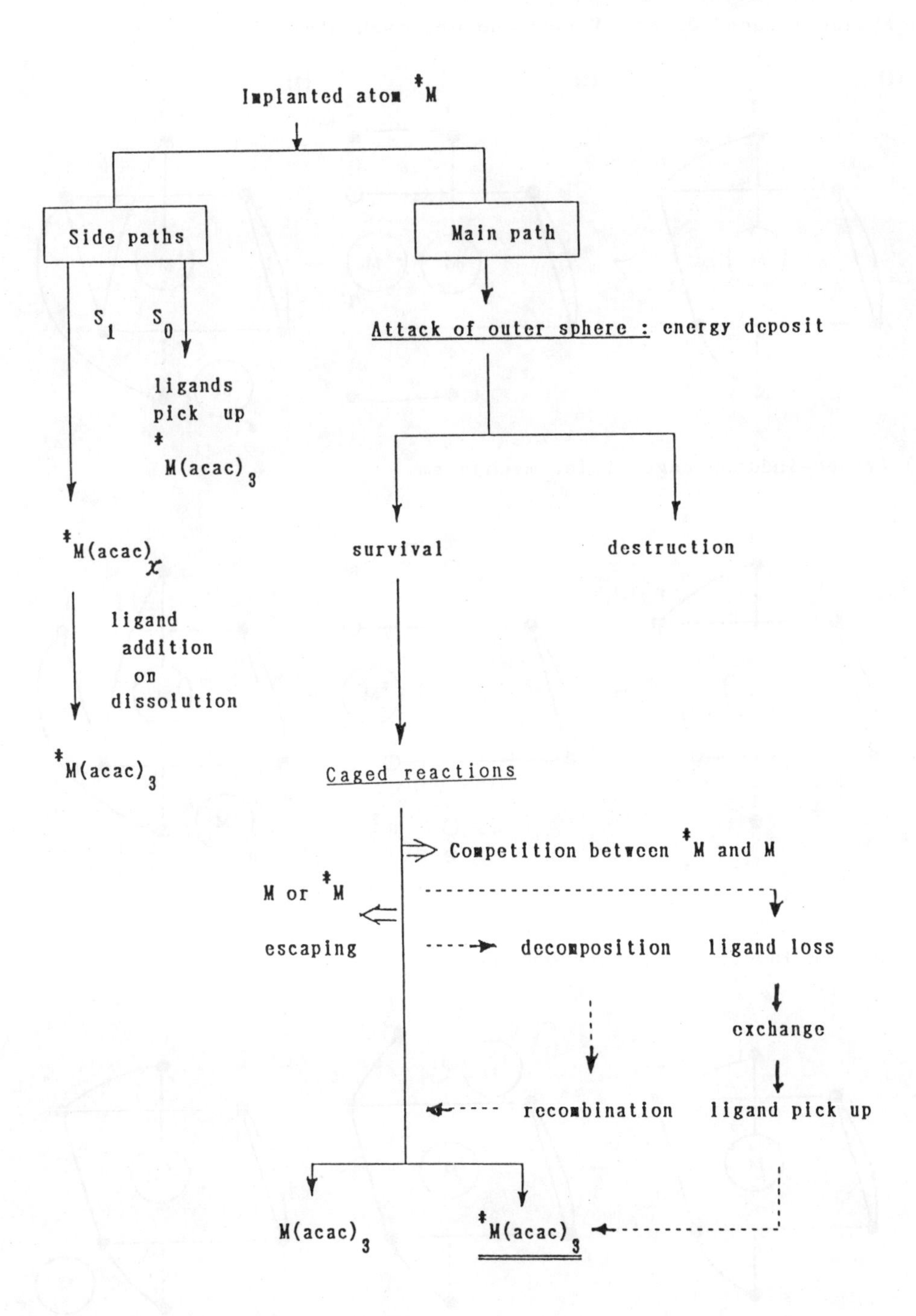

Fig. 2. Possible mechanism for $^{*}M(acac)_3$ formation by recoil implantation.

(a) Attack-induced directed bond rupture mechanism

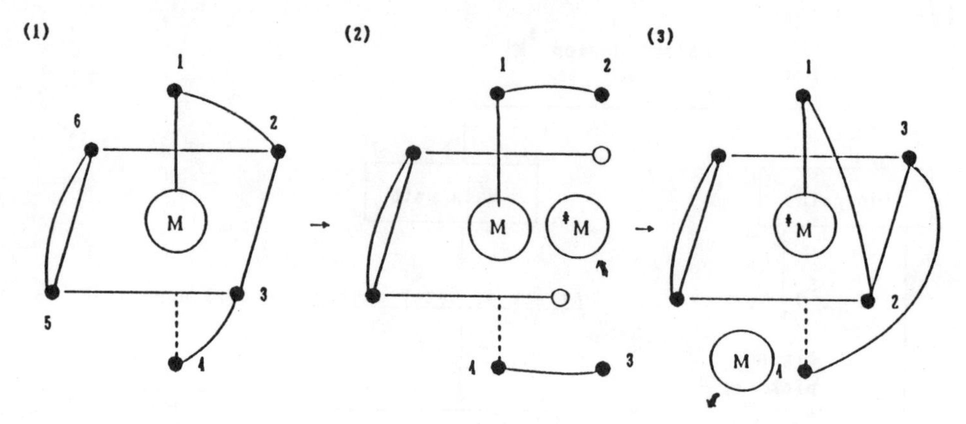

(b) Attack-induced caged twist mechanism

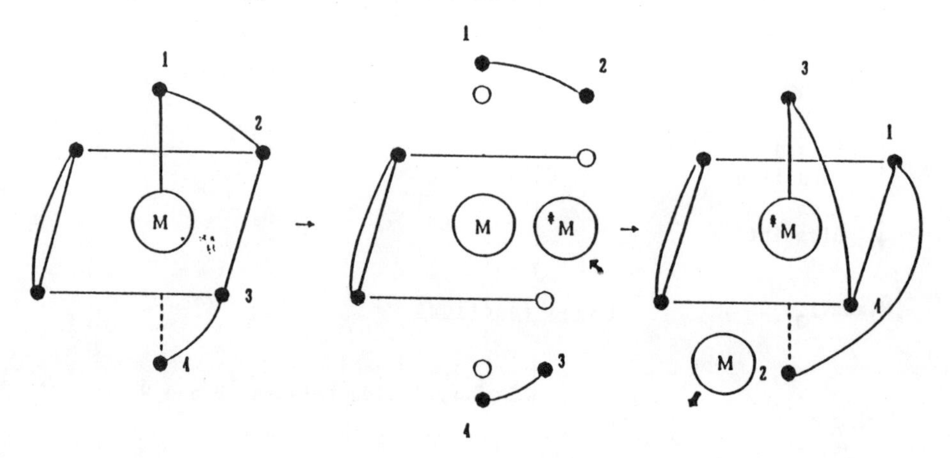

(c) Attack-induced simple recombination

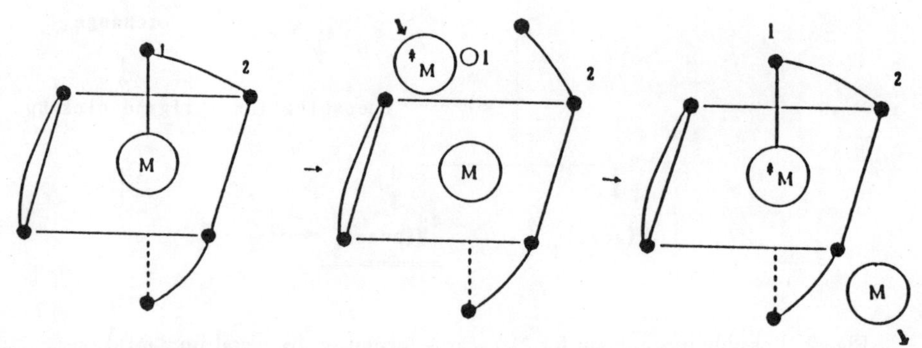

Fig. 3. Isomerization mechanisms of tris(β-diketonato)M(III) in substitution process.

the source film thickness is changed in order to vary the energy spectrum of the recoil atom. In principle, the thickness of the catcher is equivalent to an infinite thickness for the recoil implanted atom.

Fig.4 shows the energy dependence of the yield of $^{51}Cr(\beta\text{-dik})_3$ formed by implantation of ^{51}Cr recoil atoms in $Fe(acac)_3$, $Fe(dpm)_3$ and $Rh(acac)_3$[7] (Notations : β-dik = β-diketone and dpm = dipivaroylmethane). The yields are plotted against the mean implantation energy. They reach saturation at about 100 keV. The corresponding saturation value is of the order of only 200 eV in the case of a hot atom reaction inside the target [8]. The enhancement of the yield may be connected with collision processes. The meaning of the higher saturation energy is not yet clear, but it may be related to the spacial extent of the collision-induced processes. Studies to elucidate the specific features of the implantation reactions are in progress.

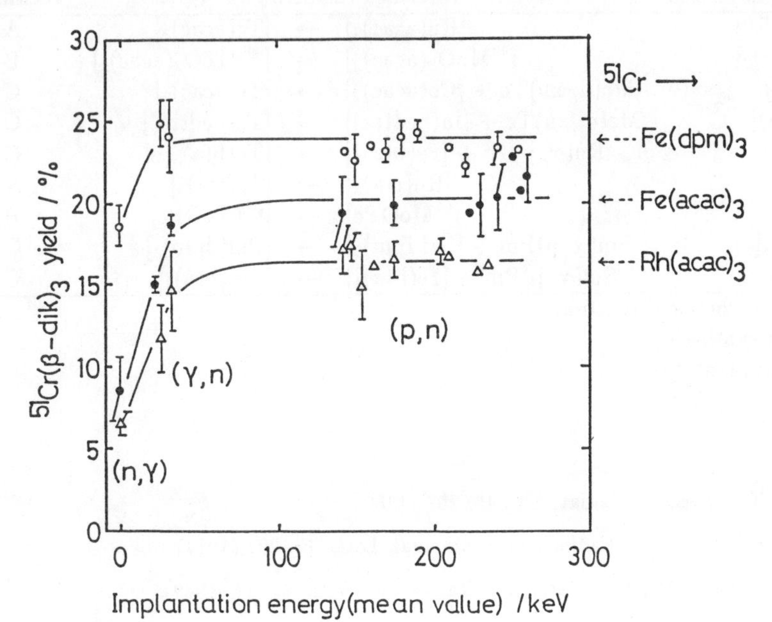

Fig. 4. Implantation energy dependence on the yield of $^{51}Cr(\beta\text{-dik})_3$

4. Chemical species synthesized with implanted atoms

Recoil implantation has been applied for the synthesis of some new chemical species. For example, in a deuteron-irradiated mixture of molybdenum and In·hedtra where hedtra = hydroxyethylendiaminetriacetic acid, the formation of Tc^{III} hedtra was confirmed [9]. A new acetylacetone complex of divalent technetium $Tc^{II}(acac)_2$, was obtained by displacement of Co from $Co(acac)_2$ with recoil implanted Tc[10]. Though the principle of fission recoil synthesis was introduced by Baumgärtner and coworkers[11] long ago, application of the recoil technique to chemical synthesis is still an interesting topic to explore. Table 1 shows a list of new substances synthesized using the recoil techniques, including implantation[12].

Apart from the synthesis induced by recoil implantation, the chemical behavior of the implanted atom which comes at rest at an interstitial position is quite interesting. In the system Mo + $Cr(acac)_3$ irradiated with deuterons, TcO_4^- and its reduced forms, as well as

$Tc(acac)_3$, were observed[13]. The former two were considered to result from the interstitial atoms implanted (1) by the Mo(d, xn)Tc reaction and (2) by the $^{98}Mo(d, p)^{99}Mo \xrightarrow{\beta^-} {}^{99m}Tc$ processes. The second route favored the formation of pertechnetate. This is believed to show the interaction of positive charge on the Tc interstitial atom with negative oxygen in the neighborhood of the implanted atom. The life time of the technetium ion is not known but the difference between the ionization potential(8.1 eV) of $Cr(acac)_3$ and that (7.3 eV) of metallic technetium suggests a considerable stability of the Tc^+ ion in such circumstances.

Table. 1. New compounds synthesized by radiochemical techniques.

Product synthesized	Nuclear processes			Technique
$[Tc(acac)_3]$	$[Ru(acac)_3]$	→	$[Tc(acac)_3]$	A
$[TcO_2(acac)_2]$	$[^{99}MoO_2(acac)_2]$	→	$[^{99m}TcO_2(acac)_2]$	B
$[Tc(acac)_2]$	Mo(d, xn)Tc + $[Co(acac)_2]$	→	$[Tc(acac)_2]$	C
[Tc(hedtra)]	Mo(d, xn)Tc + [In(hedtra)]	→	[Tc(hedtra)]	C
$[Tc(bta)_3]$	Ru(γ, p)Tc + $[Fe(bta)_3]$	→	$[Tc(bta)_3]$	C
$[Tc(tta)_3]$	$[Ru(tta)_3]$	→	$[Tc(tta)_3]$	A
[TcOPc]	$[^{99}MoOPc]$	→	$[^{99m}TcOPc]$	B
$[Pm(dpm)_3]$	Sm(γ, p)Pm + $[La(dpm)_3]$	→	$[Pm(dpm)_3]$	C
$[Pm(bta)_3]$	Sm(γ, p)Pm + $[Fe(bta)_3]$	→	$[Pm(bta)_3]$	C

A: Hot atom chemical reaction
B: β-decay synthesis
C: Recoil implantation

References

1) Rössler, K., Pross, L : Radiat. Eff., 48, 207 (1980).

2) Rössler, K., Pross, L, : Radiochem. Radioanal. Lett., 18, 291 (1974).

3) Sekine, T., Sano, M., Yoshihara, K. : Radiochim. Acta, 48, 17 (1989).

4) Sekine, T., Yoshihara, K. : "International Symposium on Advanced Nuclear Energy Research - Near-Future Chemistry in Nuclear Energy Research", Japan Atomic Energy Research Institute, Oarai, 1989, p.108.

5) Meinhold, H.,Reichold, P. : Radiochim. Acta, 11, 175 (1969).

6) Sekine, T., Yoshihara, K. : Radiochim. Acta, in press.

7) Miyakawa, A., Sekine, T., Yoshihara, K. : Radiochim. Acta, 48, 11 (1989).

8) Yoshihara, K., Kudo. H. : J. Chem. Phys., 52, 2950 (1970).

9) Yoshihara, K., Omori, T., Sekine, T., Saito, M. : Radiochim. Acta, 29, 131 (1981).

10) Sekine, T., Yoshihara, K. : Radiochim. Acta, 29, 139 (1981).

11) Baumgärtner, F., Reichold, P. : "Chemical Effects of Nuclear Transformations", vol.2, International Atomic Energy Agency, Vienna, 1961, p.319.

12) Yoshihara, K. : Sci. Rpts. Tohoku Univ. First Series LXXII, 1 (1989).

13) Sekine, T., Yoshihara, K. : Radiochim. Acta, 33, 87 (1983).

4.7 Hot Atom Chemistry of Single Crystals

G. William A. NEWTON
Chemistry Department, Manchester University, Manchester M13 9PL, U.K.

The work relevant to single crystals was reviewed up to the mid 1970's [1]. Several experiments on single crystals carried out at that time had shown the importance of impurities such as H_2O [2], OH [3,4] and O [5] etc. in determining the distribution of recoil species measured after dissolution of the solids. Several had hinted at the importance of radiation defects (electron and hole centres) in this role as [6,5], but none had proved that these were reducing or oxidising. Some [7] discarded the concept that V centres were involved in the oxidation of recoil atoms because they were "localised on ionic defects"; the same authors [6] make a positive assignment of the role of F centres.

Much of this early work was done on polar chlorides measuring ^{35}S [8] and ^{32}P [9], however other crystals were studies, for example K_2CrO_4 [10] where the crystal perfection and annealing atmosphere were considered important.

All these experiments suffered the fate of most recoil chemistry work, in that deductions were being made about solid state reactions by measuring species formed on dissolution of the solid. Changing the solvent [11] was ingenious but did not solve the problem.

Several measurements on the solid directly, using a wide range of techniques, have been made on radioactive atoms in single crystals. In general, they give information on the final position of the atom in the solid; movement, annealing and the recoil range are also considered, and only rarely are various chemical species measured.

A review of the literature reveals that since the work on polar chlorides in the early seventies there has been no further developments in this area. The recent literature on single crystals and recoils is dominated by work on elements, carbides and oxides. The properties measured are those mentioned above with the notable exception that NO chemistry of recoil species is reported. Some indication of the type of results obtained is given below.

The position of ^{73}Ge in single crystals of Ge has been measured. The ^{73}Ga parent was embedded in Ge single crystals by the reaction $^{74}Ge(\gamma,p)^{73}Ga$; ^{73}Ga decays to ^{73}Ge which has a Moessbauer transition of 13.3 keV. The authors [12] suggest that the 1.2 MeV beta recoil of ^{73}Ga "gives rise to interstitial Ge with an excited nucleus"; they describe Moessbauer spectra for free, trapped and converted insterstitials and discuss these in terms of a crystal field approach.

Interesting though this work is, it does not reveal the mechanism of the production of a range of solid state precursors for the species observed on dissolution. Moessbauer spectroscopy was used [13] to identify the position of implanted impurities in single crystals, e.g. Te in single crystals of Si, Ge and diamond. The I formed by decay of ^{129}Te was reported to be in substitutional and interstitial sites. B implanted in single crystals of Ge and Si have been shown to occupy low-symmetry non-substitutional sites by resonance depolarisation spectra [13]. Perturbed angular correlation measurements on implanted ions in single crystals of Te and Zn show the importance of radiation defects and electric field gradients [15,16]. Some of the work on implanted species in single crystals has been reviewed [17].

Nuclear resonance fluorescence of radioactive atoms embedded in single crystals of W and WSe_2 show that the recoil atoms slow down along and perpendicular to the hexagonal axis of WSe_2 [18]. Secondary Ion Mass Spectroscopy [19] has detected the residual damage in Si single crystals implanted with ^{75}As. The effect of alpha recoils on producing radiation damage in zircon single crystals has been studied by X-ray and I.R. [20]; the results suggest glass formation at very high alpha doses. An interesting result using ENDOR on single crystals of lithium acetate dihydrate indicates that at 77K the irradiation produced methyl radical is oriented very similar to the methyl group in the undamaged molecule [21]. The recoil displacement of the methyl radical along the broken C-C bond is less than 0.3 angström. Moessbauer studies [22] using oriented single crystal absorbers of SnS_2 and $SnSe_2$ have shown that the Sn atom executes a motion at 295K parallel to the S layer which is about a factor of 2 larger than motion perpendicular to this plane.

Annealing, radiation and thermal, have been fundamental in hot atom chemistry, but again nearly all measurements have been made on species formed after dissolution of the solid. NMR on F produced by $^{19}F(n,\gamma)^{20}F$ in single crystals of alkaline earth fluorides [23] generates a series of activation energies which could be related to similar results obtained by dissolution of the solids. Oscillating annealing patterns have been observed by neutron diffraction in calcium fluoride single crystals which have been related to similar results found after dissolution of a solid [24].

All the above measurements on the solid directly are concerned with anything but the chemistry of the recoils. Since the early seventies there appears to be only two such experiments: in a Moessbauer experiment on 5sp implanted impurities (^{119}In, ^{119}Cd and ^{119}Sb) in Cu, Ag and Au single crystals it would appear that thermal diffusion of O gives Sn(IV) and recoil implantation from a surface oxide layer gives a mixture of Sn(IV) and Sn(II) [25]. I.R. spectroscopy was used to study the form of stabilisation of hot atoms of tritium in poly- and single crystals of $LiAlO_2$, Li_2MoO_4 and Li_2WO_4. Two forms of tritium, OT^- and T^+ were found and the roles of impurities, rotation defect structures and surfaces were discussed [26].

An indication has been given of the range of techniques that might be used to make measurements on the solid directly. It is hoped this will stimulate researchers to invent experiments where results from the solid are compared directly with results obtained on dissolution of the solid. One example would be to measure activation energies and rate constants for different types of annealing processes; another would be to use electric field gradients on irradiated large single crystals to determine the sign and magnitude of the charge of recoil species in the solid.

There is a considerable range of interesting experiments to be done on the chemistry of recoil species in single crystals and it is hoped there will be revitalisation in this area.

References

1. Harbottle G., Maddock A.G., eds.: "Chemical Effects of Nuclear Transformations in Inorganic systems", North-Holland Publishing Company, 1979, ISBN 0-444-85054-6.
2. Ackerhalt R., Ellerbe P., Harbottle G.: Radiochimica Acta 18, 73 (1972).
3. Baptista J.L., Newton G.W.A., Robinson V.J.: Trans. Far. Soc., 64, 456 (1968).
4. Baptista J.L., Marques S.S.N.: J. Inorg. Nucl. Chem., 36, 1683 (1974).
5. Anderson, Torkild, Baptista J.L.: Trans. Far. Soc. 67, 1213 (1971).
6. Bogdanov R.V., Olevskii E.B.: Radiokhimiya, 15, 590 (1973).
7. Bogdanov R.V., Olevskii E.B., Tamonov A.A.: Khim. Vys. Energ. 3, 394 (1969).
8. Cifka J.: ref.1 p.323.
9. Newton G.W.A.: ref. 1 p.343.
10. Anderson, Torkild, Baptista J.L.: Trans. Far. Soc. 67, 1203 (1971).
11. Maddock A.G., Mahmood A.J.: Inorg. Nucl. Chem. Lett., 9, 509 (1973).
12. Matsui K., Konno O., Ishino S.: Radiation Damage and Defects in Semiconductors. Proc.Int.Conf., Meeting 1972, Inst. Phys. (1973.)
13. Hafemeister D., De Waard H.: Moessbauer Effect Methodology, 8, 151 (1973).
14. McDonald R.E., McNab T.K.: Phys. Rev. B, 13, 39 (1976).
15. Roesch Ph.L., Horber F., Seiler H.P., Kulessa R.: Int. Conf. Hyperfine Interact. Stud. Nucl. React. Decay, p.222, Stockholm, Sweden (1974) .
16. Sandner W.: INIS Atomindex, 11, Abstr. N° 497929 (1980).
17. Murnick D.E.: Angular Correlation Nucl.Disintegration, Proc. Int. Conf., Meeting 1970, Ed. Van Krugten H., Rotterdam University Press, Rotterdam, Netherlands, p. 455 (1971).
18. Treml K., Langhoff H.: Z. Phys. B, 25, 123 (1976).
19. Yen C.A.: J. Vac. Sci. Technol., 18, (1981).
20. Vance E.R.: Radiation Effects, 24, 1 (1975).
21. Toriyama K., Nunome K., Iwasaki M.: J. Chem. Phys., 64, 2020 (1976).
22. Herber R.H.: J. Phys. 40, C2, 386 (1979).
23. Buttler W., Stoeckman H.J., Fujara F., Heitjans P., Kiese G., Ackerman H., Bader K., Doerr K., Grupp H., Lauter H.: J. Phys. 41, C6, 381 (1980).
24. Dimotakis P.N.: Radiation Effects.Lett. 68, 45 (1982).
25. Andreasen H., Damgaard S., Nielsen H.L., Petersen J.W., Weyer G.: Hyperfine Interact 23, 43 (1985).
26. Kurilenko L.N., Sokolova N.P.: Zh. Fiz. Khim. 61, 3093 (1987).

4.8 Hot Atom Chemistry of Mixed Crystals and Mixed Ligand Coordination Compounds

Horst MÜLLER*,[a] and Hitoshi SHOJI**,[b]

* Institute of Inorganic and Analytical Chemistry, University of Freiburg, D-7800 Freiburg i. Br., Germany
** Department of Chemistry, University of Tsukuba, Tsukuba, Ibaraki 305, Japan

1. Introduction

The substantial progress of hot atom chemistry investigations in gases and (mostly organic) liquids is mainly caused by two features of such systems: (1) mixtures and solutions can be examined and (2) the chemical composition of the targets can be changed step-by-step. Therefore in many cases it is possible to decide unequivocally if the recoil atoms are still part of their original molecule or of a slightly modified one or if they have reacted with another molecule, may be even of the same kind. Inorganic solids usually can be investigated only as such with the result that in most cases even the above mentioned simple questions remained unanswered.

As early as 1950 a first attempt was made to overcome this inherent problem by introducing mixed crystals of simple inorganic coordination compounds as targets for hot atom chemistry research.

Three types of mixed crystals of components with simple anionic ligands may be distinguished: (1) Mixed crystals from components containing different central atoms but identical ligands, e.g. $KMnO_4$-$KClO_4$[1]; (2) mixed crystals from components containing the same central atom but different ligands, e.g. K_2ReBr_6-K_2ReCl_6[2] and (3) mixed crystals from components containing both different central atoms and ligands, e.g. (a) K_2ReBr_6-K_2SnCl_6[3] or (b) K_2CrO_4-K_2BeF_4[4]. Systems published before 1979 have been reviewed in the past.[5]

When investigating mixed crystal systems the main purpose is to determine the chemical fate of the recoil atom, which can be accomplished when it is found associated (or in other words: when it is labelled) with other atoms or atom groups as before the recoil event. Systems which in principle do not allow one to discriminate between old bonds and new ones are less promising. Since usually the activated targets are dissolved for the purpose of analytical separation the

---

[a] Part 1 - 4.2
[b] Part 4.3, 4.4

newly formed bonds should be inert against hydrolysis or any other kind of bond breaking. This restricts more promising investigations to type (2) and (3a) mixed crystal systems while type (1) and (3b) ones are of less importance. In any case, however, the advantage of such simple systems is that the damage effects following the nuclear event can be discussed mainly in the physicist's language, the disadvantage is that aspects which are regarded as characteristically chemical do fade away. Conclusions drawn from one system are not necessarily applicable to others.

In addition to systems with more simple ligands, several attempts have been made since the 1970's with the intention discussed previously but also with the purpose of a better insight into the more chemical aspects by using mixed crystals of coordination compounds with large organic ligands such as phthalocyanine, porphyrin and cyclopentadienyl.

2. Mixed Crystal Preparations

Unfortunately in most cases preparation of useful mixed crystals is very difficult or even impossible, investigations can be found in the literature where one must doubt that mixed crystals were really used because no details of their preparation and properties were presented.[6] In the work using inorganic coordination compounds with halide ligands which is reviewed here it was shown in each case (and typically published in a separate paper to which reference is made in the pertaining hot atom chemistry publication) that real mixed crystals were used. In the case of coordination compounds with large organic ligands, however, evidence was more indirect.

3. Analytical Separations

One of the mistakes very often made in hot atom chemistry investigations is concerned with the type and the number of products expected. Even when the main products may be known from earlier investigations or may be anticipated because of general chemical knowledge it is by no means obvious that only two fractions will appear. Therefore separation methods which separate only two fractions, such as liquid-liquid distribution between two phases or precipitation can be used only if it is evident that there really exist only two different species. In some reported cases this was not true and it has not been checked in almost all cases. Therefore methods should always be used which allow separation of many species without prior knowledge of their identity such as electrophoresis[7,8,9] or chromatography[10,11,12,13]. In the case of complexes with organic ligands, however, there are very often no separation or detection techniques for the presumptive recoil species with the degraded ligand.

Care must always be taken not to misinterpret radiation chemistry degradations with hot atom chemistry effects. No ligand exchange or similar reactions are permissible when hot atom chemistry phenomena are to be investigated.

4. Investigated Systems

4.1. Ligand Recoil in $K_2M'X_6$-$K_2M''Y_6$ Mixed Crystals and in $K_2MX_nY_{6-n}$ Mixed Hexahalogenometallate Coordination Compounds

4.1.1. Ligand Recoil in $K_2M'X_6$-$K_2M''Y_6$ Mixed Crystals

After neutron activation of A_2MBr_6 (A = K, NH_4, Rb; M = Re, Os, Ir, Pt) ^{80m}Br and/or ^{82}Br was found in two fractions, the yield $*Br^-$ and the retention $M*BrBr_5^{2-}$, typical results obtained were 7-12% and 88-93%, respectively.[14] The retention consists of two components, the primary retention R_{prim} and the secondary or reaction retention R_{sec}. Each of them arises from two contributions: R_{prim} from R_1 (nuclear events that fail to rupture the parent molecule) plus R_2 (nuclear events in which dissociation of the molecule is followed very quickly by reformation from the same constituent atoms or atom groups), R_{sec} from R_3 (reformation reactions involving hot atoms) plus R_4 (reformation processes involving thermalised product species which usually were not bound together before the nuclear event).[15] R_2 and R_4 are expected to be zero only at very low temperature when no chemical analysis can be done, therefore only indirect conclusions can be drawn concerning their contributions. In this review R_{prim} and R_{sec} will not be subdivided further.

R_{prim} and R_{sec} can be distinguished when using K_2ReBr_6-K_2ReCl_6 as target (# for interstitial; ---> for solid state reactions; ···> for reactions during dissolution).

Yield: $K_2ReBr_6(n,\gamma)*Br$ ---> $*Br_\#$ ···················> $*Br^-$ (1)

R_{prim}: $K_2ReBr_6(n,\gamma)K_2Re*BrBr_5$ ·····················> $Re*BrBr_5^{2-}$ (2)

R_{sec}: $K_2ReBr_6(n,\gamma)*Br_{hot}$ (3)

$*Br_{hot}$ + K_2ReBr_6 ---> $K_2Re*BrBr_5^{2-}$ + Br ···> $Re*BrBr_5^{2-}$ (4a)

$*Br_{hot}$ + K_2ReCl_6 ---> $K_2Re*BrCl_5^{2-}$ + Cl ···> $Re*BrCl_5^{2-}$ (4b)

Reactions (1) and (2) are independent of the mixed crystal composition, the billiard ball or displacement reactions (4a) and (4b), however, are not, therefore their contributions can be evaluated from an investigation of the mixed crystal system.

Six K_2ReBr_6-K_2ReCl_6 mixed crystals with K_2ReBr_6 mol fractions between 0.12 and 0.84 and pure K_2ReBr_6 were investigated for $^{81}Br(n,\gamma)^{82}Br$ recoil events, from which the following formal mathematical relations - which should not be regarded directly as describing reaction orders or the like - between the fractions of the labelled species and the mixed crystal composition were obtained ({fraction of labelled species}, [mol fraction of respective component or intermediate species in the solid]).[2] For figures when not presented in this review the reader should consult the original literature.

$$\{^{82}Br^-\} = 0.11_5 \quad (5a)$$

$$\{Re^{82}BrBr_5^{2-}\} = 0.08_5 + 0.80_5\cdot[K_2ReBr_6] \quad (6a)$$

$$\{Re^{82}BrCl_5^{2-}\} = 0.74_0 - 0.74_0\cdot[K_2ReBr_6] = 0.74_0\cdot[K_2ReCl_6] \quad (7a)$$

These results can be interpreted definitely in the following way:

yield ($\{^{82}Br^-\}$): 0.11$_5$ (11.5%)
R_{prim} ($\{Re^{82}BrBr_5^{2-}\}$): 0.08$_5$ (8.5%)
R_{sec} ($\{Re^{82}BrCl_5^{2-}\}$ + $\{Re^{82}BrBr_5^{2-}\}$ - 0.085): 0.740-0.80$_5$ (74-80.5%)

Comparing (6a) with (7a) indicates directly that a proportionality exists between $\{Re^*BrBr_5^{2-}\}$ and $[K_2ReBr_6]$ on the one side and between $\{Re^*BrCl_5^{2-}\}$ and $[K_2ReCl_6]$ on the other one with slightly differing proportionality factors; it might be concluded with some caution that a $^*Br_{hot}$ recoil atom has a slightly better chance of 0.80$_5$/0.74$_0$ = 1.09 to substitute in a hot reaction a Br ligand rather than a Cl ligand.

Only a total of 5% of other mixed labelled species $\Sigma Re^{82}BrBr_nCl_{5-n}^{2-}$ (n = 1-4) were found. The source of these will be revealed later in a detailed manner, but the most important conclusion can be drawn already from these preliminary data presented here in detail to make clear the argument: only very simple reactions occur; and there does not exist any appreciable highly disturbed, may be even melted, zone (hot spot or hot zone[16])) following the recoil event, in which the atoms are mixed thoroughly because in that case one expects that all mixed species $Re^{82}BrBr_nCl_{5-n}^{2-}$ should have been found

$$^*Br_{hot} + K_2ReCl_6/K_2ReBr_6 \longrightarrow \Sigma K_2Re^{82}BrBr_nCl_{5-n} \cdots\rightarrow \Sigma Re^{82}BrBr_nCl_{5-n}^{2-} \quad (4c)$$

following a statistical distribution

$$\{Re^{82}BrBr_nCl_{5-n}^{2-}\} = \begin{vmatrix}5\\n\end{vmatrix}\cdot[K_2ReBr_6]^n\cdot[K_2SnCl_6]^{5-n} \quad (n = 0\text{-}5) \quad (8)$$

but instead only a slightly disordered zone - characterised by few vacancies, interstitials, displacements, replacements, focussons, and crowdions - which led to the designation "disorder model" for such behaviour.[9,17)] The disorder model is the chemical analogue of the physical model of radiation damage as was developed for crystalline solids, especially metals.[18,19,20)]

These conclusions were supported by an independent investigation[21,22)] resulting in only slightly different results (as usual in hot atom chemistry investigations, mainly due to the different irradiation conditions):

$$\{^{82}Br^-\} = 0.25 - 0.05\cdot[K_2ReBr_6] \quad (5b)$$
$$\{Re^{82}BrBr_5^{2-}\} = 0.14 + 0.66\cdot[K_2ReBr_6] \quad (6b)$$
$$\{Re^{82}BrCl_5^{2-}\} = 0.61 - 0.61\cdot[K_2ReBr_6] = 0.61\cdot[K_2ReCl_6] \quad (7b)$$

and

yield ($\{^{82}Br^-\}$): 0.20-0.25 (20-25%)
R_{prim} ($\{Re^{82}BrBr_5^{2-}\}$): 0.14 (14%)
R_{sec} ($\{Re^{82}BrCl_5^{2-}\}$ + $\{Re^{82}BrBr_5^{2-}\}$ - 0.085): 0.61-0.66 (61-66%)

In this case the preference for Br substitution compared with Cl substitution is 0.66/0.61 = 1.08.

The type and quantity of the different labelled products should be dependent upon the recoil energy of the halide ligand. Decreasing it should result in an increase of the primary retention $Re^{*}BrBr_5^{2-}$ at the expense of the yield of $^{82}Br^-$ and the secondary retention, especially significant in a decrease of $Re^{82}BrCl_5^{2-}$ in mixed crystals with low K_2ReBr_6 content. For this purpose the chemical effects of the ^{80m}Br-^{80g}Br isomeric transition were investigated in six $K_2Re^{80m}BrBr_5$-K_2SnCl_6 mixed crystals with 11-85 mol fraction K_2ReBr_6, prepared by isotope exchange between $ReBr_6^{2-}$ and $^{80m}Br^-$, in any case no bond breaking occurred: the $K_2Re^{80g}BrBr_5$ retention, measurable because ^{80g}Br is radioactive, amounted to 100^{+0}_{-5}%.[23] A rough calculation of the recoil energy resulting from the inner Coulomb repulsion as a consequence of the Auger vacancy cascade resulted in 9-25 eV which is expected to be insufficient for any displacement in an ionic solid. The results therefore are in very good accordance with physical models, see also Ref. 28. In these salts of bromometallates it is known that isomeric transition does not lead to chemical effects so that intermediate transitions such as $^{82m}Br \dashrightarrow ^{82g}Br$ are not considered to influence the experimental results in the work reported here.

Increasing the recoil energy of the Br ligand should result in more mixed species of the type $Re^{*}BrBr_nCl_{5-n}^{2-}$ (n = 1-4). This implication was tested by using nuclear reactions producing recoil atoms with higher recoil energy than ^{82}Br (maximum and mean recoil energy 374 and 100 eV, respectively): ^{38}Cl (528 and 294 ev, respectively), and ^{36}Cl (1096 and 650 eV, respectively). The following (extrapolated) experimental results were obtained for mixed crystals with vanishing concentration of the Szilard-Chalmers component: K_2OsBr_6-$K_2SnCl_6(n,\gamma)^{82}Br$[24]: 7.9% $Os^{82}BrBr_5^{2-}$, 3.4% $\Sigma Os^{82}BrBr_nCl_{5-n}^{2-}$ (n = 1-4), 88.7% $^{82}Br^-$. - K_2OsCl_6-$K_2OsBr_6(n,\gamma)^{38}Cl$[25]: 5.4% $Os^{38}ClCl_5^{2-}$, 1.1% $\Sigma Os^{38}ClCl_nBr_{5-n}^{2-}$ (n = 1-4), 81.0% $Os^{38}ClBr_5^{2-}$, 12.4% $^{38}Cl^-$. - K_2ReCl_6-$K_2ReBr_6(n,\gamma)^{36}Cl$[11]: 5.7% $Re^{36}ClCl_5^{2-}$, 11.4% $\Sigma Re^{36}ClCl_nBr_{5-n}^{2-}$ (n = 1-4), 60.0% $Re^{36}ClBr_5^{2-}$, 22.9% $^{36}Cl^-$. - K_2ReBr_6-$K_2ReCl_6(\gamma,2n)^{77}Br$[5,26]: 3-5% $Re^{77}BrBr_5^{2-}$, 32-35% $\Sigma Re^{77}BrBr_nCl_{5-n}^{2-}$ (n = 1-4), 44-49% $Re^{77}BrCl_5^{2-}$, 16% $^{77}Br^-$. While the proportions of the more extensively mixed species for ^{82}Br and ^{38}Cl atoms, with their similar recoil energies do not differ significantly their contribution is higher in the ^{36}Cl case and much higher for ^{77}Br recoil atoms from the nuclear reaction $^{79}Br(\gamma,2n)^{77}Br$ in K_2ReBr_6-K_2ReCl_6 mixed crystals which have an estimated recoil energy of 1-10 keV. The proportions of the more extensively mixed species reach a maximum of 12%, 13%, 30%, and ca. 50%, respectively, for these mixed crystals with a 50:50 composition.

The simple model discussed so far does not account for the occurrence of these more extensively mixed species $M^{*}BrBr_nCl_{5-n}^{2-}$ (M = Re, Os; n = 1-4) the production of which during the recoil event became obvious when better methods of separation were used than employed in the first experiments.

A model can be developed by discussing the results of the $^{81}Br(n,\gamma)^{82}Br$ nuclear reaction in K_2OsBr_6-K_2SnCl_6 mixed crystals[24]. In this case the following relations between the fractions of the main labelled species and the mixed crystal composition were obtained:

$\{^{82}Br^-\} = 0.88_7 - 0.82_3 \cdot [K_2OsBr_6]$ (9)

$\{Os^{82}BrBr_5^{2-}\} = 0.07_9 + 0.57_9 \cdot [K_2OsBr_6] + 0.21_6 \cdot [K_2OsBr_6]^2$ (10)

$\{Os^{82}BrBr_4Cl^{2-}\} = 0.01_7 + 0.26_2 \cdot [K_2OsBr_6] - 0.27_1 \cdot [K_2OsBr_6]^2$ (11)

$\{Os^{82}BrBr_3Cl_2^{2-}\} = 0.00_4 + 0.05_4 \cdot [K_2OsBr_6] - 0.05_1 \cdot [K_2OsBr_6]^2$ (12)

The central point of the model is the production of transient ligand vacancy complex anions $MX_n\Box_{6-n}^{2-}$ (MX = OsBr, SnCl; $\Box$ = ligand vacancy) as were discussed by Rössler and Pross[27] and earlier by Bell et al.[21] and Rössler et al.[22] for the single vacancy complex $MX_5\Box^{2-}$. (Only for simplicity it is assumed that the charge of the ligand vacancy complex anions is 2-, the halogens occupying the vacancies therefore must be formulated as being Cl or Br atoms and not ions.)

In order to perform more rigorous mathematical calculations on the experimental results a more formal description of the solid state reactions induced by recoil halide atoms was needed. This model is called "Impact-induced MUltiple Ligand Abstraction" (IMULA) and concerns the reactions of halide recoil atoms at the end of their trajectory.

Reactions of the recoil halide within its original complex anion are designated as $L_s(n)$: L for ligand, s for self, n is defined as the sum of substitutions (^{82}Br substitutes Br) which is zero or one, plus the number of transient ligand vacancies which can be occupied by halide atoms from the adjacent lattice which is between zero and five. $L_s(0)$ (no substitution, no vacancy) stands for primary retention, $L_s(1)$ (one substitution, but no vacancy available for occupation by halides from other MX_6^{2-} anions) for ligand-change (which also contributes to the primary retention). No experimental method so far available can distinguish between $L_s(0)$ and $L_s(1)$. $L_s(2)$ characterises self-substitution: a ^{82}Br recoil atom ejects another Br ligand of the same complex anion taking its site and leaving one vacancy. In the $L_s(3)$ process $Os^{82}BrBr_3\Box_2^{2-}$ is obtained as transient species when still a second Br ligand is pushed away from the complex anion. These processes are regarded responsible for the production of the more extensively mixed species in mixed crystals with vanishing content of the Szilard-Chalmers component as mentioned earlier.

^{82}Br recoil atoms not being trapped as interstitials or not being involved in $L_s(n)$ processes will react with foreign $OsBr_6^{2-}$ or $SnCl_6^{2-}$ complex anions in $L_f(n)$ processes (f for foreign, n defined as before). In $L_f(n)$ processes there is always exactly one substitution. Because the $L_f(1)$ (billiard ball or displacement) reactions

$$OsBr_6^{2-} + {}^{82}Br \longrightarrow Os^{82}BrBr_5^{2-} + Br \quad (13)$$

$$SnCl_6^{2-} + {}^{82}Br \longrightarrow Sn^{82}BrCl_5^{2-} + Cl \quad (14)$$

are the most important $L_f(n)$ reactions the $Os^{82}BrBr_5^{2-}$ portion should increase and the $^{82}Br^-$ yield (mainly from hydrolysis of $Sn^{82}BrCl_5^{2-}$) should decrease with increasing K_2OsBr_6 concentration which was, indeed, observed. $Os^{82}BrBr_4Cl^{2-}$ from the $L_s(2)$ reaction of which 1.7% is found in mixed crystals with vanishing K_2OsBr_6 content, however, should decrease because the ligand vacancy of the transient species $Os^{82}BrBr_4\Box^{2-}$ is expected to be populated more and more by Br instead of Cl in mixed crystals with increasing K_2OsBr_6 content producing

$Os^{82}BrBr_5^{2-}$ instead of $Os^{82}BrBr_4Cl^{2-}$, but on the contrary it increases up to 8% for a 50:50 mixed crystal followed by a decrease to (an extrapolated) zero for pure K_2OsBr_6. This result can be explained easily by a $L_f(2)$ process at $OsBr_6^{2-}$

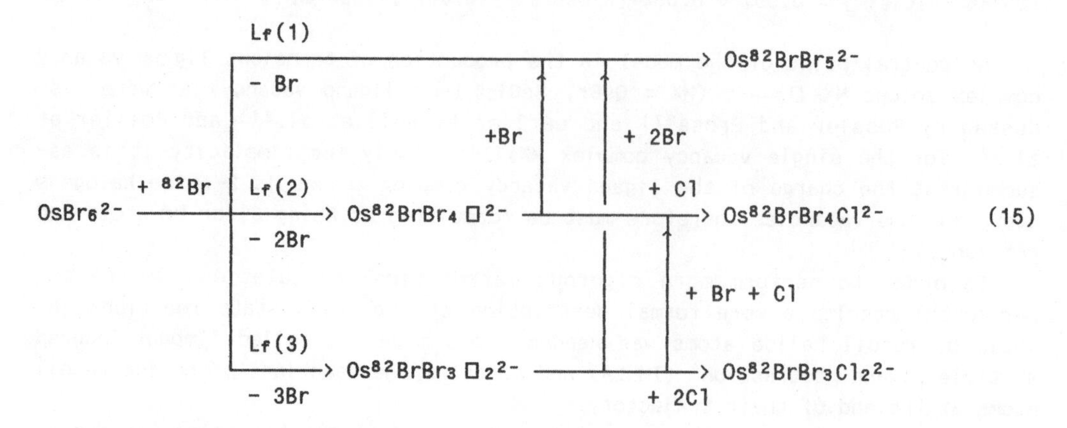

which produces additional $Os^{82}BrBr_4\square^{2-}$ by an impact in which a ^{82}Br substitutes one Br ligand but transfers so much energy that a further ligand is lost. The vacancy may now be populated by halides from the lattice following scheme (15) which includes the $L_f(3)$ process, too. A corresponding reaction scheme exists for the Sn complex anions, but all these reaction products hydrolyse with formation of $^{82}Br^-$ and cannot be observed. The yield of $L_f(2)$ produced $Os^{82}BrBr_4Cl^{2-}$ is expected to be proportional to the concentration of $Os^{82}BrBr_4\square^{2-}$ and the concentration of Cl^-

$$[Os^{82}BrBr_4Cl^{2-}] \approx [Os^{82}BrBr_4\square^{2-}][Cl^-] \qquad (16)$$

Substituting

$$[Os^{82}BrBr_4\square^{2-}] \approx [K_2OsBr_6] \qquad (17)$$
$$[Cl^-] \approx [K_2SnCl_6] = 1 - [K_2OsBr_6] \qquad (18)$$

we obtain

$$\{Os^{82}BrBr_4Cl^{2-}\} \approx [K_2OsBr_6]\cdot(1 - [K_2OsBr_6]) \qquad (19)$$

which reaches its maximum at $[K_2OsBr_6] = 0.5$ as observed.

The correlation between terms usually used in solid state hot atom chemistry and the new nomenclature is presented in table 1.

While the contributions of the different $L_s(n)$ reactions can be derived without difficulty from the results for the most dilute mixed crystals this cannot be done for the $L_f(n)$ processes if $n > 2$ because most species are the result of more than one reaction, see (15). A program PRIMULA was developed which allows the calculation of the contributions of all possible $Os^{82}BrBr_nCl_{5-n}^{2-}$ and $Sn^{82}BrBr_nCl_{5-n}^{2-}$ species.[24] The program starts with assumed initial $L_s(n)$ and $L_f(n)$ contributions. Now the vacancies of the transient species are thought to

Table 1. Relations between conventional and formal IMULA designations for ^{82}Br recoil reactions in K_2OsBr_6 including the assumed transient ligand vacancy complexes. For explanation of s, f, n see text.

n	transient ligand vacancy complex	$L_s(n)$	$L_f(n)$
0	none	primary retention	indefinite
1	none	ligand-change	billiard ball substitution
2	$Os^{82}BrBr_4\square^{2-}$	self-substitution	–
3	$Os^{82}BrBr_3\square_2^{2-}$	–	–
4	$Os^{82}BrBr_2\square_3^{2-}$	–	–
5	$Os^{82}BrBr\square_4^{2-}$	–	–
6	$Os^{82}Br\square_5^{2-}$	hot spot, (statistical distribution, see Eq. (8))	

be populated by halides from the surrounding lattice according to their concentration in the particular mixed crystal. The contributions from all $L_s(n)$ and $L_f(n)$ processes are summarised for each reaction product. The contributions of all $Sn^{82}BrBr_nCl_{5-n}^{2-}$ species are summed in order to obtain the free $^{82}Br^-$ yield resulting from the hydrolysis of these species. The calculated and experimental results are compared and in the next loop $L_s(n)$ and $L_f(n)$ values are varied in such a way that experimental and calculated results converge.

The program contains 15 parameters available for variation: $L_s(0,1)...L_s(6)$, $L_f(1)...L_f(6)$, the number N of "quasi-free" ligands in the reaction zone available for populating the vacancies which includes those which have become free during formation of $Os^{82}BrX_n\square_{5-n}^{2-}$ transient species, a complex discrimination factor D_c which simulates for $L_f(n)$ processes a preferred ($D_c > 1$) or a diminished ($D_c < 1$) reaction probability of the recoil ^{82}Br atom with $OsBr_6^{2-}$, and a ligand discrimination factor D_L which simulates for $L_s(n)$ and $L_f(n)$ processes a preferred ($D_L > 1$) or diminished ($D_L < 1$) reaction probability of $M^{82}BrX_n\square_{5-n}^{2-}$ transient species with Br in the reaction zone.

It might be suspected that any experimental result can be simulated with 15 free parameters but strong restrictions exist for most of them. The contributions of all $L_s(n)$ processes are derived directly from the experiments with only a small error and are not free for variation. The almost vanishing contributions of $Os^{82}BrBr_nCl_{5-n}^{2-}$ (n = 0,1,2) in mixed crystals with considerable K_2OsBr_6 content show that $L_f(4)...L_f(6)$ processes are of minor importance. (Moreover, for each of the $L_f(n)$ contributions an upper limit can be calculated which cannot be exceeded because this would lead for at least one $Os^{82}BrBr_nCl_{5-n}^{2-}$ species to a calculated contribution greater than the respective experimental one.) The small yield of $Os^{82}BrBr_3Cl_2^{2-}$ reflects an only small contribution of $L_f(3)$ of roughly 10% or less. This leaves only $L_f(1)$ and $L_f(2)$ as essential variants. Variation of N (when $N > 20$), D_c (ca. 1) and D_L (ca. 1) has little influence upon the result.

The results of the calculation for the K_2OsBr_6-$K_2SnCl_6(n,\gamma)^{82}Br$ system[24] are presented together with those for K_2OsCl_6-$K_2OsBr_6(n,\gamma)^{38}Cl$ experiments[25] in table 2.

Table 2. Calculated parameters and reaction channels for the IMULA model

	Dc	*X %	Ls(0,1) %	Ls(2) %	Lf(1) %	Lf(2) %	Lf(3,4,5,6) %
K_2OsBr_6-$K_2SnCl_6(n,\gamma)^{82}Br$	1.04	7.1	7.9	1.7	52.5	22.0	8.0
K_2OsCl_6-$K_2OsBr_6(n,\gamma)^{38}Cl$	1.30	11.4	5.4	0	62.0	14.0	7.0

A K_2ReCl_6-$K_2ReBr_6(n,\gamma)^{36}Cl$ investigation by the Jülich group[22] gave results very different from all other systems discussed here, especially for K_2ReBr_6 rich mixed crystals. This led them to another interpretation called "kinetic theory" the main attributes of which are that ligand vacancies when generated are not fixed but may diffuse to other complex anions and that the impact of ^{38}Cl recoil atoms with $ReBr_6^{2-}$ complex ions does not result in the production of $ReBr_5\square^{2-}$ ligand vacancy complexes or direct substitution to $Re^{38}ClBr_5^{2-}$, instead they end with a 95% probability as free $^{36}Cl^-$ ions. The experiments were repeated in the K_2ReBr_6 rich mixed crystals region with results which coincided with those of all other systems.[25] This author therefore believes that only in this special case the experimental results of the Jülich group are erroneous and the conclusions are unfounded.

Computer calculations of collision dynamics applied to hot atom chemistry were performed for pure K_2ReX_6 (X = Cl, Br) as well as for infinitely dilute K_2ReBr_6-K_2ReCl_6 mixed crystals.[20,28] The median vector ranges of Cl recoils in K_2ReBr_6 and of Br recoils in K_2ReCl_6 (1000-1500 pm) are slightly greater than those in the respective parent substances. This reflects the fact that the energy transfer Cl/Br amounts at most to 85% in a single collision, so that the number of collisions is enlarged compared with the pure substances and hence the recoils travel farther. Apparently 50% of the primary recoils make direct replacement collisions ($L_f(1)$), compare the experimental figures in table 2. The agreement of the experimental with the calculated results for the primary retention (2-12%) and the yield of the free halide (6-14%) is good for all investigated systems with the only exception of the $^{36}Cl^-$ yield in K_2ReBr_6 as found by the Jülich group (95%)[22] but not by the Freiburg group (10-14%)[25]. It must be mentioned, however, that the recombination radius of 800 pm (that means the maximum distance within which a ligand vacancy and a recoil atom recombine to a complex anion) was not calculated but was deduced from a comparison of the experimental free halide yield with the recoil range distributions, and that a (rather small) displacement threshold of 5 eV was assumed.

4.1.2. Ligand Recoil in $K_2MX_nY_{6-n}$ Mixed Hexahalogenometallate Coordination Compounds

Mixed potassium hexabromochloro-metallates(IV), $K_2MBr_nCl_{6-n}$, (M = Re, Os) may be used to check the IMULA model.[29] Different nuclides were produced by the nuclear reactions $^{81}Br(n,\gamma)^{82}Br$, $^{79}Br(n,\gamma)^{80m}Br$, $^{37}Cl(n,\gamma)^{38}Cl$ and $^{35}Cl(n,\gamma)^{36}Cl$ in order to see if the the experimental results depend upon the nature and the energy of the recoil atom (and, of course, the central metal atom).

Table 3. Calculated reaction channels*[1] (in %) in mixed potassium hexabromochloro-metallates(IV) according to IMULA model.[29)]

	*X	$L_s(0)$	$L_f(1)$	$L_f(2)$	$L_f(3)$	$L_f(2,3)$
$K_2ReBr_nCl_{6-n}(n,\gamma)^{82}Br$	13.5	16	42	11	16	27
$K_2ReBr_nCl_{6-n}(n,\gamma)^{82}Br$[30)]	16.6	16	40	0	25	25
$K_2OsBr_nCl_{6-n}(n,\gamma)^{82}Br$[31)]	9.0	12	<61	?	?	>16
$K_2ReBr_nCl_{6-n}(n,\gamma)^{80m}Br$	16	18	42	25	0	25
$K_2OsBr_nCl_{6-n}(n,\gamma)^{80m}Br$	19	11	47	23	0	23
$K_2ReCl_nBr_{6-n}(n,\gamma)^{38}Cl$	11.8	7	50	19	11	30
$K_2OsCl_nBr_{6-n}(n,\gamma)^{38}Cl$	20.3	4	49	1	26	27

*[1] Estimated errors: $L_s(0)$ 3%; $L_f(1)$ 5%; $L_f(2)$ 4%; $L_f(3)$ 4%; $L_f(2,3)$ 5%.

The results of the evaluation of the reaction channels are shown in table 3. The correspondence between experimental and calculated results is rather good. The summarised results are: No difference exists for Re and Os target atoms. Differences in the values for $L_f(2)$ and $L_f(3)$ for ^{80m}Br, ^{82}Br and ^{38}Cl recoil atoms should not be taken too seriously, very probably the sum of $L_f(2)$ and $L_f(3)$ is more characteristic. The slightly differing results for ^{38}Cl in comparison with ^{82}Br and ^{80m}Br may be due to the larger recoil energy of ^{38}Cl, the effect is, however, rather small. Compared with the mixed crystal results (see table 2) the contribution of $L_s(0)$ is greater and the contribution of $L_f(2,3)$ is smaller. This may be due to the fact that in the hexabromochloro complexes Br and Cl are more homogeneously mixed than in the mixed crystals with their Cl_6 and Br_6 clusters. The experiments did not - as was also the case for the mixed crystal experiments[24,25] - give any indication that Cl and Br recoil atoms behave distinctly differently because of their different masses. - It was not possible, however, to discuss the experimental results of the $K_2ReBr_nCl_{6-n}(n,\gamma)$ ^{36}Cl nuclear process by application of the IMULA model. The distribution of the products is even flatter than predicted by any mixture of $L_s(0)$, $L_f(1)$ and $L_f(6)$ processes. In the $K_2OsBr_nCl_{6-n}(n,\gamma)^{82}Br$ case only an upper limit for $L_f(1)$ and a lower limit for $L_f(2,3)$ can be deduced.[31)]

4.2. Central Metal Atom Recoil in $K_2M'X_6$-$K_2M''Y_6$ Mixed Crystals and in $K_2MX_nY_{6-n}$ Mixed Hexahalogenometallate Coordination Compounds

4.2.1. Central Metal Atom Recoil in $K_2M'X_6$-$K_2M''Y_6$ Mixed Crystals[9)]

The mixed crystal systems discussed so far have the advantage that, besides the recoil behaviour of the central atoms, the recoil behaviour of the ligands can also be examined. Therefore they represent one of the rare cases in hot atom chemistry where two elements may be investigated in the same compound.

The models concerning the mechanisms of chemical reactions following the production of recoil atoms can be studied also by an investigation of the fate of the central atoms as will be demonstrated for the $^{185}Re(n,\gamma)^{186}Re$ nuclear reaction in K_2ReBr_6-K_2SnCl_6 mixed crystals. As in the case of the ^{82}Br recoil different species are expected for the different reaction channels:

Yield: $K_2ReBr_6(n,\gamma)^{186}Re \dashrightarrow {}^{186}Re^* \cdots\cdots> {}^{186}ReO_4^-$ (20)

R_{prim}: $K_2ReBr_6(n,\gamma)K_2{}^{186}ReBr_6 \cdots\cdots> {}^{186}ReBr_6^{2-}$ (21)

R_{sec}: $K_2ReBr_6(n,\gamma)^{186}Re_{hot}$ (22)

$^{186}Re_{hot} + K_2ReBr_6 \dashrightarrow K_2{}^{186}ReBr_6 + Re \cdots> {}^{186}ReBr_6^{2-}$ (23a)

$^{186}Re_{hot} + K_2SnCl_6 \dashrightarrow K_2{}^{186}ReCl_6 + Sn \cdots> {}^{186}ReCl_6^{2-}$ (23b)

$^{186}Re_{hot} + K_2ReBr_6/K_2SnCl_6 \dashrightarrow$
$\Sigma K_2{}^{186}ReBrBr_nCl_{5-n} + ??? \cdots> \Sigma^{186}ReBrBr_nCl_{5-n}{}^{2-}$ (23c)

At first the results for the K_2ReBr_6-$K_2SnCl_6(n,\gamma)^{186}Re$ investigation and similar ones are very difficult to understand. All mixed species are found even for mixed crystals with a very small proportion of the Szilard-Chalmers component. (With increasing concentration of the Br containing Szilard-Chalmers component the contribution of $^*MBr_6^{2-}$ increases and that of $^*MCl_6^{2-}$ decreases significantly while the contributions of the other more extensively mixed species decrease slightly. In the K_2ReCl_6-K_2SnBr_6 system, however, $^{186}ReCl_6^{2-}$ increases and $^{186}ReBr_6^{2-}$ decreases.) The extrapolated results are shown in table 4. Even for the most dilute mixed crystals a distinct enrichment of the bromide containing species is found for the first three systems and of the chloride containing species for K_2ReCl_6-K_2SnBr_6. Such an enrichment can only be understood if it is assumed that the recoil range and the reaction zone are both very small and that the reaction zone contains still the six ligands which were originally coordinated to the recoil metal atom. The content of the reaction zone can be calculated from the proportions of the different labelled species. Cl and Br have almost the same chance for re-combination with the recoil metal atom, which was proven by the fact that in K_2ReBr_6-K_2SnCl_6 an enrichment of Br was found but in K_2ReCl_6-K_2SnBr_6 an enrichment of Cl. Making use of the fact that the lattice parameters of the mixed crystals belonging to the cubic K_2PtCl_6 type are of the order of 1000 pm and that the unit cell contains 24 halide ligands the size of the reaction zone - assumed that it is a sphere - can be calculated easily, its radius of ca. 500 pm may be taken also as recoil range which is reasonable for a maximum recoil energy of 100 eV. All these results are also presented in table 4. A schematic portrayal of the entire behaviour has been published.[5,35,36] Similar results have been obtained for $^{191}Ir(n,\gamma)^{192}Ir$ recoil atoms in K_2IrBr_6-K_2PtCl_6 mixed crystals.[37]

It may be suspected that the experimental results can be accounted for by a mini hot spot (of only 10% the size that was calculated for the hot spot model[16]) that means that recombination reactions occur statistically in the calculated small reaction zone containing the six originally coordinated ligands and 5...14 of the other kind homogeneously mixed. The expected reaction probabilities are calculated for a reaction zone containing 6 (original) and 10 (other) halide ions following

$$\{^*MBr_nCl_{6-n}{}^{2-}\} = \left|\begin{matrix}6\\n\end{matrix}\right| \cdot [K_2ReBr_6]^n \cdot [K_2SnCl_6]^{6-n} \quad (n = 0\text{-}6) \qquad (24)$$

and shown for comparison in the last column of table 4, for a figure see Ref. 17. It follows that a mini hot spot reaction should not be considered. Instead in agreement with the collision dynamics model[27] it is assumed that central

Table 4. Labelled species (in %) following M(n,γ)*M in $K_2M'X_6$-$K_2M''Y_6$ (M = Re, Os, Sn; X = Cl, Br) mixed crystals and enrichment of the originally coordinated ligand (in %), volume and number of halides in the reaction zone for mixed crystals with vanishing Szilard-Chalmers component.

Ref.:	17	34	33	32	17		
	K_2ReBr_6-K_2SnCl_6 $(n,\gamma)^{186}Re$		K_2ReBr_6-K_2OsCl_6 $(n,\gamma)^{186}Re$	K_2OsBr_6-K_2SnCl_6 $(n,\gamma)^{191}Os$	K_2ReCl_6-K_2SnBr_6*1 $(n,\gamma)^{186}Re$		R_{sec} stat.*2 calc
$^*MO_4^-$	10.2	1.8	35.6(!)	-		8.4	10.0*6
$^*MBr_6^{2-}$	12.7	6.1	13.6	13.0	$^*MCl_6^{2-}$	18.2	0.3
$^*MBr_5Cl^{2-}$	6.6	9.5	5.0	9.5	$^*MBrCl_5^{2-}$	11.0	2.5
$^*MBr_4Cl_2^{2-}$	6.4	6.5	7.8	8.8	$^*MBr_2Cl_4^{2-}$	9.2	10.4
$^*MBr_3Cl_3^{2-}$	7.7	8.9	12.0	10.4	$^*MBr_3Cl_3^{2-}$	9.2	23.1
$^*MBr_2Cl_4^{2-}$	11.6	11.0	12.8	14.8	$^*MBr_4Cl_2^{2-}$	10.0	29.0
$^*MBrCl_5^{2-}$	13.5	20.8	11.7	19.2	$^*MBr_5Cl^{2-}$	12.6	19.4
$^*MCl_6^{2-}$	32.0	35.3	3.6	26.0	$^*MBr_6^{2-}$	21.3	5.4
Br*3	36	30	55	40	Cl*3	48	37.5
Σ halide*4	17	20	11	15		13	16
Volume*5	690	820	430	620		640	670*7

*1 K_2ReCl_6(2.3 mol%)-K_2SnBr_6
*2 statistical distribution of labelled $^*MBr_nCl_{6-n}^{2-}$ products obeying Eq. (24)
*3 respective proportion (in %) in the recoil labelled species, normalised for 100% labelled mixed species
*4 Number of halides (Br, Cl) in the reaction zone
*5 Volume of reaction zone in pm^3 *6 estimated *7 for 24 halides/1000 pm^3

metal recoil atoms jump at adjacent empty lattice sites preferably at ½,0,0 and ½,½,½, respectively, followed by re-coordination of six adjacent ligands. A schematic portrayal of this behaviour has been published.[27,36] Displacement (billiard ball) reactions (table 4, line 8) are considered unimportant because of only 3.6% $^{186}ReCl_6^{2-}$ product in the K_2ReBr_6-K_2OsCl_6 reaction, it may be even smaller because the calculated recoil range of 500 pm is smaller than the smallest distance of 700 pm between two metal atoms in the investigated mixed crystals. The primary retention (table 4, line 2) cannot be more than 18%, but may be even smaller. Computer calculations are in accord with these results, the recoil range, however, was found to be larger, 1500 pm.[20,28]

The distribution of the different mixed hexabromochloro complexes is expected to be distinctly influenced by changing the distance between the complex anions in the irradiated substance. Using $Na_2IrCl_6\cdot6H_2O$-$Na_2PtBr_6\cdot6H_2O$(1:10) mixed crystals only 5% $^{192}IrCl_6^{2-}$ were found. No mixed forms have been observed in this system because of the greater distance between the $IrCl_6^{2-}$ and $PtBr_6^{2-}$ ions.[37] In a similar way it is expected that an increase of the atomic mass of the central atoms and/or the ligands of the non Szilard-Chalmers component should result in a decrease in the size of the reaction zone. This was (see table 4) actually found for the systems K_2ReBr_6-$K_2SnCl_6(n,\gamma)^{186}Re$ (V = 690 and 820 pm^3, respectively); K_2OsBr_6-$K_2SnCl_6(n,\gamma)^{191}Os$ (620 pm^3); K_2ReCl_6-$K_2SnBr_6(n,\gamma)^{186}Re$ (640 pm^3); and K_2ReBr_6-$K_2OsCl_6(n,\gamma)^{186}Re$ (430 pm^3). In the last mentioned case the very small contribution of $^{186}ReCl_6^{2-}$ indicates directly that only very few recoil atoms reach a region free of bromide.

In annealing experiments with neutron activated K_2ReBr_6-K_2SnCl_6 mixed crystals it was observed that extrapolating the practically linear pseudoplateaux region back to zero time the proportions for most of the $^{186}ReBr_nCl_{6-n}^{2-}$ species (n = 1-5) increase smoothly with annealing temperature. But for $^{186}ReBr_6^{2-}$ there is a virtually discontinuous increase around 40-60 °C.[34] These results can be interpreted supposing that one third of the recoil $^{186}Re_*$ interstitials are still located inside the original ligand cage and that the pertinent annealing reaction is controlled mainly by an electronic process. Again this indicates a small recoil range.

Quite different results were obtained in the K_2ReBr_6-$K_2SnCl_6(\gamma,n)^{186}Re$ experiment.[38] Irradiations were made with 50 MeV γ quanta. The recoil energy of the Re atoms may be estimated at 10 keV, the recoil range should be of the order of 10000 pm. The distribution of the different hexabromochlororhenates is nearly statistical following (24) with only a slight preponderance of the chloride containing species. The primary retention is zero because $^{186}ReBr_6^{2-}$ vanishes for mixed crystals with very low K_2ReBr_6 concentration. The formation of mixed forms excludes the billiard ball model. Libby's ligand-loss model[39] must be excluded because $^{186}ReBrCl_5^{2-}$ vanishes for low K_2ReBr_6 content. This implies that no intermediate $^{186}ReBr^{x+}$ species with one bromide ligand was formed, which could complete its ligand sphere. The same argument is valid for all other bromide containing species $^{186}ReBr_n^{x+}$ (n = 2-5). Neither hot spot nor disorder models are excluded by the experiments, but in the light of all other experiments the aforementioned collision dynamics model is preferred. In this a central metal recoil atom when it comes to rest re-coordinates with six adjacent Cl and Br ligands and this is expected to occur statistically if the recoil range is of the estimated order.[36,27] The billiard ball retention cannot exceed 13% which is the smallest sum found for $^{186}ReBr_6^{2-}$ + $^{186}ReCl_6^{2-}$, but probably it is only 1% or even smaller.

No direct evidence is available concerning the formation of $^*ReO_4^-$ in mixed crystals and mixed hexahalogenometallate complexes. It is believed that this species results from surviving ligand vacancy complex anions $ReX_n\square_{6-n}^{2-}$ which suffer hydrolytic oxidation upon solution. No comparable yield fraction was found in the system with K_2OsBr_6 as Szilard-Chalmers target.

4.2.2. Central Metal Atom Recoil in $K_2MX_nY_{6-n}$ Mixed Hexahalogenometallate Coordination Compounds

The chemical effects of the nuclear reactions $^{190}Os(n,\gamma)^{191}Os$, $^{184}Os(n,\gamma)$-^{185}Os, $^{185}Re(n,\gamma)^{186}Re$, $^{192}Os(\gamma,n)^{191}Os$, $^{186}Os(\gamma,n)^{185}Os$, $^{187}Re(\gamma,n)^{186}Re$, and $^{185}Re(\gamma,2n)^{183}Re$ have been investigated in $K_2MBr_nCl_{6-n}$ mixed hexahalogenometallate complexes.[30] In table 5 only the results for the Os nuclear reactions in the $K_2OsBr_3Cl_3$ target are presented. A significant isotope effect is found which is due to the different recoil ranges. From the experiment it must be concluded that ^{191}Os from the (n,γ) nuclear reaction has a smaller recoil energy than ^{185}Os while the isotopes from the (γ,n) reactions have the largest recoil energy, in this case the experimental proportions are very similar to those cal-

Table 5. Labelled species (in %) following $^{190}Os(n,\gamma)^{191}Os$, $^{184}Os(n,\gamma)^{185}Os$, $^{186}Os(\gamma,n)^{184}Os$, and $^{192}Os(\gamma,n)^{191}Os$ nuclear reactions in $K_2OsBr_3Cl_3$; and calculated proportions for statistical distribution (in %).

	$^{190}Os(n,\gamma)^{191}Os$	$^{184}Os(n,\gamma)^{185}Os$	$^{186}Os(\gamma,n)^{185}Os$ $^{192}Os(\gamma,n)^{191}Os$	R_{sec} stat.*1 calc.
$^*OsBr_6^{2-}$	1.1	1.6	2	2
$^*OsBr_5Cl^{2-}$	3.3	4.5	10	9
$^*OsBr_4Cl_2^{2-}$	11.2	13.1	23	23
$^*OsBr_3Cl_3^{2-}$	45.3	38.1	34	31
$^*OsBr_2Cl_4^{2-}$	19.5	21.3	21	23
$^*OsBrCl_5^{2-}$	9.0	9.3	8	9
$^*OsCl_6^{2-}$	10.6	12.1	2	2

*1 statistical distribution of labelled $^*OsBr_nCl_{6-n}^{2-}$ products obeying Eq. (24)

Table 6. Labelled species (in %) following $^{185}Re(n,\gamma)^{186}Re$ and $^{187}Re(\gamma,n)^{185}Re$ nuclear reactions in K_3ClReF_6; and calculated proportions for statistical distribution (in %).

	$^{185}Re(n,\gamma)^{186}Re$	$^{187}Re(\gamma,n)^{186}Re$	R_{sec} stat.*1, calc.
$^{186}ReO_4^-$ *2	45.4	48.0	46.7*3
$^{186}ReCl_6^{2-}$	0	–	0
$^{186}ReCl_5F^{2-}$	0.3	–	0
$^{186}ReCl_4F_2^{2-}$	0.8	–	0.2
$^{186}ReCl_3F_3^{2-}$	3.2	2.7	2.0
$^{186}ReCl_2F_4^{2-}$	11.2	11.5	8.8
$^{186}ReClF_5^{2-}$	19.8	17.0	21.1
$^{186}ReF_6^{2-}$	19.3	20.8	21.1

*1 statistical distribution of labelled $^{186}ReCl_nF_{6-n}^{2-}$ products obeying Eq. (24)
*2 including some % unidentified species *3 estimated

culated for a statistical distribution. Again this is not regarded as proof of a hot spot.

For K_2ReF_6-$K_2SnCl_6(n,\gamma)^{186}Re$ experiments a less pronounced enrichment of fluorine ligands in the recoil species was expected because the recoil range should be larger in a lattice with lighter (F instead of Br) atoms. Efforts to prepare K_2ReF_6-K_2SnCl_6 mixed crystals were, however, unsuccessful but resulted in the preparation of a new compound $K_3Cl[ReF_6]$ crystallising in an anti-perovskite structure.[40] Both nuclear processes $^{185}Re(n,\gamma)^{186}Re$ and $^{187}Re(\gamma,n)^{186}Re$ produced mixed $^*ReCl_nF_{6-n}^{2-}$ ions in amounts very similar and almost corresponding to the statistical distribution, see table 6.[41] The obvious reason for this at first sight unexpected behaviour is the very thorough mixture of Cl and F already in the target substance, it should not be regarded as proof of a hot spot.

4.3. Central Atom Recoil in Mixed Crystals of Coordination Compounds with Identical Large Organic Ligands

4.3.1. Phthalocyanine Mixed Crystals

Central metal atom recoils in mixed crystals of phthalocyanine complexes have been investigated since the beginning of the 1970's. Phthalocyanine complexes are suitable for the preparation of mixed crystals because many metal phthalocyanines are isomorphous. Crystalline phthalocyanines are resistant to radiation and it has been confirmed by a radio-tracer technique that little isotopic exchange occurred during the wet chemical separation process after the nuclear transformation, which fulfils an essential condition for recoil chemistry. In general, a phthalocyanine complex has two stable crystalline modifications, i.e. the α- and β-forms. All the isomorphous metal phthalocyanines used for mixed crystals have very similar crystalline structures.[42,43,44,45] Therefore their X-ray powder diffraction patterns are also much too close to prove that mixed crystals with microscopic homogeneity are really produced.[46,47,48] At present, we have only one method of the preparation of phthalocyanine mixed crystals: a mixture of the pure complexes is dissolved in cooled sulphuric acid and the solution is poured into ice-water. Because a precipitate forms instantaneously it is believed that real mixed crystals have been produced.

In the recoil process, the β-crystal form gives a higher retention than the α-form, the reason is generally attributed to the difference in crystal structure[49] and/or conductivity[50].

So far, the following combinations of mixed crystal systems have been investigated, where Pc denotes the phthalocyanato ligand:

(α,β)-CuPc-H_2Pc[51], (α,β)-CoPc-H_2Pc[52], (α,β)-ZnPc-H_2Pc[53];
(α,β)-CoPc-CuPc[54,55], α-Cupc-ZnPc[47], α-CoPc-ZnPc[56].

The former three systems, each containing H_2Pc as a component, were subjected only to thermal neutron irradiation, while the latter three mixed metal phthalocyanines were irradiated both with thermal neutron and bremsstrahlung.

In MPc-H_2Pc systems the retention of the nuclides increased with increase of the H_2Pc mole fraction, which seems reasonable because H_2Pc is a material for producing the labelled complex.

In CoPc-CuPc systems the retentions of the nuclides of both elements increased with increasing mole fraction of CuPc, linearly in α-crystals and logarithmically in β-crystals. The retention of the cobalt nuclide was higher than that of the copper in both irradiations.[54,55] This shows a marked influence of the crystal form on the fate of the recoils in the mixed crystals.

For α-CoPc-CuPc, α-CoPc-ZnPc, and α-CuPc-ZnPc, we can compare the behaviour of a nuclide in the retention-mole fraction relation in bremsstrahlung irradiation with that of a nuclide of the same element in thermal neutron irradiation. The data are shown in Figs. 1-3. The retention of cobalt and copper in the CoPc-CuPc system, that of cobalt in the CoPc-ZnPc system, and copper in the CuPc-ZnPc system were clearly linearly related to the composition and gave parallel plots in the two kinds of irradiation.

The retention arises partly from nuclear events that fail to rupture the molecule containing the affected atom, or in which rupture is quickly followed

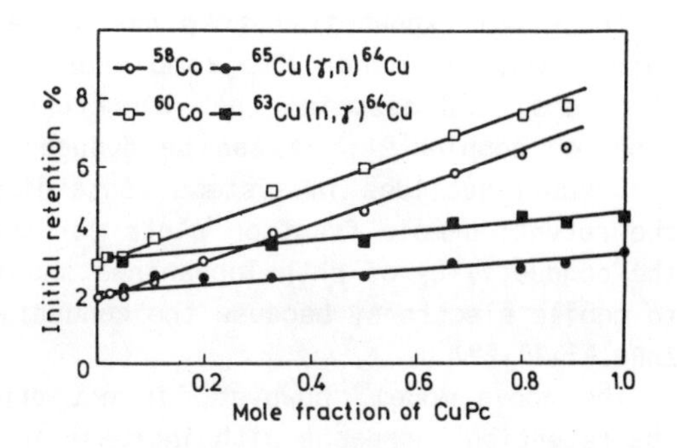

Fig. 1. Retentions of ^{58}Co, ^{60}Co and ^{64}Cu in α-mixed crystals of CoPc and CuPc.

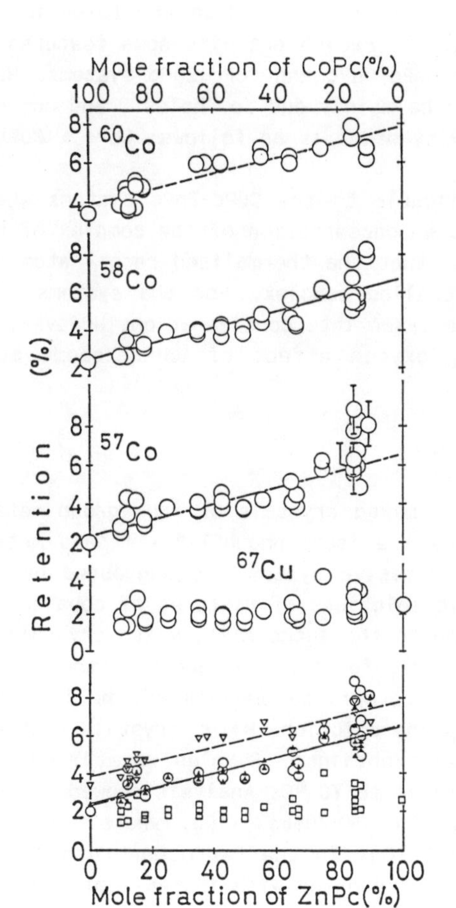

Fig. 2. Retentions of cobalt and copper recoils in α-CoPc-ZnPc mixed crystals. ^{59}Co(n,γ)^{60}Co: ▽; ^{59}Co(γ,n)^{58}Co: ▲; ^{59}Co(γ,2n)^{57}Co: o; ^{68}Zn(γ,p)^{67}Cu: □.

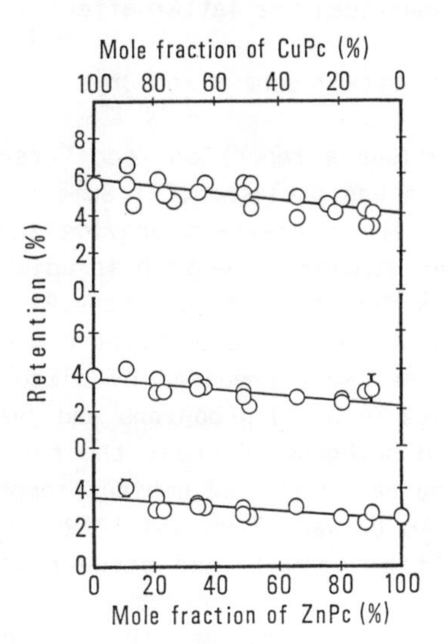

Fig. 3. Retentions of copper recoils in α-CuPc-ZnPc mixed crystals. ^{63}Cu(n,γ)^{64}Cu; ^{65}Cu(γ,n)^{64}Cu; ^{68}Zn(γ,p)^{67}Cu; (top to bottom).

by recombination, and partly from reactions leading to reformation of the parent species by reaction with the matrix. The latter includes direct replacement of an inactive atom by the recoiling radioactive atom. The former term should be independent of the composition of the mixed crystals. The fact that the retentions for nuclides of the same element formed by the (n,γ) and (γ,n) reaction show a difference that is independent of composition of the mixed crystal suggests that this difference is equal to the primary retention in the (n,γ) process, assuming that the primary retention is negligibly small in the case of the (γ,n) reaction.

It is well known that CoPc has a special affinity for oxygen molecules compared with the other MPc complexes. The adsorbed oxygen is liable to trap electrons, and assuming that electrons are necessary for the formation of the labelled complex[50], it can be deduced that CoPc will reduce the retention of all recoil nuclides in systems containing CoPc, which explains some features of the retention-mole fraction plots for the CoPc-CuPc and CoPc-ZnPc systems. Here the conductivity of phthalocyanines should be mainly due to "holes", and not due to mobile electrons, because the conductivity order is as follows: CoPc > CuPc > ZnPc.[57,58,59]

The above model, however, is not applicable to the CuPc-ZnPc systems where the retention increases with increase in the concentration of the complex of the same element. In this case, it is thought that the thermalised recoil atom (or ion) reacts preferentially to form the labelled complex. For the systems containing CoPc, this tendency should also be taken into consideration. However, at present, we must acknowledge that the "oxygen effect of CoPc" seems much stronger than the latter effect.

4.3.2. Metallocene Mixed Crystals

In 1989 a report on recoil reactions in mixed crystals of iron group metallocenes was published.[60] Some metallocenes are isomorphous[61,62,63] and metallocene mixed crystals provide another informative system, as suggested by the former studies of neutron irradiated liquid solutions of mixtures of cobaltocene with nickelocene or ferrocene.[64] According to the authors[60], mixed crystals of pairs of metallocenes (ferrocene-ruthenocene, ferrocene-osmocene, ruthenocene-osmocene) were prepared by dissolving the appropriate amounts of the two components in boiling benzene and evaporating the solution. Mixed crystals that appeared homogeneous under the microscope were obtained. Samples were irradiated in the reactor at an ambient temperature close to 70 °C. Analysis showed isotope effects between ^{97}Ru and ^{103}Ru (defined as $(1-[R_{97}/R_{103}])\cdot 100$, where R denotes retention value), and between ^{185}Os and ^{193}Os. In the ferrocene-ruthenocene mixed crystals the retentions of both metals increased with increase of the mole fraction of ferrocene. The isotope effect for the ruthenium nuclides was found to decrease with the increase of retention. With increase of ferrocene concentration in the ferrocene-osmocene system the retention of osmium increased slightly, but the retention of iron remained virtually constant. The osmium isotope effect behaved similarly. The retention of ruthenium in ruthenocene-osmocene mixed crystals increased with the decrease in its concentration, while that of osmium hardly changed. The isotope effect for the ruthenium isotopes decreased with increase in ruthenium retention and thus with increase of osmocene concentration. The isotope effect for the osmium isotopes was unchanged.

The explanation proposed[60] was based on the result of Jacobson et al.[65,66] in their gas phase studies of ion-molecule reactions in metallocenes using ion cyclotron resonance mass spectrometry. They proposed a mechanism of a series of reactions involving the existence of a polarised complex ion intermediate $^{+}M'{-}{-}{-}MCp_2$. The charge distribution within the intermediate complex ion would be affected by the difference in ionisation potentials between M' and MCp_2, that is, $\Delta IP = [IP(M') - IP(MCp_2)]$. The transfer of charge in $^{+}M'{-}{-}{-}MCp_2$ is expected to be faster for higher values of ΔIP. The bond energy of M-Cp can also affect the rate. The retention increases with the increase of ΔIP, except for the osmium retention in ruthenocene-osmocene mixed crystals. (For ionisation potentials used see the literature[67,68,69].)

The isotope effect was attributed to the fact that the nuclides (^{97}Ru and ^{185}Os) more frequently suffer K shell conversion than the other isotopes (^{103}Ru and ^{193}Os), and during the neutralisation to ions with one positive charge, their kinetic energy falls below the critical energy required for the ion-molecule reaction, leading to different reaction rates for the two isotopes.[60,70] The target matrix with lower ionisation potential gives rise to a faster electron transfer process and leads to a higher kinetic energy for the unipositive ion. This was the explanation of Yassine et al.[60] for the decrease in the isotope effect with increase in the mole fractions of ferrocene or osmocene. However, the osmium isotope effect in the osmocene-ruthenocene mixed crystals seems anomalous.

The formation of true mixed crystals was not established in this work.

Very recently the recoil behaviours of ^{97}Ru and ^{103}Ru in bremsstrahlung irradiated ferrocene-ruthenocene mixed crystals, prepared similarly, were reported.[71] In the (γ,n) reaction the ruthenium retention increased with increase in ferrocene mole fraction, while the isotope effect for ^{97}Ru and ^{103}Ru, which was not observed in pure ruthenocene, (defined as $(1-[R_{103}/R_{97}])\cdot 100$, because $R_{97} > R_{103}$ in this case) increased in a different way from the (n,γ) case. The tendencies in the ruthenium isotope effects including the (n,γ) case were interpreted as due to a more favourable enhancement of ^{97}Ru retention on the addition of ferrocene to the matrix than on that of the ^{103}Ru retention, considering a metastable state of ^{97}Ru (0.23 ns) and no such state in ^{103}Ru.

4.3.3. Stereoselectivity of Recoils in Mixed Crystals

When crystals of a stereoisomer of a metal complex are irradiated with thermal neutrons, the steric configuration of the parent isomer is usually conserved in the labelled complex produced during or after the irradiation. Since a matrix template effect may play an important role in the conservation of the configuration, the use of mixed crystals of the stereo-isomers of the complexes might be a good way of exploring the origin of stereoselective labelling, the relative contributions of a memory effect corresponding to primary retention plus immediate reformation of complex, and the matrix or "template effect" on other reformation processes. For that purpose, Sasaki et al.[72] prepared mixed crystals of Λ-$[Ru(phen)_3](ClO_4)_2$ with Λ-, Δ-, and rac-$[M(phen)_3](ClO_4)_2$ (M = Fe or Ni) by dissolution of the chlorides and precipitation of mixed crystals of their perchlorates. These mixed crystals were subjected to thermal neutron irradiation at dry ice temperature. These authors measured the radiochemical yields of Λ- and Δ-$[^{103}Ru(phen)_3]^{2+}$ (Y(Λ) and Y(Δ)) in mixed crystals of different compositions. The initial (meaning unannealed) Y(Λ) and Y(Δ) are plotted in Fig. 4 versus the mole ratio of Δ-$[M(phen)_3]^{2+}$ to the sum of Λ-$[Ru(phen)_3]^{2+}$ and Λ-$[M(phen)_3]^{2+}$ (Δ/Λ). The Y(Λ) showed no significant dependence on Δ/Λ, while the Y(Δ)'s increased with the increase in Δ/Λ and reached a constant value at and above Δ/Λ = 1. The saturation values of Y(Δ) were much lower than Y(Λ).

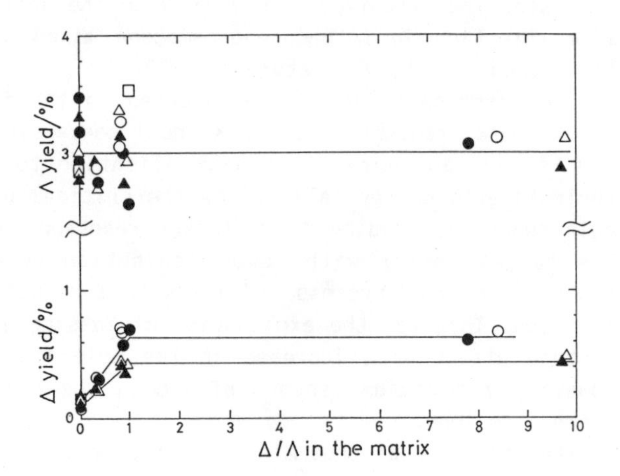

Fig. 4. Initial (Λ) and (Δ) yields in the irradiation of pure Λ- and rac-$[Ru(phen)_3](ClO_4)_2 \cdot 1.5H_2O$ crystals and the crystalline mixtures of Λ-$[Ru(phen)_3]$-$(ClO_4)_2$ with Λ-, Δ-, or rac-$[M(phen)_3](ClO_4)_2$ (M = Fe, Ni). Ru-Fe mixtures: 1st batch (▲), 2nd batch (Δ); Ru-Ni mixtures: 1st batch (●), 2nd batch (o); pure Ru-complex salts: (□). Δ/Λ: mole ratio of the Δ isomer to the sum of the Λ isomers.

The X-ray powder diffraction pattern of the unirradiated 1:1 mixture of Λ-$[Ru(phen)_3](ClO_4)_2$ and Δ-$[M(phen)_3](ClO_4)_2$ (abb. 1:1 ΛRu-ΔNi) agreed with that of the pure racemates of the rutheninum, iron, and nickel complexes. On the other hand, the powder X-ray diffraction patterns of other samples (with $\Delta/\Lambda \neq 1$) showed the crystals of both the racemate and that of the dominant optically active isomer. (In this case, therefore, the system dealt with was not a real mixed crystal but a mixture of an optical isomer and a racemate.) These observations show that when $\Delta/\Lambda < 1$ the target Λ-$[Ru(phen)_3]^{2+}$ was incorporated both in the active racemate and in the Λ-isomer crystals, and that when $\Delta/\Lambda > 1$, all the target Λ-$[Ru(phen)_3]^{2+}$ was incorporated only in the active racemate crystals. In other words, when $\Delta/\Lambda = 0$, the Y(Λ) (≈3%) and Y(Δ) (≈0.10-0.15%) reflect yields only in the Λ matrix, and when $\Delta/\Lambda > 1$, Y(Λ)(≈3%) and Y(Δ) (≈0.7% for M = Ni, ≈0.4% for M = Fe) reflect those only in the active racemate matrix. This explains why the Δ yields increased with the Δ/Λ ratio when the ratio was less than unity and saturated at $\Delta/\Lambda = 1$.

In every case in Fig. 4, the initial Y(Δ) was much lower than Y(Λ). This shows that the initial labelling reaction took place in an only slightly disturbed region in the crystals; the memory effect, or reconstruction of complex[73] played an important role in the initial labelling. The higher Y(Δ)'s in active racemate may be explained by template effects, which are not as significant as the memory effect for the higher Λ yield.

The post-irradiation annealing of the crystal-mixtures increased both the Y(Λ) and Y(Δ) at 160 °C. In the initial stage of annealing (up to 1 hr) the increase in Y(Λ) was about three times as large as in Y(Δ) regardless of the composition of the matrix. In the later stages, however, in a Λ-isomer matrix, the increase of the yield followed the same trend as in the initial stages, while in the active racemate, the Y(Λ) and Y(Δ) increased by almost equal amounts. These results show that the stereoselectivity in the initial stage originates mainly from the memory effect, while that in the later stages was mainly controlled by the template effect.

4.4. Central Atom Recoil in Water-soluble Metalloporphyrin Ion Associates[74,75]

The retention in metal complexes generally arises from contributions of several different processes. Few systems permit the measurement of a single process. This difficulty might be overcome by the use of mixed crystals of metal complexes, but true solid solutions are hard to prepare when ligands are large. However, useful results can be obtained with double complexes of the type ML·M'L'. The ion associates of $[M(TMPyP)]^{4+}$ and $[M'(TCPP)]^{4-}$, where TMPyP is α,β,γ,δ-tetrakis(4-N-methylpyridyl)porphine and TCPP is tetra(p-carboxyphenyl)-porphine, (see Fig. 5), can be made by mixing aqueous solutions of the cationic and anionic compounds of the complexes: the ion associate separates and can be centrifuged down, washed, and slurry freeze-dried. Compounds with M = Zn and M' = Cu, M = Cu with M' = Zn, and M = M' = Zn or Cu were made in this way.

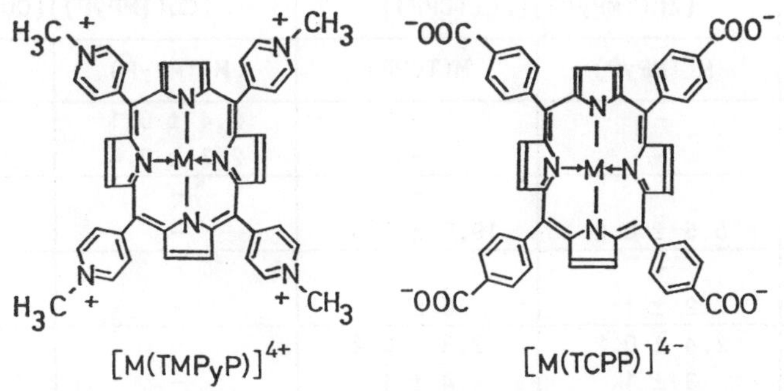

Fig. 5. Structural Formulae of Water-soluble Metalloporphyrins Used

Samples were irradiated with thermal neutrons at -78 °C and by bremsstrahlung of 50 Mev maximum energy at -130 °C. After irradiation the compound was dissolved in an ice-cold mixture of 3M ammonium chloride, 1M ammonia water and ethanol, in proportions 1:1:2 by volume. The anionic and cationic components were separated on ion exchange columns. The results are shown in table 1.

It can be seen that the probability of recoil copper substitution for zinc is high regardless of the recoil energy and is greater for the Zn(TCPP) species than for the Zn(TMPyP). It may be noted that zinc porphyrins are more easily demetallated by acid than the corresponding copper compounds.[76,77] The only marked isotopic differences are between ^{69m}Zn and the other zinc isotopes. For the (n,γ) reaction the average recoil energies are 166 eV for ^{69m}Zn and 446 eV for ^{65}Zn [48] and the behaviour of the ^{65}Zn from the (n,γ) and the very high recoil (γ,n) process are substantially the same, as is the ^{69m}Zn from the (γ,n) process. Assuming that the different target substances have rather similar structures and that there is no exchange during the separation process the data can be analysed as follows. The distribution of the radioactive products arises from (see table 2):

Table 1. Complex Yields(%)*1

Compound Used	[Zn(TMPyP)][Cu(TCPP)]		[Cu(TMPyP)][Zn(TCPP)]	
Fraction	M(TMPyP)	M(TCPP)	M(TMPyP)	M(TCPP)
^{64}Cu	9.1 ± 0.2 9 ± 1	3.6 ± 0.2 2.8 ± 0.6	2.4 ± 0.2 2.8 ± 0.4	19.7 ± 0.5 21 ± 2
^{67}Cu	– 9.0 ± 0.1	– 3.0 ± 0.1	– 2.5 ± 0.1	– 22.1 ± 0.3
^{62}Zn	– 2.3 ± 0.4	– 3.8 ± 0.3	– 3.3 ± 0.4	– 4.6 ± 0.5
^{65}Zn	2.4 ± 0.1 2.2 ± 0.4	3.6 ± 0.1 3.6 ± 0.5	3.3 ± 0.2 4 ± 1	2.7 ± 0.3 4.0 ± 0.7
^{69m}Zn	6.8 ± 0.2 1.5 ± 0.8	3.6 ± 0.1 3.9 ± 0.6	3.1 ± 0.2 4.4 ± 0.8	6.9 ± 0.4 2 ± 2

Compound Used	[Zn(TMPyP)][Zn(TCPP)]		[Cu(TMPyP)][Cu(TCPP)]	
Fraction	M(TMPyP)	M(TCPP)	M(TMPyP)	M(TCPP)
^{64}Cu	– –	– –	2.4 ± 0.1 2.3 ± 0.4	2.3 ± 0.1 2.3 ± 0.4
^{67}Cu	– 5.5 ± 0.2	– 19.0 ± 0.3	– –	– –
^{62}Zn	– 2 ± 1	– 5 ± 1	– –	– –
^{65}Zn	2.4 ± 0.2 3 ± 1	2.3 ± 0.2 4 ± 1	– –	– –
^{69m}Zn	4.2 ± 0.1 3 ± 1	4.5 ± 0.1 5 ± 1	– –	– –

*1 Upper value: Thermal neutron irradiation
Lower value: Bremsstrahlung irradiation.

1. Primary retention i.e. fraction of nuclear events not affecting molecular rupture. Denote this by P with ' and " to denote Cu and Zn and subscripts 1 and 2 to denote TMPyP and TCPP complexes, respectively.

2. Retention by reaction with surroundings. Denote by R with the same primes and subscripts.

3. Substitution products, such as [Cu(TCPP)] formed from [Zn(TCPP)]. Denote by S_2' etc.

4. A special case, corresponding to primary retention, where atomic number changes in the nuclear event as for ^{67}Cu by $^{68}Zn(\gamma,p)$. In (TMPyP), denote by μ_1', in (TCPP) by μ_2'.

Although the probable errors are substantial and the quantities not very large, the values shown in table 3 have at least qualitative significance. It is reassuring to find the primary retentions are zero in the large recoil cases. The values give a more quantitative expression to the greater probability of replacement of Zn by Cu in the two complexes. It is noteworthy that the R and S

Table 2. Possible Recoil Processes for Complex Yields*[1]

Sample	[Zn(TMPyP)][Cu(TCPP)]		[Cu(TMPyP)][Zn(TCPP)]	
Fraction	M(TMPyP)	M(TCPP)	M(TMPyP)	M(TCPP)
^{64}Cu	S_1'	$P_2' + R_2'$	$P_1' + R_1'$	S_2'
^{67}Cu	$S_1' + \mu_1'$	R_2'	R_1'	$S_2' + \mu_2'$
^{62}Zn, ^{65}Zn, ^{69m}Zn	$P_1'' + R_1''$	S_2''	S_1''	$P_2'' + R_2''$

Sample	[Zn(TMPyP)][Zn(TCPP)]		[Cu(TMPyP)][Cu(TCPP)]	
Fraction	M(TMPyP)	M(TCPP)	M(TMPyP)	M(TCPP)
^{64}Cu	–	–	$P_1' + R_1'$	$P_2' + R_2'$
^{67}Cu	$S_1' + \mu_1'$	$S_2' + \mu_2'$	–	–
^{62}Zn, ^{65}Zn, ^{69m}Zn	$P_1'' + R_1''$	$P_2'' + R_2''$	–	–

*[1]For both kinds of irradiation

Table 3. Estimated Recoil Reaction Probabilities (%)*[1]

Reaction	(Bremsstrahlung) ^{64}Cu	^{67}Cu	*Zn	(Thermal Neutrons) ^{64}Cu	^{65}Zn	^{69m}Zn
P_1'	≈ 0	–	–	≤ 1	–	–
P_2'	≈ 0	–	–	1-3	–	–
P_1''	–	–	≈ 0	–	<1	≈ 5
P_2''	–	–	≈ 0	–	<1	≈ 5
R_1'	≈ 2.5	≈ 2.5	–	≈ 2	–	–
R_2'	≈ 3	≈ 3	–	>1	–	–
R_1''	–	–	2-3	–	≈ 2	≈ 2
R_2''	–	–	4-5	–	≈ 2	≈ 2
S_1'	≈ 9	≈ 9	–	≈ 9	–	–
S_2'	≈ 20	≈ 20	–	≈ 20	–	–
S_1''	–	–	≈ 3	–	≈ 3	≈ 3
S_2''	–	–	≈ 3.5	–	≈ 3.6	≈ 3.6
μ_1'	–	≈ 0	–	–	–	–
μ_2'	–	≈ 0	–	–	–	–

*[1] *Zn = ^{62}Zn, ^{65}Zn, ^{69m}Zn (supposed to be equal)

reaction probabilities are similar to each other in both irradiations, which leads us to the already common concept that the recoils react with neighbouring ligands after loosing their initial high kinetic energy and/or high charge and that the reaction probabilities are therefore almost independent of the nuclear reaction or initial recoil energy.

References

1. Rieder, W., Broda, E., Erber, J.: Monatsh. Chemie, 81, 657 (1950).
2. Müller, H., Martin, S.: Inorg. Nucl. Chem. Letters, 5, 761 (1969).
3. Müller, H.: Naturwissenschaften, 49, 182 (1962).
4. Green, J.H., Harbottle, G., Maddock, A.G.: Trans. Faraday Soc., 49, 1413 (1953).
5. Müller, H.: "Chemical Effects of Nuclear Transformations in Inorganic Systems" (G. Harbottle, A.G. Maddock, Eds.) North-Holland, Amsterdam, New York and Oxford, 1979, p. 441.
6. Müller, H.: Radiat. Phys. Chem., 27, 25 (1986).
7. Müller, H.: Z. anal. Chem., 189, 336 (1962).
8. Müller, H.: Z. anorg. allg. Chem., 336, 24 (1965).
9. Müller, H.: Proceedings IAEA Symposium Chemical Effects Associated with Nuclear Reactions and Radioactive Transformations, Vol.II, 359, IAEA, Vienna 1965.
10. Müller, H.: Z. Anal. Chem., 247, 145 (1969).
11. Müller, H., Diefallah, E.M., Martin, S.: J. Phys. Chem., 85, 3514 (1981).
12. Müller, H., Bekk, P.: Fresenius Z. Anal. Chem., 314, 758 (1983).
13. Obergfell, P., Müller, H.: Fresenius Z. Anal. Chem., 328, 242 (1987).
14. Herr, W., Heine, K., Schmidt, G.B.: Z. Naturf., 17a, 590 (1962).
15. Vargas, J.I., Maddock, A.G.: "Chemical Effects of Nuclear Transformations in Inorganic Systems" (Harbottle, G., Maddock, A.G., Eds.) North-Holland, Amsterdam, New York and Oxford, 1979, p. 461.
16. Harbottle, G., Sutin, N.: J. Phys. Chem., 62, 1344 (1958).
17. Müller, H.: J. Inorg. Nucl. Chem., 27, 1745 (1965).
18. Gibson, J.B., Goland, A.N., Milgram, M., Vineyard, G.H.: Phys. Rev., 120, 1229 (1960).
19. Vineyard, G.H.: Disc. Faraday Soc., 31, 7 (1961).
20. Robinson, M.T., Rössler, K., Torrens, I.M.: J. Chem. Phys., 60, 680 (1974).
21. Bell, R., Rössler, K., Stöcklin, G., Upadhyay, S.R.: J. inorg. nucl. Chem., 34, 461 (1972).
22. Rössler, K., Otterbach, J., Stöcklin, G.: J. Phys. Chem., 76, 2499 (1972).
23. Müller, H., Cramer, D.: Radiochim. Acta, 14, 78 (1970).
24. Müller, H., Bekk, P., Bicheler, U.: Radiochim. Acta, 36, 115 (1984).
25. Müller, H., Obergfell, P., Hagenlocher, I.: J. Phys. Chem., 90, 3418 (1986).
26. Müller, H., Martin, S.: J. Physique, 37 [C7], 540 (1976).
27. Rössler, K., Pross, L.: Radiat. Effects, 48, 207 (1980).
28. Rössler, K. Robinson, M.T.: "Atomic Collisions in Solids" (Datz, S., Appleton, B.R., Moak, C.D., Eds.) Plenum Publ. Corp., New York, 1974, Vol. 1, p. 237.
29. Müller, H., Hagenlocher, I.: J. Radioanal. Nucl. Chem., Articles, 140, 37 (1990).
30. Bekk, P.: Dissertation, Freiburg, 1982.
31. Müller, H., Bekk, P.: Radiat. Effects, 64, 183 (1982).
32. Müller, H.: J. inorg. nucl. Chem., 28, 2081 (1966).
33. Müller, H.: J. inorg. nucl. Chem., 29, 2167 (1967).
34. Müller, H.: Radiochim. Acta, 34, 173 (1983).
35. Müller, H.: Umschau, 68, 534 (1968).
36. Müller, H.: Atomkernenergie, 16, 237, 323 (1970).
37. van Ooij, W.J.: Thesis, Delft, 1971.
38. Müller, H.: J. inorg. nucl. Chem., 31, 1579 (1969).
39. Libby, W.F.: J. Am. Chem. Soc., 62, 1930 (1940).
40. Müller, H., Abberger, S.: to be published.
41. Müller, H., Abberger, S.: Radiochim. Acta, 19, 176 (1973).
42. Ashida, M., Uyeda, N., Suito, E.: Bull. Chem. Soc. Japan, 39, 2616 (1966).

43. Linstead, R.P., Robertson, J.M.: J. Chem. Soc., 1736 (1936).
44. Brown, C.J.: J. Chem. Soc., (A), 2488 (1968).
45. Scheidt, W., Dow, W.: J. Am. Chem. Soc., 99, 1101 (1977).
46. Kujirai, O.: Dr. Thesis, Tokyo Kyoiku Univ. (1975).
47. Shoji, H., Oki, Y., Ikeda, N.: Radiochem. Radioanal. Letters, 58, 347 (1983).
48. Oki, Y.: Dr. Thesis, Univ. of Tsukuba (1988).
49. Yoshihara, K., Ebihara, H.: J. Chem. Phys., 45, 896 (1966).
50. Scanlon, M.D., Collins, K.E.: Radiochim. Acta, 15, 141 (1971).
51. Kudo, H.: Bull. Chem. Soc. Japan, 45, 392 (1972).
52. Kujirai, O., Ikeda, N.: Radiochem. Radioanal. Letters, 18, 197 (1974).
53. Ikeda, N., Kujirai, O.: Radiochem. Radioanal. Letters, 23, 125 (1975).
54. Kujirai, O., Ikeda, N.: Radiochem. Radioanal. Letters, 15, 67 (1973).
55. Kujirai, O., Ikeda, N., Shoji, H.: Radiochem. Radioanal. Letters, 26, 5 (1976).
56. Oki, Y., Shoji, H., Ikeda, N.: J. Radioanal. Nucl. Chem., Letters, 126, 269 (1988).
57. Lever, A.B.P.: "Advances in Inorganic Chemistry and Radiochemistry", Academic Press, New York, 7, 27 (1965).
58. Shakhverdov, P.A., Terenin, A.N.: Dokl. Akad. Nauk S.S.S.R., 160, 1141 (1965).
59. Abkowitz, M.A., Lakatos, A.I.: J. Chem. Phys., 57, 5033 (1972).
60. Yassine, T., Blackburn, R.: Radiat. Phys. Chem., 33, 341 (1989).
61. Seiler, P., Dunitz, J.D.: Acta Crystallogr., B36, 2946 (1980).
62. Seiler, P., Dunitz, J.D.: Acta Crystallogr., B38, 1741 (1982).
63. Boeyens, J.C.A., Levendis, D.C., Bruce, M.I., Williams, M.I.: J. Crystallogr. Spectrosc. Res., 16, 519 (1986).
64. Sato, H., Yoshida, M., Tominaga, T.: Radiochem. Radioanal. Letters, 44, 159 (1980).
65. Jacobson, D.B., Byrd, G.D., Freiser, B.S.: J. Am. Chem. Soc., 104, 2320 (1982).
66. Jacobson, D.B., Freiser, B.S.: Organometallics, 4, 1048 (1985).
67. Rosenblum, M.: "Chemistry of the Iron Group Metallocenes", Interscience, New York, 1965.
68. Rosenstock, H.M., Draxl, K., Steiner, B.W., Herron, J.J.: J. Phys. Chem. Reference Data, Vol. 6, Suppl. No. 1 (1977).
69. Green, J.C.: Structure and Bonding, 43, 37 (1981).
70. Blackburn, R., Yassine, T.: Radiat. Phys. Chem., 33, 337 (1989).
71. Matsue, H., Sekine, T., Yoshihara, K.: presented at the "61st Annual Meeting of Japan Chemical Society", (Yokohama), March, 1991.
72. Sasaki, K., Furukawa, M., Yamatera, H.: Radiochim. Acta, 36, 123 (1984).
73. Müller, H.: Radiochim. Acta, 28, 233 (1981).
74. Ogawa, K., Shoji, H., Ikeda, N.: Res. Rep. Lab. Nucl. Sci., Tohoku Univ., 19, 63 (1986) (in Japanese).
75. Ogawa, K., Shoji, H., Ikeda, N.: presented at the 13th "International Symposium of Hot Atom Chemistry" (Mt. Fuji, Japan), May, 1987.
76. Phillips, J.N.: Rev. Pure Appl. Chem., 10, 35 (1960).
77. Falk, J.E.: "Porphyrins and Metalloporphyrins", Elsevier, New York, 1964.

4.9 Production of Radionuclides Using Hot Atom Chemistry

Hiroshi EBIHARA[1] and Kenneth E. COLLINS[2]

[1] Department of Chemistry, Tsukuba University, Tennodai, Tsukuba, 305, Japan

[2] Instituto de Química, Universidade Estadual de Campinas
Caixa Postal 6154, 13081 Campinas, SP, Brasil

Radionuclides of interest to the medical, biological, chemical and agricultural communities can be produced using either nuclear reactors or particle accelerators. Since a nuclear reactor produces neutrons, the useful direct reactions are based on the (n,γ), (n,p) and (n,α) activations of suitable target species while a particle accelerator uses protons, deuterons, tritons and helium nuclei to induce reactions such as (p,n), (d,n), $(d,2n)$, (t,n) and (α,n) on appropriate target species.

Steps in Production of Radionuclides

The production of radionuclides, either in a nuclear reactor or a cyclotron, usually follows several main steps: (1) target preparation, usually of a pure solid but occasionally of pure liquids or gases; (2) irradiation and the operations incidental to this; (3) target chemistry, including putting the radioactive species in a chemical form appropriate for the separation; (4) quantitative separation of the radionuclide in question; (5) if necessary, synthesis of the labelled compound appropriate to the desired application and (6) quality validation of the final product.

The production of such radionuclides is carried out at two different levels, each requiring its appropriate infrastructure: up to several tens of megabequerels, for research use, and above terabequerels, for routine medical or industrial work and for the preparation of radiation sources.

All the nuclear reactions except the (n,γ) reaction produce chemically different species, making it possible to obtain no-carrier-added radionuclides by a chemical separation of the produced radionuclide from the target material. The overall radioactivity will depend on the irradiation time and the particle flux. Recent advances in positron emission computed tomography and single photon computed tomography have made pharmaceuticals labelled with short-lived radionuclides, produced by small on-site cyclotrons, a matter of great importance.

Hot Atom Enrichment

When the (n,γ) process occurs in a nuclear reactor, the radionuclides produced are always isotopic with the target element and the radionuclides are diluted with inactive nuclides of this element, from which they can not be separated by chemical means. This results in specific activities which depend on the neutron flux of the reactor used. High specific activities are obtained with neutron fluxes of 10^{15} n cm^{-2} s^{-1} but much lower specific activities result from use of the 10^{12} -10^{13} n cm^{-2} s^{-1} fluxes available in medium-sized research reactors.

To obtain higher specific activities from the (n,γ) reaction, at medium to low fluxes, use can be made of the chemical effects of the nuclear transformation by a process commonly known as hot atom enrichment or Szilard-Chalmers enrichment, after the scientists who first noted the separation of high specific activity radioiodide from neutron-bombarded ethyl iodide.

The recoil resulting from the nuclear transformation, when this occurs in a chemical compound, breaks the chemical bonds and produces some fraction of the newly-formed, thermalized radioactive species in a different, separable, chemical form, the identity of which depends on the environment. The enrichment factor, defined as the ratio of the specific activity of the separated product to that of the bulk-bombarded substrate, measures the effectiveness of the hot atom enrichment. Although enrichment factors in excess of 1000 have been reported, in practical terms, with reasonable bombardment times suitable for atual radionuclide production, such high values are rarely approached. Thus, hot atom enrichment is usually restricted to radionuclides with relatively short half-lives.

The fact that both the newly formed radionuclide and it target compound are separated is a further advantage of the use of the hot atom enrichment process, since it permits target recovery and recycling, important when it is necessary to use enriched targets to produce higher overall radioactivities.

Hot atom enrichment procedures have been reported for many of the elements of the periodic table,[1] using as targets inorganic or metal complex systems. The recoil separation can be successful when:

(1) the target element exists in two or more stable oxidation states and/or is available in the form of a substitution inert complex;

(2) the chosen target compound is stable to radiation and thermal decomposition;

(3) the target compound is available in a pure state;

(4) the recoiling radionuclides have sufficient energy to rupture all the chemical bonds involved;

(5) the irradiation is carried out at low temperature to reduce rapid chemical exchange between the radioactive and inactive atoms;

(6) the irradiation is carried out with a high thermal neutron to gamma ratio to reduce radiolytic decomposition of the target compound;

(7) the irradiation is carried out with a high Cd ratio to reduce the secondary reactions induced by fast or epithermal neutrons;

(8) the irradiation time is as short as is consistent with the desired radioactive yield to reduce thermal- or radiaction-induced annealing of the recoiled atoms to the target form;

(9) storage between irradiation and separation is at low temperature, to reduce thermal annealing;

(10) there is an efficient, rapid chemical processing procedure to separate the radioactive atom from the large mass of isotopic inactive target material, either by separation of two different oxidation states or by separation of free species from a complexed one.

Practical Procedures

The production of several radionuclides on a commercial basis, using medium power reactors and utilizing hot atom enrichment have been reported. Several procedures are summarized below:

(1) ^{51}Cr

Target compound: potassium chromate.

Separation method: adsorption of chromic hydroxide by the sintered glass filter,[2,3] or co-precipitation of chromic hydroxide with lanthanum hydroxide, oxidation and leaching.[4]

Separation yield: 8 - 10%

Enrichment factor: 500 - 1000

Specific activity: 0.4 - 4 TBq/g.Cr

(2) ^{76}As

Target compounds: triphenylarsine or cacodylic acid

Separation method: co-precipitation with ferric hydroxide or extraction of arsenate ions by water.[5,6]

Separation yield: 35%

Enrichment factor: 800

Specific activity: 0.5 - 1.8 TBq/g.As

(3) ^{59}Fe (and ^{55}Fe)

Target compound: potassium ferrocyanide

Separation method: elution of ferric ions from cation exchange resin (Dowex 50)[3,7]

Separation yield: 40%

Enrichment factor: 400

Specific activity: 10 - 30 GBq/g.Fe

(4) ^{65}Zn

Target compound: zinc phthalocyanine

Separation method: dissolving in concentrated sulfuric acid followed by reprecipitation of target compound[5,8]

Separation yield: 45%

Enrichment factor: 500

Specific activity: 7 - GBq/g.Zn

(5) ^{64}Cu

Target compound: copper phthalocyanine

Separation method: same as for zinc phthalocyanine[8,9]

Separation yield: 55% - 94%

Enrichment factor: 1000 - 2500

Specific activity: 1.8 - 37 TBq/g.Cu

Production of ^{99}Mo

Most of the medically interesting radionuclides currently in use are cyclotron-produced. A most significant exception is ^{99m}Tc, the generator-produced daughter of ^{99}Mo. This latter radionuclide is generally obtained by neutron irradiation of natural abundance molybdenum metal or recovered as a fission product of enriched ^{235}U. The first process produces ^{99}Mo in low specific activity while the latter requires an extremely efficient separation process to obtain ^{99}Mo free from contaminating fission products.

Higher specific activity ^{99}Mo may be obtained by irradiation of enriched ^{98}Mo, a target which would be best exploited using hot atom enrichment to permit target compound recycling.

A significant number of different molybdenum-containing target compounds have been investigated. At low neutron fluences (to 10^{15}) enrichments of 150-500 with yields of 15-50% have been observed for pure molybdenum hexacarbonyl[10,11,12] and cyclopentadienyltricarbonylchloromolybdenum[10] and for mixtures of molybdenum hexacarbonyl with oxalic acid[10,13] and molybdenum oxinate with ammonium oxalate.[10] However, when neutron fluences of greater than 10^{19} were applied to these compounds and mixtures, the complexes suffered considerable decomposition, resulting in negligible enrichments.[10]

The use of simpler target compounds. such as MoS_2 and $MoCl_x$, either pure or mixed with various catcher compounds, has not been particularly successful either. Even at low fluences, the enrichment factors are not very large and these are reduced at higher fluences.[10]

Thus the challenge still remains to devise an appropriate molybdenum-containing compound which would permit recycling of enriched molybdenum for reactor-production of high specific activity ^{99}Mo by hot atom enrichment.

References

1. Harbottle, G., Hillman, M.: "Szilard-Chalmers Procedures for Isotope Production", in "Radioisotope Production and Quality Control", IAEA Technical Report nº 128, International Atomic Energy Agency, Vienna (1971) p. 617

2. IAEA Technical Report nº 128, International Atomic Energy Agency, Vienna (1971) p. 633.
3. Henry, R.: Commissariat à l'énergia atomique Rapport nº 27, (1959).
4. Shibata, N., Amano, H., Yoshihara, K., Ebihara, H.: Atompraxis, 15, 43 (1969).
5. Douis, M., Valade, J.: Commissariat à l'énergia atomique Rapport nº 2073 (1961).
6. Sharp, R.A., Schmitt, R.A.: General Atomics Division, General Dynamics Corp. Report 910 (1959).
7. IAEA Technical Report nº 128, International Atomic Energy Agency, Vienna (1971) p. 653.
8. Payne, B.R., Scargill, P., Cook, G.B.: "Radioisotopes in Scientific Research", Pergamon Press, London (1958) p. 154.
9. Ebihara, H.: Radiochim. Acta, 6, 120 (1966).
10. Krüger, A., Lieser, K.H.: Radiochim. Acta, 28, 29 (1981).
11. Harbottle, G., Zahn, U.: Radiochim. Acta, 8, 114 (1967).
12. Zahn, U., Collins, C.H., Collins, K.E.: Radiochim. Acta, 11, 33 (1969).
13. Colonomos, M., Parker, W.C.: Radiochim. Acta, 12, 163 (1969).

4.10 Hot Atom Chemistry and Activation Analysis

Edward P. RACK and Alan J. BLOTCKY
Medical Research, Department of Veterans Affairs Medical Center, Omaha, Nebraska 68105, U.S.A. and University of Nebraska-Lincoln, Lincoln, Nebraska 68588-0304 U.S.A.

1. Introduction

Ehmann et al.[1] in their excellent 1990 review of nuclear and radiochemical analysis in *Analytical Chemistry* discuss various major activation analysis methods. Activation analysis has become more than just a neutron activation technique as originally reported in 1936 by Levi and Hevesy[2] in their classic paper developing the field. In the earlier volume *Hot Atom Chemistry -- Recent Trends and Applications in the Physical and Life Sciences and Technology*, Koyama presents an interesting and informative perspective of Hot Atom Chemistry's relevance to Activation Analysis. We will add to this perspective by not only describing hot atom chemistry's relevance but discussing some applications and limitations of these techniques to analysis.

In addition to research nuclear reactors of varying power levels, 14 MeV neutron generators, isotopic neutron sources such as Am-Be sources, accelerators and high-intensity photon sources have been used for activation analysis. Hot atom chemistry and activation analysis are both involved in the production of radioactive atoms produced by a nuclear transformation. While hot atom chemists are interested in the study of chemical effects of the nuclear transformations producing the radioactive atoms, the activation analyst is concerned with producing the radioactive atoms in the most efficacious manner to indicate the elemental composition in a sample. The hot atom chemist and activation analyst both employ high resolution gamma-ray spectroscopy and, when necessary state of the art analytical instrumentation such as gas and high performance liquid chromatography. Hot atom chemistry is an excellent training ground for the activation analyst. Figure 1 depicts a flow diagram showing the various active areas in activation analysis.

We can see from this figure that neutron activation has been and still remains the predominant choice in activation analysis. However, charged particle activation analysis (CPAA) should increase in importance because of the increased number of compact, variable-energy accelerators made available in various laboratories throughout the world. Reviews of this specialized technique can be found elsewhere[5] and will not be covered in this review. Photon Activation Analysis (PA) has yet to reach a level of utilization of other activation methods because of the lack of access to high-intensity photon sources. Segebade[6] describes some applications of photonuclear reactions to activation analysis. Applications of hot atoms to thermal neutron activation analysis, molecular neutron activation analysis and the application of hot atoms as interactive tracers for determining site information in a matrix will be discussed in the following three sections.

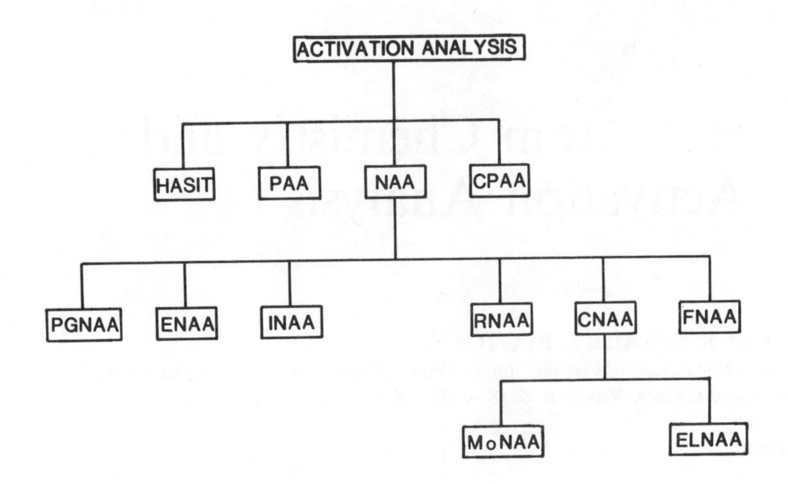

Fig. 1. The many facets of activation analysis: HASIT-Hot atom information techniques; PAA-Photon Activation analysis; NAA-Neutron activation analysis; CPAA-Charged particle activation analysis; PGNAA-Prompt gamma neutron activation analysis; ENAA-Reactor fast neutron and epithermal neutron activation analysis; INAA-Instrumental neutron activation analysis; RCAA-Radiochemical neutron activation analysis; CNAA-Chemical neutron activation analysis; MoNAA-Molecular neutron activation analysis; ELNAA-Elemental neutron activation analysis.

2. Thermal Neutron Activation Analysis

Our discussion in this section will be restricted entirely to instrumental neutron activation analysis (INAA), radiochemical neutron activation analysis (RNAA), and chemical neutron activation analysis (CNAA). These techniques are capable of high sensitivity elemental analysis with excellent precision. Depending upon favorable nuclear properties such as thermal neutron cross section, half-life and natural elemental abundance, detection limits in the parts per billion range can be approached. Thermal neutron activation analysis has been a powerful technique for determining numerous trace elements in a large variety of matrices, such as archeological artifacts, environmental samples and biological samples. For historical artifacts or valuable pieces of art, most probably non-destructive neutron activation analysis will be performed. For many biological samples containing high concentrations of the radioactivatible elements, separation procedures prior to neutron activation (CNAA) or after neutron activation (RNAA) must be employed. This is necessary to allow determination of the radioactive element's photo peak by gamma-ray spectrometry. Provided that the radioactivatible element analyzed has favorable nuclear properties for activation, neutron activation analysis is superior in precision, accuracy, selectivity and sensitivity to such techniques as atomic absorption spectrometry, atomic emission spectrometry, solution absorption spectroscopy and solution fluorescence spectrometry for certain elements. However, one severe limitation of neutron activation analysis is the limited number of research nuclear reactors currently available worldwide.

2.1. Instrumental Neutron Activation Analysis (INAA)

INAA is the most popular choice if a rapid, nondestructive multielemental analysis of the sample is required. As shown in Figure 2, INAA requires minimum manipulation of the sample since no chemical separation is performed; therefore, it is inexpensive compared to the other NAA methods. The sample is only irradiated, allowed to decay and counted. One of the advantages over the other methods is its nondestructive character and its being free from possible contamination from chemical reagents regularly used during chemical separation. A complete analysis can be performed without significantly altering the physical or chemical nature of the sample. It is usually the method of choice for delicate samples, such as works of art, and samples whose physical identity needs to be preserved, such as forensic, lunar and geological samples.

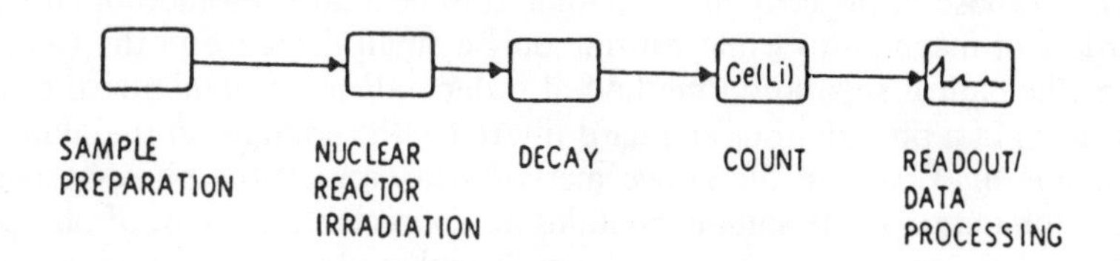

Fig. 2. Typical instrumental neutron activation analysis (INAA) experiment.

Like many other analytical methods, INAA has its limitations. Activation without chemical separations can be applied only in special conditions. In the ideal case, the ratio of the activities induced in the matrix to that of the element to be determined should be low or even zero. Koyama in his review "Hot Atom Chemistry and Activation Analysis" in the earlier volume *Hot Atom Chemistry* discusses the hot atom chemistry effects mainly due to recoil of the activated atoms and vaporization losses. Even in INAA, the analyst must be familiar with the chemical and hot atom properties of the elemental analyte.

If the matrix activity is low, chemical separations can be avoided for the analysis of minor constituents, but generally not in the case of trace levels. In certain instances, when the matrix activity is shorter lived than the activity induced in the element to be measured, determination down to the trace element level is possible. In this case, activity of the matrix can be allowed to decay before the activity of the element is measured. However, INAA has limited application for the trace element determination in biological (and other complex matrices). Biological matrices are rich in Na and Cl. The activity generated by the more abundant ^{24}Na ($t_{1/2}$ = 15.02 h) and ^{38}Cl ($t_{1/2}$ = 37.2 m) is very intense and thus obscures most of the short-lived trace elements. In order to determine these elements, a chemical separation procedure must be employed. For example in their study of the determination of trace iodine in biological samples[7)], Blotcky and Rack compared INAA and RNAA methods for the determination of trace iodine in saliva. From the experimental results they concluded that the most suitable procedure was the wet chemistry destructive procedure which allows a reduction of the Compton continuum under the iodine photopeak. In the INAA method the Compton continuum contribution to the iodine photopeak was 77% of the total counts at the photopeak.

Another source of error may be induced by the reaction of fast neutrons with other elements in the matrix. Although the main neutron flux in research reactor consists of thermalized neutrons (0.025eV) capable of producing only (n,γ) reactions, neutrons of higher energy that are in the process of being thermalized are also present. These neutrons which have energies $\geq$ 1 MeV are called fast neutrons and can lead to (n,p) and (n,γ) reactions. The extent to which these neutron induced reactions interfere with thermal neutron activation analysis depends on the relative concentration of the target nucleus in the matrix, the ratio of cross-sections and the ratio of fast to thermal neutron fluxes. Since the relative intensities and energy distribution of fast neutrons depends on the location of the sample within the reactor and varies from reactor to reactor, the extent of interference varies. A typical interfering reaction can be observed when performing INAA on aluminum in biological samples. In that case the interaction of fast neutrons with the phosphorus in the sample produces a $^{31}P(n,\alpha)^{28}Al$ reaction. Several methods have been utilized to correct for this increased aluminum assay. Gatschke and Gawlik[9)] and Alfassi and Lavi[10)] employed mathematical separation after the samples had been irradiated with and without cadmium shielding. The purpose of the cadmium shielding is to decrease considerably the (n,γ) yield (over two orders of magnitude) while causing only a small decrease in the (n,α) and (n,p) yield. The mathematical separation method also depends upon obtaining the ratio of the aluminum assayed in a phosphorous standard filtered with cadmium to the aluminum in an unshielded standard. Errors in the above method can occur if the phosphorous standard contain some aluminum. If the sample contains an appreciable amount of phosphorous, as in some biological samples, the assay of the sample with and without cadmium will be large in comparison to the trace level of aluminum actually in the sample. Consequently, when the assay with cadmium is subtracted from the assay without cadmium the propagation of error becomes large. This laboratory recently analyzed NIST Standard Reference Material Bovine Liver 1577a by the INAA Mathematical Separation Method and by CNAA and determined the assay of aluminum to be 1.9 $\pm$ 0.8 ug Al/g BVL and 2.1 $\pm$ 0.2 ug Al/g BVL respectively. Markesbery and Ehmann et al.[11)] use a 14 Mev neutron generator to activate the phosphorous in the sample by the $^{31}P(n,\alpha)^{28}Al$ reaction and then measure the quantity of aluminum in the sample. Knowing the quantity of aluminum generated in the reactor from a phosphorous standard irradiated under the same conditions as the sample, each sample can be assayed for aluminum by INAA and the phosphorous-aluminum contribution substracted. Since the accuracy of this method depends not only on errors in performing the thermal neutron irradiation and assay, but also on the errors associated with the neutron generator analysis, the propagation of error can also become very large.

2.2. Radiochemical Neutron Activation Analysis (RNAA)

Unlike INAA, this method involves a chemical separation step after irradiation, as shown in Figure 3.
A separation procedure becomes necessary when the activity induced in the matrix is high and interferes in the analysis of the desired species. Efficacious radiochemical separations can be performed in various levels of radiochemical decontamination, depending on the problem at hand. The simplest form is the removal of one or a few interfering radionuclides in a single operation, enabling subsequent measurements of a variety of elements of interest, using high-resolution germanium spectrometry.

The other extreme is the isolation of one or a few radionuclides in a state that is almost radiochemically pure, to take advantage of the high efficiency of some detectors such as NAI

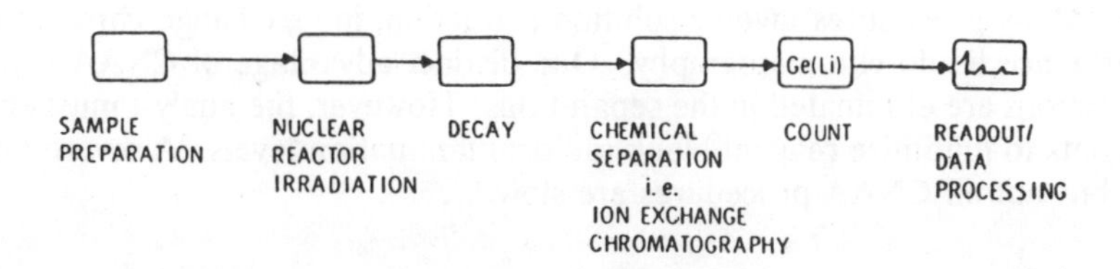

Fig. 3. Typical radiochemical neutron activation analysis (RNAA) experiment.

(Tl); thus enabling analysis in the parts-per-billion range. RNAA procedures are unsuitable for the determination of short-lived trace elements, such as aluminum and vanadium. There are two potential problems because of hot-atom reactions involving the trace element in RNAA procedures. If the trace element is born in an isomeric state after neutron irradiation, such as ^{82m}Br or ^{130m}I, a post-irradiation analysis may be complicated by hot atom reactions induced by the isomeric transitions occurring after neutron irradiation[8)]. For example, for a biological sample being analyzed for trace bromine, the bromine-82 by the $^{82m}Br(I.T.)^{82}Br$ reactions can undergo hot atom reactions in the sample, the sample container, the solvent or the solute used in the post-irradiation chemistry. These reactions can stabilize the bromine-82 activity in a chemical form not amenable to the chemical separation procedures employed. The second problem is general for all neutron irradiations. Because of the radiative neutron capture reactions occurring in the reactor, a trace element not only acquires a radioactive label but a high kinetic energy allowing it to undergo hot atom reactions within the sample. This may lead to a new molecular or ionic form of the trace element and care must be taken to devise suitable post-irradiation separations so that the desired trace element is in a form suitable for analysis.

2.3. Elemental Chemical Neutron Activation Analysis (CNAA)

A chemical separation procedure is employed prior to irradiation as shown in Figure 4. For short-lived radionuclides, pre-irradiation chemistry is necessary if INAA cannot be employed. Due to the short half-life, there would be an appreciable loss of activity in most post-irradiation chemical procedures. The CNAA approach has been used for the analysis of various analytes such as aluminum[12,13)] ($t_{1/2}$ = 2.3m) and vanadium[14-16)] ($t_{1/2}$ = 3.76m), especially in biological samples.

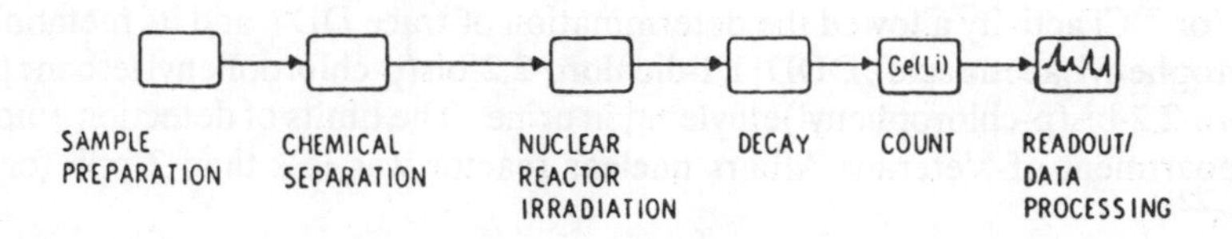

Fig. 4. Typical chemical neutron activation analysis (CNAA) experiment.

In elemental CNAA, the sample matrix, such as tissue, bone or bodily fluid is decomposed into soluble elemental ions of known oxidation state by the use of acids such as ultrapure nitric acid. Many procedures involve solution extraction, ion exchange chromatography or high performance liquid chromatography. One distinct advantage of CNAA is that effects of HAC reactions are eliminated in the separations. However, the analyst must employ high purity reagents to minimize reagent blank radiocontamination levels. A severe limitation is that most, but not all CNAA procedures are slow.

3. Molecular Neutron Activation Analysis (MoNAA)

Grant and Rowland[17)] were the first to coin the expression "molecular activation analysis" in their experiments involving ^{38}Cl reactions in chloranilic acid-water in an attempt to find "site" information. In a true application of hot atom chemistry and techniques to activation analysis, Wiles and his colleagues[18-21)] attempted to determine methylmercury in fish. However, they were unsuccessful. The reasons for the failure were three fold; a matrix dilution of the species sought; a scavaging effect, probably of methyl groups by components of the fish powder; and a methylation of some unidentified components associated with the fish fats. Undoubtably the major problem was employing HAC as a molecular activation analysis tool in a highly complex matrix.

We must remember the main advantage of activation analysis is to be able to determine a radioactivatable analyte to at least the sub-ppm or the ppb region. Unless the HAC approach to molecular activation analysis is able to detect the hot atom fragments containing the radionuclide in the desired range, its application would only be an academic exercise.

Rack, Blotcky and their colleagues[22-26)] developed CNAA procedures for the determination of metabolites containing radioactivatable elements in biological fluids. Typical digestion procedures employing oxidizing acids such as nitric acid cannot be employed. Separation procedures mainly involved ion-exchange and high performance liquid chromatography. Thus this approach employing CNAA procedures in biological fluids, separating the analyte containing the radioactivatable element can be called Molecular Neutron Activation Analysis (MoNAA). The main advantage of MoNAA is the determination of the individual analyte in the biological or environmental matrix. The limitations of the technique are similar to those described in the CNAA Section.

The biological matrices of choice are biological fluids such as serum or urine. For the determination of iodoamino acids and thyroid hormones in a urine matrix, Rack and Blotcky[23)] employed combination gel filtration and high performance liquid chromatography to separate the iodine metabolites, followed by neutron activation detection. Metabolites in the sub-parts-per-million range could be readily determined. This study demonstrated the feasibility of nuclear activation for speciation determination in complex biological samples.

A MoNAA procedure employing solvent extraction and high-performance liquid chromatography separation techniques with subsequent irradiation of the eluted fractions and radioassay for ^{38}Cl activity allowed the determination of trace DDT and its metabolites DDA [bis(p-chlorophenyl)aceticacid], DDD [1,1-dichloro-2,2-bis(p-chlorophenyl)ethane], and DDE [1,1-dichloro-2,2-bis(p-chlorophenyl)ethylene] in urine. The limits of detection employing the Omaha Department of Veterans Affairs nuclear reactor was less than 2 ppb for the DDT metabolites[22)].

Selenium is a vital micronutrient with a narrow range of intake consistent with health, outside of this range deficiency disease or toxicity occurs. Employing ion exchange chromatography and neutron activation detection, trimethylselenonium ion (TMSe), selenite ion and total selenoamino acids were determined in a urine matrix[24-26)]. Presented in

Figure 5 is a schematic describing the determination of TMSe and SeO_3^{2-} by the MoNAA approach.

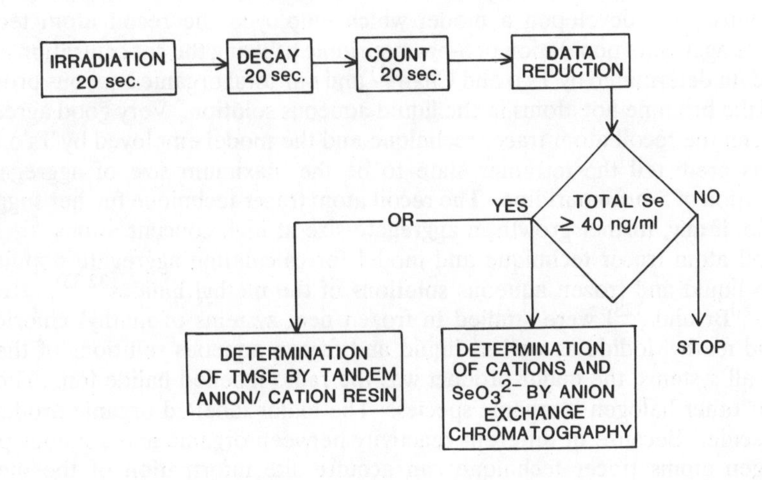

Fig. 5. Schematic describing the MoNAA procedure for the determination of TMSe and SeO_3^{2-} in a urine matrix.

4. Hot Atoms as Site Indicators

A "hot atom" can be utilized as an interactive tracer especially in multiphase systems where site information can be determined. It is important that the hot atom has distinctly different reactivities within the phases. By measuring the labelled reaction products and their yields, information may be acquired as to the nature of the immediate vicinity of the hot atoms. An application of hot atom chemistry as a site indicator was the interesting demonstration that excess ^{129}Xe and ^{128}Xe from nuclear transmutation $^{127}I(n,\gamma)^{128}I \rightarrow {}^{128}Xe$ were being released at the same temperature during the heating of neutron-irradiated meteorite samples[27]. If the ^{129}Xe were present in microscopic iodide crystals within the meteorite, then it would be released at about the same temperature as ^{128}Xe.

In an important preliminary study, Willard et al.[28] found unusually high organic yields - the fraction of the ^{128}I in dilute aqueous solutions of CH_3I. Because of the lack of suitable analytical procedures, no conclusions could be made as to the mechanism of the process. However, the authors suggested that any mechanisms may relate to the probability of the formation of $(CH_3I)_n$, CH_3I_2, CH_3I and $(I_2)_n$ aggregate or complexes in solution.

It is now known from other studies that bases and nucleosides undergo extensive association in aqueous solutions, which not only proceeds to the dimer but to higher polymers[29]. Our first experiments involved the study of recoil ^{38}Cl, ^{80}Br and ^{128}I in crystalline systems of 5-halouracil, 5-halo-2'-deoxyuridine and 5-halouridine[29]. In all of the systems studied, except crystalline 5-iodouracil, the major product was the radio-labelled halide ion. The major labelled organic product was the parent molecule. For the liquid systems, the tendency for aggregation diminished as the solute concentration approached zero, where the probable state of the solute approached a monomolecular dispersion. Unlike the liquid state, the frozen ice lattice demonstrated a caging effect for the solute aggregates which resulted in constant product yields over the entire concentration range. Ts'o and Chan[31)] studied the association of 5-bromouridine over the concentration range of 0.1 to 0.4 molal by a mathematical analysis. Their calculations suggested that the association of 5-bromouridine does not proceed beyond the tetramer stage and the monomer prevails in dilute solutions. We developed a model which employed the recoil atom technique to determine the aggregate population of 5-bromouridine utilizing the concentration and activity coefficient data determined by Ts'o and Chan[31)] and our total organic aqueous product yields by virtue of the bromine hot atoms in the liquid aqueous solution. Very good agreement was found between the recoil atom tracer technique and the model employed by Ts'o and Chan. Both models predicted the tetramer state to be the maximum size of aggregates in the aqueous solution of 5-bromouridine. The recoil atom tracer technique further suggested that there is little, if any, further growth in aggregate size at high concentrations.

The recoil atom tracer technique and model for calculating aggregate populations was extended to liquid and frozen aqueous solutions of the methyl halides[32,33)]. Reactions of recoil ^{38}Cl, ^{80}Br and ^{128}I were studied in frozen neat systems of methyl chloride, methyl bromide and methyl iodide as well as liquid and frozen aqueous solutions of these methyl halides. In all systems, the major product was the radio-labelled halide ion. There was no evidence for other halogen inorganic species. The major labelled organic product was the parent molecule. Because of different reactivity between organic and aqueous phases, the recoil halogen atoms tracer technique can acquire site information of the methylhalide solutes in the liquid and frozen aqueous systems. For all liquid and frozen systems, the methyl halide molecules tended to aggregate. For liquid systems, the tendency for aggregation diminished as the solute concentration approached zero, where the probable state of the solute approached a monomolecular dispersion. Unlike the liquid state, the frozen ice lattice demonstrated a "caging effect" for the solute aggregates which resulted in constant product yields over the whole concentration range.

References

1. Ehmann, W.D., Robertson, J.D., Yates, S.W.: Anal. Chem. 62:12, 50R (1990).
2. Hevesy, G., Levi, H.: Det. Kgl. Danske Videnskabernes Selskab. Mathematisk Fysiske Meddelelser 14:5, 3 (1936).
3. Vandecasteele, C.: "Activation Analysis with Charges Particles", Ellis Horwood: Chichester, UK, 1988, p. 171.
4. Hoste, J., Vandecasteele, C., Strijokmans, K.: Isotopenpraxis 24, 49 (1988).
5. Szabo, A.S., Sasin, L.I.: Elelmiszervisgalati Kozl. 34, 229 (1988).
6. Segebade, C., Weise, H.P., Lutz, G.L.: "Photon Activation Analysis", Walters de Gruyter, Hawthorne, NY, 1987, p. 705.
7. Blotcky, A.J., Hobson, D., Rack, E.P.: Radiochem. Radioanal. Let. 24:4, 291 (1976).
8. Lambrecht, R.M., Rack, E.P.: Analyst 93, 550 (1968).
9. Gatschke, W., Gawlik, D.: J. Radio. Anal. Chem. 56, 203 (1980).
10. Alfassi, Z.B., Lavi, N.: Analyst 109, 959 (1984).
11. Markesbery, W.R., Ehmann, W.D., Hossain, T.I., Alauddin, M., Goodin, D.T.: Annl. Neurol. 10, 551 (1981).
12. Blotcky, A.J., Hobson, D., Leffler, J.A., Rack, E.P., Recker, R.R.: Anal. Chem. 48, 1084 (1979).
13. Garmestani, K., Blotcky, A.J., Rack, E.P.: Anal. Chem. 50, 144 (1978).
14. Blotcky, A.J., Falcone, C., Medina, V.A., Rack, E.P.: Anal. Chem. 51, 1789 (1979).

15. Blotcky, A.J., Hamel, F.G., Stranik, A., Ebrahim, A., Sharma, R.B., Rack, E.P., Solomon, S.S.: J. Radioanal. Nucl. Chem. 131, 319 (1989).
16. Blotcky, A.J., Duckworth, W.C., Ebrahim, A., Hamel, F.K., Rack, E.P., Sharma, R.B.: J. Radioanal. Nucl. Chem. 134, 141 (1989).
17. Grant, P.M., Rowland, F.S.: "Molecular Activation Analysis", IAEA Status Report, Vienna, 1975, p. 219.
18. DeJong, I.G., Omori, T., Wiles, D.R.: Chem. Commun. 189, (1974).
19. DeJong, I.G., Wiles, D.R.: Radiochem. Radioanal. Lett. 17, 343 (1974).
20. DeJong, I.G., Wiles, D.R.: J. Fish Res. Board Can. 33, 1324 (1976).
21. Schmit, J.P., Wiles, D.R.: Can. J. Chem. 56, 1956 (1978).
22. Opelanio, L.R., Rack, E.P., Blotcky, A.J., Crow, F.W.: Anal. Chem. 55, 677 (1983).
23. Firouzbakht, M.L., Garmestani, S.K., Rack, E.P., Blotcky, A.J.: Anal. Chem. 53, 1746 (1981).
24. Blotcky, A.J., Hansen, G.T., Opelanio-Buencamino, L.R., Rack, E.P.: Anal. Chem. 57, 1937 (1985).
25. Blotcky, A.J., Hansen, G.T., Borkar, N., Ebrahim, A., Rack, E.P.: Anal. Chem. 59, 2063 (1987).
26. Blotcky, A.J. Ebrahim, A., Rack, E.P.: Anal. Chem. 60, 2734 (1988).
27. Renolds, J.: Ann. Rev. Nucl. Sci. 17, 253 (1976).
28. Wilkey, D.D., Brensike, J.E., Willard, J.E.: J. Phys. Chem. 71, 3580 (1967).
29. Ts'o, P.O.P.: "Basic Principles in Nucleic Acids Chemistry", Vol. 1, Academic Press, New York, 1964, p. 517.
30. Arsenault, L.J., Blotcky, A.J., Firouzbakht, M.L., Rack, E.P.: Radiochim. Acta 31, 171 (1982).
31. Ts'o, P.O.P., Chan, S.I.J.: J. Am. Chem. Soc. 86, 4176 (1964).
32. Opelanio-Buencamino, L.R., El-Amri, F.A., Grauer, W.M., Rack, E.P.: Radiochim. Acta 37, 191 (1984).
33. Opelanio-Buencamino, L.R., Rack, E.P.: Radiochim. Acta 38, 87 (1985).

Chapter 5

Radiation - Chemical and Other Hot Atom Chemistry Related Processes

5.1 Comparison of Recoil T Atoms with H(D) Atoms Produced by Radiolysis and Photolysis in the Solid Phase

Tetsuo MIYAZAKI
Department of Applied Chemistry, Faculty of Engineering, Nagoya University,
Chikusa-ku, Nagoya 464, Japan

1. Identification of Hot Processes in The Solid Phase at Low Temperature

In this autoreview the behavior of recoil T atoms produced by the nuclear reaction $^6Li(n,\alpha)T$ in the solid phase at low temperature is compared with that of H(D) atoms produced by radiolysis or photolysis. The hydrogen (H, D, T) atoms have initially excess kinetic energies and are called hot atoms. The hot atoms react with neighboring molecules, or lose their energies by collisions and are eventually thermalized.

According to a well-known criterion for hot atom reactions in the gas phase, hot atoms react without any activation energy, while thermal atoms generally react with activation energy. Thus, scavenger effects and the temperature dependence of reactions are commonly adopted for distinguishing hot and thermal reactions.

This criterion, however, cannot be applied to the reactions of hydrogen atoms in the solid phase at low temperature. Thermal H, D, and T atoms can react below 77 K by quantum-mechanical tunneling without any activation energy. According to the classical theory of chemical reaction, thermal reactions take place by passing over the potential energy barrier for the reaction and thus the reactions are suppressed at low temperature. Since hydrogen atoms are the lightest atoms and have the character of a wave, the thermal atoms can pass through the energy barrier for the reaction by their wave character, this is called a quantum-mechanical tunneling effect.[1] For example, the reaction $HD + D \longrightarrow H + D_2$ takes place easily at 4.2 and 1.9 K with rate constants 2.3×10^{-3} and 2.1×10^{-3} $cm^3\ mol^{-1}\ s^{-1}$, respectively,[2] where the apparent activation energy for the reaction is zero though a potential barrier for this reaction is 40 kJ mol^{-1}. Thermal T atoms also react with H_2 and C_2H_6 below 77 K by tunneling.[3-5] Tunneling reactions generally do not depend upon temperature. Conventional radical scavengers are ineffective in the solid phase at low temperature because of the small activation energy of their reaction and the competition with tunneling. Therefore at low temperature it is very difficult to discriminate a hot atom reaction from a tunneling reaction of thermal hydrogen atoms.

Miyazaki[6] has pointed out that a large isotope effect and a high selectivity are observed in tunneling reactions of hydrogen atoms at low temperature. On the contrary, hot atom reactions are characterized by a small isotope effect and a low selectivity. Therefore the isotope effect and the selectivity can be used a measure for distinguishing hot reactions from thermal tunneling in the solid phase at low temperature.

2. Initial Energy of Hot Hydrogen Atoms

The photolysis of HI or HBr with monochromatic light produces H atoms with an excess of kinetic energy, estimated from the wavelength of the light and the bond energy of HI (or HBr). For example, the initial energy of H atoms produced by 254-nm photolysis of HI is 1.8 eV when ground-state I atoms are produced, but 0.9 eV when I atoms are produced in the first excited state.

The initial energy of H atoms produced by radiolysis in the solid phase has not yet been estimated, except for an argon-alkane mixture at 4.2 K. In the Ar matrix at 4.2 K, hot H atoms are trapped in substitutional sites and interstitial sites, which can be distinguished by ESR spectroscopy.

Figure 1 shows the ratio ($[H_I]/([H_I]+[H_S])$) as a function of the initial energy of H atoms,[6-8] where $[H_I]$ and $[H_S]$ represent the yields of H atoms trapped in the interstitial and substitutional sites, respectively. The trapping ratio of the interstitial sites increases with increasing initial energy of H atoms. When H atoms are produced by radiolysis of Ar-C_2H_6(or C_3H_8 or i-C_4H_{10}) mixtures at 4.2 K, the trapping ratios, indicated by triangles in Fig. 1, amount to 0.94 - 0.99 . Such high ratios suggest that H atoms produced by radiolysis of the alkanes had an initial kinetic energy of about 6 eV (cf. dashed arrows in Fig. 1).

Recoil T atoms produced by the nuclear reaction $^6Li(n, \alpha)T$ have an initial kinetic energy of 2.7 MeV, higher than the energies of hot H atoms produced by photolysis or radiolysis.

Let us consider two mechanisms, a priori, for reactions of recoil T atoms in the solid phase. The first mechanism assumes that the behavior of recoil T atoms in the solid phase is different from that of H(D) atoms in the photolysis and radiolysis in the solid phase since the initial energy of the recoil T atoms is much higher than that of the H(D) atoms. The alternative one considers that in the gas phase several tenths percent of the total recoil T atoms lose their energy and become thermalized. Thus, if the same moderation process takes place in the solid phase, the behavior of recoil T atoms in the solid phase is somewhat similar to that of H(D) atoms in the photolysis and radiolysis in the solid phase. Now the two possible mechanisms will be examined experimentally.

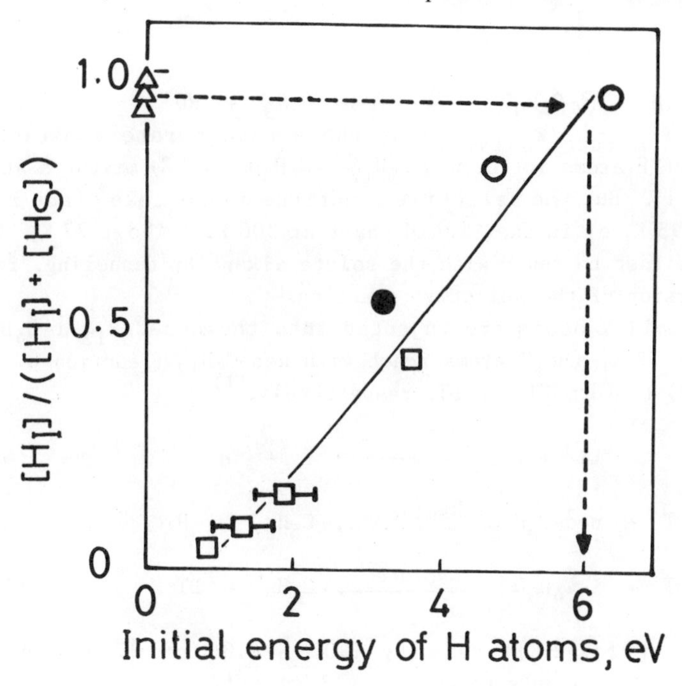

Fig. 1. Ratio of yields of H_I to total trapped H atoms against initial energy of H atoms in an Ar matrix at 4.2 K. □ , H atoms produced by photolysis of HI; ○ ; H atoms produced by radiolysis of H_2 or HD; ● , $[D_I]/([D_I]+[D_S])$ for D atoms produced by radiolysis of HD. △ , $[H_I]/([H_I]+[H_S])$ for H atoms produced by radiolysis of Ar-alkane mixtures. $[H_I]$ and $[H_S]$ represent yields of H atoms trapped in interstitial and substitutional sites, respectively. (quoted from ref. 6)

3. Comparison of Recoil T Atoms with H(D) Atoms Produced in Radiolysis and Photolysis

3-1. Solid Neopentane

When H atoms are produced at 77 K by γ-radiolysis of neopentane("solvent") containing a small amount of other alkane("solute") or by photolysis of HI in the neopentane-alkane mixtures (reactions 1 and 2), the H atoms migrate through crystalline neopentane and react selectively with the solute, for example i-C_4H_9D, probably by tunneling (reaction 4) and produce C_4H_9 radicals and HD in significant yields.[9, 10]

$$\text{neo-}C_5H_{12} \rightsquigarrow C_5H_{11}^{\cdot} + H \qquad (1)$$

$$HI \xrightarrow{h\nu} I + H \qquad (2)$$

$$H + \text{neo-}C_5H_{12} \xrightarrow{k_{solvent}} C_5H_{11}^{\cdot} + H_2 \qquad (3)$$

$$H + i\text{-}C_4H_9D \xrightarrow{k_{solute}} C_4H_9^{\bullet} + HD \qquad (4)$$

The ratio ($k_{solute}/k_{solvent}$) of the apparent rate constants for the reactions of H atoms in the neo-C_5H_{12}-i-C_4H_9D(2 mol%) mixtures at 77 K is 38 (cf. Table 1). But the selective reactions do not take place in the solid phase at 195 K, or in the liquid phase at 300 K. Above 77 K, H atoms may diffuse too fast to react with the solute alkane by tunneling, resulting in the suppression of the selective reaction.

When recoil T atoms are injected into the neo-C_5H_{12}-i-C_4H_9D(2 mol%) mixtures at 77 K, the T atoms react with neo-C_5H_{12} (reaction 6) and i-C_4H_9D (reaction 7) to form HT and DT, respectively.[11]

$$^{6}Li + n \longrightarrow T + \alpha \qquad (5)$$

$$T + neo\text{-}C_5H_{12} \xrightarrow{k_{solvent}} C_5H_{11}^{\bullet} + HT \qquad (6)$$

$$T + i\text{-}C_4H_9D \xrightarrow{k_{solute}} C_4H_9^{\bullet} + DT \qquad (7)$$

The ratio ([DT]/[HT]) is only 0.02 - 0.06 at 77 K and the ratio $k_{solute}/k_{solvent}$ amounts to about 1 - 3.[12, 13]

Table 1. Ratio ($k_{solute}/k_{solvent}$) of the rate constants for hydrogen atom abstraction reactions.

Temp. K	neo-C_5H_{12}-i-$C_4H_9D^a$ (2 mol%)		n-$C_{10}D_{22}$-n-$C_{10}H_{22}{}^a$ (10 mol%)		D_2-H_2	
	radiolytic H	recoil T	radiolytic D	recoil T	radiolytic D^b	recoil T^c
4					$>3\times10^4$	~1
77	38	1 - 3	31	2.3		
195	~1	0.25	8.8	2.3		
300	<1	0.39	6.5	2.2		

a, quoted from ref. 12 and 13. b, quoted from 19. The value is $k(D+H_2)/k(H+D_2)$. c, quoted from ref. 21.

The very low yields of DT indicate that only about 5 % of recoil T atoms are thermalized to the energy characteristic of H atoms produced by radiolysis and photolysis. Almost all recoil T atoms react with solid neopentane by a hot atom reaction. In the gas phase, however, about 30 - 40 % of the total recoil T atoms are thermalized in alkanes.[14-17] If the energy loss of recoil hot T atoms in the solid phase is assumed to be the same as that in the gas phase, there is a question why the thermalized T atoms do not react with the solute alkane in the neopentane matrix at 77 K. The previous calculation of rate constants of hydrogen atoms with alkane shows that there is no significant difference in tunneling rate constants between H(D) atoms and T atoms.[3] Before we discuss the cause of the characteristic behavior of recoil T atoms in the solid phase, the tritium behavior in other systems will be described.

3-2. Solid Decane

When $n\text{-}C_{10}D_{22}\text{-}n\text{-}C_{10}H_{22}$ mixtures are irradiated at 77 K with γ-rays, D atoms produced react selectively with the solute $n\text{-}C_{10}H_{22}$.[10]

$$n\text{-}C_{10}D_{22} \rightsquigarrow C_{10}D_{21}^{\cdot} + D \qquad (8)$$

$$D + n\text{-}C_{10}D_{22} \xrightarrow{k_{solvent}} C_{10}D_{21}^{\cdot} + D_2 \qquad (9)$$

$$D + n\text{-}C_{10}H_{22} \xrightarrow{k_{solute}} C_{10}H_{21}^{\cdot} + HD \qquad (10)$$

The ratio ($k_{solute}/k_{solvent}$) of apparent rate constants for reactions 9 and 10 is 31 at 77 K (cf. Table 1).

When recoil T atoms are injected into the $n\text{-}C_{10}D_{22}\text{-}n\text{-}C_{10}H_{22}$ mixtures at 77 K, the ratio ($k_{solute}/k_{solvent}$) of apparent rate constants for reactions 11 and 12 is only 2.3 (cf. Table 1).[13]

$$T + n\text{-}C_{10}D_{22} \xrightarrow{k_{solvent}} C_{10}D_{21}^{\cdot} + DT \qquad (11)$$

$$T + n\text{-}C_{10}H_{22} \xrightarrow{k_{solute}} C_{10}H_{21}^{\cdot} + HT \qquad (12)$$

The low value of the ratio ($k_{solute}/k_{solvent}$) at 77 K indicates that only 3 to 5 % of all recoil T atoms are thermalized and diffuse into the decane matrix.[18]

3-3. Solid Hydrogen

The reaction of hydrogen atoms in solid hydrogen can be considered as a prototype solid-state reaction that can be discussed unequivocally. When D atoms are produced by radiolysis or photolysis in solid D_2-H_2 mixtures at 4.2 K, D atoms react selectively with H_2 by a tunneling reaction $D + H_2 \rightarrow HD + H$.[19, 20] The ratio of rate constants ($k(D + H_2 \rightarrow HD + H)/k(H + D_2 \rightarrow HD + D)$) exceeds 3×10^4 (cf. Table 1).

When recoil T atoms are injected into the D_2-H_2 mixtures at 4.2 K, the ratio of the rate constants ($k(T + H_2 \rightarrow HT + H)/k(T + D_2 \rightarrow DT + D)$) is about 1 (cf. Table 1),[21] which is similar to the ratio (1.0) of the rate constants for hot T atom reactions in the gas phase.[22] A large value (7.5×10^5) for the ratio of rate constants is expected theoretically for tunneling reactions of thermal T atoms.[23] Thus, it is concluded that less than 10 % of recoil T atoms are thermalized in solid hydrogen, though 20 - 30 % of recoil T atoms are thermalized in gaseous hydrogen.[24]

4. Characteristic Behavior of Recoil T Atoms in The Solid Phase

The experimental results in the previous sections indicate that only less than 10 percent of recoil T atoms are thermalized and diffuse into the solid matrix, though a large fraction (50 - 90 %) of H(D) atoms produced by radiolysis and photolysis diffuse and react selectively with solutes.[10] Among possible explanations for the characteristic behavior of the recoil T atoms in the solid phase, the following mechanism is most plausible. First, the efficiency of moderation of hot T atoms in the solid phase may be lower than that in the gas phase, resulting in the low yields of thermal T atoms. Second, a recoil T atom produced has an initial energy of 2.7 MeV and produces a high-LET track along its trajectory in the solid phase. The local concentration of free radicals and the local temperature in the track are probably much higher than those in the bulk matrix. Even if the T atoms are thermalized, most of them react with radicals in the track without diffusion into the bulk matrix.

Acknowledgement

The author wishes to thank Dr. E. Tachikawa, Dr. Y. Aratono, and Dr. M. Saeki of the Japan Atomic Energy Research Institute and Mr. Y. Fujitani of Nagoya University for their collaboration in the study of tritium reactions.

References And Note

1. Caldin, E. F.: Chem. Rev., 69, 135 (1969).
2. Miyazaki, T., Lee, K., Fueki, K., Takeuchi, A.: J. Phys. Chem., 88, 4959 (1984).
3. Aratono, Y., Tachikawa, E., Miyazaki, T., Nagaya, S., Fujitani, Y., Fueki, K.: J. Phys. Chem., 87, 1201 (1983).
4. Lee, K., Ito, Y., Fujitani, Y., Miyazaki, T., Fueki, K., Aratono, Y., Saeki, M., Tachikawa, E.: J. Phys. Chem., 90, 5343 (1986).
5. Fujitani, Y., Miyazaki, T., Fueki, K., Masaki, N. M., Aratono, Y., Saeki, M., Tachikawa, E.: Bull. Chem. Soc. Jpn., 63, 520 (1990).
6. Miyazaki, T.: Radiat. Phys. Chem., 37, 635 (1990).
7. Miyazaki, T., Wakahara, A., Usui, T., Fueki, K.: J. Phys. Chem., 86, 3881 (1982).
8. Gotoh, K., Miyazaki, T., Fueki, K., Lee, K.: Radiat. Phys. Chem., 30, 89 (1987).
9. Miyazaki, T., Hirayama, T.: J. Phys. Chem., 79, 566 (1975).
10. Miyazaki, T., Kasugai, J., Wada, M., Kinugawa, K.: Bull. Chem. Soc. Jpn., 51, 1676 (1978).
11. Though a substitutional reaction T + neo-$C_5H_{12} \rightarrow H + C_5H_{11}T$ is another main reaction besides a hydrogen atom abstraction reaction, only the abstraction reaction are shown here.

12. Aratono, Y., Tachikawa, E., Miyazaki, T., Sakurai, M., Fueki, K.: Bull. Chem. Soc. Jpn.: 54, 1627 (1981).
13. Aratono, Y., Tachikawa, E., Miyazaki, T., Kawai, Y., Fueki, K.: J. Phys. Chem.: 86, 248 (1982).
14. Wolfgang, R.: Progress Reaction Kinetics, 3, 97 (1965).
15. Urch, D. S., Welch, M. J.: Trans. Faraday Soc.: 62, 388 (1966).
16. See, D., Wolfgang, R.: J. Chem. Phys., 47, 143 (1967).
17. Baker, R. T. K., Wolfgang, R.: Trans. Faraday Soc.: 65, 1153 (1969).
18. Aratono, Y., Tachikawa, E., Miyazaki, T., Fueki, K.: Bull. Chem. Soc. Jpn., 55, 1957 (1982).
19. Tsuruta, H., Miyazaki, T., Fueki, K., Azuma, N.: J. Phys. Chem., 87, 5422 (1983).
20. Miyazaki, T.: Bull. Chem. Soc. Jpn., 58, 2413 (1985).
21. Fujitani, Y., Miyazaki, T., Fueki, K., Masaki, N. M., Aratono, Y., Saeki, M., Tachikawa, E.: J. Phys. Chem., 95, 1651 (1991).
22. Malcome-Lawes, D. J.: J. Chem. Soc., Faraday Trans. I, 79, 2735 (1983).
23. Takayanagi, T., Sato, S., Tsunashima, S.: Proceedings of 32nd Japanese Conference on Radiation Chemistry, Hiroshima, Oct., 1989.
24. Malcome-Lawes, D. J., Oldham, G., Ziadek, Y. Z.: J. Chem. Soc., Faraday Trans. I, 78, 961 (1982).

5.2 On Solvated Electrons in Condensed Phase

Masaaki OGASAWARA
Faculty of Engineering, Hokkaido University, Sapporo 060, Japan

1. Introduction

An electron released from a molecule by ionizing radiation diffuses through matter until it is captured by a molecule or an atom having positive electron affinity. However, if the condensed matter consists of molecules with negative or zero electron affinity, the electron may be trapped by a potential energy well induced by its own polarization field. Such a trapped electron, now called the hydrated electron e_{aq}^- in water and solvated electron e_{sol}^- in general, is playing an important role in the radiolysis of solutions. For instance, it is well established that the reaction of e_{aq}^- with a water molecule leads to the formation of OH^- and H radical.[1)]

$$e_{aq}^- + H_2O \rightarrow OH^- + H$$

Solvated electrons possess extremely high electron donor capacity, because the electron is only surrounded by solvent molecules and not incorporated into the orbitals of a molecule. Reaction takes place quite easily in liquids when the trapped electron and an electron acceptor reach some encounter distance, provided the electron affinity of the acceptor is higher than that of the solvent trap; thousands of rate constants for various kinds of electron acceptors have accumulated already.[2,3)] Indeed, the discovery of solvated electrons opened the door to a new field of chemistry which had relevance to different branches of science.

In this chapter, we describe basic characteristics of solvated electrons first and, in the following sections, survey recent information on the electron capturing process, the solvent relaxation process, the solvation structure, and the charge distribution. Emphasis is particularly on the hydrated electron because of its importance in radiation chemistry.

2. Basic Characteristics of Solvated Electrons

The nature of the hydrated electron may be summarized as follows. (1) The electron is bound in the solvent by an energy of 1-2 eV. (2) The electron is surrounded by more than one solvent molecules and localized in a relatively small area. (3) It has a broad, asymmetric absorption spectrum with E_{max} at 1.73 eV and a long tail to the higher energy side. (4) It has a narrow singlet ESR spectrum with a g-value close to that of the free electron.

Perhaps, a solvated election can be compared to a ball on a sponge-mat. The electron is trapped by the polarization of the solvent molecules induced by itself. Two different approaches were made for the calculation of the binding energy of the electron in earlier times: a continuum model and a tetrahedron model. In the continuum model, a cavity with a radius of several angstroms was assumed in the medium. The potential energy is constant within the cavity, and, outside of the cavity, it is proportional to the reciprocal of the distance r from the center of the cavity.[4)]

$$V(t) = (1/\varepsilon_{op} - 1/\varepsilon_{s})(e^2/r) \tag{1}$$

Where ε_{op} and ε_{s} stand for an optical dielectric constant and a static dielectric constant, respectively. Thus, only the long range interaction is considered in this model. In the tetrahedron model, solvent molecules are treated as point-dipoles and only the short-range interactions between the electron and the point dipoles placed at the corners of a tetrahedron are calculated.[5,6)] These two extreme models are combined and unified in a semi-continuum model, in which both the long-rang interactions and the short-range interactions are considered.[7)] In this model, the first solvation shell round the cavity and the electron is assumed to consist of point-dipoles, and the solvent molecules beyond the first solvation shell are treated as a continuum medium. The short range interaction is expressed by the sum of the electron-permanent dipole interaction V_0 and the electron-induced dipole interaction. The semicontinuum model is accepted widely as a conventional model for solvated electrons, since the computational results obtained in the framework of this model fit the experimental data quite well.

Figure 1 summarizes the absorption spectra of solvated electrons observed in a variety of solvents.[8)] As solvated electrons are usually unstable with lifetime less than 1 ms at room temperature, most of the spectra shown in this figure were measured by using pulse radiolysis. As shown in this figure, the position of E_{max} is independent of the dipole moment of the solvent molecule, but affected by the local structure of the solvent, as arising from OH or ether groups. In alcohols, E_{max} is observed almost at the same position even if the solvent is changed from methanol to undecanol with the static dielectric constant being decreased from 34 to 5.[9)] The continuum model is obviously invalid in this case. As far as the absorption spectrum is concerned, only the interaction between the electron and the OH group seems to be important. The absorption spectra of solvated electrons are very wide in general; the half-width of the hydrated electron spectrum is as large as 0.93 eV. The long tail extending to the higher energy side is ascribed to bound-continum transitions.

3. Electron Trapping and Solvent Relaxation

Ionization of molecules induced by the interaction between ionizing radiation and solvent proceeds in the time range of 10^{-16}s, which is comparable

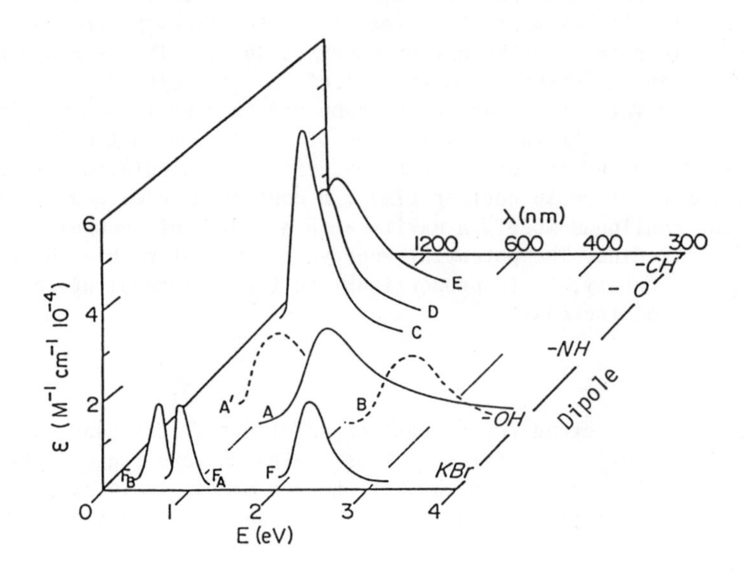

Fig. 1 Intensity and energy of optical transition of solvated electron as a function of molecular dipole and liquid structure. (A) Normal alcohols, (A) tertiary alcohols, (B) chelating alcohol, (C) ammonia, (D) ether, (E) alkane, (F) KBr F center, ($F_{A,B}$) absorption and stimulated emission from F_A(II) center in KBr.

to that of usual electronic transitions.[10] High energy electrons produced by high-energy radiation are called pseudo-free electrons e_{qf}^-, because they can migrate in the matter by spreading over the conduction band. The pseudo-free electrons quickly become thermalized electrons e_{th}^- as a result of repeated collisions with solvent molecules. They are ultimately stabilized by solvent within 1 ps, via at least one more state e_{loc}^- (see the processes (3)). In water, all the processes necessary to form a fully relaxed solvated electron e_{sol}^- are complete within 10^{-13} s after ionization.

$$H_2O \qquad H_2O^+ + e_{qf}^- \tag{2}$$
$$e_{qf}^- \qquad e_{th}^- \qquad e_{loc}^- \qquad e_{sol}^- \tag{3}$$

The subpicosecond time-domain is an important one in the radiolysis of water where the processes from the pseudo-free electron to the fully relaxed solvated electron take place successively. Recently, the observation of the events in this time-domain became feasible owing to the development of the femtosecond laser facilities. Two-photon photoionization experiments carried out by Gauduel et al. revealed that an infrared absorption band, which increases continuously

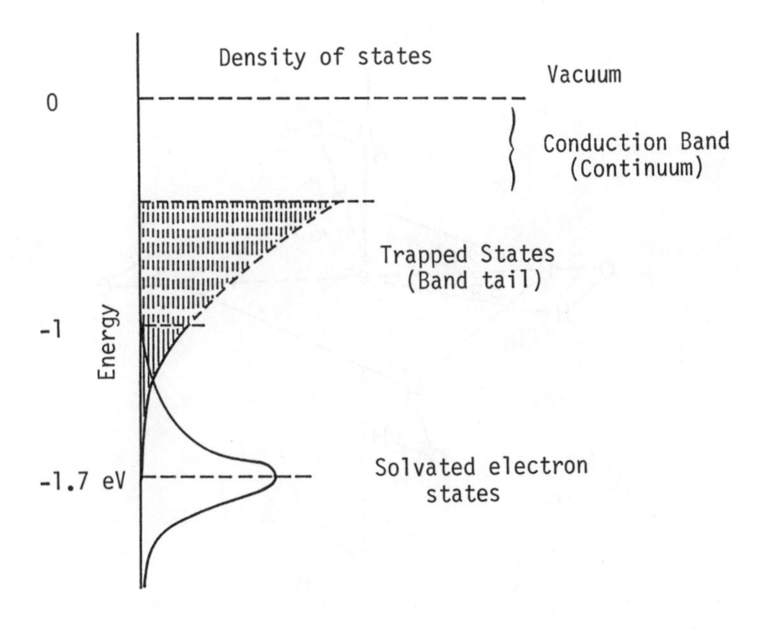

Fig. 2 The energy diagram and the density of states for pre-solvated and solvated electron in liquid water. The dotted line is drawn by speculation.

up to 1 250 nm, appeared first with a time constant of 110 20 ± fs.[11,12] The band converted to the usual hydrated electron absorption peaking at 720 nm with a time-constant of 240 20 fs. Figure 2 illustrates the relation between these two absorption bands schematically. Long et al. confirmed the existence of an isobestic point at 850 nm by subtracting the overlapping absorption due to H_2O^+.[13] The spectral change is not continuous, but is ascribed to a sudden conversion from a state giving rise to the infrared band to the fully relaxed hydrated electron band; the solvation shell is not formed by the successive reorientation of solvent molecules around the excess electron.

A plausible candidate for the state giving rise to the infrared band is a presolvated electron in the electronic ground state. Gauduel et al explained that an electron was trapped by pre-existing potential fluctuations in water and became a cluster anion $(H_2O)_n^-$ consisting of a small number of water molecules.[14] Then a question arises as to what kind of potential exists in water before the injection of the excess electrons.

A model of electron-trap due to the random orientation of solvent molecules was first proposed by Tachiya and Mozumder more than a decade ago.[15] The idea has been developed remarkably over several years in the modern quantum simulations such as quantum path integral molecular dynamics calculations or Monte-Carlo simulations. According to the results obtained by Schnitker et al., the potential gap due to the polarization of electron density and molecular

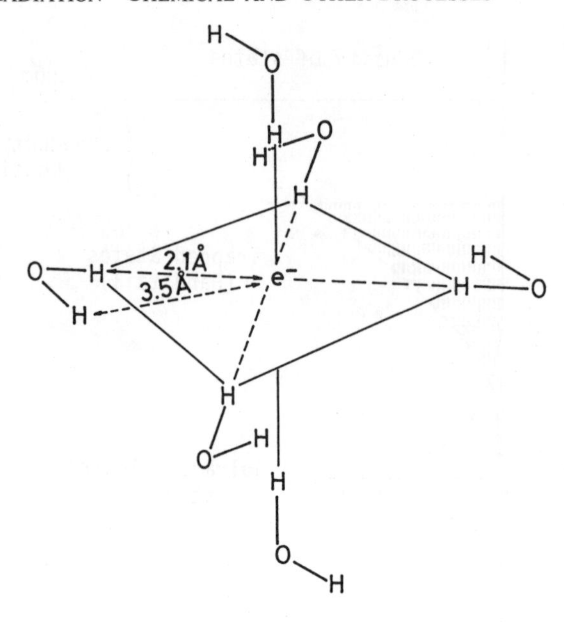

Fig. 3 Geometrical structure of e_t^- in 10 M NaOH aqueous glasses determined from electron spin echo modulation analysis.

orientation increases from -1.4 eV toward 0 eV continuously.[16] This is consistent with the infrared absorption in Fig. 2 which increases in intensity from the visible toward the infrared region beyond 1 250 nm. The spectral change from the infrared to the visible band is ascribed tentatively to a quick contraction of the cluster anions formed in water[14]; the excess electron may also "shrink" simultaneously into a cavity.

However, there is a dispute about the idea that the state giving rise to the infrared band is in an electronic ground state. A group of Eisenthal argues that the electron is first trapped by a pre-existed deep trap in an excited state and then converts to the ground state by nonradiative transition.[13]

4. Solvation Structure

The ESR spectrum of electrons trapped in various aqueous systems shows a narrow symmetric singlet.[17] This spectrum is not useful for solvation structure analysis, because hyperfine structure due to the protons composing the solvation shell is not found. Electron spin echo (ESE) measurements, on the other hand, provide detailed information about the geometrical structure of trapped electrons (e_t^-) in amorphous matrices.

The decay envelope of ESE observed in pulsed electron spin resonance experiments contains a modulation function, which is compared with the theory based on a certain assumed geometry of e_t^-. Kevan et al. analyzed the ESE modulation pattern from the e_t^- produced in 10 M NaOH by x-irradiation and ascribed it as due to a nearest solvation of six water molecules with their OH bonds oriented toward the center of the cavity as shown in Fig. 3.[18] The solvation shell consisting of three water molecules with their molecular dipoles oriented toward the center is an alternative model.[19] However, Kevan et al. rejected this possibility on the basis of the second moment analysis of the ESR spectra recorded from samples of oxygen-17 enriched water.

The model shown in Fig. 3, however, is too idealized and simplified: the real picture of solvated electrons in disordered media must show statistical fluctuations. The information about the statistical fluctuations is now available from various kinds of computer experiments. In quantum simulation the electron is treated as a quantum system and the surrounding molecules, in many cases, are treated classically. The interactions between the test charge and the solvent molecules are usually described by a so-called pseudo-potential.[20,21,22)

$$V(e\text{-}X) = V_{coul} + V_p + V_e + V_x \qquad (4)$$

Where, V_{coul} is the electrostatic attractive force between the electron and the partial charge of the molecule which is fixed on the H, O, H atoms of a rigid water molecule; V_p and V_e are the attractive force due to polarization of the molecule and the repulsive force derived from Pauli's principle; and V_x stands for the electron exchange energy between the test electron and the molecular electrons. Among these terms V_p is the most critical, and Rossky et al. used the following spherically symmetric function in the path integral calculation of solvated electrons.[21]

$$(\alpha_0/2r^4)\{1 - \exp[(r/r_0)^6] \qquad (5)$$

In this equation, α_0 is the isotropic term of the molecular polarizability and r_0 is a cut-off parameter. They used the sum of the bond-length of OH and Bohr's radius for r_0.[21]

The results of the calculations on a cluster anion composed of one excess electron and 200-500 water molecules show that the coordination number is six and the OH groups are pointing to the center of the cavity,[21] consistent with the Kevan model.[18] The distribution of the e-H distances has a peak at 2.3 Å with several subpeaks beyond it. The curve in Fig. 4 visualizes the statistical fluctuation in the solvation structure.

5. Charge Distribution

Transient ESR spectra of hydrated electrons are observable at 22 ℃ by use of an induction-detecting ESR spectrometer system. The g-value of the spectrum was found to be 2.000 47, which was smaller than that of free electron. The g-value shift is ascribed to the spin density in the proximity of oxygen nuclei of the water molecules. According to the ESE study on hydrated electrons in aqueous glasses, however, the total unpaired electron spin density on the first

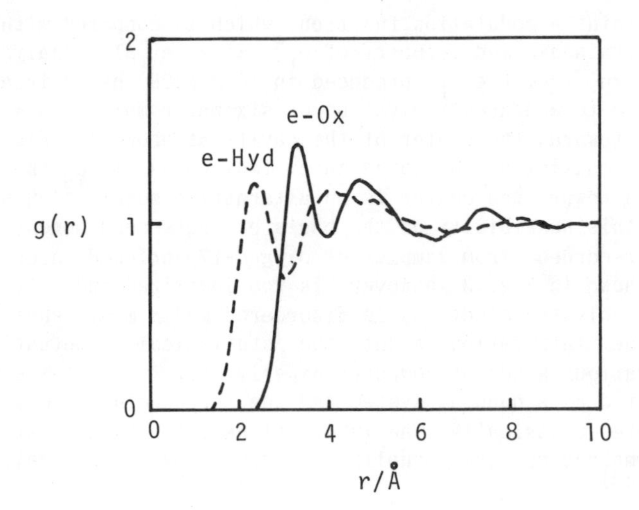

Fig. 4 Radial pair correlation functions between electronic center of mass and either oxgene (e-Ox) or hydrogen (e-hyd) nuclei of the solvent.

solvation shell molecules is as small as 4%.[18] It follows that 96 % of the spin density is distributed in the cavity surrounded by the solvent molecules.

Charge distribution of water cluster anions is extensively studied in current computer experiments. Results of quantum molecular dynamics simulation show that the negative charge is pushed out to the surface of the cluster anion (surface state) when the size of cluster $(H_2O)_n$ is small ($8 \leq n \leq 32$), but it is included in the cluster (interior state) when the size is large ($n>32$).[23] In the interior state the electron is characterized by a localized, roughly spherical, density fluctuation in a ground state, which is very much like a hydrogenic 1s state. The average radius for a system comprising of 500 water molecules and one electron was found to be 2.05 Å with a mean-square fluctuation of about 0.1 Å.[21] The results of the calculation show three p-like states above the s-like localized ground state. The wavefunctions corresponding to these three states are localized with a radius of about 3 Å and with approximately mutually perpendicular orientations. This triple of localized states is distinctly nondegenerate. The most probable energy splitting between the lowest and highest eigenvalue is about 0.8 eV, which reflects a distorted solvent cavity. Above the p-like states lies a band of apparently unbound delocalized states of indefinite symmetry.

However, E_{max} obtain by quantum molecular dynamics simulation is shifted, in comparison with the observed value, toward the higher energy side by as much as 0.7 eV.[23] A current ab-initio MO calculation on cluster anions $(H_2O)_n^-$ by Tachikawa et al. gives a better value of ca. 2.0 eV for E_{max}, although the statistical fluctuations in the solvation structure is not included in this

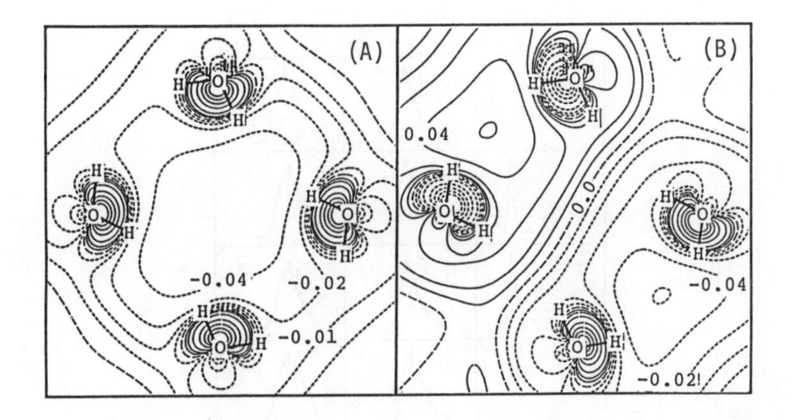

Fig. 5 The contour maps for the excess electron in water cluster anion $(H_2O)_6^-$ obtained by ab-initio MO calculation. (A) An 1s-like wave function for the ground state and (B) and a 2p-like wave function for the first excited state (Ref. 24).

calculation.[24] In their model calculations, the interactions between the excess electron and water molecules in the first solvation shell are explicitly calculated by ab-initio MO methods and those in the second and third solvation shells are represented by fractional charges. The contour maps for the ground state and the first excited state are shown in Fig. 5.

The theoretical predictions, mentioned above, may be tested by the measurement of the photodetachment of electron from water cluster anions. The photoelectron spectra of $(H_2O)^-_{n=2,6,7}$ observed by Coe et al. exhibit a structure, with vibrational features appearing on the high electron binding energy (EBE) side of the main peaks (Fig. 6).[25] The spectra of $(H_2O)^-_{n\geq11}$ consist of single, broad, asymmetric peaks, the EBEs of which correspond to vertical detachment energies. The vertical detachment energies for $n\geq11$ shifted to successively higher EBEs and showed a liner dependence vs. $n^{-1/3}$ in accord with the continuum model of the hydrated electron. It follows that the water cluster anions $n\geq11$ exist as internal states, and thus, are considered as embryonic hydrated electrons.

Information on the anisotropy of the charge distribution of anion clusters has also been obtained.[26] Campagnola et al. measured the angular distribution of the photoelectron ejected from $(H_2O)_{18}^-$ to determine the orbital angular momentum character of the orbital in which an excess electron was localized. The integrated photoelectron yields at various angles between the electric field vector of the laser and TOF drift axis are obtained. The result suggests that the orbitals have mostly s character, but an asymmetry parameter due to the distribution of the ground state electron is also obtained. This angular distribution can be compared with the results of quantum simulations to provide an interesting insight into the charge distribution of hydrated electrons.

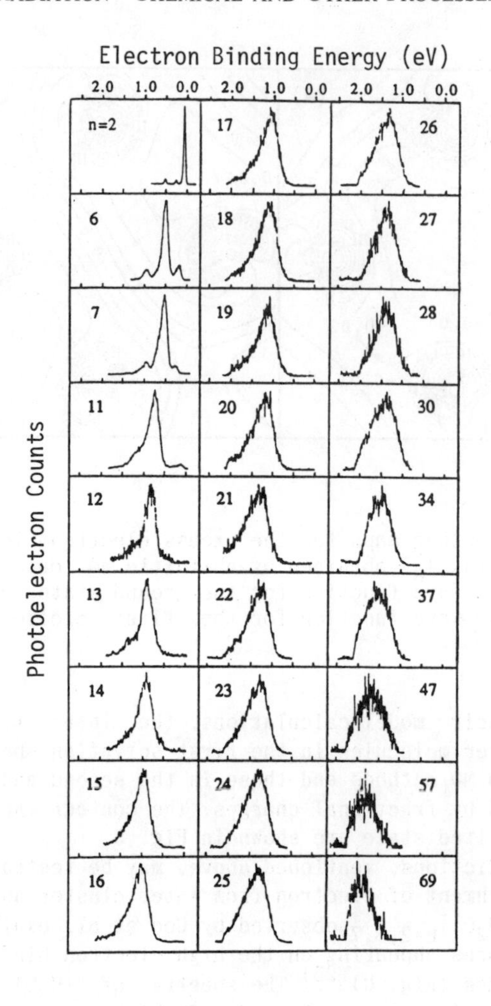

Fig. 6 The negative ion photoelectron (photodetachment) spectra of $(H_2O)_n^-$, n=2,6,7,11,28,30,34,37, 47,57,69.

Acknowledgment

The author wishes to express his sincere thanks to Mr. Hiroto Tachikawa of Hokkaido University for his useful discussion for preparing the manuscript.

References

1. Hart, E. J., Anber, M. : "The Hydrated Electron" Wiley-Interscience, New York, 1970, P. 5.
2. Anber, M., Bambenek, M., Ross, A. B. : Selected Specific Rates of

Reactions of Transient from Water in Aqueus Solution. 1. Hydrated Electron" U.S. Department of Commerce, National Bureau of Standards, 1973.
3. Ross, A. B. : Selected Specific Rates of Reactions of Transient from Water in Aqueus Solution. Hydrated Electron, Supplemental Data" U. S. Department of Commerce, National Bureau of Standards, 1975.
4. Jortner, J.: "Radiation Chemistry of Aqueous Systems" (G. Stein ed.) Wiley-Interscience, New York, 1968, p.91.
5. Natori, M., Watanabe, T.: J. Phys. Soc. Jpn., 21, 1573 (1966).
6. Natori, M.: J. Phys. Soc. Jpn., 24, 913 (1968).
7. Fueki, K., Feng, D. F., Kevan, L.: J. Phys. Chem., 74, 1976 (1970).
8. Kenney-Wallace, G. A.: Acc. Chem. Res., 11, 433 (1978).
9. Hentz, R. R., Kenney-Wallace, G. A.: J. Phys. Chem., 78, 514 (1974).
10. Mozumder, A. : Radiat. Phys. Chem., 34, 1 (1989).
11. Gauduel, Y., Migus, A., Chamberet, J. P., Antoniett, A. : Rev. Phys. Appl., 22, 1755 (1987).
12. Migus, A., Gauduel, Y., Martin, J. L., Antonetti, A.: Phys. Rev. Lett., 58, 1559 (1987).
13. Long, F. H., Lu, H., Shi, X., Eisenthal, K. B. : Chem. Phys. Lett., 160, 464 (1989).
14. Gauduel, Y., Pommeret, S., Migus, A., Antonieti, A. : Radiat. Phys. Chem., 34, 5 (1989)
15. Tachiya, M., Mozumder, A.: J. Chem. Phys., 60, 3037 (1974).
16. Schnitker, J., Rossky, P. J., Kenney-Wallace, P. J. : J. Chem. Phys., 85, 2986 (1986).
17. Pikaev, A. K. : "The Solvated Electron in Radiation Chemistry" Israel Program for Scientific Translation, Jerusalem, 1971, p 243.
18. Kevan, L.: Acc. Chem. Res., 14, 138 (1981).
19. Newton, M.: J. Phys. Chem., 79, 2795 (1975).
20. Barnett, R. N., Landman, U., Cleaveland, C. L., Jortner, J. : J. Chem. Phys., 88, 4421 (1988).
21. Rossky, P. J., Schnitker, J.: J. Phys. Chem., 92, 4277 (1988).
22. Bartczak, W. M., Sopek, M., Kroh, J.: Radiat. Phys. Chem., 34, 93 (1989).
23. Barnett, R. N., Landman, U., Cleaveland, C. L., Jortner, J.: J. Chem. Phys., 88, 4431 (1988).
24. Tachikawa, H., Lund, A., Ogasawara, M.: unpublished data.
25. Coe, J. V., Lee, G. H., Eaton, J. G., Arnold, S. T., Sarkas, H. W., Bowen, K. H., Ludewigt, C., Haberland, H., Worsnop. D. R.: J. Chem. Phys., 92, 3980 (1990).
26. Campagnola, P. J., Posey, L. A., Johnson, M. A. : J. Chem. Phys., 92, 3243 (1990).

5.3 Scavenger Reaction in Hot Atom Chemistry and Radiation Chemistry

Shin-ichi OHNO and Yasuyuki ARATONO
Japan Atomic Energy Research Institute, Tokai, Ibaraki, 319-11 Japan

1. Scavenging Effects in the Study of HAC

Hot atoms, generally created with a very high kinetic energy, pass through a medium which consists of a reactive component (a reactant) and a non-reactive component (a moderator). The hot atoms slow down through successive atom-molecule collisions until they have an adequate energy to react. The energy region ($E_1 < E < E_2$) of a HAC-reaction is dependent on the type of reaction and on the energy of the hot atom. Presumably hot atoms with kinetic energy outside of this energy region can be removed from the system. Suppression of reactions due to high-energy atoms may be accomplished by adding to the system varying amounts of an inert moderator (such as a noble gas).[1] The kinetic theory developed on this model[1] has been applied to numerous experimental systems over the years,[2] thus enabling theoretical descriptions of hot atom reactions in terms of cross-sections or an excitation function. On the other hand, addition of a small amount of a "scavenger" to the system suppresses reactions in which low-energy (i.e. $< E_1$) or thermalized atoms take part.[2] The scavenger will effectively react with the low-energy or thermalized atoms to give a product different of that from a hot-atom reaction.

Regarding role of the scavenger in hot atom chemistry experiments, three factors which yield additional complications in interpreting the results should be mentioned: Firstly, the scavenger, being highly reactive towards thermalized atoms, is likely to show a significant reactivity towards the hot atoms. Thus competition for hot atoms between the scavenger and the reactants may occur. Secondly, the scavenger is likely to react with free radicals and fragments formed by concomitant radiation damage in the system. These reactions may give rise to additional molecules which can react with hot atoms. In some studies, computer simulation and correction to the kinetic theory for the effects of scavenger competition have been studied.[3] Thirdly, there may be circumstances in which the hot reaction product is formed with a high degree of translational or internal excitation so that some of the reaction products may subsequently undergo decomposition and may not contribute to the observed yield.

Radiation chemists have more widely used scavenger techniques over forty years to investigate the behavior of free radicals, atoms, ions, and electrons, which are formed in the irradiated system and which are mostly thermalized at the time of the reaction. Fast charged particles passing through matter dissipate their energy in a number of limited spherical volume called "spurs" with a radius of about 30 Å or in a cylindrical volume called a "track" which consists of overlapped spurs to initiate chemical reactions. The processes in the spur or in the track can be conveniently divided into three stages: physical, physico-chemical and chemical stage. One way to elucidate these processes is to use high concentrations of solute (= scavenger) and to get information from the product analysis on the reactive species and on their yields in an attempt to explain the early kinetics (10^{-11} - 10^{-7} s) in terms of the diffusion model. Another way to study early events in radiation chemistry is to employ pulse radiolysis techniques. Below we briefly report the progress in the study of scavenger reaction mainly in the field of radiation chemistry.

2. Diffusion Model of Radiolysis of Hydrocarbon Liquids

The primary energy loss events occur along the track of a charged particle in a liquid. Each event produces a single ionization or a small cluster of ionizations. In a non-polar liquid like a hydrocarbon, where the Coulombic interaction has a comparatively large range, most of the electrons formed in the ionizations are thermalized within the field of attraction of the parent positive ion. This results in the recombination of the ion with the electron. When solutes (= scavenger) are present which react with the charged species during their lifetime, the course of the chemical reactions is changed. Assuming an initial distribution of the electrons and positive ions, the diffusion and the mutual reactions in each other's coulombic field will be considered below.

2.1 Diffusion

The diffusion of a particle in three dimensions starting at the origin of a spherical coordinate system is considered. The probability density $c(r,t)$, which is the probability of finding the particle at a given time in a shell between r and $r + dr$ divided by $4\pi r^2 dr$ is described by

$$\partial c/\partial t = (D/r^2)\partial/\partial r(r^2 \partial c/\partial r) \quad (1)$$

with the solution:

$$c(r,t) = 1/(4\pi Dt)^{3/2} \exp(- r^2/4Dt) \quad (2)$$

The most probable distance to find the particle is obtained from $(\partial/\partial r)[4\pi r^2 c] = 0$, and which corresponds to $r = (4Dt)^{1/2}$.

2.2 The Smoluchowski Equation

It can be shown that the diffusion of the two neutral particles can also be described by Eq. (1), where D is now the sum of the diffusion coefficients of the two particles and where the origin of the coordinate system is taken at the site of one of the two particles. When the particles are ions, they exert a force on each other, and the diffusion equation is now described by

$$\partial/\partial t = (D/r^2)\partial/\partial r(r^2\partial c/\partial r + r_c c) \tag{3}$$

where $r_c = e^2/4\pi\varepsilon_0 k_B T$, the distance at which the potential energy between the ions is equal to $k_B T$. This equation is often referred to as the Smoluchowski equation for a pair of ions.[4]

When a pair of ions is initially separated by a distance r_0, $c(r,0)$ at $t=0$ is $\delta(r - r_0)/4\pi r_0^2$. The time and space developement of $c(r,t)$ (Eq.2) has a sink at $r = \infty$ representing the pairs that escape reaction and a sink close to the origin representing the recombination between the ions. The first sink is expressed as $c(\infty, t) = 0$, while the second sink can be expressed as:

$$c(R, t) = 0 \tag{4}$$

where R is the reaction radius at which the particles react on encounter. The rate of the reaction may be expressed as the product of $c(R, t)$ and a specific rate k_R.

2.3 Survival and escape from initial recombination[5]

The probability that the ions have not reacted at a given time, or survival probability, $W(t)$, is

$$W(t) = \int_R^\infty c(r, t)4\pi r^2 dr \tag{5}$$

The probability that the ions have not survived at t, $1 - W(t)$, is the probability that the ions have reacted with each other:

$$1 - W(t) = \int_0^t k_R c(R, t)dt \tag{6}$$

The probability for escape from recombination is equal to $W(t = \infty)$. It is interesting to note that Laplace transformation of above equations gives useful information. The escape probability $W_{esc} = W(t = \infty)$ is simply given by $1 - W_{esc} = k_R c(R, s = 0)$. For $k_R \gg 4\pi D r_c$ and $r_c \gg R$, The Onsager's equation is obtained:[6]

$$W_{esc} = \exp(- r_c/r_0) \tag{7}$$

An approximation to this equation was presented by Mozumder:[7]

$$W(t) = \exp[- (r_c/r_0)(1 - \mathrm{erfc}(r_0/4Dt)] \tag{8}$$

2.4 Scavenging reaction[5]

If a solute S is present which may react with the ion, the Smoluchowski Eq. (3) will have an additional sink term,

$- k_s C_s c$, where k_s is the specific rate of reaction with the scavenger and C_s the scavenger concentration,

$$\partial c/\partial t = (D/r^2)\partial/\partial r[r^2 \partial c/\partial r + (c/k_B T)dV/dr] - k_s C_s c \tag{9}$$

The solution $c(r, t)$ is now related to the $c_0(r, t)$ in the absence of solute:

$$c(r, t) = c_0(r, t)\exp(-k_s C_s t) \tag{10}$$

The probability for reaction with the scavenger per unit time is equal to the local rate of reaction , $k_s C_s c(r, t)$, per unit volume and the time integrated over space

$$S(t) = \int_R^\infty k_s C_s c(r, t) 4\pi r^2 dr \tag{11}$$

$$= k_s C_s W_0(t)\exp(-k_s C_s t) \tag{12}$$

where $W_0(t)$ is the probability of survival in the absence of S. The probability for the ion to have reacted with the solute at $t = \infty$, $P_s(k_s C_s)$, is obtained by integrating $S(t)$ over time.

$$P_s(k_s C_s) = \int_0^\infty k_s C_s W_0(t)\exp(-k_s C_s t)dt \tag{13}$$

Several authors have presented calculations of the scavenging probability. At low concentrations it approaches a $C_s^{1/2}$ dependence:[8)]

$$P_s(k_s C_s) = \exp(-r_c/r_0)[1 + (k_s C_s r_c^2/D)^{1/2}] \tag{14}$$

In a non-polar liquid, the range of the Coulombic interaction is much larger than the thermalization distance of the electrons, so that only a small fraction of the ions and electrons escapes from each other. Those ions that escape will react with ions coming from other spurs or tracks (homogeneous recombination). The yields of ions which have escaped from initial recombination bear information about the initial spatial distribution of the ions and electrons.

It is often assumed that the total yield of ions in the liquid is equal to that in the gas and that the distance between the ion and electron is distributed according to a Gaussian distribution:

$$f(r) = 4\pi r^2/(\pi b^2)^{3/2}\exp(-r^2/b^2) \tag{15}$$

which is based on a random walk picture of the thermalizing electron. In TABLE 1 are shown free ion yields, and b values for various liquids.[9)] It has also been observed that in liquid with a large thermalization length r_c the excess electron have high mobilities.

TABLE 1. Yield of Escaped Ions in Some Liquids , Values of Onsager Length r_c, and Initial Ditsribution Radius b.[9]

	G_{esc} (/100 eV)	r_c (nm)	b (nm)
n-Hexane	0.13	29.9	6.7
n-Tetradecane	0.12	27.7	6.1
2,2,4-Trimethylpentane	0.33	28.6	9.5
Neopentane	1.2	31.8	23.0
Cyclohexane	0.13	27.9	6.1
Benzene	0.053	24.8	4.2
Perfluoromethyl-cyclohexane	0.028	30.5	4.4
CCl_4	0.096	25.3	5.1
CS_2	0.31	31.4	7.2
Tetramethylsilane	0.76	31.3	15.9

The yield of scavenging reaction as a function of scavenger concentration has been studied. As seen, for single ion pairs and small concentrations, the scavenging probability is given by Eq.(14) and the probability of survival at long times is given by Eq.(8) with $t \rightarrow \infty$. On the other hand, experimental studies have been made of the scavenging of the ions and thermalized electrons in various liquids. The experimentally obtained concentration dependence of the yield may conveniently be approximated over a large range of concentration by an empirical equation:[10]

$$G_s(C_s) = G_{esc} + B(aC_s)^n/[1 + (aC_s)^n] \qquad (16)$$

where n varies between 0.5 and 0.7. In TABLE 2 are presented values of B, a and the specific rates k_s of the reaction of the solutes with charged species as obtained for charge scavenging with different scavengers in cyclohexane,[10,11] using Eq.(16). B is obtained by plotting $(G_s - G_{esc})^{-1}$ against $C_s^{-0.5}$ and extrapolating to $C_s = \infty$.

TABLE 2 Values of G_{esc}, a, B,and Specific Rates k_s Obtained from Scavenging Reactions with Different Scavengers in Cyclohexane[10,11]

	G_{esc} (/100eV)	a dm³/mol	B (/100eV)	k_s (10^{12}dm³/mol s)
$CH_3Br + e^-$	0.12	16.2	3.8	4.1
	0.12	11.2	4.9	-
	0.13	9	5	-
$CH_3Cl + e^-$	0.12	5.6	3.8	1.4
	0.13	3.5	5	-
	0.12	5	4.2	-
ND_3 + hole	0.12	0.85	3.8	0.26
$c-C_3H_6$	0.10	0.4	3.8	0.10
+ hole	0.13	0.18	5	-

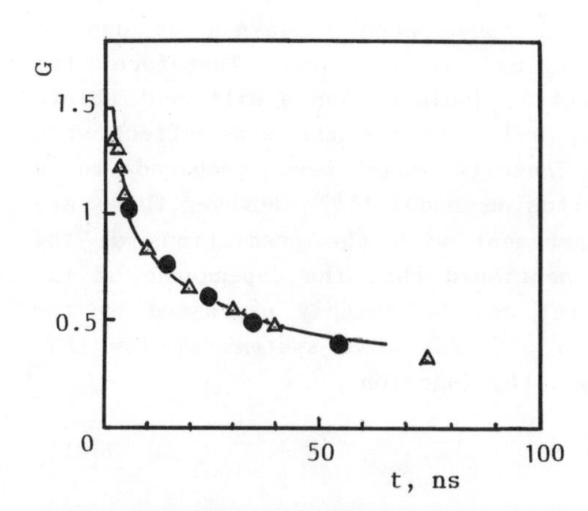

Fig. 1 Yield of biphenyl ions as a function of time after pulse radiolysis of cyclohexane; ●, 0.1 mol/dm^3 biphenyl, △, 0.5 mol/dm^3. The curve is plotted following Eq. (17).

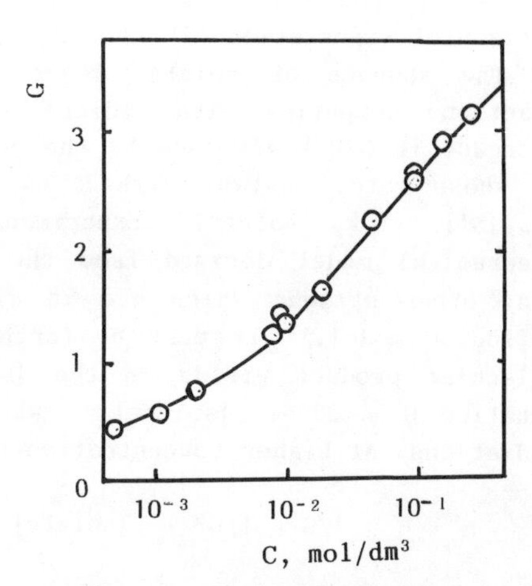

Fig. 2. Yield of the scavenging of electrons in cyclohexane containing CH_3Br. The curve is calculated with G_0 = 4.6.[13]

The survival of ions in biphenyl solutions in cyclohexane was studied by measuring the optical absorption of the biphenyl ions.[12] Fig. 1 shows the yield of biphenyl ions as a function of time according to the equation:

$$G(t) = G_{esc} + B \exp(k_s t/\alpha) \mathrm{erfc}[(k_s t/\alpha)^{1/2}] \qquad (17)^{5)}$$

with the values B = 5, G_{esc} = 0.13, α =9 dm^3/mol, and k = 4.1x10^{12} dm^3/mol s for electron scavenging by CH_3Br. Fig. 2 shows the yield of scavenged electrons in cyclohexane containing CH_3Br, together with a calculated curve. Thus, the yield of scavenging as a function of concentration as well as the yield of survival with time is in good agreement with the expectation on the basis of a single-ion-pair treatment. However, no information is obtained about the initial distribution of the ions and electrons.

3. Spur Reactions in Aqueous Solution

For aqueous solutions,[4] the generally assumed reactive species at the beginning of the chemical stage are OH, e^-_{aq}, and H_3O^+. The initial spatial distribution of OH and H_3O^+ would be essentially the same, whereas that of the e^-_{aq} would be more spread out. As the concentration of these species within the spur is high, there is a relatively high probability for reacting with each other, before diffusion into the bulk of the solution. The mathematical treatment of this model predicts the formation of H_2, H_2O_2, and H atoms in the spur. Thus, this model is useful in deriving information on the spur reaction from the effect of added solute on the radiolytic product yields.

The yields of H_2 and H_2O_2 decrease at high concentrations of certain solute. Plots of $G(R_2)/G^0(R_2)$ against log[solute], obtained for different solutes (NO_3^-, NO_2^-, Cu^{2+}, H_2O_2, Br^-, etc.) can be made to coincide by horizontal translation.[14] Here R_2 stands for H_2 or H_2O_2, $G^0(R_2)$ is the yield in the absence of solute. These results have been explained as due to reactions competing with radical scavenging in the spur. Therefore, the decrease in $G(R_2)$ governed by the product k_{RS}[solute] and a different solute S' whose rate constant with R is k'_{RS} will produce the same effect when $k'_{RS}[S'] = k_{RS}$[solute]. Experimental results have been compared to a theoretical model derived from the diffusion model.[4,13] However,there are many other systems which are in disagreement with the predictions of the diffusion model.[4] It must be further mentioned that the dependence of the molecular product yields on the [solute] may be roughly expressed by the function $G = G^0 - a[\text{solute}]^{1/n}$ where n = 3 for most systems at low LET-radiations. At higher concentration range, the function

$$1/G = 1/G^0 + a[\text{solute}] \tag{18}$$

has been proposed.[4,13] Corresponding to the decrease of the molecular yield, radical yields increase at high concentrations of solutes. The increase in G(R) is also a function of $k_{RS}[S]$, and the results can be fitted to the curve derived from the diffusion model (See Eq. 16).

At higher solute concentrations, discrepancies from the spur diffusion model appear and can be explained by different models: existence of different types of spur, reaction of the precursors of e^-_{aq} and OH, or time dependent dielectric constant, etc.[4]

References

1) P. J. Estrup and R. Wolfgang, J Amer. Chem. Soc., 82, 2665 (1960).
2) D. J. Malcolme-Lawes, in "Hot Atom Chemistry,"ed. by T. Matsuura, Kodansha-Elsevier (1984), p. 39.
3) D. J. Malcolme-Lawes, J. Chem. Phys., 57, 2476, 2481 (1972).
4) " Handbook of Radiation Chemistry," ed. by Y. Tabata, CRC Press, Boston (1991), p. 892.
5) A. Hummel,in "Kinetics of Nonhomogeneous Processes," ed. by G. R. Freeman, John-Wiley & Sons, New York (1987), p. 215.
6) L. Onsager, Phys. Rev., 54, 554 (1938).
7) A. Mozumder, J. Chem. Phys., 48, 1659 (1968).
8) J. L. Magee and A. B. Taylor, J. Chem. Phys., 56, 3061 (1972).
9) A. O. Allen, NSRDS-NBS-57, US Government Printing Office, Washington DC,(1976).
10) J. M. Warman, K.D. Asmus, and A R. H. Schuler, J. Phys. Chem., 73, 931 (1969).
11) C. Klein and R. H. Schuler, J. Phys. Chem., 77, 978 (1973); E. L. Davids, J. M. Warman and A. Hummel, J. Chem. Soc. Faraday Trans.I, 71, 1252 (1975).
12) J. K. Thomas, K. Johnson, T. Klippert and R. Lowers, J. Chem. Phys., 48, 1608 (1968).; Y. Yoshida, S. Tagawa and Y. Tabata, Radiat. Phys. Chem., 23, 279 (1984).
13) S. J. Rzad and J. M. Warman, J. Chem. Phys., 52,485 (1970).
14) H. A. Schwarz, J. Phys. Chem., 73, 1928 (1969); T. J. Sworski, Advan. Chem. Ser., 50, 163 (1965).

5.4 Theoretical Study on Tritium Decay

Shigeru IKUTA and Masashi IMAMURA†

General Education Department, Tokyo Metropolitan University, 1-1 Minami-Ohsawa, Hachioji-shi, Tokyo 192-03 and †Tokyo University of Information Sciences, 1200-2, Yatoh-cho, Chiba 265, Japan

β-Decay events of tritium atoms contained in gaseous compounds were experimentally studied by using a specially designed mass spectrometer (charge spectrometer) in the late '50s and early '60s;[1,2] typical results[3-7] are summarized in Table 1.

Table 1. Ions produced by β-decay events[3-7]

Parent	Ions	Yield		Parent	Ions	Yield
(i)H^3H	HHe^+	89.5*1,	93.2*2	(iii)$C_2H_5{}^3H$	$C_2H_5{}^+$	80
	He^+	8.2*1,	5.1*2	(iv)$C_6H_5{}^3H$	$C_6H_5{}^+$	72
	H^+	2.3*1,	1.55*2	(v) o-$CH_3C_6H_4{}^3H$	$C_7H_7{}^+$	78
	He^{2+}		0.14*2	m-$CH_3C_6H_4{}^3H$	$C_7H_7{}^+$	79
(ii)$CH_3{}^3H$	$CH_3{}^+$	82.0		p-$CH_3C_6H_4{}^3H$	$C_7H_7{}^+$	76
	$CH_2{}^+$	4.9		(vi)$C_6H_5CH_2{}^3H$	$C_7H_7{}^+$	79
	CH^+	4.0		(vii)c-$C_4H_7{}^3H$	$C_4H_7{}^+$	~80
	C^+	4.9		(viii)c-$C_5H_9{}^3H$	$C_5H_9{}^+$	~75
	H^+	2.4				

*1 Reference 3. *2 Reference 4.

Upon a β-decay event a tritium atom (^3H) changes into a helium ion ($^3He^+$). When a tritium decays *in a tritiated molecule* (called to be a parent), a ground- or excited-state daughter with a He atom (with the same geometry as the parent) is produced; the daughter dissipates energy along its potential energy surface, most of the daughters resulting in the ground-states. On the basis of a sudden approximation, transition probabilities (P_{if}) from a parent into a daughter can be defined by the overlap of the wavefunctions of the initial (ϕ_i) and final (ϕ_f) states corresponding respectively to the parent and the daughter of the ground- or one of the excited-states. In Fig. 1, three types of potential energy curves (PEC) for a ground-state daughter are shown as a function of the X-He distance.[8] A parent changes into a daughter with the same geometry as the parent, indicated as point **a**. The daughter having the potential like I or II dissociates into fragments. On the other hand, the daughter having the curve III may have a chance to survive dissociation. In addition to the considerations on PEC, the recoil effect on the internal energy due to β-ray have to be taken into consideration for the quantitative prediction of the final ions resulting from the β-decays.

In 1941, Migdal[9] calculated the transition probabilities (P_{if}) from a ^3H atom to the ground- and excited-state daughters (He^+). Seventy percent of the parents changes into the ground-state daughters, while 30 % produces the excited-states. In 1965 Wolniewicz[10] performed state-of-the-art calculations on P_{if} from a H^3H parent by using a James-Coolidge 64 term expansion method; P_{if} to the ground-state daughter was found to be 60 %. He also indicated that the ground-state HHe^+ has a fairly large binding energy (2.04 eV) and therefore very stable, but all the excited ions decompose into fragments.

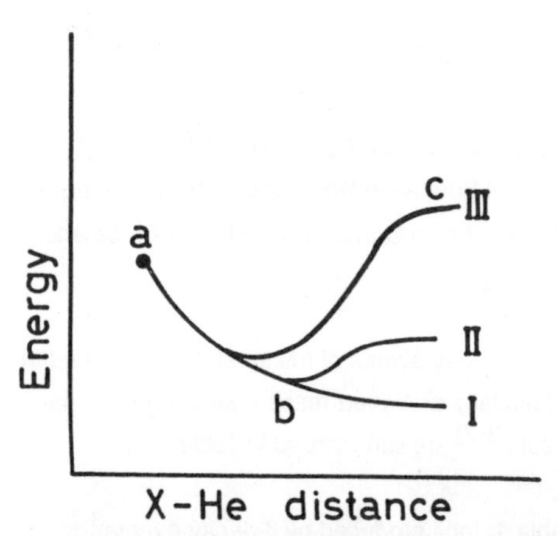

Fig. 1 Three types of potential energy profiles of the ground-state daughter as a function of the X-He distance.

Ikuta, Iwata, and Imamura[11] calculated P_{if} and PEC in H^3H, $CH_3{}^3H$, $NH_2{}^3H$, OH^3H, and $^{14}CH_4$ β-decay events by using an *ab initio* Hartree-Fock MO method. In ^3H β-decay, P_{if} to the ground-state daughter has no dependence on the parent, being 60 %, and P_{if} in ^{14}C β-decay is somewhat larger (about 70 %).

They indicated that the orbital and state symmetry rule should be considered in defining the dissociation path of daughters. They furthermore pointed out that the absolute yield of HHe^+ (90%) cannot be interpreted in terms of only considerations based on a sudden-approximation. Their calculations, however, omitted polarization functions and electron correlation, both of which are important though the ground-state daughter dissociates into two closed-shell fragments.

PEC of the ground-state HHe^+ has only one double-occupied molecular orbital throughout the whole internuclear distance. HHe^+ ions both at a geometry of a H^3H parent and at a global minimum have one σ orbital, which correlates with the $(1s)^2$ of He atom at the dissociation limit. Thus one can assume that the electron correlation effect on PEC may be small. On the other hand, a ground-state daughter, for example $OHHe^+$, possesses five occupied molecular orbitals, $(1a')^2(2a')^2(3a')^2(4a')^2(1a'')^2$, near the global minimum. These five orbitals are classified into two groups at the dissociation limit, i.e., four double-occupied molecular orbitals of OH^+ ($^1\Delta$) and one $(1s)^2$ of He. Although the total numbers of electron pairs are the same in these two geometries, no inter-system electron correlation between OH^+ ($^1\Delta$) and He is present at the dissociation limit. Thus there may exist an appreciable change in an inter-system electron correlation between the two geometries at the global minimum and at the dissociation limit.

Since currently available quantum chemical techniques allow us fairly precise calculations compared with a decade ago, the basis set extension and electron correlation effects on the equilibrium geometries and on the potential energy profiles of daughters (resulting from tritium β-decay) are now studied. The present short summary reports the recent (state-of-the-art) theoretical results on the tritium β-decay in H^3H, Li^3H, BeH^3H, $CH_3{}^3H$, $NH_2{}^3H$, OH^3H, and F^3H parents.

The geometries of the ground-state daughters at points **a** and **b** and that of the fragment at the dissociation limit **c** are determined by a second-order Møller-Plesset perturbation method (MP2)[12,13] using a 6-31G** basis set.[14] Final energy computations are performed at the optimized geometries (**a**, **b**, and **c**) using a fourth-order Møller-Plesset perturbation method[15] including the single, double, and quadruple excitations (MP4SDQ(FULL)). The basis sets[16] used are H: (5s2p1d/3s2p1d), He:(5s2p1d/3s2p1d), Li:(11s4p2d1f/5s2p2d1f), Be:(10s5p2d1f/5s3p2d1f), C, N, O, and F: (11s6p2d1f/5s4p2d1f), where both primitive and contracted basis sets are noted.

Table 2. Energy relationship in the potential curves of the ground-state daughters

Parent	Fragments	$DE(E_c-E_b)$*1	$\Delta(E_c-E_a)$*2	Potential type
H^3H	(H^+, He)	47.03	46.33	III
Li^3H	(Li^+, He)	1.60	-0.16	II
BeH^3H	(BeH^+, He)	14.05	5.54	III
$CH_3{}^3H$	($CH_3{}^+(^1A)$, He)	1.80	-17.56	II
$NH_2{}^3H$	($NH_2{}^+(^1A)$, He)	5.46	-10.19	II
OH^3H	($OH^+(^1\Delta)$, He)	23.70	13.64	III
F^3H	($F^+(^1S)$, He)	65.98	60.63	III

*1 Energy difference between points **c** and **b**, in kcal/mol. *2 Energy difference between points **c** and **a**, in kcal/mol.

Dissociation energies and their potential types calculated for their ground-state daughters are summarized in Table 2.[17] Even PEC of the ground-state CH_3He^+ calculated at beyond the Hartree-Fock level of theory has a shallow minimum at a large C-He distance, where $CH_3{}^+$ and He interact very weakly. PECs in the ground-state daughters, $LiHe^+$, CH_3He^+, and NH_2He^+, show Type II, whereas those of HHe^+, $BeHHe^+$, $OHHe^+$, and FHe^+, Type III.

In Fig. 2 shown is the potential energy curve in the ground-state $OHHe^+$, calculated by the MP4SDQ method; the potential energy curve is a striking contrast to that by the Hartree-Fock (HF) one. These significant differences between HF and MP4SDQ results are attributable to the energy differences between points **b** and **c**, since the energy differences between points **a** and **b** are both 10 kcal mol^{-1} in the two methods.

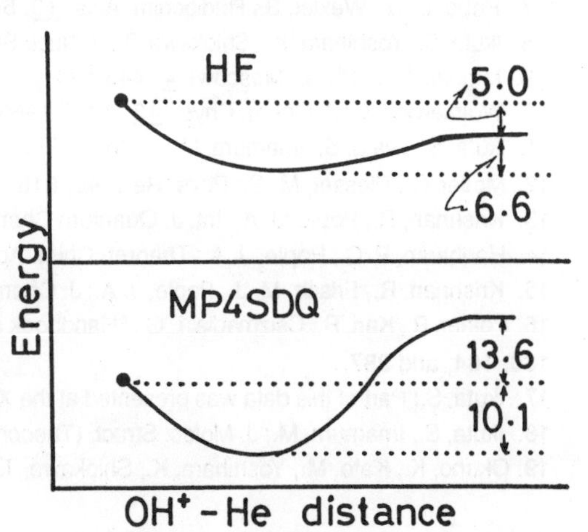

Fig. 2 MP4SDQ potential energy profile of the ground-state $OHHe^+$ is compared with that of the HF one.

The larger binding energy in the MP4SDQ PEC is due to the smaller electron correlation energy at the dissociation limit ($OH^+(^1\Delta)$ and He). These theoretical results indicate the remarkable contributions of the electron correlation to PEC, suggesting that some of the experimental results should be re-examined with meticulous care regarding background-contamination.[18] For example, some of the ground-state $OHHe^+$ ions may survive dissociation, even if the considerations on the recoil energies transformed by a tritium β-ray were included; Okuno et. al.[19] have observed only OH^+ ion from OH^3H. The experimental yield of $OHHe^+$ will provide us with a useful hint to estimate the internal energy transformed by recoil effects.

The present article emphasizes the importance of an electron correlation effect on PEC in the ground-state daughters. To evaluate the quantitative yields of product ions, both accurate PECs in excited-state daughters and quantitative considerations on the internal energy transformed by the recoil effect are needed. Theoretical approaches to these problems are still future subjects.

Acknowledgement

One of the authors (S. I.) thanks the Institute for Molecular Science for providing him with the chance to use the HITAC S-810 computer.

References

1. International Atomic Energy Agency, "Chemical Effect of Nuclear Transformations", IAEA, Vienna, 1961.
2. International Atomic Energy Agency, "Chemical Effect of Nuclear Transformations", IAEA, Vienna, 1965.
3. Snell, A. H., Pleasonton, F., Leming, H. E. : J. Inorg. Nucl. Chem., 5, 112(1957).
4. Wexler, S.: J. Inorg. Nucl. Chem., 10, 8(1959).
5. Wexler, S., Hess, D. C.: J. Phys. Chem., 62, 1382(1958).
6. Wexler, S., Anderson, G. A., Singer, L. A.: J. Chem. Phys., 32, 417(1960).
7. Pobo, L. G., Wexler, S.: Radiochim. Acta, 19, 5(1973).
8. Ikuta, S., Yoshihara, K., Shiokawa, T.: J. Nucl. Sci. Technol. (Japan), 14, 661(1977).
9. Migdal, A.: J. Phys. (Moscow), 4, 449(1941).
10. Wolniewicz, L.: J. Chem. Phys., 43, 1087(1966).
11. Ikuta, S., Iwata, S., Imamura, M.: J. Chem. Phys., 66, 4671(1977).
12. Møller, C., Plesset, M. S.: Phys. Rev., 46, 618(1934).
13. Krishnan, R., Pople, J. A.: Int. J. Quantum Chem. Symp., 14, 91(1978).
14. Hariharan, P. C., Pople, J. A.: Theoret. Chim. Acta, 28, 213(1973).
15. Krishnan, R., Frisch, M. J., Pople, J. A.: J. Chem. Phys., 72, 4244(1980).
16. Poirier, R., Kari, R., Csizmadia, I. G.: "Handbook of Gaussian Basis Sets", Elsevier, Amsterdam, 1985, PP. 160, 164, and 287.
17. Ikuta, S.: Part of this data was presented at the XIII IHAC Symposium, Yamanaka, Japan, 1987.
18. Ikuta, S., Imamura, M.: J. Molec. Struct. (Theochem), 153, 269(1987).
19. Okuno, K., Kato, M., Yoshihara, K., Shiokawa, T.: Radiochem. Radioanal. Lett., 37, 191(1979).

5.5 Luminescence from Irradiated Materials

Hari Jeevan ARNIKAR[1], Somaji Fakira PATIL[1] and Tetsuo HASHIMOTO[2]
[1] Department of Chemistry, University of Poona, Pune, 411 007, India
[2] Department of Chemistry, Faculty of Science, Niigata University, Niigata, 950-21 Japan

1. Introduction

1.1 Thermoluminescence Dosimetry (TLD)

When a substance absorbs energy in some form or other, a fraction of this absorbed energy may be reemitted as electromagnetic radiation in the visible or near-visible region of the spectrum. The emission resulting on heating is referred to as thermoluminescence (TL). A curve of intensity of emission (I) versus time (t) of uniform rate of heating is called a glow curve. These curves provide information about the energy of the excited levels involved and of their initial occupancy (at t=0). The TL is to be distinguished from blackbody radiation which obeys the laws of Kirchhoff and Wien[1]. Levy and coworkers[2] were amongst the earliest to develop the subject, after the theoretical basis of TL dosimetry was established by Daniels and Rieman[2a]. Amongst the alkali halides LiF was found to best suited for TL dosimetry. Levy reported 28 glow peaks, collectively, from X- or γ-irradiated crystals of LiF over the temperature range of 20-550 K, the most intense one being at 140 K.

Since then radiation dosimetry by TL from LiF (TLD 100) has been developed extensively, specially in respect of the role of major and minor dopants[3-6]. As an example, LiF with 80 ppm of Mg and 3 ppm of Ti and given a dose of 1.7 kGy displays five glow peaks at 60, 130, 175, 200 and 280 ℃, all with spectral maxima at 420 and 640 nm (Fig. 1)[6]. A model proposed by Mayhugh[7] explains the results for LiF (TLD 100) satisfactorily. In the pre-irradiated crystal the major dopant Mg is stated to be present as (Mg^{++} + Li^{+} vacancy) in equilibrium with its dimer and trimer, besides other complex species. Electrons released from Mg centres interact with an intermediate defect such as a two-hole trap (V_3), and release the second hole to convert Ti^{3+} ions back to Ti^{4+} with the emission of blue light.

$$Ti^{3+} + \text{hole(from } V_3 \text{ centre)} \rightarrow Ti^{4+} + h\nu \text{ (TL, bluish emission)}$$

Studies of TL from other alkali halide crystals variously doped and exposed to ionizing radiation have been exhaustively reviewed[5,6,8] and discussed in international conferences specially devoted to work on luminescence over the past few decades[9].

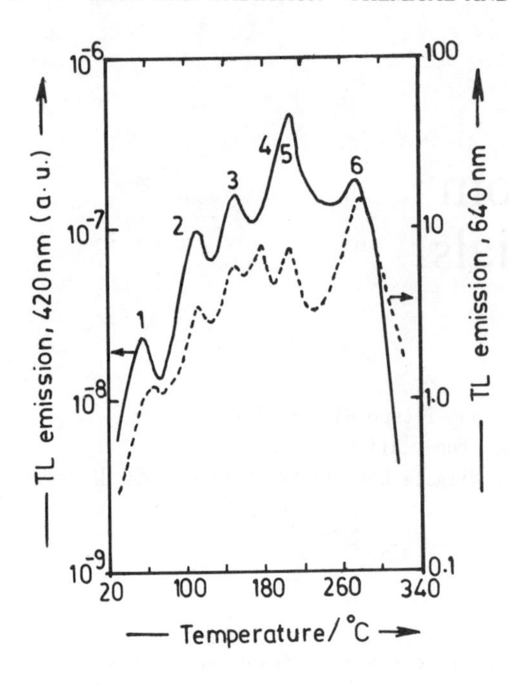

Fig. 1. Typical TL glow peak curves from LiF(+ 80 ppm Mg+3 ppm Ti) after an X-ray dose of 1.7 kGy, measured at wavelengths of 420 and 640nm (Crittenden et al[6]).

1.2 Colour Centres: F, Hole and their Derivatives

Besides TL dosimetry, basic aspects of the formation and decay of radiation-induced defects, colour centres, as F and its derivatives, F*, F *, F_2, F_3 etc, and hole centres as V_K, V_3, H, etc. have been studied in detail[10-12]. Newton and his group[13-15] have contributed significantly to the understanding of the production and decay of F * centres in alkali halides, NaF, NaCl, KBr and KI employing pulse radiolysis. They have shown that the F^- species decays by a mixture of thermal and photolytic processes. However, the thermal process deminates at higher temperatures following first order kinetics with a mean life-time 100-200μs, independent in all cases of both the dose per pulse and the previous history of the sample. These results point to the conclusion that the F* centres decay by thermal ionization rather than by vacancy capture, as postulated earlier by Luty[16]. Recently, the same group[17] have investigated the decay of the excited states of F and F_2 centres in X-irradiated NaF and KCl under the action of 337 and 532 nm laser pulses respectively. They have suggested in this context the formation of quasi-free electron pairs ($e^{-2}{}_2$) in the crystal lattice which decay back to F centres.

Wide as the scope of the subject of luminescence from irradiated materials has been, we per force limit our interest here to following emissions from nominally pure crystals having radiation-induced colour centres.

i) Thermoluminescence at room temperature (RTL) [or 'after glow' (AG),]

ii) Aqualuminescence (AL) or lyoluminescence (LL) during the dissolution of the irradiated crystal in water, and

iii) Thermoluminescence from irradiated minerals, combined with colour imaging (TLCI).

2. Room Temperature Thermoluminescence (RTL)

A study of RTL, sometimes referred to as after-glow (AG), from alkali halide single crystals irradiated at room temperature, brought to light two interesting aspects, viz.

(i) the complex nature of its decay comprising several monomolecular terms and

(ii) the possibility of repeated regeneration of the luminescence (RRTL), after its decay, by exposure to F-light.

2.1 Decay Kinetics of RTL

The decay of RTL from irradiated crystals follows complex rate laws, the traps involved being of varying depths. Most RTL log intensity-time curves can be approximated to two straight lines (a) an initial fast decay obeying first order kinetics and (b) a slower decay showing pseudo-first order characteristics. it is generally assumed that all the electrons released by radiation are not in the same energy state, and that the hole centres and interstitial clusters (vide infra) have a nearly continuous energy spread. Of the electrons released into the conduction band during irradiation, some recombine immediately with holes and some get trapped at anion vacancies in the lattice to form F centres, while the rest are trapped at different depths[18] . Those within an Onsager radius[19] from holes recombine rapidly giving rise to the initial fast order decay component. The rest of the electrons at greater distances must suffer many more interactions with phonons. These make up the slower component of RTL decay, and contribute to observed photoconductivity of γ-irradiated crystals[20]

2.2 Repeated Regeneration of Thermoluminescence (RRTL)

The second result of interest is the effect of the F band light which regenerates room temperature thermoluminescence in a crystal[21]. The regenerated luminescence, designated RTL-II in turn decays in the same manner as RTL-I. The initial intensity of RTL-II increased linearly with the intensity of F light for a constant exposure time of 1 min. Increase in duration of exposure at constant intensity leads to saturation in about 60 s. Except for lowered intensity, the spectrum of RTL-II is similar to that of RTL-I.

The results of Furst and Kallmann[22] on γ-irradiated NaCl doped with 1 % AgCl, would correspond to RTL. The authors attributed the phenomenon to instantaneous phosphorescence with periods of the order of "minutes, hours and even days". After this glow had decayed considerably, a fresh emission could be induced by exposing the crystal to near uv or visilbe light. This was described as stimulated phosphorescence. Clearly, this is same as RTL-II. γ-irradiated halide ions lose one or more electrons by the Varley or Pooley process (see Crawford[23]). They diffuse into interstitial sites, and cluster around F centres. An electron microscopic study by Hobbs at al[24] showed these clusters can glow upto 10-100 nm at room temperature. Acting as acceptor species, they combine radiatively with electrons lying in troughs. The resulting emission would be a continuum, as observed in RTL. As a consequence, the band gap will be narrowed in the damaged region forming an energy trough (Fig. 2). Some unit cells away from the defect region, the lattice becomes normal[18] .

3. Aqualuminescence

A glow during the dissolution of cathode ray-treated NaCl was first reported by Wiedemann and Schmidt[25] in 1895. The observation seems to have remained unnoticed for over 60 years till Ahnstrom and Ehrenstein[26] observed light emission from X-, or γ-, or neutron-irradiated glucose, sorbitol, amylopectin, saccharose and glycine, both in the irradiated solids and during their dissolution.

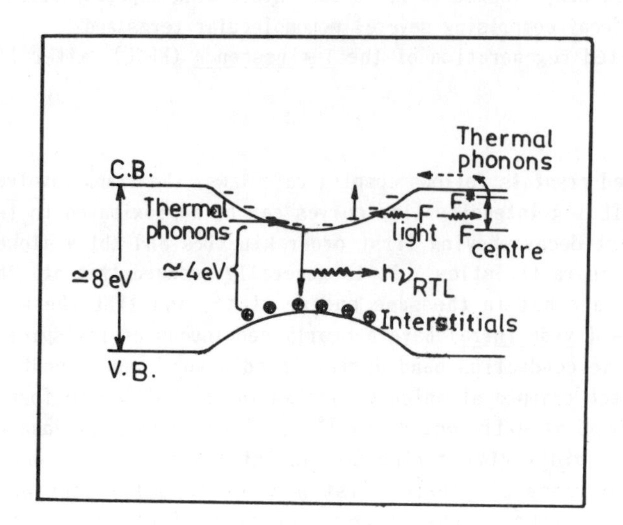

Fig. 2. Proposed band gap model for defect region in γ-irradiated crystals showing RRTL.

3.1 Early Work on Aqualuminescence

Westermark and Grapengiesser[27] reported luminescence during the dissolution of γ- or electron irradiated crystals of NaCl, KI and LiF. The authors studied the emission upon dissolution in liquid scintillators and in the presence of surfactants and substances known to fluoresce in the uv or under X-rays. The presence of Tl^+ ions in 0.05 M concentration and dyes of the fluorescein group, and in particular, luminol increased markedly the intensity of the glow. Westermark[28] observed that the phenomenon with irradiated NaCl could be used to monitor the γ-dose received by the crystal and hence as a new means for radiation dosimetry. Lelievre and Adloff[29] showed that the concentration of F centres in the crystal was related linearly to the intensity of the luminescence during dissolution. The name aqualuminescence (AL) was proposed by Arnikar[30,31] as more appropriate for the light emission during dissolution in water of the irradiated crystal.

3.2 The Spectrum of Aqualuminescence

The spectrum of AL was obtained by Arnikar and Kalkar[32] by a photographic recording on a Fuoss spectrograph (Fig. 3). Recently, a systematic investigation of the emission was carried out by Atari and Ettinger[33-35] using a gallium arsenide photocathode with a flat response from 200-930 nm and sensitized silicon detector stated to resolve the spectrum to within 4 nm. The results confirmed that

1) The luminescence intensity on standardization can serve to monitor doses over a wide range from 10^{-2} to 10^5 Gy within ± 5 %.

2) The AG and LL spectra of any irradiated alkali halide are nearly identical, as shown by the spectra of 6 alkali halides in Fig. 4, confirming thereby Arnikar's earlier results for the spectra of RTL and AL[33-35]. On the basis of the similarity of their mechanisms, viz.

$$Cl^{\cdot} + e^- \text{ (from F centre)} \longrightarrow (Cl^-)^* \longrightarrow Cl^- + h\nu \text{ (TL) Solid state}$$

$$Cl^{\cdot} + e^-_{aq} \text{ (from F centre after hydration)} \longrightarrow (Cl^-)^*_{aq} \longrightarrow Cl^-_{aq} + h\nu \text{ (AL) Solution state}$$

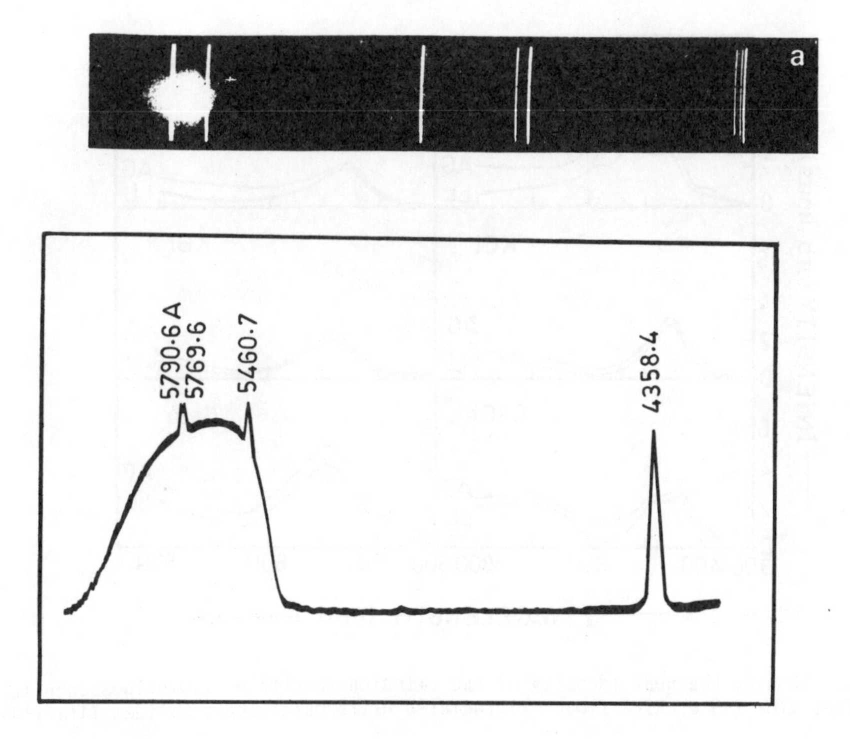

Fig. 3. Emission spectrum of aqualuminescence from γ-irradiated NaCl in the presence of eosin (5×10^{-6}M) as an activator. (a) Spectrum taken on Fuoss spectrograph, film 400 ASA, (b) Microphotometric analysis.

3) Crystals of NaCl additively coloured by heating in sodium vapour give rise to only F centres but no hole centres. Such crystals do not display AG or AL, nor oxidising reactivity, vide infra (Burns and Williams[28a]).

4) The emission from trehalose dihydrate is best suited for dosimetry over the range of 10^{-2} to 10^{5} Gy.

5) On account of their chemical composition and solubility, the saccharides approach a tissue-equivalent material[35].

3.3 The Mechanism of AL

The mechanism of AL is essentially the same as that of TL. This is well supported by the similarity of the spectra of the two emissions[30, 31, 33]. In AL the electrons liberated from F centres during dissolution, are first hydrated in the relaxation time of the water dipoles (10^{-11} s) prior to the recombination reactions[35, 36]

$$e^{-}\text{ (from F centre)} \xrightarrow{H_2O} e^{-}_{aq}$$

$$X \text{ (from } X_2^{-}) + e^{-}_{aq} \xrightarrow{H_2O} X^{-*}_{aq}$$

$$X^{-*}_{aq} \longrightarrow X^{-}_{aq} + h\nu \text{ (AL)}$$

$$(X = Cl, Br, I)$$

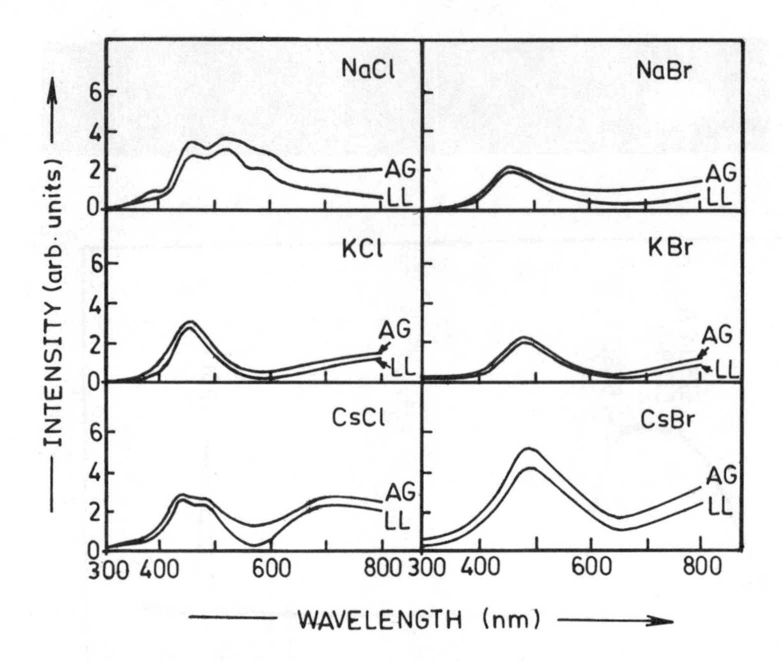

Fig. 4. Showing the near identity of the emission spectra of lyoluminescence (LL or AL) and after glow (AG or RTL) from γ-irradiated ultra pure alkali halides (Atari[33])

The ESR studies of Hart et al[36] of a rapidly cooled solution of γ-irradiated NaCl in 9 M NaOH provided clear evidence of the formation of the hydrated electron prior to the emission of AL. This also substantiated the prediction of Walker[38] that crystals with F centres should be a convenient source of obtaining hydrated electrons in situ.

The subject has been recently reviewed in 1984 by Avotinsh, Dzelme, Buganko and Tiliks[39]. Burns and Williams[28a] showed that the electron excess and defect concentrations are equivalent, each being of the order of 2 x 10^{19} cm $^{-3}$ in several alkali halides, given a saturation γ-dose. They also measured the yields of some of the redox reactions induced by γ-irradiated NaCl during dissolution, as oxidation of I^- to I_2, of toluidine and the polymerization of acrylonitrile. None of these reactions could be observed with unirradiated NaCl, nor with additively coloured specimens.

4. Exchange due to Energy Stored in Irradiated Crystals

Westermark[28] first pointed out that γ-irradiated crystals, because of the energy stored in them in the form of F and hole centres, are the equivalent to a radiation source. This energy upon dissolution, he showed, promotes the oxidation of Fe^{2+}, I^- and other reactions. Later, Bosi, Lazzarini and Lazzarini[40] found that the Co III complex $[Co(NH_3)_6]^{3+}$ is reduced to Co^{2+} by γ-irradiated crystals. The reduction was found to be proportional to the oscillator strength of the centres in the crystal in the case of 16 alkali halides.

4.1 The Origin of Activity: the Active Species

In the creation of F and hole centres in a crystal like NaCl, a certain number of free Na and Cl atoms are formed[41]. On dissolution, the F centres and Na atoms generate powerful reducing species, viz. the hydrated electron and the H radical:

$$\text{F centre} \xrightarrow{\text{water}} e^-_{aq}$$

$$Na \xrightarrow{\text{water}} e^-_{aq} + Na^+_{aq}$$

$$e^-_{aq} \longrightarrow H + OH^-_{aq}$$

At the same time, the hole centres form powerful oxidising species, viz. Cl. Also in the presence of dissolved O_2, HO_2 is formed which is a strong oxidising species. Depending on the redox potential of the solute the resulting reaction will be one of the oxidation or reduction. These redox reactions have been observed at room temperature with NaCl, KCl, Li_2SO_4, Na_2SO_4, K_2SO_4, and $BaCl_2$ irradiated to γ-doses in the range 20-170 kGy.

4.1.1 Inorganic reactions

The inorganic reactions induced by γ-irradiated NaCl* reported[42-44], are

(a) $I^- + BrO_3^- \xrightarrow{NaCl*} I_2 + IO_3^- + Br^-$ (products)

(b) $NO_2^- + BrO_3^- \xrightarrow{NaCl*} NO_3^- + Br^-$ (products)

In the case of irradiated $BaCl_2$, the state of hydration had a marked effect on the yields of the redox products[45]. The concentration of F centres in irradiated NaCl calculated from the yields of above reactions come to (1.9-2.3) x 10^{19}/mole NaCl which is close to the value of 1.9 x 10^{19}/mole NaCl reported by Seitz[46] and Burns and Williams[28a].

4.1.2 Organic reactions

(a) Fluorecein and similar dyes are reduced from the quininoid to benzenoid form on the addition of γ-irradiated NaCl, KCl or Li_2SO_4.

$$C_{20}H_{12}O_5 + 2e^-_{aq} \xrightarrow{Li_2SO_4} C_{20}H_{14}O_5 + 2OH^-$$

The reduction is indicated by a suppression of the peak absorption of the quininoid form[47].

(b) The methylene blue group of dyes is similarly reduced to their leuco form by NaCl*, the reduction being followed by a suppression of the characteristic absorption peak. Electron scavengers as acetone lowered the reduction[48a].

(c) The peroxidation of pyrogallol and o-dianisidine dihydrochloride has been effected by NaCl* even in the absence of H_2O_2 or other oxidisers of peroxidase[48b].

4.1.3 Bioreactions: oxido-reduction reactions in coenzymes

The redox reactions of coenzymes, NAD^+, $NADP^+$, FAD and cytochrome C ox, play a vital role in life processes as hydrogen and electron carriers in respiratory process, and in the liberation and transport of energy-rich ATP. These bioreactions can be induced in vitro by the transfer of energy stored in γ-irradiated salts. The amounts of oxidising and reducing species liberated in situ during the dissolution of the irradiated salts being equal, in the absence of scavengers, the resulting reactions depend on the effective redox potential of the coenzymes present. Generally these are within ±0.1 V of the standard hydrogen electrode potential[49]. The monitoring of these reactions is facilitated for NADH by the large separation of the absorption maxima viz. the oxidised form (NAD) at 260 nm and the reduced form (NADH) at 340 nm.

The redox yields in all coenzyme pairs studied varied linearly with the amount of energy transferred i.e. to the amounts of irradiated salts added.

5. Thermoluminescence Colour Images (TLCI)and 3-Dimensional TL-Spectra from Natural Quartzes

Classical TL acquired a new dimension when colour imaging and conventional TL-spectrometry were coupled to it[50]. The themoluminescence colour image (TLCI) technique, developed by Hashimoto[50-54], has yielded results which are very meaningful in revealing the petrogenesis, mineralzation process and the microcomposition of quartzes of different origins as well as in the establishment of the reliable quartz inclusion TL-dating using red-region TL measurements[55-56]. The on-line 3-dimensional TL-spectrometric analysis, of spectrum as a function of temperature, has been also developed by using image intensified unit coupled to photodiode array reader. X- or γ-irradiated quartz sands examined by the new techniques show different colour images, readily distinguishable as red or blue TL emitting grains[56].

5.1 Sample Irradiation and TL Measurements

The sample was irradiated by X-rays to a dose of 8.7 kGy. The TL measurements were carried out after storing the irradiated specimen for two months at room temperature to let RTL decay. The irradiated sample was placed on a heater controlled at a linear rate of 1℃. The TLCI system permitted taking photographs at any desired temperature interval by programming on a personal computer. The colour fims were the commercially available high-sensitive film (ASA-1600). In more quantitative TL-spectrometric analysis, the spectral data in every second were stored in floppy disk files and followed by the "three dimensional plot" of TL intensity as a function of heating temperature. The spectrum files could be also converted to the glow-curves in the desired wavelength regions and extracted for the comparison of each spectrum at the preferred temperatures.

5.2 Provenance and Cause Search of the Red and Blue TL Emitting Quarzes

TLCI patterns over the temperature range 80-400℃ indicate unmistakably the provenance, i.e. the geological origin and the genesis of the specimen. In general quartzes from volcanic ashes, containing β-quartz mineralized at high temperature showed a strong red TLCI, while quartzes of pegmatite/hydrothermal origin, attributable to plutonic association and containing α-quartz, mineralized at low temperature gave rise to blue TLCI[51]. The 3-dimensional spectra are shown in Fig. 5(a) and (b). The Tazawa lake sands (a) are selected as a typical red TL emitting quartz. Extracted from volcanic ash layer they give intense TL emission at higher temperature side beyond 250℃, with a broad emission peak at 620 nm. On the other hand, the Madagascar quartz crystal of hydrothermal origin shows a distinct blue TL peak, with a broad emission peak at 470 nm,

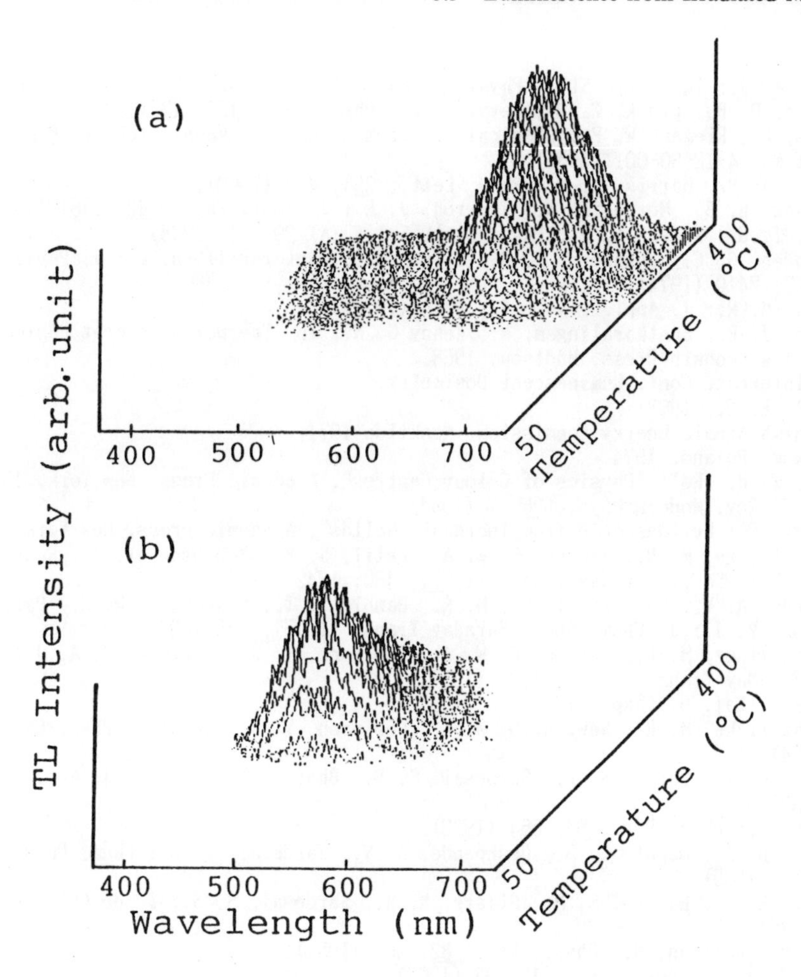

Fig. 5. Typical three dimensional spectrograms of TL from natural quartzes.
(a) Tazawa Lake quartz sands (volcanic ash origin),
(b) Madagascar crystal quartz (hydrothermal origin).

at relatively lower heating temperature around 200℃.

Besides shedding light on the origin and mode of formation of the quartz specimens, the present TL studies have been helpful in correlating the spectra with the microcomposition of the samples, in respect of trace impurities. Instrumental neutron activation analysis tentatively confirmed that the red TL emission is due to the higher concentration of impurities, involving Al (above 100 ppm) and light rare earth elements (chiefly Eu and/or Sm)[52]. It was also verified that Al impurities or dopants give rise to blue TL emission when quartz glasses were synthesised by the sol-gel technique. In the recent studies it has been clarfied that the Al impurites beyond 100 ppm cause red TL emission when the quartzes, originally with blue TL properties, were annealed for 100 hrs at high temperature above 1000 ℃. The increase of Al signals in the ESR measurements is also correlated to the conversion from blue TL intensity into red one after annealing treatments[55, 56].

References

1. Dekker, A. J.: in "Solid State Physics", MacMillan, London, 1962, pp. 398 and 405.
2. Townsend, P. D., Clark, C. D., Levy, P. W.: Phys. Rev., 155, 17 (1977).
2a. Daniels, F., Rieman, W. P.: Chemical Procurement Agency, Washington DC, Final Report Project No. 4-12-80-001 (1954).
3. Jackson, J. H., Harris, A. M.: Phys. Lett., 29A, 423 (1969).
4. Podgorsak, E. B., Moran, P. R., Cameron, J. R.: J. Appl. Phys., 42, 2761 (1971).
5. Stoebe, T. G., Watanabe, S.: Phys. Stat. Sol., (A) 29, 11 (1975).
6. Crittenden, G. C., Townsend, P. D., Gilkes, J., Wintersgill, M. C.: J. Phys. D., Appl. Phys., 7, 2410 (1974).
7. Mayhugh, M. R.: J. Appl. Phys., 41, 4776 (1970).
8. Cameron, J. R., Suntharalingam, N., Kenny G. N.: in "Thermoluminescent Dosimetry", Univ. of Wisconsin Press, Madison, 1968.
9. Proc. Internat. Conf. Luminescent Dosimetry,
II US A. E. C., 1968;
III Danish Atomic Energy Commission, Roskilde 1971;
IV Krakow, Poland, 1974
10. Fowler, W. B. (Ed): "Physics of Colour Centres", Academic Press, New York, 1968.
11. Seitz, F: Rev. Modern Phys., 26, 7 (1954).
12. Goldberg, P.: Luminescence from Inorganic Solids", Academic Press, New York, 1966
13. Chandratillake, M. R., Newton, G. W. A., Patil, S. F., Robinson, V. J., Rodgers, M. A. J.: J. Chem. Soc., Faraday Trans. II, 74, 480; 1342 (1978).
14. Deshpande, A. V., Chandratillake, M. R., Hamblett, I., Newton, G. W. A., Patil, S. F., Robinson, V. J.: J. Chem. Soc., Faraday Trans. II, 77, 135 (1981).
15. Chandratillake, M. R., Newton, G. W. A., Robinson, V. J., Rodgers, M. A. J.: J. Chem. Soc., Faraday Trans. II, 73, 1739 (1977).
16. Luty, F., (Ref. 9, Chap. 3).
17. Chandratillake, M. R., Newton, G. W. A., Robinson, V. J.: Radiat. Phys. Chem., 23, 29, 33 (1984).
18. Arnikar, H. J., Patil, S. F., Sardesai, S. S., Bhatia, P. J.: Jap. J. App. Phys., 24, 128 (1985).
19. Onsager, L.: Phys. Rev., 54, 554 (1938).
20. Arnikar, H. J., Bapat, L. B., Deshpande, A. V., Sardesai, S. S.: Chem. Phys. Lett., 115, 187 (1985).
21. Arnikar, H. J., Rao, B. S. M., Gijare, M. A., Sardesai, S. S.: J. de Chim. Phys., 72, 654 (1975)
22. Furst, M., Kallman, H.: Phys., Rev., 82, 964 (1951).
23. Crawford, J. H.: Adv. Phys., 17, 93 (1968).
24, Hobbs, L. W., Hughes, A. E., Pooley, D.: Proc. Roy. Soc., (London), A332, 167 (1973).
25. Wiedemann, E., Schmidt, G. C.: Ann. d. Physik, 56, 210 (1895).
26. Ahnstrom, G., Ehrenstein, G. V.: Acta. Chem. Scand., 13, 199 (1959).
27. Westermark, T., Grapengiesser, B.: Nature, 188, 395 (1960).
28. Westermark, T., Grapengiesser, B.: Archiv. Kemi., 17, 139 (1961).
28a. Burns, W. G., Williams, T. F.: Nature, 175, 1043 (1955).
29. Lelievre, B., Adloff, J. P.: J. Physique, 25, 789 (1964).
30. Arnikar, H. J., Damle, P. S., Chaure, B. D., Rao, B. S. M.: Nature, 228, 357 (1970); Naturwissenschaften, 57, 541 (1970).
31. Arnikar, H. J., Damle, P. S., Chaure, B. D.; J. Chem. Phys., 55, 3668 (1971).
32. Arnikar, H. J., Kalkar, C. D.: J. Lum., 15, 227 (1977).
33. Atari, N. A., Ettinger, K. V., Fremlin, J. H.: Radiation Effects, 17, 45 (1973); 20, 135 (1973); 26, 39 (1975).
34. Atari, N. A.: J. Lum., 21, 305, 387 (1980).
35. Atari, N. A., Ettinger, K. V.: Nature, 247, 193; 249, 341 (1974).
36. Ahnstrom, G.: Acta Chem. Scand., 19, 300 (1965).
37. Gopinathan, C., Damle, P. S., Hart, E. J.: J. Phys. Chem., 76, 3694 (1972).
38. Walker, D. C.: Adv. Chem. Series; Radiation Chem.-I: Hydrated Electron, 81, 49 (1968).
39. Avotinsh, Yu. E., Buganko, L. T., Dzelme, Yu. R., Tiliks, Yu. F.: "Lyoluminescence", (a Review in Russian), (1984).

40. Bosi, L., Lazzarini, A. L. F., Lazzarini, E.: Phys. Stat. Sol. (b) 66, 285 (1974); 69, 519 (1975).
41. Hacksylo, M., Otterson, D.: J. Chem. Phys., 21, 552, 1434 (1953).
42. Arnikar, H. J., Patil, S. F., Rao, B. S. M., Bodhe, A. A., Pokharkar, R. D.: Radiochimica Acta, 23, 109 (1976).
43. Arnikar, H. J., Rao, B. S. M., Bedeckar, M. J.: Radiochem. Radioanal. Lett., 36, 73 (1978).
44. Patil, S. F., Ravishankar, D., Bhatia, P., Chowdhary, I. B.: Int. J. Appl. Isot., 35, 459 (1984).
45. Patil, S. F., Ravishankar, D., Bhatia, P.: ibid., 35, 1095 (1984).
46. Seitz, F.: Rev. Modern Phys., 26, 7 (1954).
47. Arnikar, H. J., Kapadi, A. H., Bavadekar, V. K., Nilegaonkar, S.: Biovigyanam, 11, 192 (1985)
48. Arnikar, H. J., Nilegaonkar, S., Bhosale, S. B., Kapadi, A. H.: J. Radioanal. Nucl. Chem., (a) Lett., 131, 95 (1989); (b) Articles, 125, 57 (1988); (c) Lett., 108, 229 (1986).
49. Lehninger, A. L.: in "Biochemistry", Worth Publishers, New York, (1977).
50. Townsend, P. D., Kirsh, Y.: Contemp. Phys., 30, 337 (1989).
51. Hashimoto, T., Hayashi, Y., Yokosaka, K., Koyanagi, A., Kimura, K.: Nuclear Tracks Radiat. Meas., 11, 229 (1986).
52. Hashimoto, T., Yokosaka, K., Habuki, H.: ibid., 13, 57 (1987).
53. Hashimoto, T., Yokosaka, K., Habuki, H., Hayashi, Y.: ibid., 16, 3 (1989).
54. Hashimoto, T., Koyanagi, A., Yokosaka, K., Hayashi, Y., Sotobayashi, T.: Geochem. J., 20, 111 (1986).
55. Hashimoto, T., Habuki, H., Tanabe, I., Sakai, T., Takahashi, S: Geochemistry, 33, 35 (1989).
56. Hashimoto, T., Kojima, M., Sakai, T.; Archeology and Natural Science, 23, 13 (1991).

5.6 Linear Energy Transfer (LET) Effects of Radiation Chemistry

Masashi IMAMURA
Tokyo University of Information Sciences, 1200-2, Yatoh-cho, Chiba, Chiba, 265 Japan

1. Introduction

Chemical changes produced in matter exposed to ionizing radiation are the result of energy transfer from the radiation. The energy transfer occurs along the trajectories of the radiation and produces primary reactive species, ions, excited molecules, and free radicals. The overall result of the absorption of any type of radiation by matter is thus the formation of tracks of these reactive species.

These species may be the same in a given matter regardless of the type or energy of the radiation. All ionizing radiations may, therefore, give rise to qualitatively similar chemical effects in matter. However, radiations of different types and energies lose energy at different rates and consequently form tracks that are densely or sparsely populated with the reactive species, resulting in differences in the subsequent radiolytic yields.[1]

The rate of the energy transfer is described by the linear energy transfer, or LET, of the radiation. The dependence of the radiolytic yields on LET is termed the LET effect.

The LET effects are more important in liquids, where the reactive species are hindered from moving apart by the proximity of other molecules, than in gases, where they can move apart with relative ease. Thus, in gases no pronounced LET effect is observed on the product yields compared with liquids.

This article presents a brief description of LET and its effects in the radiolysis of water and aqueous solution and of typical liquid organic compounds.

2. Energy Loss of Radiation

2.1. Heavy Charged Particles

A semiclassical expression for the rate of energy loss of heavy charged particles (protons, deuterons, α-particles) in matter was derived by Bethe, based on the basic hypothesis that the main mechanism of energy dissipation is by electrostatic coulombic interaction between the heavy particle and the electrons of the medium.

When a particle of charge ze and velocity v traverses a medium in which the density of electrons (the number of electrons per unit volume of the medium) is n, the rate of energy loss (energy loss per unit path length) is given by

$$-\frac{dE}{dx}=\frac{4\pi z^2e^4n}{mv^2}\ln\left(\frac{2mv^2}{I}\right) \quad (1)$$

where m is the mass of the electron and I is the mean excitation potential for the electrons, which increases linearly with the charges of the nuclei of the medium. The value of I calculated for water is 65.1 eV.[2]

The rate of energy loss, -dE/dx, is called the stopping power or linear energy transfer (LET). Equation 1 breaks down when the velocity of the incident particle is too high or too low ($E < 0.6$ MeV for protons; $E<2.5$ MeV for α-particles).[3]

2.2. Electrons

When the incident particle is an electron, the situation is only slightly changed. The main difference is that the factor 2 in the logarithmic term of Eqn. 1 disappears because the reduced mass of the two electrons is m/2, whereas the reduced mass of the system consisting of a heavy particle and an electron is close to the mass of the electron.

Another factor is that both particles involved in the collision are electrons, i.e., they are identical. As a result, the rate of energy loss of incident electrons is given by

$$-\frac{dE}{dx}=\frac{4\pi z^2e^4n}{mv^2}\ln\left(\frac{mv^2}{2I}\frac{\varepsilon}{2}\right) \quad (2)$$

where ε is the basis of natural logarithmus. At very high energies, Eqn.2 is modified to take into account the relativistic change of the mass of the electron.

2.3. High-Energy Photons

High-energy photons, such as X rays and γ rays, lose energy in photoelectric absorption, Compton scattering, and pair production. Their relative contribution to the total energy loss depends on the energy of the incident photon and on the nuclear charges of the medium. For photons of 100 keV —2MeV the main mechanism of energy loss in water is by Compton scattering. The energy distribution of Compton electrons depends on the energy of the incident photons.

On the basis of these facts, it is concluded that the main effect of the absorption of high-energy photons by matter is the production of energetic electrons, which dissipate their energy as described before.

3. LET Effects

Examination of Eqns. 1 and 2 leads to the following conclusions. First, the rate of energy loss of a charged particle in a given medium is proportional to the electron density of the medium. Second, because the factor v^2 outside the logarithmic term is more important than the one inside, the rate of energy loss increases with decreasing velocity of the particle. Third, if we compare two particles of equal energy but different mass, the heavier one has a smaller velocity and hence has a larger LET.

As a consequence, the density of encounters along an α-particle track is several thousand times larger than that along an electron track of the same energy.

This fact is of great importance in the interpretation of the quantitative differences between the reactions induced by fast electrons and those induced by heavy particles.

If a charged particle has a low LET value, spurs (clusters of ions created by low-energy-loss events along the trajectory of the particle) are widely spaced like a "string of beads", and they develop in time without any interference from neighboring spurs (isolated spurs). On the other hand, for a high-LET particle the spurs overlap and form a cylindrical track, in which reactive species from neighboring spurs along the track can intermingle and react.

Thus, the kinetics in radiation chemistry reflects the initial spatial distribution.

4. Radiolysis of Water

Radiation chemistry of water and aqueous solutions has been intensively studied and well documented compared with any other liquids.[4]

A water molecule is ionized by radiation on a time scale of an electronic transition. The positive ion H_2O^+ undergoes the ion-molecule reaction to produce OH and H_3O^+. The electron released in the ionization has sufficient energy to ionize further water molecules, leading to the formation of clusters of ions (spurs) along the track of the ionizing particle. Since the average energy loss per event is assumed to be about 50 eV, each spur may contain 2-3 pairs of ions.

Eventually the energy of the electron falls below the ionization threshold of water and finally the electron is localized in a potential energy well long enough to be hydrated (hydrated electron: e_{aq}^-).

Some water molecules, instead of being ionized, may be excited to upper electronic states, from which they can autoionize, dissociate, or fall back to the ground electronic state.

These physicochemical processes described above are complete by about 10^{-12} sec after ionization. Hydrated electrons, H_3O^+, radicals (H, OH), and molecular products (H_2, H_2O_2) resulting from the dissociation of excited water molecules are clustered in the spur.

The primary products then begin to diffuse. A fraction of them encounter one another to form molecular and secondary radical products, while the remainder escape into the bulk to be homogeneously distributed. This spur expansion is complete by about 10^{-7} sec.

The spur diffusion model described above is verified by the following features: (1) A fraction of radicals (e_{aq}^- , H, OH) are readily scavenged by low concentrations of solutes ($<10^{-3}$ M) in yields that are independent of the solute concentration, while the molecular products (H_2, H_2O_2) are formed in constant yields. (2) When the solute concentration is increased above 10^{-3} M, the yields of scavenged radicals increase and the yields of H_2 and H_2O decrease; the changes in the yields are approximately proportional to the change in log [scavenger] .

The radical and molecular yields thus determined with radiations with various LET values are listed in Table 1. The yields are expressed by G, which is the number of species produced (or destroyed) per 100 eV absorbed dose.

Table 1. LET dependence of the yields of radicals and molecular products in the radiolysis of water[4,5)]

Radiation	LET	G				
	(eV/Å)	e_{aq}^-	H	OH	H_2	H_2O_2
Co-60 γ	0.02	2.63	0.55	2.72	0.45	0.68
18 MeV D^+	0.5	1.48	0.62	1.78	0.68	0.84
32 MeV He^{2+}	2.3	0.72	0.42	0.91	0.96	1.00
12 MeV He^{2+}	5.0	0.42	0.27	0.54	1.11	1.08

5. LET Effect in the Radiolysis of Aqueous Ferrous Sulfate Solution

The radiation-induced oxidation of aqeous ferrous sulfate solution containing 0.4 M sulfuric acid has been extensively studied and is the basis for the Fricke dosimeter in wide use. On exposure to ionizing radiation the ferrous ions are oxidized to ferric ions by the oxidizing species produced from water:

$$Fe^{2+} + OH \longrightarrow Fe^{3+} + OH^-$$
$$H + O_2 \longrightarrow HO_2$$
$$Fe^{2+} + HO_2 \longrightarrow Fe^{3+} + HO_2^-$$
$$HO_2^- + H^+ \longrightarrow H_2O_2$$
$$2Fe^{2+} + H_2O_2 \longrightarrow 2Fe^{3+} + 2OH^-$$

Thus the yield of ferric ion for every 100 eV absorbed, $G(Fe^{3+})$, expressed by

$$G(Fe^{3+}) = G_{OH} + 3G_H + 2G_{H2O2}$$

in which G_{OH}, G_H , and G_{H2O2} stands for the yields of the primary species in the bulk of the solution.[4)]

The oxidation yield, $G(Fe^{3+})$, which is 15.6 for Co-60 γ-rays, decreases steadily with increasing LET. In Fig. 1 the oxidation yields obtained with protons, deuterons, helium ions, carbon ions, and nitrogen ions are plotted as a function of initial LET values of these particles.[6)]

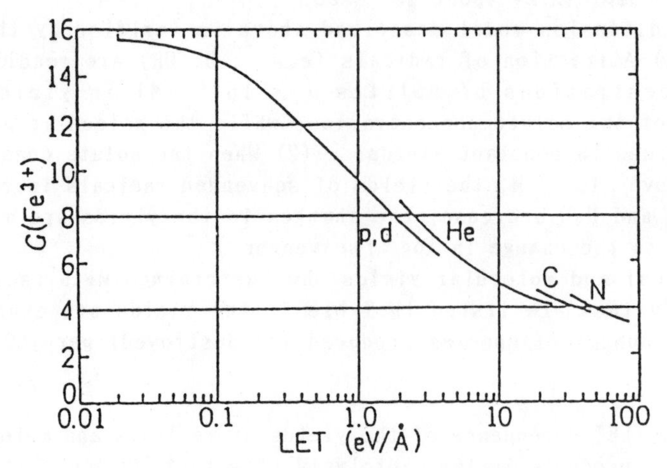

Fig. 1. Variation of $G(Fe^{3+})$ for the aerated ferrous sulfate solution with the initial LET of protons, deuterons, helium ions, carbon ions, and nitrogen ions.

The decrease in $G(Fe^{3+})$ with increasing LET is explained on the basis of the decreasing yields of primary radicals, H and OH, with increasing LET in the radiolysis of water.

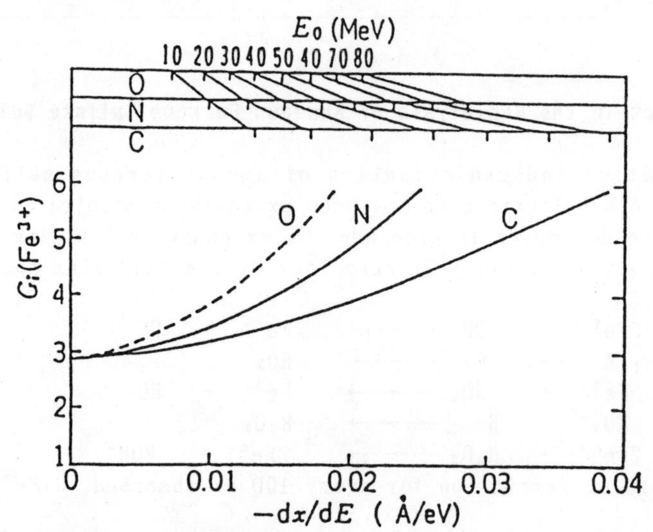

Fig. 2. Variation of instantaneous yields of ferric ion, $G_i(Fe^{3+})$, with reciprocal LET for C and N ions. The curve for O ions is estimated from a single experimental result. The extrapolated G-value for infinite LET is 2.9.

The discontinuities observed among these particles at the same LET values are regarded as being due to the different contributions of δ-rays emitted out of the tracks by head-on collisions of these heavy particles with water molecules. It is known that heavy particles also lose their energy by head-on collisions and eject energetic electrons (δ-rays). The heavier particle ejects the more energetic electrons, which produce low-LET branch tracks outside the main track, resulting in the higher overall yield at the same LET. The difference in $G(Fe^{3+})$ between particles (carbon and nitrogen ions) at the same LET is shown more clearly in Fig. 2,[6] in which "instantaneous yields", $G_i(Fe^{3+})$, are plotted as a function of reciprocal LET. The instantaneous yield at a given particle energy are calculated from the slope of a curve obtained by plotting $G(Fe^{3+}) \times E$ against E: $G_i(Fe^{3+}) = d[G(Fe^{3+})E]/dE$, where E is the initial energy of the particle.

6. LET effects in the Radiolysis of Liquid Organic Compounds

LET effects in organic compounds have been less extensively studied; these studies have been reviewed[7] and a summary of recent references has been published elswhere.[8]

The main radiolytic product from hydrogenous organic compounds is hydrogen, with a yield generally increasing with the LET.

6.1. Benzene

One of the most remarkable LET effects is observed on the hydrogen yield from liquid benzene. $G(H_2)$ from benzene is very low (0.038) in γ-radiolysis and shows only a slight increase at modest LETs; however, the yield increases markedly for a heavy particle toward the end of its track.

Using various heavy particles, LaVerne and Schuler[9] extensively studied the LET effect on the hydrogen yield from benzene. Plots of $G(H_2) \times E$ vs. E for these particles, shown in Fig. 3, indicate that the instantaneous yields

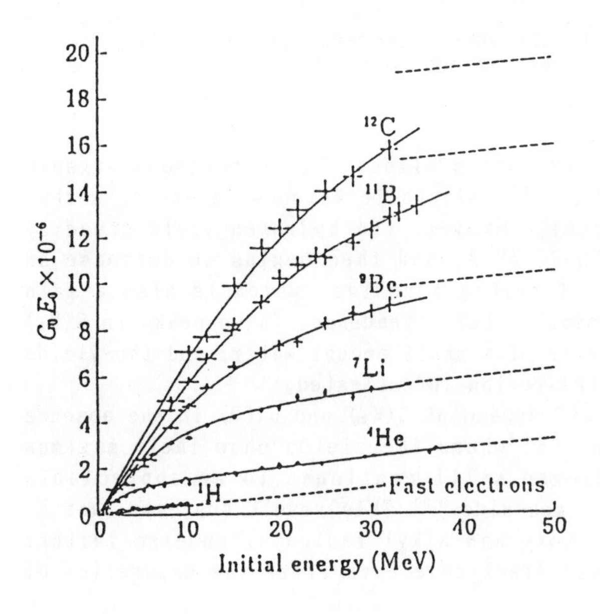

Fig. 3. Integral hydrogen produced (G × E) from benzene. The dashed lines represent the limiting instantaneous yields at high energies, which are the same as the yield for fast electrons.

(obtained from the slope at a given E) at low energies show pronounced increase with the atomic number of the particles ,but the limiting instantaneous yields at very high energies, where LET is low, approach that of low-LET fast electrons.

These results suggest that the increase in $G(H_2)$ from benzene with increasing LET can be ascribed to the marked increase in $G(H_2)$ near the end of the track of the heavy particles.

When the instantaneous hydrogen yields are plotted as a function of LET, the yields show a decrease at the same LET with increasing atomic number of the particle, as shown in Fig. 4. LaVerne and Schuler concluded that this decrease with the atomic number cannot be explained by the δ-ray effect, but rather reflects the increased diameter of the track core produced by the more highly charged particles.

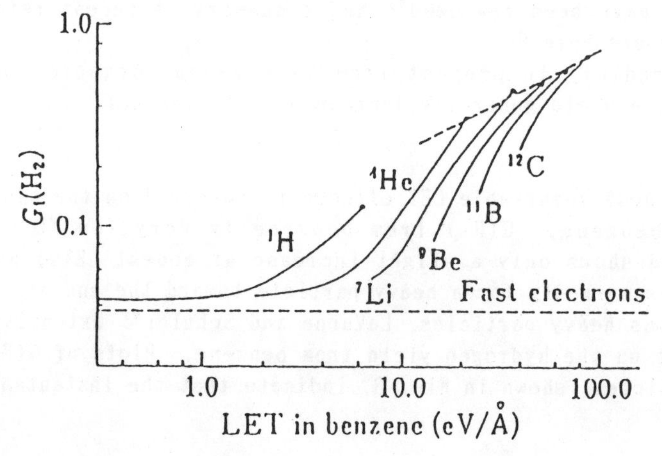

Fig. 4. Variation of the instantaneous hydrogen yields, $G_i(H_2)$, with LET in benzene for the various ions.

6.2. Aliphatic Ketones

As mentioned, the hydrogen yield from almost all hydrogenous organic compounds increases with the LET. For aliphatic ketones (acetone, methyl ethyl ketone, and diethyl ketone), however, the hydrogen yield steadily increases with the LET up to 50-70 eV/A, and then begins to decrease as shown in Fig. 5.[10] The yield of carbon monoxide, which is also a main product next to hydrogen, show similar LET dependence. These peaks in $G(H_2)$ and $G(CO)$ disappear on the addition of a small amount water, and the yields continue increasing in the high LET region investigated.[11]

The detailed analysis of the LET-dependent $G(H_2)$ and $G(CO)$ in the absence of water reveals that,above the LET where the yields show their maximum values, the formation of hydrogen still continues to an appreciable extent,but almost not for carbon monoxide.[10] This result suggests that H-containing primary radicals, alkoxy and alkyl radicals, undergo further decomposition within the high-LET track core even after the saturation of primary radical formation from parent ketone. This conclusion, though tentative, is based on the fact that the decomposition of a ketone molecule could produce several H_2 molecules, but only one for CO molecule, and that the activation energies of the decomposition of the primary radicals are as high as 20-40 kcal/mol.

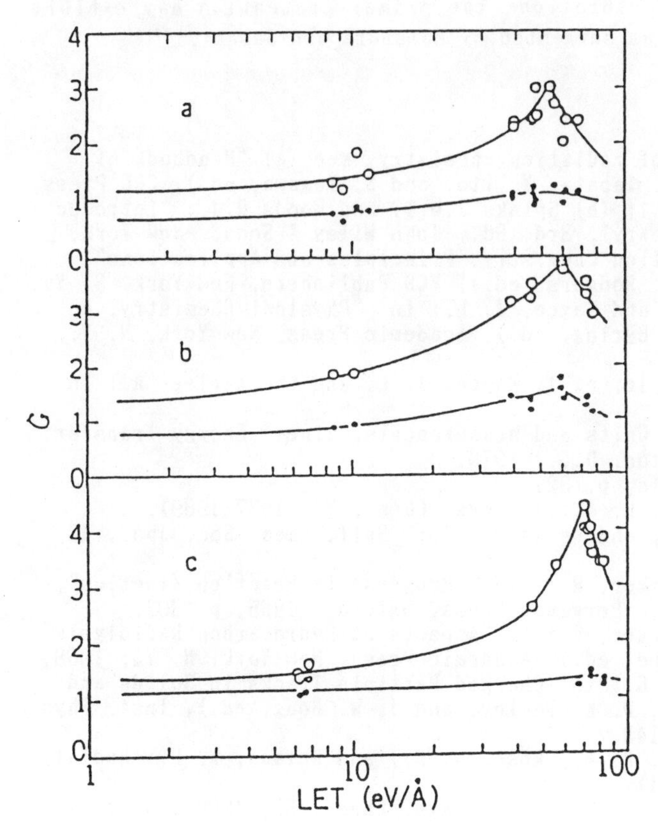

Fig. 5. Variation of $G(H_2)$ G(CO) from aliphatic ketones with the initial LET of He, C, and N ions. a, acetone; b, methyl ethyl ketone; c, diethyl ketone; ○, $G(H_2)$; ●, G(CO).

7. Concluding Remarks

With increasing LET, a heavy ion particle imparts an enomorous amount of energy to a medium, giving rise to dense ionization and excitation of the molecules of the medium. In a simple molecule like water, most of the primary species react with each other and produce molecular products, which then diffuse out of the track with the rest of the species that have escaped recombination. Excess energy may rapidly dissipate to the bulk. In organic compounds, the excess energy may also dissipate to the bulk when the "thermal conductivity" of a medium is relatively high.

When the "thermal conductivity" is low, however, the excess energy could cause further decomposition of primary species that have high activation energies; this is the case for the radiolysis of ketones containing no water, as described in the last section. In such a medium, one could observe an apparent saturation of product formation above a certain LET value, in contrast to aqueous systems in which rapid thermal diffusion takes place.

In hot-atom chemistry, recoiled particles behave as high-LET radiation, resulting radiolysis of the medium and, depending on the energy of the particles and on the medium, give rise to the local temperature increase due to excess thermal energy. If the high local temperature is retained for a time longer than molecular vibration, the primary retention may exhibit negative temperature effect as suggested by Matsuura and Sasaki.[12]

References

1. For general references of radiation chemistry, see (a) "Handbook of Radiation Chemistry",(Y. Tabata, Y. Ito, and S. Tagawa, ed.), CRC Press, Boca Raton, Florida, 1991; (b) Spinks J.W.T. and Woods R.J.: "Introduction to Radiation Chemistry", 3rd. Ed., John Wiley & Sons, New York, N. Y., 1990; (c) "Radiation Chemistry. Principles and Applications", (Farhataziz and M. A. J. Rodgers, ed.), VCH Publishers, New York, N. Y., 1987. (d) Mozumder,A. and Magee, J. L.: in "Physical Chemistry. An Advanced Treatise", (H. Eyring, ed.), Academic Press, New York, N. Y., 1975, p. 700.
2. Chatterjee, A.: in ref. 1c, p. 1; Magee, J. L. and Chatterjee, A.: in ref.1c, p. 137.
3. Int. Comm. on Radiation Units and Measurements. Linear Energy Transfer, ICRYU Rep. 16, Washington, D.C., 1970.
4. Buxton, G. V.: in ref. 1c, p. 321.
5. Appleby, A. and Schwarz, H. A.: J. Phys. Chem., 75, 1937(1969).
6. Imamura, M., Matsui, M., and Karasawa, T.: Bull. Chem. Soc. Jpn., 43, 2745 (1970).
7. (a) Burns, W. G. and Barker, R.: in "Progress in Reaction Kinetics", Vol. 3 (G. Porter, ed.), Pergamon Press, Oxford, 1965, p. 303; (b) Burns, W. G. and Barker, R.: in "Aspects of Hydrocarbon Radiolysis", (T. Gaumann and J. Hoigne, ed.), Academic Press, New York, N. Y., 1968, p. 33; (c) Burns, W. G.: in "Charged Particle Tracks in Solids and Liquids", (G. E. Adams, D. K. Bewley, and J. W. Boag, ed.), Inst. Phys. & Phys. Soc., 1970, p. 143.
8. LaVerne, J. A., Schuler, R. H., Ross, A. B., and Helman, W. P.: Radiat. Phys. Chem., 17, 5 (1981).
9. LaVerne, J. A. and Schuler, R. H.: J. Phys. Chem., 88, 1200 (1984).
10. Matsui, M. and Imamura, M.: Bull. Chem. Soc. Jpn., 47, 1113 (1974).
11. Matsui, M. and Imamura, M.: Bull. Chem. Soc. Jpn., 48, 2346 (1975).
12. Matsuura, T. and Sasaki: K.: Radiochim. Acta, 49, 17 (1990).

5.7 α-Recoil Damage and Hot Atom Chemistry

Tetsuo HASHIMOTO
Department of Chemistry, Faculty of Science, Niigata University, Ikarashi-Ninocho, Niigata, 950-21 Japan

1 Introduction

The α-decay of U, Th, and their daughter elements causes accumulated natural radiation damage in minerals over geological time-periods. Such radiation damage in minerals can be resolved into two parts; one is α-particle exposure and another is the bombardment of the α-recoil atoms[1,2]. The effects of α-recoil are significantly greater than those of the α-particles themselves, because of higher LET owing to high atomic number and mass of the recoil atoms. Hence the α-recoil damage will be dealt with first in this article.

In the recoil energy region corresponding to α-decay of both natural and artificial α-emitters, the recoil atoms cause mainly atomic displacements and result in many interstitial atoms along their tracks. Thus, the latent α-recoil tracks can give rise to locally amorphous regions, which become easily etchable, or porous parts in dielectric materials, including natural minerals. These damaged parts are considered to be associated with the preferential enrichment of daughter nuclides in natural waters, resulting in high activity ratios of $^{234}U/^{238}U$ and $^{224}Ra/^{228}Ra$. This may be considered as an example of a naturally occurring hot atom effect[3–6]. In a few minerals such as micas, parts damaged by α-recoil can be revealed by phase-contrast microscopy following a suitable chemical etching treatment[7,8].

Recently, considerable attention has also been paid to the remarkable effects of α-recoil damage that occur during long storage times. Solidification of long-lived actinides in radwaste[9] gives rise to such situations.

In a preceding review, the author has compared the experimental α-recoil ranges with theoretically estimated values[1]. In the present article, the α-recoil phenomena are discussed from the standpoint of the elution and annealing behavior of the incident heavy ions introduced as recoil atoms onto muscovite surfaces. Rn-emanation effects and the effects of α-recoil atoms on thermoluminescence in natural systems are also considered.

1.1 Elution and annealing behavior of α-recoil atoms[10,11]

In a vacuum chamber, an annealed mica target was exposed to an electroplated ^{232}U-source, which had been stored for the growth of thorium descendants. The mica thus subjected to α-recoils showed an α-particle spectrum typical of all members of the thorium decay series, in particular, ^{228}Th, ^{224}Ra, and ^{212}Po. However, ^{232}U, the parent nuclide, was never been observed on the target mica surfaces, even after protracted irradiation. This indicates that all activities found on the mica surface were transferred by the recoil effect following α-decay on the surface of the source. Since some of the recoil atoms may undergo successive decay processes, the transferred atoms and their descendants should be implanted in the mica layer. Accordingly, the mica surface was repeatedly etched with HCl and/or HF solutions. The residual activity changes of the ^{224}Ra and ^{212}Po (fed from ^{212}Pb) on the mica are illustrated in Fig. 1 as a function of total etching time. Apparently, the ^{224}Ra component is removed at an earlier stage of etching, whereas the ^{212}Po is eluted at a relatively slow rate. The half removal times of ^{224}Ra and ^{212}Po activity were found to be 23 and 5.2 m etching time, respectively. From these findings, it is concluded that the fraction of ^{212}Po generated by repeated alpha decay could penetrate more deeply into the mica layer. On the other hand, all of the ^{224}Ra originates directly from the parent ^{228}Th on the ^{232}U source through only a single-decay process, so that the corresponding depth of ^{224}Ra should be shallower than for the ^{212}Po (or ^{212}Pb) on the mica surface. In this event, it is understandable that the elution of ^{224}Ra precedes that of ^{212}Po.

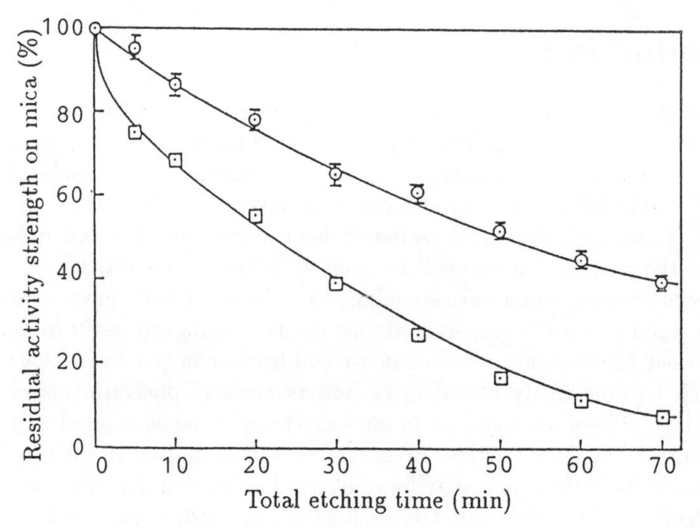

Figure 1. Changes in residual activity on a mica surface etched with (1+1)HF: ⊙:^{212}Po (fed from ^{212}Pb); □:^{224}Ra.

Several micas implanted with the recoil atoms were subjected to a thermal annealing treatment at various temperatures before washing with HCl solution. The results obtained are summarized in Table 1. Following annealing at 500 for 1h, it was found that the acidic washing unexpectedly removed up to 90% of the ^{224}Ra activity and 45% of the ^{212}Po activity. These values are consistent with the results obtained with a mica target irradiated at atmospheric pressure, so that the thickness of the surrounding layer of air corresponded to the range of single α recoil atoms. In contrast, the un-annealed mica showed less than 10% removal for both ^{224}Ra and ^{212}Po activities. It appears certain that similar effects of annealing on washing also occur at lower temperatures, *i.e.*, in the range 230-235°C. These results suggest that the injected recoil atoms in the mica surface are preferentially expelled from the inner layers, where they are initially implanted, to the outer surface, in the course of annealing. The greater extent of removal of ^{224}Ra with compared to ^{212}Po is also compatible with a shallower depth of ^{224}Ra injection in comparison with that of ^{212}Po. These effects can be rationalized by the multiple α-decay process mentioned above.

Table 1. Effect of thermal annealing on extraction by washing with 0.5N HCl solution

Annealing temp. (°C)	Annealing period (h)	Removed percentage ^{224}Ra	Activity with washing $^{212}Po(^{212}Pb)$
500	1	86.2	43.9
500 [a]	1	91.3	45.8
380–420	1	13.0	20.6
230–235	1	14.6	12.1
No	–	8.4 ± 2.6	8.9 ± 4.6
No [b]	–	87	43

a: Annealing was performed in a vacuum.
b: Recoil collection at atmospheric pressure.

Table 2. Variation of F_T and F_r values (retention efficiency on collector surfaces) using each collector

Collector material	F_T-value	F_r-value*
Stainless steel plate	0.30	0.95
Platinum plate	0.27	0.69
Glass plate	0.28	0.84
Biotite	0.32	1.00
Feldspar	0.28	0.84
Quartz	0.23	0.72

* This value was normalized to the highest F_T-collector, biotite, which was assumed to retain almost completely ^{222}Rn within its surface (for comparison with previous results see reference 10)).

The ejection efficiency of ^{222}Rn was also determined from the ratio of the ^{226}Ra activity in the source to the ^{222}Rn transferred to various targets or collectors in vacuum[12,13]. The experimental collector efficiency, F_T, of targets was expressed using the relation $F_T = F_c \cdot F_r$, where F_c is the ejection efficiency from the source and F_r is a retention efficiency of ^{222}Rn. The retention efficiency, F_r, of ^{222}Rn implanted on several target materials is summarized in Table 2. All targets examined were capable of retaining ^{222}Rn to an extent greater than 70%; conversely, the "escape ability" of the ^{222}Rn was greatly dependent on the target material. These results suggest that the ability of ^{222}Rn to escape immediately following α-recoil implantation is remarkably low from all the targets, including minerals.

It was concluded from these experiments that the effects of α-recoil due to either single or multiple decays, together with natural thermal influences, should be important factors in determining disequilibrium of radionuclides in the environment.

1.2 Thermoluminescent phenomena and α-recoil effects in lepidolite mica[14)]

A sample of natural lepidolite mica from Madagascar was split into 15 batches, of which all but one were annealed at a temperature of 400°C for various times. TL glow-curves were obtained by irradiation with γ-rays. After etching treatment, all mica surfaces were coated with a thin silver layer by vacuum evaporation and examined with a Nomarski differential interference-contrast system; α-recoil track densities were measured for each batch.

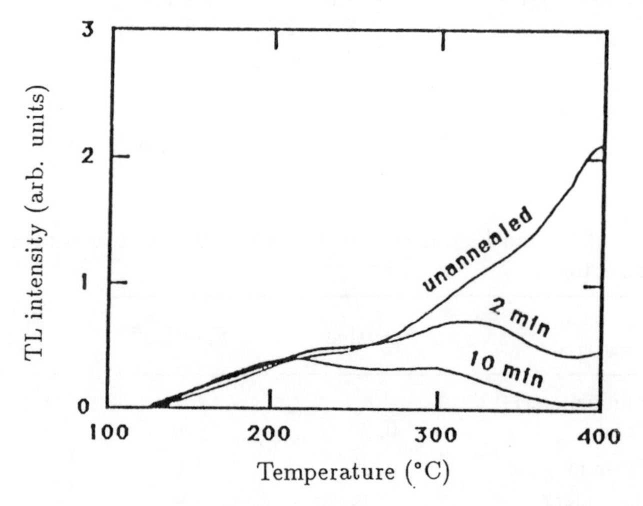

Figure 2. Effect of pre-annealing (400°C) on the TL glow-curve of γ irradiated lepidolite. The glow-curves represent unannealed, 2-min annealed, and 10-min annealed samples. The γ-ray dose was 8.7 kGy, and the heating rate was $1°Cs^{-1}$

Figure 2 presents TL glow-curves for three selected samples following γ-ray irradiation. Annealing prior to γ-ray irradiation lowers the TL sensitivity of lepidolite and a higher temperature has a more pronounced effect than a lower. The effect of pre-annealing on TL sensitivity is also evident in Fig.3. When the sample is annealed for 5 min or longer at 400°C, the integrated TL intensity in the range 320-400°C is reduced to one-tenth of that of the unannealed control; the TL intensity in the 150-250°C range is independent of the pre-annealing time.

The α-recoil track density is also reduced to one-tenth of the original density when the sample was annealed at 400°C, for 3 min; α-recoil tracks completely disappeared when the sample was annealed for more than 30 min. The concomitant decrease in TL sensitivity and decrease in α-recoil track density suggests that latent α-recoil tracks play an important role as electron trapping sites or lattice defects in lepidolite. It is concluded that thermoluminescence detection in various natural minerals may constitute a useful research tool in studing accumulated α-recoil effects.

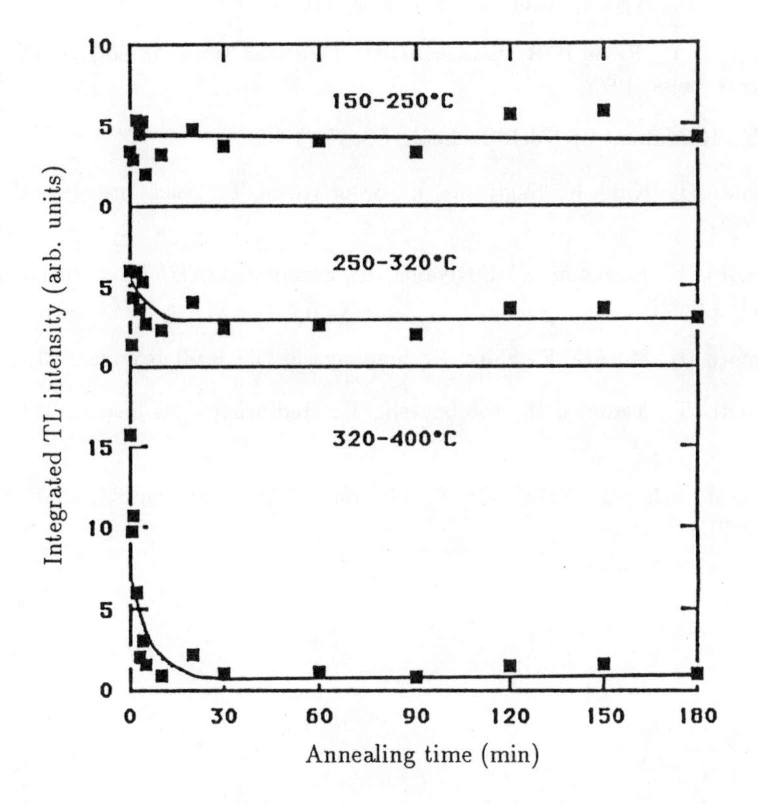

Figure 3 Effect of pre-annealing (400°C) on the integrated TL intensity of γ irradiated lepidolite. The integrated ranges of glow-curve temperature are 150-250°C, 250-320°C and 320-400°C.

References

1. Sakanoue, M., Hashimoto, T.: "Hot Atom Chemistry" (Matsuura, Ed.) Kodansha, Tokyo and Elsevier, Amsterdam, 1984, p.460.

2. Fleischer, R. L., Raabe, O. G.: Geochem. Cosmochim. Acta, **42**, 937 (1978).

3. Ordonez Regil, E., Schleiffer J. J., Adloff, J. P., Roessler, K.: Radiochim. Acta, **47**, 177 (1989).

4. Roessler, K. in Gmelin Handbook "Uranium" Suppl. Vol. A6 (1983) p. 135.

5. Roessler, K. in Gmelin Handbook "Thorium" Suppl. Vol. A4 (1988) p. 199.

6. Adloff, J. P., Roessler, K.: Radiochem. Acta, **52/53**, 269 (1991).

7. Huang, W. H., Walker, R. M.: Science, **155**, 1103 (1976).

8. Fleischer, R. L., Price, P. B., Walker, R. M.: "Nuclear Tracks in Solids", University of California Press, 1975.

9. Eyal, Y., Kaufman, A.: Nucl. Technol., **58**, 77 (1982).

10. Hashimoto, T., Kido, K., Sugiyama, H., Sotobayashi, T.: Nucl. Instrum. Meth., **150**, 509 (1978).

11. Hashimoto, T., Komatsu, K., Sugiyama, H., Sotobayashi, T.: Nucl. Instrum. Meth., **178**, 437 (1980).

12. Hashimoto, T., Maruta, F., Saito, H., Sotobayashi, T.: Radioisotopes, **33**, 1 (1984).

13. Hashimoto, T., Yamada, H., Sotobayashi, T.: Radiochem. Radioanal. Lett., **41**, 323 (1979).

14. Kasuya, M., Sakai, T., Takahashi, S., Hashimoto, T.: Nucl. Tracks Radiat. Meas., **16**, 283 (1989).

5.8 Radiation Damage of Solids

Noriaki ITOH
Department of Physics, Faculty of Science, Nagoya University,
Furocho, Chikusaku, Nagoya 464-01, Japan

1. Introduction

When solids are subjected to irradiation, defects in the crystal lattice are generated, inducing changes in their macroscopic properties. This phenomenon is called radiation damage.[1-4] The way the radiation damage evolves in each solid varies from material to material. The present chapter gives only the fundamental aspects of the processes of radiation damage, which may be of use in understanding the phenomena and predicting qualitatively or even quantitatively radiation damage evolution in solids on irradiation under given conditions. Since the radiation damage is initiated by deposition of the energy of incident particles into solids, we discuss on energy deposition in section 2 and show the two important types of energy deposition: as kinetic energy of atoms and as electronic excitation. In section 3, we deal with radiation damage originating from the energy deposition as electronic excitation and in section 4 that from the energy deposition as to atomic kinetic energy.

2. Energy deposition

The energy of incident particles is deposited in a solid by collisions with the lattice atoms. We do not treat the effects induced by nuclear reactions, since their cross section is usually small, but confine ourselves to the effects induced by atomic collisions. Any effect of irradiation by incident particles arises from direct collisions of the incident particles with the atoms of the crystal lattice or those of the primary displaced atoms with the lattice. Since the latter occur for any type of incident particles, we deal first with the collisions of displaced atoms.

2.1. Collisions of energetic atoms in solids

An atom can be regarded as a massive nucleus of which charge is shielded by surrounding electrons. Energetic atoms travelling in solids are not neutral;

some electrons are removed because of the collisions with the atoms in the lattice.[5] Usually the elastic and inelastic collisions are assumed to occur independently.[6] The former imparts kinetic energy to the atoms in the lattice and the latter produces electronic excitation of the solids.

2.1.1. Cross sections of elastic encounters

The maximum energy T_m transfered by an atom of energy E to an atom at rest in an elastic encounter is derived from the energy and momentum conservation laws[6]:

$$T_m = \frac{4m_1m_2}{(m_1 + m_2)^2} E \quad , \tag{1}$$

for non-relativistic particles and

$$T_m = \left(\frac{2m_e}{m_2}\right)\left(\frac{E+2m_ec^2}{m_ec^2}\right) E \quad , \tag{2}$$

for relativistic particles, where c is the light velocity and m_1 and m_2 are the masses of the colliding and target atoms, respectively.

More sophisticated treatment of elastic collisions between atoms rely on quantum mechanics. Lindhard et al. have developed a semi-classical theory of collisions of energetic atoms[5,7] Their treatment is based on the Thomas-Fermi model of atoms.[8] One of the advantages of using their model is that universal equations for several quantities can be derived. According to Lindhard, the universal differential cross section $d\sigma$ for collisions between two atoms of atomic number Z_1 and Z_2 and of masses m_1 and m_2 is given by

$$d\sigma = \pi a^2 \frac{dt}{2t^{3/2}} f(t^{1/2}) \quad , \tag{3}$$

where a is the Thomas-Fermi radius given by

$$a = 0.8853 \frac{a_B}{\{Z_1^{2/3}+Z_2^{2/3}\}^{1/2}} \quad , \tag{4}$$

and t a reduced variable representing the energy T imparted to the target atom and the scattering angle θ, and a_B is the Bohr radius. Using the universal energy ε given by

$$\varepsilon = \frac{0.8853}{2Z_1Z_2\{Z_1^{2/3}+Z_2^{2/3}\}^{1/2}} \frac{m_2}{(m_1+m_2)} \frac{E}{E_R} , \tag{5}$$

t is related to θ or T as follows:

$$t = \varepsilon^2 \sin^2(\frac{\theta}{2}) , \tag{6}$$

$$t = (\frac{T}{E}) \varepsilon^2 . \tag{7}$$

In these equations, E_R is the Rydberg energy. f(t) can be obtained numerically[8] or approximated by[10]

$$f(t^{1/2}) = \frac{1.309t^{1/6}}{[1 + (2.618t^{2/3})^{2/3}]^{3/2}} . \tag{8}$$

Fig. 1 shows the function f(t), which for large t approaches the cross section of the Rutherford scattering. At the low energy limit the collisions are usually assumed to be hard-sphere collisions.

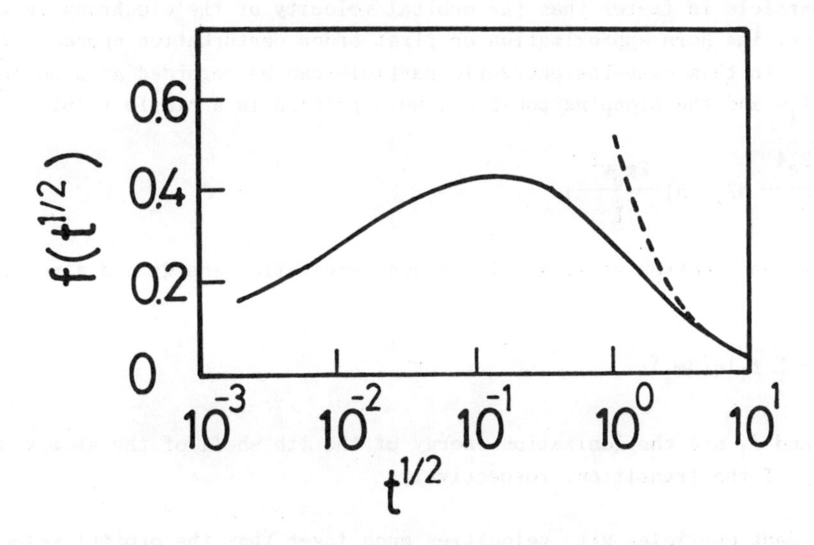

Fig. 1. The function $f(t^{1/2})$ (solid line). The dashed line shows the Rutherford scattering cross section.

2.1.2. Stopping power due to elastic encounters

The linear rate of energy deposition from particles to solids can be expressed using the stopping power, which is defined by

$$S = N \, \Sigma\sigma_i T_i = N \int_0^{T_m} T d\sigma \quad , \tag{9}$$

where σ_i is the cross section for the ith collision, T_i is associated energy loss and N the number of molecules per unit volume. Lindhard[7] has obtained the universal nuclear stopping power s_n, which is related to the stopping powers given by Eq (9) by:

$$s_n = \frac{1}{Z_1 Z_2 e^2} \frac{1}{4\pi N} \frac{m_1+m_2}{m_1} S \quad .$$

The universal nuclear stopping power is given numerically in Ref. (8) and often approximated by

$$s_n(\varepsilon) = 0.6 + 1.0\varepsilon^{1/2} + 2.0\varepsilon^{3/2} \tag{10}$$

The theories of electronic encounters between two atoms are more elaborated, and here we expose only the concept and the results. When the velocity of the incident particle is faster than the orbital velocity of the electrons in the target atoms, the Born approximation or first order perturbation approach is applicable. In this case the energetic particle can be regarded as a point charge of Z_1e and the stopping power can be expressed in a simple form:

$$S_e = \frac{4\pi Z_1{}^2 e^4}{m_e v^2} NZ_2 \ln\left(\frac{2m_e v^2}{I}\right) \quad , \tag{11}$$

where m_e is the electron mass, and I the mean excitation energy and given by

$$\ln I = \frac{1}{Z} \sum_i f_i \ln(\hbar\omega_i) \tag{12}$$

where $\hbar\omega_i$ and f_i are the ionization energy of the ith shell of the atom and the probability of the transition, respectively.

For incident particles with velocities much lower than the orbital velocity, the energy loss due to formation of quasi-molecules between the incident and target atoms should be involved. In this energy region phenomenological treatments by Firsov[10] and Lindhard[11,12] are often used. Firsov treated the exchange of electrons between the colliding atoms (quasimolecules) classically, and Lindhard assumed that both the incident and target atoms can be treated as electron gases. These authors have arrived at the conclusion that the electronic stopping power is proportional to the velocity. According to Lindhard et al., the electronic energy loss is given by

$$s_e = k\varepsilon^{1/2} \tag{13}$$

where s_e and ε are reduced stopping power and energy, respectively and

$$k_e = 3.955\xi_e\left(\frac{m_1+m_2}{m_1}\right)^{3/2}\left(\frac{m_e}{m_2}\right)^{1/2}\left(\frac{Z_1Z_2}{Z}\right)^{1/2} \tag{14}$$

and $Z = (Z_1^{2/3} + Z_2^{2/3})^{3/2}$.

A typical diagram for the elastic and electronic stopping power is shown in Fig. 2. Clearly the elastic encounters dominate for lower energies and the electronic encounters dominate at higher energies. Kinchin and Please[13] assumes that there is a critical energy E_A: $E<E_A$ only the elastic collisions occurs and $E>E_A$ only the electronic collisions occur. It has been shown that, at the energy region where Born approximation holds, the electronic stopping power is about 10^3 times the elastic stopping power.[1]

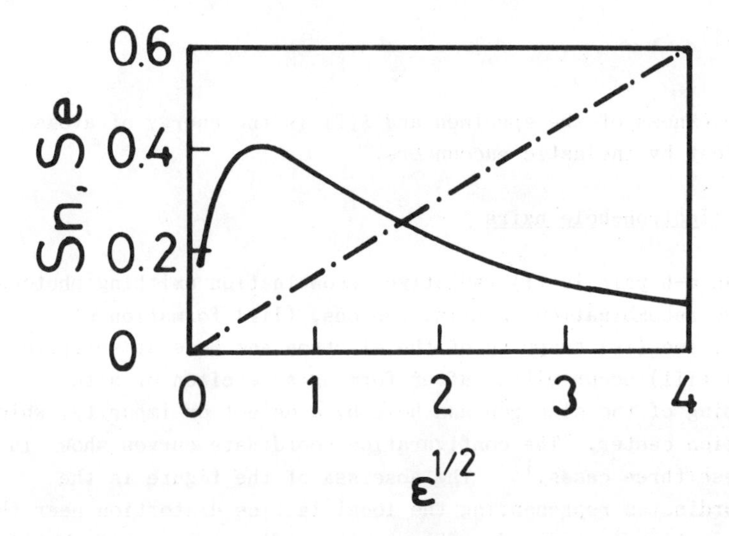

Fig. 2. The universal elastic (solid line) and electronic (dash-dot line) stopping powers.

3. Effects of Electronic Energy Deposition on Solids

In this section we deal with the modification of solids which may be induced by electronic excitation. Primary electronic interaction of charged particles with solids produces fundamental electronic excitation; generation of electron-hole (e-h) pairs and also excitons, complex particles comprising an electron-hole pair bound by Coulomb force between each other. The excited state has a limited lifetime and de-excites mostly to the ground state. However, local lattice rearrangements can also arise as a result of electronic excitation, which is the main concern in this section[14,15].

3.1. Creation of electron-hole pairs

The number n of e-h pairs (including excitons) created is proportional to the absorbed energy ε_a and often expressed as

$$n = \frac{\varepsilon_a}{W} \tag{15}$$

where W is called W-value and usually 2-3 times the band-gap energy.[16] Eq. (15) includes the e-h pairs generated directly by incident particles and by ejected energetic atoms. Since the traveling distance of the ejected atoms is small, practically ε_a can be evaluated as

$$\varepsilon_a = NL\int \xi(T)d\sigma(E,T) \quad , \tag{16}$$

where L is the thickness of the specimen and $\xi(T)$ is the energy of atoms ejected at an energy T, lost by inelastic encounters.

3.2 The fates of electron-hole pairs

The fates of an e-h pair is (i) radiative recombination emitting photons, (ii) non-radiative recombination emitting phonons, (iii) formation of a metastable defect, and (iv) trapping of the electron and hole at separate sites. The processes (i)-(iii) occur either after forming an exciton or after consecutive trapping of the electron and hole by a defect or impurity, which is called recombination center. The configuration coordinate curves shown in Fig. 3 illustrates these three cases.[17] The abscissa of the figure is the configuration coordinates representing the local lattice distortion near the site where recombination is induced. The process (iv) results in formation of a pair of metastable electron- and hole-trapped centers. Usually the lifetime for radiative recombination is longer than 10^{-9} s, while the processes (ii) and (iii) occur much faster. The non-radiative recombination emits lattice phonons, which are widely spread within the crystal, while the formation of metastable states means coupling with specific local phonons and lead to local lattice rearrangements[18]. For the context of radiation damage, the process (ii) produces the thermal spike, which is not very effective in damage formation,[1] while process (iii) leads directly to damage formation, although not in all materials. We discuss the process (iii) in the next section.

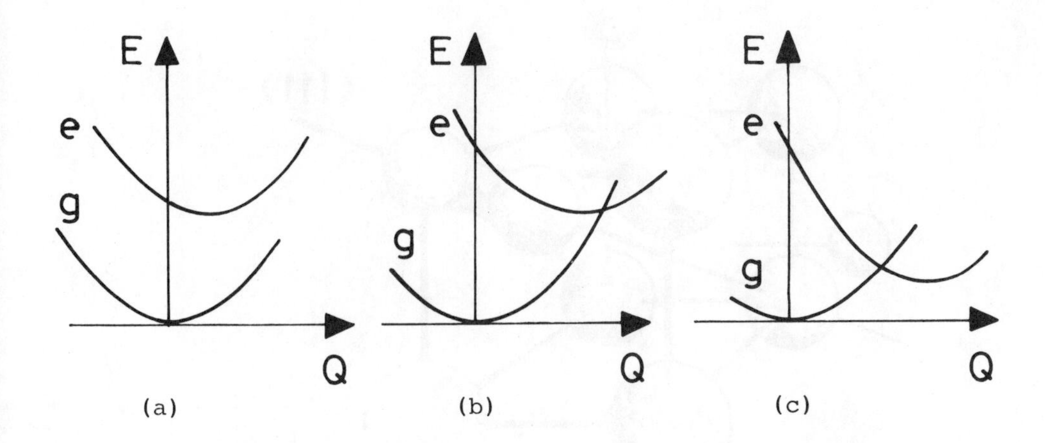

Fig. 3. Configuration coordinate diagrams for the ground state (g) and an excited state (e), representing (a) the radiative recombination and (b) non-radiative recombination and (c) formration of the metastable states.

3.3. Self-trapping of excitons and defect formation

An exciton in some insulating solids is self-trapped, or stabilized by itself creating lattice distortion. Alternatively a hole is self-trapped first, followed by successive electron trapping by the self-trapped hole, forming a self-trapped excitons. The self-trapping is induced in solids with strong electron-lattice coupling; by forming a potential well for the particle by virtue of the lattice relaxation.[17] It has been shown that the self-trapping of holes is induced in several insulators including alkali halides, alkaline earth fluorides and silver halides, while the self-trapping of excitons is induced in SiO_2 in addition to the materials described above.[14] Formation of self-trapped excitons in ionic oxides, such as MgO and Al_2O_3, is still controversial.[19] Although no experiments are available for insulators with molecular anions, it is very likely that self-trapping is induced in these solids. Schematic diagrams for the self-trapped holes and the self-trapped excitons in alkaline earth fluorides are shown in Fig. 4. The self-trapped exciton in alkaline earth fluoride can be regarded as a nearest Frenkel pair comprising a vacancy and interstitial in the halogen sublattice. The yield of the self-trapped excitons is probably not less than 1/10 of that of electron-hole pairs.

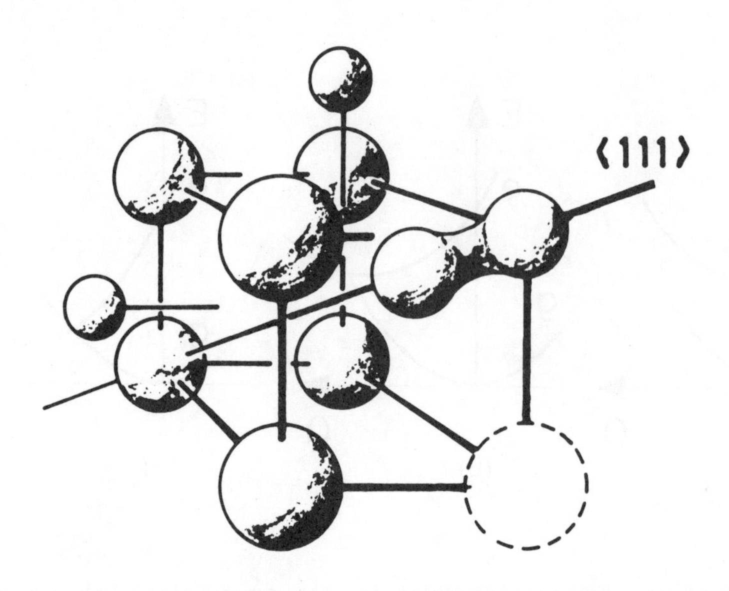

Fig. 4. A schematic diagram of a self-trapped exciton in alkaline earth flurides. Small spheres represent cations, large spheres anions and the composite sphere the F_2^- molecular ion.

In crystals in which self-trapping of excitons is not induced, the fates of e-h pairs are limited to (i), (ii) and (iv). On the other hand, the self-trapped excitons, once generated, are often converted to a distant Frenkel pair, which comprises a vacancy and interstitial (process (iii)). For instance, the yields of distant Frenkel pairs in alkali halides and alkali earth fluorides are about 1/100 of that of the self-trapped excitons.

As described above, lf-trapping of holess and excitons play a crucial role in formation of defects by electronic excitation. It has been shown that the self-trapping is induced if the electron-lattice relaxation energy E_{LR} of an exciton is larger than a half of the width of the exciton band.[17,20] E_{LR} is the energy gained by the lattice relaxation of an exciton. Self-trapping of excitons does not necessarily leads to formation of stable defects in solids. In fact in crystalline SiO_2 permanent defects are not produced by conventional ionizing radiation, while they are produced in amorphous SiO_2. However, it is known that defects are created in both crystalline and amorphous SiO_2 along tracks of energetic heavy ions.[21] This track registration is due to entirely electronic origin and observed in many insulators. The process was long interpreted by the 'ion explosion mechanism'[22], which assumes that the electric field due to non-uniform electron-hole distribution damages the lattice. Recently it has been suggested[23] that formation of self-trapped excitons at high densities results in highly disordered region and can be the cause of the track registration.

4. Effects of Kinetic Energy Deposition on Solids

The kinetic energy is directly imparted to atoms comprising solids by elastic collisions. We first consider the situation where the collision cross section is so small that each collision can be treated independently. Conventionally a threshold energy T_d for ejection of an atom from a lattice point can be defined: let the energy imparted to an atom be T and if $T>T_d$ the atom is ejected and if $T<T_d$ the atom stays in the lattice and only lattice vibration is excited. We should consider that if $T>>T_d$ many atoms are displaced from the lattice point by the collision cascade initiated by the atom to which energy T is imparted. A theory for the number $\nu(T)$ of atoms produced by a collision cascade started by the initial kinetic energy T was developed by Kinchin and Pease[13] using the hard-sphere collision potential and the threshold energy T_d. They found that

$$\nu(T) = \frac{T}{2T_d} \qquad \text{for } T > 2T_d$$

$$= 1 \qquad \text{for } 2T_d > T > T_d. \tag{17}$$

Kinchin and Pease assumed that $\nu(T) = E_A/2T_d$ for $T > E_A$, where E_A is the critical energy above which the elastic energy loss dominates. More recently, Norget et al.[24] suggested an equation which takes the electronic energy loss of ejected atoms into consideration:

$$\nu(T) = \kappa \frac{\xi(T)}{2T_d} \tag{18}$$

where $\xi(T)$ is the energy lost by elastic encounters and conventionally given by

$$\xi(T) = \frac{T}{1 + k\{3.4008\varepsilon_T^{1/6} + 0.40244\varepsilon_T^{3/4} + \varepsilon_T\}}, \tag{19}$$

where k is given already in Eq. (14) and ε_T is T converted to the reduced energy.

Suppose particles having a fixed incident energy E and a small cross section for elastic encounters are incident at a flux φ on a solid and primary knock-ons with energy T are produced by a cross section $d\sigma(E,T)$, the number n_d of knock-ons can be calculated by integrating $\nu(T)$;

$$n_d = N\varphi t \int_{T_d}^{T_m} \nu(T) d\sigma(E,T) \quad . \tag{20}$$

n_d/N is called DPA or displacements per atom. T_m is the maximum energy imparted by an elastic encounter given by Eq. (1). DPA can be regarded as a universal expression for flux φt; the value indicates the number of knock-ons and is convenient to compare the doses of particles of different types.

Eq. (19) is valid for particles with large penetration, for example neutrons. For energetic charged particles, it is valid only when the thickness of the target is thin enough so that the particles do not lose the energy significantly as they penetrate the target. For thick targets, the energy degradation has to be taken into account in calculating the number of knock-ons. Since the electronic energy loss dominates, the distance of the travel of a particle while it is decelerated from energies E+dE to E is approximated by $S_e^{-1}(E)\, dE$. Thus one obtains the number n_d of knock-ons for a heavy charged particles while it is decelerated from an energy E_0 to be approximately

$$n_d = N \int_0^{E_0} S_e^{-1}(E) dE \int_{T_d}^{T_m} \nu(T) d\sigma(E,T) \tag{21}$$

More sophisticated theories[25)] and computer codes[26)] to calculate the number of knock-ons produced by heavy ions have been developed.

For electrons of energies of about 1 MeV, relativistic consideration should be made in calculating the number of knock-ons. First we note that the average value of T imparted by collisions is given by[1)]

$$\langle T \rangle = T_d\{\ln(T_m/T_d) - 1 + \pi\alpha\},$$

where $\sigma = 1/137$ and is of the same order of magnitude as T_d, and hence practically $\nu(T)=1$. Thus the number of n_d can be obtained by simply integrating the differential cross section $d\sigma\ (E,T)$ from T_d to T_m.

A few comments should be made on the threshold energy for knock-ons. Evidently the assumption of the sharp threshold at T_d for displacement is not strict, as seen from the results of calculation using molecular dynamics computer programmes.[27)] In a molecular dynamics calculation differential equations for a cluster of atoms simulating a crystal are solved under appropriate boundary conditions. To calculate T_d, trajectories of atoms in the crystal are followed after a certain amount of energy is imparted to an atom, to see whether any Frenkel pair is generated as a consequence of the energy deposition. The minimum energy above which a Frenkel pair is permanently formed is recorded. The value of the threshold energy depends on the direction of the momentum initially imparted. Thus more appropriate expression for the knock-on is to take a probability function p(T) which is 0 for $T \ll T_d$ and unity for $T \gg T_d$. Conventionally it is assumed that T_d is T at which $p(T)=1/2$.

Experimental determination of T_d cannot be straightforward. Earlier T_d was determined from the results of measurements of the electron-induced damage rate as a function of the incident energy[3]. Damage can be detected if $p(T_m)$ is deviated from 0 appreciably. Thus it has been pointed out, rather recently, that the threshold energy obtained from the damage production as a function of the incident energy of electrons is not T_d but the value of T at which p(T) starts to deviate from zero. Thus it is often the case that T_d is determined by combining the experimental results of electron-damage and the results of computer simulation. The values of T_d thus obtained are listed in Table I.

Table I. The values of the knock-on threshold energy for some metals.

substance	threshold energy (eV)
Al	27
Ni	33
Cu	29
Ag	39
Au	43

The number of defects actually created in a specimen is much smaller than DPA, because of spontaneous recombination and annealing during irradiation, of which the amount may depend on temperature. Although interstitials are very mobile at not very low temperatures, they form clusters or are adsorbed to dislocation, leaving vacancies behind. Thus a substantial fraction of knocked-on atoms remains and permanent radiation damage results, even at high temperatures.

Particles with a high stopping power may collide target atom so frequently that the collision cascade initiated from each of target cannot be independent. In this case a concept of displacement spike has been suggested.[28] Such displacement spike may be produced at the end of the range of heavy charged particles, like fission fragments. A displacement spike includes a cluster of defects consisting many vacancies and interstitials, and consequently the lattice is completely disordered.

References

1) F. Seitz and J. S. Koehler: "Solid State Physics", (F. Seitz and D. Turnbull, Eds) Vol. 2, Academic Press, New York, (1956), p.305.
2) G. J. Dienes and G. H. Vineyard: "Radiation Effects in Solids", John Wiley, New York (1957); D. S. Billington and J. H. Crawford, Jr.: "Radiation Damage in Solids", Princeton Univ. Press, Princeton, (1961); J. W. Corbett: "Electron Radiation Damage in Semiconductors and Metals", Suppl. 7 of Solid State Physcis, Academic Press, New York, (1966)
3) L. T. Chadderton: "Radiation Damage in Crystals", Methuen, London, (1965), D. M. Thompson: "Radiation Damage in Metals", Cambridge University Press, Cambridge, (1969).
4) N. L. Petersen and A. S. Harkness (Eds): "Radiation Damage in Metals", American Society of Metals, Ohio, (1975).
5) J. Lindhard: NBS Publication 1133, (1963).
6) J. Lindhard and M. Scharff Mat: Mat. Fys. Medd. Dan. Vid. Selsk. 27, No. 15 (1953).
7) J. Lindhard, V. Nielsen and M. Scharff: Mat. Fys. Medd. Dan. Vid. Selsk. 36, No. 10, (1968)
8) P. Gombas, "Handbuch Physik", Springer Verlag, Berlin Vol. 36, p.109. (1965)
9) S. Kalbitzer and H. Oetmann: Rad. Effects, 47, 57, (1980).
10) O. B. Firsov, Sov. Phys. JETP 9, 1076 (1959).
11) J. Lindhard and A. Winther, Met. Fys. Medd. Dan. Vid. Selsk 34, No. 4 (1964).
12) J. Lindhard and M. Scharff: Phys. Rev. 124, 128, (1961).
13) G. H. Kinchin and R. S. Pease: Rep. Prog. Phys. 18, 1, (1955).
14) R. T. Williams and K. S. Song, J. Phys. Chem. Solids 51, 679 (1990).
15) N. Itoh and K. Tanimura, J. Phys. Chem. Solids 51, 717 (1990).
16) W. Shockley: Czech. J. Phys. B11, 81, (1961).
17) Y. Toyozawa: Physca B+C 23, 117/118, (1983)
18) W. Hayes and A. M. Stoneham, "Defects and Defect Processes in Nonmetallic Solids", John Wiley, New York (1985).
19) J. A. Valbis and N. Itoh, Radiat. Eff. Defects Solids 116, 171 (1991).
20) Y. Toyozawa: "Vacuum Ultraviolet Radiation Physics", (E. E. Koch, R. Haensel and C. Kunz, Eds) Pergamon Press, Braunschweig, (1974), p.317.
21) J. P. Duraud, F. Jollet, Y. Langevin and E. Dooryhee: Nucl. Instrum. Methods B 32, 248, (1988).
22) R. L. Fleisher, P. B. Price and R. M. Walker: "Nuclear Tracks in Solids" Univ. California Press, Berkeley, (1975).
23) N. Itoh: Radiat. Effects Defects Solids 110, 19, (1989)
24) M. J. Norgett, M. T. Robinson and I. M. Torrens, Nucl. Eng. 33, 50 (1974).
25) K. B. Winterbon, P. Sigmund and J. B. Sanders: Mat. Fys. Medd. Dan. Vid. Selsk. 37, No. 14, (1970).
26) J. P. Biersack and L. G. Haggmark, Nucl. Instrum. Methods, 194 607 (1980).
27) P. Jung and W. Shilling, Phys. Rev. B5, 2046 (1972).
28) J. A. Brinkman, J. Appl. Phys. 25, 961 (1954).

5.9 Theory of Sputtering

Robert E. JOHNSON, John W. BORING and Raul BARAGIOLA
Dept. of Nuclear Engineering and Engineering Physics
University of Virginia, Charlottesville, VA 22903, USA

Energetic ions incident on solids, sputter (eject) neutrals and ions due to both electronic[1,2] and nuclear elastic energy deposition[3]. The ejected species may be the intrinsic molecular species, fragments, or chemically altered species. In fact, very large organic molecules (~50,000 amu) can be ejected intact by the energy deposited by fast heavy ions[2].

Of great interest to HA chemists is the sequence of elastic collisions, which produces cascades of 'hot' atoms, following the production of an energetic atom. Since such cascades may also produce sputtering, the measured energy spectra of the sputtered atoms and molecules in the ejecta can be used to describe the nature of the cascades[4]. The cascades of moving particles also produce chemically altered species that are seen in the ejecta. In this paper we first review the various sputtering regimes that have now been identified, we then discuss the energizing mechanisms, and finally we consider certain observed chemical alterations.

1. **Sputter Regimes**

An incident ion penetrating a solid produces events along its path through the solid (electronic excitations, elastic collisions, nuclear reactions). The <u>average</u> number of such events per unit path length in the material is often determined, using a mean energy deposited per event, ΔE, from the stopping power, (dE/dx), the average energy lost by the ion per unit path length in the solid. If these events lead to molecular motion, are energetic enough, and occur close to the surface, then sputter ejection of material may occur. When the mean spacing between events, $\lambda = ((dE/dx)/\Delta E)^{-1}$, is large, then the probability of a single event occurring close to the surface is small. For this case the yield is easily written. Note that $dz/(\lambda \cos\theta_i)$ is the probability of an event occurring over a depth interval dz, at depth into the solid z, where θ_i is the angle of incidence. If $Y(z)$ is the yield from an event initiated at depth z then the net yield from all depths can be written[1,2] as:

$$Y = \Delta z/(\lambda \cos\theta_i) \tag{1}$$

This gives the simple linear dependence of Y on λ^{-1}, hence on (dE/dx), seen at low excitation densities. Here, Δz is an effective 'sputter depth'[1] to be discussed.

If the events which lead to sputtering produce molecular motion over a distance of the order of Δs, then when $\lambda \approx \Delta s$ the possibility becomes significant that the events act cooperatively, instead of singly, to produce ejection[1,2,5,6]. In this regime the yield is non-linear in (dE/dx) (i.e. λ^{-1}). Two ejection processes have been identified in this regime, one determined by the increase in the instantaneous local energy density at the surface and the other by the net impulse produced by the excitation events[7,8]. For both of these processes the yield can be written quite generally[9] as:

$$Y = \int d^2\vec{\rho} \int dt\, \Phi(\vec{\rho}, t) \tag{2}$$

where Φ is the flux of particles from the surface and ρ is the location on the surface.

The ejection process which is determined by the local energy density is like sublimation and, hence, is often referred to as a 'thermal' spike, though clearly thermodynamic equilibration is generally not achieved in the transiently energized region. Because the resulting sputtering is an 'activated' process[10], chemical activation in the bulk can also be produced by this spike. In Eq. 2 one writes $\Phi(\vec{\rho},t) = \Phi(\epsilon_s(\vec{\rho},t))$, for the surface flux. That is , Φ is determined only by the value of the energy density, ϵ_s, at the surface[7]. This process has been associated with the very low energy ejecta seen in many sputtering experiments and corresponds to 'late' ejection times. For a highly penetrating ion (penetration depth >> λ and Δs) a roughly cylindrical region is energized. If the energy density $\epsilon(\vec{r},t)$ is obtained from a diffusion equation

$$\nabla(\kappa\nabla\epsilon) = \partial\epsilon/Zt \tag{3}$$

where κ is a diffusivity, then it is straight forward to show[11,12] that at high excitation density Eq. 2 gives

$$Y \approx C_s \left[\frac{\ell}{U} \; f \; \left(\frac{dE}{dx}\right)\right]^2 (\cos\theta_i)^{-1.6} \tag{4}$$

where U is the cohesive energy of the solid and ℓ the mean molecular spacing ($\ell \approx n_M^{-1/3}$, n_M the molecular number density). The quantity f is that fraction of the deposited energy which results in molecular motion and, therefore, can lead to sputtering. The yield above is seen to be proportional to λ^{-2} and can be simply understood by considering the volume of material removed. That is, we can write the yield in Eq.2 as[9]

$$Y \approx n_M(\pi\rho_s^2)\Delta z_s \tag{5}$$

In Eq. 5 the yield is determined by an effective surface area excited which is $(\pi\rho_s^2)$ and a depth, $\Delta z_s \approx \bar{v}\Delta t_s$, determined by the length of time a spike is sustained, Δt_s, and an average speed, $\bar{v}$, for the ejecta. The largest radial extent, ρ_s, for which $\epsilon_s > n_M U$ is $(\pi\rho_s^2) \approx (f\ dE/dx)/(n_M U)$. Further, via Eq. 4, $\Delta t_s \approx \kappa(\pi\rho_s^2)$. Taking the product of these in Eq. 5 gives the form in Eq. 4. The angular dependence is derived in ref. 12.

In Eq. 4 C_s is a number which is determined by the dependence of the diffusivity on ϵ and the dependence of Φ on ϵ_S. For an equilibrium process the standard vapor pressure relationship should be used for Φ. This is based on a Maxwell-Boltzmann velocity distribution of moving molecules at each point in the solid, as determined by the local ϵ. However, as the radial scale is often small and the decay of the energy rapid, a delta function velocity spectrum is more appropriate[5]. In this case each molecule has the average local energy, E, determined from ϵ in Eq. 3 (i.e. $n_M E = \epsilon$). Using a simple estimate of the diffusivity ($\kappa \propto \epsilon^{\frac{1}{2}}$) then $C_S \approx 0.2$ for the Maxwellian case and $C_S \approx 0.02$ for the delta function case.

The rapid deposition of energy in a narrow volume also creates a transient impulsive force[13], determined by the steep gradients in the local energy density[7], which produces 'prompt' sputtering. For the roughly cylindrical excitation region discussed above, this produces a radial and outwardly directed 'pressure pulse', often referred to as a 'shock'. The local impulsive force is roughly proportional to $(-\nabla\epsilon)$ in Eq 3. And the flux at the surface in Eq (2) must be integrated over the time during which this force is applied. Writing the net impulse given to a molecular volume of the material as

$$n_M \vec{p} = \beta' \int_0^\infty (-\nabla\epsilon)\, dt \tag{6}$$

where β' is a proportionality constant determined by the material properties. Using this the yield in Eq. 2 for normal incidence can be estimated by including in the escape flux all those species receiving a component of the net impulse normal to the surface, p_n, greater than some minimum, p_c[7,14]. This ignores any rebound, which is appropriate for this 'prompt' ejection process. Using solutions to Eq. 3 in Eq. 6 and evaluating $p_n \approx p_c$ we can estimate the size of the ejected volume rather than integrate over the flux as in Eq. 2. For normal incidence this volume is roughly hemispherical with r_I proportional to $[f(dE/dx)(\ell/U)]$. Therefore, the yield for $\theta_i = 0$ is

$$Y \approx n_M \frac{2\pi}{3} r_I^{\,3} \approx C_I \left[\frac{\ell}{U} f \frac{dE}{dx}\right]^3 \tag{7}$$

which is roughly proportional to λ^{-3}. An estimate of the constant $C_I \approx 0.002$, is obtained analytically[7] and also using molecular dynamics simulations[15,16]. The angular dependence in this regime is also conceptually simple but involves a more complicated geometry[14].

When the geometry of the energized region is not cylindrical, as in bombardment by a low energy heavy ion (spherical geometry) or a laser pulse (planar geometry), somewhat different forms for the sputtering yield apply. However, the results above are all quite general for penetrating particles and have been applied successfully to a number of sputtering experiments. In the following we will discuss two energizing processes: quasielastic collisions between the primary particle and atoms of the target material, and then electronic excitations. We will not consider nuclear decays, but charged particles from such decays obviously deposit their energy both collisionally and electronically.

2. **Collision Cascade Sputtering**

Energy deposited by the primary particle in nuclear elastic collisions produces a cascade of moving secondaries[3]. When these cascades (IV.2) are well separated so that most of the atoms in the vicinity of interest are still moving at energies ($\tilde{}kT_s$) determined by the temperature of the solid, T_s, then this cascade is described by a simple transport equation which can be treated analytically. The energy spectra of recoils in a cascade started by an atom of the material of kinetic energy T is far from Maxwellian. The number of recoils of atoms of the same type produced with energy between E and (E + dE) is:

$$(dN(E)/dE)dE \approx (\beta T/E^2)dE \text{ for } E>>U>kT_s \tag{8}$$

where β is a constant depending on the interaction of the energetic atoms with the material[2]. This simple equation forms the basis of collision cascade sputtering theory. Sigmund[17] evaluated β for power law interatomic potentials and suggested using $\beta \approx 6/\pi^2$ for cascades in solids, a constant roughly appropriate for a Born-Mayer (exponential) potential. As the collisional energies approach U, the material properties dominate and a diffusive process occurs, as in Eq. 4, involving all of the molecules locally. Therefore, following the energetic collisions in the cascade, a 'spike' always occurs as the energized region spreads. This spike may or may not be energetic enough to produce an effect, such as 'thermal' spike sputtering or chemical activation.

The standard procedure for calculating the yield of particles ejected from the surface is to assume a sputter depth, Δz in Eq. 1, proportional to the collisional mean-free-path, $(n_M\sigma_d)^{-1}$, determined by the average diffusion cross section, σ_d. Because it has been shown by simulation[18,19] and experiment that the ejecta primarily originate from the surface layer, a useful average value is $\sigma_d \approx n_M^{-2/3}$. (Very energetic particles can actually exit from layers below the surface). If we require for ejection that a cascade particle is moving out from the surface with the perpendicular component of kinetic energy greater than U, then, using Eq. 8, we obtain the standard expression for the yield due to individual, energetic primary recoils,

$$Y \approx \frac{3}{2\pi^2}\,\frac{\alpha S_n}{U\bar{\sigma}_d}\,\cos\theta_i^{-1.6} \tag{9}$$

where it is customary to write $(dE/dx)_n = n_M S_n$. For atomic solids Sigmund[3] used $\sigma_d \approx 3.7Å^2$ giving the well known expression $Y \approx (0.042\alpha S_n/UÅ^2)$ for normal incidence. This expression has been used to organize the sputtering data and Andersen and Bay[20] have shown that the α determined semi-empirically depends only on the ratio of the incident and target particle masses. Recently, σ_d was shown to be underestimated[19,21], which would increase α slightly. The dependence on angle of incidence is also remarkably close to that given in Eq (5). Fewer results exist for the sputtering of molecular solids; the case of refractory molecular solids has been reviewed by Betz and Wehner[22]. Boring and coworkers[23] have shown that using $\sigma_d \approx n_M^{-2/3}$, (the molecular size) and using the value of α determined by Andersen and Bay[20] gives total yields in reasonable agreement with those measured for low temperature condensed gas solids.

The expression in Eq. 8 is also roughly verified by molecular dynamics calculations and by measurements of the ejected atom energies. When the yield is relatively small, the measured energy spectra[20] have the form

$$Y(E)/Y \approx 2EU/(E+U)^3 \tag{10}$$

predicted using a planar binding condition[3]. For large yields more low energy particles are seen and Boring et al[24] have found that

$$Y(E)/Y \approx U/(E+U)^2$$

predicted assuming 'spherical' binding, is more appropriate for sputtering of the rare-gas solids in the linear regime. As the excitation increases, the non-linear processes contribute and a quasi-thermal component occurs, as discussed above[25].

3. Electronically-induced Sputtering

Although the process of electronically stimulated desorption of absorbed species was well-known, the discovery by Brown et al.[26] of exceptionally large sputtering yields for low temperature (77K) water ice by MeV protons led to considerable activity in the study of electronically-induced sputtering, partly in response to its relevance to planetary science[27]. The desorption and sputtering processes are both driven by excitation of repulsive states which produce atomic (molecular) motion. This is most clearly demonstrated in the detailed studies of the sputtering of condensed rare-gas solids in which both the luminescence and the sputter ejecta are correlated[28-31] so that the participating states involved can be identified.

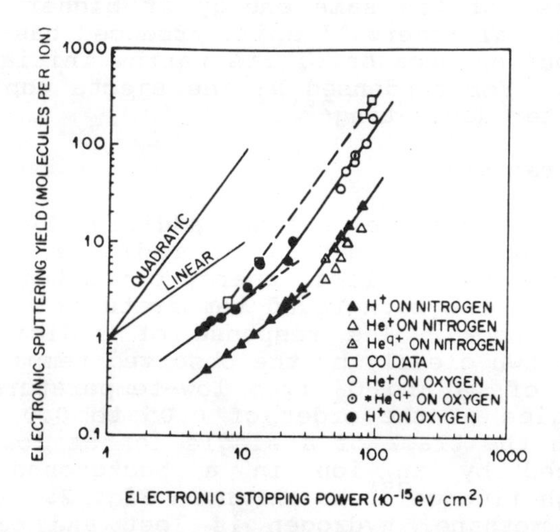

Fig.1 **The yield in molecules removed per ion incident for MeV protons and helium ions plotted versus the electronic stopping power given as n_M^{-1} $(dE/dx)_e$: q implies charge equilibrated state (q≈2) (from ref. 33)**

Excitations can produce exothermic reactions with neighbors, which result in molecular motion, or can decay by the repulsive dissociation of molecular species. Such motion may produce desorption if initiated at the surface. For ordered solids, the excitation produced by an incident ion, electron or photon may first migrate away from the initial excitation site and eventually be trapped at defects, grain boundaries, or the surface[32]. Such defects have been shown to affect the sputter yield.

The nature of an excitation energetic enough to eject the atoms depends on the cohesive energy and electronic properties of the materials. Roughly speaking, if electronic transport and recombination are rapid, electronic sputtering does not occur. Furthermore, if the cohesive energy is large, deep excitations at the surface are required to cause desorption. Electronic sputtering has been extensively studied in alkali-halides, condensed-gas solids, organic solids, and polymers. In these materials yields for normal incidence have been measured which are linear (e.g. condensed N_2, O_2, rare-gas solids, and alkali-halides), quadratic (condensed-gas solids), and roughly cubic (solids of large organic molecules) in the electronic stopping power $(dE/dx)_e$, representing the processes described earlier. In all of these processes neutrals are by far the dominant ejecta (i.e. smallest U) with the possible exception of the alkali-halides. The processes driving the linear yields closely correspond to those leading to desorption, i.e. repulsive decays. Computer simulations of eV decays in condensed gas solids[19] give a recoil distribution similar to that for energetic collision cascades as given in Eq. 8. The nicest examples of the effect of overlapping cascades are the measured yields for condensed O_2 and N_2 sputtered by MeV protons and helium shown in Fig(1). There is a sharp transition[33] from a linear to a quadratic dependence on $(dE/dx)_e$. This is well described by individual impulses (< 3 eV in N_2 and < 8 eV in O_2) in the linear regime, which act as overlapping spikes of the same energy at higher $(dE/dx)_e$[5]. The resulting cylindrical 'thermal' spike produced has a non-Maxwellian velocity distribution because of its narrow initial dimensions and rapid spreading. For condensed N_2 the ejecta contains both N and N_2, with the latter dominating[25].

4. Chemical Alterations

In the more reactive solids additional new species are produced following the formation of radicals. This production occurs in response to the local energy deposited (e.g. hot atoms) and in response to the background temperature[34] and is a primary concern of this book. The response of radicals to background temperature is shown clearly by the observed temperature dependence of the ejection of D_2 and O_2 from low-temperature condensed D_2O. Activation energies of the order of 0.05 to 0.07 eV are measured for reactions in the track of a single ion at low fluence and for reactions induced by an ion in a background of dissociated fragments at high fluence[35] as shown in Fig. 2. In the erosion of low-temperature methane, hydrogen is lost and carbon chains are formed[36]. On the other hand, an example of a hot atom reaction is shown by the measurements of new species produced in a mix of D_2O and CO_2[37]. In the thermal ejecta produced on heating of the solid, formaldehyde is seen which exhibits the insertion[38] of a C atom into a D_2O molecule. Recent IR studies of such material give little evidence for formaldehyde <u>in</u> the ice, but do show that carbonates occur[39]. Therefore, formaldehyde forms during ejection. It is seen by these examples that desorption/sputtering experiments are closely related to those hot atom processes discussed elsewhere in this text.

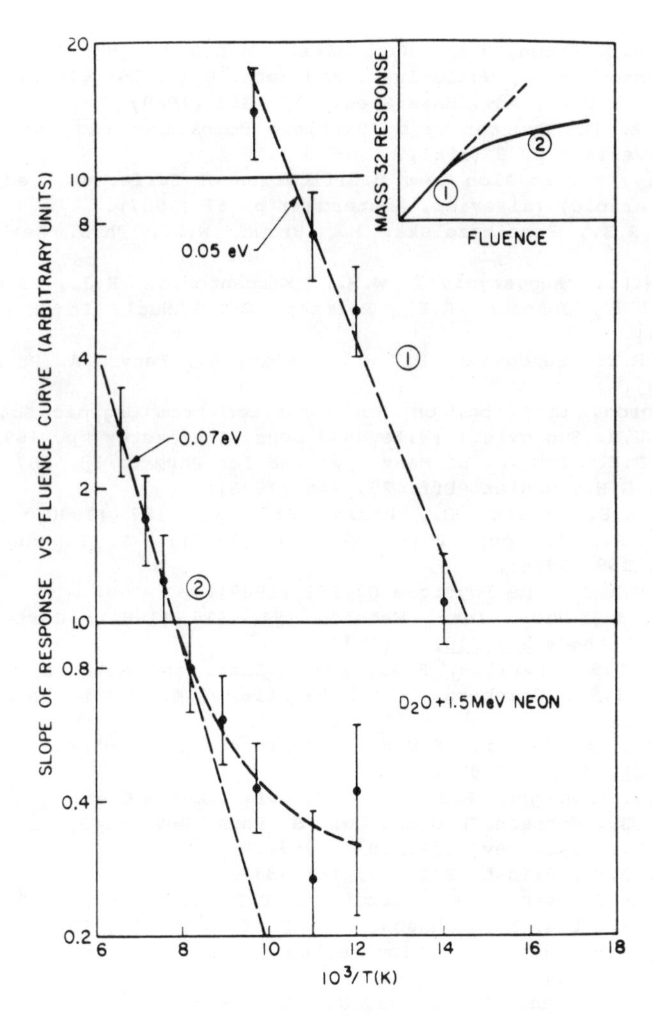

Fig.2 Slope of the yield vs. fluence of O_2 ejected from D_2O ice plotted vs. the inverse of the ice temperature (inset). Region (1) correspond to O_2 formed in a single ion track; region (2) corresponds to overlapping tracks. Derived activation energies are given. (from ref. 35).

5. Conclusions

Measuring the ejecta due to individual ions, electrons or photons incident on solids allows one to study both the initial energizing processes occurring in solids as well at the later chemical processes. Such results complement those studied by more conventional HAC methods.

Acknowledgements

This work is supported by grants from the Astronomy Division and the Division of Materials of the U.S. National Science Foundation.

References

1. Johnson, R.E. Brown, W.L., Nucl. Inst. and Meth. 198, 103 (1982). Brown, W.L., Johnson, R.E., Nucl. Inst. and Meth. B 13, 295 (1986).
2. Sundqvist, B.U.R., Adv. Mass Spec. 11A, 363 (1989).
3. Sigmund, P. in "Sputtering by Particle Bombardment I" (ed. R. Behrisch, Springer-Verlag) p. 9 (1981).
4. e.g. Kelly, R., in "Ion Beam Modification of Surfaces", (ed. P. Mazzoldi and G.W. Arnold) (Elsevier, Amsterdam) p. 57 (1987).
5. Johnson, R.E., Pospieszalska, M., Brown, W.L., Phys. Rev. B 44, 7263 (1991).
6. Brown, W.L., Augustyniak, W.M., Marcantonio, K.J., Simmons, E.H., Boring, J.W., Johnson, R.E., Reimann, C.T., Nucl. Inst. and Meth. B1, 307 (1984).
7. Johnson, R.E., Sundqvist, B.U.R., Hedin, A., Fenyö, A. Phys. Rev. B 40, 49 (1989).
8. R.E. Johnson. in "Proc. on Ion Formation from Organic Solids" (ed. A. Hedin, B.U.R. Sundqvist) (Wiley and Sons, Chechester) p. 189 (1990).
9. Johnson, R.E., Int. J. of Mass Spec and Ion Physics 78, 357 (1987).
10. Vineyard, G.H., Radiat. Eff. 29, 245 (1976).
11. Johnson, R.E., Evatt, R., Radiat Eff. 52, 187 (1990); Sigmund, P., Claussen, R., J. Appl. Phys. 52, 990 (1981); P. Sigmund Appl. Phys. Lett. 25, 169 (1974).
12. Johnson, R.E., J. de Physique C2 251 (1989).
13. Yamamura, Y., Nucl. Inst. Methods 194, 515 (1982); Carter, G., Nucl. Inst. and Methods 209/210, 1 (1983).
14. Bitensky, I.S., Parilis, E.S., Nucl. Inst. and Methods B2, 26 (1986). Bitensky, I.S., Goldberg, A.M., Parilis, E.E. J. de Physique C2, 213 (1989).
15. Fenyö, D., Sundqvist, B.U.R., Karlsson, B., Johnson, R.E., J. de Physique C2, 33-35 (1989).
16. Cui, S.T., Johnson, R.E. Int. J. of Quant. Chem. 23, 575 (1989). Banerjee, S., Johnson, R.E and Cui, S. Phys. Rev. B 43, 12707 (1991).
17. Sigmund, P., Phys. Rev. 184, 383 (1969).
18. Harrison, D.E., Raidat. Eff. 70, 1 (1983).
19. Cui, S.T., Johnson, R.E., Cummings, P.T. Surf. Sci. 222, 491 (1989). Banerjee, S., Liu, M., Johnson, R.E. Surf. Sci. 255, L504 (1991).
20. Andersen, H.H., Bay, H.L. "Sputtering by Particle Bombardment I" (ed. H. Behrisch) (Springer-Verlag, Berlin) 9 (1981).
21. Vicanek, M., Jimenez Rodriguez, J.J. and Sigmund, P., Nucl. Instr. Meth. B36,124 (1989).
22. Betz, G., Wehner, G.K. in "Sputtering by Particle Bombardment II" ed. H. Behrische. (Springer-Verlag, Berlin) p. 11 (1983).
23. Boring, J.W., Garrett, J.W., Cummings, T.A., Johnson, R.E., Brown, W.L., Nucl. Instrum. Meth. B1, 327 (1984): Surf. Sci. 147, 227 (1984).
24. O'Shaughnessy, D.J., Boring, J.W., Phipps, J.A., Johnson, R.E. Surf. Sci. 203, 227 (1988).
25. Pedrys, R., Vostra, D.J., Haring, A., Radiat. Eff. Def. in Solids 109, 239 (1989).
26. Brown, W.L., Lanzerotti, L.J., Poate, J.M., Augustyniak, W.M., Phys. Rev. Lett. 49, 1027 (1978).
27. Johnson, R.E., "Energetic-Ion Bombardment of Atmospheres and Surfaces" (Springer-Verlag, Berlin) (1990).
28. Reimann, C.T., Johnson, R.E., Brown, W.L., Phys. Rev. Lett. 53, 600 (1984); Phys. Rev. B 37, 1455 (1988); in DIET IV, Vol. 19 of "Springer Series in Surface Science" (Betz, G., Varga, P., eds) (Springer-Verlag, Berlin) p. 226 (1990).

29. Arakawa, I., Takahashi, M., Takeuchi, K. J. Vac. Sci. Technol. A7, 2090 (1989).
30. Feulner, P., Muller, T., Puschman, A., Menzel, D., Phys. Rev. Lett. 59, 791 (1987).
31. Kloiber, T., Loach, W., Zimmerer, G., Coletti, F., Debever, J.M. Europhys. Lett. 7, 77 (1988). Coletti, F., Debever, J.M., Zimmerer, G., F. Phys. Lett. 45, L467 (1984).
32. Boring, J.W., Johnson, R.E., O'Shaughnessy, D.J., Phys. Rev. B 39, 2689 (1989).
33. Gibbs, K., Brown, W.L., Johnson R.E. Phys. Rev. B 38, 1 (1988).
34. Rossler, K. Radiat. Eff. 99 21 (1986).
35. Reimann, C.T., Boring, J.W., Johnson, R.E., Garrett, J.W., Farmer, K.R., Brown, W.L., Surf. Sci. 147, 227 (1984).
36. Lanzerotti, L.J., Brown, W.L., Marcantonio, K.J., Astrophys. J. 313, 910 (1987). Foti., G., Calcagno, L., Zhu, Z., Strazzulla, G., Nucl. Instru. Methods B24/25, 522 (1987).
37. Pirronello, V., Brown, W.L., Lanzerotti, L.J. Marcantonio, K.J., Simmons, E., Astrophys. J. 262, 636 (1982).
38. Roessler, K., Radiat. Eff. 99, 21 (1986).
39. Moore, M.H., Khanna, R., Donn, B., J. Geophys. Res. (Planets) 96, 17,541 (1991).

Chapter 6

Relation to Other Nuclear Techniques

6.1 Moessbauer Spectroscopy Applied to Hot Atom Chemistry

Kazutoyo ENDO[1] and Hirotoshi SANO[2]
1) Showa College of Pharmaceutical Sciences,
Higashitamagawagakuen, Machida, Tokyo 194, Japan
2) Department of Chemistry, Faculty of Science,
Tokyo Metropolitan University,
Minami-Ohsawa, Hachioji, Tokyo 192-03, Japan

1. Introduction

The studies of the chemical effects associated with nuclear transformations or nuclear decay in solids have been carried out in a variety of kinds of systems. In metals, mobility of conducting electrons is so fast that the aftereffects of nuclear events can hardly be observed, whereas in semiconducting materials or especially in insulators such as chemical compounds, electrons are tightly bound to a molecule so that the transient chemical states formed through the nuclear event have been observed. Although the nuclides that can be used as Mössbauer probes are limited in number, the hyperfine parameters obtained by the spectroscopy give important information not only about the Mössbauer atom itself, but also the anions or the ligands which surround the Mössbauer atom.

Most of the experiments on emission spectroscopy have been performed on the system of ^{57}Co-labelled or doped compounds. The nuclear decay of ^{57}Co leads to nuclear excited states of the product ^{57}Fe-atoms. The transition to the first excited nuclear state of ^{57}Fe is rather fast; i.e., the lifetime of the second excited state is 8.8 ns; the transition from the first excited state to the ground state with a half-life of 97.7 ns is accompanied by the emission of a 14.4 keV gamma-radiation; hence, abnormal valence states or chemical relaxation of the nucleogenic atom initiated by EC decay can be observed by Mössbauer spectroscopy (Fig. 1).

Emission Mössbauer spectroscopy is useful for dynamic studies of short-lived chemical species during the excited nuclear lifetime or times of the same order of magnitude, and it has an advantage that it detects the chemical states of Mössbauer active atoms decayed from the parent nuclide in ultra-microquantities in the solid. The concentration of metastable or unstable species produced after EC-decay is usually too low to be detected by ordinary physicochemical techniques. The spectroscopy,

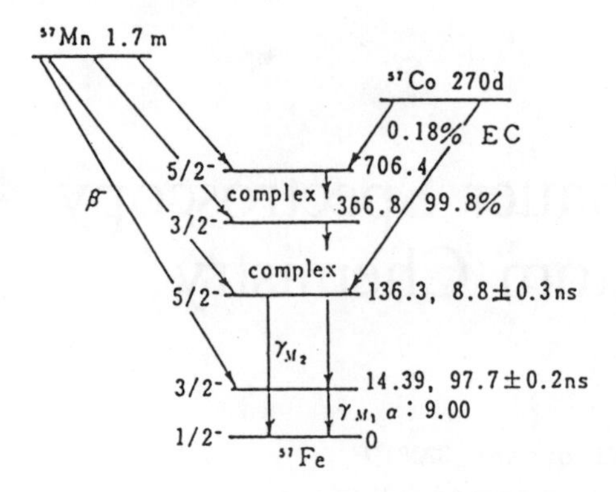

Fig. 1 Decay scheme of ^{57}Co.

therefore, gives us unique hyperfine parameters for the decayed atoms in the solid.

In the last decade, Mössbauer emission studies of chemical aftereffects have been reviewed several times.[1-4] Investigations on the aftereffects in compounds using Mössbauer spectroscopy are focused on examining the aliovalent charge states, or their initial population, relaxation processes of the nucleogenic iron-atoms and electron transfer in coordination compounds. Apart from the examples in crystalline compounds, the aliovalent Fe(I) state has been observed as daughter of a ^{57}Co atom in a matrix of solid Xenon.[5] The rare gas matrix isolation experiments also supply interesting data from the aspect of hot atom chemistry. Implantation of radioactive ^{57}Co into non reactive frozen gases like Ne, Ar, N_2, Xe, CH_4 and C_2H_4[6,7] and reactive oxygen at 4.2 K[8] have been investigated. In this chapter, however, only compounds in the crystalline states will be reviewed.

2. Time integral Emission Mössbauer spectroscopy

2.1. Emission spectra of ^{57}Fe generated from the ^{57}Ni-^{57}Co-^{57}Fe double decay

The systems of ^{57}Co-doped dihydrated oxalates of some divalent metals, $M^{II}C_2O_4 2H_2O$(with M = Mg, Mn, Fe, Co, Ni, and Zn) were investigated in order to examine the matrix influence on the distribution of ^{57}Fe-atoms as a function of the nature (ionic radius) of the host cations.[9,10] With these isomorphous metal(II) oxalate matrices, a strong matrix influence on the stabilization of Fe(III) has been observed for $NiC_2O_4 2H_2O$. These effects were further supported by experiments on mixed Co(II)/Ni(II) compound, and have been assigned to thermodynamic (formation constant) and steric effects related to the ionic size of Fe^{2+}, Fe^{3+}, and Ni^{2+}.

Emission Mössbauer spectra of ^{57}Fe generated from the ^{57}Ni-^{57}Co-^{57}Fe double decay in ^{57}Ni-labelled Ni(II) oxalate have been compared with the results for the corresponding ^{57}Co-doped compound as shown in Fig. 2.

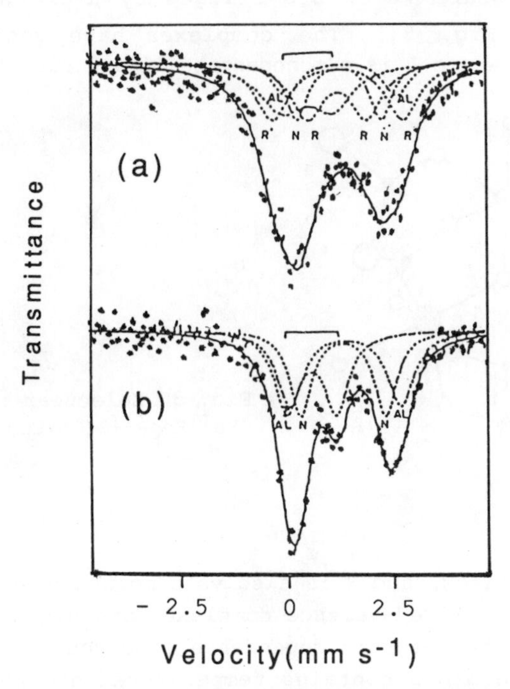

Fig. 2 Emission Mössbauer spectra at 90 K of ^{57}Ni-labelled NiC_2O_4 (a) after decay at 77 K before annealing, (b) annealing at 295 K.[10]

Highly perturbed chemical states of ^{57}Fe-atoms generated from the ^{57}Ni-^{57}Co-^{57}Fe sequence were observed when the ^{57}Ni decays at low temperature (77 K). The recoil effects of nucleogenic ^{57}Co-atoms are observed at 90 K. The main difference between the related spectra of the ^{57}Co-doped and ^{57}Ni-labelled systems concerns the amount of the unstable ferrous species denoted as Fe_{AL}^{2+} in their spectra (Fig.2). The spectrum measured at 90 K after ^{57}Ni decay at 77 K gave superimposed doublets with large line widths corresponding to Fe(II) (δ = 2.32 mm s^{-1}, ΔE_q = 1.32 mm s^{-1}; 78 %) and Fe(III) (δ = 0.72 mm s^{-1}, ΔE_q = 1.61 mm s^{-1}; 22%) On the other hand, the spectrum at 90 K after warming to room temperature for two days showed a completely different spectrum; i.e., initial line broadening has decreased drastically, and the annealed ^{57}Ni-labelled sample actually gave a similar spectrum to the ^{57}Co-labelled samples at 90 K as well as at room temperature.

2.2 Mixed-valence trinuclear complexes

Oxo-centered trinuclear iron acetate complexes have one Fe(II) and two Fe(III) ions in a molecule which are bridged by μ-oxo and μ-acetato ligands as shown in Fig. 3. The complexes have general formulae $[Fe^{II}Fe_2^{III}O(CH_3CO_2)_6L_3]S$ where L is a monodentate ligand such as water,

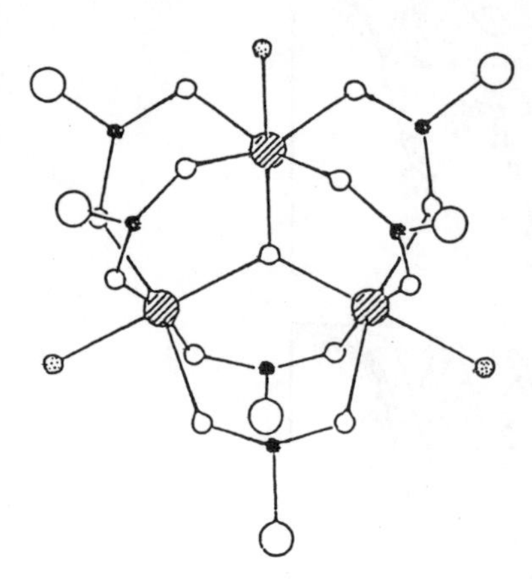

Fig. 3 Molecular structure of $[Fe^{II}Fe_2^{III}O(CH_3CO_2)_6(L_3)]$.

pyridine and its derivatives, and S is a solvate molecule such as pyridine and its derivatives. The mixed-valence complexes are classified into two categories based on the temperature dependence observed in the absorption Mössbauer spectra. One group contains temperature-independent trapped-valence type compounds, whose Mössbauer spectra consist of mutually independent high-spin Fe(II) and high-spin Fe(III) components, the latter with double intensity, at all accessible temperatures, typically from 4.2 K to room temperature. The other is a temperature-dependent trapped-to-averaged valence type compounds which show the spectral change from a trapped-valence state to an averaged-valence state with increase in the temperature.

With the use of emission Mössbauer spectroscopy, information on the decayed ^{57}Fe-atoms in the complexes gives us a new insight into the stabilization process of the nucleogenic atoms in the complexes, and the mechanism of averaged and trapped valence states in the solid.

Emission spectra of ^{57}Co-labelled $[CoCr_2O(CH_3CO_2)_6(py)_3]py$ consist of components ascribed to Fe(II)-species and a smaller component of Fe(III)-species.[11] The comparison of the spectrum at 78 K with that at room temperature indicates that there is no significant temperature dependence due to intramolecular electron transfer.

Figures 4 and 5 show emission spectra of $[CoFe_2O(CH_3CO_2)_6(H_2O)_3]$ and $[CoFe_2O(CH_3CO_2)_6(py)_3]py$, respectively.[12] There are two remarkable features compared with the emission spectrum of $[CoCr_2O(CH_3CO_2)_6(py)_3]py$. First, the amount of $^{57}Fe(III)$-species in the cobalt-iron trinuclear complexes is substantially larger than that of the cobalt-chromium trinuclear complex. Second, the valence states of both the $^{57}Fe(II)$ and $^{57}Fe(III)$ atoms produced are found to be temperature-dependent as is found in the absorption Mössbauer spectra of $[Fe_3O(CH_3CO_2)_6(H_2O)_3]$ and $[Fe_3O(CH_3CO)_6(py)_3]py$. The results indicate that the three iron atoms in one molecule having a decayed ^{57}Fe-atom are not in the form of $^{57}Fe(III)Fe_2(III)$ but either $^{57}Fe(III)Fe(III)Fe(II)$ or $^{57}Fe(II)Fe_2(III)$ at 78 K, because both $[Fe_3{}^{III}O(CH_3CO_2)_6(H_2O)_3]^+$ and $[Fe_3{}^{III}O(CH_3CO_2)_6(py)_3]^+$ salts do not exhibit any appreciable temperature dependence of their Mössbauer spectra. These experimental results show that most of the ^{57}Fe atoms produced through EC-decay in ^{57}Co-labelled $[CoFe_2O(CH_3CO_2)_6(H_2O)_3]$ and $[CoFe_2O(CH_3CO_2)_6(py)_3]py$ keep their position at the sites of the original ^{57}Co atoms and that the valence electrons are transferred through

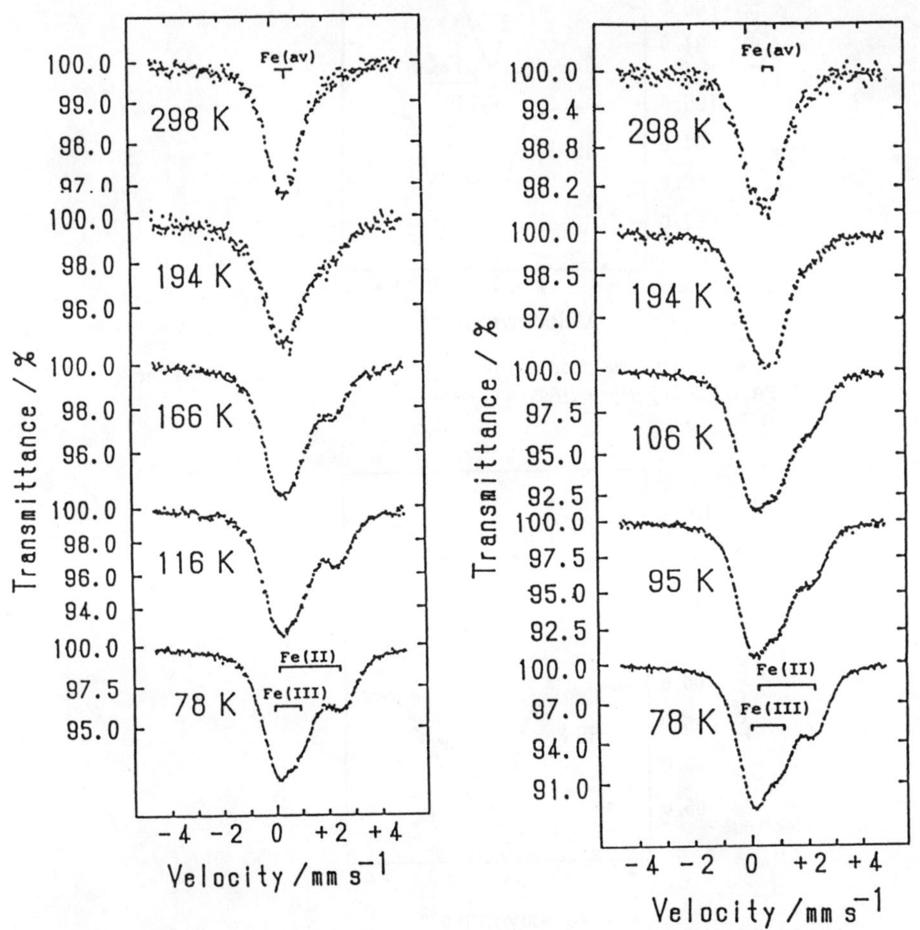

Fig. 4 Emission Mössbauer spectra of ^{57}Co-labelled $[CoFe_2O(CH_3CO_2)_6(H_2O)_3]$.[11)]

Fig. 5 Emission Mössbauer spectra of ^{57}Co-labelled $[CoFe_2O(CH_3CO_2)_6(py)_3]py$.[11)]

the intramolecular bondings, although there are nucleogenic local disturbances to some extent as found in their line broadening. The temperature dependence of the mixed-valence state of ^{57}Fe atoms produced in ^{57}Co-labelled trinuclear cobalt-iron complex, $[CoFe_2O(CH_{3-n}X_nCO_2)_6(H_2O)_3]$

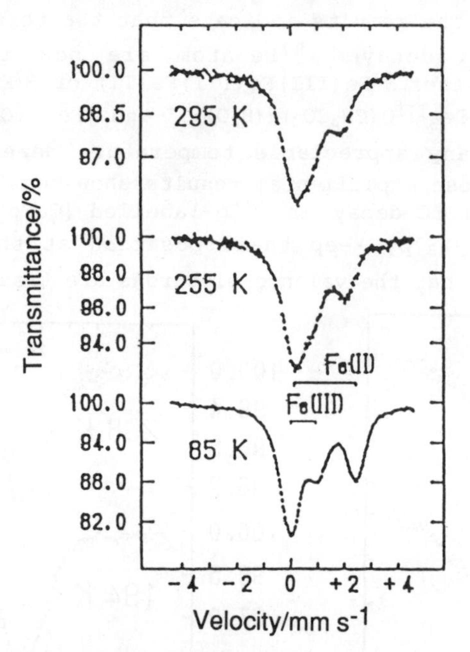

Fig. 6 Emission Mössbauer spectra of ^{57}Co-labelled $[CoFe_2O(CHCl_2CO_2)_6(H_2O)_3]$.[12)]

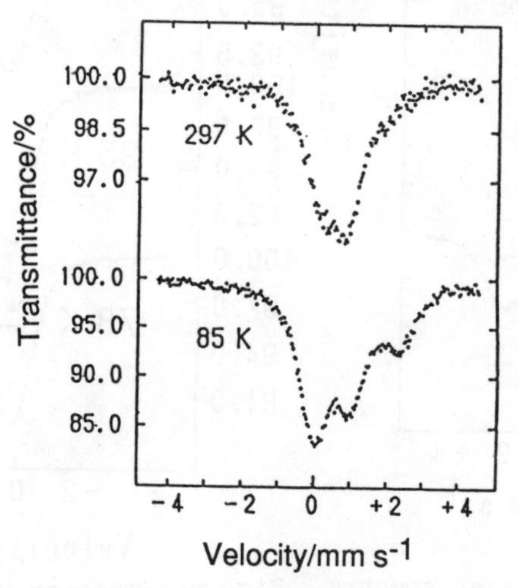

Fig. 7 Emission Mössbauer spectra of ^{57}Co-labelled $[CoFe_2O(CCl_3CO_2)_6(H_2O)_3]$.[12)]

(0<n<3, X = Cl, Br, and I) has been also observed. Emission Mössbauer spectra of ^{57}Co-labelled [$CoFe_2O(CCl_3CO_2)_6(H_2O)_3$] show the temperature-dependent trapped-to-averaged process as found in the absorption spectra of [$Fe_3O(CCl_3CO_2)_6(H_2O)_3$]. It seems that the energy released in the EC-decay or the anomalous charge states of ^{57}Fe atoms are rapidly spread all over the affected molecule and the surrounding molecules through delocalized π-electrons. Figures 6 and 7 show the emission spectra of [$CoFe_2O(CHCl_2CO_2)_6(H_2O)_3$] and [$CoFe_2O(CCl_3CO_2)_6(H_2O)_3$], whose analogous trinuclear iron complexes are classified as temperature-independent trapped valence type. Although the spectra show less temperature dependence, neither spectrum can be explained only by individual components of high-spin Fe(II) and Fe(III) states. In contrast to the fact that [$Fe_3O(CHCl_2CO_2)_6(H_2O)_3$] and [$Fe_3O(CH_2ClCO_2)_6(H_2O)_3$], which show no significant temperature dependence in their Mössbauer absorption spectra, the emission spectra of ^{57}Co-labelled complexes show line-broadening for Fe(II) and a remarkable decrease in the Fe(III) quadrupole splitting on rise in temperature. The same trends are also observed in the emission spectra of [$CoFe_2O(CH_2BrCO_2)_6(H_2O)_3$]. Even though ^{57}Fe atoms produced in the trinuclear cobalt-iron matrix which has an isomorphous structure to the trapped-valence type trinuclear iron complex, the valence states fluctuate over the Mössbauer time scale as a consequence of the intramolecular electron transfer.

3. Application of coincidence technique

3.1. X, γ-Ray coincidence

Combining emission Mössbauer spectroscopy with a coincidence technique gives more detailed and selective information. If a Mössbauer spectrum is measured in a gated mode with a particular radiation among the

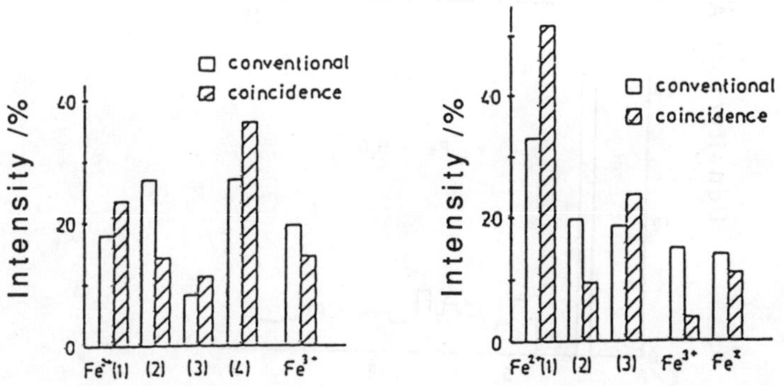

Fig. 8 Distribution of ^{57}Fe-species observed by conventional and X,γ coincidence Mössbauer spectra for ^{57}Co-labelled $FeSO_4H_2O$(left) and $FeSO_4$(right) at room temperature.[16]

several associated with the de-excitation of nuclear or atomic states, the chemical states accompanied by the transition can be observed. It is often pointed out that in many hot atom reactions, the chemical valence states of decayed atoms or the atoms formed through nuclear reaction are affected by low energy Auger electrons after the nuclear events. However, no direct experimental evidence has been reported in solid state hot atom chemistry that discriminates the chemical effect of Auger electrons and KX-ray emission. Kobayashi and co-workers demonstrated clearly such effects using a coincidence technique in ^{57}Co-doped $CoCl_2$ nH_2O(n=2, 6), and $FeSO_4$ $7H_2O$.[13-16] In the case of ^{57}Co, the influence of low energy electrons which are emitted during the Auger cascade after EC-decay is approximately twice as large when the K-Auger process occurs than that in the case of the competitive KX-ray emission. The first report on coincidence between KX-ray and 14.4 keV was based on a conventional Mössbauer spectrometer with a time window of 400 ns, which is nearly three times the mean lifetime, and the spectrum was compared with the non gated window spectrum after subtracting random coincidence fraction. The relative intensities of the conventional Mössbauer spectrum and of the spectrum for coincidence with the KX-rays are shown in Fig. 8 for ^{57}Co-doped $FeSO_4H_2O$ and $FeSO_47H_2O$.

In the KX-ray emission, multiple ionization is less pronounced than Auger electron emission. The redistribution of electronic shells after KX-ray emission does not cause a very large perturbation in the ^{57}Fe-atoms and the neighboring atoms as does the Auger process. The KX-ray emission and subsequent de-excitation process lead to the formation of oxidizing radicals in smaller amounts. When water molecules are coordinated to

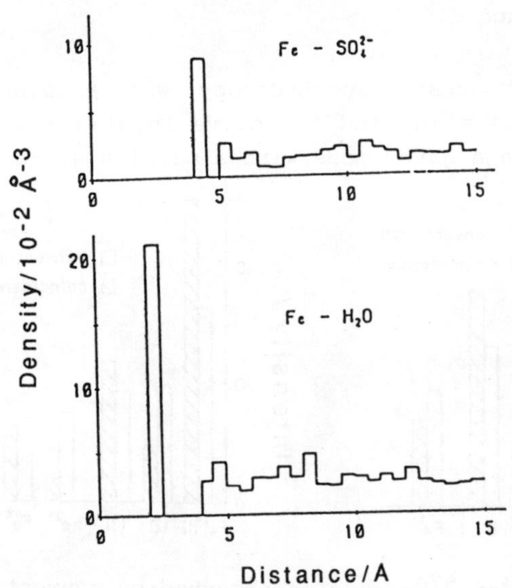

Fig. 9 Densities of H_2O and SO_4^{2-} as a function of distance from an Fe atom in $FeSO_47H_2O$.[15]

the decayed atom or are involved as hydrates in the vicinity, the water molecules are decomposed by the Auger process, resulting in the formation of oxidative OH radicals.

Kobayashi interpreted the Fe^{2+} fraction in the emission Mössbauer spectra in terms of density of water molecules and anions as a function of distance from an iron atom to an oxygen atom. Two distinct coordination shells of H_2O and SO_4^{2-} are shown at about 2A and 4A respectively from the decayed ^{57}Fe atom (Fig. 9). The Fe^{3+} component is considered to arise from the oxidation of ^{57}Fe-atoms by free OH radicals formed through radiolysis by Auger electrons. In addition, due to a widely distributed distance between the decayed atom and a SO_3^- radical through radiolysis of a SO_4^{2-} anions, Fe^{2+} is hardly oxidized by the radicals. In fact, absorption Mössbauer spectra of gamma-ray irradiated $FeSO_4$ and $FeSO_4 7H_2O$ in earlier study indicate that SO_4^{2-} has no oxidizing ability.

Analogous effects of water molecules have been found for the system of ^{57}Co-labelled CoF_2 and $CoF_2 2H_2O$[17] and $Co(SeO_4)_2 nH_2O$ (n= 0 and 1).[18] KX-ray gated emission Mössbauer spectra of ^{57}Co-labelled anhydrous and dihydrated cobalt(II) fluoride are shown in Figs.10 and 11 together with the conventional (non-gated) emission spectra. Two sets of quadrupole doublets are assigned to $^{57}Fe(II)$-species from the I.S. and Q.S. values and another two sets to $^{57}Fe(III)$-species. The Fe(II)-species and Fe(III)-species with larger Q.S. values are described as Fe(II)-1 and Fe(III)-1, while the others with smaller Q.S. values as Fe(II)-2 and Fe(III)-2, respectively. The former has Mössbauer parameters similar to the

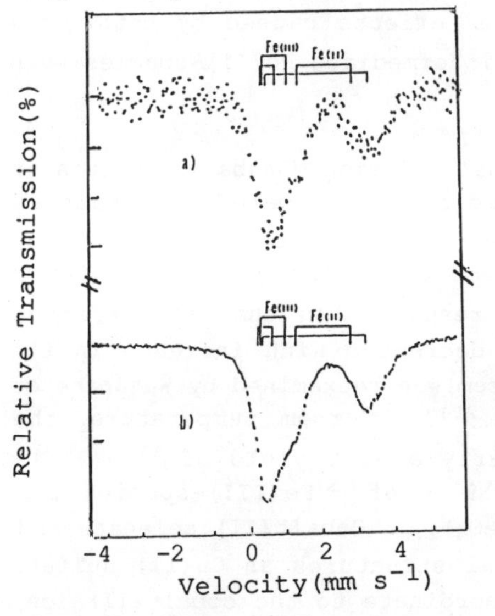

Fig. 10 Conventional and X,γ coincidence Mössbauer spectra for ^{57}Co-labelled CoF_2[15]

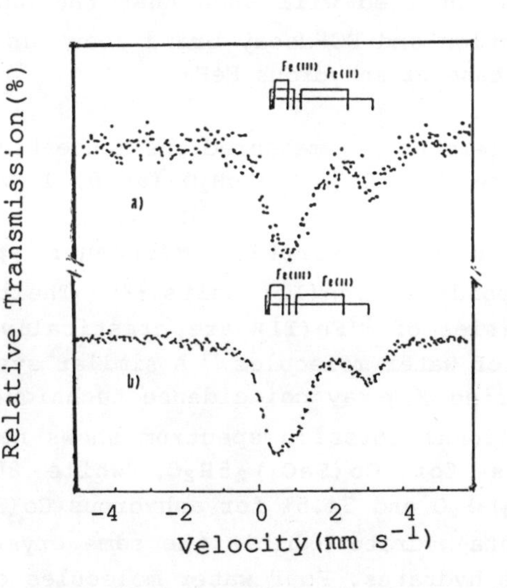

Fig. 11 Conventional and X,γ coincidence Mössbauer spectra for ^{57}Co-labelled $CoF_2 2H_2O$[15]

absorption spectra of iron(II) fluoride. In the case of the dihydrate, appreciable differences are found in the relative intensities for the Fe(II)-species and Fe(III)-species between the non-gated and the X-ray gated spectrum. However, these differences are found only for the components Fe(II)-1 and Fe(III)-1. In contrast, the difference is hardly discernible in the case of the anhydrous fluoride. The results indicate that only the components with larger Q.S. value; i.e., Fe(II)-1 and Fe(III)-1 are affected differently in the presence of water of crystallization, depending on whether the process after EC-decay is mainly X-ray emission or Auger electron emission.

In order to compare the chemical effect of EC-decay with those caused by γ-ray induced radiolysis, FeF_2 and $FeF_2\ 2H_2O$ were irradiated with γ-rays emitted from ^{60}Co and the chemical species produced were studied by absorption Mössbauer spectroscopy.[17] An absorption Mössbauer spectrum of the irradiated $FeF_2 2H_2O$ shows a large fraction of ^{57}Fe(III)-species, which is formed through oxidation of Fe(II) by radicals. Although the difference of the ^{57}Fe(III)-fraction between the two spectra of the unirradiated and irradiated anhydrous FeF_2 is not as large as in the case of the dihydrated fluoride, an additional component of an ^{57}Fe(II)-species with a small Q.S. value is found in the irradiated sample. It is well known that Fe(II) sulfate in an aqueous solution is oxidized to Fe(III) by oxidizing radicals, originated from the radiolysis of water. A similar radiolytic oxidation is known to occur in the solid phase only in the presence of water of crystallization for $FeSO_4\ nH_2O$(n=0,1,4, and 7).[18] The results obtained will show that the Auger effects caused by both γ-ray irradiation and EC-decay bring about an intermediate Fe(II)-species even in the case of anhydrous FeF_2.

Ladriere et al. measured the conventional emission Mössbauer spectra of ^{57}Co-labelled $Co(SeO_4)_2 nH_2O$ (n= 0, 1, and 5) and compared the chemical states of the nucleogenic ^{57}Fe atoms formed through EC-decay with those found in the absorption Mössbauer spectra of the γ-ray irradiated corresponding iron(II) salts.[19] Their results show that the relative intensities of ^{57}Fe(II) are drastically decreased with increace in the number of water molecules. A similar system was reexamined by Watanabe et al., using X,γ-ray coincidence technique.[20] At room temperature, the conventional emission spectrum shows nearly a 90 % yield of ^{57}Fe(III)-species for $Co(SeO_4)_2 5H_2O$, while 80.9 % of ^{57}Fe(III)-species for $Co(SeO_4)_2 H_2O$ and 54.5% for anhydrous $Co(SeO_4)_2$. Cobalt(II) selenate and the penta-hydrate exhibit the same crystal structures as Cu(II) sulfate and its hydrates. Four water molecules coordinate to the cobalt(II) ion, and one water molecule links through a hydrogen bond to the two selenate ions. The water molecules coordinated to ^{57}Co(II) will decompose through the EC-decay, resulting in a formation of oxidizing OH radicals. These radicals oxidize the nucleogenic ^{57}Fe-atoms to a high oxidation state which is most stable in the chemical matrix; i.e., ^{57}Fe(III) in the case of

$Co(SeO_4)_2nH_2O$. The KX-ray gated Mössbauer spectra of ^{57}Co-labelled $CoSeO_4$ and $CoSeO_4H_2O$ have been measured at room temperature. In this system, a similar result was obtained to CoF_2 and CoF_22H_2O. No difference in the relative intensity of $^{57}Fe(II)$ was observed for anhydrous $CoSeO_4$, while a larger relative intensity of Fe(II) was observed for the KX-ray gated spectrum of $CoSeO_4$ H_2O than for non-gated one. Since the X,γ-ray coincidence method requires one to detect the 6.3 keV KX-rays of Fe-atoms, the experiment at low temperature is rather difficult. Once this problem has been overcome, this coincidence will be a promising method to study the aftereffects as suggested by Spieling et al.[4)]

3.2 Time-differential Mössbauer spectroscopy

Time-differential Mössbauer spectroscopy (or γ-γ coincidence Mössbauer spectroscopy) is based on the delayed coincidence between the 122 keV and

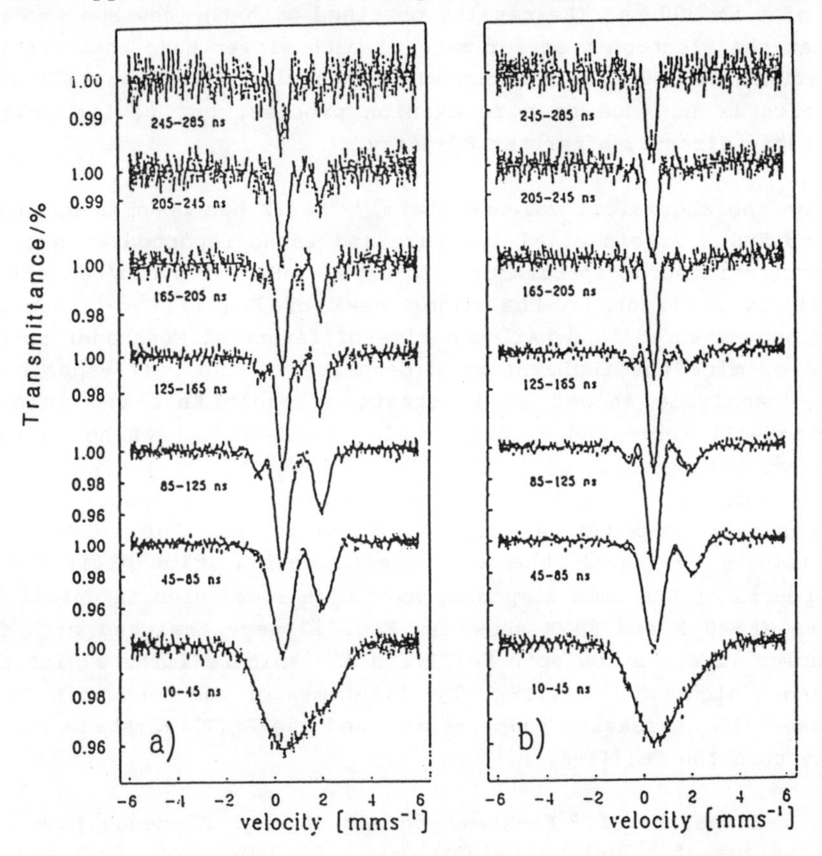

Fig. 13 Time differential Mössbauer spectra of ^{57}Co-labelled $CoSeO_4$ H_2O at room temperature; (a) 0-20 ns, (b) 35-60 ns, (c) 77-123 ns, (d) 125-180 ns (e) 180-302 ns, (f) random. coin.[29)].

14.4 keV γ-rays, and gives unique information on the dynamic state of decayed ^{57}Fe atoms. Although the spectroscopy was developed soon after the discovery of Mössbauer effect, the application to chemical effects is limited in number and reviewed briefly in the previous publication of this series.[2]

Goldanskii and co-workers reported an electron transfer rate of the order of 10^8 s^{-1} for ^{57}Co-labelled Prussian Blue analogous system of $^{57}Co^{2+}/[Fe^{III}(CN)_6]^{3-}$, using time-differential Mössbauer spectroscopy.[21] They explained their results in terms of an activation tunneling process. Recently, Gütlich's group reexamined the same system using a newly-developed spectrometer.[22] The time-resolved spectra were analyzed into two different iron high-spin species, taking into account the crystal structure of Prussian Blue.[23] The spectra show a slight decrease of the iron(II) fraction with decreasing temperature. In addition, the time-resolved spectra at 78 K showed the iron(II) fraction is constant for the time range of 0 to 300 ns. The results obtained with the new spectrometer indicate that the electron transfer rate is much slower than that reported by Goldanskii et al. Gütlich's group claims the iron(II)/iron(III) ratio in the spectra is not due to a relaxation process, but is the initial population ratio directly after the EC-decay.

A study on the anormalous valence-state, $^{57}Fe(I)$ has been investigated in ^{57}Co-doped ZnS. Garcin et al., Gerard and Lerho reported a resonance line in the time-integral spectra of ^{57}Co-doped ZnS, which can be assigned to an Fe(I) in addition to the major peak of Fe(II).[24,25] Recently, Gütlich's group measured in detail the time-differential Mössbauer spectra in order to examine the temperature dependence of the Fe(I)-species.[26] The spectral analysis showed an interesting result that the relative intensity of Fe(I) increased with the delay time, for which no definite explanation has been given.

The first application of time differential Mössbauer spectroscopy to the spin-crossover compound was done by Grimm et al. for ^{57}Co-labelled $[Co(phen)_3](ClO_4)_2$.[27] With the new spectrometer, time-differential Mössbauer spectra of the same compound have been remeasured in detail.[28] The spectra at 40 K and 80 K shown in Fig. 12 were analyzed with four sets of doublet, i.e., a low spin Fe(II), a low spin Fe(III), a high spin Fe(II)-1, and a high spin Fe(II)-2. The lifetimes of the high-spin states both decrease with increasing temperature, and the Fe(II)-2 state relaxes more rapidly than the Fe(II)-1.

Chemical relaxations of ^{57}Fe-atoms formed through EC-decay have been studied in systems of ^{57}Co-labelled $Co(IO_3)_2$, $Co(SeO_4)_2nH_2O$, CoF_2 and its hydrate in relation to their chemical stability (the redox couple of the cation and anion, or crystallographic stability of corresponding iron salts).[17,20,29]

Time differential Mössbauer spectra of $CoSeO_4H_2O$ are shown Fig. 13. A time dependence on the relative area of the $^{57}Fe(II)$ component was observed. The relative area of the $^{57}Fe(II)$ at each time window decreased with the delay time. The relaxation time was estimated by assuming that the reaction proceeds as,

$$^{57}Fe(II) + A^* \longrightarrow {}^{57}Fe(III) + A$$

where A* represents oxidizing radicals formed in the vicinity of the decayed ^{57}Fe atoms. If A* is in sufficient amounts, at least, on the time scale of the lifetime of the ^{57}Fe nucleus, the chemical reaction can be treated as pseudo first-order kinetics. A numerical calculation yielded the $^{57}Fe(II)$ fraction at the time of the 122 keV emission to be (56.5 ± 2.5) % and the chemical decay constant, $\lambda_c = (1.94 \pm 0.12) \times 10^{-2}\ ns^{-1}$ (or the mean lifetime to be 51.6 ± 3.3 ns) for the rapidly decaying fraction. Although the radicals represented by A* are not identified, the IR data on the gamma-ray irradiated K_2SeO_4, $FeSeO_45H_2O$, $CoSeO_4$ and $CoSeO_4H_2O$ indicated the formation of selenite ions. In the case of the monohydrate, $^{57}Fe(II)$ formed through EC-decay may be oxidized by the

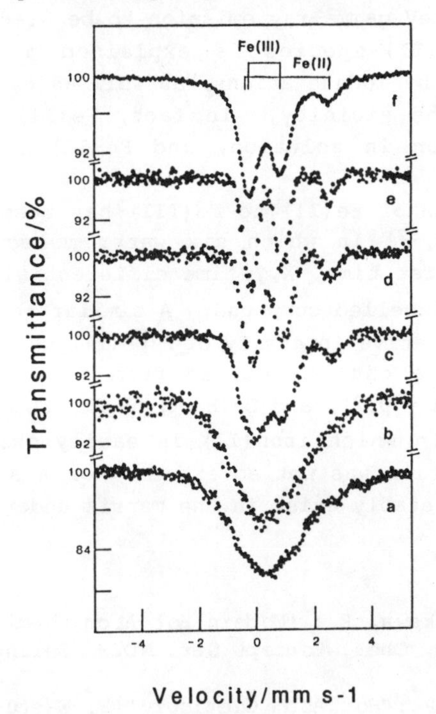

Fig. 13 Time differential Mössbauer spectra of ^{57}Co-labelled $CoSeO_4H_2O$ at room temperature; (a) 0-20 ns, (b) 35-60 ns, (c) 77-123 ns, (d) 125-180 ns, (e) 180-302 ns, (f) random. coin.[29].

strongly oxidizable OH and/or selenite radicals. It has been reported in an ESR study of ^{60}Co γ-ray irradiated K_2SeO_4 that γ-ray induced radiolysis gives rise to such radicals as SeO_4^-, SeO_3^-, and SeO_2^- and that selenite radicals have a lifetime of 4.5 hr at room temperature.[30,31] In fact, IR spectra indicated that the stronger intensity of selenite ions (a characteristic stretching vibration; 720 cm^{-1}) are observed by irradiation of ^{60}Co γ-rays for selenate salts with a greater number of water molecules. The radicals formed in selenate ions through the local radiolysis of EC-decay may accelerate the oxidation of $^{57}Fe(II)$ in ^{57}Co-labelled $CoSeO_4\ H_2O$. Since the chemical species formed through EC-decay are highly (vibrationally and electronically) excited states, the relaxation of $^{57}Fe(II)$ to $^{57}Fe(III)$ in the labelled compound may be initiated by "hot atom reaction" as well as normal redox reaction.

The time differential Mössbauer spectra of ^{57}Co-labelled $Co(IO_3)_2$ were measured at room temperature in our first coincidence experiments with poor time resolution and Mössbauer driving system.[29] The results were treated to a similar analysis to that mentioned for cobalt(II) selenate. The mean lifetime of the unstable $^{57}Fe(II)$ species formed through EC-decay is estimated to be 43 $\pm$ 5 ns and the initial distribution ratio of Fe(II)/Fe(III) at 122 keV gamma-ray emission to be 0.46 $\pm$ 0.13. The short lifetime of the $^{57}Fe(II)$-species is explained as the oxidation of nucleogenic iron atoms by iodate anions, as well as by the radicals formed through EC-decay in the vicinity. In fact, Fe(II) ion is immediately oxidized by iodate ion in solution, and Fe(II) iodate has not been isolated as a solid.

Analogous relaxation of Fe(II) to Fe(III) has been observed for ^{57}Co-labelled $Co(BrO_3)_2 6H_2O$,[32] in which six water molecules coordinate to cobalt(II). For the first time, X,γ time differential Mössbauer spectra were measured for the labelled compound. A similar relaxation time of the $^{57}Fe(II)$, but a high relative intensity of $^{57}Fe(II)$ was observed.

The following facts can be deduced from the results on $Co(IO_3)_3$, $Co(SeO_4)2H_2O$, $CoF_2nH_2O(n = 0,2)$, and $Co(BrO_3)_2 6H_2O$. Chemical relaxation was observed for systems in which iron(II) is easily oxidized by the anion itself, and the relaxation was not so extreme for a system in which both Fe(II) and Fe(III) can stably exist in the matrix under investigation.

References

1. Tominaga, T., Tachikawa, E.: "Modern Hot Atom Chemistry and its Application", Inorg. Chem. Concept Ser. NO.3 Springer-Verlag, New York (1981).
2. Sano, H., Gütlich, P.:"Hot Atom Chemistry"(T. Mastuura, Ed.) Kodansha, Tokyo(and Elsevior, Amsterdam), 1984, p.265.
3. Sano, H.: "Chemical Mössbauer Spectroscopy (R. H. Harber, Ed.) Plenum Pub. Corp. New York (1984), p.177
4. Spieling, H., Alflen, M., Gütlich, P., Hauser, A., Hennen, C., Manthe,V., Tuczek, F.: Hyperfine Int., 53, 113 (1990).
5. Van Rossum, M., Orders, J. Pattyn, H., De Troyer, J., Verbiest, E.,

Coussement, R., and Bukshpan, S., Phys. Lett., 75A, 241 (1980).
6. Van der Heyden, M., Pasternak, M., Langousche, G. Hyperfine Int.: 29, 1315 (1986).
7. Vander Heyden, M., Michliz, H., Bukshpan, S., and Langouche, M., Phys. Rev., B36, 38 (1987).
8. Bukshpan, S., Van Rossum, M., Pattyn, H., Verbiest, E., Coussement, R.: Phys. Lett., 82A, 40 (1981).
9. Devillers, M., Ladriere, J., Apers, D.: J. Phys. Chem. Solid, 49, 909 (1988).
10. Devillers, M., Ladriere, J., Apers, D.: J. Phys. Chem. Solid, 49, 921 (1988).
11 Sato, T., Katada, M., Sano, H.: J. Radioanal. Nucl. Chem. Lett., 144, 195 (1990).
12. Sato, T., A Thesis for Doctor of Science, Tokyo Metropolitan Univ., (1991).
13. Kobayashi,.T.: Radiochim. Acta, 35,43 (1984).
14. Kobayashi, T., Friedt, J. M.: Bull. Chem. Soc. Jpn., 59, 631 (1986).
15. Kobayashi, T.: Bull. Chem. Soc. Jpn., 62, 576 (1989).
16. Kobayashi, T., Makita, T., Fukumura, K.: Hyperfine Int., 56,1533 (1990).
17. Watanabe, Y., Nakada, M., Endo, K., Nakahara, H., Sano, H.,: J. Radioanal. Nucl. Chem. Lett., 136, 257 (1989).
18. Meyers, J., Ladriere, J., Chavee, M., Apers, D.:J. Phys.(Paris), Colloq., 37, C6-905 (1976).
19. Ladriere, J., Krack, C. J., Apers, D., J. Phys.(Paris), Colloq., 40, C2-434 (1979).
20. Watanabe, Y., Nakada, M., Endo, K., Nakahara, H., Sano, H.: Bull. Chem. Soc. Jpn., 63, 2790 (1990).
21. Alekseev, V. P., Goldanskii, V. I., Prusakov, V. E., Nefedev, A. V., Stukan, R. S.: JETP Lett., 16,43 (1972).
22. Albrecht, R., Alflen, M., Gütlich, P. Kajcsos, Zs., Schulze, R., Spieling, H., Tuczek, F.: Nucl. Instr. and Meth., A257, 209 (1987).
23. Hennen, C., Alflen, M., Spieling, H., Gütlich, P.: Hyperfine Int., 47, 596 (1989).
24. Garcin, C., Imbert, P., Jehanno, G., Regnard, J. R., Ferey, G., Leblanc, M., Gerard, A.: J. Physique, 47, 1977 (1986).
25. Gerard, A. and Lerho, M., Hyperfine Int., 29, 1373 (1986).
26. Alflen, M., Hennen, C., Tuczek, F., Spieling, H., Gütlich, P.: Hyperfine Int., 47, 115 (1989)
27. Grimm, R., Gütlich, P., Kankeleit, E., Link, R., J. Chem. Phys., 67, 549 (1977).
28. Hennen, C., Alflen, M., Spieling, H., Gütlich, P.: Hyperfine Int., 56, 1527 (1990).
29. Watanabe, M., Endo, K., Sano, H.: Bull. Chem. Soc. Jpn., 61, 2785 (1988).
30. Atkins, P. W., Symons, M. C. R., Wardale, H. W.: J. Chem. Soc., 1964, 5215.
31. Aiki, K.: J. Phys. Soc. Jpn., 29, 379 (1970).
32. Nakada, M., Tamegaya, K., Nakahara, H., Endo, K.: Hyperfine Int., 1992 (in press).

6.2 Hot Atom Chemistry and Positronium Chemistry

Yasuo ITO
Research Center for Nuclear Science and Technology, The University of Tokyo, Tokai, Ibaraki 319-11, Japan
Ennio LAZZARINI
Instituto di Ingegneria Nucleare-CESNEF Politecnico, Milano, Italy
and Hans J. ACHE
Institut fur Radiochemie, Kernforschungszentrum Karlsruhe GmbH, D-7500 Karlsruhe, Germany

1. Introduction

1.1 Fundamentals of Positron Annihilation [1-16]

A positron injected into a substance loses energy by a sequence of inelastic collisions and, before it is annihilated with one of the electrons, takes various physical and chemical states. For example, in metals and alloys, it diffuses in the interstitial sites of perfect crystals or is trapped in vacancy-type defects. In insulators it forms an atom called "positronium" (chemical symbol : Ps) which further undergoes various reactions.

The positron is eventually annihilated with an electron by emitting γ-rays. The selection rule for the γ-ray emission is derived from conservation of energy and momentum,

$$E = 2\, m_e c^2 + E_+ + E_- = 2 \cdot 511.0 \text{ keV} + E_+ + E_- \qquad (1)$$

where E_+ and E_- are the kinetic energy of e^+ and e^-, respectively, and conservation of momentum and charge-parity. When the pair e^+/e^- annihilates with their spins anti-parallel, two γ-rays with energies

$$E = 511.0 \text{ keV} \pm c/2\, P_X \qquad (2)$$

are emitted in the directions slightly deviating from 180° by an angle

$$\theta = P_Z / m_e c \qquad (3)$$

P_X and P_Z are the components of the total momentum of the e^+/e^- pair. The deviation of energy from 511.0 keV, $\pm c/2\, P_X$, is called the "Doppler shift" and that of the angle from 180° is called the "angular correlation", and both carry information about the momentum of the annihilating pair.

When the pair e^+/e^- annihilates with their spins parallel, three γ-rays are emitted. The energy of the three γ-rays ranges from 0 to 511.0 keV and consequently the angular correlation is not determined unequivocally.

In "free" annihilation of e^+, i.e. when e^+ picks up electron spins randomly, both types of annihilation are possible, but the efficiency of the three γ-ray annihilation is very low and the ratio of $3\gamma/2\gamma$ is 1/372.

The mean lifetime of positrons is inversely proportional to the electron density at the position of e^+. The cross section for 2γ annihilation is

$$\sigma_a = \pi r_e^2 c / v \tag{4}$$

where r_e is the classical electron radius, c is the velocity of light in vacuum, and v is the velocity of e^+. The annihilation rate is thus,

$$\lambda = n Z_{eff} \sigma_a v = \pi r_e^2 c n Z_{eff} \tag{5}$$

where n is the number density of molecules, and Z_{eff} is the effective number of electrons per molecule available for annihilation.

Positronium is a neutral particle composed of e^+ and e^-, and is the simplest hydrogen-like atom. The energy levels of Ps differ from those of H atom by a scaling factor of approximately 2. There are two substates of Ps: para-Ps (p-Ps) with e^+/e^- spins anti-parallel (S=0) and ortho-Ps (o-Ps) with the spins parallel (S=1). The intrinsic annihilation of p-Ps is by 2γ-emission and its rate is

$$\lambda^0 \text{(p-Ps)} = 8.0 \times 10^9 \text{ s}^{-1} \tag{6}$$

or the mean lifetime is $1/\lambda$=125 ps.

The intrinsic annihilation of o-Ps is by 3γ-emission and its mean lifetime is $1/\lambda^0$ (o-Ps)= 140 ns. In most substances, however, e^+ in o-Ps can overlap with an electron in the medium and is annihilated before it can attain its intrinsic lifetime. This is a purely quantum mechanical process called "pick-off" annihilation and, similar to the "free annihilation", the ratio of 2γ to 3γ annihilations is 372 in the pick-off process. Due to the pick-off annihilation, the lifetime of o-Ps becomes shorter in materials having higher electron densities, and is less than several ns in many condensed materials. Thus in condensed materials e^+ annihilation is dominated by 2γ-emission even when Ps is formed abundantly.

The basic experimental methods of positron annihilation are [18] :

1) Positron annihilation lifetime measurement (PAL)
2) Angular correlation of 2γ-annihilation radiation (ACAR)
3) Doppler broadening of positron annihilation radiation lines (DBPA)

PAL measures the lifetime spectrum of positrons. Different positron states are resolved by the difference in the corresponding mean lifetimes, and PAL is the most useful method in positron chemistry. ACAR and DBPA, measuring the momentum distribution of the annihilating pair as described in Eqs.2 and 3, are equivalent methods for isotropic samples. In positron chemistry they are regarded as a complementary method to PAL, but offer completely different and important information especially regarding the p-Ps component, which cannot be easily obtained by PAL due to its very short lifetime.

Positron emitting radioisotopes (^{22}Na, ^{68}Ge, ^{64}Cu, ^{58}Co) have been used as the positron source for these experiments. It is difficult to control the energy and the direction of these "white source" positrons, and recently techniques have been developed to obtain mono-energetic slow positron beams. Due to the advent of the slow positron beam, it has become possible to obtain fundamental data of positron interactions and our knowledge about positron chemistry is being expanded. Details of experimental methods using white positron sources are described in ref.(18).

2. Overview of Positron and Positronium Chemistry [19-22]

"Positron annihilation" is studied by observing the annihilation, hence every observed event is the final state of each e^+. The time window of observation is from about 0.1 ns to several tens of ns (for the condensed phases), during which most of the positron states are already in equilibrium with the medium. Events in non-equilibrium processes, i.e. events corresponding to epithermal stages and inhomogeneous spur processes, are finished at the very early stage of this time window and, indeed, such have not yet been observed directly excepting in gaseous media[23]. This is partly due to the limit of the time resolution (0.2~0.3 ns). The intensity, I_3, and the lifetime, τ_3, of the longest lived component are the two major parameters that can be measured with high accuracy.[1] Normally this component corresponds to o-Ps, and the lifetime τ_3 carries information of the state and the reactivity of o-Ps on a time scale of ns. The intensity I_3, on the other hand, is related to positronium formation processes which take place at much earlier times: ps or less.

2.1 Reactions of Positronium

In gases o-Ps may exist as a free particle. It may annihilate by itself with the intrinsic lifetime of 140 ns, or e^+ in o-Ps may pick-off an external electron (e^- not bound to e^+) on collision with the molecules. Its lifetime is thus inversely proportional to the density of molecules.

$$1/\tau = \lambda^{0}(\text{o-Ps}) + \pi r_0^2 c N\, {}^1Z_{eff} \qquad (7)$$

${}^1Z_{eff}$ is the number of electrons available for the pick-off annihilation. Since o-Ps cannot penetrate into molecules due to the repulsive molecular force, ${}^1Z_{eff}$ is only a fraction of the total number of electrons, Z; for ex-

---

1. The components in a PAL spectrum are numbered from the shortest to the longest lived, and are usually 3. But when the time resolution is not good enough as was the case in the earlier studies, the PAL spectrum is resolved into only two components, in which case the longest lived one, denoted as (τ_2,I_2) can be the o-Ps component. When the PAL spectrum is resolved into four components as in some polymers or porous materials, (τ_4,I_4) corresponds to o-Ps. In such cases (τ_3,I_3) may also correspond to o-Ps (as in porous materials) but the assignment is not yet determined as in polyethylene.

ample, ${}^1Z_{eff}(Z)$=0.35(2), 0.26(14), 0.48(22) for He, N_2, CO_2, respectively. For some molecules ${}^1Z_{eff}$ becomes comparable to or larger than Z; ${}^1Z_{eff}(Z)$= 14(16), 200(13), $\sim 10^5$(19) for O_2, CCl_2F_2, NO_2, respectively. In such cases o-Ps is considered to be reacting with the molecules, and for these molecules it is better to describe the reactivity by a usual kinetic treatment than in terms of ${}^1Z_{eff}$. In actual experimental conditions non-reactive gases (e.g. N_2, Ar) are used as a buffer gas and reactive molecules are added as impurity. Considering the annihilation rate due to pick-off in the buffer gas (Eq.7) as a constant, the overall annihilation rate is given by,

$$\lambda_3 = \lambda_{po} + k\,[X] \tag{8}$$

where λ_{po} is equal to the right hand side of Eq.7 but can be directly determined by PAL measurement in the buffer gas. λ_3 is also measured by PAL, and the reaction rate constant is calculated from Eq.8.

In liquids Ps is considered to reside in a void created by Ps itself, called "Ps bubble".[22-25] The size of the "Ps bubble" is determined by the balance between tension of the internal surface of the bubble and the zero-point energy of Ps, and is approximately 0.4 nm in radius in many hydrocarbon liquids. O-Ps annihilates by picking-off an electron in the wall of the bubble, and its lifetime is about $1/\lambda_{po}$=3~4 ns. Reactions of o-Ps in liquids is dealt with in the same way as in the gases using Eq.8.

Compounds can be divided into two categories regarding reactivity toward Ps.[19,21] The first one which shows only weak interaction ($k < 10^8\ M^{-1}s^{-1}$) is composed of hydrocarbons, halogenated hydrocarbons, aliphatic nitro compounds, and diamagnetic inorganic ions whose standard redox potential in aqueous solution are more negative than -0.9 eV. In these cases the interaction is governed by weak attractive Van der Waals force of the collision complex and the reactivity is correlated with the polarizability of the molecules as was demonstrated for n-hydrocarbons. The second group shows strong reactivity toward Ps ($k > 10^8\ M^{-1}s^{-1}$) and contains nitroaromatics, quinones, halogens, conjugated anhydrides, cyanoethylenes, organic ions, and inorganic ions with a standard redox potential larger than -0.9 eV. The strongly reactive organic substances are highly conjugated and are strong electron acceptors which form stable molecular complexes. The reaction between o-Ps and these compounds may be a "Ps complex" formation as,

$$\text{o-Ps} + M \rightarrow PsM \rightarrow 2\gamma + M \tag{9}$$

Since e^+ incorporated in a stable compound feels a dense electron cloud and is annihilated at a rate of ca. 0.3 ns, it is removed from the long lived component.

The strong interaction observed in aqueous solutions of simple inorganic ions may be understood as electron transfer reactions;

$$\text{o-Ps} + A_{aq}^{n+} \rightarrow e^+_{aq} + A_{aq}^{(n-1)+} \tag{10}$$

This reaction can take place when it is energetically possible, and there is a correlation between the standard redox potentials and the rate constants.

Similar to H-atoms, abstraction and displacement reactions may be postulated for Ps as;

$$\text{o-Ps} + \text{RX} \rightarrow \text{PsX} + \text{R} \quad (11)$$
$$\text{o-Ps} + \text{RX} \rightarrow \text{RPs} + \text{X} \quad (12)$$

These reactions are normally endothermic and would take place with energetic Ps. Since "hot" Ps reactions affect the intensity, I_3, and are not responsible for the lifetime, τ_3, they will be viewed in more detail in the next section.

Another important aspect of o-Ps reactions is spin exchange. This occurs when Ps encounters paramagnetic molecules as;

$$\text{o-Ps}(\uparrow\updownarrow) + \text{M}(\downarrow) \rightarrow \text{p-Ps}(\downarrow\updownarrow) + \text{M}(\uparrow) \quad (13)$$

The spin exchange reaction is also possible for p-Ps leading to conversion to o-Ps. But, since the p-Ps lifetime is short, it is not efficient and only the spin exchange of o-Ps is usually observed. O_2, NO and NO_2 are known to exchange their unpaired spin with Ps. Spin exchange reaction of o-Ps with gaseous O_2 takes place both in inelastic and elastic collisions, and the cross section for the former is more than 100 times larger than that of the latter (1×10^{-9} cm^2).[26,27] But spin exchange is not the sole reaction channel, and Ps compound formation is also possible for these molecules. Spin exchange and compound formation are considered to be different channels for the same collision complex as;[28]

$$\text{o-Ps} + \text{M} \rightarrow [\text{Ps--M}]^* \rightarrow \text{o-Ps/p-Ps} + \text{M} \quad \text{spin exchange} \quad (14)$$
$$\rightarrow \text{PsM} \quad \text{Ps compound} \quad (14')$$

When the excess energy of the collision complex [Ps--M]* is removed efficiently by a third body, the complex is stabilized (Ps compound formation). For O_2, for example, spin conversion is efficient in gases while Ps compound formation takes over in small pores or in liquids.

3. Ps Formation

3.1 The Ore Model

There are two basic models of Ps formation.[29,30] The Ore model[31] simply considers that e^+ abstracts an electron from a substance to form Ps;

$$e^+ + M \rightarrow Ps + M^+ \quad (15)$$

Owing to the small binding energy of Ps (=6.8 eV), this reaction is normally endothermic and thus there is an energy threshold, E_{th}, below which Ps formation is impossible;

$$E_{th} = E_i - 6.8 \text{ eV} \quad (16)$$

where E_i is the ionization energy of the substance. At positron energies larger than for electronic excitations and ionization, the cross sections are considered to become larger than that of Ps formation and an upper boundary, E_{max}, for Ps formation was supposed to exist somewhere near or between the first electronic excitation energy, E_{ex}, and the ionization energy, E_i. Ps formation is considered to be efficient only for e^+ having an energy between

E_{th} and E_{max}, and this energy region is called the "Ore gap". Ps formation by the Ore model process is thus an epithermal process.

The Ore model could not explain the experimental fact that Ps formation probabilities differ for liquids having similar Ore gap structures: for example I_3=0.42 for n-hexane while I_3=0 for CCl_4. In order to explain many similar experimental facts from the viewpoint of the Ore model, the ideas of hot-atom chemistry were borrowed :[2]

1) capture of positrons at energies above E_{th} reduces Ps formation
2) rapid moderation of e^+ energy below the Ore gap reduces Ps formation
3) nascent "hot Ps" is capable of reaction before being thermalized, which leads to an apparent reduction in Ps formation

The processes 1) and 2) remain mere speculative possibilities at present. A reaction, $e^+ + CCl_4 \rightarrow e^+$ compound, was postulated to explain non Ps formation in CCl_4, but it has not yet been substantiated. It is also difficult to imagine according to 2) that CCl_4 is more efficient at moderating epithermal e^+ energies than n-hexane.

But the process 3), often called the "Ore model plus hot-Ps reaction" model, deserves some consideration. Ps formed by the Ore model process will have an energy ranging from thermal to $E_{max}-E_{th}$, i.e. it is born as a "hot" particle. It is reasonable to expect that the hot o-Ps undergoes abstraction or displacement reactions as in Reactions (11) and (12). An example is halogenated hydrocarbons. Although they do not react with thermalized o-Ps they are efficient inhibitors of Ps formation, and the efficiency of the inhibition is larger for the molecules having smaller bonding energy between the carbon and halogen atoms. Theoretical calculation suggests that Ps can bind to halogen atom,[32] for example the binding energy between Ps and Cl is calculated to be 1.4-2.0 eV, which is less than the binding energy of C-Cl (3.0 eV for $Cl-CCl_3$). The following endothermic reaction is thus reasonably suggested.

$$\text{o-Ps}^* + RX \rightarrow PsX + R \tag{17}$$

Another example is the effect of inorganic ions in aqueous solution.[33] Ions like Sn^{4+}, Sn^{2+}, Pb^{2+}, Cd^{2+}, Zn^{2+}, Tl^{2+} and Na^+ are efficient inhibitors of Ps formation and their efficiency is described by a Stern-Volmer type function;

$$I_3 = I_3{}^0 / (1 + \alpha\ [M]) \tag{18}$$

where $I_3{}^0$ is the o-Ps yield in the pure solvent. The parameter α is called the inhibition coefficient and it describes, within the "hot Ps" model, competition between scavenging and thermalization of Ps^*. A reasonable correlation is found between the α value and the free energy $-\Delta G^0$ for the one-electron transfer reaction to the ions, and this was considered to imply that the following hot Ps reaction causes the inhibition.

$$Ps^* + A_{aq}{}^{n+} \rightarrow e^+ + A_{aq}{}^{(n-1)+} \tag{19}$$

It is also important to note that the inhibition effect levels off at some value, I^{sat}, which differs for different ions and shows a good correlation with the redox potential of these ions. For endothermic reactions, only the Ps having sufficient energy to overcome the barrier may be able to take part in the reaction, and I_{sat} is the measure of the fraction of Ps having energies below the threshold of Reaction 10.

A theoretical approach to hot Ps reactions have also been made. One is an application of the Estrup-Wolfgang equation, and another treats the energy loss process of hot Ps by inelastic collisions.[34] In both cases the derived theoretical expressions appear to be able to explain the experimental results at least qualitatively.

3.2 The Spur Model[30,35.36]

The spur model of Ps formation was proposed in 1974.[37] A positron, injected into a substance, is slowed down by successive ionization and excitation processes by depositing its energy in a microscopic restricted region, called the "spur", at every several 100 nm. In the spur model it is assumed that the positron stops in the terminal spur that it has created by depositing its last ca 200 eV and that the positron combines with one of the excess electrons in this spur and forms Ps.

$$e^+ + e^- \rightarrow Ps \qquad (20)$$

An important point of this model is that e^+ and e^- are, before they combine, separated at some distance with nearly thermal energies. The Ps formation probability is determined by the number and initial distribution of the excess electrons in the spur, their energy states and mobilities, the number and reactivity of the parent ions, as well as the energy state and mobility of e^+.[38] Any change in these parameters can affect Ps formation. This situation gives the model a flexibility in interpreting subtle effects of temperature, phase change, and admixture on Ps formation which are, if not impossible at all, not easy to explain from the Ore model because the latter is essentially an epithermal model. Various intraspur reactions that affect Ps formation and inhibition are summarized in Table.

Table Intraspur reactions in the Positron spur

Basic Reactions	
$e^+ + e^- \rightarrow Ps$	Ps formation
$M^+ (h^+) + e^- \rightarrow M*$	geminate recombination
$e^- \rightarrow$ escape	escape from the spur
$e^- + R_0 \rightarrow R_0{}^-$	e^- capture by free radicals
Reactions that inhibit Ps formation	
$e^- + RX \rightarrow R + X^-$	e^- scavenging
$e^+ + RX \rightarrow RXe^+$	e^+ scavenging
$e^- \rightarrow e^-_{sol}$	e^- solvation
$e^+ \rightarrow e^+_{sol}$	e^+ solvation
$e^+ + e^- / E$	electric field effect
Reactions that enhance Ps formation	
$h^+ + X \rightarrow MX^+$	hole scavenging
$e^- + S \rightarrow S^-$	shallow e^- trap
$S^- \xrightarrow{e^+} Ps + S$	followed by e^- abstraction by e^+
$R_0 + X \rightarrow RX$	radical scavenging

Among many experiments to test the validity of the spur model, the effects of electron scavengers are the most widely adopted, since their effects can be compared quantitatively with the data of radiation chemistry. In aqueous systems the inhibition effects are described by one of the following three functions;[39,40]

$$I_3/I_3^0 = \frac{1}{1 + \alpha C} \quad (21)$$

$$I_3/I_3^0 = \frac{f}{1 + \alpha C} + (1 - f) \quad (22)$$

$$I_3/I_3^0 = \frac{1 + \beta C}{1 + \alpha C} \quad (\text{with } \beta > \alpha) \quad (23)$$

Eq.21 corresponds to the case where Ps formation is totally inhibited at high inhibitor concentrations, and Eq.22 to the case where the inhibition is only partial. The precursor of Ps can be either "dry" or "damp" (i.e. incompletely solvated) electrons, and the scavengers showing the effect of Eq.22 are considered to capture only the damp electrons, and the unscavengable fraction (1-f) corresponds to Ps formation from dry electrons. Total inhibitors may capture both dry and damp electrons. The inhibition coefficient α appears to be correlated with the rate constant k_{aq} of reaction with hydrated electrons, or with the parameter $1/C_{37}$ (C_{37} is a term from picosecond pulse radiolysis and is the scavenger concentration at which the number of "dry" electrons is intercepted to $1/e$[41]). The scavengers of Eq.23 enhances Ps formation, and one of the possible explanations for the enhancement is scavenging OH radicals which would otherwise have captured electrons.

Scavenger experiments have also been performed extensively for Ps formation in nonpolar solvents.[36,42-45] In these cases the inhibition function does not follow the Stern-Volmer type function suggesting that Ps formation in them is a non-homogeneous process as in the spur reactions in radiation chemistry. The inhibition coefficients of Ps formation, α', are found to be very close to the electron scavenging coefficients, α, obtained in radiation chemistry, too.[46] Especially for the scavengers called "normal inhibitors" α' is almost the same as α. For "strong inhibitors" α' is much larger than α in which case additional effects of the solute, for example capture of e^+ as well as the capture of e^-, had to be assumed. There are also another type scavengers and they have weak inhibition effects ("partial inhibitor") or even enhance Ps formation ("enhancer"). Examples of the enhancer are aromatic hydrocarbons and fluorinated aromatic hydrocarbons. Taking C_6F_6 as an example, the enhancement effect is explained as follows;

$$e^- + C_6F_6 \rightarrow C_6F_6^- \quad (e^- \text{ capture}) \quad (24)$$

$$e^+ + C_6F_6^- \rightarrow Ps + C_6F_6 \quad (e^- \text{ pick-up by } e^+) \quad (25)$$

In reaction 24 the geminate recombination of e^- is prevented and its lifetime is extended, giving more chance for e^+ to form Ps in reaction 25. Thus the effect of the enhancer is called "anti-recombination". When different types of scavengers, inhibitor and enhancer, are present in nonpolar solvent, their effects can be treated as a simple competition for electron capture.

3.3 Comprehension of the Ore Model and the Spur Model

Whatever the model, supporters of each model have tried to explain as many experimental facts as possible, and each model has eventually received modifications; the Ore model was modified to include hot Ps reactions (Ore model plus hot-Ps reaction), and the spur model was modified to include secondary reactions of excess electrons as already described. If one wants to interpret the anti-inhibition effect from the stand point of the Ore model, it becomes necessary to consider participation of excess electrons (Ore model plus spur reaction effect).[45] Notwithstanding all these efforts, however, both models together with their modifications do not seem satisfactory and a better model is being sought.

It is important to note that the two models are not exclusive of each other in either energy or time domains. From the viewpoint of energetics, if $E_+ + E_-$ (E_+ and E_- are the energy of e^+ and e^-, respectively, just after the ionization action of positron) is smaller than the binding energy of Ps (6.8 eV), the pair is already bound, and the Ore model may operate. But if $E_+ + E_-$ is larger than the binding energy the pair separates, and the spur model will operate.[47] From the viewpoint of time scale, the Ore model precedes the spur model in time because the former is an epithermal process. Where Ps formation by both models is possible, the Ore model might take precedence. However in polyatomic substances in which e^+ energy is moderated efficiently, there is less chance for the Ore model. Thus the two models are considered complementary, and a proper question would be to ask what fraction of Ps comes from the Ore model and what from the spur model.

Experimental attempts to separate contributions from the two different Ps formation processes are not straightforward usually. For example, scavengers can almost always influence both processes. But they can be resolved in some special cases. A study of the effect of static electric field on Ps formation in several polymers suggests a 60% contribution from the Ore model.[48]

A monochromatic slow positron beam may also be used for the purpose of distinguishing the two models. In one experiment the Ps formation probability in ice was measured as a function of the incident e^+ energy.[49] Ps started to be formed at an e^+ energy corresponding to the threshold E_{th} of Ps formation as expected from the Ore model. But at e^+ energies much higher than the Ore gap, Ps formation was still substantial. The results indicate Ps formation is possible by both mechanisms. In an another experiment where alkali halides were used as the sample,[50] the energy of the produced Ps was measured as a function of the energy of the incident e^+. The assumption here was that Ps formed by the different processes may have different initial energies at the time of formation: Ps formed by the Ore model may have energies ranging between zero and the Ps binding energy, while that formed by the spur model should be larger than the binding energy. The latter assumption is not straightforward, because we do not know what is the energy when Ps is formed from e^+ and e^- pair in the condensed phase. In vacuum it will be the binding energy plus the kinetic energies of e^+ and e^- as stated, but in the condensed phase interactions with the aggregated environment make the situation very complicated and it is probable that the energy of the pair is reduced at the time of formation of Ps.

This complexity is common in radiation chemistry and hot atom chemistry, and not yet well understood.

The use of a monochromatic slow positron beam in studying Ps formation in the gaseous phase is also important to test the Ore model. An example of such studies is found in ref.51, where the Ps formation probability was measured as a function of the incident e^+ energy. The Ps formation probability rises from the threshold E_{th} as expected from the Ore model. But it is interesting to note that the peak of the Ps formation probability is located near the excitation energy E_x. This is not in accord with the Ore model, because the Ore model predicts that Ps formation probability should fall above E_x.

Recently a new model of Ps formation has been proposed.[52] Here Ps formation is supposed to be formed through resonant formation of a complex involving a molecular excited state M^*, $[e^+:M^*]$. This complex may be formed either by collision of energetic e^+ on a ground state molecule,

$$e^{+*} + M \rightarrow [e^+:M^*] \rightarrow Ps + M^+ \qquad (26)$$

or from reaction between nearly thermalized e^+ and excited molecular state.

$$e^+ + M^* \rightarrow [e^+:M^*] \rightarrow Ps + M^+ \qquad (27)$$

Reaction (26) resembles the Ore model, and reaction (27) is essentially an extension of the spur model since it involves an electron excited due to the energy of the incident e^+. The new model aims to sublimate the Ore model and the spur model to a model of "resonant Ps formation", but certainly needs detailed examination both experimentally and theoretically.

4. Conclusion

Positron and positronium chemistry contains many important subjects closely related with hot atom chemistry and radiation chemistry. Some of them, mostly the chemistry of positronium, are now well understood, but there are others that are as yet poorly understood. The mechanism of Ps formation belong to the latter category. It is necessary to do detailed and critical investigations from a fundamental viewpoint. For example, it is important to ask with what energy Ps emerges after combination between e^+ and e_- in the spur ? This question resembles a question in radiation chemistry, namely what is the energy of the product of geminate recombination M^+ and e^- ? And if we can ever find an answer to these questions, it is most probably from a study of Ps formation because it is the simplest system.

We have mainly described the problems in positron and positronium chemistry because they present a worthy challenge for chemists. But it will not do justice to stress only the unsolved problems. From the other side positron and positronium chemistry is growing up and is mature for use as important and unique tools in physics and chemistry. The readers are referred to suitable reviews and papers concerning studies of free volumes[53-55] and micro pores of porous materials[56,57] and amorphous Si[58], micells,[59] phase changes,[60] density fluctuations in gases,[61] studies of surface, thin films and interfaces.[62]

References

General Reviews and Text Books

1. J. Green and J. Lee, "Positronium Chemistry", Academic Press (1964)
2. V.I. Goldanskii, Atomic Energy Review, 6, 3 (1968)
3. "Positron and Muonium Chemistry" (Advances in Chemistry Series 175), (H. J. Ache, Ed.), American Chemical Society, 1974
4. "Positron and Positronium Chemistry", (D.M. Schrader and Y.C. Jean, Eds.), Elsevier, 1988
5. R.N. West, "Positron Studies of condensed Matter", Advances in Physics, 22(3), 1973

Proceedings of International Conferences and Workshops, Special Issues

6. Proc. 3rd ICPA, Hautojarvi, P. and Seeger, A. eds., Otaniemi, Finland, August 1973, Springer Verlag (Offprints from Applied Physics)
7. Proc. 4th ICPA, Helsingor, Denmark, August 1976
8. Proc. 5th ICPA, (R.R. Hasiguti and K. Fujiwara, Eds.), Yamanaka, Japan, April 1979, The Japan Inst. Metals
9. Proc. 6th ICPA, (P.G. Coleman, S.C. Sharma and L.M. Diana, Eds.), North-Holland, Texas, USA, April 1982
10. Proc. 7th ICPS, (P.C. Jain, R.M. Singru and K.P. Gopinathan, Eds.), World Scientific, New Delhi 1985
11. Proc. 8th ICPA, (L. Dorikens-Vanpraet, M. Dorikens and D. Segers, Eds.) World Scientific, Gent Belgium 1988
12. Proc. 3rd Int. Workshop Positron [Electron]-Gas Scattering, Detroit, Michigan, (W.E. Kauppila, T.S. Stein and J.S. Wadehra, Eds.) World Scientific 1985
13. "Atomic Physics with Positrons" (Proc. NATO Advanced Res. Workshop, London England, 1987), (J.W. Humberston and E.A.G. Armour, Eds.), Plenum Press 1987
14. "Positron Annihilation Studies of Fluids", Arlington, Texas, (S.C. Sharma, Ed.) World Scientific, 1988
15. Proc. 3rd Int. Workshop Positron and Positronium Chemistry, July 1990, Milwaukee, USA (Y.C. Jean, Ed.), World Scientific 1990
16. "Positron Solid-State Physics" (Proc. Int. School Physics Enrico Fermi), (W. Brandt and A. Duapsquier, Eds., North-Holland 1983
17. Special Issue Positron and Muon Chemistry, Radiat. Phys. Chem, 28(1), 1986 (Y. Tabata, Ed.)

Theses

18. Y.C. Jean and D.M. Schrader, Chapter 3 of Ref. 4 offers extensive description of the methods.
19. H.J. Ache, Chapter 1 of Ref.3
20. Chapters 5-6 of Ref.4
21. V.I. Goldanskii and V.P. Shantarovich, Ref.6, (Appl. Phys. 3, 335 (1974))
22. S.J. Tao, Ref.6, (Appl. Phys. 3, 1 (1974))
23. T.C. Griffith and G.R. Heyland, Physics Report, 39, 169-277 (1978)
24. J.P. Hernadez and S. Choi, Phys. Rev., 188, 340 (1969)
25. A.P. Buchikhin, V.I. Goldanskii, A.O. Tatur and V.P. Shantarovich, Zh. Eksp. Teor. Fiz., 60, 1136 (1971)
26. M. Deutsch and S. Berko, Aalpha-, Beta- and Gamma-ray Spectroscopy, (K. Siegbahn, Ed., North-Holland, Amsterdam, 1965) p.1583
27. M. Kakimoto, T. Hyodo and T.B. Chang, J. Phys.B, 23, 589 (1990)
28. V.I. Goldanskii, A.D. Mokrushin, A.O. Tatur and V.P. Shantarovich, Appl. Phys., 5, 379 (1975)
29. E. Lazzarini, "Hot Atom Chemistry" (T. Matsuura, Ed.) Kodansha, Tokyo (and Elsevier, Amsterdam), 1984, p.373
30. Y. Ito, Chapter 4 of Ref.4
31. A. Ore, Univ. i Bergen Arbok. Naturwitenskapp Rekke, Nr.9 (1949)
32. D. M. Schrader, Chapter 10 of Ref.3; Chapter 2 of Ref.4

33. L.J. Bartal, J.B. Nicholas and H.J. Ache, J. Phys. Chem. 76, 1124 (1972)
34. A. Foglio Para and E. Lazzarini, J. Inorg. Nucl. Chem. 40, 1473 (1978)
35. S.J. Tao, Chapter 8 of Ref.3
36. Yu. N. Molin and O.A. Anisimov, Chapter 9 of Ref.3
37. O.E. Mogensen, J. Chem. Phys. 60, 998 (1974)
38. J.M. Warman, p.306 of Ref.15
39. G. Duplatre, J.Ch. Abbe, A.G. Maddock and a. Haessler, Radiat. Phys. Chem. 11, 199 (1978); ibid. 15, 617 (1980)
40. J. Talamouni, J.Ch. Abbe, G. Duplatre and A. Haessler, Chem. Phys. 58, 13 (1981)
41. K.Y. Lam and J.W. Hunt, Radiat. Phys. Chem. 7, 317 (1975)
42. G. Wikander, Chem. Phys. 38, 181 (1979); 39, 21 (1979); 39, 309 (1979); 43, 344 (1976); 66, 227 (1982)
43. G.Wikander and O.E. Mogensen, Chem. Phys. 72, 407 (1982)
44. O.A. Anisimov, S.V. Vocel and Yu. N. Molin, Chem. Phys. 44, 367 (1979); 56, 261 (1981)
45. B. Djermouni and H.J. Ache, J. Phys. Chem. 82, 2378 (1978)
46. Y.Ito, Y. Katsumura, T. Azuma and Y. Tabata, J. Phys. Chem. 88, 1921 (1984)
47. S.J. Tao, Applied Physics, 10, 67 (1976)
48. A. Bisi, G. Gambarini and L. Zappa, Nuovo Cimento 2D, 1465 (1983)
49. M. Eldrup, A. Vehanen, P.J. Schultz and K.G. Lynn, Phys. Rev. Lett. 51, 2007 (1983)
50. M. Tuomisaari, R.H. Howell and T. McMullen, Phys. Rev.B, 40, 2060 (1989)
51. M. Charlton, T.C.Griffith, G.R. Heyland, K.S. Lines and G.L. Wright, J. Phys. B13, L757 (1980)
52. Z. Zhang and Y. Ito, J. Chem. Phys. 93, 1021 (1990)
53. H. Nakanishi, S.J. Wang and Y.C. Jean, p.292 of Ref.14
54. H. Nakanishi and Y.C. Jean, Chapter 5 of Ref.5
55. Y.C. Jean, p.1 of Ref.15
56. Y. Ito and M. Hasegawa, Applied Physics A45, 193 (1988)
57. Y.Ito, M. Hirose and Y. Tabata, Appl. Phys. A50, 39 (1990)
58. Y.J. He, M. Hasegawa, R. Lee and S. Berko, Phys. Rev. B33, 5924 (1986)
59. H.J. Ache, Chapter 1 of Ref.3; Chapter 10 of Ref.5
60. W.W. Walker, Chapter 2 of Ref.3
61. S.C. Sharma, p.20 of Ref.14
62. P.J. Schultz and K.G. Lynn, Rev. Mod. Phys. 60, 701 (1988)

6.3 Chemical Effects in Nuclear Decay Processes: Applications in Hot Atom Chemistry

David S. Urch
Chemistry Department, Queen Mary and Westfield College, University of London, Mile End Road, LONDON E1 4NS, United Kingdom.

1. Introduction

The elucidation of hot atom chemical reactions in solids is greatly complicated by the need, in most cases, to dissolve the solid so that a chemical analysis of the labelled species may be carried out. Clearly this procedure will allow the once recoil but now trapped atom to relax, and possibly react, either with the solvent or with other species (radicals etc.,) present in the lattice as a result of the passage of the recoil atom. It is therefore most desirable that direct methods be sought of probing the chemical state and local environment of the recoil atom at its rest site within the lattice. As the recoil atom in a typical HAC experiment is radioactive, perturbations in radioactive decay that can be correlated with chemistry are required. And although it is claimed that radioactivity is unaffected by the chemical environment this is not always so. The purpose of this chapter is to identify those radioactive decay processes in which chemical effects have been observed and to discuss their relevance to HAC. Such processes include:

i) variations in half-life (or decay constant),
ii) events associated with γ-ray internal conversion,
  (a) autophotoelectron emission
  (b) X-ray emission
iii) events following electron capture, X-ray emission
iv) the angular correlation of γ-rays emitted in cascade
v) recoil-less γ-ray emission (Mössbauer effect).

Of these effects the latter is the subject of a separate chapter in this book (6.1) whilst the first is difficult to determine. Some slight changes in decay constants associated with valency changes have been reported for ^{117m}Sn (SnII-SnIV)[1], ^{51}Cr (CrIII-Cr VI)[2], ^{54}Mn (MnII-MnVII)[3] and also ^{99m}Tc[4]. But because this effect has been little studied and is not easy to utilise effectively it will not be discussed further. (ii) and (iii) will be considered in more detail in this chapter and (iv) in the next. In all cases if there are applications in HAC these will be emphasised.

2. γ-ray Internal Conversion (γIC)

Some radioactive nuclei which have long-lived (more than a nanosecond) metastable states decay by internal conversion of a γ-ray with the ejection of an electron from an inner shell. As the energy made available by the nuclear transformation is quite precise this process can be described as autophotoelectron emission. Following the creation of this core hole in the circum-nuclear electron cloud, an outer electron will relax with the consequent emission of either an X-ray or an Auger electron. Whilst no detailed study of the Auger electrons initiated by such an internal conversion process has yet been made both γIC autophotoemission and γIC X-ray emission have been investigated. So far studies have been restricted, in both cases, to compounds of technetium.

3. γIC: Autophotoemission

Gerasimov et al.[5] established that the direct decay of ^{99m}Tc by γ emission was a strongly forbidden process, but that relaxation to the ground state could proceed ($T_{1/2}$ 6 hours) by internal conversion with the emission of an electron from the M (or N) shell. As the energy for this process (2172.6 eV) is highly monochromatic the γIC electron should strongly resemble a photoelectron produced in X-ray photoelectron spectroscopy (XPS) in all respects, including that of exhibiting the phenomenon of 'chemical shift'. The effective local charge at any atomic site modifies slightly, but to a readily observable degree, the binding energies of all the electrons of that atom. Thus the kinetic energies of ejected photoelectrons vary with valence state and with ligand environment, following bombardment with monochromatic X-rays. This expectation was confirmed by both Gerasimov et al.,[6] and also Fiser and Dragoun et al.,[7] who found that the same shifts were found for γIC induced autophotoemission as had been established[8] for a series of technetium compounds by XPS.

Subsequently the list of compound types and technetium valencies studied was greatly expanded by Fiser, Dragoun and their coworkers [9], and more recently by Burke et al.,[10]. The nature and range of binding energy shifts for technetium is summarised in Table 1. It can be seen that a change of +1 in the valence state causes a binding energy change of roughly 1 eV. Rather more importantly it has also been established that for a variety of compounds with technetium in a specific state the range of binding energies does not usually exceed ±0.2 eV. It therefore follows that γIC autophotoemission as well as XPS can be used to establish the valence state of technetium.

Table 1

Binding Energies of some Technetium orbitals as a function of valency

Tc valence	M level binding energies (average values)			
	3p(1/2)	3p(3/2)	3d(3/2)	3d(5/2)
1			256.3	252.9
3			258.3	254.8
5	449.2	430.0	259.4	256.0
7	452.4	432.6	262.8	259.3

Whilst the papers by Czech, Russian and British groups have shown the validity of this method for the determination of the valency of technetium and have shown how it may be successfully applied it to many compounds of use in nuclear medicine, γIC autophotoemission spectroscopy does not appear to have been used in HAC. Burke et al.,[10] have reported that about 2×10^{13} technetium atoms (185 MBq) are required to give a satisfactory signal. Furthermore it must be remembered that what ever may happen in the bulk of a sample only those ^{99m}Tc atoms within about 2nm of the surface will be able to contribute to the γIC autophotoemission process. This is because the mean free path of electrons with a kinetic energy of about 2keV will not be greater than 2nm. The potential of this method for HAC is thus strictly limited and useful results may more easily be obtained by studying the X-rays that result from the relaxation of γIC produced core holes.

4. γIC: X-ray Emission

X-ray emission will follow the creation of a core hole by γIC. But as the chemical shifts described above are almost the same for all the core orbitals it follows that changes in the energies of X-rays that result from transitions between two such core hole states will be very small. However, sometimes changes can be found in the relative intersities of X-rays, which can be related to chemical state, valency and/or ligand environment. Thus for first row transition metal ions such changes have been recorded[11] for $[I(K_{\beta1,3}):I(K_{\alpha1,2})]$, the ratio of the intensity of the peak that results from the $3p \rightarrow 1s$ transition to that from the $2p \rightarrow 1s$ transition. In the case of technetium there are three isotopes which decay by γIC, ^{99m}Tc[12], ^{97m}Tc and ^{95m}Tc (4%). For all three isotopes the intensities of both the $K_{\beta1,3}$ ($3p \rightarrow 1s$) and $K_{\beta2}$ ($4P \rightarrow 1s$) peaks relative to the intensity of the $K_{\alpha1,2}$ peak have been measured[13]. $I(K_{\beta2}):I(K_{\alpha1,2})$ showed the greater variation with chemical state of the technetium, as might be expected since the 4p shell is nearer the valence band. For ^{95m}Tc this ratio was found to have values of 0.0267 for Tc_2S_7, 0.0270 for $K_2TcC\ell_6$ and 0.0280 for $KTcO_4$; a similar trend, but characterised by slightly higher intensity ratios was found for both ^{97m}Tc and ^{99m}Tc. This ratio is not a simple function of valence state but can be correlated with the ionicity of the bond to technetium. No other studies of X-ray emission following γIC appear to have been reported although such emission (or the production of an Auger electron) will necessarily follow any γIC event. Changes in the pattern of X-ray emission that may be correlated with chemical state, have, however, been investigated for some radioactive isotopes that decay by electron capture.

5. Electron Capture (EC): X-ray Emission

The core hole ionised state that follows γIC autophotoionisation can also be created directly by isotopes that decay through electron capture. In this case it is the 1s electron that is captured and so K X-ray lines will be emitted, in the first instance. The possibility of using the changes in X-ray emission that can be related to valence state etc., have been investigated for some first row transition metal isotopes that decay by EC, e.g. ^{51}Cr[11,14] and ^{55}Fe[14].

Changes in the relative intensities of the $K_{\alpha1,2}$ ($2p \rightarrow 1s$) and $K_{\beta1,3}$ ($3p \rightarrow 1s$) X-rays for compounds doped with ^{51}Cr were first reported by Tamasaki et al.[11], although, of course, such changes can equally well be observed in the X-ray emission spectra of unlabelled chromium compounds. The $I(K_\beta):I(K_\alpha)$ intensity ratio was found to increase slightly with an increase in the valency of chromium. This trend was confirmed by Lazzarini et al.[14], who also used ^{51}Cr, either in labelled compounds or in samples doped with this isotope. In all cases the $I(K_\beta):(K_\alpha)$ ratio is in the range 0.12-0.15 with the lower valencies favouring the lower valence states. However it was also found that each valence state covers a range of values, e.g. for Cr(III) 0.125 ± 0.004 - Cr(VI) 0.134 ± 0.004. Surprisingly both elemental chromium and iron have unexpectedly large values for this ratio, corresponding to a valency of about IV! Whilst it would seem that this method could be used in HAC to determine the valency of a recoil atom once it had come to rest in a lattice, there is very little 'clear water' between the uppermost bound for Cr(III) and the lowest value for Cr(VI).

Related work on X-ray peak shapes and peak shifts has shown that there are other quite large chemical effects to be found in X-ray spectra. The largest effects are incurred with X-rays generated by transitions that originated in the valence band, but unfortunately such peaks are usually the least intense. Paci-Mazzilli[15] and also Arber, Urch and West[16] investigated changes in the $K_{\alpha 1,2}$, $K_{\beta 1,3}$ and $K_{\beta 2,5}$ peak positions and peak profiles, as well as $I(K_\beta):I(K_\alpha)$, for correlations with the valence state of chromium. They also studied the intensity ratio, $I(K_{\beta'}):I(K_{\beta 1,3})$; $K_{\beta'}$ is found as a satellite to $K_{\beta 1,3}$ but with an energy of about 13-15 eV less than the main peak. Its intensity, relative to the that of the $K_{\beta 1,3}$ peak can be shown to be directly related to the number of unpaired 3d electrons [17], for the lighter first row transition elements. For such elements this ratio is thus inversely proportional to the valency. As a way of determining the valence state of chromium[16] or manganese [17] Urch and coworkers have established the measurement of $I(K_{\beta'})$: $I(K_{\beta 1,3})$ as the method of choice. (It has also been shown [18], however, that this particular intensity ratio is strangely indifferent to valency changes in iron, both Fe(II) and Fe(III) giving values that differ by only a few per cent.) The measurement of other intensity ratios, or the measurement of peak shifts was rejected as not giving such reliable results either because, although the peaks were intense the shift was small (e.g. $K_{\alpha 1,2}$) or because large shifts were only associated with very weak peaks (e.g. $K_{\beta 2,5}$). In the case of the $I(K_\beta):I(K_\alpha)$ ratio it was found that the ranges for a variety of compounds associated with each valence state overlapped somewhat[15].

In closely defined systems, however, (e.g. a recoil atom coming to rest in a crystal lattice of known chemical structure and composition) it is possible to use this ratio to establish the valence state of the emitting atom, as Collins et al.[19], have shown. Potassium chromate crystals were doped with ^{51}Cr in the trivalent state and then subjected to annealing at different temperatures. As annealing is a procedure which often follows neutron irradiation in an HAC experiment, it is important to establish what chemical reactions may befall the recoil atom during this process. Measurement of the $I(K_\beta):I(K_\alpha)$ intensity ratio showed that up to about 230°C the valence of the ^{51}Cr is unchanged but that at slightly higher temperatures, 250°-300°C, the ratio increased reaching the Cr(VI) value at about 300°C. This represents the first use of X-ray intensity measurements to investigate solid state processes related to HAC. Preliminary experiments have also been reported[20] in which the $I(K_\beta):I(K_\alpha)$ ratio was used to study directly the thermal annealing reactions in neutron irradiated potassium chromate and also in ^{51}Cr doped K_2CrO_4. Unfortunately the results were not so clear cut as in the Collins experiments. This indicates the shortcomings of this particular intensity ratio as a probe of valence state and suggests that future experiments should use other X-ray peaks to obtain unequivocal results (e.g. $K_{\beta'}$, $K_{\beta 1,3}$).

6. Conclusions

The few experiments that have been carried out so far on γIC and EC isotopes have shown that both γIC 'photo' electrons and X-rays can be used to determine directly the chemical state of the emitting atom. It is also clear that much more work needs to be done to establish the optimum conditions and also to determine those peaks that will yield the best results. Once this has been done then both Electron and X-ray Spectroscopies will be able to play a leading role in Solid State HAC.

References

1. Bondarevskij, S. I., Ermin, V. V., Murin, A. N.: Sov. Radiochem. (Eng. Trans. of Radiokhimiya), 28, 606 (1987)
2. Murin, A. N., Bondarevskij, S. I., Ermin, V. V.: Radiokhimiya, 22, 918 (1980) and 23, 933 (1981)
3. Murin, A. N., Bondarevskij, S. I., Ermin, V. V.: Radiokhimiya, 23, 424 (1981)
4. Johannsen, B., Mänze, R., Dostal, K. P., Nagel, M.: Radiochem. Radioanal. Lett., 47, 57 (1981)
5. Gerasimov, V. N., Zelenkov, A. G., Kulakov, V. M., Pchelin, V. A., Soldatov, A. A., Stepanchilov, V. A., Chistyakov, L. V.: Yad. Fiz., 34, 3 (1981) (Eng. Trans., Sov. J. Nucl. Phys., 34, 1 (1981))
6. Gerasimov, V. N., Zelenkov, A. G., Kulakov, V. M., Pchelin, V. A., Sokolovekaya, V. A., Soldatov A. A., Chistyakov, L. V.: Zh. Eksp. Teor. Fiz., 82, 362 (1982)
(Eng. Trans., Sov. Phys. JETP, 55, 205 (1982))
7. Dragoun, O., Fiser, M., Brabeck, V., Kovalik, A., Kuklik, A., Mikusik, P.: Phys. Lett., 99A, 187 (1983)
8. Gerasimov, V. N., Kryuchkov, S. V., Kuzina, A. F., Kulatov, V. M., Pirozhkov, S. V., Spitzyn, V. I.: Dokl. Akad. Nauk. SSR, 266, 148 (1982)
(Eng. Trans., Dokl. Phys. Chem., 266, 688 (1982))
9. Fiser, M., Brabeck, V., Dragoun, O., Kovalik, A., Frana, J., Rysavy, M.: Int. J. Appl. Radiat. Isot., 36, 219 (1985)
Fiser, M., Dragoun, O., Brabeck, V., Kovalik, A., Rysavy, M.: Technetium Chem. Nucl. Med., 2, 57 (1986)
Fiser, M., Brabeck, V., Dragoun, O., Kovalik, A., Rysavy, M., Dragounova, N.: Appl. Radiat. Isot., 39, 943 (1988)
10. Burke, J. F., Archer, C. M., Wei Chiu, K., Latham, I. A., Edgell, R. G.: Appl. Radiat. Isot., 42, 49 (1991)
11. Tamaki, Y., Omori, T., Shiokawa, T.: Radiochem. Radioanal Lett., 20, 255 (1975) and Jpn. J. Appl. Phys., suppl. 17, 425 (1978)
12. Yoshihara, K., Hibino, A., Yamoto, I., Kaji, H.: Radiochem. Radioanal. Lett., 48, 303 (1981)
Yamoto, I., Kaji, H., Yoshihara, K.: J. Chem. Phys., 84, 522 (1986)
13. Yoshihara, K.: Topics in Current Chem. (pub. Springer-Verlag, Berlin, Germany), 157, 1 (1990)
14. Lazzarini, E., Lazzarini-Fantola, A.-L., Mandelli-Bettoni, M.: Radiochim. Acta, 25, 81 (1978)
15. Paci-Mazzilli, B.: Ph. D. Thesis, London University, 1982

16. Arber, J. M., Urch, D. S., West, N.: Analyst, 113, 779 (1988)
17. Urch, D. S., Wood, P. R.: X-ray Spectrometry, 7, 9 (1978)
18. Urch, D. S.: Unpublished results
19. Collins, K. E., Collins, C. H., Heitz, C.: Radiochim. Acta, 28, 7 (1981)
20. Tamaki, Y., Omori, T., Shiokawa, T.: Bull. Miyagi Univ. Educ., 17, 1 (1982)

6.4 PAC Techniques to Study Chemical Effects of Nuclear Transformations

Kenji YOSHIHARA and Harumi KAJI
Department of Chemistry, Faculty of Science, Tohoku University, Sendai 980 Japan

1. INTRODUCTION

As shown in Fig. 1, when an excited nucleus in the energy level A undergoes deexcitation to the ground level C through the intermediate level B by emission of two γ-rays in cascade, an angular correlation is observed between the directions of the emitted γ-rays. The theory of electromagnetic radiation predicts that the intensity of the radiation emitted from a polarized spin level is nonisotropic. The angular correlation function $W(\theta)$ is expressed:

$$W(\theta) = 1 + A_2P_2(\cos\theta) + A_4P_4(\cos\theta) + \cdots \quad (1)$$

where θ is the angle between γ_1 and γ_2 , P_2 and P_4 are the Legendre polynomials, and A_2 and A_4 are the angular correlation coefficients. Fig.2 shows the relations between the emission angle and the intensity for various combinations of the spins of the nuclear levels and multipolarities of the γ-rays. For example, the ratio $W(\theta)/W(90)$ (normalized with respect to the intensity at $\theta = 90°$) in the case of a 2(D)2(Q)0, transition between spin states $2 \rightarrow 2 \rightarrow 0$ with emission of dipole and quadrapole γ's, increases from 90° to 180°. It decreases from 90° to 0°, symmetrically with respect to the 90° axis.

When the intermediate level B has a short but definite lifetime of the order of nanoseconds to hundreds of nanoseconds, external electric and magnetic fields can interact with the nucleus to perturb the angular correlation within the time inverval. This phenomenon is called perturbed angular correlation (PAC), and gives useful information about the local states surrounding the decaying nucleus. The perturbed angular correlation function is:

$$W(\theta,t) = \exp^{-t/\tau_N}[1 + G_2(t)A_2P_2(\cos\theta) + G_4(t)A_4P_4(\cos\theta) \quad + \cdots] \quad (2)$$

where t is the delay between the two successive emissions, τ_N is the lifetime of the intermediate level, and $G_2(t)$ and $G_4(t)$ are the differential attenuation factors.

Observation of PAC is performed using the apparatus of (i) time-integral (TIPAC) and of (ii) time-differential (TDPAC) types. The latter technique is more sophisticated and gives us more detailed informations[1)] when it is applied to hot atom chemistry than the former, though it is not so familiar to most chemists. A simplified technique called the 'sum peak method'[2)] has been developed in place of ordinary TIPAC, as will be described later.

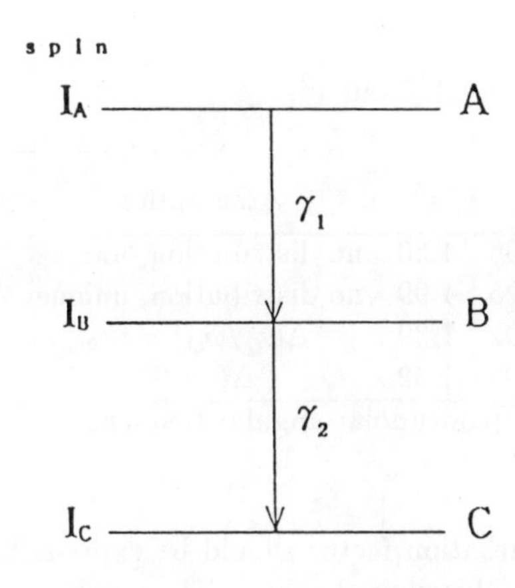

Fig. 1. Nuclear transition with cascade γ-ray emission.

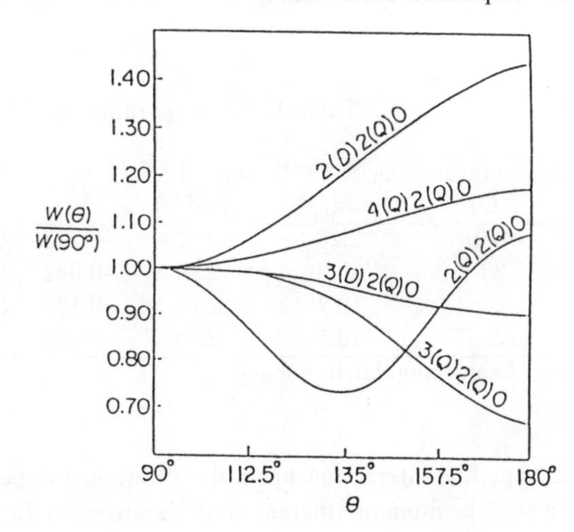

Fig. 2. Angular correlation patterns for various nuclear transitions in cascade.

2. PAC STUDIES APPLIED TO HOT ATOM CHEMISTRY

Only a limited number of papers of PAC applied to hot atom chemistry have appeared. Sato et al.[3] used a TIPAC technique to detect the hot atom effect in neutron irradiated pottasium perrhenate $KReO_4$, while Vargas and coworkers[4,5] observed the effects in hafnium complexes by the technique of TDPAC. The TDPAC study by Abbé and coworker[6] on hafnium-edta complex neutron-irradiated and labeled with ^{181}Hf also revealed the presence of a limited number of well-defined sites as shown by Vargas et al. In the present review, however, details of their papers are omitted because these were already described in the previous book.[7]

It is worthwhile reporting briefly that TDPAC spectra of ^{111}In incorporated in iron oxides have been studied by the RIKEN (Institute of Physical and Chemical Research) group.[8] The results of these experiments shed new light on the after-effects of nuclear transformations in solid matrices. The TDPAC time spectra of ^{111}In doped in α-Fe_2O_3 are shown in Fig.3 which involves the results of measurement at 420°C and 20°C. In their paper the perturbation factor $G_{22}(t)$ is defined by the following form:

$$G_{22}(t)_{uniq} = \sum_{N,m_1,m_2,n_1,n_2} (-1)^{2I+m_1+m_2} \begin{pmatrix} I & I & 2 \\ m_1' & -m_1 & N \end{pmatrix} \begin{pmatrix} I & I & 2 \\ m_1' & -m_2 & N \end{pmatrix}$$
$$\times \exp\left[\frac{-i}{\hbar}(E_{n_1} - E_{n_2})t\right] < n_1|m_2 >^* < n_1|m_1 >< n_2|m_2' >< n_2|m_1' >^* \quad (3)$$

where $\begin{pmatrix} I & I & 2 \\ m_i & -m_i & N \end{pmatrix}$ denotes the Wigner 3-j symbol, I the spin quantum number of the $5/2^+$ intermediate state of ^{111}Cd, $|m_i>$ the state assigned by its Z-component $m_i, |n_i>$ the eigenstate of the interaction Hamiltonian, and E_{n_i} its energy eigen value. If

Table 1. Fitted parameters $\omega_L, \omega_Q, C_1, C_2$ and χ^2

Temperature (°C)	$\omega_L \times 10^{-7}$ (rad/s)	$\omega_Q \times 10^{-7}$ (rad/s)	C_1	C_2	χ^2	Assumption
420	8.28	2.52	-0.113	-0.006	1.30	no distribution, unique
20	10.8	2.41	-0.042	-0.025	1.99	no distribution, unique
20	10.7	2.54	-0.134	-0.002	1.39	$\Delta\omega_Q/\omega_{Q_0} = 8\%$
20	10.7	2.54	-0.111	-0.009	1.32	$\Delta\theta = 6°$

ω_L: Lamor angular frequency ω_Q: quadrupolar angular frequency

the hyperfine interaction has a distribution, the perturbation factor should be expressed as a superposition of different $G_{22}(t)$'s corresponding to distributed values. The spectra in Fig.3 can be analyzed when the parameters in Table 1 are adopted.

By a semi-empirical formula $A_{22}G_{22}(t) = C_1 \times G_{22}(t) + C_2$, the functions shown in Fig.3 are calculated using the parameters in Table 1. The spectrum observed at 420°C can be analyzed well with a unique set of a hyperfine magnetic field and an electric field gradient. However, the one measured at 20°C is poorly reproduced if the unique set is used. This means that a distribution of hyperfine parameters should be used for the spectrum at 20°C due to the presence of after-effects by the nuclear decay $^{111}In \rightarrow ^{111}Cd$. Using a Gaussian type distribution for ω_Q or θ (the angle between the direction of H_{hf} and the Z-axis of electric field gradient EFG), the time spectrum at 20°C is fitted as shown in Fig.4. It is reproduced fairly well in the whole range of time observed. The difference between the spectrum at 420°C and the one at 20°C is probably due to an annealing effect at higher temperature.

The TDPAC spectra of ^{111}In doping Fe_3O_4 was measured between 85 and 300K by the same RIKEN group.[9)] Each spectrum revealed a well-define hyperfine frequency component above the Verwey temperature (T_V = 120K), but a remarkably broadened at lower temperature. This effect again reflected after-effects as in the case of α-Fe_2O_3 doped with ^{111}In.

The TDPAC spectra were compared with Mössbauer spectra in α-Fe_2O_3 doped with ^{111}In and ^{119}Sb, both EC nuclides.[10)] Apparently much more pronounced after-effects were revealed in TDPAC measurement of EC decay of ^{111}In, while such effects were hardly observed in Mössbauer spectra of ^{119}Sb. This could be attributed to the fact that the EC decay of ^{111}In gives rise to a distribution of e^2qQ, but the shift of each Mössbauer line $\varepsilon(= e^2qQ(3\cos^2\theta - 1)/8)$ is only slight.

From the measured spectra of TDPAC of ^{111}In doped in $Fe_{3-X}M_XO_4$ (ferrimagnetic oxides with a spinel structure), the super-transferred hyperfine magnetic fields, H_{STHF}, were obtained.[11)]

The RIKEN group[12)] elaborated their measurements and interpretation of TDPAC spectra of ^{111}In doped α-Fe_2O_3 in a wide temperature range from 85 to 987K. The spectra are classified into three categories.

(1) Above 700K, the observed hyperfine interaction is unique and free from after-effects.

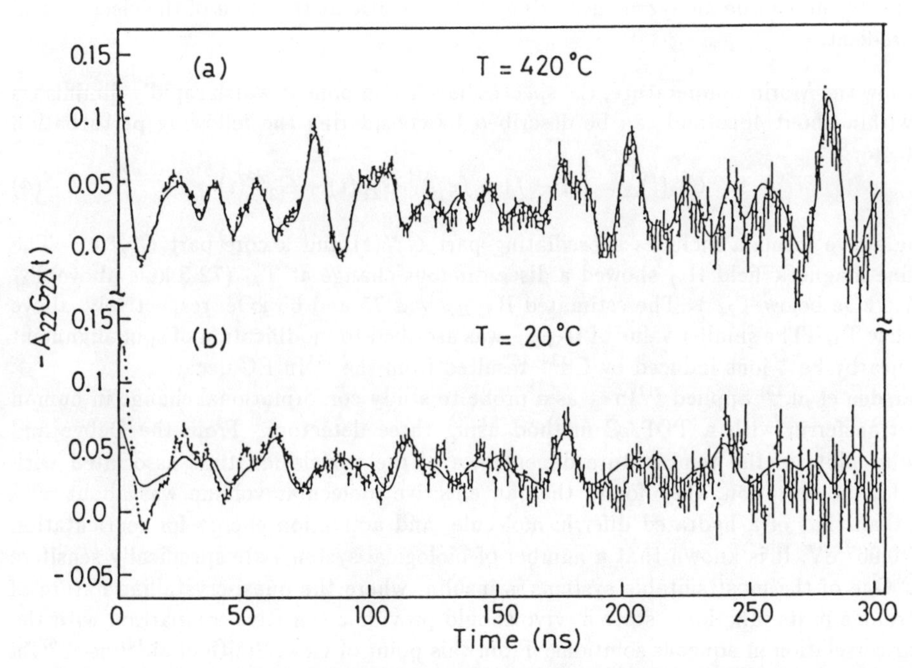

Fig. 3. TDPAC coefficients $A_{22} \cdot G_{22}(t)$ of the $^{111}Cd(\leftarrow {}^{111}In)$ $\gamma - \gamma$ correlation in $\alpha{-}Fe_2O_3$ (a): at 420°C, and (b): at 20°C. The solid curves represent the fittid values of $C_1 \times G_{22}(t)_{\mathrm{uniq}} + C_2$.

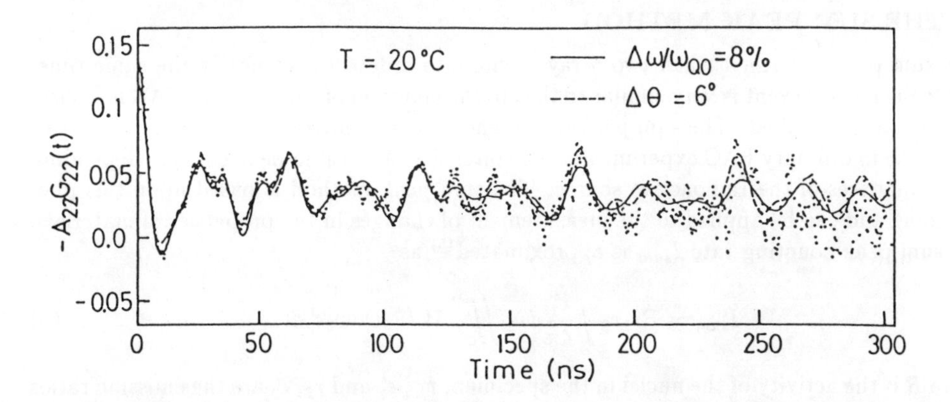

Fig. 4. TDPAC coefficient $A_{22} \cdot G_{22}(t)$ of the $^{111}Cd(\leftarrow {}^{111}In)$ $\gamma - \gamma$ correlation in $\alpha{-}Fe_2O_3$ at 20°C. The solid curve represents the fitted values assuming a distribution of $\Delta\omega_Q/\omega_{Q0} = 8\%$, and the dotted line represents the values assuming $\Delta\theta = 6°$.

(2) Above the Morin temperature (T_M = 260K), the spectra are modified by the after-effects and can be analyzed successfully with a static distribution of the electric field gradient.

(3) Below the Morin temperature, the spectra have a component which rapidly diminishes within about 40ns and can be described by considering the following perturbation factor:

$$G_{22}(t)_{\triangle} = \left[(1-f) + fe^{-\lambda t}\right] G_{22}^{\rm osc}(t) + G_{22}^{\rm core}(t) \tag{4}$$

The above formula includes a oscillating part $G_{22}^{\rm osc}(t)$ and a core part $G_{22}^{\rm core}(t)$. The hyperfine magnetic field H_{hf} showed a discontinuous change at T_M (72.5 kOe above T_M and 67.6 kOe below T_M). The estimated H_{STHF} was 75 and 65 kOe, respectively, above and below T_M. The smaller value of H_{STHF} was ascribed to modification of spin alignment of the nearby Fe^{3+} ions induced by Cd^{2+} resulted from the ^{111}In EC decay.

Marsden et al.[13] applied ^{111}In as a probe to study conformational change in human serum transferrin with a TDPAC method using three detectors. From the Debye and Arrhenius plots of the temperature dependence of the correlation time associated with molecular reorientation, they found that an effective molecular volume was about 50% larger than that of a hydrated diferric molecule, and activation energy for reorientation was $\sim$ 0.067 eV. It is known that a number of biological systems are specifically sensitive to Zn. One of the most suitable systems is insulin, where the quasi-crystalline nature of the hormone in its functional state in vivo should provide a sensitive comparison with the angular correlation in aqueous solutions. From this point of view, Smith et al.[14] used ^{62}Zn as a probe by the TDPAC method with three NaI(Tl) detectors in both aqueous solution at pH$\sim$ 6.0 and incorporated it into crystalline 2Zn-insulin. The solution data showed a fast relaxation time of (75$\pm$25)ns, while the three 2Zn-insulin data gave an electric quadrupole frequency of (77 $\pm$ 8)MHz using a static interaction assumed axial asymmetry.

3. THE SUM PEAK METHOD

A sum peak is formed when two γ-rays come into a detector at nearly the same time. This 'coincidence' event is very similar to that in the emission of γ-rays in the PAC measurement already described. The sum peak is influenced by the environment of the radioactive atom alike in ordinary PAC experiments. The intensity of the sum peak changes depending on the matrices of the radioactive source. The sum peak method is based upon this phenomenon, and can be applied to the measurement of changes in the properties of materials. The sum peak counting rate I_{sum} is approximated[15] as

$$I_{sum} = Rr_1r_2 \int \frac{\epsilon_1'}{4\pi} d\omega_1 \iint_0^{2\pi} W(\theta,t) d\omega_2 \epsilon_2' dt \tag{5}$$

where R is the activity of the nuclei in the specimen, r_1 , ϵ_1' and r_2, ϵ_2' are the emission ratios and the detection probabilities of the photons γ_1 and γ_2, respectively, $d\omega_1$ and $d\omega_2$ are the differential solid angle measured from the specimen over the detector, and $W(\theta,t)$ is the time differential PAC function. To estimate the attenuation factor of PAC, the following formula is available

$$I_{sum}/I_1 = r_2\epsilon_2[1 + A\bar{G}_2F_{geo}] \tag{6}$$

where I_1 is the counting rate of γ_1, $\bar{G}_2$ is the time integral attenuation factor, and F_{geo} is a geometrical factor. For the samples of ^{111}In-tropolone complex and $^{111}InCl_3$(in an aqueous solution with pH 6.5) the value of the attenuation factor calculated from Eq.(6) are 0.79 and 0.35 which agree with 0.74[17] and 0.33[16] obtained by the normal PAC technique using two detectors. Demille et al.[16] studied the attenuation factor of an aqueous solution of ^{111}In at various pH values, and they argued the following change of chemical species by application of the normal PAC technique.

$$[In(H_2O)_6]^{3+} \longrightarrow [In(H_2O)_5OH]^{2+} \cdots \rightarrow [In(OH)_6]^{3-} \tag{7}$$

Smith et al.[18,19] studied the formation of aqueous ^{111}In complexes as a function of pH, time after preparation of the ^{111}In and temperature using TIPAC and TDPAC methods. The mean radius of the molecular complex was found to increase with pH, until at pH 7.4 the attenuation of the angular correlation became dominated by the contribution from a damped static interaction having a correlation time in excess of 24 ns. Such a long correlation time is inconsistent with the free rotational diffusion of a complex no larger than $In_4(OH)_6^{+6}$ as suggested by x-ray and potentiometric measurements.

The sum peak method could be applied to the same system at much lower pH.[20] In spite of formation of $[InCl_6]^{3-}$ in higher concentration of hydrochloric acid, change of the integral attenuation factor was not observed. H. Singh et al.[21] studied $\bar{G}_2$ in different concentrations (0.05 mM $\sim$ 5.0 mM) of bovine sesum albumin (BSA) using ^{133}Ba as a probe, and they observed $\bar{G}_2$ is inversely proportional to the correlation time of 356-81 keV cascade radiations and to the concentration of BSA surrounding the probe. The results indicate a variation of the $\bar{G}_2$ factor with a change of the ligands. This variation is caused due to the rotational correlation time of the molecules bound to the probe nucleus ^{133}Ba.

Dhillon et al.[22] studied the nuclear quadrupole interaction frequencies at the nucleus ^{133}Cs which is resulted from electron-capture decay of ^{133}Ba in barium compouds, and they found the electric field gradient varies with different compounds of barium and the small value of the frequency for $Ba(NO_3)_2$ due to weak interactions between barium and nitrate ions.

References

1) Boyer, P., Baudry, B.: "Hot Atom Chemistry, Recent Trends and Applications in the Physical and Life Sciences and Technology" (T. Matsuura, ed.) Kodansha-Elsevier, Tokyo-Amsterdam 1984, p.315.

2) Yoshihara, K.: "Chemical Applications of Nuclear Probes" (K.Yoshihara, ed.) Springer-Verlag, Heidelberg 1990, p.1.

3) Sato, J., Yokoyama, Y., Yamazaki, T.: Radiochim. Acta, 5, 115 (1966).

4) Béraud, R., Berkes, I., Danière, J., Lévy, M., Marest, G., Rougny, R., Vargas, J.I.: Proc. Roy. Soc., A 311, 185(1969).

5) Vargas, J.I., Berthier, J., Hocquenghem, J.C., Ribot, J.J., Boyer, P.: Proc. Roy. Soc., A 311, 191 (1969).

6) Abbé, J.Ch., Marques-Netto, A.: J. Inorg. Nucl. Chem., 37, 2239 (1975).

7) Boyer, P., Baudry, A.: Hot Atom Chemistry, Recent Trends and Applications in the Physical and Life Sciences and Technology (ed. Matsuura, T.) Elsevier-Kodansha, Amsterdam-Tokyo 1984, p.315.

8) Asai, K., Ambe, F., Ambe, S., Sekizawa, H.: J. Phys. Soc. Jpn., 53, 4109 (1984).

9) Asai, K., Okada, T., Sekizawa, H.: J. Phys. Soc. Jpn., 54, 4325 (1985).

10) Ambe, F., Asai, K., Ambe, S., Okada, T., Sekizawa, H.: Hyp. Interactions, 29, 1197 (1986).

11) Asai, K., Okada, T., Sekizawa, H.: Hyp. Interactions, 34, 435 (1987).

12) Asai, K., Ambe, F., Ambe, S., Okada, T., Sekizawa, H.: Phys. Rev. B 41, 6124 (1990).

13) Marsden, P. J., Smith, F. A., Evans, R. W.: Appl. Radiat. Isot., 40, 715 (1989).

14) Smith, F.A., Martin, P.W., Shukri, A.: Hyp. Interactions, 23, 375(1985).

15) Kudo, T., Tsuchihashi, N., Yui, T., Mitsugashira, T., Kaji, H., Yoshihara, K.: Appl. Radiat. Isot., 39, 131 (1988).

16) Demille, G.R., Livesey, D.L., Mailer, K., Turner, S.P.: Chem. Phys. Lett., 44, 164 (1976).

17) Smith, F.A., Lurie, D.J., Brady, F., Danpure, H.J., Kensett, M.J., Osman, S., Silvester, D.J., Waters, S.L.: Int. J. Appl. Radiat. Isot., 35, 501 (1984).

18) Shukri, A., Smith, F. A., Marsden, P. J.: Appl. Radiat. Isot., 39, 9 (1988).

19) Smith, F. A., Marsden, P. J.: Appl. Radiat. Isot., 39, 15 (1988).

20) Kaji, H., Yoshihara, K.: J. Radioanal. Nucl. Chem., Lett., 119, 143 (1987).

21) Singh, H., Binarh, H.S., Ghumman, S.S., Sahota, H.S.: Appl. Radiat. Isot., 41, 797 (1990).

22) Dhillon, K.S., Singh, K.: J. Radioanal. Nucl. Chem., Lett., 145, 425 (1990).

Chapter 7

Correlation with Life-, Geo-, and Space Sciences

7.1 Practical Production of Simple Positron Emitting Compounds by Hot Atom Chemical Method

Ren IWATA and Alfred P. WOLF
CYRIC Tohoku University, Aoba-ku, Sendai, 980 Japan and Chemistry Department, Brookhaven National Laboratory, Long Island, NY11973, U.S.A.

1. Introduction

The positron emitters ^{11}C, ^{13}N, ^{15}O and ^{18}F are the radioisotopes of elements essential to life or found in many pharmacologically active compounds. As listed in Table 1 they are very short-lived, in comparison with conventional reactor-produced radioactive tracers which have long been used for biological and medical purposes, and as seen in the nuclear reactions for their production listed in Table 2 they can theoretically be produced in a carrier-free state. Due to these characteristics they have found their application in medical diagnosis as ideal radiotracers for humans. In addition, recent developments in cyclotrons and positron emission tomography (PET) have accelerated this advanced technology and is now wide spread. They can be produced easily with a small medical cyclotron and a variety of compounds are prepared as positron-emitting radiopharmaceuticals to provide functional images by PET and to study organ biochemistry in vivo. Fig.1 illustrates some typical PET radiopharmaceuticals.

The short-lived positron emitters are certainly indebted to extensive basic research in the past for their great success in medical applications. However, hot atom chemistry (HAC) of these radionuclides has not yet provided definitive versions of the reactions of energetic atoms. The needs of the medical field has turned the HAC approach from fundamental research using low dose

Table 1 Physical properties of short-lived positron emitters

Nuclide	Half-life (min)	Theoretical specific activity (Ci/mol)	Maximum β^+ energy (MeV)	Maximum β^+ range (mm in H_2O)
^{11}C	20.4	9.23×10^9	0.96	4.1
^{13}N	9.96	9.08×10^{10}	1.19	5.4
^{15}O	2.04	1.89×10^{10}	1.72	8.2
^{18}F	109.8	1.71×10^9	0.63	2.4

Table 2 Principal reaction for production of short-lived positron emitters

Nuclide	Reaction	Threshold energy (MeV)	Maximum cross section (mb)	Particle energy at max. cross sect.(MeV)
^{11}C	$^{10}B(d,n)^{11}C$	0	- 200	3.0 - 5.4
	$^{11}B(p,n)^{11}C$	3.0	- 360	8.7 - 10
	$^{14}N(p,\alpha)^{11}C$	3.1	- 140	- 6.9
^{13}N	$^{12}C(d,n)^{13}N$	0.3	- 150	- 4.7
	$^{13}C(p,n)^{13}N$	3.2	- 211	- 6.9
	$^{16}O(p,\alpha)^{13}N$	5.5	- 53	- 11.0
^{15}O	$^{14}N(d,n)^{15}O$	0	- 210	- 4.1
	$^{15}N(p,n)^{15}N$	3.7	- 140	- 6.4
^{18}F	$^{16}O(\alpha,pn)^{18}F$	23.2	- 130	- 35
	$^{16}O(^{3}He,p)^{18}F$	0	- 370	- 7
	$^{18}O(p,n)^{18}F$	2.5	- 700	- 5.1
	$^{20}N(d,\alpha)^{18}F$	0	- 320	- 7.0

irradiations to applications using high dose irradiations.

The application as radiotracers or radiopharmaceuticals requires mass production utilizing a high dose irradiation of a target, especially because of their short half-lives. Under intense radiation, in general, only simple molecules such as completely oxidized or reduced compounds are produced, dependent on ambient target conditions, whatever chemical form the HAC reaction initially produces, and it cannot be expected that more complex compound can be directly produced. For example, ^{11}C produced in highly purified nitrogen takes mainly the chemical form of $^{11}CO_2$, resulting from the reaction of ^{11}C with a trace amount of oxygen and subsequent radiation-induced oxidation,[1] while $^{11}CH_4$ is found as the dominant product in a mixed target of nitrogen and hydrogen, and intermediate products such as $H^{11}CN$ and $^{11}CH_3NH_2$ are usually suppressed.[2]

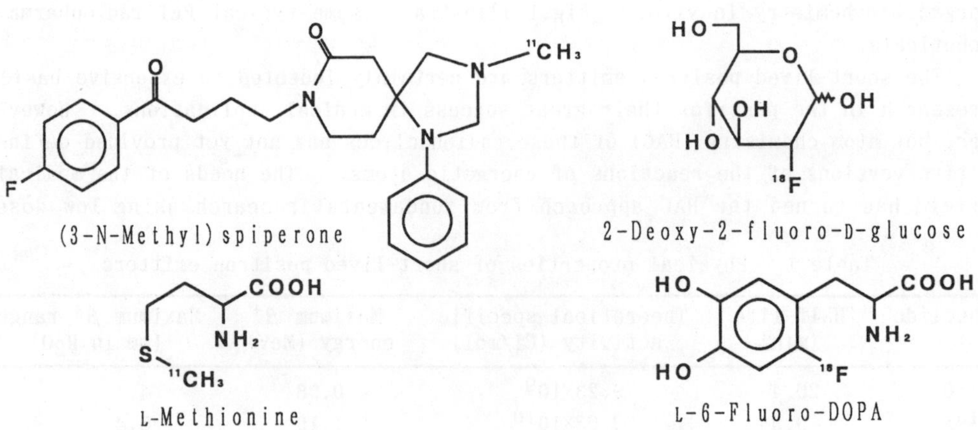

(3-N-Methyl)spiperone

2-Deoxy-2-fluoro-D-glucose

L-Methionine

L-6-Fluoro-DOPA

Fig.1 Examples of frequently used PET radiopharmaceuticals

Table 3 Synthetic preparation of ^{11}C-labeling precursors

Product	Starting compound	Procedure
^{11}CO	$^{11}CO_2$	Zn reduction
$^{11}CH_4$	$^{11}CO_2$	Ni reduction with H_2
$H^{11}CN/^{11}CN^-$	$^{11}CH_4$	Pt conversion with NH_3
$^{11}CH_3OH$	$^{11}CO_2$	Reduction with $LiAlH_4$
$^{11}CH_2O$	$^{11}CH_3OH$	Ag oxidation with O_2
$^{11}CH_3I$	$^{11}CH_3OH$	Iodination with HI
$^{11}CH_3NH_2$	$H^{11}CN$	PtO_2 hydrogenation with H_2
$^{11}COCl_2$	^{11}CO	Chlorination with $PtCl_4$
$^{11}CO(NH_2)_2$	$^{11}COCl_2$	Amination with NH_3
$CH_3{}^{11}COOH$	$^{11}CO_2$	Grignard reaction with CH_3MgBr
$^{11}CH_2N_2$	$^{11}CH_4$	Conversion with hydrazine via $^{11}CHCl_3$

However, several attempts to bring product spectra under control have been made. In this section the subject focus will be on the description of a practical approach to the production of simple but useful positron emitting molecules by the HAC method, that is, nonsynthetic methods. This subject has also previously been reviewed,[3,4] and further synthetic aspects of these radioisotopes can be found in recent reviews and texts.[5,6,7]

2. Carbon-11 Labeled Compounds

From the viewpoint of chemical synthesis, ^{11}C has as big a potential as ^{14}C, which has long been used for the preparation of many useful radiotracers for biological studies. However, besides its short half-life the limitation in chemical form available in practise from the target restricts this mul tivalent radionuclide from incorporation into many organic compounds and the possibilities of positional labeling by ^{11}C. Table 3 and 4 list major ^{11}C-labeling precursors which have so far been developed using synthetic and HAC

Table 4 Production of major ^{11}C-labeling precursors by HAC method

Precursor	Target system	Nuclear reaction	Ref.
$^{11}CO_2$	N_2(+<10 ppm O_2)	$^{14}N(p,\alpha)^{11}C$	1
$^{11}CH_4$	N_2 + 5% H_2	$^{14}N(p,\alpha)^{11}C$	2
$H^{11}CN$	N_2 + 1% H_2(flowing)	$^{14}N(p,\alpha)^{11}C$	17
$^{11}CH_3I$	N_2 + HI(flowing)	$^{14}N(p,\alpha)^{11}C$	21
$H^{11}CCH$	CaC_2	$^{12}C(p,pn)^{11}C$	23
	cyclopropane	$^{12}C(p,pn)^{11}C$	24
$^{11}COCl_2$	N_2 + CO + Cl_2	$^{14}N(p,\alpha)^{11}C$	27
$H_2{}^{11}CN_2$	NH_4X (X=Cl, Br, I)	$^{14}N(p,\alpha)^{11}C$	37
$^{11}CN_2{}^{2-}$	Ca_3N_2	$^{14}N(p,\alpha)^{11}C$	33
$(H_2N)_2{}^{11}CN_2$	liq.NH_3 + N_2O	$^{14}N(p,\alpha)^{11}C$	37

methods, respectively.

2.1 $^{11}CO_2$ and $^{11}CH_4$ Production

As can be clearly seen in Table 3, $^{11}CO_2$ is the most commonly used primary product from the target. Historically, this precursor was first produced using a solid target of B_2O_3.[8] It seems that lack of knowledge about radiation chemistry and supposed requirement of oxygen in the target led to the use of this material. A very complex target, as shown in Fig.2, was developed to obtain $^{11}CO_2$ in high efficiency for practical use. The target had to be kept molten facing a horizontal beam so as to liberate $^{11}CO_2$ formed in the solid matrix.[9] HAC and radiation chemistry of gaseous targets revealed that a trace amount of oxygen is enough to almost quantitatively oxidize ^{11}C produced for routine $^{11}CO_2$ production.

$$^{11}C^* + O_2 \longrightarrow {}^{11}CO + O \qquad (1)$$

$$^{11}CO + O_2 \xrightarrow{\text{radiolysis}} {}^{11}CO_2 + O \qquad (2)$$

On the other hand, addition of 5% H_2 to a nitrogen target brings a marked change in the product spectra. More than 90 % of ^{11}C is found in the form of $^{11}CH_4$ using an intense irradiation. Trace amounts of $H^{11}CN$ are also formed.[2,10] When low beam densities are used one finds considerable quantities of $H^{11}CN$.

Carbon-11 has a specific activity of 9.23X10^9 Ci/mol if carrier free. Thus, ^{11}C-labeled compounds are suitable as diagnostic probes to investigate human brain functions, such as receptors, where the carrier level injected is usually required to be less than a few nmols. However, during production and synthetic use of $^{11}CO_2$ inevitable isotopic dilution usually by a factor of over 2000 with ^{12}C occurs. This is mainly due to the abundance of CO_2 under natural circumstances. Consequently irradiation at high beam currents has often been carried out for large scale production in expectation that it may enable one to

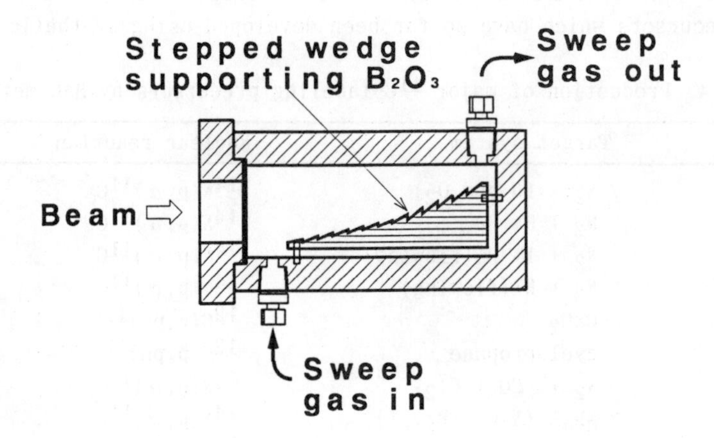

Fig.2 B_2O_3 target for $^{11}CO_2$ production[43]

increase the specific activity. In this connection, charged particle penetration in gas targets has been studied to optimize gas target performance in practical production, and the serious density reduction observed under intense irradiation has been attributed to thermal heating of the target gas in the beam path,[11-14] A profile of beam scattering in the target gas was shown photographically,[11,14] and a conical target chamber was thus designed to minimize the necessary target volume and eliminate the beam striking the walls of the chamber,[12] as can be seen in Fig.3. Radiation effects induced by intense irradiation, however, have been recently reported to cause the serious loss of newborn ^{11}C in pure N_2 on the target walls without additional O_2[15], and the coproduction of carrier CO_2 from the target walls has been observed.[16] Interaction of nucleogenic ^{11}C atoms with the walls under intense irradiation seems to be gaining more importance in practical production.

2.2 $H^{11}CN$ Production

As one of the useful precursor for ^{11}C-labeling, several methods for the direct production of ^{11}CN were investigated. As for solid targets, neither sodium cyanide[10] nor lithium amide[17] was promising for further use in synthetic labeling because the former gave a low specific activity and the latter a low yield. A gaseous target consisting of N_2 and 1% H_2 gave $H^{11}CN$.[10] However, this recoil reaction is easily overwhelmed by secondary radiation-induced reduction with increased proton irradiation, resulting in $^{11}CH_4$ production as described above. Although a rapid flow of the target with a lower content of hydrogen (approx. 1%) suppresses strong reductive effects of radiation and results in a 20% radiochemical yield of $H^{11}CN$,[17] it is currently produced by catalytic conversion of $^{11}CH_4$ or $^{11}CO_2$ in almost quantitative radiochemical yield.[2,18,19]

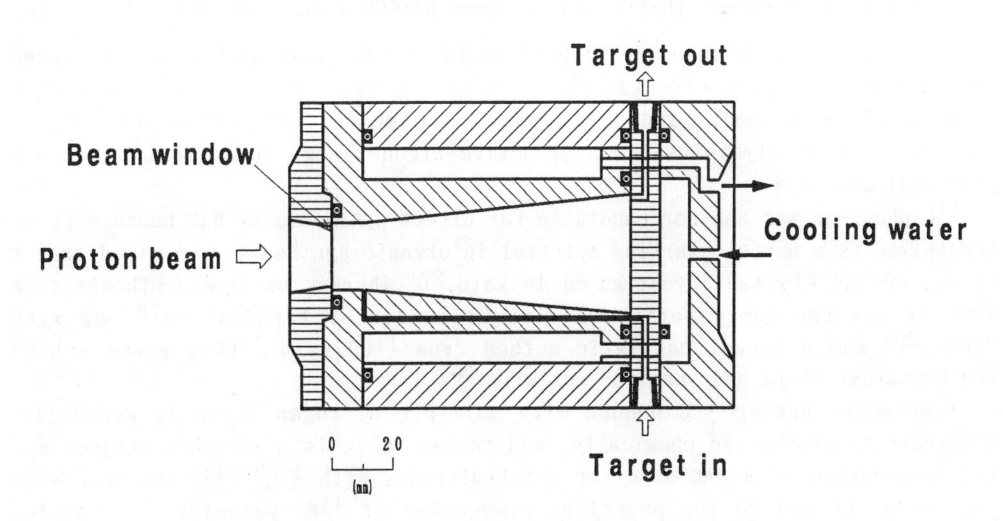

Fig.3 A sectinal side-view of a conical target gas chamber for $^{11}CO_2$ production (designed and used at CYRIC)

$$^{11}CO_2 + H_2 \xrightarrow[450^\circ C]{\text{Ni or Ru}} {}^{11}CH_4 \qquad (3)$$

$$^{11}CH_4 + NH_3 \xrightarrow[950^\circ C]{\text{Pt}} H^{11}CN \qquad (4)$$

2.3 $^{11}CH_3I$ Production

^{11}C-methyl iodide has wide versatility for preparation of pharmacologically active ^{11}C-radiopharmaceuticals by ^{11}C-methylation as follows[20]:

$$^{11}CO_2 \xrightarrow[2)H_2O]{1)LiAlH_4/THF} {}^{11}CH_3OH \xrightarrow{HI} {}^{11}CH_3I \qquad (5)$$

Direct production sometimes seems to be very attractive especially for replacing a synthetic method using multiple steps like the above procedure. In-target production of this valuable labeling precursor was examined using a flowing target of N_2-HI(10 %) to control strong radiation effects.[21] The yield of $^{11}CH_3I$, however, was observed to drop drastically from 25% to less than 10% with increasing radiation dose, while the yield of high boiling by-products was enhanced. This in-target production also suffered from rather low specific activity whereas high specific activity is usually required.

2.4 Miscellaneous ^{11}C-molecule Production

^{11}C-acetylene is a useful labeling precursor. A few attempts have been made to prepare this precursor,[22,23] but the particular character of the C≡C bond led the production of too low a specific activity $H^{11}CCH$ for conventional chemical synthesis. On the other hand, HAC seemed to be more promising because only excited ^{11}C atoms abstract carbon from a hydrocarbon to form $H^{11}CCH$ in nearly carrier-free state in a good yield.[24,25]

$$^{11}C^* + H\text{-}CH_2\text{-}R \longrightarrow [H\text{-}^{11}C\text{-}CH_2\text{-}R]^* \longrightarrow H^{11}CCH + HR \qquad (6)$$

Although cyclopropane gave the highest yield of 50%, this method also suffered from strong radiation effects and therefore it has not yet been practically applied to large scale production and at the moment conversion of $^{11}CH_4$ by carrier added pyrolysis using an inductive argon plasma seems to be the only practical method.[26]

^{11}C-phosgene was another candidate for direct synthesis by HAC because it is recognized as a useful starting material in organic synthesis. A mixed target of N_2, CO and Cl_2 was investigated in vain,[27] whereas on-line synthesis from ^{11}CO is now routinely performed with Cl_2 under UV irradiation[28] or with $PtCl_4$,[29] and a recent catalytic method from $^{11}CH_4$ via $^{11}CCl_4$ gives a high radiochemical yield and specific activity.[30]

A molecule having ^{11}C bonded with multiple nitrogen atoms is generally difficult to synthesize chemically, and therefore it is a suitable subject for HAC application. A HAC study on metal nitrides with ^{14}C[31,32] has been successfully applied to the practical production of ^{11}C-cyanamide. Calcium nitride gave the maximum yield of approximate 30 mCi of ^{11}C-cyanamide with a 7 μA-30 min proton irradiation, and this ^{11}C-precursor was demonstrated to be useful for synthesis of ^{11}C-guanidine derivatives.[33]

$$H_2{}^{11}CN_2 + H_2N\text{-}R \longrightarrow H(R)N\text{-}{}^{11}C(=NH)NH_2 \quad (7)$$

On the other hand, ammonia has been considered to be a good target to produce a ^{11}C-product having a ^{11}C-N bond. Gaseous and liquid NH_3 give only $^{11}CH_4$ and $^{11}CH_3NH_2$,[34,35] while the formation of ^{11}C-guanidine was observed when N_2O was added to liquid NH_3 as a scavenger of solvated electrons.[36] A 42% radiochemical yield for direct ^{11}C-guanidine production was obtained for a 5 μA-30 min irradiation by controlling radiation effects with the optimized addition of N_2O.[37] Besides these target systems, a solid ammonium halide system has been reported to give the same ^{11}C-precursors[38] although the yields have not been optimized for more intense radiation.

Microwave discharge is an alternative method for direct production of simple compounds. It was successfully applied to the preparation of $^{11}CS_2$ from $^{11}CO_2$ with H_2S and Ar.[39] After the reaction conditions were optimized as to microwave power and discharge time, $^{11}CO_2$ was converted to $^{11}CS_2$ in about 9 % yield.

Recoil labeling is more attractive when it can be applied to production of useful but complex ^{11}C-labeled compounds which usually require several synthetic steps. Thus, a number of optically active amino acids have been directly labeled with ^{11}C using the $^{12}C(\gamma,n)^{11}C$ reaction,[40] however, this method produces a complex mixture of low specific activity and yield.

3. Nitrogen-13 Labeled Compounds

The number of ^{13}N-labeled compounds available as ^{13}N-synthetic precursors or ^{13}N-radiopharmaceuticals is somewhat limited, probably due to its short half-life. The major products are only ^{13}NN and $^{13}NH_3$. Table 5 summarizes the approaches to non-synthetic production of simple ^{13}N-labeled compounds developed for PET use.

3.1 ^{13}NN Production

A preliminary HAC study on ^{13}N in the gas phase system showed for the first time that a CO_2 target containing a trace of N_2 gave a distribution of approxi-

Table 5 Production of simple ^{13}N-labeled compounds by HAC method

Product	Target system	Nuclear reaction	Ref.
^{13}NN	CO_2(trace N_2)	$^{12}C(d,n)^{13}N$	43
	Charcoal	$^{12}C(d,n)^{13}N$	43
	^{13}C-enriched charcoal	$^{13}C(p,n)^{13}N$	44
	$H_2O + NH_3$	$^{16}O(p,\alpha)^{13}N$	46
$^{13}NO_2$	O_2	$^{16}O(p,\alpha)^{13}N$	55
$^{13}NO_2^-/^{13}NO_3^-$	H_2O	$^{16}O(p,\alpha)^{13}N$	51
$^{13}NH_3$	CH_4(flowing)	$^{12}C(d,n)^{13}N$	48
	$^{13}C + H_2$	$^{13}C(p,n)^{13}N$	53
	$H_2O + H_2$	$^{16}O(p,\alpha)^{13}N$	52

mate 50% ^{13}NN and 50% ^{13}NNO[41] in low dose irradiations, and this was confirmed later by a more systematic study.[42]

$$^{13}N^* + N_2 \longrightarrow [^{13}NN]^* + N \quad (8)$$
$$[^{13}NN]^* + M \longrightarrow {}^{13}NN + M^* \quad (9)$$
$$[^{13}NN]^* + CO_2 \longrightarrow {}^{13}NNO + CO \quad (10)$$

This target system was successfully applied to the practical production of ^{13}NN because it produced ^{13}NN in almost 99% radiochemical yields due to instability of the other in-target product, ^{13}NNO, towards intense radiation.[43]

$$^{13}NNO \xrightarrow{\text{radiolysis}} {}^{13}NN + O \quad (11)$$

An alternative method for practical production of ^{13}NN is a use of a solid charcoal target with both the $^{12}C(d,n)^{13}N$[43] and $^{13}C(p,n)^{13}N$[44,45] nuclear reactions. A special treatment such as heating during irradiation or pre-activation is usually necessary for efficient extraction of ^{13}NN from a solid matrix target.

A convenient method for ^{13}NN production was developed using a water target and the $^{16}O(p,\alpha)^{13}N$ reaction.[46,47] The formation of 60% ^{13}NN and 40% $^{13}NH_3$ in an aqueous NH_3 target was observed, independent of irradiation dose. The reaction mechanism has not yet been fully elucidated, but it seems to involve radiolytic reactions. Since $^{13}NH_3$ is reused to produce ^{13}NN, the radiochemical yield of ^{13}NN increases with irradiation dose until the NH_3 is completely consumed.

3.2 $^{13}NH_3$ Production

^{13}N-ammonia is a frequently used PET radiopharmaceutical mainly for myocardial imaging, and it is also utilized for enzymatic synthesis of ^{13}N-labeled amino acids. Direct production of $^{13}NH_3$ was first attempted with deuteron irradiation of a flowing CH_4 target.[48] Only small quantities of the impurities $CH_3{}^{13}NH_2$ and $HC^{13}N$ were found in the product spectra. Irradiations in the range from 0.2 to 15 μA significantly affected the $^{13}NH_3$ production ratio.

On-line preparation of $^{13}NH_3$ from ^{13}NN with microwave discharge is a notable method for direct $^{13}NH_3$ production.[45] ^{13}NN was converted to $^{13}NH_3$ in approximate 65% radiochemical yield with a 10 min discharge.

Water is a good target to produce ^{13}N in high yield and high specific activity via the $^{16}O(p,\alpha)^{13}N$ reaction. Although the reaction mechanism of recoil ^{13}N atoms in water is not clearly understood in low dose systems, ^{13}N forms $^{13}NO_3^-$ mainly plus a small quantity of $^{13}NO_2^-$ and $^{13}NH_4{}^+$ in high dose systems.[49,50] Therefore, $^{13}NH_3$ is routinely prepared by reduction of $^{13}NO_3^-$ and $^{13}NO_2^-$ with DeVarda's alloy followed by distillation for purification.[51]

$$^{13}N^* + H_2O \xrightarrow{\text{radiolysis}} {}^{13}NO_2{}^- + {}^{13}NO_3{}^- \xrightarrow[\text{NaOH}]{\text{DeValda's alloy}} {}^{13}NH_3 \quad (12)$$

A new method for direct production of $^{13}NH_3$ has recently been developed.[52] More than 95% of the ^{13}N produced by proton irradiation of water under H_2

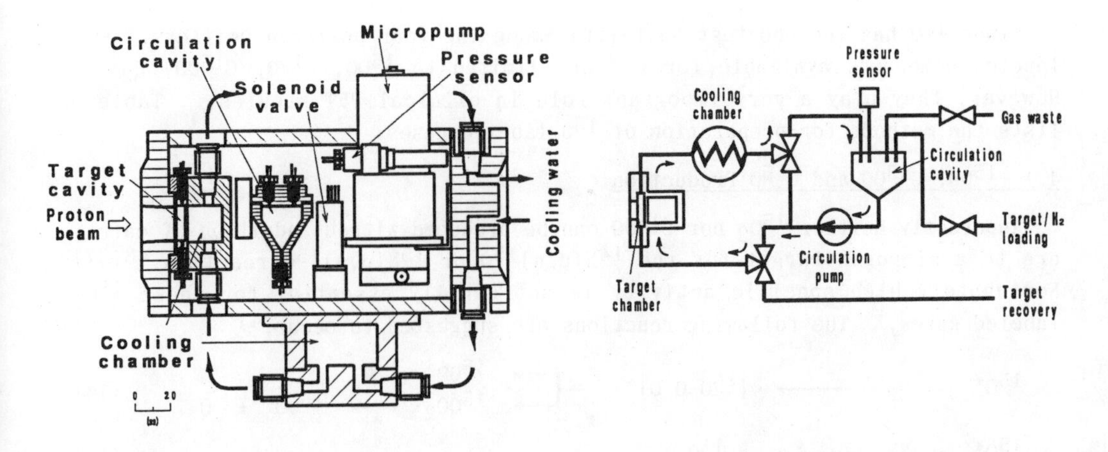

Fig.4 An assembled side-view and flow chart of a circulating water target system for direct production of $^{13}NH_3$ (a courtesy of NKK Corp., Japan)

pressure was found as $^{13}NH_3$ at a proton current of 20 μA. Radiation-induced reduction processes take over from radiation-induced oxidation processes, which are predominant without the addition of H_2 as scavenger of any oxidative radiolytic species. This excellent method is considered to be suitable for routine production of $^{13}NH_3$ as it is easily purified for clinical use by passing through an ion exchange column (see Fig.4). An alternative method for direct $^{13}NH_3$ production using a slurry of ^{13}C powder in water has also been developed.[53] Although radiation effects on the ^{13}N product spectra was observed, over 50% of the ^{13}N produced by the $^{13}C(p,n)^{13}N$ reaction was $^{13}NH_3$ with 15 μA-20 min irradiations, and the radioactive products were easily recovered from the target and purified with an ion exchange column as well.

3.3 Other ^{13}N-molecule Production

It is known that recoil ^{13}N atom is almost inert to O_2 in low dose irradiations because no ^{13}NO or $^{13}NO_2$ are detected in such irradiations.[42,51] However, when 10-15 atm high purity O_2 was irradiated by a 5-10 μA proton beam,[55] $^{13}NO_2$ was produced together with ^{13}NN and ^{13}NNO in a ratio of 3.5:8:1, respectively. The $^{13}NO_2$ was recovered from the target in a cryogenic trap.

^{13}N-nitrous oxide is expected to be a good PET tracer for measurement of cerebral blood flow. Although the formation of ^{13}NNO is observed in many target systems under low irradiation conditions, no practical method for direct production has been developed due to its radiation instability. This ^{13}N-labeled compound was prepared by pyrolysis of ^{13}N-ammonium nitrate.[56]

$$^{13}NO_3^- + NH_4^+ \longrightarrow NH_4{}^{13}NO_3 \xrightarrow[H_2SO_4]{} {}^{13}NNO \qquad (13)$$

4. Oxygen-15 Labeled Compounds

Since ^{15}O has the shortest half-life among the four positron emitters, ^{15}O-labeled compounds available for PET are limited to ^{15}OO, $C^{15}O$, $C^{15}OO$, $H_2{}^{15}O$. However, they play a very important role in clinical PET studies. Table 6 lists the methods for preparation of ^{15}O-labeled gases.

4.1 ^{15}OO, $C^{15}OO$ and $C^{15}O$ Production

Apparently neither $^{15}O_2$ nor $C^{15}OO$ can be produced without addition of carriers to a nitrogen target for the $^{14}N(d,n)^{15}O$ or $^{15}N(p,n)^{15}O$ reaction.[43,57] Fortunately high specific activity is not usually essential for these ^{15}O-labeled gases. The following reactions are suggested to occur.[4]

$$^{15}O^* + O_2 \longrightarrow [^{15}O\text{-}O\text{-}O]^* \rightarrow \begin{cases} ^{15}OO + O \\ ^{15}OO_2 \longrightarrow {}^{15}OO + O \end{cases} \quad (14)$$

$$^{15}O^* + N_2 \longrightarrow N_2{}^{15}O \quad (15)$$

$$^{15}O^* + CO_2 \longrightarrow [^{15}O\text{-}CO_2]^* \rightarrow \begin{cases} ^{15}OO + CO \\ C^{15}O + O_2 \end{cases} \quad (16)$$

$$C^{15}O + O^* \longrightarrow C^{15}OO \quad (17)$$

Thus, it seems probable that ^{15}OO is mainly a primary hot atom product and $C^{15}OO$ is a radiolytic product from $C^{15}O$ or ^{15}OO. Both products are recovered in high radiochemical yields with a carrier content of more than 1%. Tolerance of low specific activity for ^{15}-labeled gases allowed one to adapt an O_2 target for ^{15}OO production with the $^{16}O(p,pn)^{15}O$ reaction.[58]

In a recent study the ^{15}O exchange reaction between O_2 and CO_2 assisted by a metal oxide catalyst was successfully applied to efficient on-line interconversion of ^{15}OO and $C^{15}OO$.[59]

$$^{15}OO + CO_2 \xrightarrow[500^\circ C]{\text{Hopcalite II}} C^{15}OO + O_2 \quad (18)$$

$$C^{15}OO + O_2 \xrightarrow[650^\circ C]{\text{Hopcalite II}} {}^{15}OO + CO_2 \quad (19)$$

These reactions offer a very convenient method for the production of all the three ^{15}O-gases from one in-target product, ^{15}OO or $C^{15}OO$ because $C^{15}O$ is also

Table 6 Production of ^{15}O-labeled compounds by HAC method

Product	Target system	Nuclear reaction	Ref.
^{15}OO	N_2 + 1-4% O_2	$^{14}N(d,n)^{15}O$	43
	O_2	$^{16}O(p,pn)^{15}O$	58
	$^{15}N_2$ + 1% O_2	$^{15}N(p,n)^{15}O$	57
$C^{15}OO$	N_2 + 1-4% CO_2	$^{14}N(d,n)^{15}O$	43
$H_2{}^{15}O$	N_2 + 5% H_4(flowing)	$^{14}N(d,n)^{15}O$	61
	H_2O	$^{16}O(p,pn)^{15}O$	62

quantitatively produced from either ^{15}OO or $C^{15}OO$ with heated charcoal.

$$^{15}OO \text{ or } C^{15}OO \xrightarrow[900°C]{\text{charcoal}} C^{15}O + CO \quad (20)$$

For clinical use of this toxic gas, a lower content of carrier is quite desirable. A novel approach to direct production of $C^{15}O$ using a heated carbon filament in the target[60] can be expected to reduce the carrier content to less than 1%.

4.2 $H_2{}^{15}O$ Production

^{15}O-labeled water is routinely prepared by on-line catalytic conversion of ^{15}OO over palladium with H_2.[43] Direct production of $H_2{}^{15}O$ with a mixed target of N_2 and H_2[61] also seems practical. However, it may suffer from a considerable loss in a transferring tube from the targetry to the PET site due to its high specific activity. On the other hand, another direct production method has recently been reported.[62] Nearly one Ci of $H_2{}^{15}O$ was produced by irradiating natural water with a 26 MeV proton beam.

4.3 Other ^{15}O-molecule Production

No practical method is available by direct production of ^{15}O-labeled compounds other than the above four products. As for chemical synthesis, $N_2{}^{15}O$ was prepared in 15-20% radiochemical yields from ^{15}OO by catalytic oxidation of anhydorus NH_3.[63]

$$^{15}OO + NH_3 \xrightarrow[310°C]{\text{Pt}} N_2{}^{15}O + H_2O \quad (21)$$

The synthesis of ^{15}O-labeled butanol[64] and DOPA[65] from ^{15}OO is also notable.

5. Fluorine-18 Labeled Compounds

Fluorine-18, the only usable radionuclide of fluorine, has rather unique characteristics among the four positron emitting radionuclides. Although fluorine is not a naturally occurring constituent of the living body, many pharmacologically active compounds contain this element. In addition, ^{18}F has numerous advantages derived from the physical properties over the other three positron emitters in PET use. The short range of β^+ emitted by ^{18}F gives high resolution in PET imaging. The relatively long half-life (109.8 min) favors frequent use in multistep syntheses and consequent PET studies of moderately slow physiological processes. Thus, many methods have been developed for production of ^{18}F-labeled synthetic precursors and preparation of ^{18}F-radiopharmaceuticals. Table 7 lists the production methods of ^{18}F-labeling precursors. They have also been reviewed in the literature.[7,66-68]

5.1 ^{18}FF Production

Molecular ^{18}FF was developed as a strong electrophilic ^{18}F-fluorinating agent[69-73]. This in-target product has been utilized for labeling many

Table 7 Production of ^{18}F-labeled synthetic precursors by HAC method

Product	Target system	Nuclear reaction	Ref.
^{18}FF	Ne + 0.1% F_2	$^{20}Ne(d,\alpha)^{18}F$	70
	$^{18}O_2$ / Ne + F_2	$^{18}O(p,n)^{18}F$	73
$H^{18}F$	Ne + 5% H_2	$^{20}Ne(d,\alpha)^{18}F$	79
$^{18}F^-$	Water	$^{16}O(\alpha,pn)^{18}F$	82
		$^{16}O(^{3}He,p)^{18}F$	81
	$H_2{}^{18}O$ (enriched)	$^{18}O(p,n)^{18}F$	86

useful compounds with ^{18}F by addition reactions across double bonds such as 2-deoxy-2-^{18}F-D-glucose,[74] which is the first successful application and one of the most established and frequently used positron emitting radiopharmaceuticals.

The direct production of ^{18}FF by the fluorine exchange reaction was first investigated by deuteron irradiation of the mixed gas target of Ne and F_2[69] and then fully optimized for F_2 amount and target pressure.[70] Due to the high reactivity of ^{18}FF the Ni target walls were passivated with F_2 in advance. A 0.1% content of carrier F_2 at a target pressure of 24 atm was found to be high enough to prevent lose of ^{18}F, moderated by Ne, by diffusing to the walls. In the practical production at a deuteron current of 15 μA, nearly 95% of the theoretically produced ^{18}F was recovered from the target as ^{18}FF. Fig.5 shows a routine ^{18}FF production system for preparation of various ^{18}F-radiopharmaceuticals.

An alternative method for ^{18}FF production using the ^{18}O-enriched oxygen target with the $^{18}O(p,n)^{18}F$ reaction was developed for a small proton .LH 8 cyclotron.[73] The method consists of two sequential proton irradiations: (a) for production of ^{18}F via the $^{18}O(p,n)^{18}F$ reaction on $^{18}O_2$; and (b) for recovery of ^{18}F as ^{18}FF by the radiation-induced exchange reaction between the ^{18}F

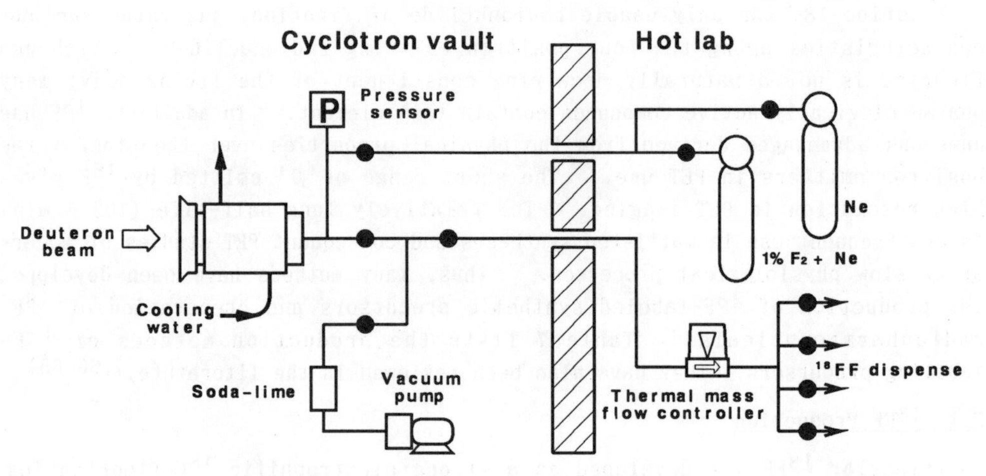

Fig.5 A schematic diagram of a routine ^{18}FF production system

deposited on the walls of a passivated Ni target and the F_2 contained in the Ne. A 40-60% recovery yield was attained.

In general, it is difficult to moderate and control the reactivity of ^{18}FF. Electrophilic fluorination with acetyl hypofluorite was developed instead.[75,76] ^{18}F-labeled acetyl hypofluorite is easily obtained by on-line conversion of ^{18}FF as below:

$$^{18}FF + CH_3COOK \longrightarrow CH_3COO^{18}F + KF \quad (22)$$

Consequently, ^{18}FF has been replaced by ^{18}F-acetyl hypofluorite in many preparations.

5.2 $H^{18}F$ and $^{18}F^-$ Production

Nucleophilic fluorination using ^{18}F-fluoride with a phase transfer catalyst such as crown ether, alkylammonium salt and aminopolyether is a rather recent technique. Especially after a remarkable success in the synthesis of 2-deoxy-2-^{18}F-D-glucose using $^{18}F^-$,[77] a large number of applications have been reported. Currently ^{18}F-fluoride is recognized as a readily available and valuable precursor for ^{18}F-labeled radiopharmaceuticals mainly because this ^{18}F-labeling precursor also gives high specific activity (no-carrier-added) positron emitting radiopharmaceuticals.

Anhydrous $H^{18}F$ was obtained by deuteron irradiation of a Ne gas target followed by washing the glass target walls with a suitable organic solvent.[78] The production and recovery method was greatly improved by addition of 5% H_2 to the Ne target,[69] or adoption of a flowing target of Ne and 5% H_2 in a heated target system.[72,79] However, due to the difficulties with target handling and poor reproducibility in the recovery yield, it seems that this method has been completely replaced by an alternative method utilizing aqueous targets.

Once aqueous $^{18}F^-$ has won its way in no-carrier-added synthesis of ^{18}F-labeled radiopharmaceuticals, water is the best target, which can provide a nearly quantitative recovery of $^{18}F^-$ from a target vessel. ^{18}F-fluoride is produced by α or ^3He irradiation of natural water via the $^{16}O(\alpha,pn)^{18}F$ or $^{16}O(^3He,p)^{18}F$ reaction.[80-84] However, these two particle irradiations require a multi-particle accelerator, and especially the latter requires a recovery system of this expensive gas. An alternative choice is the use of the $^{18}O(p,n)^{18}F$ reaction, which is well suited to a small proton cyclotron. Although an $^{18}O_2$ gas target was again investigated,[85] it is clear that a water target is more convenient to handle than a gas target. Therefore much effort have been focused on the practical aspects of efficient production with the smallest volume of expensive ^{18}O-enriched water.[86-93] Proton irradiation of a less than 5 mm thick water target with a current of more than 15 μA may form many bubbles due to boiling water, resulting in a sudden decrease in the production yield of $^{18}F^-$. An interesting approach to these practical problems is to use photographic methods for probing the processes occurring during irradiation[94], and this method verified the formation of voids in the beam path and clearly showed that overpressure on the target.can significantly reduce the boiling of the water. While reproducibility remains in question among different target systems, $^{18}F^-$ can be produced in high yield using less than 1 ml ^{18}O-water with a current of more than 15 μA. For recovery of target water and preparation of reactive $^{18}F^-$ for subsequent synthesis convenient and efficient methods of separation of $^{18}F^-$ from ^{18}O-water have also been developed.[95-98]

5.3 Miscellaneous ^{18}F-labeled Molecule Production

Before the above two ^{18}F-molecules had been established as the powerful and irreplaceable labeling precursors, direct production of several ^{18}F-labeled compounds were sought using the neon gas target systems. They are $NO^{18}F$,[69,99] $C^{18}FFO$,[69] $Cl^{18}F$[69] and $Xe^{18}FF$.[100] However, no notable progress in this field has been made in the past decade.

Apart from its usefulness in medical diagnosis, ^{18}F-chlorofluoromethane is a good target for recoil labeling from this viewpoint.[101,102] The ^{18}F-labeled compounds of $CCl_3{}^{18}F$, $CCl_2{}^{18}FF$, $CCl^{18}FF_2$ and $C^{18}FF_3$ were produced in high yields by ^{18}F-for-Cl substitutions for respective starting substrate of CCl_nF_{4-n} (n=1-4) added to a neon gas target. No significant radiation effects were observed on these product spectra.

A ^{18}F-for-F substitution was observed for perfluorodecalin coated on the walls of the irradiation vessel to reduce radiation effects.[47] Recoil ^{18}F atoms produced in Ne via the $^{20}Ne(d,\alpha)^{18}F$ reaction drifted towards the walls and then the substitution took place. Although it was not clearly shown how thermalized ^{18}F atoms were involved in the substitution reaction and which position was labeled with ^{18}F, a nearly 15-20% radiochemical yield was obtained for the 10 μA-60 min irradiations.

It should be noted that the exchange reactions have been alternatively applied to practical on-line preparation of versatile ^{18}F-labeled precursors. Diethylamino sulfur trifluoride (DAST),[103,104] XeF_2,[105] and CsF[106] were labeled with ^{18}F on-line via the ^{18}F-for-OH exchange from $H^{18}F$. On-line conversion of ^{18}FF to ^{18}F-acetyl hypofluorite with potassium acetate[76] and to ^{18}F-perchloryl fluoride with potassium perchlorate[107] were also successfully carried out.

6. Conclusion

PET chemistry has been expanding, for more than two decades, on the foundation of basic HAC studies. It seems likely that the production methods for simple positron emitting compounds, especially labeling precursors, have been fully established and that there will be no more room for HAC to contribute to PET chemistry, or at least to the increasing demands for the preparation of new positron emitting radiopharmaceuticals. However, target chemistry for PET is presently entering a new age after a low energy but high current cyclotron has begun to be introduced, and it will soon be established as a new field dealing with practical aspects of production under intense irradiation involving interactions of radioactive atoms with the walls of an irradiation vessel. In addition, it is certain that no target system has been fully understood or systematically investigated under intense particle irradiation. Consequently, it is expected that HAC can still play a fundamental but very important role in this field by providing clues for understanding reaction processes in the target.

References

1. Ache, H.J., Wolf, A.P.: J. Phys. Chem., 72, 1988 (1968).
2. Christman, D.R., Finn, R.D., Karlstrom K.I., Wolf, A.P.: Int. J. Appl. Radiat. Isot., 26, 435 (1975).
3. Brinkman, G.A.: Int. J. Appl. Radiat. Isot., 33, 525 (1982).
4. Ferrieri, R.A., Wolf, A.P.: Radiochim. Acta, 34, 69 (1983).
5. Fowler, J.S., Wolf, A.P.: "The synthesis of carbon-11, fluorine-18, and nitrogen-13 labeled radiotracers for biomedical applications" Nucl. Sci. Ser. NAS-NS-3201 (1982).
6. Sajjad, M., Lambrecht, R.M.: "Radiochemistry of carbon, nitrogen and oxygen" Nucl. Sci. Ser. NAS-NS-3019 (1988).
7. Kilbourn, M.R.: "Fluorine-18 labelling of radiopharmaceuticals" Nucl. Sci. Ser. NAS-NS-3203 (1990).
8. Long, F.A.: J. Am. Chem., 61, 570 (1939).
9. Welch, M.J., Ter Pogossian, M.M.: Radiat. Res., 36, 580 (1968).
10. Finn, R.D., Christman, D.R., Ache, H.J., Wolf, A.P.: Int. J. Appl. Radiat. Isot., 22, 735 (1971).
11. Heselius, S.-J., Lindblom, P., Solin, O.: Int. J. Appl. Radiat. Isot., 33, 653 (1982).
12. Vandewalle, T., Vandecasteele, C.: Int. J. Appl. Radiat. Isot., 34, 1459 (1983).
13. Wieland, B.W., Schlyer, D.J., Wolf, A.P.: Int. J. Appl. Radiat. Isot., 35, 387 (1984).
14. Heselius, S.-J., Malmborg, P., Solin, O., Langstroem, B.: Appl. Radiat. Isot., 38, 49 (1987).
15. Tewson, T.J., Banks, W., Franceschini, M., Hoffpauir, J: Appl. Radiat. Isot., 40, 765 (1989).
16. Ferrieri, R.A., Alexoff, D.L., Wolf, A.P., Schlyer D.J., Fowler, J.S.: 8th Int. Symp. Radiopharm. Chem. Abst. pp.186, Princeton, June (1990).
17. Lamb, J.F., James, R.W., Winchell, H.S.: Int. J. Appl. Radiat. Isot., 22, 475 (1971).
18. Christman, D.R., Finn, R.D., Karlstrom, K.I., Wolf, A.P.: J. Nucl. Med., 14, 864 (1973).
19. Iwata, R., Ido, T., Takahashi, T., Nakanishi, H, Iida, S.: Int. J. Appl. Radiat. Isot., 38, 97 (1987).
20. Marazano, C., Maziere, M., Berger, G., Comar, D.: Int. J. Appl. Radiat. Isot., 28, 49 (1977).
21. Wagner, R., Stoecklin, G., Schaack, W.: J. Label. Compd. Radiopharm., 18, 1557 (1981).
22. Cramer, R,D., Kistiakowsky, G.B.: J. Biol. Chem., 137, 549 (1941).
23. Myers, W.G.: J. Nucl. Med., 13, 699 (1972).
24. Wolf, A.P., Christman, D.R., Fowler, J.S., Lambrecht, R.M.: Radiopharmaceuticals and Labeled Compounds. IAEA, Vienna, Vol.1, pp.345 (1973).
25. Machulla, H.J., Laufer, P., Stoecklin, G.: J. Radioanal. Chem., 32, 381 (1976).
26. Crouzel, C., Sejourne, C., Comar, D.: Int. J. Appl. Radiat. Isot., 30, 566 (1979).
27. Brinkman, G.A., Hass-Lisewska, I., Veenboer, J.T., Lindner, L.: Int. J. Appl. Radiat. Isot., 29, 701 (1978).
28. Roeda, D., Crouzel, C., Van Zanten, B.: Radiochem. Radioanal. Lett., 33,

175 (1978).
29. Crouzel C., Roeda, D., Berridge, M., Knipper, R., Comar, D.: Int. J. Appl. Radiat. Isot., 34, 1558 (1983).
30. Landais, P., Crouzel, C.: Appl. Radiat. Isot., 38, 297 (1987).
31. Kuhry, J., Adloff, J.: Bull. Soc. Chim. Fr., 9, 3414 (1967).
32. Finn, R.D., Ache, H.J., Wolf, A.P.: J. Phys. Chem., 73, 3928 (1969).
33. Iwata, R., Ido, T.: Int. J. Appl. Radiat. Isot., 34, 973 (1983).
34. Yang, J.Y., Wolf, A.P.: J. Am. Chem. Soc., 82, 4488 (1960).
35. Cacace, F., Wolf, A.P.: J. Am. Chem. Soc., 87, 5301 (1965).
36. Iwata, R., Ido, T., Tominaga, T.: Radiochem. Acta, 33, 195 (1983).
37. Iwata, R., Ido, T., Tominaga, T.: Int. J. Appl. Radiat. Isot., 32, 303 (1981).
38. Vogt, M.: "Festkoerperreaktionen von energetischen Kohlenstoffatomen aus dem KernprozeB $^{14}N(p,\alpha)^{11}C$", Thesis, Univ. Koeln (1983).
39. Niisawa, K., Ogawa, K., Saito, J., Taki, K., Karasawa, T., Nozaki, T.: Int. J. Appl. Radiat. Isot., 35, 29 (1984).
40. Gundlach, G., Sattler, E.L., Wagenbach, U.: Appl. Radiat. Isot., 40, 637 (1989).
41. Welch, M.J.: Chem. Commun., 1968, 1354.
42. Stewart, G.W., Dymerski, P.P., Hower, C.O.: J. Chem. Phys., 61, 483 (1974).
43. Clark, J., Buckingham, P.: "Short-lived radioactive gases for clinical use", Butterworths, London (1975).
44. Austin, S.M., Galonsky, A., Bortins, J.: Nucl. Instrum. Methods, 126, 373 (1975).
45. Ferrieri, R.A., Schlyer, D.J., Wieland, B.W., Wolf, A.P.: Int. J. Appl. Radiat. Isot., 34, 897 (1983).
46. Suzuki, K., Iwata, R.: Radiochem. Radioanal. Lett., 28, 263 (1977).
47. Ido, T., Iwata, R., Takahashi, T.: Radiochim. Acta, 43, 71 (1988).
48. Tilbury, R.S., Dahl, J.R., Monahan, W.G., Laughlin, J.S.: Radiochem. Radioanal. Lett., 8, 317 (1971).
49. Tilbury, R.S., Dahl, J.R., Marano, S.J.: J. Label. Compd. Radiopharm., 13, 208 (1977).
50. Parks, N.J., Krohn, K.A.: Int. J. Appl. Radiat. Isot., 29, 754 (1978).
51. Vaalburg, W., Kamphuis, J.A.A., Beerling-van der Molen, H.D., Reiffers, S., Rijskamp, A., Woldring, M.G.: Int. J. Appl. Radiat. Isot., 26, 316 (1975).
52. Mulholland, G.K., Sutorik, A., Jewett, D.M., Mangner, T.J., Kilbourn, M.R.: J. Nucl. Med., 30, 926 (1989).
53. Bida, G., Wieland, B.W., Ruth, T.J., Schmidt, D.G., Hendry, G.O., Keen, R.E.: J Label. Compd. Radiopharm., 23, 1217 (1986).
54. Malcolme-Lawes, D.J.: Nature, 247, 540 (1974).
55. Parks, N.J., Peek, N.F., Goldstein, E.: Int. J. Appl. Radiat. Isot., 26, 683 (1975).
56. Nickles, R.J., Gatley, S.J., Hichwa, R.D., Simpkin, D.J., Martin, J.L.: Int. J. Appl. Radiat. Isot., 29, 225 (1978).
57. Wieland, B.W., Schmidt, D.G., Bida, G., Ruth, T.J., Hendry, G.O.: J. Label. Compd. Radiopharm., 23, 1214 (1986).
58. Ruth, T.J.: Int. J. Appl. Radiat. Isot., 36, 107 (1985).
59. Iwata, R., Yamazaki, S., Ido, T.: Appl. Radiat. Isot., 39, 1207 (1989).
60. Votaw, J.R., Satter, M.R., Sunderland, J.J., Martin, C.C., Nickles, R.J.: J. Label. Compd. Radiopharm., 23, 1211 (1986).
61. Ruiz, H.V., Wolf, A.P.: J. Label. Compd. Radiopharm., 15, 185 (1978).
62. Mulholland, G.K., Kilbourn, M.R., Moskwa, J.J.: Appl. Radiat. Isot., 41, 1193 (1990).
63. Diksic, M., Yamamoto, Y.L., Feindel, W.: J. Nucl. Med., 24, 603 (1983).
64. Kabalka, G.W., Lambrecht, R.M., Sajjad, M., Fowler, J.S., Kunda, S.A.,

McCollum, G.W., MacGregor, R.: Int. J. Appl. Radiat. Isot., 36, 853 (1985).
65. Maddaluno, J.F., Faull, K.F.: Appl. Radiat. Isot., 41, 873 (1990).
66. Nickles, R.J., Gatley, S.J., Votaw, J.R., Kornguth, M.L.: Appl. Radiat. Isot., 37, 649 (1986).
67. Berridge, M.S., Tewson, T.J.: Appl. Radiat. Isot., 37, 685 (1986).
68. Tewson, T.J.: Nucl. Med. Biol., 16, 533 (1989).
69. Lambrecht, R.M., Neirinckx, R., Wolf, A.: Int. J. Appl. Radiat. Isot., 29, 175 (1978).
70. Casella, V., Ido, T., Wolf, A.P., Fowler, J.S., MacGregor, R.R., Ruth, T.J.: J. Nucl. Med., 21, 750 (1980).
71. Bida, G.T., Ehrenkaufer, R.L., Wolf, A.P., Fowler, J.S., MacGregor, R.R., Ruth,T.T.: J. Nucl. Med., 21, 758 (1980).
72. Blessing, G., Coenen, H.H., Franken, K., Qaim, S.M.: Appl. Radiat. Isot., 37, 1135 (1986).
73. Nickles, R.J., Daube, M.E., Ruth, T.J.: Int. J. Appl. Radiat. Isot., 35, 117 (1984).
74. Ido, T., Wan, C-N., Casella, V., Fowler, J.S., Wolf, A.P.: J. Label. Compd. Radiopharm., 14, 175 (1978).
75. Rozen, S., Brand, M.: Synthesis, 665 (1981).
76. Fowler, J.S., Shiue, C-Y., Wolf, A.P., Salvador, P.A., MacGregor, R.R.: J. Label, Comp. Radiopharm., 19, 1634 (182).
77. Hammacher, K., Coenen, H.H., Stoecklin, G.: J. Nucl. Med., 27, 235 (1987).
78. Nozaki, T. Tanaka, Y.: Int. J. Appl. Radiat. Isot., 18, 111 (1967).
79. Ehrenkaufer, R.E., MacGregor, R.R., Wolf, A.P., Fowler, J.S., Ruth, T. J., Schlyer, D.J., Wieland, B.W.: Radiochim. Acta, 33, 49 (1983).
80. Clark, J.C., Silvester, D.J.: Int. J. Appl. Radiat. Isot., 17, 151 (1966).
81. Tilbury, R.S., Dahl, R., Mamacos, J.P., Laughlin, J.S.: Int. J. Appl. Radiat. Isot., 21, 277 (1970).
82. Lindner, L., Suer, T.H.G.A., Brinkman, G.A., Veenboer, J.T.: Int. J. Appl. Radiat. Isot., 24, 124 (1973).
83. Fitscher, J., Beckmann, R., Holm, V., Nevert, H.: Int. J. Appl. Radiat. Isot., 28, 781 (1977).
84. Knut, E.J., Machulla, H.J.: Int. J. Appl. Radiat. Isot., 34, 1627 (1983).
85. Nickles, R.J., Hichwa, R.D., Daube, M.E., Hutchins, G.D., Congdon, D.D.: Int. J. Appl. Radiat. Isot., 34, 625 (1983).
86. Kilbourn, M.R., Hood, J.T., Welch, M.J.: Int. J. Appl. Radiat. Isot., 35, 599 (1983).
87. Wieland, B.W., Wolf, A.P.: J. Nucl. Med., 24, p122 (1983).
88. Kilbourn, M.R., Jerabek, P.A., Welch, M.J.: Int. J. Appl. Radiat. Isot., 36, 327 (1985).
89. Dejesus, O.T., Martin, J.A., Yasillo, N.J., Gatley, S.J., Cooper, M.D.: Appl. Radiat. Isot., 37, 397 (1986).
90. Vogt, M., Huszar, I., Argentini, M., Oehninger, H., Weinreich, R.: Appl. Radiat. Isot., 37, 448 (1986).
91. Keinonen, J., Fontell, A., Kairento, A.-L.: Appl. Radiat. Isot., 37, 631 (1986).
92. Iwata, R., Ido, T., Brady, F., Takahashi, T., Ujiie, A.: Appl. Radiat. isot., 38, 979 (1987).
93. Tewson, T.J., Berridge, M.S., Bolomey, L., Gould, K.L.: Nucl. Med. Biol., 15, 499 (1988).
94. Heselius, S.-J., Schlyer, D.J., Wolf, A.P.: Appl. Radiat. Isot., 40, 663 (1989).
95. Solin, O., Bergman, J., Haaparanta, M., Reissell, A.: Appl. Radiat. Isot., 39, 1065 (1988).
96. Alexoff. D., Schlyer, D.J., Wolf, A.P.: Appl. Radiat. Isot., 40, 1 (1989).

97. Schlyer, D.J., Bastos, M.A.V., Alexoff, D., Wolf, A.P.: Appl. Radiat. Isot., 41, 531 (1990).
98. Jewett, D.M., Toorongian, S.A., Bachelor, M.A., Kilbourn, M.R.: Appl. Radiat. Isot., 41, 583 (1990).
99. Welch, M.J., Lifton, J.F., Gaspar, P.P.: J. Nucl. Med., 12, 405 (1971).
100. Adloff, J.P., Schleiffer, J.J.: Inorg. Nucl. Chem. Lett., 4, 403 (1968).
101. Palmer, A.J.: Int. J. Appl. Radiat. Isot., 29, 545 (1978).
102. Brinkman, G.A., Visser, J.: Int. J. Appl. Radiat. Isot., 30, 517 (1979).
103. Straaman, M.G., Welch, M.J.: J. Nucl. Med., 18, 151 (1977).
104. Straaman, M.G., Welch, M.J.: J. Label. Compd. Radiopharm., 14, 210 (1977).
105. Schrobilgen, G., Firnau, G., Chirakel, R., Garnett, E.S.: Chem. Commun., 1981, 198.
106. Tewson, T.J., Welch, M.J., Raichle, M.C.: J. Nucl. Med., 19, 1339 (1978).
107. Ehrenkaufer, R.E., MacGregor, R.R.: J. Label. Compd. Radiopharm., 34, 613 (1983).

7.2 β-Decay Effects of Tritium Incorporated in Organic Molecules and Living Matter

Takeyoshi ASANO
Research Institute for Advanced Science and Technology, University of Osaka Prefecture, Sakai, Osaka, Japan.

1. Introduction

The β-decay effects of tritium incorporated in organic and biomolecules or in living systems have been extensively studied. Attention has been paid to chemical or biological damage and to the biological hazards that might arise from accidental or permanent incorporation of tritium into genetic material.

There are several excellent reviews of this subject.[1-7] It has also been discussed at meetings organized by the IAEA and NCRP agencies.[8-12] When tritium is bound in an organic molecule, the daughter helium departs as a neutral atom, leaving behind an excited molecular cation (see below). On the other hand, the emitted β^--particles cause internal radiolysis (radiation effect) of the surrounding molecules, similar to the effects occurring upon external electron irradiation. In the condensed phase, often it is difficult to distinguish between the relative importance of these two effects. Nevertheless, some understanding of the problem has been achieved as shall be shown later in this review.

2. Cause of molecular effects due to β-decay

2.1. β-Decay effects of tritium

Tritium decays to form ^3He by emission of β^--particles with the maximum energy of 18.6 keV[13] and an average energy of 5.7 keV[14,15]. The half-life of ^3H is 12.33 years.[13]

The following physical processes may be responsible for the molecular consequences occurring when a β^--emitter bound in a molecule or a biological system decays.[5,7]

1) the increase of the atomic number by one unit in a transformed atom,
2) the creation of a positive charge,
3) the acquisition of electronic excitation energy by the sudden change of nuclear charge and

4) the acquisition of recoil energy due to β^--particle emission.

The conversion of a tritium atom to helium, possessing different chemical properties, brings about instability in the molecule. Moreover, the creation of a positive charge through the β^--particle emission would lead to electronic excitation.

In β-decay, the change of nuclear charge by one unit in a short time compared with orbital periods of the orbital electron motion causes perturbation of the shell. In most β^--particle emissions, there will be an adiabatic shrinkage of the electron shell to accommodate to the new charge. In this case there is no electronic excitation. But sometimes there is a high probability of nonadiabatic emission of the β^--particle. This sudden perturbation causes excitation of the electron shell or additional ionization.[16,17] From Migdal'equation[16,33] one obtains the relative probability of transitions from the ground state of H to the various states of He^+:

$$W_{1,n \atop (n=1)} = 2^6 \frac{[ZZ_1]^3}{[Z + Z_1]^6} \tag{1}$$

$$W_{1,n \atop (n \neq 1)} = 2^6 \frac{[n(Z_1/Z)-1]^{2n-4}}{[n(Z_1/Z)+1]^{2n+4}} \times n^5 (Z_1/Z)^3 ((Z_1/Z)-1)^2 \tag{2}$$

where Z_1 and Z are the charge on the nucleus before and after the β decay and n is the principal quantum number for the final state. The sum of these probabilities is subtracted from unity to obtain the probability of electron ejection. In Table 1 the results of calculation of electronic transition probability are shown. Thus 70 % of $^3He^+$ is in the ground state, 27.5 % in various excited states with energies between 40.8 and 54.4 eV and the residual 2.5 % lead to He^{2+} ions. An average electronic excitation energy is calculated to be about 11 eV ($40.8 \times 0.25 + 48.3 \times 0.013 + \cdots \simeq 11$ eV). The resulting electronic excitation energy is expected to be transfered to the bonded partner of ^3He, and cause the dissociation of C-C and C-H bonds in its daughter molecule ion.[18]

Table 1. Electronic transition probability in β-decay of tritium

States of $^3He^+$	probability of transition/%	energy level/eV[1]
1s	70	0
2s	25	40.8
3s	1.3	48.4
.	.	.
.	.	.
∞	2.5	> 54.4

[1] NSRDS-NBS 34, National Bureau of Standards, Washington (1970).

The nucleus recoil energy, E_R, is given by[19]

$$E_R \text{ (eV)} = \frac{547 E_\beta}{M} + \frac{536_\beta{}^2}{M} \tag{3}$$

where E_β is the energy of a β^--particle in MeV and M is the mass of the recoil atom in a.m.u.. In the β-decay of a free tritium atom, the maximum recoil energy is 3.3 eV and the mean recoil energy, 1.1 eV. If the tritium atom is bounded chemically, part of the recoil energy is converted to the translational energy of the molecule.[20] Thus the recoil energy is generally lower than bond energies (e.g., 4.3 eV for C-H and 3.6 eV for C-C). The week He-C bond (the energy of which is 0.05 eV[21]) may be ruptured by the recoil energy; but it is unlikely that the recoil energy would make great contribution to the β-decay effects. Therefore, for a low energy β^--particle emitter such as tritium, the ionization and electronic excitation are of major importance.

2.2. Dosimetry of tritium β-ray

In turn, I describe briefly the dosimetry of tritium in an aqueous solution of a labelled compound and in living matter.

In a dilute aqueous solution of a labelled compound, the energy of the β-ray emitted is absorbed almost entirely in water through the process of excitation and ionization which results in the formation of the water-radicals. The radiolysis of the labelled compound takes place by interaction of the water-radicals. This is called the indirect action of radiation. In such systems direct action of the β-particle is of minor importance.[22,23]

The absorbed radiation dose for tritium β-ray, D is calculated by the following equation[6]:

$$D\ (Gy) = N(decay/g) \cdot 5700(eV/decay) \cdot 1.6\times10^{-16}(Gy \cdot g/eV) \qquad (4)$$

where N is the number of decays per gram of solution. The dose per one tritium decay per gram of solution is calculated to be 9.1×10^{-13} Gy.

In the living system containing tritium, because of the short range of tritium β-rays in water and the high concentration of constituents in the microvolume of the cell, the radiation effects are not easily recognized.

The ranges of β-rays of tritium in water have been calculated from a consideration of the β-rays spectrum.[24] It was shown that a tritium β-ray can travel a maximum of 6 μm and 1 μm in average. The track length of tritium β-rays in water is comparable to the size (0.1 - 10 μm) of the living cell. In a cell containing high molecular genetic materials, the energy of β-ray is absorbed by both water and solute. Hence it should be predicted that both indirect action of radiation and direct action would play a role. The concepts of microdosimetry were applied to tritium.[25]

There are several ways to calculate the absorbed radiation doses in a eukaryotic cell (e.g., animal cell) and in a prokaryotic cell (e.g., bacterial cell and bacteriophage).

If tritium is distributed uniformly in the nucleus of eukaryotic cell, an absorbed radiation dose over the sphere of the nucleus is given by[26]

$$D\ (Gy) = \frac{N(decay/nucl) \cdot 5700(eV/decay) \cdot 1.6\times10^{-16}(Gy \cdot g/eV) \cdot (1 - 0.2)}{270\times10^{-12}(g)} \qquad (5)$$

where N is the number of decays per nucleus, 0.2 is fraction of energy escaped from the nucleus (correction value for edge effects) and the denominator is the mass of the "Standard cell nucleus" considered a sphere of 4 μm in radius.[27] The dose per one tritium decay in the cell nucleus is calculated to be 2.7×10^{-3} Gy.

In the case of a prokaryotic cell, the microscopic dose distributions are computed with the use of the programs designed to simulate tritium decay in the geometrical volume of the cell.[76,78] These calculations are carried out with consideration of 1) the tritium distribution in the cell, 2) the shape of the tritium β-spectrum and 3) the exponential energy absorption model. In the model the absorbed dose at a distance x from a point source is given by[76]

$$D = k \frac{F(e^{-\nu x})}{x^2} \qquad (6)$$

where ν is the absorption coefficient, k is a proportionality constant.

For the model bacterium in the shape of a cylinder with hemispherical ends (length: 2.2 μm, width: 0.88 μm, volume: 1.16 μm^3 and bacterial density: 1.08 g/cm^3), the radiation doses of the centrally located nuclear body are calculated to be 1.04 Gy per one tritium decay if tritium is distributed in the central part of the cell, and to be 0.361 Gy per one tritium decay if tritium is distributed in the whole cell.[77]

3. Chemical effects

3.1. Decomposition of organic molecules

The studies for simple organic molecules in the gas phase are important to clarify the mechanism of the primary molecular effects of β-decay, and provide the valuable clues for understanding the β-decay effects occurring in biomolecules and biological systems. Only a brief discussion of some relevant data will be given below.

In an early chemical study, the positive charge of the daughter atom following β-decay of tritium gas (H^3H, $^3H_2$) was measured with a positive ion collection chamber.[28] Later, the destruction of small molecules of tritiated hydrocarbons by β-decay were extensively investigated by charge spectrometry.[29-33] It has become apparent that the β-decay of a constituent tritium atom causes a C-$^3He^+$ bond disruption and furthermore these initial fragment ions dissociate in a variety of modes to give a complex pattern of ionic fragments.

In the measurement of various charged fragments formed by the β-decay of monotritiated benzene, $C_6H_5{}^3H$, it was found that in about 70 % of the events singly charged $C_6H_5^+$ fragments were formed. In the other 30 % of the events, the $C_6H_5^+$ fragments were further excited and produced more than 30 different charged fragments.[33]

The β-decay effects of tritium were also studied chemically by multilabelling and radio-gaschromatography.[34,35] These studies enable one to observe final chemical products. In the multilabelling technique, the molecule is labelled with two or more tritiums at chemically equivalent positions. The chemical fate

Table 2. Comparison of experimental and calculated yields of labelled products formed following the decay of gaseous [1,2-^{3}H]propane.

	yield/ %								
Prod.	H^3H	$CH_3{}^3H$	$C_2H_5{}^3H$	$C_2H_3{}^3H$	C_2H^3H	$C_3H_5{}^3H$	$C_3H_3{}^3H$	$C_4H_9{}^3H$	Total act.*
Exp.[35]	9.3	7.9	1.9	4.9	0.7	6.0	4.9	···	35.6
Cal.[30]	9.8	6.5	1.6	4.1	1.0	1.2	2.0	···	33.5

* Total activity in products other than $C_3H_7{}^3H$

of the labelled molecule following β-decay of tritium is traced by the measurement of the distribution of the remaining tritium. The radiochemical yields of labelled products after β-decay of gaseous [1,2-^{3}H]propane in the presence of an excess of inactive propane are shown in Table 2.[35] The results are in fair agreement with the yields calculated by taking into account the fragmentation pattern obtained in a charge spectrometric experiment[35] and succeeding ion-molecule reactions. $C_3H_6{}^3H^+$ ions are assumed to be the predominant species (abundance: about 60 %). It is considered that in the presence of excess propane, the propane ions undergo a hydride ion (H^-) transfer reaction:

$$C_3H_6{}^3H^+ + C_3H_8 \longrightarrow C_3H_7{}^3H + C_3H_7{}^+ \quad \text{(hydride ion transfer reaction)} \quad (7)$$

Monotritiated propane can not be detected by gaschromatography which does not allow its separation from the large excess of [1,2-^{3}H]propane.

The multilabelling technique which leads to the formation of a labelled daughter cation has been widely exploited in the mechanistic, structural and kinetic studies of ion-molecule reactions in gaseous and condensed media.[34,36,37]

Another experimental technique, namely that of the spin trapping ESR spectroscopy, was utilized to identify and quantify the radicals formed when tritium decayed in labelled methanol and benzene.[38,39]

Theoretical studies on the dissociation of tritium labelled molecules following β-decay have been carried out. Molecular orbital calculations were made for H^3H, $CH_3{}^3H$ and $C_2H_5{}^3H$.[40-42] The transition probabilities from ground state of parent molecules to the ground state ions of HHe^+, CH_3He^+ and $C_2H_5He^+$ were computed to be 62.9, 66.5 and 64.8 %, respectively. The calculation of potential energy curves indicated that the ground state $HHe+$ ion exists as a bound ion, whereas ground state CH_3He^+, $C_2H_5He^+$ ions dissociate instantly into a He atom and the residual fragment ion. Details of these studies are described in Chapter V in this book.

3.2. Decomposition of biomolecules and DNA

^{14}C-labelled products resulting from the decomposition of ^{3}H and ^{14}C-double labelled DNA were studied *in vitro*.[43] Isolated E. coli DNA containing [2-^{14}C,5-^{3}H]cytosine was stored at -196 °C to accumulate β-decay. In a TLC analysis of products, following hydrolysis of the DNA, ^{14}C-labelled uracil was observed as a major product with an efficiency of 28 %/^{3}H decay. By the ionizing irradiation of the same DNA, no ^{14}C-labelled uracil was observed. A possible reaction mechanism leading to the formation of uracil from [5-^{3}H]cytosine decay was suggested:

$$[5\text{-}^3H]Cy \xrightarrow{\beta\text{-decay}} [5\text{-}He^+]Cy \xrightarrow{-He} Cy(C^5)^+ \xrightarrow{+OH^-} [5\text{-}OH]Cy \xrightarrow{\text{deamination}} Ur \quad (8)$$

It was further proposed that uracil possesses the genetic coding properties of thymine and would account for the high efficiency of C ⟶ T transitions revealed in mutagenic studies employing [5-^{3}H]cytosine.[58]

Recently ^{3}H labelled products formed by the decomposition of multilabelled [C^3H_3]thymidine incorporated in DNA of HeLa cells was studied under the condition of the cell growing at 37 °C.[46] For control, the ^{137}Cs-γ irradiation of [6-^{3}H]thymidine labelled cell was also carried out. In a HPLC analysis of products, following hydrolysis of the DNA, large amounts of tritium labelled [5-CH_2OH]uridine (HMUd) was found from the cell containing [C^3H_3]thymidine. In the analysis of the [6-^{3}H]thymidine labelled cells which were irradiated, the yield of tritium labelled HMUd was small. These facts indicate that HMUd can be formed exclusively by the β-decay of [C^3H_3]thymidine. Thus a mechanism for the formation of HMUd through β-decay of tritium was proposed as

$$[C^3H_3]\text{Thd} \xrightarrow{\beta\text{-decay}} [C^3H_2He^+]\text{Thd} \xrightarrow{-He} [^+C^3H_2]\text{Thd} \xrightarrow{+OH^-} [5\text{-}C^3H_2OH]\text{Urd} \qquad (9)$$

On the other hand, the decomposition of tritium labelled nucleic acid bases in aqueous solutions was studied by the combination of techniques of double (or multi) labelling and reduction of radiolysis.[44,45] The resultant labelled products were analysed by HPLC.

At first an attempt was made to evaluate the relative importance of the β-decay effects and the radiation effects for the formation of end-products.[44] For that, the ^{14}C-products formed from [2-^{14}C,5-^{3}H]uracil, which is capable of causing both effects, and the [2-^{14}C]uracil mixed with tritiated water, which is capable of causing only the radiation effects, were compared in the presence of scavengers of water-radicals, t-butanol or oxygen. It was found qualitatively that the β-decay and irradiation result in the formation of the same end-products and that the G-values of many of the ^{14}C-products formed from [2-^{14}C,5-^{3}H]uracil are usually higher than those formed from the [2-^{14}C]uracil.

Next the decomposition of double labelled [2-^{14}C,5-^{3}H]uracil, [2-^{14}C,5-^{3}H] cytosine and mulitilabelled [C^3H_3]thymine (in this case single labelled [2-^{14}C]thymine is simply mixed) in oxygenated and degassed aqueous solutions was studied in the presence of a large amount of nonradioactive bases.[45] By this method the radiolysis of radioactive bases can be reduced by a factor of several hundreds compared with that of carrier free labelled bases. In the case of [2-^{3}H, 5-^{14}C]uracil or -cytosine, the decomposition, as determined from ^{14}C radioactivity, is due to both the β-decay effects and the radiation effects, while that from ^{3}H radioactivity, solely due to the radiation effects. Contrary to the case of mixture of [C^3H_3]thymine and [2-^{14}C]thymine, above situation is reversed. Therefore, the extent of decomposition of [2-^{3}H, 5-^{14}C]uracil or -cytosine due to the transmutation (β-decay) effects (T %/^{3}H decay) is calculated by the equation that corrects for the contribution of the radiation effects:

$$T\ (\%/^{3}H\ \text{decay}) = \frac{(\text{obs. B} - \text{obs. A})}{\alpha(1 - \exp -\lambda t)(1 - R)} \qquad (10)$$

where R is the rate of decomposition of radioactive base by radiolysis (R = obs. A / 100 in eq. (10)), λ is the decay constant for ^{3}H, t is a storage time, α is the rate of ^{3}H labelling of the base, obs. A is the percentage decomposition of radioactive base determined from the measurement of ^{3}H radioactivity and obs. B is the similar value determined from the measurement of ^{14}C radioactivity (Definition shown below is for [2-^{3}H, 5-^{14}C]uracil as well as for [2-^{3}H, 5-^{14}C]cytosine):

$$\text{obs. A (\%)} = \frac{(\text{act. of } {}^3\text{H-Ur})_{t=0} \exp -\lambda t - (\text{act. of } {}^3\text{H-Ur remained})_{t=t}}{(\text{act. of } {}^3\text{H-Ur})_{t=0} \exp -\lambda t} \times 100 \quad (11)$$

$$\text{obs. B (\%)} = \frac{(\text{act. of } {}^{14}\text{C-Ur})_{t=0} - (\text{act. of } {}^{14}\text{C-Ur remained})_{t=t}}{(\text{act. of } {}^{14}\text{C-Ur})_{t=0}} \times 100 \quad (12)$$

For the $[C^3H_3]$thymine/$[2\text{-}^{14}C]$thymine system, the extent of decomposition is calculated by

$$\text{T (\%/}^3\text{H decay)} = \left\{\frac{(\text{obs. A - obs. B})}{(1 - \exp -\lambda t)(1 - R)} - 100\right\} \times \frac{1}{2} \quad (13)$$

where R = obs. B / 100, and obs. A and obs. B are experimentally observed percentage decomposition determined from ^{3}H radioactivity and ^{14}C radioactivity, respectively, and are defined by

$$\text{obs. A (\%)} = \frac{(\text{act. of } {}^3\text{H-Thy})_{t=0} - (\text{act. of } {}^3\text{H-Thy remained})_{t=t}}{(\text{act. of } {}^3\text{H-Thy})_{t=0}} \times 100 \quad (14)$$

$$\text{obs. B (\%)} = \frac{(\text{act. of } {}^{14}\text{C-Thy})_{t=0} - (\text{act. of } {}^{14}\text{C-Thy remained})_{t=t}}{(\text{act. of } {}^{14}\text{C-Thy})_{t=0}} \times 100 \quad (15)$$

In equation (13), 100 and 1/2 are the values for the correction for the activity of decay tritium which is contained in the obs. A value and the overlapping count of $^3H_2$-products, respectively. This equation is applicable to the state where the decays of the second tritium in the methyl group ($C^3H_2 \longrightarrow C^3HHe$) are negligible. The results thus obtained are shown in Table 3. One may compare the extent of decomposition of tritium labelled uracil, cytosine and thymine, which increase in that order. The extent of decomposition in oxygenated aqueous solution is larger than that in degassed aqueous solution.

Table 3. The decomposition of tritium labelled bases (%/^{3}H decay)

	$[2\text{-}^{14}C,5\text{-}^3H]$Ur	$[2\text{-}^{14}C,5\text{-}^3H]$Cy	$[C^3H_3]$thy
oxyge. aq. soln.	55	70	95
degas. aq. soln.	12	59	80

The decomposition of bacterial DNA was studied with three tritium compounds.[47] In the experiment, E. coli 15 was doubly labelled with $[2\text{-}^{14}C]$thymine in their DNA, and either $[CH_3\text{-}^3H]$thymine, also in their DNA, $[5\text{-}^3H]$uracil in their RNA, or $[^3H]$histidine in their protein. These labelled cells were stored at 6 °C. The amount of ^{14}C radioactivity remaining incorporated in the cells was assayed by a filtration method. As much as 80 % of the cellular DNA was decomposed by tritium decays, but the rates of decomposition varied, being greater for $[CH_3\text{-}^3H]$thymine than for $[5\text{-}^3H]$uracil and ^{3}H histidine decays. Further the kinetics of DNA decomposition for each of three tritium compounds showed differences which are similar to the differences of cell killing efficiencies obtained for the same compounds in the same cell line.[75] It has become apparent that these differences between different tritium compounds can be explained approximately by consideration of the microscopic radiation doses of the centrally located DNA.[77]

Tritium incorporated into DNA gives rise to single strand DNA breaks (SSBs) or double strand DNA breaks (DSBs) either by the radiation effects or by the β-decay effects. These strand breaks are considered as a more objective indication of the biological effects and have been studied in various living materials *in vitro* and *in vivo* (in culture) experiments as shown in Table 4.[48-54] The number of strand breaks is calculated from the molecular weight determined by a sucrose density-gradient centrifugation[54] or is measured directly by analysis with agarose gel electrophoresis.[50]

In a *vitro* experiment SSBs formed appreciably by the decay of [6-^{3}H] uridine (or -uracil), [6-^{3}H]cytosine and [CH_3-^{3}H]thymidine, but DSBs could not be detected or were negligible.[48,49] Further, SSB did not occur by ^{3}H-β^--particle irradiation of ^{14}C-labelled DNA. Additionally a significant difference between the SSB with the cytosine labelled in the 6-position and in the 5-position was found.[49] Therefore, it was concluded that the β-decay effects largely contribute to the SSB with pyrimidine labelled in the 6-position and in the methyl group.

On the other hand, *in vivo*, the efficiency of SSB was larger than that observed *in vitro* for any labelled compound. In comparison with breakage by X-rays, it was found that the efficiency of the SSB by tritium is equivalent to that caused by the irradiation dose (:115 eV/cell = 4.8×10^{-3} Gy) which is close to the dose per decay (:3.8×10^{-3} Gy/decay).[51] The lower efficiency of the SSB

Table 4. DNA Strand breaks by the decay of tritium incorporated into DNA of living matter.

Living matter	D.pneu Ua	E.coli WWU	Colici E1	C.ham V79 ce	Chinese hamster V79-S171 cell		phage λ	Human T1cell
DNA storage;	*in vitro*			*in vivo* (in culture)				
Temp(°C)	-30	-60	-25	-196	-196		-196	0-1
Labelled sample	6^{3}H Ud (or 6 ^{3}H U)	6^{3}H Cy 5^{3}H Cy	CH_3-^{3}H dT	CH_3-^{3}H dT	CH_3-^{3}H dT ^{14}C dT (5^{3}H Ud in RNA)	^{3}H dT ^{14}C dT bifil d.labe	CH_3-^{3}H dT	6^{3}H dT
SSB/decay	0.30	U:0.37 L:0.09	(85)	2.1	U:2.2 - 2.3 L: 0.43	U:4.4 L:3.9	0.2	1.25 in O_2 0.760 in N_2
DSB/decay	0.01	0	(15)	—	—	—	0	—
Control sample	^{14}C T β-ray	^{14}C dT β-ray	^{14}C T β-ray	^{14}C dT X-ray	^{14}C dT X-ray	—	—	6^{3}H dT ^{60}Co γ
SSB/energ abs/cell	0	0	~ 0	1.0 / 115 eV	1.0 / 130 eV	—	—	4.5 / 100 eV
Ref. No.	48	49	50	51	52		53	54

D.pneu Ua: Diplococcus pneumoniae Ua which is a uracil requiring strain; Colici E1: colicinogenic factor E1; bifil d.labe: bifilar double labelled DNA; SSB/decay, DSB/decay: the number of breaks per decay; SSB/abs energ/cell: the number of breaks per absorbed energy in cell ; ( ) : % of the total breaks; U and L: for upper and lower labelled samples, respectively.

for decays originating in RNA was estimated to be due to different irradiation doses delivered to the DNA by the different distributions of tritium in RNA and DNA.[52] The *in vivo* condition increases the relative β-ray irradiation of DNA compared to the *in vitro*. Accordingly, it was explained that the majority of the SSBs is due to the radiation effects. Induction of DNA strand breaks *in vivo* was also studied with the use of bacteriophage labelled with [CH_3-^{3}H]thymidine.[53] The breakage efficiency is similar to that observed *in vitro*. Is the difference in magnitude of energy transfer of β-ray on DNA volume attributed to the difference of efficiency of SSB between cell and phage *in vivo* ?

Recently, the effects of oxygen on SSB and DSB by [6-^{3}H]thymidine labelled human cells was measured.[54] A low OER (the oxygen enhancement ratio) value of 1.7 (1.25/0.76) compared with an OER value of 4.9 obtained in electron beam irradiation, was found for the SSBs. Assuming that the β-decay effects is solely responsible for a lowering of OER, the efficiency of the SSB due to the decay effects was calculated to be 0.28 per tritium decay. This value agrees with the efficiency of 0.3 SSB/decay obtained in the condition of *in vitro*.[48]

4. Biological effects

4.1. Mutation

Mutagenic β-decay effects of incorporated tritium have been studied in prokaryotic cells (E. coli bacteria and bacteriophages) and eukaryotic cells (yeasts and mammalian cells). The fraction of surviving mutant after β-decay is given by[55]

$$S_m/S_o = kA \qquad (16)$$

where S_m and S_o are the number of mutants and survivors, respectively, k is the mutation frequency per decay and A is ^{3}H decays per organism. In Table 5 the relative mutation frequencies for various tritium labelled precursors in organisms are shown. Many data were obtained in the studies by Person and his co-workers.[55,56,58,59,61]

In comparison with the mutation frequencies for [5-^{3}H]uridine (or [5-^{3}H]uracil) RNA precursor), [CH_3-^{3}H]thymidine (DNA precursor) and ^{3}H-amino acids (protein precursor) in E. coli, [5-^{3}H]uridine caused a higher mutation frequency.[55] On the other hand, in a theoretical calculation, the irradiation doses to the nuclear region of E. coli incorporated ^{3}H-amino acid, [5-^{3}H]uridine and [CH_3-^{3}H]thymidine were 0.29, 0.44 and 0.73 Gy per decay, that is, were in the ratio of 1 : 1.5 : 2.5, respectively.[76,77] For the ^{3}H-amino acids (proline and histidine) and [CH_3-^{3}H]thymidine, the difference of observed mutation frequency was similar to that of the theoretical irradiation dose. In addition, the efficiency of mutation production by ^{3}H-amino acids (0.28×10^{-8}) was very nearly the same as that by the ^{3}H-water (0.23×10^{-8}) bringing about the irradiation effects.[59] Accordingly it was concluded that the mutation frequencies for ^{3}H-amino acids and [CH_3-^{3}H]thymidine are explainable only by the radiation effects on the bacterium, while a large difference for the [5-^{3}H]uridine decays is not and is preferably indicative of the β-decay effects.

The β-decay effects on the mutation can be examined more readily by using the same two nucleic acid precursors labelled with tritium in the different positions to each other. The effects associated with β-decay depend on the position labelled, while the radiation effects are independent. Therefore the presence of decay effects are revealed by a comparison of the biological effects due to the decay of the two labelled precursors. These relations are called *positional effects.*[56]

In this connection, the comparative mutation frequencies for the tritium decay at positions 5 and 6 of uracil (or uridine) showed the former ([5-^{3}H] uracil) to be more effective than the latter ([6-^{3}H]uridine).[56,59] As described above, it was explained that the mutation by the [6-^{3}H]uracil decay is due to the radiation effects, while the mutation by the [5-^{3}H]uracil decay is mainly due to the decay effects. The extent of the decay effects of [5-^{3}H]uracil was estimated by subtracting the mutation frequency for [6-^{3}H]uracil. The difference in the mutation frequency was regarded as the β-decay effects.

Assignment of base changes induced by the [5-^{3}H]uracil decay mutagen was made by comparing the pattern of phage growth obtained to the ^{3}H-labelled bacteria strain with that obtained with suppressed mutants.[57,60] It was proved that most mutations caused by [5-^{3}H]uracil decays are attributed to the GC ⟶AT base pair changes occurring at the site of labelled bases in DNA. Therefore it was assumed as hereunder. A metabolic conversion of [5-^{3}H]uracil to [5-^{3}H]cytosine occurs in an organism and results in the incorporation of the [5-^{3}H]cytosine formed into the DNA. The decay of tritium leads to deamination of the cytosine. The deaminated cytosine, that is, uracil, possesses the same genetic coding properties as thymine.

Finally clear evidence of the β-decay effects of mutation attributed to the genetic coding change caused by [5-^{3}H]cytosine decay has been shown.[60] In this study the mutation frequency for incorporated [5-^{3}H]cytosine in bacteriophage is 400 times higher than that for [6-^{3}H]cytosine.[58]

The considerably greater mutagenic effects by the decays of [5-^{3}H] cytosine have been also observed in yeast cells and λ phage.[64,66] With respect to the origins of the mutation, it was demonstrated that [5-^{3}H]cytosine decay in yeast causes a GC ⟶AT coding change, while the mutagenic effects on λ phage are associated with the modified mispairing bases but not with uracil residues (see studies for *ung* mutation described below).

From the biological data, one can calculate the probability, P, of mutagenesis by the β-decay effects per decay at one of the nucleoside pair sites where mutation occurs[61]:

$$P = [\{(1) - (2)\}/(3)] \; / \; [(4)/(5)] \qquad (17)$$

where 1) overall mutation frequency,
2) mutation frequency due to the radiation effects,
3) the ratio of distribution of labelled nucleosides in DNA among whole bacterium (or cell),
4) the total number of particular nucleoside per bacterium (or cell),
5) the number of nucleoside pair sites where mutation occurs in a DNA.

In calculation for [5-^{3}H]cytosine decay[58], the observed value of k, 790×10^{-6}, leads to a probability of mutagenesis per decay of 18 ~ 28 %, which is comparable to the efficiency of uracil production by [5-^{3}H]cytosine decay (: 28 %/decay).[43]

Such mutagenesis by the β-decay effects was also studied by the comparison between [6-^{3}H]- / [CH_3-^{3}H]thymidine,[61,62,64,67] [2-^{3}H]- / [8-^{3}H]adenosine,[61] and [8-^{3}H]guanosine / [8-^{3}H]adenosine.[65]

The decays of [6-^{3}H]thymidine and [2-^{3}H]adenosine in E. coli induce mutation showing the *positional effects*, although with a lower mutation frequency than in the case of [5-^{3}H]cytosine.[61] The frequencies for [CH_3-^{3}H]thymidine and [8-^{3}H]adenosine were explained on the basis of the radiation effects. Therefore it was considered that the higher mutation frequencies for [6-^{3}H]thymidine and [2-^{3}H]adenosine are largely due to the β-decay effects. The probabilities of mutagenesis were calculated to be 3 and 8 %/decay for [6-^{3}H]thymidine and [2-^{3}H]adenosine, respectively. Although the mechanism of mutation remains unclear, it was found that the decays of [2-^{3}H]adenine in bacteriophages cause DNA crosslinks with an efficiency of 50 %/decay.[79]

In additional comparative studies in mammalian cell, [6-^{3}H]thymidine decays were similarly 2 to 3 times as mutagenic as [CH_3-^{3}H]thymidine decays, while [CH_3-^{3}H]thymidine decays showed no difference from expectations of the mutation frequency from X-ray irradiation at an equivalent dose.[62] In this study the number of SSBs induced by decays at the 6 or methyl position does not correlate with the mutation frequency.

Table 5. Relative mutation frequencies by tritium labeled compounds incorporated in living matter.

Living matter	Bacterium				phage		cell			
	E.coli WWU				S13	λ	C.ham[§]	Yeas[§2]	Yeas[§3]	mouse[#]
Storage tepm(°C)	4	8	37	-75	—	—	-79	2	2	37
5-^{3}H uridine or 5-^{3}H uracil	6.6[a]	6.6[b]	6[c]							
6-^{3}H uridine or 6-^{3}H uracil		1	1							
CH_3-^{3}H thymidine	2.4		2.2							
^{3}H proline	1									
^{3}H histidine	1									
5-^{3}H cytosine					400[e]	14		[†]482[g]		
6-^{3}H cytosine					1					
6-^{3}H thymidine				2.5[d]			2.2[f]	[†2]33	(0.5)	1
CH_3-^{3}H thymidine				1	0.5	1	1	[†3]42	(0.6)	1
^{3}H alanine								1		
2-^{3}H adenosine				1						
8-^{3}H guanosine				0.5					[†4]1.5[h]	
8-^{3}H adenosine				0.5					[†5]1	
Reference No.	55	56	59	61	58	66	62	64	65	67

[§]C.ham: Chinese hamster V79-S171 cell; [§2]Yeas: Yeast, Saccharomyces cerevisiae U9-158-P4; [§3]Yeas: Yeast, Saccharomyces cerevisiae U9-15V-P4; [#]mouse: mouse L5178Y cell.

Mutation frequency per decay, k = [a]1.84×10^{-8};[b]1.84×10^{-8};[c]1.44×10^{-8}; [d]1.98×10^{-8};[e]790×10^{-6};[f]8.2×10^{-8};[g]0.41×10^{-6};[h]8.7×10^{-8}.

[†]5-^{3}H cytidilic acid;[†2]6-^{3}H thymidilic acid;[†3]CH_3-^{3}H thymidilic acid; [†4]8-^{3}H guanylic acid;[†5]8-^{3}H adenylic acid.

In yeast, mutation frequency by both [8-^{3}H]guanosine and [8-^{3}H]adenosine was twice that by [6-^{3}H] and [CH_3-^{3}H]thymidine.[64,65] On the other hand, in the analysis of tritium distribution in purine bases of DNA it was shown that the metabolic conversion of [8-^{3}H]adenosine to [8-^{3}H]guanosine occurs, and in the measurement of mutation spectra for both [8-^{3}H]guanosine and [8-^{3}H]adenosine decays it was found that GC ⟶AT coding changes occur. Hence it was assumed that [8-^{3}H]guanosine decay plays a major role in mutation and the enhanced mutagenesis for [8-^{3}H]adenosine decays is due to [8-^{3}H]guanosine derived from [8-^{3}H]adenosine.

Recently, an interesting study was carried out to confirm the C ⟶T transition. The mutation by [5-^{3}H]cytosine decay or [6-^{3}H]cytosine decay in DNA of wild type E. coli strain was compared with *ung* strain defective in uracil-DNA-glycosidase.[63] This enzyme functions in the repair of DNA containing accidentally introduced uracil residues. Hence it is expected that the mutation frequency in the *ung* cell is greater than in the wild cell. The mutation frequency for [5-^{3}H]cytosine was certainly grater than [6-^{3}H]cytosine, but no difference in the mutation frequency could be observed between the *ung* strain and wild type labelled with [5-^{3}H] cytosine. The study of yeast incorporating the same labelled compound also showed no dependence of mutation for the enzyme.[66] Therefore it was suggested that the uracil observed chemically in hydrolyzed DNA (see section 3.2 in text), after [5-^{3}H]cytosine decay, does not exist in situ to any significant extent, and some other intermediate that is an unaffected substrate for uracil-DNA-glycosidase should be considered.[63]

4.2. Killing

The killing of organisms by radioiactive decay was first revealed in E. coli phage containing radio phosphorus ^{32}P (Hershey et al. 1951[68]). With use of the Watson and Crick DNA structure model presented at that time, a hypothesis of that the nuclear transformation of ^{32}P incorporated into the backbone of DNA causes the DSB (double strand break) of the DNA molecule, and results in killing was proposed.[69] Futher DNA damage was studied by comparison of DSB by the decays of ^{32}P and ^{33}P, and it was demonstrated that the DSB is a significant factor in killing of coliphage[70] (see review by Krisch and Zelle [3]). The study of the killing by the decay of incorporated tritium was first carried out with use of a bacterium of E. coli.[72,74] A tabulation of killing efficiencies for the decay of various tritium labelled compounds in living materials is shown in Table 6. The fraction of survivors is given by

$$\ln S/S_o = -\alpha A \tag{18}$$

where S and S_o are the number of organisms after decay and before decay, respectively, α is killing efficiency per decay and A is ^{3}H decays per organism.

A comparison of killing of E. coli was attempted in the decay of [CH_3-^{3}H]thymidine and the irradiation with X-rays.[72] On the basis of a theoretical calculation of dose of tritium β-rays at uniform distribution of tritium in an organism, it was revealed that the killing due to the tritium decay is explainable by the β-ray irradiation. Further the comparative killing efficiencies for the decay of [6-^{3}H]- and [CH_3-^{3}H]thymidine did not show the *positional effects*.[73]

In the comparative studies for the decays of tritium labelled precursors incorporated into DNA ([CH_3-^{3}H]thymidine), RNA ([5-^{3}H]uridine) and protein (^{3}H-histidine) in E. coli strain, the data showed that the decay of [CH_3-^{3}H]thymidine is more effective in producing lethality than either [5-^{3}H]uridine or ^{3}H-histidine.[74,75] According to the theoretical calculation, the irradiation doses to the nuclear region by the decays of ^{3}H-histidine, ^{3}H-uridine and ^{3}H-thymidine were in the ratio of 1 : 1.5 : 2.5 as mentioned before (section 4.1). The reported killing efficiencies for ^{3}H-histidine, [5-^{3}H]uridine and [CH_3-^{3}H]thymidine[75] were in the ratio of 1 : 1.4 : 2.6, and correspond to mean lethal doses (D_{37}) of 27, 29 and 25 Gy, respectively. These mean lethal doses are similar to one another and to the experimental mean lethal dose under X-rays. Therefore, it was suggested that differential killing efficiencies are the result of differential dose rates to the DNA volume and that inactivation by tritium decays are due to β-particle ionizations.

A comparative study for the decays of different tritium labelled precursors ([CH_3-^{3}H]thymidine, [CH_3-^{3}H]thymine, [6-^{3}H]uracil, ^{3}H-amino acids (Leu, Lys, Pro, Phe, His) in a "bacteriophage" gave the same conclusion.[78] That is to say, the ratio of killing efficiency (α for decays originating predominantly in a DNA volume / α for decays originating predominantly in phage protein) is 2.6, while the ratio of effective energy transfer paths through the phage DNA from decays originating in the DNA to those originating in protein is calculated to be 2.6 for a 6.5 nm protein-coat thickness.

In the study with mouse cells it was shown that the decay of [CH_3 ^{3}H]thymidine is 8 times as efficient in causing killing as that of ^{3}H-histidine or ^{3}H-lysine. When the cells were pulse labelled with [5-^{3}H]uridine, or were pulse labelled with tritiated uridine and chased for one generation, the magnitude of the killing efficiencies lay between those of [CH_3-^{3}H]thymidine and ^{3}H-amino acids.[80] The distribution of tritium in five fractions (DNA, RNA, proteins and acid soluble fraction) from the cells was determined in each case, that is, most of the tritium activity in ^{3}H-thymidine, ^{3}H-uridine and ^{3}H-amino acids are present in the DNA fraction, mRNA and acid soluble fractions (pulse labelling) or rRNA and sRNA fractions (pulse labelling and chasing) and acid soluble fraction, respectively. Recently, in a comparison of the killing efficiencies for [6-^{3}H]thymidine, [6-^{3}H]uracil and ^{3}H-histidine incorporated into Chinese hamster cells, it was shown that [6-^{3}H]thymidine is more effective than the others, although to a lesser extent than above.[84] These facts also indicate that there is a definite "local effect" due to tritium decays and the efficiency of tritium decay in causing cell killing clearly depends on the location of the ^{3}H atom. For the moment, however, without the data of microscopic radiation dose to sensitive volume (i.e., DNA) of nucleus, the relative importance of the β-decay effects and the radiation effects cannot be assigned to the different killing efficiencies.

The killing effect on a mouse cell by the decay of [CH_3-^{3}H]thymidine incorporated in only one strand of DNA (unifilarly labelled DNA) and in both strands (bifilarly labelled DNA) were compared.[81] The killing by ^{60}Co γ-ray irradiation was also examined. The bifilar labelling is twice as efficient in killing as the unifilar labelling. For unifilarly and bifilarly labelled cells, the mean lethal doses were revealed to be 0.90 and 0.40 Gy, respectively. These are less than the value of 3.00 Gy for ^{60}Co γ-ray irradiation. Therefore, it was assumed that the major difference in efficiency between both types of labelling is due to the fact that when the tritium decay occurs in both strands of DNA there is additional DNA damage leading to cell killing. Consequently the importance of the β-decay effects in cell killing was suggested in the case of tritium decay on bifilarly labelled DNA. Later an additional experiment using the same mouse cell line was carried out in order to examine previous findings in further detail.[82] The result for unifilar labelling is very similar to that of previous work; but there is no significant difference between unifilar and bifilar labelling modes. In a recent study using a different mouse cell line unifilar and bifilar modes of [6-^{3}H]thymidine incorporation gave similar results for cell killing, too.[83] The difference between the former and the latter two studies remains unsolved.

The next data show the existence of β-decay effects in cell killing. The relation between killing, DNA crosslinks and SSBs by the decay of [2-^{3}H]adenosine or [8-^{3}H]guanosine(-adenosine) was studied with use of labelled bacteriophage and its isolated (*in vitro*) phage DNA.[79] In the process of tritium labelling the metabolic conversion of guanosine to adenosine occurs. Accordingly, DNA labelled with [8-^{3}H]guanosine contains both [8-^{3}H]guanine and -adenine. Killing efficiency for [2-^{3}H]adenosine is 3 times greater than that of [8-^{3}H]guanosine(-adenosine) decay. In the study for isolated DNA the crosslinks-causing ability was measured to be 0.41 to 0.54 per tritium decay for [2-^{3}H]adenosine and not detected for [8-^{3}H]guanosine(-adenosine), while the SSBs were formed with efficiencies of 0.08 to 0.50 per tritium decay for [2-^{3}H]adenosine and 0.08 per tritium decay for [8-^{3}H]guanosine

Table 6. Killing efficiencies[a] by tritium labelled compounds incorporated in living matter.

Living matter	Bacterium, E.coli			phage		Mammalian cell		
	B_1 3	15	15	T4	T4	L5178Y	L5178Y	Don
Storage temp(°C)	-196	4	4	5	4	-196	-196	-196
6-^{3}H thymidine	.00058							.0008[d]
								.0009[e]
CH_3-^{3}H thymidine	.00058	0.022	0.029	0.12		.0060[d]	.0045[d]	
						.0125[e]	.0044[e]	
5-^{3}H uridine			0.015			.0015[b]		
						.0010[c]		
6-^{3}H uracil				0.12				.0006[b]
								.0003[c]
^{3}H amino acids.(His,Leu,Lys,Pro)			0.011	0.0460		.0007		.0004
2-^{3}H adenosine					0.34			
8-^{3}H adenosine					0.12			
8-^{3}H guanosine					0.12			
Reference No.	73	74	75	78	79	80,81	82	83,84

[a]killing efficiency per decay, α. [b]pulse labelling. [c]pulse labelling plus one generation chasing. [d]unifilar labelling (only one strand in double strand DNA is labelled). [e]bifilar labelling (both strand are labelled).

(-adenosine). Therefore, it was suggested that the high killing efficiency for [2-^{3}H]adenosine is due to the DNA crosslinks caused by tritium decay.

5. Conclusion

The β-decay effects of incorporated tritium on the decomposition of molecules, DNA strand breaks, mutation and killing have been demonstrated experimentally in various systems, in spite of the difficulty in distingwishing the decay effects from radiation effects in condensed systems. As far as killing effects are concerned, it is necessary to watch the progress in the studies before a general conclusion is derived. The present author is really interested in the relationship between chemical and biological effects. Although some of chemical problems have been explained in the biological studies, the studies of the β-decay effects reported so far are still insufficient to account for the relationship between these effects as a result of chemical changes.

I shall conclude with brief remarks on the description of biological hazard associated with the β-decay of tritium.

Regarding to the biological hazard for human, a calculation of the probability of occurrence of tritium decay in a genetic important molecule, that is in the 5 position of cytosine ring in DNA, was attempted on the basis of tritium concentration in terrestrial water and of incorporation of tritium as a result of ingestion of its water.[12] The probability of the tritium decay in the 5 position of the cytosine ring in cell nucleus was given to be 4×10^{-10} decays/year. This is not a serious number. But such calculations should be made in cases of accidental exposure to tritium, when DNA bases may get labelled.

Acknowledgement

The author wishes to express his thanks to Dr. A. Halpern of Research Center Jülich (KFA) and Professor M. Imamura of Tokyo University of Information Sciences for their kind interest and useful suggestions for improving this paper. The continuous encouragement from Professor T. Matsuura of Rikkyo University should also be thankfully acknowledged by the author.

References

1. Strauss, B. S.: Radiat. Res. 8, 234-247 (1958).
2. Wimber, D. E.: in "Advances in radiation biology", Vol. 1, Ed. Augenstein, L. G., Mason, R. and Quastler, H., Academic press, New York, 1964, p 85-115.
3. Krisch, R. E. and Zelle, M. R.: in "Advances in radiation biology", Vol. 3, Ed. Augenstein, L. G., Mason, R. and Zelle, M., Acadmic Prss, New York, 1969, p 177-213.
4. Feinendegen, L. F.: in "Hot atom chemistry status report" Panel proceeding series, Vienna 1974, IAEA, 1975, p285-316.
5. Halpern, A. and Stöcklin, G.: Radiat. Environ. Biophys. 14, 167-183 (1977) ; *ibid.* 14, 257-274 (1977).
6. Carsten, A. L.: in "Advances in radiation biology", Vol. 8, Ed. Lett, J. T. and Adler, H., Acadmic Prss, New York, 1979, p 419-458.
7. Halpern, A.: in "Hot atom chemistry" Ed. Matsuura, T., Kodansha, Tokyo, 1984, p 430-459.
8. "Chem. eff. nucl. transformations", Vol 1, (Pub. 34) Proc. symp., Prague

1960, IAEA, 1961.
9. "Chem. eff. nucl. transformations", Vol 1 and 2, (Pub. 91) Proc. symp., Vienna 1964, IAEA, 1965.
10. "Biological effects of transmutation and decay of incorporated radioisotopes" (Pub. 183) Proc. of an Panel, Vienna 1967, IAEA, 1968.
11. "Hot atom chemistry status report" Panel proceeding series (Pub. 393), Vienna 1974, IAEA, 1975.
12. "Tritium and other radionuclide labelled organic compounds incorporated in genetic material" Cairman: Cronkite, E. P., NCRP Report No. 63 (1979).
13. "Table of Isotopes" 7th ed.. Ed. Lederer, C. M. and Shirley, V. S., Lawrence Radiation Lab., John Wily & Sons, Inc. New York, 1987, p 1.
14. Jenks, G. H., Ghormley, J. A. and Sweeton, F. H.: Phys. Rev. 75, 701-702 (1949).
15. Pillinger, W. L., Hentges, J. J. and Blair, J. A.: Phys. Rev. 121, 232-233 (1961).
16. Migdal, A.: J. Phys. (USSR) 4, 449-453 (1941).
17. Wexler, S.: J. Inorg. Nucl. Chem. 10, 8-16 (1959).
18. Feinendegen, L. E.: in "Tritium" Ed. Moghissi, A. A. and Carter, M. W., Messenger Graphics, Publishers, Phoenix, USA, 1973, p 221-231.
19. Edwards, R. R. and Davies, T. H.: Nucleonics 2, No. 6, 44-56 (1948). Libby, W. F.: J. Am. Chem. Soc. 69, 2523-2534 (1947).
20. Suess, H.: Z. Physik. Chem. B45, 312-322 (1940).
21. Hsiung, C. H.: J. Chem. Phys. 36, 947-953 (1962).
22. Spinks, J. W. T. and Woods, R. J.: "An introduction to radiation chemistry" John Wiley and Sons, Inc., New York, 1964. p 6.
23. Sanders, E. B.: in "CRC handbook of radiation measurement and protection", Section A. Vol. 1, Ed. Brodsky, A. B., CRC Press, 1978, p 529-546.
24. Robertson, J. S. and Hughes, W. L.: in "Proc. 1st natl. biophys. conf., Columbus, Ohio" Ed. Quastler H. and Morowitz, H., 1957, Yale Univ. Press, New Haven, 1959, p 278-283.
25. Ito, A.: in "Proc. of advisory group meeting on nuclear and atomic dates for radiotherapy and related radiobiology" Sept. 1985, IAEA, 1987, p 413-429.
26. Bond, V. P. and Feinendegen, L. E.: Health Phys. 12, 1007-1020 (1966).
27. Chaudhuri, J. P., Haas, R. J. Schreml, W., Knörr-Gärtner, H and Fliedner, T. M.: Teratology 4, 395-404 (1971).
28. Wexler, S.: Phys. Rev. 93, 182-187 (1954).
29. Snell, A. H. and Pleasonton, F.: J. Phys. Chem. 62, 1377-1382 (1958).
30. Wexler, S.: in "Chem. eff. nucl. transformations", Vol 1, Proc. symp., Prague 1960, IAEA, 1961, p 115-145; Wexler, S.: in "Actions Chimiques et Biologiques des Radiations", Vol 8, Ed. Haissinsky, M., Masson, Paris, 1965, p 103-241.
31. Wexler, S.: Science 156, 901-907 (1967).
32. Izawa, G., Nagashima, K., Hiraga, M., Yoshihara, K. and Shiokawa, T.: Mass Spectrometry 21, 179 (1973).
33. Carlson, T. A.: J. Phys. Chem. 32, 1234-1239 (1960).
34. Cacace, F.: in "Hot atom chemistry status report" Proc. of a panel, Vienna 1974, IAEA, 1975, p 229-239.; in "Hot atom chemistry" Ed. Matsuura, T., Kodansha, Tokyo, 1984, p 161-179.
35. Cacace, F., Caroselli, M and Guarino, A.: J. Am.. Chem. Soc. 89, 4584-4588 (1967).
36. Cacace, F., Cipollini, R. and Giacomello P.: J. Phys. Chem. 86, 2062-2065 (1982).
37. Cacace, F.: Science 250, 392-399 (1990).
38. Halpern, A.: Chem. Phys. Lett. 103, 523-526 (1984).
39. Halpern, A.: Chem. Phys. Lett. 119, 331-334 (1985).
40. Ikuta, S., Iwata, S and Imamura, M.: J. Chem. Phys. 66, 4671-4676 (1977).
41. Ikuta, S., Okuno, K., Yoshihara, K. and Shiokawa, T.: J. Nucl. Sci. & Technol. (Japan) 14, 131-134 (1977).
42. Ikuta, S., Yoshihara, K. and Shiokawa, T.: J. Nucl. Sci. & Technol. (Japan) 14, 661-663 (1977).
43. Krasin, F., Person, S., Snipes, W. and Benson, B.: J. Mol. Biol. 105, 445-451 (1976).

44. Asano, T., Halpern, A. and Stöcklin, G.: Radiochim. Acta 33, 75-80 (1983).
45. Asano, T., Kiritani, R., Fujita, S. and Kawanishi, T.: unpublished.
46. Teebor, G. W., Frenkel, K. and Goldstein, S.: Proc. Natl. Acad. Sci. USA 81, 318-321 (1984).
47. Person, S. and Sclair, M. H.: Radiat. Res. 33, 66-73 (1968).
48. Rosenthal, P. N. and Fox, M. S.: J. Mol. Biol. 54, 441-463 (1970).
49. Krasin, F., Person, S. and Snipes, W.: Int. J. Radiat. Biol. 23, 417-420 (1973).
50. Kupersztoch-Portnoy, Y. M. and Helinski, D. R.: Biochim. Biophys. Acta, 374, 316-323 (1974).
51. Clever, J. E., Thomas, G. H. and Burki, H. J.: Science 177, 996-998 (1972).
52. Burki, H. J., Bunker, S., Ritter, M. and Cleaver, J. E.: Radiat. Res. 62, 299-312 (1975).
53. Boye, E. and Krisch, R. E.: Int. J. Radiat. Biol. 37, 119-133 (1980).
54. Tisljar-Lentulis, G., Hanneberg, P., Feinendegen, L. E. and Commerford, S. L.: Radiat. Res. 94, 41-50 (1983).
55. Person, S. and Bockrath, C. B. Jr.: Biophysic. J. 4, 355-365 (1964).
56. Person, S. and Bockrath, R.: J. Mol. Biol. 13, 600-602 (1965).
57. Osborn, M., Person, S., Phillips, S. and Funk, F.: J. Mol. Biol. 26, 437-447 (1967).
58. Funk, F. and Person, S.: Science 166, 1629-1631 (1969).
59. Sands, J. A., Snipes, W. and Person, S.: Int. J. Radiat. Biol. 22, 197-202 (1972).
60. Philips, S. L., Person, S. and Newton, H. P.: Int. J. Radiat. Biol. 21, 159-166 (1972).
61. Person, S., Snipes, W. and Krasin, F: Mutat. Res. 34, 327-332 (1976).
62. Clever, J. E.: Genetics 87, 129-138 (1977)
63. Bockrath, R., Wolff, L. and Person, S.: Radiat. Res. 96, 635-640 (1983).
64. Korolev, V. G. and Ivanov, E. L.: Radiobiologiya 23, (4) 458-461 (1983). (Russ)
65. Korolev, V. G. and Ivanov, E. L.: Mutat. Res. 149, 359-364 (1985).
66. Konevega, L. V. and Kalinin, V. L.: Radiobiologiya 25, (3) 319-323 (1985). (Russ)
67. Furuno-Fukushi, I., Ueno, A. M. and Matsudaira, H: Radiat. Res. 110, 428-438 (1987).
68. Hershey, A. D., Kamen, M. D., Kennedy, J. W. and Gest, H.: J. Gen. Physiol. 34, 305-319 (1951).
69. Stent, G. S. and Fuerst, C. R.: J. Gen. Physiol. 38, 441-457 (1955).
70. Tomizawa, J. and Ogawa, H.: J. Mol. Biol. 30, 7-15 (1967).
71 Ley, R. D. and Krisch, R. E.: Int. J. Radiat. Biol. 25, 531-537 (1974).
72. Apelgot, S. and Latarjet, R.: Biochim. Biophys. Acta 55, 40-55 (1962).
73. Apelgot, S.: Int. J. Radiat. Biol. 10, 495-508 (1966).
74. Person, S. and Lewis, H. L.: Biophysic. J. 2, 451-463 (1962).
75. Person, S.: Biophysic. J. 3, 183-187 (1963).
76. Koch, A. L.: Radiat. Res. 24, 398-411 (1965).
77. Bockrath, R., Person, S. and Funk, F.: Biophysic. J. 8, 1027-1036 (1968).
78. Funk, F., Person, S. and Bockrath, C. B. Jr.: Biophysic. J. 8, 1037-1050 (1968).
79. Krasin, F., Person, S., Ley, R. D. and Hutchinson, F.: J. Mol. Biol. 101, 197-209 (1976).
80. Burki, H. J. and Okada, S.: Biophys. J. 2, 445-456 (1968).
81. Burki, H. J. and Okada, S.: Radiat. Res. 41, 409-424 (1970).
82. Bedford, J. S., Mitchell, J. B., Griggs, H. G. and Bender, M. A.: Radiat. Res. 63, 531-543 (1975).
83. Panter, H. C.: Radiat. Res. 87, 79-89 (1981).
84. Panter, H. C.: Cytobios 38, 107-114 (1983).

7.3 Molecular Consequences of the Auger Effect

A. HALPERN
Institute of Chemistry 1, Research Center Jülich, 5170 Jülich, Germany

1. Introduction

The Auger effect occurs as a possible relaxation process whenever a vacancy in an inner shell of an atom emerges. The filling of such an electronic vacancy in the atom by one electron from a less tightly bound state occurs either with the simultaneous emission of a fluorescence X-ray photon (radiative relaxation), or of a second electron from another less tightly bound state (non-radiative relaxation). The latter case is called Auger effect and the ejected electron - Auger electron, in honour of Pierre Auger, a pioneer in the study of the effect (cf. his personal recollections[1]). It has been since well established that this non-radiative process plays a fundamental role in different physical phenomena with relevance to atomic, solid state and surface physics and material sciences. The Auger effect attracted also the attention of radio- and radiation chemists who studied chemical effects associated with the decay of radionuclides via electron capture or internal conversion ("Auger emitters") and radiolysis upon X-rays, as well as of radiation biologists who started extensive studies of the lethal and mutagenic effects caused by the Auger emitters (more recently also by photoelectric absorption of X-rays) in cells with the aim to improve the understanding of biological damage and in search of a potential therapeutic application. This review deals with the chemical and biological consequences of the Auger effect initiated by the photoelectric absorption of low-energy X-rays or by the radioactive decay of ^{125}I. We shall deal mainly with condensed organic matter with emphasis on DNA and cells in vitro. The effects in isolated atoms and gas-phase molecules will be largerly neglected. Almost none of early papers and only a small portion of more recent ones will be cited, since our intention was not to give an extensive coverage of the literature, but rather to highlight some of the main problems currently under investigation. This will be achieved by refering to, and quoting from, the selected publications which can be regarded as the most important or representative. They, in turn, contain further references. Relevant reviews[2-5] can also be consulted. A brief restatement of well-established physical principles might be useful as an introduction to this review.

2. Physical principles

The interaction of photons having energy up to 30 keV with atomic systems is nearly completely photoelectric. In the photoelectric process the incident photon interacts with the electron cloud of an atom transfering its entire energy $h\nu$, whereby one electron is ejected from the atom (photoelectron) with the kinetic energy $T = h\nu - E_B$, where E_B is the binding energy of the ejected electron in a given shell. Momentum is conserved by the recoil of the entire residual atom. The most tightly bound atomic electrons have the greatest probability of absorbing a photon. Typically, at least 80 per cent of the photoelectric absorption takes place in the K shell, provided $h\nu$ exceeds the K-shell binding energy. At low photon energies, the photoelectrons tend to be ejected in the direction of the electric vector of the incident radiation, hence at right angles to the direction of incidence. Following the emission of a photoelectron the atom is left with a vacancy in the inner (most frequently K) shell.

Another process which leads to the formation of an inner-shell vacancy is the radioactive decay via electron capture. When energetically allowed, a nucleus Z may capture one of its own atomic electrons transforming to the isobar of atomic number Z-1, e.g. ${}^{125}_{53}I \xrightarrow{EC} {}^{125m}_{52}Te$. Usually the electron capture transition involves an electron from the K-shell, because these have the greatest probability density in the vicinity of the nucleus.

Whenever an atom has been ionized in an inner-shell, the created vacancy will be filled (within 10^{-15}-10^{-16} s) by an electron from a higher, less tightly bound shell. The excess energy that evens up the difference between the electron binding energy in the inner shell E_i (i = K,L ...) and the higher shell E_j (j = L,M ...) is released in one of the two competing processes. Either it is emitted as a X-ray fluorescence photon with the energy $E_{h\nu} = E_i - E_j$, or it is transmitted to another higher shell electron which is then ejected (Auger electron) with the energy $E_e = E_i - (E_j + E_k')$, where E_k' is the binding energy of the electron about to be ejected (i.e. the binding energy of an electron in the atom that is already ionized in the inner shell); k may be the same shell as j or another one less tightly bound than i. For the Auger transition to be energetically possible, of course, $E_i - (E_j + E_k') \geq 0$. If the atomic number of the atom which undergoes the Auger effect is Z, then $E'_k(Z)$ is often approximated by taking its value as equal to $E_k(Z+1)$, although this produces some energy disbalance. Fluorescence and Auger processes are competitive relaxation mechanisms. The fluorescence yield (ω) is the number of quanta emitted per vacancy in a particular shell. The Auger yield is $1-\omega$. The Auger process dominates for the K-shell vacancies of elements with Z<30, and for the L-shell vacancies of almost all elements.

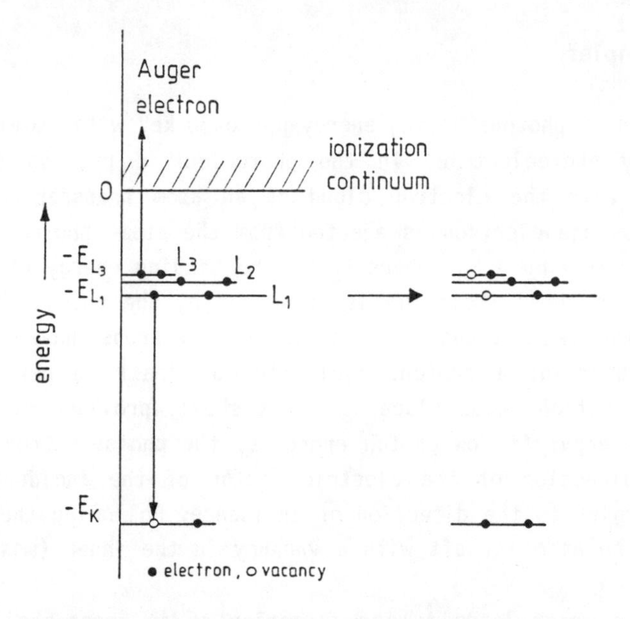

Fig. 1 Schematic representation of a single Auger process.

Fig. 1 schematically illustrates a possible electronic rearrangement that follows the formation of a vacancy in the K-shell and results in the emission of an Auger electron. The downward arrow indicates the transition of an electron from the L_1 orbital to fill the K-shell vacancy, thus releasing an energy equal to the difference in binding energies, E_K-E_{L1}, which is transferred to an L_3 electron ejecting it from the atom with a kinetic energy $E_e = E_K-(E_{L1}+E'_{L3})$. As can be seen, at this stage the L shell is already doubly ionized instead of one primary vacancy in the K-shell. The process continues shell by shell, until the valence shell is reached and no further transitions are possible. Thus, each Auger process creates one extra vacancy. The vacancy cascade leads finally to a multiple ionization of an atom. One can think of the effect as a lost of valence (bonding) electrons. In Fig. 1 the KL_1L_3 transition is shown. Transitions can also occur with other combinations of the three L-shell orbitals, as well as may involve M-shell orbitals (e.g. KLM type). Matters are further complicated by the presence of Coster-Kronig transitions in which a vacancy is shifted to a higher orbital within the same principal shell as the primary vacancy, e.g. L_1L_2M. Consequently, the Auger electron spectra are usually complex. They may be simulated by a Monte Carlo computing procedure in which the computer picks at random one possible route for filling the initial vacancy and follows it interaction-by-interaction, accounting at each step for the relative transition probabilities and energies, until no more transition can occur. Then other possible routes, i.e. other cascades, are followed in a similar way. Examples of such calculations are to be found in refs.[6-8]. However, as the cascade proceeds and the atoms acquire several vacancies, the calculation becomes increasingly speculative.

The next question is what happens when a vacancy cascade occurs in an atom bound in a molecule. Primarily the multiple positive charge resides on the atom that had undergone the Auger cascade. However, an <u>intramolecular</u> electron transfer will promptly take place due to the electrostatic repulsion, driving the charges to periphery of the molecule, hence creating repulsive centers within it. (Recall that two electronic charges separated by a distance of 0.1 nm repel each other with an energy of 14 eV). In gases under low pressure, when molecules are in collision-free space, the molecule may virtually explode, as the now highly charged regions within it repel one another apart due to Coulomb forces[10]. In the condensed phase, especially in solids, it is unlikely that the multiple ionization will lead to the coulombic explosion. Now a multicharged molecule will rather rapidly draw-in electrons from the adjacent molecules. These <u>intermolecular</u> interactions may have profound consequences for the fate of the molecule. In the conducting media, the multicharged ion may not survive long enough, say 10^{-13} s, to permit the intramolecular charge redistribution and hence the creation of repulsive centers, a prerequisite for the "explosion". In insulators or poor conductors, the multicharge centers may form and last for an appreciably long time ($> 10^{-13}$ s) divided between the atom that experienced the cascade and the remaining part of a molecule. In such a case, a neutralization of the charge settled on the latter moiety, by catching electrons from the neighbouring molecules, would deposit some tens or hundreds eV of excitation energy in this moiety what may lead to excitation decomposition[43]. To what extent this occurs depends on the chemical nature of the parent molecule. This point will be mentioned again later (§ 4.4). It may be noted here that dry DNA has low concentration of charge carriers and hence low conductivity, but the conductivity of hydrated DNA increases exponentially with the water content[11].

Another process which contributes to the fragmentation of molecules in the condensed phase is the internal radiolysis by secondary low-energy electrons. For the elements of low or medium atomic number these electrons have energies up to a few keV with a relatively high LET of 1 to 10 eV/nm. Since such electrons dissipate their energy in material of unit density within a distance of the order of 10-100 nm, they may efficiently damage molecules in the nearness of the target site. The contemporary interpretation of the radiation effects caused by low-energy electrons is afforded by the microdosimetric approach (cf. § 4.3).

3. Effects associated with the photoelectric absorption of low-energy X-rays

3.1. Absorption of low-energy X-rays

The characteristic feature of low-energy X-rays is that, as they interact with matter predominantly by photoelectric effect, the atomic interaction coefficients vary rapidly with both photon energy and the atomic number of the material (approximately proportional to $Z^4(h\nu)^{-3}$). This is in contrast to high-energy photons which interact mainly by Compton scattering and pair production for which the corresponding coefficients only slightly depend on Z.

Let us consider two molecules containing bromine, bromouracil $C_4H_3N_2O_2Br$ (BU, M.wt. 191) and the DNA molecule in which 55 % thymine was replaced by bromouracil (BU-DNA, M.wt. $4.5\cdot10^6$). When they are subjected to 1 MeV photons, the mass absorption coefficient is the same for both compounds, namely 0.027 cm^2/g. Moreover, these photons interact with the component atoms with the relative probabilities correlating well with the ratio of the number of electrons from each element (e.g. in BU-DNA 37 % with C, 18 % with N, 30 % with O, 11 % with P and 3.7 % with Br). In contrast, for incident photons of 50 keV energy the mass absorption coefficient is 1.48 cm^2/g for BU and 0.17 cm^2/g for BU-DNA. Now bromine contributes 99 % to the total absorption in BU, and 68 % in BU-DNA (plus 16 % in P and 16 % in C, N and O). Thus, reducing the energy of the incident photons from the MeV to the keV region not only the interaction coefficient significantly increases, but also the topography of absorption drastically changes. Especially critical is an energy interval immediately around the absorption edges. This is visualized in Table 1 in which the mass energy absorption coefficients for 13.35 keV and 13.51 keV X-rays, i.e. on both sides of, and close to the K-shell binding energy in bromine (13.47 keV), are given for BU and BU-DNA, together with the per cent absorption in the constituent elements.

Table 1. Differential absorption of X-rays in BU and BU-DNA

Substance	M.wt.	μ_{en}/g (cm^2/g)	% absorption in Br	C	N	O	P
BU	191.0	9.30	91.7	2.3	2.2	3.8	
		34.13	97.7	0.6	0.6	1.0	
BU-DNA	$4.5\cdot10^6$	3.44	20.4	8.7	7.6	7.6	45.6
		5.48	50.0	5.4	4.8	11.2	28.6

Upper values: 13.35 keV, lower values: 13.51 keV

Thus as the photon energy is raised from values below the K-edge for Br to the values above this edge, the total absorption abruptly increases, and so does the relative contribution of bromine to this total absorption. Low-energy electrons set in motion by photons traversing through an absorber and interacting with the component atoms are the main agent through which the radiation effects arise. The ionization density, the number of ionizations in unit length of the path of an electron, is inversely related with the electron velocity (energy). In low Z elements, which are characteristic of biological matter, an electron causes roughly 30 ionizations per 1 keV of its energy before being thermalized. Thus, an electron of energy 1.82 keV (e.g. phosphorus $KL_1L_{2,3}$ Auger electron) will produce only 50 ionizations along a short track. In contrast, when 1.24 MeV γ-rays interact, 71 % of the initial energy is carried out by recoil electrons of energy 875 keV which originate from the Compton scattering through 90°. In this case each recoil electron will produce roughly 2600 ionizations along long tracks. This microscopic fashion is essential since the efficacy of different radiations (e.g. of high or low LET) to produce damage increases with the ionization density in the track. In recent years it has become possible to obtain greatly improved description of radiation tracks by Monte-Carlo computer simulations which include all atomic interactions of the primary charged particles and all their secondaries until they come to rest[12]. This enabled to analyse the three-dimensional structures of tracks over dimensions down to less than 1 nm[13,14]. Another feature of low-energy X-rays is that, as photon mean free paths are several orders of magnitude greater that the ranges of electrons of the same energy, the charge particle equilibrium exists even in the absence of the photon equilibrium.

3.2. Biological response to low-energy X-rays

The current work concentrates along two lines of research. First, ultra-soft (< 4.5 keV) X-rays have been used as a tool to test the microscopic mechanisms of radiation effects in cells. Second, low-energy X-rays have been utilized to study the highly destructive molecular processes following their absorption and the concomitant Auger cascade, which in cells may manifest themselves as an enhancement of a radiobiological damage. Our review is biased towards this second area (cf. § 3.4). This will be, however, preceded by a brief outline of the experiments in which ultra-soft X-rays were used to study the size within which biological lesions arise (cf. § 3.3). This work, apart of being of fundamental importance for molecular radiobiology, contributed to a better understanding of some aspects of the Auger enhancement of radiobiological effects.

3.3. Selective probing with ultra-soft X-rays

Since late seventies, Goodhead et al[15-17] have been using X-rays of energies 0.28 keV, 1.5 keV or 4.5 keV (carbon, aluminium and titanium K X-rays) to determine their effectiveness in killing mammalian cells and inducing chromosome aberrations and mutations. These photons interact with matter by photoelectric absorption (cf. § 3.1) in which photo and Auger electrons of well-defined low energy are released with ranges of 7 nm, 70 nm and ~ 550 nm, respectively. These X-rays turned out to be more effective in inducing biological effects than ^{60}Co γ-rays or 250 keV ("hard") X-rays. As an example, Fig. 2 shows the survival vs dose curves for Chinese hamster cells. It is evident that the efficiency varies inversely with the photon energy. The lowest energy X-rays (0.28 keV) which produce the shortest electron tracks ($\leq$ 7 nm) are the most effective per unit dose. Similar relationship was observed for other biological end-points, e.g. chromosome aberration[17]. These results imply that the sensitive site in cells involved in a radiobiological effect cannot be greater than this dimension (only three times the diameter of the DNA double

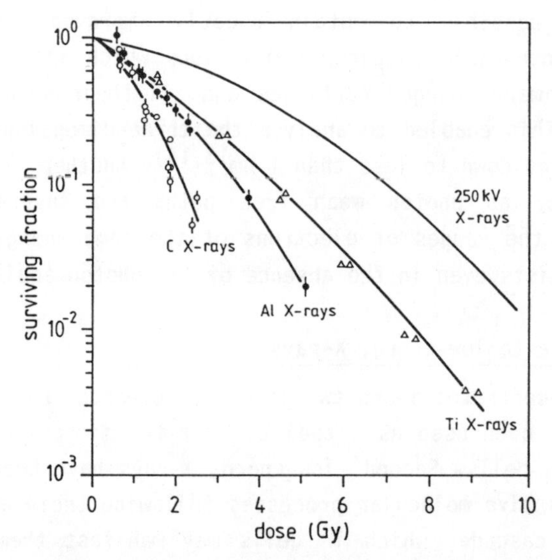

Fig. 2 Survival of Chinese hamster cells after irradiation with ultrasoft X-rays (experiments by Goodhead et al)

helix) within which several ionizations occur and a small amount of energy (< 280 eV) is deposited. This discovery was of fundamental theoretical importance and stimulated re-examination of the existing models or radiobiological action[18]. The topic is beyond the scope of the present review and shall not be discussed here. Instead, we consider one particular aspect which is directly linked with our main topic of the Auger enhancement effects.

The ultra-soft X-rays experiments provide evidence that the biological damage results from occasional local deposition of energy in very small volumes of a few nm. Secondary electrons released from all component atoms which interacted with photons serve as the energy carriers. None of the particular component element alone can be regarded as responsible for a radiation effect. Rather, in the first approximation, each of them will contribute according to its relative contribution to dose. More exactly, numbers and energies of electrons from individual elements should be taken into account since the effectiveness of electrons depends on the track length and the ionization density within the track. It was therefore not surprising that Goodhead et al[16] did not find cellular phosphorus to play any dominant role in killing the irradiated cells. These authors compared the relative biological effectiveness of Al K and Ti K X-rays, i.e. with energies on either side of the P K-edge (2.148 keV). As seen from Fig. 2, 1.5 keV X-rays were more effective than 4.5 keV X-rays although the latter produced more P K-shell ionizations. It should be noted that both these energies are well above the K-edge for oxygen which in tissue makes the most significant contribution to the total dose.

More recently groups of Japanese researchers carried out more straightforward experiments to prove the "special" role of the photon absorption in phosphorus. They irradiated different cells with monoenergetic X-rays (from a synchrotron radiation source) of energies 2.146 keV, 2.153 keV and 2.160 keV, i.e. just below, at and just above the P K-edge. The results reported in annual Photon Factory Activity Reports 1986-1989 (I am not aware of any journal publication) are inconclusive as yet. In some cases they indicated no difference in the effect produced by X-rays below and above the K-edge while at the edge there was a small enhancement. This observation can perhaps be attributed to the extended fine structure in phosphorus, i.e. an oscillation of the absorption coefficients which extends up to several hundreds eV beyond the edge*.

More extensive work intended to prove the Auger enhancement effect has been carried out using molecules or cells which contained higher atomic number elements (Br, I).

3.4. Auger enhancement of biological damage

The guiding concept stems from the fact that the photoelectric absorption of photons having energies slightly above the K-edge ($h\nu \geq E_K$) is followed by the

*After completion of this paper, a work on the effects in yeast cells caused by the absorption of X-rays around the P K-edge appeared[50].

Auger cascade and leaves the atom involved highly ionized. Both the low-energy Auger and Coster-Kronig electrons set in motion, and the excitation energy released in charge neutralization are capable of producing extensive bond rupture and damage (cf. § 2). Obviously, if $h\nu < E_K$ these physical processes do not proceed. Therefore, experiments designed to show or disprove the Auger enhancement involve irradiation of given specimens with monoenergetic X-rays on both sides of, and close to, the K-shell binding energy in the selected (the heaviest) component atom.

Experiments with small molecules demonstrate that the damage per unit dose at photon energies just beyond the K-edge is higher than that at energies below this edge. E.g., Halpern and Stöcklin[19] studied the formation of stable free radicals in irradiated solid 5-bromodeoxyuridine as a function of X-ray energy and observed a marked increase in the radical yield per unit dose at the K-edge of bromine. In another experiment[20], liquid carbon tetrachloride was irradiated with sulphur $K_{\alpha,\beta}$ X-rays (2.32 keV) or scandium $K_{\alpha,\beta}$ X-rays (4.12 keV) (the core-level binding energy of Cl is 2.82 keV), and the formed free radicals were measured using the spin-trapping ESR spectroscopy. There were 3.5 times more trapped CCl_3 radicals upon 4.12 keV X-rays than upon 2.32 keV X-rays, at an equal photon dose.

The situation is less clear in the case of brominated DNA or cells containing such DNA. Although the cross-sections for the photoeffect in component atoms of DNA (C, N, O, P) are significantly lower than in bromine, there are so many of these atoms that an electron flux originating in them might outweigh the secondary electrons from bromine. We now consider in some detail the recent work with brominated DNA (BU-DNA)[21]. Dry samples of Col E1 plasmid DNA in which 55 % of thymidine (TdR) was replaced by bromodeoxyuridine (BUdR) were irradiated with 13.35 keV or 13.51 keV X-rays (from a synchrotron radiation source), i.e. on each side of, and close to the K-shell binding energy of Br (13.47 keV), followed by the measurement of single and double strand breaks (ssb and dsb). The mean number of ssb was $3.4 \cdot 10^{-10}$ per Gray·Dalton for both photon energies; the mean number of dsb induced by 13.35 keV or 13.51 keV photons was $4.74 \cdot 10^{-12}$ per Gray·Dalton or $6.32 \cdot 10^{-12}$ per Gray·Dalton, respectively. Thus, photons of energy above the Br K-edge appeared slightly more efficient in producing dsb (but not ssb) than those of energy below this edge. The energy needed to produce one strand break in BU-DNA was estimated as 30.6 eV/ssb for both photon energies, 2.19 keV/dsb for 13.35 keV photons and 1.64 keV/dsb for 13.51 keV photons. To comprehend these results, and recalling the discussion in § 3.3, clearly the number of secondary electrons from all individual elements, and their energies, have to be taken into account. In the work discussed here, this has been achieved by a two-step procedure. First, from the differential absorption data (Table 1) the number of photoelectric interactions <u>per Gray</u> with individual component elements of the irradiated BU-DNA was calculated. Then, the number of photo and Auger electrons emitted <u>per interaction</u> from each element in question, and their mean energy, was calculated. Apparently, the product of these two numbers gives the total number of secondary electrons per Gray from individual component elements of BU-DNA, and their total kinetic energy. The data are summarized in Table 2.

Table 2. Number of electrons and total electron energy per Gy from individual component elements of BU-DNA

	C + N + O				P				Br			
hν	PE		AE		PE		AE		PE		AE	
keV	N	E	N	E	N	E	N	E	N	E	N	E
13.35	16.7	215	16.6	7	22.2	249	21.2	42	10.0	91.1	37.8	10.7
13.51	9.8	127	9.7	4	13.0	148	12.4	25	22.7	4.6	118	72.0

Symbols and units:

PE = photoelectrons, AE = Auger electrons

N = number of electrons $\cdot 10^{-4}$, E = total electron energy in keV $\cdot 10^{-4}$

What appears to be important is that fairly energetic photoelectrons are abundantly generated in light component elements (C, N, O, P), each carrying sufficient energy to cause up to hundreds further outer shell ionizations in the neighbourhood. This severly restricts the chance to visualise the effects caused by the activation of inner-shell electrons of bromine, because there are so many more secondary activations (ionizations and excitations) of outer electrons in other atoms. Indeed, the gross damage to BU-DNA, i.e. ssb, was the same below and above the Br K-edge. It remains open for speculation as to why there was a small energy-dependence of the dsb yield. The guess is that this is somehow associated with the higher number of very low energy Auger electrons released from bromine by 13.51 keV photons (Table 2) and the resulting positive charge on it (vide infra). Alternatively, according to Humm and Charlton[22] cascades generated by photons with energy above the K-edge produce a greater number of energy depositions > 100 eV, which cause dsb more efficiently than energy depositions below 100 eV.

At this stage it should be noted that in ref. 21 the frequency of the Auger electrons from bromine was calculated using a simplified procedure without regard for the contribution from individual subshells, although an advanced algorithm which accounted for every allowed transition had been developed by Humm and Charlton[22]. The appeal of this purist computation route is that it accounts for the fact that the material immediately sorrounding the absorption site may experience different effects depending upon the particulate cascade. In ref. 21, the authors did not follow this route assuming that its accuracy may be of minor importance for the interpretation of the experimental results which themselves represent averages over many cascades.

We now turn to cellular systems. It is easy to predict that to prove the Auger enhancement effect in cells is more difficult than in isolated DNA. On the one hand, the light elements of cellular water and the protein fraction, in addition to those in the DNA, will increase the flux of photoelectrons. On the other, the incorporation of halopyrimidines (e.g. BUdR) into the DNA of mammalian or bacterial cell usually sensitizes that cell toward the effects of ionizing radiation, with the imminent danger that the Auger enhancement effect will be mostly masked by the chemical sensitization. Humm and Charlton[22] calculated the contribution of the Auger cascade in bromine to the total production of dbs in a cell, concluding that it will be insignificant in comparison with the effect due to the BUdR sensitization. How this theoretical predicition compares with the experimental results?

In 1978, Halpern and Mütze[23] studied the colony-forming ability in dried bacteria Micrococcus denitrificans, in which 8 % of TdR was replaced by BUdR, following irradiation with 12.1 keV or 14.4 keV X-rays. In the dry state, repair processes ceased and no difference in survival was seen between brominated and unbrominated cells at 12.1 keV energy. Above the K-edge, however, lethality increased by 20 % (at 37 % survival) for bacteria prelabeled with BUdR. Much of the work which followed was carried out by the Japanese researchers[24-27]. Bacteriophage T1, yeast cells, and mammalian cells (E.coli, CHO, HeLa), with partially brominated DNA, were irradiated with monoenergetic X-rays of energy 12.4 keV or 13.5 keV (from a synchrotron radiation source), followed by the measurements of the cell survival or chromosome damage. Fig. 3 shows the survival vs exposure curves for HeLa cells[24] and exemplifies the authors' way of presenting the experimental results. Of course, from a plot of the radiation effect against exposure no direct conclusion regarding the Auger enhancement is possible. Exposure describes the radiation field, not the amount of energy absorbed by a material located in it, whereas an evaluation of the Auger enhancement must be based on a comparison of the effects produced by the two monoenergetic radiations normalized to the same energy expended or, even better, the same number of photoelectric interactions. Hence, the authors attempted the analysis of the results in terms of the energy absorbed and in terms of the number of the Auger events. Let us dwell upon their analysis in terms of the energy absorbed. D_0 values in Gy were calculated with the aid of roentgen-to-rad conversion factors. The enhancement ratios, obtained by dividing D_0 (in Gy) for non-brominated material by that for brominated material, were found always higher for X-rays of energy above the Br K-edge than below this edge (2.80 and 1.64 for T1, 2.52 and 2.32 for E.coli, 3.34 and

2.95 for yeast cells). This may indicate that the increase in the killing efficiency upon 13.5 keV X-rays exceeds the rise in the amount of energy absorbed. This conclusion, however, is not beyond doubt, because of the unknown

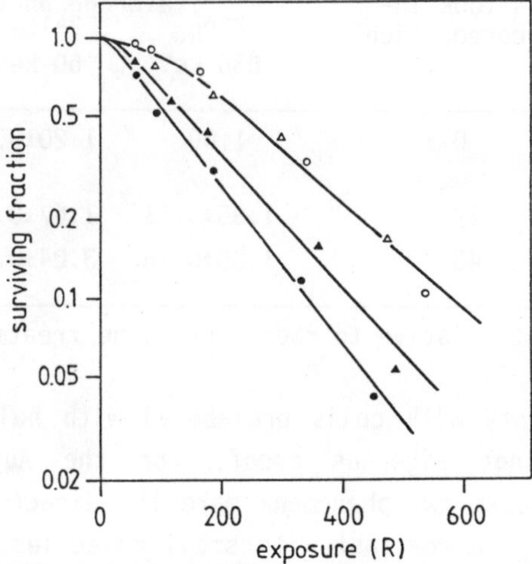

Fig. 3 Survival of HeLa, natural (open symbols) or brominated (solid symbols) after irradiation with 12.1 keV (triangles) or 14.4 keV (circles) X-rays

accuracy of the results and a lack of proper statistical analysis. Larson et al[28] performed similar experiments with V79 hamster cells (32 % replacement of TdR by BUdR). They reported no statistically substantial difference in survival fractions between the curves obtained due to irradiation with 13.45 keV or 13.49 keV X-rays.

Recently, Nath et al[29] utilized radiation sources of the type used in brachytherapy which contained ^{125}I, ^{241}Am or ^{226}Ra, i.e. emitting photons of average energy 28 keV, 60 keV or 830 keV, respectively, to irradiate Chinese hamster lung cells, in which 22 % or 45 % of TdR was replaced by IUdR (the K-edge for iodine is 33.17 keV). This technique is disadvantageous in comparison with the use of monoenergetic X-rays, but nevertheless the results are of potential interest. In Table 3, the RBE and radiosensitization data, obtained from the survival vs dose curves (at the dose rate of 0.72 Gy/h) are summarized.

These results reveal the usual IUdR radiosensitization, and moreover an additional increase in the sensitivity toward radiation which is greater upon ^{241}Am photons (of energy above the K-edge for I) than upon either ^{125}I photons (below this edge) or ^{226}Ra photons (very much above this edge). This observation of a more efficient killing efficiency of 60 keV photons compared to both lower and very much higher energy photons indicate that Auger cascade occurying in the component iodine atoms contribute to the radiation effect. However, any quantification of these cascades is here hardly possible.

Table 3. Effect of photon energy on RBE and radiosensitization

Parameter	% IUdR incorporation	Radiation (isotope and average photon energy) ^{226}Ra 830 keV	^{241}Am 60 keV	^{125}I 28 keV
RBE relative to ^{226}Ra	0	1.00	1.20±0.10	1.30±0.11
Radiosensitization factor*	22	1.35±0.11	1.67±0.09	1.47±0.08
	45	1.89±0.16	3.04±0.13	2.48±0.17

*Radiation/IUdR treatment relative to radiation alone treatment

Summing up, experiments with cells prelabeled with halogens have hitherto provided indications, not rigorous proof, for the Auger enhancement of biological damage. At least two phenomena make the direct observation of this effect difficult. First, in contrast with small molecules, the interaction of photons with the surplus of atoms other than halogen create an electron flux which outweigh the secondary electrons from a halogen. The second disturbing factor is the usual sensitization of cells by halopyrimidines. Future experiments should utilize L5178Y s/s cells in which the BUdR radiosensitization is small and therefore the Auger component easier to detect. Generally, the Auger component is not expected to be large enough to be of potential value for therapy. However, its unambiguous demonstration will be theoretically important, since it will prove that other mechanisms, besides the initial distribution of deposited electron energy, are operative when low-energy photons interact with biological matter.

4. Effects associated with electron capture decay of ^{125}I

4.1. Introduction

Whether a vacancy in the K-shell is produced by photoionization or by orbital electron capture decay, the physical processes that follow are essentially the same, except that in the latter case the atom changes its identity and there is no photoelectron emission. Obviously, lack of photoelectrons is advantageous when the consequences of the Auger cascade are of primary interest. At present, ^{125}I is the most widely used nuclide in studies of structural and functional consequences of the Auger effect in cells. The decay of ^{125}I incorporated into the DNA of a cell (via the thymidine analogue ^{125}I-iododeoxyuridine) causes severe cytotoxic and mutagenic effects. The radiobiological effects have the characteristics of a high LET phenomenon. In contrary, little or no toxicity is observed when ^{125}I decays at a distance from the DNA, e.g. in the cytoplasm, on the cell membrane, at the extracellular sites, or when it is diffusely distributed within the cell[30-32]. The effects are now of low LET character. These experimental findings have been well established and their basic understanding achieved (cf. reviews[2-5]). However, there are still some open questions regarding the physico-chemical phenomena responsible for the occurence of the post-Auger biological damage. At least two physical processes, acting concomitantly, contribute to the observable damage: (a) radiation effects by low-energy electrons, and (b) effects associated with the positive charge on the daughter atom, its migration and neutralization. In what follows we shall deal with questions of more physical or chemical, rather than biological nature. Recent biological results are well summarized by Makrigiorgos et al[5].

4.2. Experiments with ^{125}I-labeled DNA molecule or its fragments

We shall consider two questions: To what extent does the decay of ^{125}I destroy a labeled DNA base? What is the range of damage to DNA caused by ^{125}I decay? The answer to the first question can be deduced from experiments in which the fate of the parent (^{125}I-labeled) molecule is followed, while the bulk radiolysis by ^{125}I-electrons is ignored. The technique of double labeling fulfils this requirement. In this method, each molecule, besides ^{125}I, contains the long-lived ^{14}C as a marker, so that the residues remaining after ^{125}I had decayed are ^{14}C-labeled and the stable products can be determined radioanalytically. Using this technique, Deutzmann and Stöcklin[33] studied the products in an aqueous solution of doubly-labeled [2-^{14}C,5-^{125}I]-iodouracil. The major products (65 % yield), determined by radiogas chromatography, were ^{14}CO and $^{14}CO_2$. These gases were not detected when an aqueous solution of [2-^{14}C]-iodouracil was irradiated with ^{60}Co γ-rays, or when tritium, the β^--emitter, was in the 5-position of the uracil ring[34]. Subsequently, Linz and Stöcklin[35] incorporated the doubly-labeled [U-^{14}C,5-^{125}I]-iododeoxycytidine triphosphate into the plasmid pBR322 DNA and analysed the products after a desired number of ^{125}I decayed. Again, ^{14}CO and $^{14}CO_2$ were the major products. These gases were not observed with ^{125}I not incorporated into, but mixed with the DNA. The above results bear evidence that the pyrimidine base experiences an efficient and deep fragmentation following the Auger cascade, probably due to charge neutralization.

Turning now to the second above question, we shall refer to three important investigations in which the methods of molecular biology were employed to study the range of damage to DNA. Martin and Haseltine[36] incorporated ^{125}I-labeled iododeoxycytidine at a single position within a linear plasmid segment, a polynucleotide containing 59 base pairs of defined sequence, and estimated the length of the cleavage products from their mobility on polyacrylamide gels. Single strand breaks were detected in the same strand as that labeled with ^{125}I

and in the complementary strand up to 7 nm from the decay site, with the majority confined to 1.5-2.0 nm, i.e. within 4-5 nucleotides. In the later study[37], the ^{125}I-labeled sequence-selective DNA ligand Hoechst 33258 (bis-benzimidazole derivative) was prepared and liganded to specific regions of the plasmid DNA segments (176 or 346 b.p.). The location of strand breaks relative to the site of decay was then analysed from the sequencing gel data, at a resolution corresponding to the distance between neighbouring nucleotides. The results suggested that each ^{125}I decay produced multiple scission in each DNA strand, mostly within four A-T base pairs. The final lesion may be detected as a dsb, but may also lead to loss of short fragments at the site of breakage.

Since short DNA segments were used in the above experiments, distant effects a priori could not have been detected. In contrary, Linz and Stöcklin[35] used the DNA molecule consisting of 4361 b.p. into which ^{125}I-iododeoxycytidine was incorporated. The number and the length of the cleavage products were determined by electron microscopy. It turned out that dsb occured both at the site of the decay and as far as hundreds base pairs away. The important message conveyed by this study is that the decay of covalently bound ^{125}I promotes distant damage to DNA. The most plausible explanation to be suggested consists in postulating a long-range (μm range) transfer of excitation energy in DNA.

4.3. Microdosimetric approach to ^{125}I decay

As we mentioned in § 4.1, the biological damage to cells depends on the localization of ^{125}I with respect to the nuclear DNA, a presumed target for radiobiological damage. It is so since most of the Auger and Coster-Kronig electrons emitted from ^{125}I are short-ranged and deposit their energy within a few nm of the decay site. The conventional (macroscopic) dosimetry appears inadequate in such situation. It averages the doses over large volumes and, consequently, significantly underestimates the local energy deposition from short-range electrons. Of considerable importance was the application in recent years of the microdosimetric concepts to calculate the electron spectrum of ^{125}I and the energy deposition in nm sites.

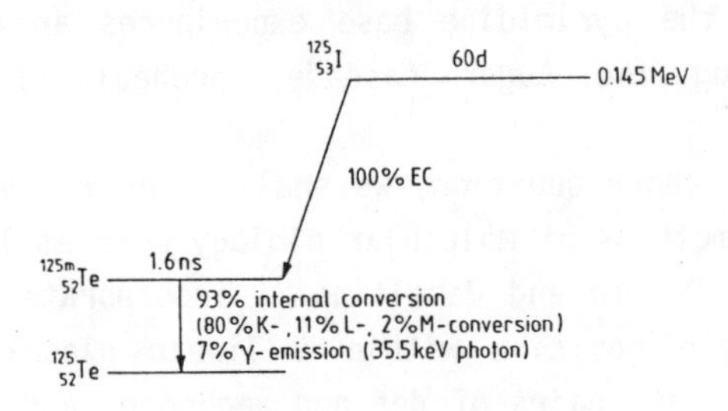

Fig. 4 Decay scheme of ^{125}I

The decay scheme of ^{125}I is shown in Fig. 4. The decay produces (in 93 %) two Auger cascades in quick succession, one due to the K-capture, the other due to internal conversion, separated by a time interval of 1.6 ns. Charlton and Booz[6)] developed a Monte Carlo computer code, later modified[8)], to estimate the number and energy of electrons released. In the condensed phase, 2 to 30 electrons may be emitted in the individual decays (in average 13 per decay[8)]). Their energy ranges from a few eV to about 35 keV, but the lowest energy electrons predominate. Most effective in the DNA damage are electrons of energy $\leq$ 500 eV[9)]. Accepting the average spectrum, Kassis et al[38)] estimated the average energy ($\triangle$E) deposited in spheres of radius r around the site of decay in unit density matter: r = 1.0 nm, $\triangle$E = 300 eV; r = 2.0 nm, $\triangle$E = 550 eV; r = 5.0 nm, $\triangle$E = 1000 eV. According to Pomplun (private communication), these values are overestimated; his estimated values of $\triangle$E are 60 eV, 130 eV and 300 eV for r = 1.0 nm, 2.0 nm and 5.0 nm, respectively. When the DNA is labeled via ^{125}IUdR, ^{125}I is on the inside of the double helix at a distance of 0.5 nm from the central axis of the DNA duplex and in the plane of the base. Thus, a high fraction of energy is deposited in the first few nm, in agreement with the ranges of the lowest energy emission electrons. This fraction then drops with the distance. This immediately makes plausible a highly localized nature of the action of ^{125}I electrons. Parallel, the probability of dsb falls by a factor of ten within the first 3 nm.

There is some controversy as to whether the average dose is an appropriate parameter in the assessment of the local damage from incorporated Auger emitters[39)]. Indeed, the radiation effect will depend upon which of the many possible cascades occurs at random. Clearly, calculations which take this stochastic behaviour into account foster a more accurate physical picture. This accuracy, however, is not necessarily needful for the interpretation of experimental results which themselves are averages over many different cascades.

Most crucial in the ^{125}I-microdosimetry approach was an attempt to convert the energy deposition in the sequential nucleotide pairs into the strand breaks. Charlton[40)] applied the electron track code to calculate the energy deposition in the immediate vicinity of the ^{125}I location (a cylinder of 2 nm diameter represented the DNA duplex). The average deposition in nucleotide pairs per decay was shown to decrease rapidly with a distance, so that beyond 5 pairs from this location it was insufficient to make a break. In subsequent papers[41,42)], the method has been refined to enable the estimation of the energy deposited in the bases and sugar-phosphate (S-P) chains separately. The DNA molecule was now modelled as a solid cylinder of diameter 2.3 nm, divided into three volumes simulating those occupied by pair of bases (diameter 1.0 nm) and two spiraling S-P moieties (0.34 nm width), the incorporated ^{125}I being placed 0.15 nm from the central axis of the base cylinder. Using individual spectra from ^{125}I decay, the energy deposition in the base and S-P volumes was calculated. Finally, by fitting different calculated values of the energy deposited in these volumes to the experimental data of Martin and Haseltine[36] on the ssb distribution, the minimum energy required for one ssb, and the location of the ssb farthest from the decay site, were determined. The best fit was obtained with the value of 17.5 eV. Higher energy depositions may produce additional ssb, also in the complimentary strand. Assuming that two ssb in opposite strands separated by not more than 10 b.p. give a dsb, the authors estimated that between 0.9 and 1.1 dsb should occur per decay in a mammalian cell, in agreement with usually quoted value of one. Note that the assessment of strand breaks by means of microdosimetry rests ultimately on a comparison of the fairly exact calculated values of the energy deposited in a volume of interest with the error-laden measured quantities. The results will not be more accurate than the approximate experimental input was.

The theoretical method of Charlton and Humm allows one to estimate the initial distribution of deposited energy within the DNA molecule. It is based on the explicit assumption that the deposition of electron energy in the critical volume of this molecule is decisive for its damage (strand breaks) which is assumed to occur at or near the sites of the initial energy deposition. The whole class of phenomena that may perturb the initial energy distribution, such as the collective excitation in DNA or the energy and charge transfer along the helix is by necessity disregarded, as these are submolecular effects and remain beyond the microdosimetric approach. It should be also kept in mind that the microdosimetric methods provide information about the quantity of energy imparted to a selected microscopic volume of the DNA molecule, and the radiation effects thereupon. These methods account for the directs effects, i.e. those occuring due to energy deposition in the DNA. They are at best a crude tool to deal with the indirects effects, i.e. those mediated by radicals from the radiolysis of water associated with DNA[9]. The relative contribution from direct and indirect effects to the damage upon the Auger electrons (or other high LET radiations) is still not known, although probably the importance of the direct action increases with LET. Pomplun[9] estimated that roughly 40 % of dsb produced by ^{125}I in DNA is due to direct effects.

The microdosimetric approach is essentially concerned with the physics of energy deposition over timescales of 10^{-16} s, whereas the chemistry eventually responsible for the biological damage occurs much later. Microdosimetry, being a purely phenomenological method, does not offer any insight into the actual mechanisms of the chemical processes involved in a damage to genetic material. Nevertheless, it has contributed significantly to the comprehension of the consequences of the Auger effect, though clearly should not be regarded as a single or sufficient explanation. A more general treatment would require the microdosimetric calculations be complement by other concepts which are beyond the scope of microdosimetry[43]. Some of them will be discussed in the following section.

4.4. Physical phenomena which escape microdosimetric interpretation

We now turn to some physical phenomena that may modify the process of the initial electron energy deposition in restricted volumes of interest. These include the phenomena of energy migration and superexcitation.

As we pointed out in § 4.2, there is experimental evidence that the decay of ^{125}I in the DNA molecule causes strand breaks not only at the site of the decay but also afar of this site. This result, which indicates at a long-distance energy transfer, is by no means surprising. The charge and energy migration have long been known to play an essential role in the radiation chemistry of DNA (upon γ-rays, fast electrons, etc). Relevant references can be found elsewhere[43,44]. In brief, in large and complex molecules, especially ones having extended sequence of double bonds, such as the DNA molecule, electronic excitation has a collective character. Like in other π-electron solid systems, the excitation energy is instantenously transmitted to the entire assembly of π-electrons with the immediate effect that the site of excitation becomes delocalized along the molecule. The close proximity and planar stacking of the bases in the DNA molecule foster the transfer of charge and excitation over long distances along the helix. There is, of course, no reason to expect that such physical processes would be less significant when the electronic excitation stems from the Auger charging. Nath et al[45-47] studied the intramolecular process of energy transfer in the molecules that experienced the Auger ionization followed by charge neutralization. This has been done by investigating the emission Mössbauer spectra of various solid phase compounds, labeled with the Auger emitters ^{57}Co or ^{129m}Te, which differed with respect to the number of the conjugated bonds (i.e. in molecules which differed in the number of delocalized π-electrons). It has been established that the higher the degree of conjugation in a molecule, the lower the probability of its fragmentation during the electronic relaxation following the Auger effect (non-conjugated molecules fragmented completely). The explanation suggested was that the energy of the excited moiety in conjugated molecules is shared collectively by the loosely bound π-electrons, and then it is rapidly lost, presumably through the emission of a single electron. Recently, it was suggested[48] that an energy or charge migration in DNA might be a non-linear process and involve solitary waves or solitons.

A frequently debated point concerns the role and consequences of the multiple charge resulting from the Auger cascade relative to the energy deposited along the tracks of the electrons. As we already mentioned, the results of Deutzmann and Stöcklin[33] on the fragmentation of ^{125}I-labeled iodouracil proved that the neutralization of this charge releases enough excitation energy to bring about the endothermic process of a rupture of the pyrimidine ring. (Recall that in these experiments the fate of the parent molecule was followed, but not the radiation effects by ^{125}I-electrons). It is, of course, difficult to distinguish between the electron irradiation and the charge neutralization on the ground of the measurements of cellular endpoints. These two phenomena are interdependent, i.e. the number of the emitted electrons and the charge on the daughter atom alter concomitantly, and both contribute to the same kind of biological effects. In recent years it was attempted to treat the neutralization process merely as a source of additional ionization[8,49]. The authors estimated an average potential energy associated with the charge on the daughter atom by adding the subsequent ionization potentials weighted by the average distribution of vacancies in the respective shells. By this procedure, the value of 926 eV per decay of ^{125}I was obtained. Further, an assumption was introduced that this energy will entirely be available for the emission of additional electrons of very low energy, just increasing the local electron dose. Objection may immediately be raised that this model keeps out of sight the basic processes acting when the initial positive charge is embadded in a large condensed-phase molecule. In reality, the problem is not limited to the simple ionization when the daughter atom (Te) is neutralized. Rather, concomitantly with the decay of ^{125}I in DNA a multiple charge accumulates and quickly redistributes over the daughter tellurium and the remaining part of the nucleotide. During the subsequent neutralization of the latter by catching electrons from the neighborhood, several hundreds eV of excitation energy is gained by this moiety which becomes superexcited. (Recall that when a molecule is excited to a level above its ionization potential, it may immediately ionize (direct ionization), or may have a transient existence in states with energies exceeding those required for ionization. It is customary to regard a molecule as superexcited when it assimilated sufficient energy to ionize, but it did not by times usually of the order of 10^{-12} s. In condensed phases each superexcited state can decay through several competing pathways. It can emit slow electrons (autoionization), or can get rid of the excess of energy by emitting a photon (radiative relaxation), or convert into lower excited states (radiationless relaxation). All these processes occur delayed in time as compared with the time required for ionization). A superexcited pyrimidine moiety can autoionize, or it may become a center of a number of vibrationally and/or electronically excited states. Due to excitation transfer, some DNA bases remote of the initial site may also be raised into excited states. As energy is put into and taken out of the restricted volume occupied by the parent moiety, the equilibrium distribution of energy will depend on the rate of transfer of energy and may differ from that estimated in the microdosimetric calculations.

5. Conclusions

The consequences of the decay of the Auger emitters in cellular DNA are apt to manifest themselves locally appropriate to the ranges of the Auger and Coster-Kronig electrons and, on a smaller scale, at sites significantly remote from the site of the decay. The former effects are accounted for by the microdosimetric approach which describes the radiation effects in terms of the quantity of energy imparted to a microscopic volume of interest, but does not offer any mechanistic information. The distant effects are interpreted in terms of energy migration from sites where the energy is originally deposited to the sites where it will be finally stored long enough to produce damage, the concept in common usage in photo and radiation chemistry of DNA.

To comprehend the physico-chemical mechanisms of the phenomena which follow a decay of an Auger emitter is a formidable task which is still far from being accomplished. Many physicists, chemists and biologists active in the field are motivated by the belief that this interdisciplinary area of research has much to offer in clarifying the basic questions of the science of the biological action of radiation.

References

1. Auger, P.: Surface Sci., 48, 1 (1975)
2. Feinendegen, L.: Radiat. Environ. Biophys. 12, 85 (1975)
3. Halpern, A., Stöcklin, G.: Radiat. Environ. Biophys. 14, 167 and 257 (1977)
4. Bloomer, W.D., Adelstein, S.J.: Pathobiology Ann. 8, 407 (1978)
5. Makrigiorgos, G., Adelstein, S.J., Kassis, A.I.: Radiat. Environ. Biophys. 29, 75 (1990)
6. Charlton, D.E., Booz, J.: Radiat. Res. 87, 10 (1981)
7. Sastry, K.S.R., Rao, D.V.: in "Physics of nuclear medicine: recent advances" (D.V. Rao, R. Chandra, M.C. Graham, eds.), Am. Inst. of Physics, N.Y. 1984, p. 169
8. Pomplun, E., Booz, J., Charlton, D.E.: Radiat. Res. 111, 533 (1987)
9. Pomplun, E.: Inst. J. Radiat. Biol. 59, 625 (1991)
10. Wexler, S.: Science 156, 901 (1967)
11. van Lith, D., Warman, J.W., de Haas, M.P., Hummel, A.: J. Chem. Soc., Faraday Trans. I, 82, 2933 (1986)
12. Paretzke, H.G.: in "Kinetics of Nonhomogenous Processes" (Ed. G.R. Freeman), Wiley, N.Y. 1987, p. 89
13. Goodhead, D.T., Nikjoo, H.: Int. J. Radiat. Biol. 55, 513 (1989)
14. Nikjoo, H., Goodhead, D.T., Charlton, D.E., Paretzke, H.G.: Phys. Med. Biol. 34, 691 (1989)
15. Goodhead, D.T., Thacker, J., Cox, R.: Int. J. Radiat. Biol. 36, 101 (1979)
16. Goodhead, D.T., Thacker, J., Cox, R.: Phys. Med. Biol. 26, 1115 (1981)
17. Thacker, J., Wilkinson, R.E., Goodhead, D.T.: Int. J. Radiat. Biol. 49, 645 (1986)
18. Goodhead, D.T.: Radiat. Res. 91, 45 (1982)
19. Halpern, A., Stöcklin, G.: Radiat. Res. 58, 329 (1974)
20. Halpern, A.: J. Chem. Soc., Faraday Trans. I, 83, 219 (1987)

21. Menke, H., Köhnlein, W., Joksch, S., Halpern, A.: Int. J. Radiat. Res. 59, 85 (1991)
22. Humm, J.L., Charlton, D.E.: in "DNA Damage by Auger Emitters" (K.F. Baverstock, D.E. Charlton, Eds.), Taylor and Francis, London 1988, p. 111
23. Halpern, A., Mütze, B.: Int. J. Radiat. Biol. 34, 67 (1978)
24. Shinohara, K., Ohara, H., Kobayashi, K., Maezawa, H., Hieda, K., Okada, S., Ito, T.: J. Radiat. Res. 26, 334 (1985)
25. Maezawa, H., Hieda, K., Kobayashi, K., Furusawa, Y., Mori, T., Suzuki, K., Ito, T.: Int. J. Radiat. Res. 53, 301 (1988)
26. Ohara, H., Shinohara, K., Kobayashi, K., Ito, T.: ref. 22, p. 123
27. Maezawa, H., Hieda, K., Kobayashi, K., Ito, T.: ref. 22, p. 135
28. Larson, D., Bodell, W.J., Ling, C., Phillips, T.L., Schell, M., Shrieve, D., Troxel, T.: Int. J. Radiat. Oncology Biol. Phys. 16, 171 (1989)
29. Nath, R., Bongiorni, P., Rossi, P.I., Rockwell, S.: Int. J. Radiat. Oncology Biol. Phys. 18, 1377 (1990)
30. Warters, R.L., Hofer, K.G., Smith, J.M.: Curr. Top Radiat. Res. Quart.: 12, 389 (1977)
31. Kassis, A.I., Fayad, F., Kinsey, B.M., Sastry, K.S.R., Taube, R.A., Adelstein, S.J.: Radiat. Res. 111, 305 (1987)
32. Whaley, J.M., Kassis, A.I., Kinsey, B.M., Adelstein, S.J., Little, J.B.: Int. J. Radiat. Biol. 57, 1087 (1990)
33. Deutzmann, R., Stöcklin, G.: Radiat. Res. 87, 10 (1981)
34. Asano, T., Halpern, A., Stöcklin, G.: Radiochim. Acta 33, 75 (1983)
35. Linz, U., Stöcklin, G.: Radiat. Res. 101, 262 (1985)
36. Martin, R.F., Haseltine, W.A.: Science 213, 896 (1981)
37. Martin, R.F., Holmes, N.: Nature 302, 452 (1983)
38. Kassis, A.I., Sastry, K.S.R., Adelstein, S.J.: Radiat. Res. 109, 78 (1987)
39. Charlton, D.E.: Radiat. Res. 114, 192 (1988)
40. Charlton, D.E.: Radiat. Res. 107, 163 (1986)
41. Charlton, D.E., Humm, J.L.: Int. J. Radiat. Biol. 53, 353 (1988)
42. Charlton, D.E.: ref. 22, p. 89 (1985)
43. Halpern, A.: Radiochim. Acta 50, 129 (1991)
44. Adams, G.G., Al-Kawizni, A.T., O'Neil, P., Fielden, E.M.: Radiat. Prot. Dosim. 31, 47 (1990)
45. Nath, A., Klein, M.P., Kündig, W., Lichtenstein, D.: Radiat. Eff. 2, 211 (1970)
46. Misroch, M.B., Schramm, C.J., Nath, A.: J. Chem. Phys. 65, 1982 (1976)
47. Nath, A., Sauer, Ch., Halpern, A.: J. Chem. Phys. 78, 5125 (1983)
48. Baverstock, K.F., Cundall, R.B.: Radiat. Phys. Chem. 32, 553 (1988)
49. Charlton, D.E., Pomplun, E., Booz, J.: Radiat. Res. 111, 553 (1987)
50. Kobayashi, K., Hieda, K., Maezawa, H., Furusawa, Y., Suzuki, M., Ito, T.: Int. J. Radiat. Biol. 59, 643 (1991)

7.4 Geochemistry and Hot Atom Chemistry

Jean-Pierre ADLOFF
Laboratory of Nuclear Chemistry, Nuclear Research Center and University Louis Pasteur, B.P. 20, 67037 Strasbourg, France and
Kurt ROESSLER,
Institute of Chemistry I, (Nuclear Chemistry), Research Centre, Postfach 1913, 5170 Jülich, FRG

1. Introduction

Nearly twenty years elapsed between the discovery of the Szilard-Chalmers effect and the first recognition of a hot atom effect in the natural environment. On geological time scales, the radioactive equilibrium between ^{238}U (T=4.668 x10^9 years) and ^{234}U (T=2.446x10^5 years) is readily established and the ratio of the activities of both uranium isotopes should be essentially unity. However, in 1955, Cherdyntsev[1)] observed that the activity ratio (AR) $^{234}U/^{238}U$ in several minerals exceeded the expected value, being as high as 3.7 in schroeckingerite. Such a huge isotope fractionation is never observed for stable elements and thus cannot be the result of chemical or physical isotope effects. It is well known that the separation of ^{235}U from ^{238}U is an extremely difficult task, which requires innumerable repetitions of elementary steps, each increasing tinily the natural isotope ratio.

It is now universally recognized that the anomaly discovered by Cherdyntsev, whatever its actual mechanism, is triggered by the recoil energy of ^{234}Th (T=24.1 d) formed by α decay of ^{238}U. Nucleogenic atoms formed in this decay acquire kinetic energies of about 100 keV and behave like hot atoms.

The rupture of radioactive equilibrium between ^{234}U and ^{238}U appears to be the rule rather than an exception and has been the subject of a very large number of investigations. Indeed the disequilibrium is not restricted to uranium isotopes, but occurs all along the natural radioactive families. The geochemical implications and the applications of the uranium series disequilibrium have been exhaustively described in a book edited by M. Ivanovich and R.S. Harmon [2)].

In recent years the behaviour of uranium and thorium (as well as rare earths) in geochemical media has been widely investigated because these elements (in form of uraninite UO_2 and thorianite ThO_2) represent natural analogues of actinides (and fission products) which are the main deleterious components of the radioactive wastes. The long-lived natural radioelements are the only means by which nuclides normally absent in nature (notably Pu, Np and Am) can be traced over the long periods (10^5 to 10^6 years) during which the noxious actinides decay to acceptable levels. It has been stated that natural analogues are a "key element of safety assessment and of confidence building in models, for both the experts and the public"[3]. Most of the long-lived actinides, like the natural U and Th isotopes, are α emitters and beget radioactive daughters. Hence hot atom effects must be considered for the artificial as well as for the natural α emitters.

The discussion will focus mainly on the various models which have been proposed for the interpretation of the disequilibrium of the uranium isotopes. The survey will cover mostly literature published starting 1984 since geochemical implications of hot atom chemistry were reviewed in a previous monography on Hot Atom Chemistry[4].

2. Alpha decay in minerals

The long-lived ancestors of the three natural radioactive families ^{238}U, ^{235}U ($7 x 10^8$ y) and ^{232}Th ($1.4 x 10^{10}$ y) have half-lives respectively very close to the age of the Earth, the two last about six times shorter and 3 times longer. Thus they are witnesses of geochemical events which have occured since the formation of our planet. In a closed system the three radioelements are in equilibrium with all descendants which comprise altogether 22 α emitters (neglecting low intensity branchings). Uranium and thorium bearing minerals are uniquely suited for observing (i) the after effects of α emission, (ii) the radiation damage induced by the radiation, (iii) the correlation between the two preceding phenomena. The occurrence of a metamict (i.e. amorphous) state in minerals like zircon is a macroscopic consequence of the chaotic disturbance of the structure brought about by the α recoils in an initially regular lattice.

For the radiochemist, the easiest access to the events following α decay, is to determine "isotope effects" in natural samples. Besides the archetype case of the $^{234}U/^{238}U$ pair, fractionations are also observed among the thorium isotopes ^{232}Th, ^{230}Th and ^{228}Th. Recoil-induced separations of nuclides from a parent matrix were known since the early days of radioactivity and have been widely used for the preparation of carrier free natural and artificial nuclides. In minerals, parent-daughter separations (such as U/Pa,Th/Ra) following α and β decays are also widely noticed but they are less amenable to interpretation in terms of hot atom effects because they may result merely from the change of chemical identity during the transmutation.

The immediate consequences of α decay with particular emphasis on uranium have been discussed elsewhere [5,6]. In general the role of electronic excitation of the daughter due to the sudden change from Z to Z-2 is negligible with respect to the effects of the very high kinetic energy of the recoiling atom, about 100 keV. The properties of uranium[7] and thorium[8] recoil atoms have been extensively reviewed, as well as the charge states of α recoils in the gas phase or ejected from thin layers. The kinetic energy of α-recoils is dissipated mainly by elastic collisions with the nuclei of the matrix.

Little is known of the actual charge of α recoils in bulk materials. From simple arithmetic the electric charge of the daughter should be decreased by two units with respect to that of the parent[5]. This reasoning holds well for the pair $U^{6+}(\alpha)Th^{4+}$ but fails for $U^{4+}(\alpha)Th^{2+}$ because it leads to a highly unstable oxidation state of the daughter. In a mineral, Th^{2+} will not survive, but rather converts to the tetravalent and only stable ionic form of thorium.

The radiation damage is intense along the path of the α particle and of the recoil atom. Both species have high LET values and are well known to produce visible tracks in a photographic emulsion and in solids such as mica. Each α particle displaces about 500 atoms in the lattice and each recoil species about 1500 atoms. The latter ends up in a highly disturbed zone since the LET increases toward the end of the trajectory. The role of radiation damage accounts for the observed disequilibrium between ^{234}U and ^{238}U in several models and has stimulated work on the effect of external irradiation, in addition to the self-irradiation, on uranium minerals.

3. The range of α-recoil atoms in minerals

Quite intuitively hot atoms produced in a mineral grain are likely to be expelled from their host if the parent is located close to the surface, i.e. lies at a depth within the recoil range. This picture has been used for a long time for the description of emanating power due to recoil[9]. It seems to have been retained as an explanation of the uranium isotope disequilibrium for the first time by Kigoshi[10]. The author suggested that the decay of ^{238}U at the surface or near the surface of solid grains ejects the nascent ^{234}Th recoil atoms into rock pores filled with water. The hot atoms are rapidly stopped in the water and decay via two fast steps to ^{234}U. Thus the water is enriched in this isotope and the AR exceeds unity (and correspondingly AR <1 at least at the surface of the grain). From the accumulation of ^{234}Th ejected from a zircon sample into water, Kigoshi deduced a suspiciously high recoil range of 55 pm. Previously, a more sensible value of 19.5 pm had been recorded from the observation of the thorium recoil tracks in mica[11]. This order of magnitude was confirmed in a different type of experiment by collecting on an aluminium plate the recoiling ^{234}Th and also ^{231}Th (from $^{235}U(\alpha)$) ejected from UO_2 and U_3O_8 as a function of the thickness of the radioactive source[12].

Range calculations using the Lindhard, Scharff, Schiott (in short LSS) theory have been performed for all natural a recoil atoms, including the extinct ^{240}U and ^{236}U in 15 different minerals[13]. The ^{234}Th range in uraninite (UO_2) is 14.6 pm, in U_3O_8 17.8 pm, in ThO_2 15.8 pm and in quartz (SiO_2) 27.2 pm. Expressed in superficial mass units, the ranges are respectively 15.9, 15.1, 15.6 and 7.2 mg per cm^2. Although the calculated values are in gross agreement with experimental data, discrepancies may result from the fact that the LSS calculations ignore structural effects (i.e. apply to amorphous samples) while measurements are performed on crystalline samples; in addition, dislocations in the matrix are expected to play some part, perhaps leading to a slow transfer of recoil atoms to the surface. The average range deduced from leaching experiments[14] on carnotite is 19.3 pm , to be compared with the LSS calculated value of 32 pm. In other cases, the measured range exceeds the calculated one, which may reveal the role of channeling. It has also been noted that the calculated data are inconsistent with the density of the selected matrices[8].

A different approach to the range of recoil atoms is based on computer simulation of collision cascades using the MARLOWE program[7,8].This procedure leads to the mean projected range of the recoil atom rather than the total path. The versatility of the program permits the computation as a function of the initial recoil energy and of the properties of the matrices. For the 72 keV ^{234}Th recoil atoms, the resulting range is 30 pm in SiO_2, 18.5 pm in MgO and 16 pm in UO_2. These values are slightly higher than those obtained by direct LSS calculations. Further information from the computation is the range distribution of the recoil atoms. For ^{234}Th projected in MgO the fwhm of the distribution is about 10 pm.

The computed range of ^{234}Th recoil atoms in water is 60 pm.This value gives an idea of the role of the porosity of the medium. In low porousity material, the distance between adjacent grains may be less than the recoil range; this allows the recoiling atom to be again embedded in a solid. After decay of ^{234}Th, the granddaughter ^{234}U may be released by diffusion or by etching of the recoil track. This mechanism has first been proposed in the theory of the emanating power, and later applied to the disequilibrium of the uranium isotopes in a model based on accelerated dissolution of α tracks[15].

4. The leaching of recoil atoms from minerals

A striking observation is the maintenance of radioactive equilibrium between ^{238}U and ^{234}U in lunar samples. The moon being deprived of any water, the terrestrial behaviour of the uranium isotopes necessarily reflects the interaction of groundwaters with the minerals. In addition, the fractionation of stable isotopes of similar magnitude to the uranium case is never observed. It may be concluded that the erstwhile hot atoms exist in minerals in loosened sites created in the decay, which facilitate their subsequent dissolution by percolation of groundwater. These considerations have prompted many leaching experiments which have lead to interesting conclusions regarding hot atom effects in minerals. Leaching is usually performed first with water and continued with increasingly chemically agressive solutions up to hot mixtures of concentrated nitric and hydrofluoric acids. The procedure can be applied continuously in a chromatographic column containing the sample (a mineral possibly ground and of selected grain size) or stepwise by stirring with the solution followed by centrifugation or filtration. The α-emitting isotopes of interest are readily identified and counted by spectrometry with silicon surface barrier detectors.

At this point, a word of caution is necessary. Many authors have neglected the unavoidable dissolution of the host minerals. By this way ^{238}U can be released in large amounts and the measured AR is no more representative of the direct ejection of ^{234}U, but rather reflects the combination of ejection and dissolution. The primary source of uranium in groundwaters is attributed to the solubility of uranium-bearing minerals of igneous rocks and the ensuing dilution of the recoil-induced separation of the uranium isotopes must be taken into account.

This problem has been thoroughly discussed by Petit et al.[16]. The authors have shown that when the dissolution rate exceeds a critical value, the direct ejection mechanism can not lead to AR's of 1.2 which have been observed in nature. Thus the various models proposed so far and based on direct or dissolution-enhanced release of ^{234}U are sufficient only for dissolution rates slower than about 3.0×10^{-5} pm per year. In comparison, the dissolution rate of major minerals estimated from weathering data would be much higher, of the order of 0.1 pm per year. Accessory minerals such as monazite and zircon, may be much less soluble, but even in this case the critical dissolution rate (reduced by a factor of 2 with respect to that estimated for major minerals) is inconsistent with the isotope fractionation induced by recoil; again dislocation may be important. In addition, the radiation damage produced by alpha decay would still accelerate the etching rate of old and uranium-rich minerals. On the other hand, annealing processes could again reduce the leaching rate.

Changes of AR ratios in leachates with the chemical aggressiveness of the leaching reagents have been observed on several occasions[14,17-18]. Attack of a mineral with water or dilute acid solutions yields generally leachates with AR slightly higher than those observed for the bulk of the sample. This is due to an increased solubility of loosely bound ^{234}U. With stronger acids, most of the uranium is dissolved and consistent with what has preceded, the preferential solubility of the recoil atoms is masked by the large amount of dissolved uranium. The highest AR are found in the residues such as silicates which contain little uranium and require leaching agents as strong as hot concentrated acids. It appears that recoil ^{234}U atoms are ejected from the adjacent uranium-rich phases to the uranium-poor phase which act as collectors of the hot atoms during geological times. AR superior to 400 have been observed in the residues of acid-treated carnotite[14]. Interestingly enough, minerals with high uranium contents (> 20%) which exhibit an average AR of unity, have a very heterogeneous isotopic distribution of ^{234}U; microsamples with very high AR can be separated by simple leaching from bulk samples with normal AR.

The easier leaching from the residues of ^{234}U vs ^{238}U confirms that the former are not strongly held in the crystal lattice. The same behaviour has been observed in a very rich (34.5 % U) sample from Oklo[19]: in the last leaching step, when nearly all uranium has been washed out, residues such as inclusions of hematite or breccia have an AR of 64 and ^{234}U is leached much better than ^{238}U and ^{235}U.

It is interesting to note that in Oklo samples part of the ^{235}U is not primordial, but is the daughter of ^{239}Pu formed by neutron irradiation of ^{238}U. This nucleogenic ^{235}U should behave like ^{234}U. Indeed a thousandfold variation in the $^{235}U/^{238}U$ AR has been observed[20]. This may reflect a selective migration of Pu during the operation of the reactor followed by a metamorphic redistribution of Pu. This anomaly is located in a 250mm wide zone, which rules out a simple recoil displacement effect.

5. Alpha-decay induced radiation damage and natural annealing

The increase of the rate of solution of solid compounds due to radiation damage is a well established fact. In the case of radioactive minerals, the crystalline disorder brought by self irradiation is called metamictization. With increasing radiation dose, zircon becomes amorphous and is progressively more leachable.

The search for radiation-resistant embedments for radwastes bearing alpha emitters has prompted intensive research on radiation effects on glasses. In order to foresee the effects of long-term irradiation in repositories, laboratory experiments have been performed by bombardment of samples with accelerated heavy ions in order to simulate the self-irradiation, followed by leaching experiments. More recently these experiments have been extended to the case of U-bearing minerals[21,22]. Implantation of heavy ions, such as Pb, with energies of the order of 1 keV/amu greatly increases the dissolution rate. The rate of etching does not increase linearly with the dose and the density of defects but is characterized by a threshold at a critical dose which is 5×10^{12} ions cm^{-2}. Although these observations confirm the synergy of radiation damage and solubility, it should be noted that the implantation concerns the outer layers of the sample rather than the bulk irradiation prevailing in nature. On the other hand, the intense dose is delivered in a very short time interval, while the self-irradiation lasts over geological periods. The validity of the simulation of internal alpha decay with heavy ion implantation remains questionable.

Here leaching experiments are also relevant[23,24] and give an idea of the age of radiation damage. ^{238}U and ^{232}Th being the heads of the radioactive series are located in non-damaged regions. On the other hand, the daughter recoil atoms come to rest in damaged regions and thus are candidates for leaching experiments, unless the damage is subsequently annealed out by some spontaneous natural process.

Information on the time scale of the latter is inferred from the half-lives of the thorium isotopes ^{230}Th and ^{228}Th. The half-life of the latter is 1.9 y; it is born amidst "fresh " radiation damage while the defects around 10^5 y- ^{230}Th (as well as ^{234}U) had hundreds thousand of years to heal. Experiments performed on a thorianite ThO_2 sample 550 My old and on a 1 Gy-old uraninite UO_2 have indicated a slight leaching of ^{234}U vs ^{238}U and of ^{230}Th vs ^{232}Th, but a very strongly enhanced leaching of the short lived ^{228}Th. From the respective half-lives it appears that the natural annealing of radiation damage occurs on a time scale between 10 y and 10^5 y. Average healing times are in the ky range. Thermal annealing reduces the leaching rate.

Self-annealing of the natural damage is not unexpected, otherwise the minerals would be uniformly damaged and all daughter recoils would be leached out. As a practical conclusion, materials which show permanent damage are not suitable for radwaste storage.

6. Hot atom chemistry of a recoil atoms in minerals

Most of the early models of uranium disequilibrium were based on the direct or delayed release of ^{234}Th or ^{234}U from minerals. A first interpretation taking into account chemical effects associated with α decay was proposed by Rosholt et al.[25]. These authors considered that ^{234}U born from ^{238}U could be incorporated in a lattice site which favours the formation of ^{234}U in the soluble hexavalent state, in contrast to much less soluble tetravalent ^{238}U. In a review[16] on the various interpretations of the uranium isotopes disequilibrium, it has been suggested that the most plausible model is that based on valence changes upon α decay.

More recently a new model of recoil chemistry in minerals has been elaborated[5-8]. It is based on the physical consequences of collision dynamics which in turn influence the oxidation state of the recoil atom. Initially the aim of this model was to interpret the observed ruptures of radioactive equilibria after α decay, taking as a typical example the $^{238}U/^{234}U$ couple. Because the immediate oxidation state of ^{234}Th in minerals cannot be determined and the wet analytical procedure would anyhow change the unstable states to $^{234}Th^{4+}$, the conclusions must be drawn from the chemical state of the final nuclide, ^{234}U.

It has been observed that in many minerals, as a consequence of α-recoil, ^{234}U is oxidized to U(VI) even if the parent ^{238}U is tetravalent.This behaviour should be associated to the presence of oxygen lattice defects. This is confirmed by the recoil chemistry of uranium in crystalline compounds containing inorganic or organic ligands.

Data on hot atom chemistry of uranium isotopes formed in n,γ and n,2n reactions are available[7,8]. When the target atom is tetravalent and incorporated in a matrix with an excess of oxygen atoms, most of the recoil atoms are formed in the oxidized hexavalent form, with a yield increasing with the recoil energy. On the other hand, in complex compounds containing many hydrogen atoms, part of the uranium atoms are found in the reduced form. Hence the behaviour of the recoil atoms is determined by reactions with oxidizing or reducing species produced along or at the end of the recoil path.

However, it is surprising that the small number (one or two approximately) of defects produced by the (n,γ) reaction is able to oxidize the recoil atoms at all. By virtue of some mechanism these defects must be concentrated at the end of the trajectory, very close to the site, where the recoil atom comes to rest.

Computer simulations described below reveal that this is indeed the case, as shown from the collision dynamics of heavy projectiles such as thorium with the light oxygen atoms in rocks and minerals. Whereas after the collision of partners of equal mass the paths are diverging, the directions are aligned when a heavy atom strikes a light one, as shown in figure 1[8]. The heavy ^{234}Th recoil atom tends to move straightforward, pushing and accumulating the light atoms in front of it.

On the other hand, the light partners move faster and will be stopped before the heavy one. The slower and still proceeding primary atoms may displace the light one for a second or third time. As a consequence of such an "aligned" cascade, the light particles end up with a high local density at the site of thermalization of the recoil atom.

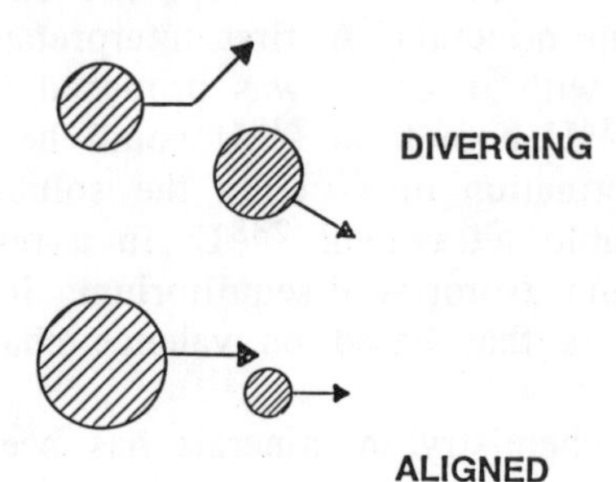

Fig.1: The distinct cascade directions in collisions of partners of equal mass (upper part) and of very different mass

This observation has prompted computer simulation studies of single collision cascades with the program MARLOWE[26]. The computed cascades were triggered by energetic U or Th atoms in model compounds such as MgO and UO_2 simulating U-rich and U-poor rocky or mineral media respectively.

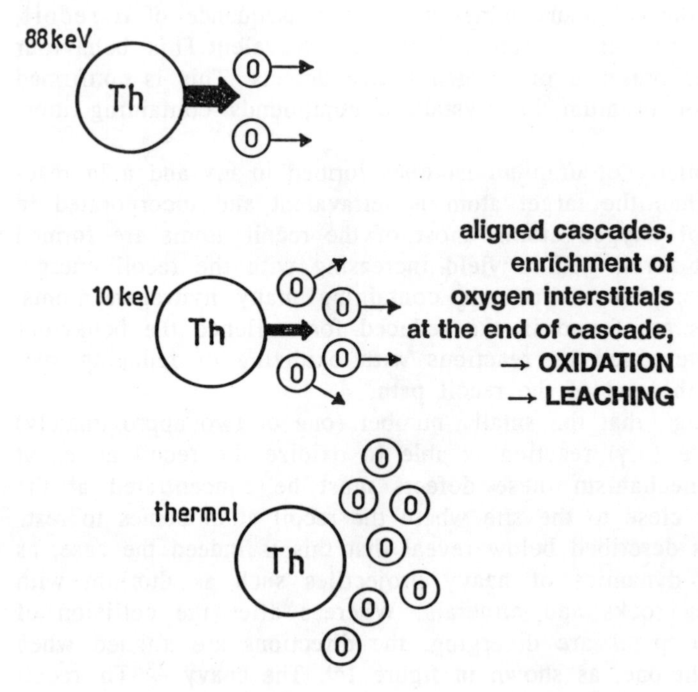

Fig.2: Schematic view of the effect of aligned cascades of Th recoils in oxygen containing targets

Figure 2 taken from ref.[5] displays a schematic view of the effect of aligned cascades of thorium recoils in oxygen containing targets. The plot in figure 3 is a representation of a typical cascade of a 100 eV Th atom in MgO as calculated by MARLOWE. The lattice is projected onto the (010) plane because the cascade appeared to be rather flat. All features derived from the theoretical considerations show up: alignement of motions, multiple knock-ons of the oxygen atoms and eventually appearance of two oxygen interstitials within a distance of less than 0.2 pm from the stopped recoil atom.

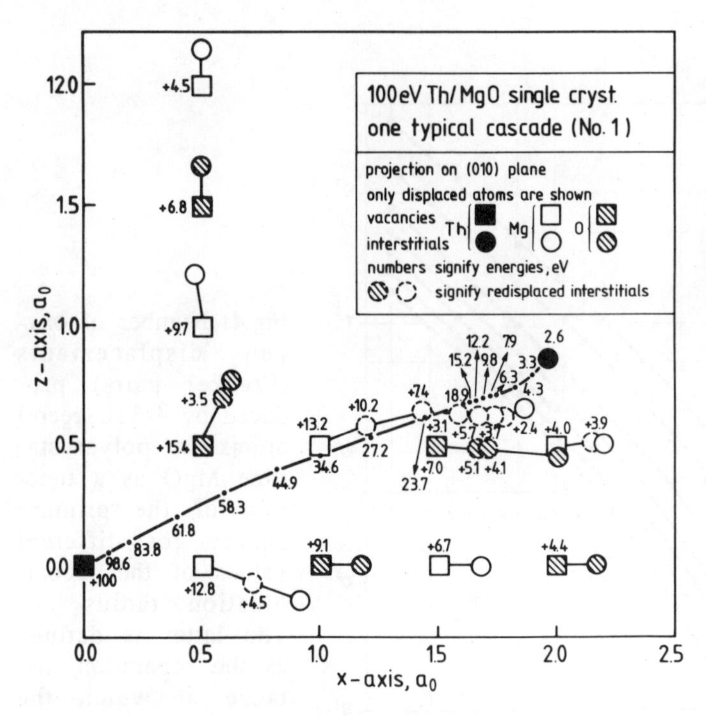

Fig.3: MARLOWE calculation of a typical binary collision cascade of a 100 eV ^{234}Th in a MgO single crystal. The figure represents the projection on the (010) plane of the three dimensional trajectory

In figure 4, the number of oxygen displacements in cascades of Th recoiling in polycrystalline MgO is shown as a function of the initial recoil energy. It is estimated that approximately 3000 oxygen interstitials are formed for a recoil atom with an energy of 70 to 80 keV. Many of these interstitials will accumulate in front of the recoiling Th atom. The collision dynamics show that when the heavy recoil atom hits an oxygen atom in the lattice, the terminal part of the trajectory is analogue to a nest of oxygen radicals in which the hot atom has come to rest. If the lattice were rich in hydrogen atoms, the latter would accumulate likewise in front of the recoil atoms which in that case would be reduced.

Figure 5 shows the effect of the oxygen atoms on the ^{234}Th recoils in the natural decay of ^{238}U. In rocks and basic minerals, uranium is generally found in the tetravalent state, U^{4+}.The decay by α emission formally reduces the charge of the daughter to Th^{2+}. Internal conversion of the energy of the 48 keV level of ^{234}Th would expectedly trigger an Auger charging process and increase the charge; however fast oxidation to Th^{3+} is due mostly to the inherent unstability of the divalent thorium ions. Th^{3+}, in its intersitial lattice position, is oxidized by the nearby oxygens to the stable valence state Th^{4+}. The following two β-decays lead formally to $^{234}U^{6+}$. Here the oxygen radicals may warrant the hexavalent state and also serve as ligands for the formation of uranyl ions already in the solid, or at least upon contact with aqueous geomedia where they will be readily complexed by carbonate ions and easily leached out of the solid host.

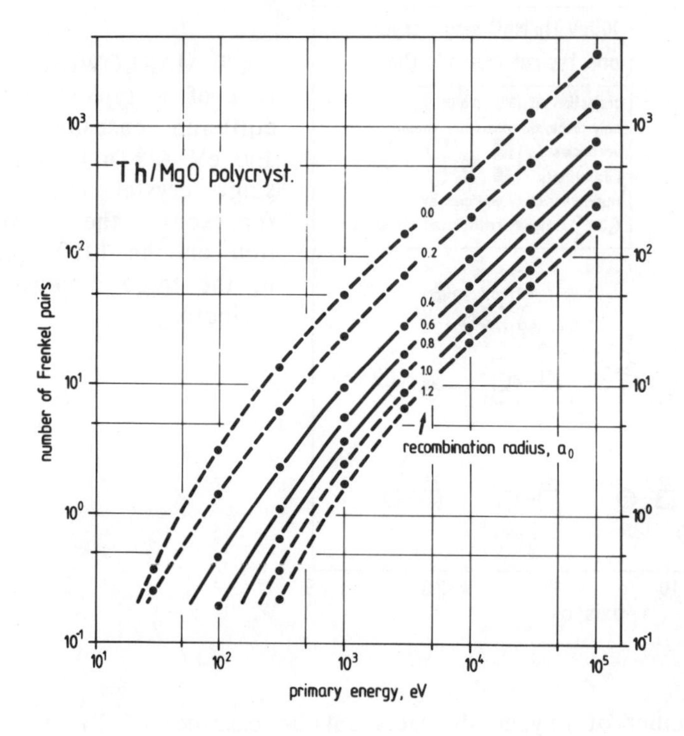

Fig.4: Number of oxygen displacements (Frenkel pairs) produced by ^{234}Th recoil atoms in polycrystalline MgO as a function of the primary energy for different values of the recombination radius a_0. The latter is defined as the separation distance at which the pair recombines immediately.

This model differs from all other "chemical" mechanisms of α-recoil proposed hitherto in postulating that the nearby oxygen defects act immediately after the recoil of the thorium daughter or even during the development of the cascade. Oxidative control of the β decay products, as well as complexation reactions, are merely auxiliary processes as compared to the primary oxidation of ^{234}Th. The main events take place as a consequence of the recoil at a moment where the oxygen radicals are still located close to the recoil atom. In the course of geological times, such oxygen radicals may diffuse away and react to form less active species.

The preceding discussion was based on the decay effects of tetravalent uranium. If U(VI) is involved, the primary charge on ^{234}Th will be higher. However, neutralization along the slower part of the trajectory will finally lead to a situation similar to that encountered for U(IV).

A premise of the model was that the recoil takes place in an environment with only few uranium atoms, i.e. minerals with low U content. If uranium is the main or an important component of the lattice, the number of oxidizing in-

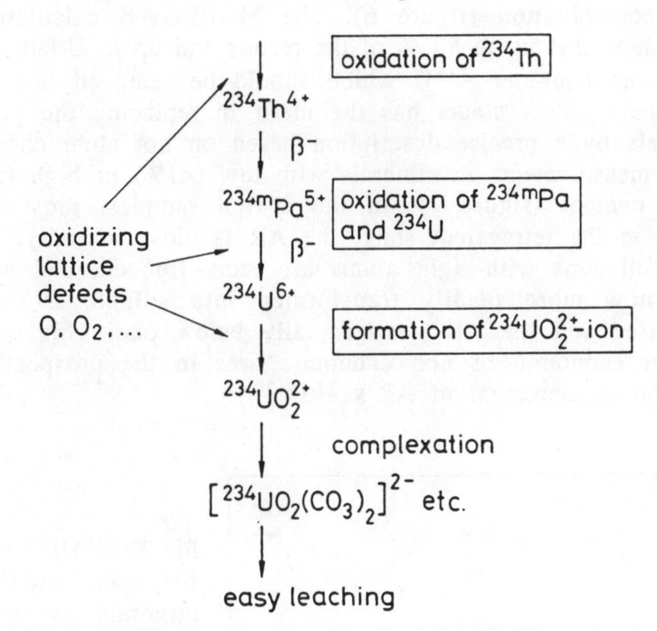

Fig.5: The chemical model for the origin of the $^{238}U/^{234}U$ disequilibrium.

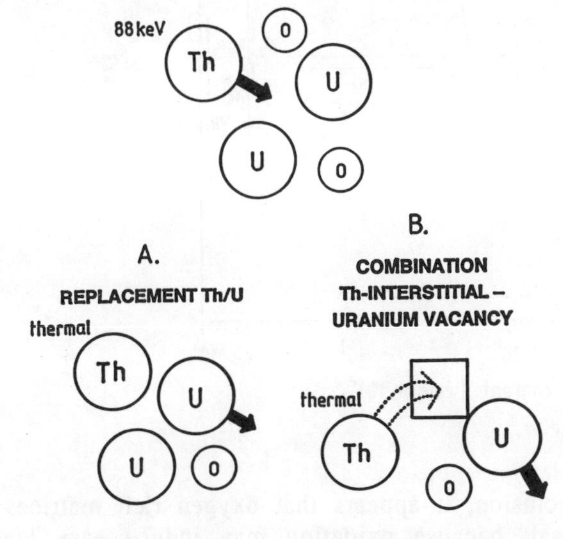

Fig.6: Schematic view of the effects of Th-recoil in uranium-rich minerals

terstitials will be lower. On the other hand, in a collision between two heavy partners (U on U or Th on U) the probability is high for the hot atom to end in a regular lattice position either by direct substitution or by trapping in a vacant site by spontaneous recombination (figure 6). The MARLOWE calculation of ^{234}Th recoils in UO_2 show that up to 80 % of the recoils end up in U-lattice sites and consequently also the daughter ^{234}U which should be removed less preferentially from the lattice. This model has the merit in replacing the previous vague "chemical" models by a precise description based on hot atom chemistry. It fits nicely with AR measurements in minerals with low (<1%) or high (> to a few percent) uranium content (figure 7). In the U-rich samples, most of the ^{234}U recoils terminate in the tetravalent state; the AR is close to unity. In the poorer materials, the collisions with light atoms are more frequent and because the ^{234}U atoms are now more readily transformed into soluble U(VI), the leaching is also increased and the AR lies generally below one. This explains why the recognition of economic or non economic ores in the prospection of uranium is based on the measurement of AR's [27-28-29].

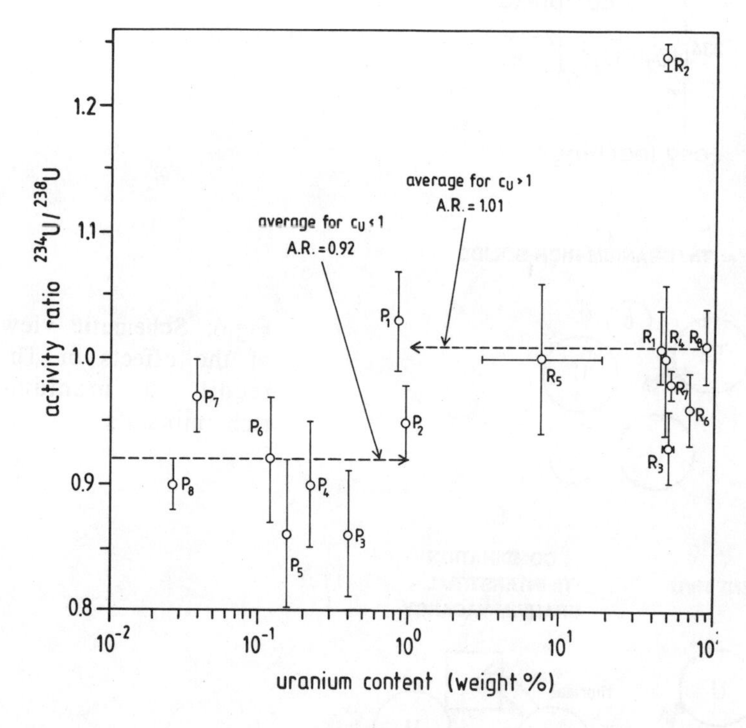

Fig.7: $^{238}U/^{234}U$ ratio for some uraniferous minerals as a function of the uranium content [7)]

As a more practical conclusion, it appears that oxygen rich matrices are less suitable for radwaste disposal, because oxidation may induce easy leaching of actinides. On the other hand, hydrogen-containing materials, such as bitumens, which impede the oxidation processes could offer a greater resistance to leaching.

References

1. Cherdyntsev, Y.V., Chalov, P.I., Khitrik, M.E., Mambetov, D.M., Khaidarov, G.Z.: Akad. Nauk SSSR,3, 175 (1954-55)
2. "Uranium Series Disequilibrium: Applications to Environmental Problems", Ivanovich, M., Harmon, R.S., Eds,Clarendon Press, Oxford,UK (1982),571 p.
3. Petit, J.C.: Radiochim. Acta, 52 / 53, 337 (1991)
4. Sakanoue,M., Hashimoto, T. in "Hot Atom Chemistry", T. Matsuura Ed., Kodansha, Tokyo, (1984) p. 460
5. Ordonez-Regil, E., Schleiffer,J.J., Adloff,J.P., Roessler, K.: Radiochim. Acta, 47, 177 (1989).
6. Adloff,J.P., Roessler, K.: Radiochim. Acta , 52 / 53, 269 (1991)
7. Roessler, K. in Gmelin Handbook "Uranium" Suppl. Vol. A6 (1983) p. 135
8. Roessler, K. in Gmelin Handbook "Thorium" Suppl. Vol. A4 (1988) p. 199
9. Adloff, J.P. : This Book , Chapter VIII. 1.
10. Kigoshi, K.: Science, 173, 47 (1971).
11. Huang, W.H., Walker, R.M.: Science,155, 1103 (1976)
12. Hashimoto, T., Kido, K., Sotobayashi, T.: J. Inorg. Nucl. Chem., 43, 2233 (1981)
13. Hashimoto, T., Aoyagi, Y., Kudo, H., Sotobayashi, T.: J. Radioanal. Nucl. Chem. Articles, 90, 415 (1985)
14. Sheng, Z.Z., Kuroda, P.K.: Radiochim. Acta , 39, 131 (1986)
15. Fleischer, R.K., Raabe, O.G.: Geochim. Cosmochim. Acta, 42,973 (1978)
16. Petit, J.C., Langevin, Y., Dran, J.C.: Bull. Minéral. , 108, 745 (1985).
17. Sheng,Z.Z., Kuroda, P.K.: Radiochim. Acta, 37, 93 (1984)
18. Sheng,Z.Z., Kuroda, P.K.: Radiochim. Acta, 40, 95 (1986).
19. Sheng, Z.Z., Kuroda, P.K.: Nature, 312, 535 (1984).
20. Hishita, S., Masuda, A.: Naturwiss. , 74, 241 (1987).
21. Petit, J.C., Langevin , Y., Dran, J.C.:Geochim. Cosmochim. Acta ,49, 871 (1985)
22. Petit, J.C., Dran,, J.C., Della Mea, G.: Bull. Minéral. 110, 25 (1987).
23. Eyal, Y. , Fleischer, R.L. : Nature, 314, 518 (1985).
24. Eyal, Y., Fleischer, R.L. : Geochim.Cosmochim. Acta , 49, 1155 (1985).
25. Rosholt, J.N., Shields, W.R., Garner, E.L.: Science, 139, 224 (1963).
26. Roessler, K.: This Book, Chapter IV.2..
27. Cherdyntsev,V.V.: Uranium 234, Atomizdat, Moscow 1969; Israel Program for Scientific Translations, Jerusalem 1971.
28. Syromyatnikov, N. G. : Soviet At. Energy 19, 964 (1965).
29. Syromyatnikov, N.G., Ibrayev, R.A., Mukashev, F.K.: Geokhimiya 697 (1967) .

7.5 The Oklo Phenomenon, Isotopic Anomaly and Hot Atom Chemistry

P.K.KURODA
Department of Chemistry, University of Nevada, Las Vegas, Nevada 89154 U.S.A.

1. Introduction

In the night of 15 July 1945, General Leslie Groves[1] at Base Camp near the Trinity Test Site, Alamogordo, New Mexico, is quoted to have stated: "I had become a bit annoyed with Fermi --- when he suddenly offered to take wagers from his fellow scientists on whether or not the bomb would ignite the atmosphere, and if so, whether it would merely destroy New Mexico or destroy the world". Emilio Segrè later recalled this historic event as follows: "--- we saw the whole sky flash with unbelievable brightness in spite of the very dark glasses we wore ---, I believed for a moment I thought the explosion might set fire to the atmosphere and thus finish the earth".

One month later in August 1945, standing in the ruins of Hiroshima, which looked like the end of the world, I felt that perhaps the beginning of the world must have been like this. Thus I became interested in the study of large-scale nuclear reactions occurring in nature. I knew that a German physicist named Flügge[2], in 1939, considered the possibility that a critical uranium chain reaction may have occurred in some uranium ore deposits. A French physicist named Noetzlin[3] then published a series of papers concerning a possible connection between volcanism and nuclear energy, while a Japanese physicist named Odagiri[4] argued that a large-scale transmutation of the elements might be occurring at the center of the earth.

After the end of WWII, a chance encounter with one of the early pioneers of hot atom chemistry in America enabled me to pursue my idea. An International Symposium on Geochemistry was held at the 75th Annual Meetings of the American Chemical Society in New York City during the first week of September 1951. When I finished presenting a paper concerning the radioactivity of hot springs in Japan, I was approached by a young gentleman, who introduced himself as Raymond R. Edwards, a hot atom chemist and Chairman of the Chemistry Department of the University of Arkansas. He invited me for lunch and told me an incredible story that his group at Arkansas was looking for the presence of radioactive strontium isotopes in the water of Hot Springs National Park, Arkansas. He apparently believed that a natural nuclear reactor was actually operating today under the ground at Hot

Springs Arkansas and was trying to prove his idea by radiochemical means. The term 'hot atom chemistry' was new to me in 1951 and I thought at that time that it was an area of chemistry populated by chemists who had 'hot' ideas such as the possible existence of nuclear reactors in nature. It is interesting to recall that in 1951 scientists believed that the age of the earth was about 3.3 billion years. Even Pope Pius XII is reported to have mentioned this age of the earth in his address to the Pontifical Academy of Sciences on 22 November 1951. Soon thereafter, Houtermans[5] revised this value to 4.5(±0.3) billion years, which is in essential agreement with the currently accepted value.

The research program which had its origin in the hot atom chemistry(HAC) laboratories at the University of Arkansas in the early 1950's led to the theory of the Oklo phenomenon[6] and the discovery of the extinct nuclide ^{244}Pu in the early solar system[7,8,9]. The concept of HAC played a key role not only in these, but also in the studies on such far reaching subjects as the age of the earth, the moon and the solar system. A brief account of some of the results from these studies during the second half of the 20th century will be presented in this chapter.

2. The Oklo Phenomenon

2.1. Early Studies

The idea of a critical uranium chain reaction occurring in nature was quite unpopular among physicists in the early 1950's. The reason for this was that if Fermi's pile theory[10] was applied to natural uranium ore deposits, it seemed to lead to an unequivocal conclusion that the chain reaction could have never become self-sustaining. According to the pile theory,

$$k_{\infty} = \epsilon \, p \, f \, \eta \qquad (1)$$

where ϵ is the fast fission factor, p is the resonance escape probability, f is the thermal utilization factor, and η is the number of fast neutrons available per neutron absorbed by uranium. The problem was that in order that the value of k_{∞} to become greater than unity, one had to increase the values of p and f so that the product p times f would increase. It turned out that as p increased, f always decreased and there was no way to increase both factors simultaneously. I spent two years from 1954 to 1956 trying to find the conditions under which the value of k_{∞} would become greater than unity, but all these calculations ended in a failure.

One day in early 1956, when I was clearing my desk by throwing away the notes containing the results of all the unsuccessful calculations, however, a thought occurred to me that I may have been using an incorrect model in these calculations. I have been assuming that a large uranium ore deposit had suddenly appeared on the earth billions of years ago, but I should have known from my past experience in the studies on hot springs and volcanoes that uranium ore deposits do not suddenly appear on the surface of the earth. Uranium had to be first leached out from the rocks, transported by water and deposited at a certain place in order to form a large uranium ore. This somewhat more complicated but geochemically more reasonable model, which I have accepted in 1956, led to the conclusion that natural reactors should have been operating on the earth approximately 2 billion years ago[6].

Soon thereafter, I proposed to the Atomic Energy Commission to initiate a research program to examine the isotopic composition of uranium in minerals and ore deposits from all over the world, but no one was interested in funding such a project.

In the same year 1956, Patterson[11] reported the age of the earth and the meteorites to be (4.55 ± 0.07) billion years. At the beginning of this famous paper, he remarked: "It seems we now should admit that the age of the earth is known as accurately and with about as much confidence as the concentration of aluminum is known in the Westerly, Rhode Island, granite". The age of the earth reported by Patterson[11] became universally accepted to be correct by scientists up to the present time. It is worthy of note here that in the equation used to calculate the age of the earth,

$$\frac{R_{1a} - R_{1b}}{R_{2a} - R_{2b}} = \frac{(e^{\lambda_1 T} - 1)}{K.(e^{\lambda_2 T} - 1)} \qquad (2)$$

where T is the age; λ_1 and λ_2 are the decay constants of ^{235}U and ^{238}U, respectively; R_1 and R_2 are the $^{207}Pb/^{204}Pb$ and $^{206}Pb/^{204}Pb$ ratios of samples a and b, respectively; and K is the $^{238}U/^{235}U$ ratio today(= 137.8). Scientists at that time believed that K should be regarded as an universal conatant.

2.2. Discovery of the Oklo Reactor

On 25 September 1972, the world's scientific community learned of an extraordinary discovery made by research workers of the French Atomic Energy Commission: uranium had been found, in the deposit at Oklo in the Republic of Gabon, Africa, with an abnormal isotopic composition that led one to arrive at the conclusion that self-sustaining nuclear chain reactions had occurred in the remote past. The reaction site consisted of several bodies of very rich uranium ore, and more than 500 tons of uranium had been involved in the reactions with a quantity of energy released equal to about 100 x 10^9 kW.h. The integrated neutron flux at certain points exceeded 1.5 x 10^{21} (n/cm^2)[12-16].

Most of the early studies on the Oklo reactors were carried out by French investigators and some 400 articles including monographs and review papers have appeared on the subject of Oklo phenomenon. Roth[17,18] published excellent review papers on the work leading to the discovery and information derived from analytical studies, particularly age of the deposit, duration of the sustained chain reactions and total power involved and so on. Migration of fission products and transuranium elements have been studied and it was found out that rare earths stayed mostly with uranium, while no indication of plutonium migration was found.

At the time of the discovery, only a Rb-Sr age of the Francevillian formation was known, which provided a 1740 ± 40 million years estimate. Uranium-lead measurements on parts of the uranium that have not reacted were then performed and a value of 1.8 x 10^9 years was obtained. Incidentally, the data showed that lead has migrated with respect to uranium. Rubidium-strontium isotopic measurements were then performed on what was expected to be fissiogenic ^{87}Rb and its ^{87}Sr daughter with the aim of providing new age determinations since their chemical abundance was high enough, of the order of a few partsper mil with respect to U. The results of analysis demonstrated, however, that ^{87}Rb from fission had been completely removed from the samples studied, and that ^{87}Rb present came from a later addition. It was found out that in the current material in the Oklo reactor less than one percent of Rb and Sr originate from fission.

Table 1 compares the migratory behaviors of elements and their melting and boiling points. Note that the elements which migrate easily in and out of the natural reactors all have relatively low melting points and the elements which are well preserved in the natural reactors have high melting and boiling points.

Table 1. Migration of the elements in and out of the Oklo reactors.

Z	Element	Migration	Melting point	Boiling point
			(°C)	
18	Argon	yes	-189.2	-185.7
19	Potassium	yes	62.3	760
37	Rubidium	yes	38.5	700
38	Strontium	yes	752	1150
52	Tellurium	yes	452	1390
53	Iodine	yes	114	183
54	Xenon	yes	-112	-107.1
57	Lanthanum	no	826	1800
82	Lead	yes	327	1613
90	Thorium	no	1750	3500
92	Uranium	no	1132	3818
94	Plutonium	no	639.5	3235

Naudet[19] reported that the water was super critical and high temperatures(at least 350 to 400 degrees in some cases) had to come into play for stabilization of the reactors. Openshaw[20] and Vidale[21] have also estimated that the aqueous solutions may have reached temperatures between 450 and 600 degrees. As shown in Table 1, the melting point of tellurium is 452°C and that of plutonium is 639.5°C and this explains why the elements with melting points higher than 600°C are generally well preserved in the Oklo reactors.

2.3. Alpha-recoil Effects

A series of papers on the alpha-recoil effects of uranium isotopes in radioactive minerals have recently been published by Sheng and Kuroda[22-25]. They performed acid-leaching experiments on a sample of uranium ore from reactor zone No.10 of the Oklo mine and observed anomalously high $^{234}U/^{238}U$ ratios accompanied by modestly increased $^{235}U/^{238}U$ ratios in uranium fractions. These results, which can be interpreted as being due to the alpha-recoil effects of ^{238}U and ^{239}Pu, provide a convenient way of calculating the conversion factor (or fraction of uranium atoms converted to plutonium) of the natural reactors from radiochemical data, obviating the necessity of mass-spectrometric measurements. It is also interesting to note here that Hishita and Masuda[26] have recently reported on a thousandfold variation in $^{235}U/^{238}U$ ratios observed in a uranium sample from Oklo.

Sheng and Kuroda[22] used 1.089-gram sample of powdered uranium ore from the Oklo deposit in the Republic of Gabon, Africa. The uranium content of this ore sample, which was a steel-grey color, was 34.5 % and the $^{235}U/^{238}U$ ratio was 0.660 atom %. It was leached in a series of experiments, beginning with 49 cm^3 of 0.1 M HCl, and was subsequently treated successively with 6 M HCl, 9 M HCl and 8 M HNO_3. The first passage of the 8 M HNO_3 solution through the column resulted in a marked increase in the rate of reaction. When this step was completed, the residue was transferred to a small beaker and treated with 8 M HNO_3 for about 3 hours at near boiling point. The residue was filtered and washed with 8 M HNO_3. The little residue which remained after this was transferred to a Teflon beaker and treated with concentrated HF. Table 2 shows the experimental results.

Most of the uranium in the ore sample had been dissolved in the acid solution by the time the 8 M HNO_3 treatment was completed and leachate fraction 7 was obtained. The observed $^{234}U/^{238}U$ ratios in leachates 3 - 7 were essentially the same as the radioactive equilibrium value of 1.00. The marked increases observed in the $^{234}U/^{238}U$ ratios in fractions 8 - 11 may be due to the fact that we are observing a preferential solution effect of recoil atoms of ^{234}U present in mineral phases whose uranium content was much lower than that of the reactor core material. The Oklo ore sample studied here contained tiny inclusions of haematite, clay and breccia. These inclusions, which contained very little uranium initially, may have been accumulating recoil atoms of ^{234}U over many years. The ^{234}U atoms which entered the crystal lattices of the mineral inclusions could be leached by the acid solutions much more easily than any ^{235}U and ^{238}U originally present. Alternatively, if the effects are due to emplacement of recoiling nuclei into a second, relatively low-uranium phase adjacent to the dominant uranium-rich mineral, direct dissolution of the surface layers would remove the implanted atoms and so produce the observed effect.

A marked increase in the $^{234}U/^{238}U$ ratio observed in leachate fractions 8 - 11 is accompanied by a modest increase in the $^{235}U/^{238}U$ ratios(see Table 2 and Fig. 1). The observed increase in the $^{235}U/^{238}U$ ratio in some of the leachate fractions of the Oklo ore samples is to be expected, because the reactions

Table 2. Variation of the isotopic composition of uranium extracted from a sample of Oklo ore deposit in the acid-leaching experiments.

Fraction	Acid used	Amount of U leached (mg)	$^{234}U/^{238}U$ (Ci/Ci)	$^{235}U/^{238}U$ (Ci/Ci)
1	0.1 M HCl*	70.6	1.15 ± 0.03	0.035 ± 0.004
2	0.1 M HCl+		1.22 ± 0.02	0.037 ± 0.003
3	6 M HCl*		0.97 ± 0.02	0.039 ± 0.003
4	6 M HCl+	110.3	1.02 ± 0.03	0.036 ± 0.004
5	9 M HCl*	91.8	1.03 ± 0.05	0.035 ± 0.006
6	9 M HCl+		1.01 ± 0.03	0.036 ± 0.005
7	8 M HNO_3*		1.01 ± 0.04	0.045 ± 0.007
8	8 M HNO_3‡	85.9	4.14 ± 0.28	0.051 ± 0.014
9	8 M HNO_3#		5.47 ± 0.42	0.065 ± 0.019
10	8 M HNO_3(hot)	0.0123	64.3 ± 3.0	0.120 ± 0.017
11	conc. HF(hot)	0.0111	21.02 ± 0.51	0.064 ± 0.006

* Initial fraction + Final fraction ‡ Final fraction 1

Final fraction 2

$$^{238}U(n,\gamma)^{239}U \xrightarrow{\beta^-} {}^{239}Np \xrightarrow{\beta^-} {}^{239}Pu$$

must have occurred on a large scale when the Oklo reactors were in operation. The alpha-recoil of the decaying ^{239}Pu atoms may have implanted the atoms of ^{235}U in the crystal lattices of nearby mineral inclusions.

The experimental data obtained here can be used to calculate the values of conversion factor for the natural reactors, which can be defined as

$$\frac{dN_{235}}{dt} = -N_{235}\,\sigma_{235}\,(1 - C)\,\Phi$$

$$= - N_{235}\,\sigma_{235}\,\Phi + N_{239}\,\lambda_{239} \tag{3}$$

where Φ is the neutron flux, σ_{235} is the neutron-absorption cross-section of ^{235}U and λ_{239} is the decay constant of ^{239}Pu. The same relationship holds for the ^{235}U atoms (N^p_{235}) which were created by the decay of ^{239}Pu atoms and hence we have the relationship

$$\frac{d\,N^p_{235}}{dt} = - N^p_{235}\,\sigma_{235}\,\Phi + N_{239}\,\lambda_{239} \tag{4}$$

and, solving equations(3) and (4), we have

$$\frac{1}{C} = \frac{\log\,(\,N_{235}/N_o\,)}{\log\left[\,1 - \left(\frac{N_{238}}{N_{235}}\right)\left(\frac{A^p_{235}}{A_{234}}\right)\left(\frac{T_{235}}{T_{238}}\right)\right]} \tag{5}$$

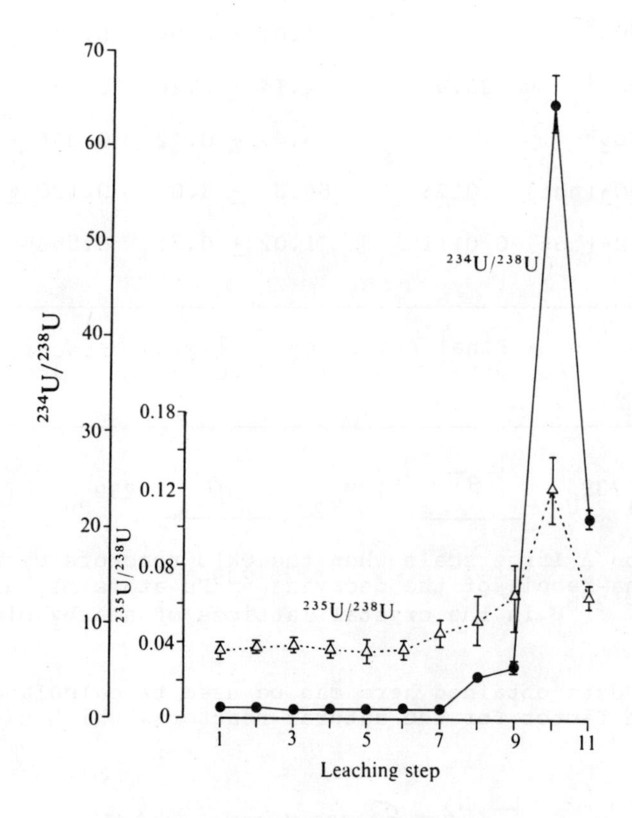

Fig.1. **Variation of the $^{234}U/^{238}U$ and $^{235}U/^{238}U$ ratios of uranium extracted from a sample of Oklo ore deposit.**

where A^{p}_{235} is the activity of recoiled ^{235}U atoms from ^{239}Pu, A_{234} is the activity of recoiled ^{234}U atoms from ^{238}U, T_{235} and T_{238} are the half-lives of ^{235}U and ^{238}U, respectively, and N_{235}/N_o is the ratio of the ^{235}U contents of the uranium in the natural reactor and in the normal uranium ore, respectively. For the uranium sample from reactor zone 10 of the Oklo mines, we have as shown in Table 2

$$(N_{235}/N_o) = 0.00660/0.00725,$$

$$(A^{p}_{235}/A_{234}) = (1.120 - 0.036)/(64.3 - 1.0)$$

$$= 0.084/63.3$$

and equation(5) yields a value of C = 0.26. Similarly, the observed $^{234}U/^{238}U$ and $^{235}U/^{238}U$ ratios for fraction 11 yield a value of C = 0.27.

2.4. Early Studies on Anomalous Xenon

In 1960, newly-elected President Kennedy declared that the United States would send man to the moon within a decade. Soon after the successful landing on the moon which occurred on 20 July 1969, scientists began to analyze the moon samples more or less assuming that the age of the moon should be close to 4.55 billion years, as reported earlier by Patterson[11] in 1956. Their attempts to accurately date the moon samples, however, led to all sorts of problems.

In 1960, Reynolds[27] made the important discovery that the decay product of 16 million-year ^{129}I was highly enriched in the meteorite, Richardton. Kuroda[7,8] then predicted that 82 million-year ^{244}Pu should have existed in nature during the early history of the solar system. Experimental evidence in support of the ^{244}Pu hypothesis was obtained five years later in 1965[9]. It so happens that ^{129}I beta-decays to ^{129}Xe and ^{244}Pu decays by the process of spontaneous fission to heavy xenon isotopes:

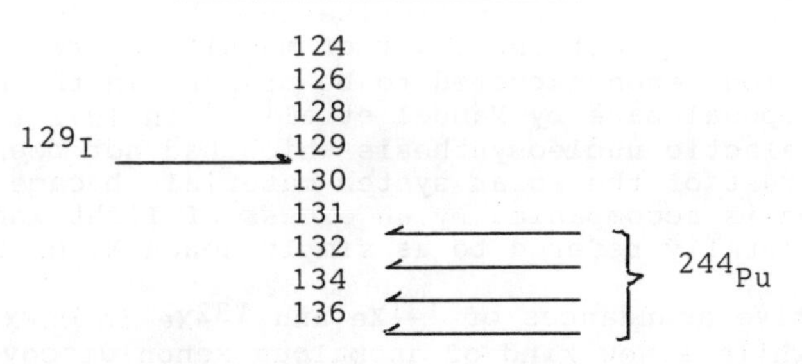

This meant that two 'nuclear clocks' would be available to date the moon samples with a very high precision, since the half-lives of ^{129}I and ^{244}Pu are both much shorter than those of ^{238}U, ^{235}U and ^{232}Th. If the moon is indeed as old as 4.55 billion years, isotopes such as ^{129}I and ^{244}Pu synthesized in stars should have been present in the lunar samples.

In the first report on the examination of the samples returned from the moon, members of the Apollo 11 Lunar Sample Preliminary Examination Team(LSPET)[28] wrote that the isotopic compositions of xenon found in the lunar fines and breccia resembled those of the carbonaceous chondrites and that decay products of ^{129}I and ^{244}Pu appeared to be absent on the moon. This was a great disappointment to most scientists who had anticipated that evidence for the existence of ^{129}I and ^{244}Pu in the early history of the solar system should have been clearly recorded and preserved in the rocks and soils which were brought to the earth.

Scientists soon found themselves confronted with another problem: excess fission xenon began to show up in some of the lunar samples, while excess ^{129}Xe was hard to find. Reynolds et al[29]and Alexander[30]were the first to observe the presence of excess fission xenon in lunar rocks 10057 and 12013, respectively, but they attributed it to the decay of ^{238}U by spontaneous fission.

After the lunar samples were returned from the Apollo 14 landing on 5 February 1971, members of LSPET[31] reported that the lunar breccia 14301, one of the five samples whose isotopic compositions of xenon were determined mass-spectrometrically, contained as much as 150 x 10^{-12}(cc STP $^{136f}Xe/g$) of excess fission xenon. This amount was clearly much more than could have been produced by the spontaneous fission of ^{238}U in 4.5 billion years. The presence of ^{244}Pu fission xenon was reported in many of the lunar samples returned from the Apollo 14 and subsequent landings on the moon, but most of the investigators in the early 1970's have concluded that the ^{244}Pu fission xenon was 'parentless' in the sence that it was not due to in situ decay of ^{244}Pu, but it had been stored in an intermediate reservoir before incorporation into the lunar samples.

At about the time these studies on the occurrence of ^{244}Pu fission xenon in lunar samples were being carried out in the early 1970's, scientists were beginning to doubt the origin of the so-called 'carbonaceous chondrite fission(CCF) xenon', which had been discovered by Reynolds and Turner[32] in the carbonaceous chondrite Renazzo in 1964. These carbonaceous chondrite contained 20 to 100 x 10^{-12}ccSTP of excess ^{136}Xe per gram of meteorite and these amounts have been regarded as being at least one order of magnitude greater than the amount of ^{244}Pu fission xenon expected to be present in the meteorites. Thus, the proposal made by Manuel et al[33] in 1972 that CCF is a product of galactic nucleosynthesis which had not been uniformly mixed with the rest of the solar system materials became widely accepted. The CCF xenon is accompanied by an excess of light xenon isotopes and is generally refered to as simply xenon X, or CCFX, xenon H,L.

The relative abundances of ^{131}Xe and ^{132}Xe in CCFX xenon is abnormally low, while a new kind of anomalous xenon discovered by Shukolyukov et al[34-36] in the Oklo natural reactor in 1976 had abnormally high abundances of ^{131}Xe and ^{132}Xe, and somewhat resembled the isotopic compositions of anomalous xenon reported by Kennett and Thode[37] in 1960.

Fig.2 shows a plot of $^{132}Xe/^{136}Xe$ vs. $^{134}Xe/^{136}Xe$ ratios for the xenon isotopes found in the solar system. There are over 3,000 analyses of xenon in meteorites and in terrestrial samples. Not all the existing xenon isotope data are plotted here, but most of the meteorite data lie within the triangle PMF, where P is Takaoka's primitive xenon(38), M is a mass-fractionated primitive xenon and F is the ^{244}Pu fission xenon. The isotopic composition of the atmospheric xenon(A) lies along the line PM. Some of the data points deviate from the line PM and lie outside of the triangle PMF. They represent the xenon found in mineral inclusions of the carbonaceous chondrites Murray and Murchison. The isotopic compositions of these anomalous xenon can be attributed to the alterations caused by thermal-neutron induced reactions, as recently reported by Kuroda and Myers.(39)

The isotopic compositions of xenon found in uranium minerals, such as uraninite, pitchblende and thucolite lie within the triangle ABC, where B is the ^{238}U spontaneous fission xenon and C is the neutron-induced ^{235}U fission xenon. Note that many of the data points lie along the line BC, indicating that a sub-critical uranium chain reaction occurs in the uranium minerals. The data points for the xenon from the Oklo reactor lie close to the point C, but some of the data points lie along the line CD, where D is the thermal neutron-induced ^{239}Pu fission xenon. This shows that ^{239}Pu is produced in the Oklo reactor and it also undergoes fission. Many of the data points for the Oklo xenon deviate toward the point Z, which represents the isotopic composition of Shukolyukov's anomalous xenon.(34-36) It is to be noted, however, that not all the data points for the Oklo xenon are confined within the triangle ZCD. Several data points deviate upward from the line ZD in Fig.2.

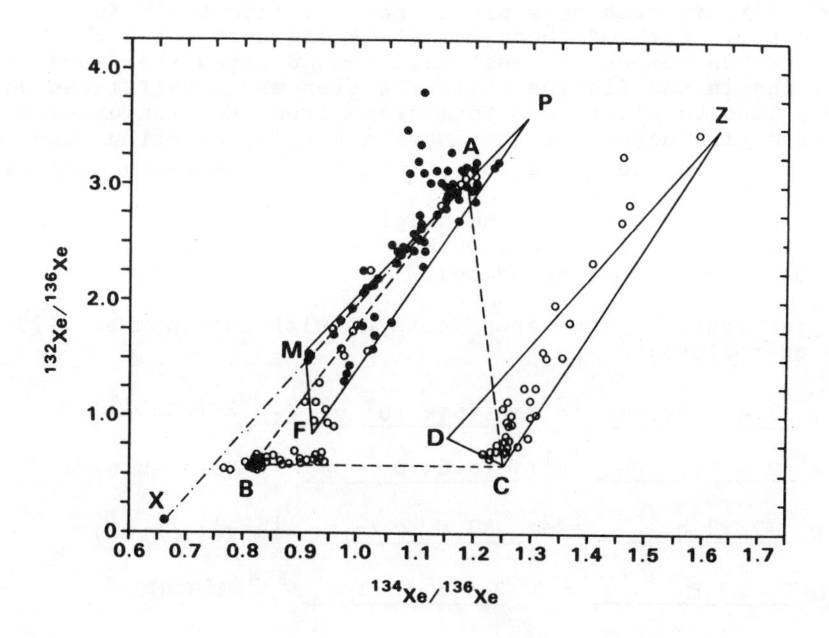

Fig.2. Isotopic compositions of xenon in the solar system.

2.5. Anomalous Xenon Isotopes from the Oklo Reactor

Table 3 shows that the isotopic composition of anomalous xenon from the Oklo reactor is different from those of the fission xenon from ^{235}U and ^{239}Pu in that the relative abundances of ^{131}Xe and ^{132}Xe in the former are much higher than those of the ^{235}U xenon and the ^{239}Pu xenon.

Table 3. Isotopic composition of the anomalous xenon from the Oklo reactor, reported by Shukolyukov et al.(36)

Mass No.	Oklo No.1348	^{235}U(thermal)	^{239}Pu(thermal)
129	0.358	0.105	0.258
131	1.20	0.456	0.594
132	3.46	0.680	0.788
134	1.59	1.239	1.102
136	1.00	1.000	1.000

The anomalous xenon from the Oklo reactor resemble that obtained by Kennett and Thode(37) from the pile-irradiated U_3O_8, but the abundance of ^{131}Xe is much more pronounced relative to ^{132}Xe in the case of the latter. Both of these investigators have noted that these anomalous xenon components must have been derived from some progenitors arising in the fission chain reaction whose half-lives were sufficiently long to allow them to migrate from the uranium oxide and accumulated elsewhere, but they have not fully described the mechanisms involved in the formation of the anomalous xenon components.

A more detailed study on the origins of these xenon components has recently been carried out by Kuroda(40) A brief summary of the results obtained is presented below.

The precursors of the xenon isotopes with mass numbers 129 through 136 are as follows:

$$^{129}Te \xrightarrow{33.4\ d, 69.5m} {}^{129}I \xrightarrow{1.6 \times 10^7\ y} {}^{129}Xe(stable)$$

$$^{131}Te \xrightarrow{32.4\ h, 25.0m} {}^{131}I \xrightarrow{8.04\ d} {}^{131}Xe(stable)$$

$$^{132}Te \xrightarrow{78.2\ h} {}^{132}I \xrightarrow{83\ m, 2.28\ h} {}^{132}Xe(stable)$$

$$^{134}Te \xrightarrow{42\ m} {}^{134}I \xrightarrow{3.5\ m, 52.5\ m} {}^{134}Xe(stable)$$

$$^{136}Te \xrightarrow{18\ s} {}^{136}I \xrightarrow{45\ s,\ 83.6s} {}^{136}Xe(stable)$$

Kennett and Thode[37] have irradiated uranium oxide in a reactor for periods of 2.5, 5 and 10 days. At the end of the irradiation, the quartz vials containing the sample were placed into high-vacuum lines connected to the mass-spectrometer. The xenon isotopes were released from the samples at various temperatures and the isotopic composition of xenon was measured mass-spectrometrically.

Fig.3.a shows the values of enhancement(Δ_{131}) of the relative abundances of ^{131}Xe in xenon fractions released at 30°C and 150°C from the samples, which had been irradiated. The $_{132}$ values for the xenon released at 150°C reveal a growth of 8.04-day ^{131}I. Fig.3.b shows a similar plot for the enhancement at mass number 132. The Δ_{132}values for the xenon fractions reveal a growth of 78.2-hour ^{132}Te. These results indicate that the precursors of ^{131}Xe and ^{132}Xe (^{131}I and ^{132}Te) play key roles in producing the anomalies at mass numbers 131 and 132,

These experimental results can be explained in terms of the melting points of iodine and tellurium shown in Table 1. In the xenon fractions released from the irradiated uranium oxide at 150°C, ^{131}Xe becomes enriched, because the release temperature is intermediate between the melting point(114°C) and the boiling point(183°C) of iodine. In the xenon fractions released at 150°C and 300°C, ^{132}Xe becomes enriched, because the release temperatures are approaching the melting point(452°C) of tellurium. It is known that some of the tellurium compounds are volatile in the temperature range between 200 and 400°C.

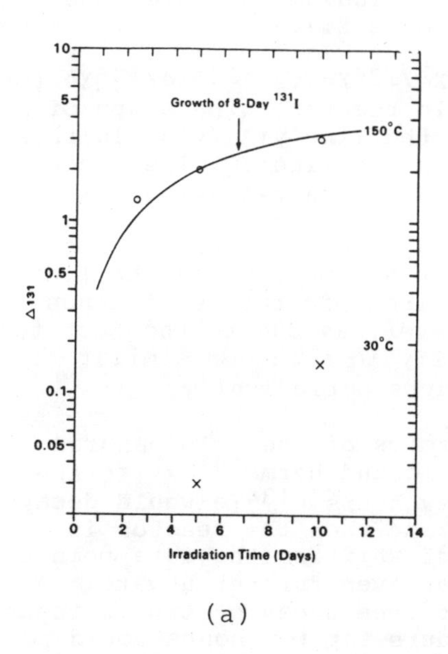

(a)

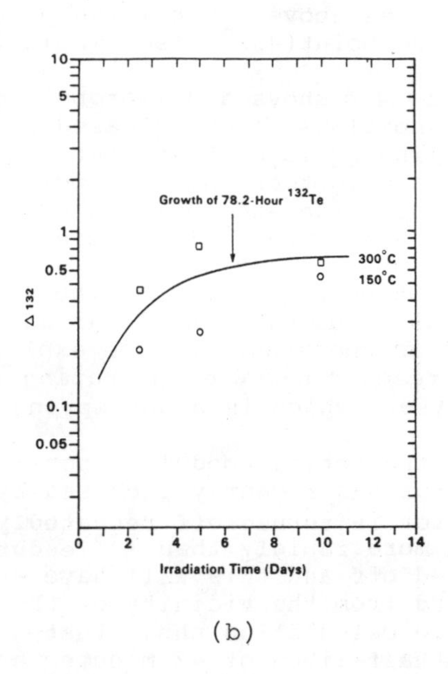

(b)

Fig.3. Release of anomalous xenon isotopes from the pile-irradiated uranium oxide.

Fig.4.a shows a 3-isotope plot of $^{129}Xe/^{136}Xe$ vs. $^{131}Xe/^{136}Xe$ for the anomalous xenon released from the Oklo reactor. Shukolyukov and Minh(36) have analyzed a total of 78 samples of xenon fractions from Specimen No.1348. The point Z represents the isotopic composition of the anomalous xenon; C and D are the xenon from thermal neutron-induced fission of ^{235}U and ^{239}Pu, respectively; and the line y_{129}/y_{131} represents the ratio of cumulative fission yields for mass 129 and 131 chains. Most of the data points lie along the line ZC, whose slope is almost identical to that of the line y_{129}/y_{131}. The longest-lived precursors of these decay chains are 1.6×10^7-year ^{129}I and 8.04-day ^{131}I. These results indicate that the enhancement of ^{129}Xe and ^{131}Xe observed for the anomalous xenon can be accounted for as due to a preferential release of xenon fractions which have been produced by the decays of the precursors, ^{129}I and ^{131}I, respectively.

Fig.4.b shows a 3-isotope plot of $^{131}Xe/^{136}Xe$ vs. $^{132}Xe/^{136}Xe$ for the anomalous xenon released from the Oklo reactor. The slope of the line y_{131}/y_{132} is much greater than that of the line ZC in this case. Note that most data points lie far below the line y_{131}/y_{132}. The downward deviations of the data points from the line y_{131}/y_{132} means that there exists a deficiency in the abundance of ^{131}Xe relative to ^{132}Xe in these xenon fractions. The precursors of ^{131}Xe and ^{132}Xe are ^{131}I(8.04 day) and ^{132}Te(78.2 hour), respectively. As it was mentioned in Section 2.2., the Oklo reactors have operated at temperatures 350 to 400°C. The fact that there exists a deficiency of ^{131}Xe relative to ^{132}Xe can be attributed to a loss of iodine relative to tellurium in the Oklo reactor, which was operating at temperatures above the boiling point(183°C) of iodine and below the melting point(452°C)(see Table 1 in Section 2.2.).

Fig.4.c shows a 3-isotope plot of $^{132}Xe/^{136}Xe$ vs. $^{134}Xe/^{136}Xe$ for the anomalous xenon released from the Oklo reactor. The slope of the line ZC is much greater than that of the line y_{132}/y_{134} in this case and most of the data points lie above the line ZC. The precursors of ^{132}Xe and ^{134}Xe which have the longest half-lives are ^{132}Te (78.2 hour) and ^{134}Te(42 minute), respectively, and they are the isotopes of the same element, so that the deviations of the data points can not be attributed to the difference in the melting and boiling points. The pattern of variation of the isotopic ratios of xenon such as shown here can be explained, however, as due to the fact that the reactor had been operating periodically in a manner similar to a geyser, which is a hot spring which erupts periodically.

A theoretical model of non-linear dynamics of the Oklo natural reactor was recently proposed by Billanovic and Harms(41). If the reactor is turned off repeatedly for a few hours, ^{134}Te would decay much more rapidly than ^{132}Te during the time when the reactor is turned off and this will have an effect of shifting the data points upward from the vicinity of the line ZC or even further upward. A simple calculation shows that a period of free decay of two isotopes with half-lives of 42 minutes and 78.2 hours for few hours would produce an upward shift of the data points such as shown in Fig.3.c.

The time period(Ξ) during which the reactor was turned off can be calculated from the ratio of excess $^{132}Xe(\Delta_{132})$ to excess $^{134}Xe(\Delta_{134})$

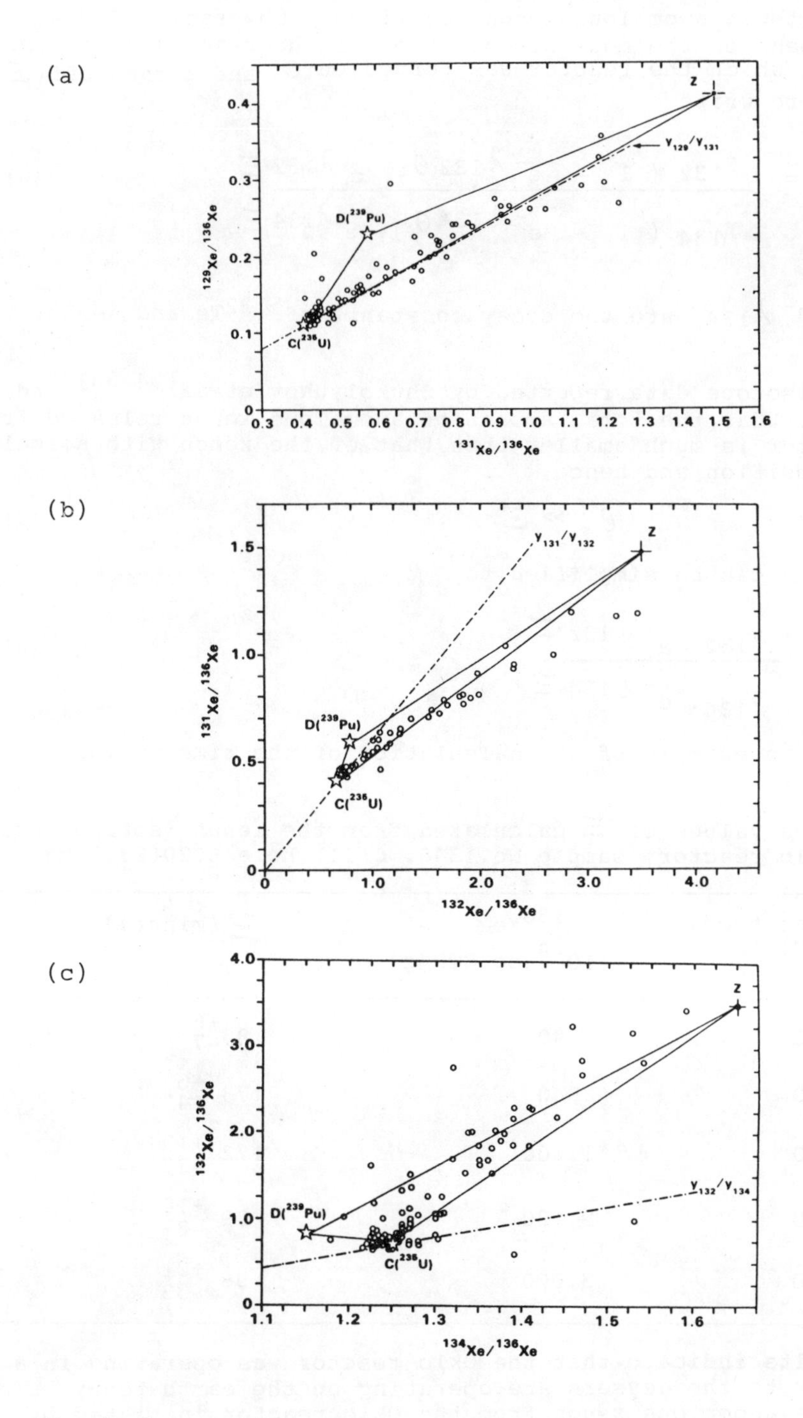

Fig.4. Release of anomalous xenon isotopes from the Oklo reactor.

in these anomalous xenon fractions. The ratio of $\Delta_{132}/\Delta_{134}$ will depend on the mode of operation of the reactor: the time periods during which the reactor was turned on(θ and turned off(Ξ). Let us therefore write

$$\Delta_{132}/\Delta_{134} = \frac{y_{132}.(1 - e^{-\lambda_{132}\cdot\theta}).\ e^{-\lambda_{132}\cdot\Xi}}{y_{134}\cdot(1 - e^{-\lambda_{134}\theta}).\ e^{-\lambda_{134}\cdot\Xi}} \qquad (6),$$

where λ_{132} and λ_{134} are the decay constants of ^{132}Te and ^{134}Te, respectively.

The xenon isotope data reported by Shukolyukov et al(34-36) indicate, however, that the total amount of anomalous xenon released from the Oklo reactor is much smaller than that of the xenon with normal isotopic composition and hence

$$\theta \gg \Xi \qquad (7),$$

and equation(6) can be simplified to

$$132/134 = \frac{y_{132}.\ e^{-\lambda_{132}\cdot\Xi}}{y_{134}\cdot\ e^{-\lambda_{134}\cdot\Xi}} \qquad (8).$$

Table 4 shows an example of the calculation of the time period.

Table 4. The values of Ξ calculated from the xenon isotope data for the Oklo reactor, sample No.1348, drill hole SC20(22.1 mg).

Release temp. (°C)	^{136}Xe (10^{-9} cc STP/g)	Ξ (minute)
400	90	185^{+6}_{-7}
600	940	173^{+6}_{-4}
800	1,100	172^{+19}_{-27}
1,000	9,100	39^{+12}_{-27}
1,100	3,600	98^{+21}_{-33}

These results indicate that the Oklo reactor was operating in a manner similar to the geysers are operating on the earth today. The studies on the anomalous xenon from the Oklo reactor initiated by Shukolyukov et al(34-36) are likely to become extremely important in future studies on the operational conditions of the natural reactors.

2.6. A Note on the Age of the Solar System

The puzzle of the xenon isotopes concerning the origin of the so-called CCF, CCFX, xenon H, L, S etc. appears to have been finally solved. Kuroda and Myers[42-46] have recently reported in a series of papers that carbonaceous chondrites as well as the lunar fines all had the initial $^{244}Pu/^{238}U$ ratios somewhat higher than one atom of ^{244}Pu to ten atoms of ^{238}U. This means that the anomalous xenon components such as CCF, X etc. do not really exist in nature. Instead, they are mixtures of ^{244}Pu fission xenon and mass-fractionated primordial xenon. Results from recent investigations[42-49] indicate that the carbonaceous chondrites and some of the lunar fines and breccias appear to have started to retain their xenon more than 4,800 million years ago. This means that the age of the solar system must be at least 250 million years greater than Patterson's estimate of 4,550 $\pm$ 70 million years[11]. The age of the solar system calculated by Patterson refers to the time of a breakup of the meteorite parent body which happened 4,550 million years ago and it does not necessarily mean that the earth, the moon and the rest of the solar system were formed all at once 4,550 million years ago.

References

1. Rhodes, R.: "The Making of the Atomic Bomb", Simon and Shuster, New York, 1986, p.664.
2. Flügge, S. : Naturwissenschaften 27, 401(1939).
3. Noetzlin, J. :Comptes rendus 208, 1662(1939).
4. Odagiri, M. : "On the Parallel Relationship between the Developments of Atoms and the Earth as a Heavenly Body"(in Japanese), 1940,p.1-52; J.Chem.Soc.Japan 63, 224,1425(1942).
5. Houtermans, F.G. : Nuevo Cimento 10, 1623(1953).
6. Kuroda, P.K. : J. Chem. Phys. 25, 781, 1295(1956).
7. Kuroda, P.K. : Nature 187, 36(1960).
8. Kuroda, P.K. : Geochim. Cosmochim. Acta 24, 40(1961).
9. Rowe, M.W., Kuroda, P.K. : J. Geophys. Res. 70, 709(1965).
10. Fermi, E. : Science 105, 27(1947).
11. Patterson, C. : Geochim. Cosmochim. Acta 10, 230(1956).
12. Bodu, R., Bouzigues, H., Morin, N., Pfiffermann, J.P.: C.R.Acad. Sc. Paris 275D, 1731(1972).
13. Neuilly, M., Bussac, J., Frejacques, C., Nief, G., Vendryes, G., Yvon, J. : C.R.Acad. Sc. Paris 275D, 1847(1972).
14. Baudin, G., Blain, C., Hagemann, R., Kremer, M., Lucas, M., Merlivat, L., Molina, R., Nief, G., Prost-Marechal, F., Regnaud, F., Roth, E. : C.R.Acad. Sc. Paris 275D, 2291(1972).
15. "The Oklo Phenomenon", International Atomic Energy Agency, Vienna, 1975.
16. Maurette, M., : "Annual Review of Nuclear Science", 26, 319(1976).
17. Roth, E. :J. Radioanal. Nucl. Chem. 37, 65(1977).
18. Hagemann, R., Roth, E., : Radiochim. Acta 25, 241(1978).
19. Naudet, R., "Natural Fission Reactors", International Atomic Ener-

gy Agency, Vienna, p.589, 1978.
20. Openshaw, R., Pagel, M., Poty, B., : ibid. p.267, 1978.
21. Vidale, R.J.: ibid. p.235, 1978.
22. Sheng, Z.Z., Kuroda, P.K. : Nature 312, 535(1984).
23. Sheng, Z.Z., Kuroda, P.K. :Radiochim. Acta 37, 93(1984).
24. Sheng, Z.Z., Kuroda, P.K. :Radiochim. Acta 39, 131(1986).
25. Sheng, Z.Z., Kuroda, P.K. :Radiochim. Acta 40, 95(1986).
26. Hishita, S., Masuda, A. : Naturwissenshaften 74, 241(1987).
27. Reynolds, J.H.,: Phys. Rev. Lett. 4, 8(1960).
28. The Lunar Sample Preliminary Examination Team(LSPET): Science 165, 1211(1969).
29. Reynolds, J.H., Hohenberg, C.M., Lewis, R.S., Davis, P.K., Kaiser, W.A.: Science 167, 545(1970).
30. Alexander E.C.Jr. : Earth Planet. Sci. Lett. 9, 201(1970).
31. The Lunar Sample Preliminary Examination Team(LSPET): Science 173, 681(1971).
32. Reynolds, J.H., Turner, G. : J. Geophys. Res. 69,3263(1964).
33. Manuel, O.K., Hennecke, E.W., Sabu, D.D. : Nature Physical Science 240,99(1972).
34. Shukolyukov, Y.A., Ashkinadze, G.S., Verkhovskii, A.B. : Atomnaya Energiya 41, 53(1976).
35. Shukolyukov, Y.A., Min, T.W. : Geokhimiya 11, 1604(1977).
36. Shukolyukov, Y.A., Minh, D.V. : Geokhimiya 12, 1763(1977).
37. Kennett, T.J., Thode, H.G. : Can. J. Phys. 38, 945(1960).
38. Takaoka, N. : Mass Spectroscopy 20, 287(1972).
39. Kuroda, P.K., Myers, W.A. : J. Radioanal. Nucl. Chem.(submitted, May 1990).
40. Kuroda, P.K.: J. Radioanal. Nucl. Chem.(in press, 1990).
41. Bilanovic, Z., Harms, A.A. : Nuclear Science and Engineering 91, 286(1985).
42. Kuroda, P.K., Myers, W.A. :J. Radioanal. Nucl. Chem.(submitted, May 1990).
43. Myers, W.A., Kuroda, P.K. :presented at the 199th National Meetings of the American Chemical Society, Boston, Massachusetts, 22-27 April 1990.
44. Kuroda, P.K., Myers, W.A. : presented at the 199th National Meetings of the American Chemical Society, Boston, Massachusetts, 22-27 April 1990.
45. Myers, W.A., Kuroda, P.K. : "50 Years With Nuclear Fission", edited by James W. Behrens and Allan D. Carlson, Vol. 2, American Nuclear Society, Inc., La Grange Park, Illinois, p. 909, 1989.
46. Kuroda, P.K., Myers, W.A. : ibid. p.901.
47. Kuroda, P.K., Sheng, Z.Z. : "Essays in Nuclear, Geo- and Cosmochemistry", edited by M.W.Rowe, Burgess International Group Inc. Edina, MN, p.183, 1988.
48. Kuroda, P.K., Sheng, Z.Z., Batchelor, J.D. : ibid. p.192.
49. Kuroda, P.K. : ibid. p.100.

7.6 Hot Atom Chemical Processes in Space

Kurt ROESSLER
Institut für Nuklearchemie, Forschungszentrum Jülich, Postfach 1913,
D-5170 Jülich, Germany

1. Introduction

Energetic atoms, ions and molecules are quite abundant in cosmos and the study of suprathermal chemistry should constitute an important issue of space research. There are some specific reasons that on the contrary the astrophysical community accepted hot atom chemistry only slowly:[1-5] The knowledge of the abundance of hot species in space dates from the last ten years. Cosmochemists and -physicists often described the actual state of a space system but did not try to elucidate the chemical mechanisms leading to it. The main obstacle, however, was the lack of clearcut kinetic data such as reaction rate constants which were not available due to the non-equilibrium character of hot processes.[5-9] Hot atom chemists on the other hand were too much concerned with inorganic and organic systems which prooved to be irrelevant for space research. They were quite aware of the importance of space relevant hot atom chemistry,[10-12] but no decided action took place. One of the inherent reasons not to step into this field, despite the fact that it was and still is quite well fonded, may have been the academic modesty of most of the hot atom chemists. There is hardly another domain in science so much based on speculation and conjecture than space research. This had been one of the major critics the author encountered from his colleagues when starting relevant suprathermal chemistry work in 1984.[13] However, the fascination of space science and the obviously important role of hot atom chemistry in it were the reasons to continue. Since then many experimental and review articles were published with the intention to introduce hot atom chemistry to the astrophysical community.[5,13-17] In the present paper this intention is reversed: What is attractive and innovative in space research with respect to hot atom chemistry?

2. Non-equilibrium reaction kinetics

The knowledge of space chemistry originates from terrestrial and mission based observation, laboratory simulation under space conditions and physicochemical theory. The latter has set up whole networks for photoionization induced ion-molecule reactions in the gas phase of interstellar clouds,[18,19] cometary comae,[2] or planetary atmospheres.[20] Starting from simple basic species, complex final products are reached in the calculations assuming concentrations and thermal reaction rates in an equilibrium of formation and destruction. Every attempt to introduce hot atom reactions into this closed world of classical physicochemistry necessitates a prediction of the rates of suprathermal processes which may compete with thermal ion-molecule reactions. A first approach to estimate the order of magnitude of hot reaction rates was achieved by a comparison of rate constants of thermal oxygen atoms in the ground and first exited states and of O^+ in the ground state with simple gases (H_2, H_2O, CH_4). The extrapolated reaction rate constants for hot oxygen were by orders magnitude higher than those for the corresponding thermal reactions.[5]

A recent approach to non-equilibrium kinetics of hot atoms used the method of inversed Laplace transformation of thermal rate constants to obtain energy dependent cross sections and hot reaction rates.[6,7] Table 1 shows that the hydrogen abstraction in H_2O and CH_4 gas proceeds many orders of magnitude faster with hot hydrogen of 1 eV kinetic energy than with species in thermal equilibrium at 293 K.

Table 1: Comparison of hot and thermal reaction rate constants, according to[6,7]

reaction	$E_{threshold}$ eV	k_{hot} (1 eV H) $cm^3 \cdot s^{-1}$	k_{therm} (293 K) $cm^3 \cdot s^{-1}$
$H + H_2O \rightarrow HO + H_2$	0.883	$1.7 \cdot 10^{-11}$	$9.6 \cdot 10^{-26}$
$H + CH_4 \rightarrow CH_3 + H_2$	0.51	$5 \cdot 10^{-11}$	$2.5 \cdot 10^{-19}$

Hot reaction rates seem to be in the order of those for the corresponding ion-molecule reactions. Since in space neutral species are much more abundant than ions, hot atom chemistry constitutes an important part of all chemical processes. This has in particular been exemplified for the inner coma of comet P/Halley.[7] Some 10 to 40 % of the destruction of the important species H_2O, CH_4, OH, etc. are due to hydrogen abstraction by hot H. The suprathermal reactions can compete with the photodissociation processes, which created the energetic hydrogens. Hot atom reactions, in particular by hydrogen but also by C and N, constitute the majority of chemical reactions in the inner coma,[7] if photolytic and radiolytic processes are not considered. Similar processes are also predicted for the atmospheres of Saturn's moon Titan which contains N_2 and CH_4.

The goal of astrophysical application has tiggered a novel and practical treatment of non-equilibrium, suprathermal reaction rates and their significance in some popular gaseous space systems. Reactions in solids will, however, be much more difficult to handle, cf.[5,17])

3. Target systems in space

The interstellar matter of our galaxy consists of 99 % gases (3 % ions and 97 % neutrals) and 1 % solids. Liquids are encountered in very few cases only such as in aerosols in atmospheres and in some oceans of planets and satellites (predicted ethane ocean on Titan). The gaseous systems are in general very diluted, corresponding to ultra-high vacuum, such as listed in Table 2. Only few of the planetary and satellite atmospheres are comparable to terrestrial conditions.

Table 2: Density of some selected gaseous systems in space

system	number density atoms or mols. cm^{-3}	equivalent pressure mbar
interstellar medium	10^{-1} - 10^{1}	some 10^{-18} - 10^{-16}
diffuse interstellar clouds	10^{1} - 10^{3}	some 10^{-16} - 10^{-14}
dark interstellar clouds	10^{3} - 10^{5}	some 10^{-14} - 10^{-12}
inner coma of comets	10^{5} - 10^{8}	some 10^{-12} - 10^{-9}
atmosphere of Mercury	$< 10^{8}$	$< 10^{-9}$
atmosphere of Mars	$1.76 \cdot 10^{17}$	6.5
atmosphere of Titan	$4.3 \cdot 10^{19}$	$1.3 \cdot 10^{3}$
atmosphere of Venus	$2.4 \cdot 10^{21}$	$9 \cdot 10^{4}$

The temperatures of these systems range from a few 10 K in dense molecular clouds to 730 K in the atmosphere of Venus and some 10^5 K in very dilute interstellar medium. The composition can vary from very simple molecules H_2, CO, H_2O, CH_4, NH_3, CO_2, HCN, C_2H_6, etc. to complicated highly unsaturated long chain molecules such as e.g. cyanoacetylene HC≡C-CN, cyanopentayne $HC-(C{\equiv}C)_5-CN$ or organic ring molecules such as the cyclopropenyl ion $C_3H_3^+$ or the propenylidene radical C_3H_2, most of which are only stable at high dilution.

Table 3 lists some selected solid systems in space, the temperatures of which range between 10 K for interstellar grains to some 100 K for planets and asteroids in the inner solar system. It can be seen that almost all systems are mixtures of minerals (silicates, oxides, iron), ices (H_2O, NH_3, CH_4, CO, CO_2 etc.), carbonaceous matter (C, SiC, a-C:H) and complex organic substances (aromates, polycyclic aromatic hydrocarbons (PAH), pyrimidine derivatives and other precursors of biomolecules).

Table 3: Some selected solid systems in space

system	diameter, m	approx. composition
interstellar grains	10^{-7} to 10^{-6}	mineral (silicate) nucleus with layers of frosts and carbonaceous (organic) refractories
interplanetary dust	10^{-7} to 10^{-3}	"
meteorites	10^{-5} to 10^{1}	minerals, carbon, organics
meteors	10^{-4} to 10^{-2}	"
ring material of planets	10^{-5} to 10^{1}	minerals, ices
comets	some 10^{3} to 10^{4}	minerals, ices, organics, carbon
asteroids	10^{5} to 10^{6}	minerals (S), organics and carbon (C)
satellites	$3 \cdot 104$ to $5 \cdot 10^{6}$	mineral nuclei, often icy surfaces
planets	$3 \cdot 10^{6}$ to $1.4 \cdot 10^{8}$	"

4. Hot species in space

High energetic species may be ions, atoms, molecules or their fragments, radicals, clusters, whole grains, colliding larger bodies, etc. Table 4 lists some of the typical sources in space, for details cf.[3-5,15,17]

Table 4: Sources for hot species in space

source	primary energy eV	approx. penetration into solids μm	formation of secondaries
photodissociation by UV photons	1 - 5	surface	no
dissociative recombination of photon produced ions	1 - 5	surface	no
collision of space craft with rest gas	3 - 10	surface	no
motion relative to the interstellar medium	10^{1} - 10^{2}	surface	no
nuclear ß-decay	1 - 10^{1}	surface	no
nuclear α-decay	10^{5}	some 10^{-2}	yes
nuclear reactions	10^{2} - 10^{8}	10^{-5} - 10^{1}	yes
shock waves in the interstellar medium	10^{1} - 10^{3}	10^{-6} - 10^{-4}	few
discharges, lightenings	10^{2} - 10^{4}	10^{-5} - 10^{-3}	few
solar (stellar) wind	10^{3} - 10^{5}	10^{-4} - 10^{-2}	yes
ion torus (Io)	10^{3} - 10^{5}	10^{-4} - some 10^{-2}	yes
pick-up-ions	10^{4} - 10^{5}	10^{-3} - 10^{-2}	yes
T-Tauri winds	10^{6}	10^{-1} - 10^{0}	yes
cosmic rays	10^{3} - 10^{23}	10^{-4} - > 10^{8}	some

Except for the cases of photodissociation and dissociative recombination, most of the species are primarily ionized. In particular in solids a fast neutralisation takes place by electron pick-up, and the hot species react as a neutrals at the end of their trajectories when chemical bonds can be formed, cf.[21] Projectiles with a kinetic energy in keV higher than the mass in a.m.u. will transfer their energy to the electronic system of the target atoms (S_e, electronic stopping) leading to excitation and ionization. Species with energies below or at the a.m.u. value will preferentially transfer energy by elastic collisions (S_n, nuclear stopping) creating point defects, replacement events, etc. S_n leads to the formation of hot secondary atoms which can undergo on their turn suprathermal reactions. The secondary atoms are in general much more numerous than the primaries and are responsible for the majority of hot reactions in space. Table 5 shows the number of secondary (and tertiary etc.) hot H, O and C atoms with kinetic energies $E \geq 2$ eV formed by typical primary solar wind ions.

Table 5: All secondary knock-on atoms with $E \geq 2$ eV formed in collsion cascades of keV ions in frozen H_2O and CH_4 at 77 K. MARLOWE computer simulation, cf.[5,15]

primary	total number of secondaries per cascade ($E \geq 2$ eV) H_2O	CH_4
1 keV H	25 H, 10 O	18 H, 15 C
4 keV He	57 H, 42 O	63 H, 30 C
10 keV C	150 H, 113 O	203 H, 63 C

Fluxes of energetic particles in space are medium to low, cf. Table 6. The long lasting irradiation in the life-time of the solar system $4.6 \cdot 10^9$ a have led to enormous fluences for some objects. Asteroids which are situated at about 3 AU from the sun (AU = astronomical unit, semimajor axis of Earth's orbit around sun, $1.496 \cdot 10^{11}$ m) have suffered a bombardment of $3.3 \cdot 10^{24}$ solar wind ions creating more than 10^{26} cm^{-2} secondary atoms. Even if the surfaces are turned from time to time by mechanical mixing of grains, the enormous number of hot processes can totally change the pristine matter of carbonaceous asteroids. Other interesting objects are planets and satellites without or almost without an atmosphere such as Mercury, cf. Table 6. Comet P/Halley is protected from solar wind near the sun (< 5 AU) by the coma, a gas phase formed by the thermal evaporation of volatiles out of the nucleus.

Table 6: Fluxes and fluences of primary hot particles in space at 1 AU.

source	major constituents	flux, $cm^{-2}s^{-1}$	fluence in $4 \cdot 10^9$a, cm^{-2}
solar wind	95 % 1 keV H^+ 4 % 4 keV He^{2+} 0.1 % 10 keV C^{6+}	$2\text{-}3 \cdot 10^8$	$4 \cdot 10^{25}$
solar flares ($1\ a^{-1}$)	95 % < MeV H^+ 5 % < MeV He^{2+}	varies	$4 \cdot 10^{19}$
interstellar medium (relative motion)	50 % 18 eV H 45 % 70 eV He 2 % ≥ 250 eV C,N,O	$6.5 \cdot 10^5$	$8 \cdot 10^{22}$
low energy cosmic rays	87 % < 1 MeV H^+ 12 % < 1 MeV He^{2+} 0.2 % < 1 MeV C^{6+},O^{8+}	10^1	10^{18}
solar UV-photons (110-300 nm)	≈ 100 % 4.3-7.3 eV (300-170 nm) 1 ‰ 7.3-11.3 eV (170-110 nm)	$2 \cdot 10^{15}$ $3 \cdot 10^{12}$	$2 \cdot 10^{32}$ $4 \cdot 10^{29}$

In the rest of its orbit, cf. Fig. 1, the bare nucleus is subjected to a fluence of about $1.3 \cdot 10^{18}$ cm^{-2} solar wind ions in each revolution. Cosmic ray ions deliver in $4.6 \cdot 10^9$ a to comets a fluence of about 10^8 cm^{-2}, which gives rise to a surface dose of about $2 \cdot 10^{11}$ rad.[5,23] The flux conditions for other objects in the solar system are compiled in Table 7, from.[16]

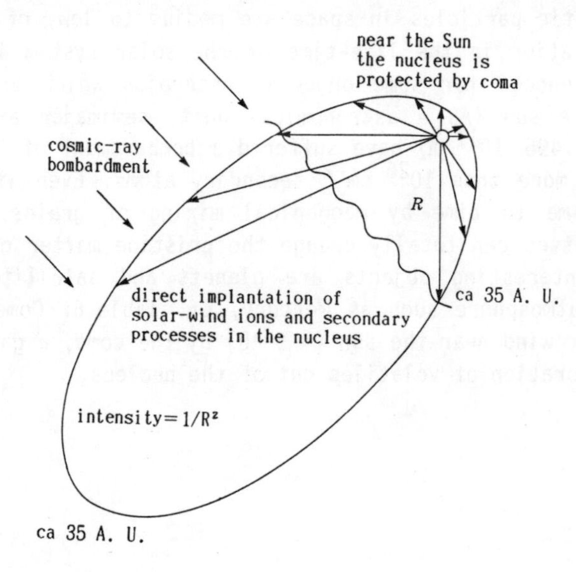

Fig. 1: Comet P/Halley in the solar and cosmic radiation field.[5]

Table 7: Solar wind fluxes for objects in the solar system, from.[17]

Object in space	Distance to sun AU	Flux of solar wind ions $cm^{-2}s^{-1}$
Mercury	0.387	2×10^9
P/Halley at perihelion	0.587	1.3×10^9
Venus	0.723	10^9
Earth	1.000	$2\text{-}3 \times 10^8$
Mars	1.524	10^8
Asteroids	3.5	2×10^7
Jupiter + moons	5.202	10^7
Saturn + moons	9.555	3×10^6
Uranus	19.21	7×10^5
Neptune	30.109	$3\text{-}4 \times 10^5$
P/Halley at aphelion	≈ 35	2×10^5

5. Dualism of radiation chemistry and hot atom chemistry

Solar photons produce hot hydrogen atoms in cometary comae by photodissociation of H_2O molecules which on their turn are then attacked by the hydrogens via H-abstraction. Both processes lead to the destruction of H_2O. The formation of hot secondary atoms by knock-on is in essence a radiolytic destruction of the substrate. Formation, motion and reaction of hot species are always accompanied by radiation physics and chemistry (photolysis, radiolysis) either by the hot atom itself or the accompanying radiation field, which change the target and the products likewise. Since the processes are interwoven and lead sometimes to similar products, a discrimination is only possible by a careful study of dose (flux, fluence) and energy density (linear energy transfer) effects, such as discussed in the next chapter.

Astrophysics has hitherto considered the radiation field in space only from the point of view of radiation physics and chemistry, in particular the formation of ions and radicals in the gas phase. Solids were considered only in the case of the icy layers on interstellar dust and comets.[23,24] Radiation processes in solids are in general an open field in space research. For example it is quite unknown at present how the annealing in the long irradiation times modified the concentration of defects.

Due to its high reaction rates (see above) and in some cases the formation of specific products (e.g. HCN in the system C/N_2) hot atom chemistry in the gas phase may well compete with radiation induced chemistry and a separate treatment is justified. Even more in the solid state since hot reactions proceed in most of the cases in a collision cascade where secondary hot atoms, excited or at least activated molecules, and a decrease of lattice binding energy add to create an activated zone. Collective or multicenter reactions are possible which cannot be induced by simple ionizing radiation. Furthermore, it can be expected that hot reactions in the solid state are also fast enough to compete with thermal radiation induced processes.[5,17]

It should be mentioned that many studies which are thought to be pure radiation chemistry, such as a treatment with MeV protons, contain a large amount of hot atom chemistry via the hot secondary atoms formed by knock-on.[25] Even UV-photolysis gives rise to (isolated) hot atoms. The formation of complex hydrocarbons out of simple ones is a good example to demonstrate the dualism of radiation and hot chemistry. Radiation chemistry in simple organic substrates leads to the preferential formation of linear, long chained aliphates and olefines, whereas hot carbon chemistry yields complex cyclic and aromatic structures such as polycyclic aromatic hydrocarbons (PAH), amorphous hydrogenated carbon, a-C:H (with a H/C ratio of about 0.4), soot, tarry substances, and amorphous carbon a-C.[25-27] One of the typical products of the a-C:H type is shown in Fig. 2, a polycyclic hydrocarbon. When irradiating one of these complex structures, simple molecules are formed together with carbonaceous matter. All processes seem to proceed in a kind of circle process in the "hydrocarbon world", such as shown schematically in Fig. 3. Hot atom chemistry takes part in build-up and destruction of complexity, but more in the first process then radiation chemistry, Figs. 4,5.

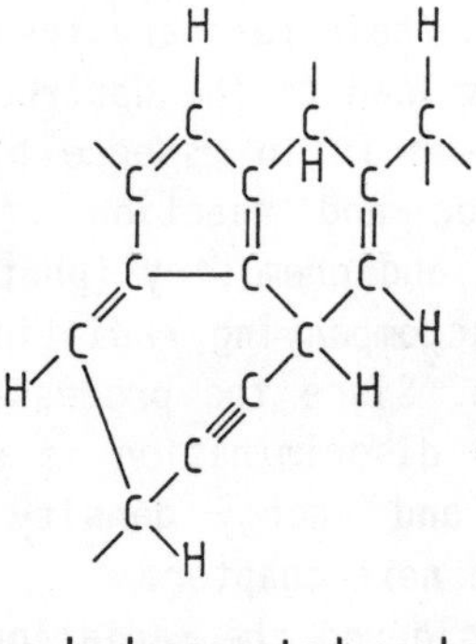

Fig. 2: Example of amorphous hydrogenated carbon a-C:H, from.[5,17]

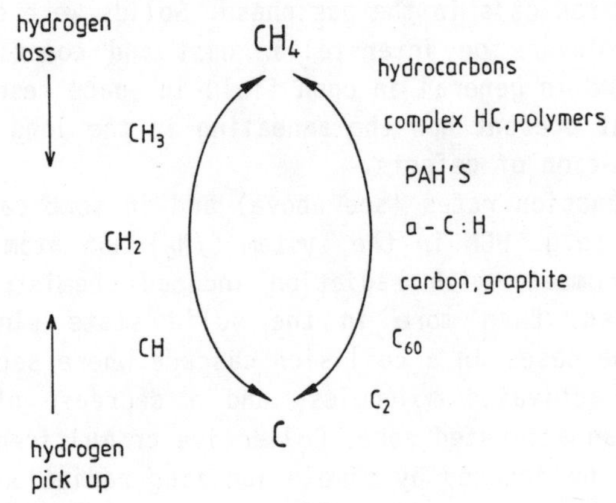

Fig. 3: Circle reactions in the "hydrocarbon world", from.[17]

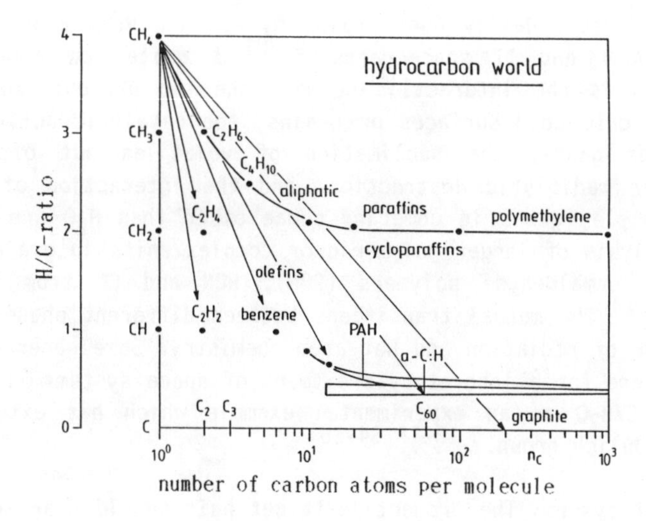

Fig. 4: Product formation by suprathermal reactions in solid CH_4 in the framework of the "hydrocarbon world", from.[17]

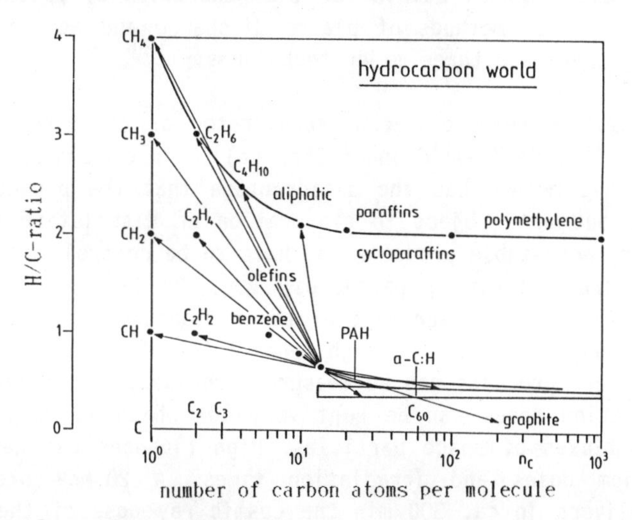

Fig. 5: Product formation by suprathermal reactions in solid anthracene in the framework of the "hydrocarbon world", from.[17]

6. Hot atom chemistry studies in the laboratory

The knowledge of cosmic chemistry is at present dramatically increasing by spacecraft based observations of gas phases via e.g. infrared, vacuum-UV and X-ray spectroscopy, gas chromatography, and mass spectrometry.[18-20,28] Solids are analyzed by remote sensing via reflectance spectroscopy, laboratory analysis of extraterrestrial samples such as meteorites, lunar matter, interplanetary dust grains from stratosphere or antarctic ices, and the direct observation of comet P/Halley dust grains by PIA and PUMA experiments aboard GIOTTO and VEGA I and II spacecrafts.[29,30] A quite new aspect of these advanced studies is the interaction between the two phases: condensation of gaseous species onto cold surfaces or grains, the catalytic activity of grain surfaces towards gases, the sublimation of volatiles out off grains, in particular after radiolytic destruction, and the interaction of grains with frosts. For example, gases in cometary comae other than H_2O are discussed to stem from photolysis of larger polymeric or complex units in grains ejected by jets (CO from formaldehyde polymers (POM), HCN and CN from CN-containing macromolecules).[2] The mutual transitions between different phases necessitate a good knowledge of radiation and hot atom chemistry. Some general guide-lines will be drawn here for a laboratory treatment of space systems. It is referred to the system C/H_2O as an experimental example which has extensively been studied by the Jülich group.[5,13-15,34-36]

6.1 Selection of system: The projectile/target pair should bear some relevance to a space system well known from astronomical or astrophysical observations.

6.2 Selection of experimental method for the generation of primaries: Besides the less frequently used methods of plasma discharge and atomic or molecular beam experiments, there are three major techniques:[5,15]

a) Recoil from nuclear reactions with accelerator or cyclotron ions such as e.g. $^{14}N(p,\alpha)^{11}C$, $^{12}C(^{3}He,^{4}He)^{11}C$ and $^{16}O(p,\alpha pn)^{11}C$ in combination with radiochromatography. This method has the disadvantage that the products cannot be analyzed in situ but are subject to evaporation or dissolution effects which may change primary metastable products and have to be controlled carefully. The advantages are: The activating particles, e.g. 20 MeV protons, provide a concomitant radiation. The measurement of the radioactivity allows for a 100 % balance of the products. Due to the high sensitivity of the radiodetection also small amounts of rare products can be measured precisely. To produce measurable effects the radiation doses can be kept very low which is very favorable in view of the low fluxes of space particles. High fluences can nevertheless be reached by medium doses and irradiation times. A 20 MeV proton beam of $1\ \mu A \cdot cm^{-2}s^{-1}$ delivers in ca. 300 min the cosmic ray dose of the duration of the solar system to a thin (1 mm) ice target.[5] The recoil atom marks the center of the collision cascade in solids and its (labelled) products are very characteristic for the in-cascade-chemistry, e.g. multicenter reactions. The radioactive primary plays among the hot but nonradioactive secondaries the role of a "primus inter pares". Last not least the nuclear recoil method may provide an approach to very diluted gas systems.
b) Ion implantation and analysis by spectroscopy (cold targets in cryostats), mass spectrometry and many other analytical methods such as discussed in.[5,15,25,26] Samples can be analyzed in situ. A disadvantage is that for many analytical tools the doses must be quite high $\gg 10^{15}$ ions cm^{-2}. The implantate

can not be discriminated from the secondary hot atoms of the same element. The products are representative for cascade and general radiolysis effects.
c) Photodissociation by VUV photons combined with chromatography, mass spectroscopy, optical spectroscopy, etc. can be analyzed in situ. The penetration of the photons in solids amounts to approx. 1 μm only. The hot atoms produced are rather isolated and can not induce a collision cascade. They will lead to smaller products than the two preceeding methods which include formation of secondaries, i.e. multicenter interactions. Table 6 lists types of space radiation which are simulated by the experimental methods discussed. It is highly desirable to apply more than one method to the systems under study and intercompare the effects.

Table 6: Simulation of space radiation by experiments

experiment	exp. energies eV	type of space radiation
atomic beam	1 - 10	shockwaves in interstellar medium
VUV photons	4.3 - 11.3	solar photons
plasma discharge	10^2 - 10^3	ion torus (Io) discharge lightenings
ion implantation	10^3 - $3 \cdot 10^5$	solar wind
cyclotron ions (nuclear recoil)	5 to $30 \cdot 10^6$	cosmic rays

6.3 Selection of substrate: It depends somewhat on the choice of the method for the projectile and should preferentially comprise both gaseous and solid state, for the reasons discussed above, and pure as well mixed systems. Sometimes it might be necessary to include also a study of the liquid state for better comparison. It is very difficult to efficiently cool gaseous targets. Furthermore it is virtually impossible to reach the high dilutions in space, since the products could not be detected in the background of impurities. Thus, it is often unavoidable to work with partial pressures of some to some ten mbar and to extrapolate to lower pressures. At high pressure all in- or metastable products may have a good chance to react with the medium whereas at high dilution they would survive. Thus, any kind of the above discussed simulations will create stable molecules and only in few cases radicals. Solids of low temperatures are easy to handle in cryostats at 77 or 5-10 K[5,15,25-26,31-36] and give reliable results also with respect to metastable states when analyzed by in situ methods.

6.4 Irradiation conditions and products: The experiments should be carried out in a way that a broad range of radiation dose is covered from very low ones in the order of 10^{-3} to 10^{-2} eV per target molecule where in particular in solids macroscopic radiolysis can not be expected, and medium to high dose of about some 10 to 10^2 eV per target molecule. 480 eV per H_2O-ice molecule is the maximum (surface) fluence of cosmic rays during the solar system to a comet. At low doses one can expect unchanged hot products, at higher doses radiolysis products. Doses beyond 10 eV will change the target molecules themselves. For the study of energy density effects which proved to be very important in the build-up of complex organic structures in frozen CH_4,[25-27,17] it is recommended to apply different kinds of activating projectiles (e.g. p, He, heavier ions) and vary the L_T values from some 10^2 to 10^4 eV μm^{-1}.

6.5 Mechanisms: For a chemist it is unavoidable to explain the formation of typical products by mechanisms. One of the best experiments in the framework of this dicussion of space chemistry was the mass spectrometric detection of m/z = 33 ejected from an ion irradiated ice mixture containing $^{13}C^{18}O_2$ and $D_2{}^{16}O$.[4,57,58] The prominent mass peak is characteristic for $D_2{}^{13}C^{16}O$ = 33, i.e. formaldehyde formed by secondary hot carbon insertion into D_2O and not by random recombination of defects and fragments. The physicist authors of the above mentioned articles did not accept this clearcut chemical explanation of their experiment, insisting on a modified defect recombination theory. Table 7 shows a collection of insertion processes of C, N, O projectiles into simple molecules, the intermediates and the final product states, from.[17] Besides the very prominent insertion there are substitution steps (direct replacement), fast defect recombination, H-abstraction and many more hot mechanisms leading to new products. Last not least there is the new theory of multicenter reaction within collision cascades.[17,25,26,33]

Table 7: Insertion processes of hot C, N and O atoms in simple molecules, from[17]

Reaction to intermediate	Successive products		
	H-elimination	1,2-H-transfer	H-uptake
$C+H_2O \rightarrow [HCOH]^*$	CO,COH,HCO	H_2CO	CH_3OH
$C+NH_3 \rightarrow [HCNH_2]^*$	HCN,CN,HNC	CH_2NH	CH_3NH_2
$C+CH_4 \rightarrow [HCCH_3]^*$	C_2H_2,C_2	C_2H_4	C_2H_6
$N+H_2O \rightarrow [HN\text{-}OH]^*$	NO,HNO	-	NH_2OH
$N+NH_3 \rightarrow [HN\text{-}NH_2]^*$	N_2	-	N_2H_4
$N+CH_4 \rightarrow [HN\text{-}CH_3]^*$	HNC,CN,CH_2NH	-	CH_3NH_2
$O+H_2O \rightarrow [HOOH]^*$	O_2,HO_2	-	-
$O+NH_3 \rightarrow [HO\text{-}NH_2]^*$	NO,HNO	-	-
$O+CH_4 \rightarrow [HO\text{-}CH_3]^*$	CO,HCO,HOC	-	-

6.6 Kinetics: As discussed above this part is still in development and very difficult to handle due to the non-equilibrium character of the suprathermal reaction. However, some preliminary results are available for hot O,[5] C[7], H[6,7] and halogen atoms.[9]

6.7 The example C/H_2O: This system shows up in all gas mixtures of H_2O with carbonaceous molecules (CO_2, CO, CH_4, etc.) which are frequent in atmospheres, in interstellar gas, in ice layers on dust particles and comets. Fig. 6 shows the main product yields obtained for hot carbon atoms from two different nuclear reaction in gaseous H_2O at 22 mbar and 295 K.[5,13,34-36] Analysis was performed by radiogaschromatography. ^{11}CO is the only primary hot atom product at low doses, $^{11}CH_4$ and $^{11}CO_2$ are radiolysis products. The mechanisms leading to CO, directly or via metastable CH_2O are described in Fig. 7. CHO and COH will also decay to CO. Radiolysis in the gas phase leads astonishingly to both oxidation (CO_2) and reduction (CH_4).

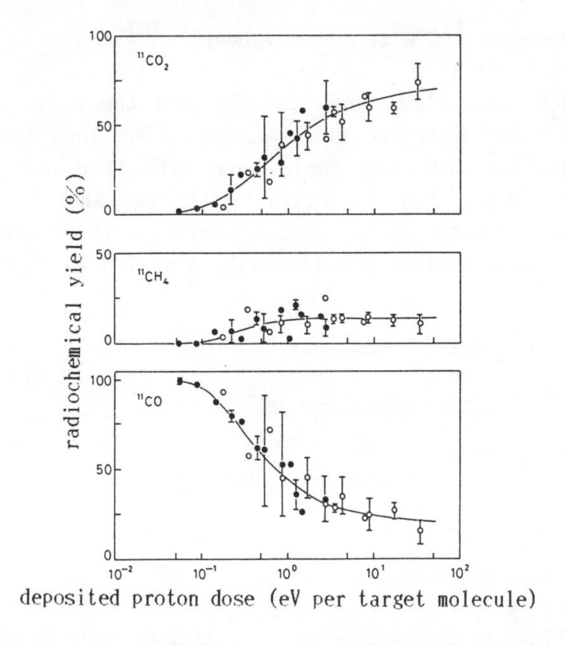

Fig. 6: ^{11}C-product yields for ^{11}C-recoils in H_2O vapour (22 mbar) at 295 K as a function of proton radiation dose, from.[5,34-36] $^{16}O(p,\alpha pn)^{11}C$, BN-$^{14}N(p,\alpha)^{11}C$.

Figs. 8 and 9 shows the yields of the main ($Y \geq 1$ %) ^{11}C labelled products after nuclear processes induced by MeV protons in liquid and frozen H_2O (77 K). The kind of products is the same in both systems, only their yields and the dose dependence are totally different. In H_2O, the radiolytic OH radicals can diffuse freely which leads to early oxidation of all species to $^{11}CO_2$ already at a dose of about $D^* = 10^{-3}$ eV per H_2O molecule. In liquid H_2O the main primary products are ^{11}CO, $H^{11}COOH$ and $H_2{}^{11}CO$, whereas $^{11}CO_2$ and $^{11}CH_3OH$ show

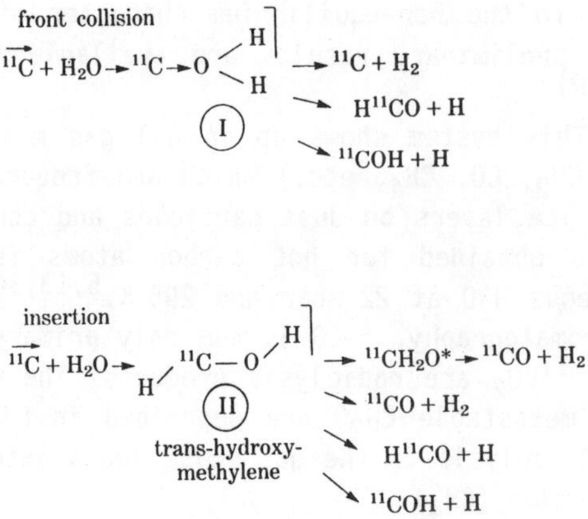

front collision
$^{11}C + H_2O \rightarrow {}^{11}C \rightarrow O$ H H
$\rightarrow {}^{11}C + H_2$
$H^{11}CO + H$
I
$^{11}COH + H$
insertion
$^{11}C + H_2O \rightarrow$ H $^{11}C - O$ H
$\rightarrow {}^{11}CH_2O^* \rightarrow {}^{11}CO + H_2$
II
$^{11}CO + H_2$
trans-hydroxy-methylene
$H^{11}CO + H$
$^{11}COH + H$

Fig. 7: Reaction scheme of ^{11}C with water vapour.[5,34)]

minor yields. In H_2O ice, $^{11}CO_2$ and $^{11}CH_3OH$ form the main primary products besides $H_2{}^{11}CO$. The other ones are not important. The long constant behaviour at lower doses signifies that one deals here with true hot products formed independently of the dose. Fig. 10 exhibits the mechanistic scheme for the formation of the hot products in H_2O ice, including a three center reaction of hot carbon with two H_2O molecules and elimination of 4 H to $^{11}CO_2$.[5,15)]

$^{11}CH_4$
$^{11}CH_3OH$
$H_2{}^{11}CO$
$H^{11}COOH$
^{11}CO
$^{11}CO_2$
Stenström 1970 ($^{16}O(p,3p3n)^{11}C$)
this work ($^{16}O(p,\alpha pn)^{11}C$)
radiochemical yield (%)
deposited proton dose (eV per target molecule)

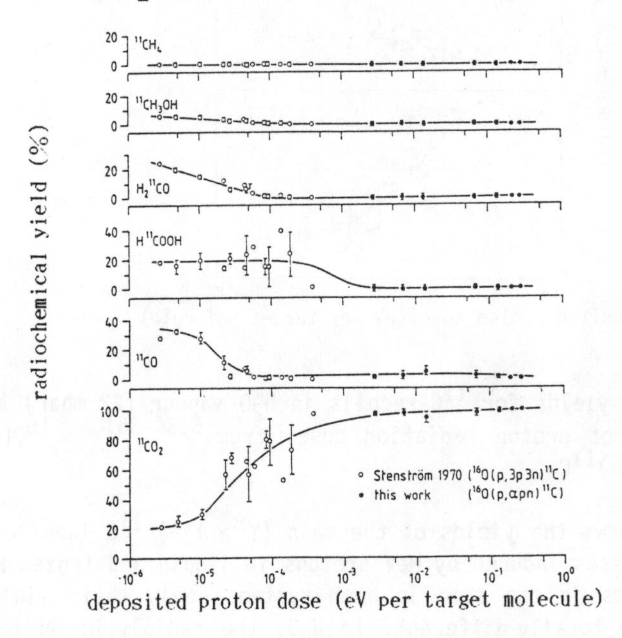

Fig. 8: Radiochemical yields of ^{11}C labelled products in liquid H_2O at 295 K as depending on the proton dose, from.[37-39)]

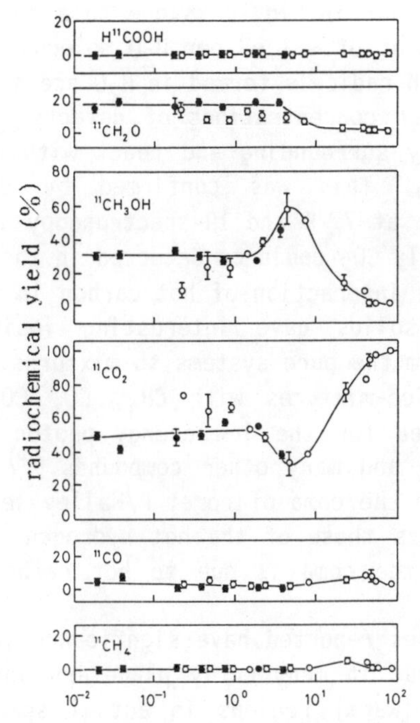

Fig. 9: Radiochemical yields of ^{11}C labelled products in solid H_2O at 77 K, from.[5,13,15,35-37] ● $^{16}O(p,\alpha pn)^{11}C$, ○ BN-$^{14}N(p,\alpha)^{11}C$.

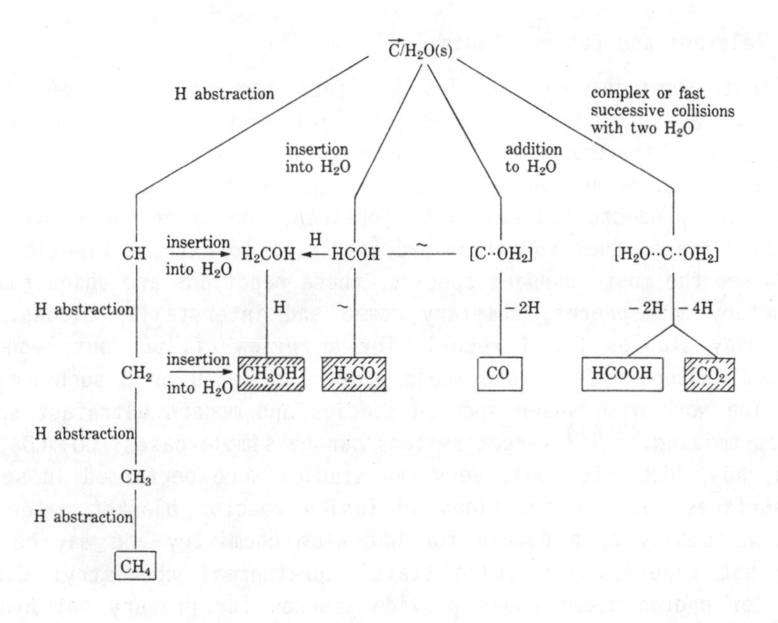

Fig. 10: Mechanistic scheme of hot carbon reaction in solid H_2O, from.[5,15]

The strange dose behaviour in Fig. 9 is due to a reduction of primary $^{11}CO_2$ with beginning radiolysis at D* ≈ 1 eV per H_2O molecule to CH_3OH by the mobile H-radicals. At 77 K the OH radicals formed in H_2O are still immobile. At higher doses > 10 eV, i.e. higher concentrations of defects, the OH can find carbon compounds in their nearby surrounding and react with them finally converting all C-species to $^{11}CO_2$. This was confirmed by the results of C^+-ion implantation into H_2O ice at 77 K and IR-spectroscopy in transmission.[40,41,5] At doses beyond 100 eV only CO_2 could be detected in the in situ spectra.

Further studies on the interaction of hot carbon in mixture of H_2O with CH_4 and NH_3 in gases and solids gave interesting insight in the change of mechanisms when going from the pure systems to mixtures.[5,36] Very important is the work in solid H_2O-ice-mixtures with CH_4, CO, CO_2, NH_3 etc. with VUV-irradiation which revealed for the low energy photon dissociation steps the formation of CH_2O, CH_3OH and many other compounds.[24] The kinetics of hot C reaction in H_2O vapour in the coma of comet P/Halley leading to CO and H_2 were treated in the same way as those of the hot hydrogen. It could be shown that about 5 % of the CO of the coma is due to hot carbon reaction of the type described in Fig. 7.[7]

The experimental studies reported have signficance for carbon chemistry not only in cometary comae but in many early planetary and satellite atmospheres and in H_2O vapour rich (warm) regions in actual space and the early solar system. The studies in H_2O ice are important for the stability of organic molecules in icy frosts, the formation of CH_3OH and CH_2O, important ingredients of evolutionary chemistry in comets, icy layers of interstellar grains and many other cold environments, cf.[5,17]

7. Some relevant and future studies

The most prominent hot species in space are hydrogen atoms from photo-dissociation and protons from solar (stellar) wind and other sources. Hot atom chemistry should therefore devote a renewed interest to hot hydrogen chemistry. Since the mechanisms are very simple: hydrogen abstraction and radical combination, and the products can easily be foreseen, the attention should be devoted to quantify the product formation process, i.e. to extract kinetic data. Since H and H_2 are the most abundant species, these reactions are ubiquitous in space in planetary atmospheres, cometary comae and interstellar clouds. There are already many studies for T recoil, for a review cf.[42], but because of the pronounced isotope effects one would prefer to use H or D such as present in nature. The work with laser induced species and modern ultrafast spectroscopy is very promising.[43-47] Target systems can be simple gases: CO, CO_2, H_2O, CH_4, NH_3, NO, NO_2, HCN, etc. Only very few studies were performed in solids or at solid surfaces, e.g. T reactions in fusion reactor blanket materials.[48,49] This is a totally open domain for hot atom chemistry and may be a clue to develop hot kinetics for solid state suprathermal chemistry. Cyclotron or accelerator proton beams could provide sources for primary hot hydrogens and their secondary knock-on products in many systems.

Next to hydrogen and in close connection from the point of view of chemical and biological evolution in space are the other "CHON" elements: carbon, nitrogen and oxygen. Many systems were studied hitherto, cf. reviews and tables therein.[5,13-19,42] Some of the first systems measured thoroughly was carbon recoil in gaseous and solid NH_3 and CH_4.[50-53] In addition to $^{11}C/H_2O$ (gls = gas, liquid, solid) the Jülich group added recently the systems: $^{13}N/H_2O$ (gls),[5,16,39,54] $^{11}C/CH_4$ (s),[31-33,25-27] $^{13}N/CH_4$ (s),[13,55] $^{11}C/H_2O$-NH_3 (g,s),[5,36] $^{11}C/H_2O$-CH_4 (g),[36] $^{11}C/NH_3$-CH_4 (g)[36] and ion implantation C^+ and N^+ in solid H_2O and NH_3 at 77 K.[5,15,40,41,56] Table 8 lists schematically the simple systems studied hitherto.[14] Table 9 reports some of the typical products of carbon and nitrogen recoil in simple ices, from.[5]

Table 8: List of projectile target systems studied hitherto, for details cf. reviews.[5,14,15,42]

Projectiles	Targets																	
	H_2	N_2	O_2	H_2O	NH_3	CH_4	C_2H_6	C_2H_4	CH_3NH_2	CO	CO_2	NO	NO_2	N_2O	PH_3	H_2S	SO_2	LiH
T	g		g	gls	g	g	g	g				g				g		s
C	g	g	g	gls	gls	gs	gl	gls	gl	g	gls	g	g	g			g	s
N	g	g	g	gls	s	gs	g	g		g	g	g		g				s
O	g	g	g	l		g	g			g	g							
P	g			l		g	g	g			g				g	g		
S	g		g	l		g	g	g		g	g					g	g	

Table 9: Typical products of ^{11}C and ^{13}N recoil and C^+ or N^+ ion

Projectile and target	Main products of high-energy reactions
C/H_2O (77 K)	CO_2, CH_3OH, CH_2O
C/NH_3 (8 + 77 K)	CH_3NH_2, CH_4, CH_3, $CH(\dot{N}H)NH_2$, etc.
N/H_2O (77 K)	NH_3, NO_2, NO, NH_2OH
N/CH_4 (77 K)	NH_3, CH_3NH_2, $(CH_3)_2NH$, $C_2H_5NH_2$, CH_3CN
C/H_2O-NH_3 (77 K)	CH_2NOH, CH_3OH, CO
C/CH_4 (77 K)	C_2H_2, C_2H_4, C_2H_6, C_3H_8, C_3H_6, ... up to C_7, △, □, ⬡, ⌬, PAHs

One of the new studies on the build-up of complex organic matter in space uses 17 MeV protons and $^3He^{2+}$-ions on solid CH_4 at 15 K and a series of modern techniques to analyze gas phase and solid residues: mass spectrometry, light microscopy, SEM (scanning electron microscopy), FT-IR (Fourier transform infrared spectrometry in transmission and reflectance), ESCA (Electron Spectroscopy for Chemical Analysis), RBS (Rutherford backscattering), ERDA (Elastic Recoil Detection Analysis), ^{1}H-FT-NMR (Fourier Transform Nuclear Magnetic Resonance Spectrometry), etc.[25-27] For PAH-formation a critical energy density value of $2 < L_T < 10$ keV μm^{-1} was obtained.

The trend of hot carbon chemistry goes to reactions in complex systems, such as benzene, styrene, polystyrene, polynees, polyoxymethylene, paraffins, cycloparaffins, PAH from naphthaline to coronene, a-C:H, C_{60}, and amorphous carbon.[30,3-5,25-27,59-60] Among the fundamental studies which lack is the reaction of hot carbon with acetylene which could give rise to cyclic intermediates such as e.g. cyclopropenylidene C_3H_2 (eq. 1), which is ubiquitous in space and seems to be a very important reaction intermediate for unsaturated and complex carbon compounds:

$$(1) \qquad \vec{C} + HC \equiv CH \rightarrow \text{c-}C_3H_2 \; (\ddot{C} \text{ bonded to } CH{=}CH)$$

Another problem is the change of satellite Titans atmosphere from primordially CO, NH_3, Ar to today N_2, CH_4, Ar along eq. 2:

$$(2) \qquad CO + 2\,NH_3 \rightarrow CH_4 + N_2 + H_2O \text{ (freezes out at 90 K).}$$

An interesting task for hot carbon and nitrogen chemistry are the the CN-rings in comets. Their formation from photodissociation of CN-containing polymers or in the gas phase itself can be governed by both radiation and hot atom chemistry.[60-63]

Biomolecule precursor materials for biochemical evolution were produced in simple inorganic solids by carbon recoil in ammonium compounds, $LiNH_2$, Ca_3N_2, etc., giving rise to the formation of e.g. HCN, cyanamide, guanidine, and other pyrimidine precursors,[5,13,64-68] proving the abiotic synthesis of building blocks for processes of life.

In order to provide a schematic overview on the organic chemical processes in space, Fig. 11 shows the two branches leading to biological precursor material and complex dark organic matter in space.

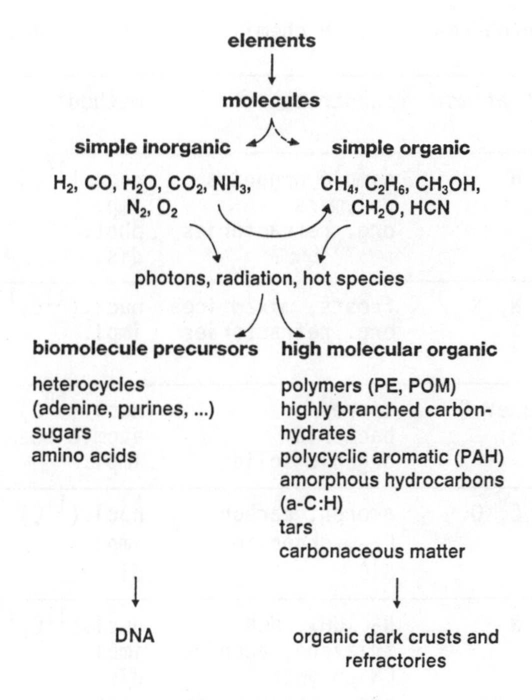

Fig. 11: Schematic flow diagram of chemical evolution in space, from.[17]

From the point of view of cosmochemistry, hot oxygen chemistry is as important as C or N chemistry, however, much less studied, cf.[69,70] It may describe the material destruction and surface ablation reactions, space crafts encounter in low earth orbits (approx. 300 km altitude) from oxygen atoms of the rest gas. The relative motion of the spacecraft with 8 km h^{-1} gives rise to a (relative) energy of 5.3 eV of the oxygen which, thus, impignes on the surface and induces very fast hot reactions.[5]

Sulphur and phosphoros recoil seems to be important for the build-up of the many compounds found in cometary comae. Last not least the minerologists and planetologists demand Si-, Al- and even Fe-hot atom chemical studies in simple silicates and oxides, but also in representative space minerals such as olivine or montmorillonite, etc. Finally mixed mineral-ice targets would be of interest for cometary research, e.g. comet simulation,[71-73] and Mars-studies. In order to give an overview, some of the most interesting problems for hot atom chemistry are listed in Table 10.

Table 10: Selected problems of space chemistry for hot atom studies

problem	hot atoms	substrate	method*	references prelim. work
asteroids (surface)	C, H	simple organics polymers org. refractories	nucl.(^{11}C) imp. phot. dis.	25,26,60,61, 76
biomolecule precursors	C, N, S	frosts, mixed ices org. refractories	nucl.(^{11}C,^{13}N) impl.	4,5,24,28,29, 30,36,42,64, 68,74-79,96
biophysical probes on space crafts	5.3 eV O	spores bacteria organic solids	nucl.(^{18}O) atomic beam impl.	5,81
carbon (degradation, reduction)	H, C, O	amorph. carbon C_{60}, graphite SiC	nucl.(^{11}C) impl. dis.	4,5,30,79,80, 89
cometary comae (CN-rings)	C, N	N_2, CH_4, HCN triazene, adenine CN-polymers org. refractories	nucl.(^{11}C,^{13}N) impl. dis. phot.	61-63,90,91
cometary comae (S-chemistry)	S, H	CH_4, H_2O, polymers org. refractories	nucl.(S) impl.	20,30,82
dark organic matter (org. refract.)	C	CH_4, C_2H_2, C_2H_4 benzene, styrene polymers, POM CN-polymers paraffins cycloparaffins PAH, kerogene tar, soot, a-C:H C_{60}, amorph. C	nucl.(^{11}C) impl. phot. dis.	4,5,17,25-28, 30-33,59-61, 79,80,83-87, 89
grain-grain collisions	H, C, O, Si, Al	SiO_2, MgO, minerals ice grains	impl. grain accel.	5
Mars (surface, atmosphere)	H, C, N, O	H_2O-CO_2 ice minerals	nucl.(^{11}C) impl., phot. dis.	20,34-39, 71-73
mineral chemistry	H, C, N, O Si, Al, Fe	SiO_2, MgO SiC, carbides oxides, silicates (olivine, montmorillonite)	nucl. impl. dis.	15,35-40,88

Table 10 continued

Table 10: continued

problem	hot atoms	substrate	method*	references prelim. work
mineral-ice interactions (catalysis)	C, O, Si	H_2O-CO_2 ice minerals cometary analogs	nucl. impl. dis.	35-39,71-73
planetary atmospheres (upper)	H, C, N, O	simple gases mixtures	nucl. impl. phot. dis.	5,14,20,27, 32,94,95
planetary atmospheres (lower)	5.3 eV O	simple gases O_2, O_3, N_2, H_2O NO, NO_2, NH_3	nucl.(^{18}O) atomic beams	5,20
ring systems C̈ CH+ HC=CH HC–CH (O)	C	C_2H_2, C_2H_4	nucl.(^{11}C) phot.	5,14,18,19, 90,91
satellite atmospheres (Io)	S	simple gases S-compounds	nucl. impl. phot.	20,82
solar photons	H, C, O	organic solids polymers	phot.	24,59-61
solar wind (space crafts, org. matter)	H, C, O He	polymers organic solids paints	nucl.(^{11}C) impl. dis.	5
space crafts (ablation by hot O)	5.3 eV O	oxides, ceramics metals polymers, paints	nucl.(^{18}O) atomic beam impl.	5,81,92,93
Titans atmosphere	C, N, H	CO + NH_3 CH_4 + N_2	nucl.(^{11}C,^{13}N) impl., phot.	20,36,95
unsaturated molecules (e.g. cyan-acetylene)	C, N	C_2H_2, C_2H_4	nucl.(^{11}C,^{13}N)	5,14,18,19

*nucl. = nuclear recoil (via activation by cyclotron ions)
impl. = ion implantation
phot. = VUV photolysis
dis. = plasma discharge processes

7. Conclusion

The problems listed in Table 10 and described in the preceeding chapters necessitate sophisticated target arrangements, many of them cryostated, and the application of more than one of the methods for generation of hot species discussed above, depending on whether one deals with dilute or dense gases, surfaces or bulk samples. Space research may trigger advanced hot atom work in close connection to physical chemistry and solid state physics. It should include the use of computer programms to simulate collision dynamics, cf.[97] Future work may include the choice of even heavier projectiles than discussed in this paper, since the hot atom chemistry due to dominance of S_n processes is more pronounced with small amounts of heavier particles (e.g. He in solar wind) than with big amounts of lighter ones (H in solar wind), cf.[25,26] It should be reminded that the acceptance of hot atom chemistry by astrophysics is linked to its content of mechanistic and kinetic solutions.

References

1. Sagan, C.: Science 188, 72 (1975).
2. Huebner, W.F.: Physics and Chemistry of Comets, Springer, Berlin, 1990.
3. Strazzulla, G., Johnson, R.E.: in Comets in the Post-Halley Era (R.L. Newburn, M. Neugebauer, J. Rahe, Eds.) Kluwer, Dordrecht, 1991, 1, p. 243.
4. Pirronello, V.: in Chemistry in Space (J.M. Greenberg, V. Pirronello, Eds.) Kluwer, Dordrecht, 1991, p. 263.
5. Roessler, K.: in Solid State Astrophysics (E. Bussoletti, G. Strazzulla, Eds.) North Holland, Amsterdam, 1991, p. 197.
6. Heyl, M., Roessler, K.: this issue.
7. Heyl, M.: Report-Jül-2409 (1990) 118 p.
8. Stiller, W.: Arrhenius Equation and Non-Equilibrium Kinetics, Teubner, Leipzig, 1988.
9. Berei, K., Gadó, J., Keszturi, A., Szatmáry, Z., Vass, Sz.: J. Phys. Chem. 94, 2362 (1990).
10. Stöcklin, G.: Die Zeit (Hamburg, FRG) 19, 55 (1966).
11. Rowland, F.S., Hathaway, L., Kambara, T.: in Chemical Effects of Nuclear Transformations, IAEA, Vienna 1961, 2, p. 255.
12. Adloff, J.P.: 3. Symposio sobre Quimica Nuclear, Radioquimica y Quimica de Radiationes, Mexico, December 1980, UNAM, Mexico, 1980, p. 55.
13. Roessler, K., Jung, H.-J., Nebeling, B.: Adv. Space Res. 4, 12-83 (1984).
14. Roessler, K.: in the Atmospheres of Saturn and Titan, ESA-SP-241, 175 (1985).
15. Roessler, K.: Rad. Eff. 99, 21 (1986).
16. Roessler, K.: Radiochim. Acta 43, 123 (1988).
17. Roessler, K.: Nucl. Instr. Meth. Phys. Res. B (1992) in press.
18. Winnewisser, G., Armstrong, J.T. (Eds.): The Physics and Chemistry of Interstellar Molecular Clouds, Springer, Berlin, 1989.
19. Duley, W.W., Williams, D.A.: Interstellar Chemistry, Academic Press, London, 1984.
20. Atreya, S.K.: Atmospheres and Ionospheres of the Outer Planets and Their Satellites, Springer, Berlin, 1986.
21. Roessler, K.: in Gmelin Handbook of Inorganic Chemistry, Thorium, Suppl. Vol. A4, Springer, Berlin, 1989, p. 199.
22. Johnson, R.E.: this issue.
23. Draganic, I.G., Draganic, Z.D., Vujosévic, S.: Icarus, 60, 464 (1984).
24. Greenberg, J.M.: Sci. American, 250, 6 (1984).
25. Kaiser, R.I.: Report-Jül-2492 (July 1991) 128 p.
26. Kaiser, R.I., Lauterwein, J., Müller, P., Roessler, K.: Nucl. Instr. Meth. Phys. Res. B, 1992, in press.
27. Kaiser, R.I., Mahfouz, R.M., Roessler, K.: Nucl. Instr. Meth. Phys. Res. B., 1992, in press.

28. Jessberger, E.K. (Ed.): Analysis of Samples from Solar System Bodies, Proc. ESF/SSC Workshop Bad Honnef, Germany, 11-13 June 1990, Space Sci. Rev., in press.
29. Kissel, J., Krueger, F.R.: Nature 326, 755 (1987).
30. Bussoletti, E., Strazzulla, G. (Eds.): Solid State Astrophysics, North Holland, Amsterdam, 1991.
31. Patnaik, A., Roessler, K., Zádor, E.: Adv. Space Res. 9, 6-49 (1989).
32. Patnaik, A., Roessler, K., Zádor, E.: Radiochim. Acta 50, 75 (1990).
33. Roessler, K., Eich, G., Patnaik, A., Zádor, E.: Lunar Planet. Sci. Conf. XXI, 1035 (1990).
34. Nebeling, B., Roessler, K., Stöcklin, G.: Radiochim. Acta. 38, 15 (1985).
35. Nebeling, B.: Report-Jül-1973 (Febr. 1985) 69 p.
36. Nebeling, B.: Report-Jül-2245 (Nov. 1988) 111 p.
37. Stenström, T.: Thesis, University of Uppsala, Sweden (1970) 190 p.
38. Nebeling, B., Roessler, K., Schmitz, G.: Adv. Space Res. 6, 12-207 (1986).
39. Schmitz, G., Nebeling, B., Roessler, K.: Report-Jül-2119 (March 1987) 68 p.
40. Bibring, J.P., Rocard, F.: Adv. Space Res. 4, 12-103 (1984).
41. Batista, M., Roessler, K.: unpublished results.
42. Stöcklin, G.: Chemie heißer Atome, Verlag Chemie, Weinheim 1969; Chimie des atomes chauds, Masson et Cie, Paris, 1972.
43. Valentini, J.J.: Radiochim. Acta 43, 105 (1988).
44. Cousins, L.M., Leone, R.: Radiochim. Acta 43, 107 (1988).
45. Wolfrum, J.: Radiochim. Acta 43, 114 (1988).
46. Kleinermanns, K.: Radiochim. Acta 43, 118 (1988).
47. Leone, S.-R.: Science 227, 889 (1985).
48. Kudo, H.: Radiochim. Acta 50, 71 (1990).
49. Kudo, H.: in Hot Atom Chemistry, (T. Matsuura, Ed.), Kodansha, Tokyo 1984, p. 501.
50. Stöcklin, G., Wolf, A.P.: J. Am. Chem. Soc. 85, 229 (1963).
51. Stöcklin, G., Stangl, H., Christman, D.R., Cumming, J.B., Wolf, A.P.: J. Phys. Chem. 67, 1735 (1963).
52. Dubrin, J., MacKay, C., Wolfgang, R.: J. Am. Chem. Soc. 86, 959 (1964).
53. Cacace, F., Wolf, A.P.: J. Am. Chem. Soc. 87, 5301 (1965).
54. Roessler, K., Schurwanz, K.: Report-Jül-1990 (April 1985) 52 p.
55. Fiergolla, J., Nebeling, B., Roessler, K.: Report-Jül-2156 (Sept. 1987) 58 p.
56. Armborst, E., Roessler, K.: Report-Jül-2089 (Oct. 1986) 84 p.
57. Pirronello, V., Brown, W.L., Lanzerotti, L.J., Marcantonio, K.J., Simmons, E.H.: Astrophys. J. 262, 636 (1982).
58. Brown, W.L., Lanzerotti, L.J., Johnson, R.E.: Science 218, 525 (1982).
59. Mahfouz, R.M., Sauer, M., Atwa, S.T., Kaiser, R.I., Roessler, K.: Nucl. Instr. Meth. Phys. Res. B, 1992, in press.
60. Sauer, M.: Diploma thesis, Fachhochschule Aachen/Jülich and Institut für Nuklearchemie der KFA Jülich, July 1991 (to appear as Report-Jül Nov. 1991).
61. Roessler, K., Sauer, M., Schulz, R.: Ann. Geophys. 1992, in press.
62. Schulz, R., Schlosser, W.: Astron. Astrophys. 214, 375 (1988).
63. Schulz, R., Schlosser, W.: in Formation of Stars and Planets and the Evolution of the Solar System, ESA-SP-315, 121 (1990).
64. Ido, T., Iwata, R.: in Hot Atom Chemistry (T. Matsuura, Ed.) Kodansha, Tokyo, 1984, p. 417.
65. Ido, T., Iwata, R., Takahashi, T.: Radiochim. Acta 43, 71 (1988).
66. Iwata, R., Ido, T.: Int. J. Appl. Radiat. Isotopes 34, 973 (1983).
67. Roessler, K., Lattke, H., Mathias, C., Al-Shukri, L.M., Vogt, M.: J. Lab. Comp. Radiopharm. 19, 1618 (1982).
68. Vogt, M.: Report-Jül-1855 (June 1983) 124 p.

69. Ferrieri, R.A.: this issue.
70. Ferrierri, R.A., Wolf, A.P.: Radiochim. Acta 34, 69 (1983).
71. Special Section: Laboratory Comet Simulation Experiments (KOSI): Geophys. Res. Letters 18, 243 (1991).
72. Roessler, K., Hsiung, P., Kochan, H., Hellmann, H., Düren, H., Thiel, K., Kölzer, G.: Proc. 20th Lunar and Planetary Science Conference, LPI, Houston, 1990, p. 379.
73. Grün, E., Kochan, H., Roessler, K., Stöffler, D.: in Diversity and Similarity of Comets, ESA-SP-278, 501 (1987).
74. Ponnamperuma, C. (Ed.): Comets and the Origins of Life, Reidel, Dordrecht, 1981.
75. Wilkening, L.L. (Ed.): Comets, Univ. of Arizona Press, Tucson, 1982.
76. Delsemme, A.H. (Ed.): Comets, Asteroids, Meteorites, University of Toledo, Toledo, 1977.
77. Mullie, F., Reisse, J.: in Topics in Current Chemistry, Vol. 139 (Organic Geo- and Cosmochemistry), Springer, Berlin, 1987, p. 83.
78. Winnewisser, G., Herbst, E.: in Topics in Current Chemistry, Vol. 139 (Organic Geo- and Cosmochemistry), Springer, Berlin, 1987, p. 119.
79. Tarter, J.C., Chang, S., Defrees, D.J. (Eds.): Carbon in the Galaxy: Studies from Earth and Space, NASA-CP-3061, 1991.
80. Bussoletti, E., Colangeli, L.: Riv. del Nuov. Chim. 13, 1 (1990).
81. Roessler, K., Horneck, G.: in ERA Follow-On Scientific Study, ESA-contract No. 8116/88/F/BZ (SC), Sept. 1989, 4-67.
82. Moore, M.H.: Icarus 59, 114 (1984).
83. Strazzulla, G., Baratta, G.A.: Astron. Astrophys. 241, 310 (1991).
84. Strazzulla, G.: in Experiments on Cometary Dust Analogues, (E. Bussoletti et al., Eds.), Kluwer, Amsterdam, 1988, p. 103.
85. Johnson, R.E., Cooper, J.F., Lanzerotti, L.J., Strazzulla, G.: Astron. Astrophys. 187, 889 (1987).
86. Roessler, K.: in Polycyclic Aromatic Hydrocarbons and Astrophysics (A. Léger, L. d'Hendecourt, N. Boccara, Eds.) Reidel, Dordrecht, 1987, p. 173.
87. Roessler, K., Eich, G.: in Amorphous Hydrogenated Films, E-MRS, Vol. XVII, Les Editions de Physique, Paris, 1987, p. 167.
88. Bibring, J.P., Langevin, Y., Maurette, M., Meunier, R., Jouffrey, B., Jouret, C.: Earth Planet. Sci. Lett. 22, 205 (1974).
89. Léger, A., d'Hendecourt, L., Boccara, N. (Eds.): Polycyclic Aromatic Hydrocarbons and Astrophysics, Reidel, Dordrecht, 1987.
90. Krueger, F.R., Korth, A., Kissel, J.: Space Sci. Rev. 56, 167 (1991).
91. Korth, A., Krueger, F.R., Mendis, D.A., Mitchell, D.L.: in Asteroids, Comets, Meteors III (C.I. Lagerkvist et al., Eds.) Reprocentralen HSC, Uppsala, 1990, p. 373.
92. Alberidge, R.G., Cole, R.K., Daech, A.F., et al.: Nucl. Instr. Meth. Phys. Res. B. 18, 582 (1987).
93. Zimcik, D.G., Maag, C.R.: J. Spacecr. Rockets 25, 162 (1988).
94. Sack, N.J., Schuster, R., Hofmann, A., Khedim, A., Koppmann, R.: Astrophy. J. 360, 305 (1990).
95. Sagan, C., Thompson, W.R.: Icarus 59, 133 (1984).
96. Khare, B.N., Sagan, C., Ogino, H., et al.: Icarus 68, 176 (1986).
97. Roessler, K.: this issue

Chapter 8

Hot Atom Chemistry and Energy and Environmental Problems

8.1 Hot Atom Chemistry of Radon and its Progeny

Jean-Pierre ADLOFF
Laboratory of Nuclear Chemistry, Nuclear Research Center and University Louis Pasteur, BP 20, 67037 Strasbourg, France

1. Introduction

During the last decade, awareness of the radiological risk associated with the emission of radon has increased steadily. On several occasions it has been claimed that radon and its progeny represent the main cause of natural radiation exposure. It contributes 40% of the annual global average dose equivalent of 2.4 mSv delivered to a single person from all radiation sources. The emanation in itself is not a serious threat because it is characterized by relative chemical inertness and low solubility. The radiotoxicity involved is mainly due to the radioisotopes of polonium, bismuth and lead formed by the decay of radon. The immediate daughters of radon are polonium atoms, which normally carry a positive charge. The ions are highly mobile and are rapidly adsorbed by atmospheric aerosols whose droplet size is generally less than one micron in diameter. Whether in adsorbed form or not, the polonium atoms decay in turn and the descendants undergo the same processes.

The solid daughter products of radon, once inhaled, are fixed along the bronchio-respiratory tract. Depending on the size of their carriers, the radionuclides are deposited at various depths within the bronchia and irradiate the surrounding tissues and cells. Recent studies on the carcinogenic effects of radon have indicated that the most sensitive cells are those of the basal layer and of the mucosa of the tracheo-bronchial epithelium.

The correlation between uranium mining and lung cancer was recognized a century ago among workers at the Sankt Joachimsthal mine in Bohemia. After Marie Curie had discovered radium in pitchblende coming from this area, the relation between radon inhalation and bronchial carcinoma became evident.

In recent years a wealth of literature, both scientific [1,2,3] and popular, has been published on radon. The control of this radioactive gas in homes and buildings and the health hazards it involves are now widely discussed topics. Further, a valid assessment of the properties of the radon daughters is complex because of the numerous parameters involved in a real situation, such as the indoor radioactivity of a dwelling. Some of the radionuclides disappear by disintegration or are eliminated by ventilation processes; others are deposited on walls and furniture. As a result, the radon daughters are never in radioactive equilibrium with their progenitor. Their radiotoxicity is related only to the so-called equilibrium fraction, i.e., that corresponding to the decay products which remain in the confined air of a dwelling. Indeed, the radon concentration is much higher indoors than outdoors, which exacerbates the radiological risk. This is an obvious consequence of the dilution factor resulting from the relative volumes of air concerned.

An understanding of the behaviour of radon descendants is evidently of great environmental importance, especially when rules can be established for the control of the equilibrium fraction. Whatever the complexity and diversity of the reactions in which the nuclides participate, the initial step will be determined by the immediate after-effects of nucleogenesis. Therefore it is instructive to recall the properties and behaviour of radon and its progeny in the course of successive decays from radon to the terminal element lead. Hot atom chemistry in natural radioactive families has been discussed previously [4].

The radioactive properties of two natural emanations and their descendants are recapitulated in Table I.

Table I. Parent and progeny of ^{222}Rn and ^{220}Rn

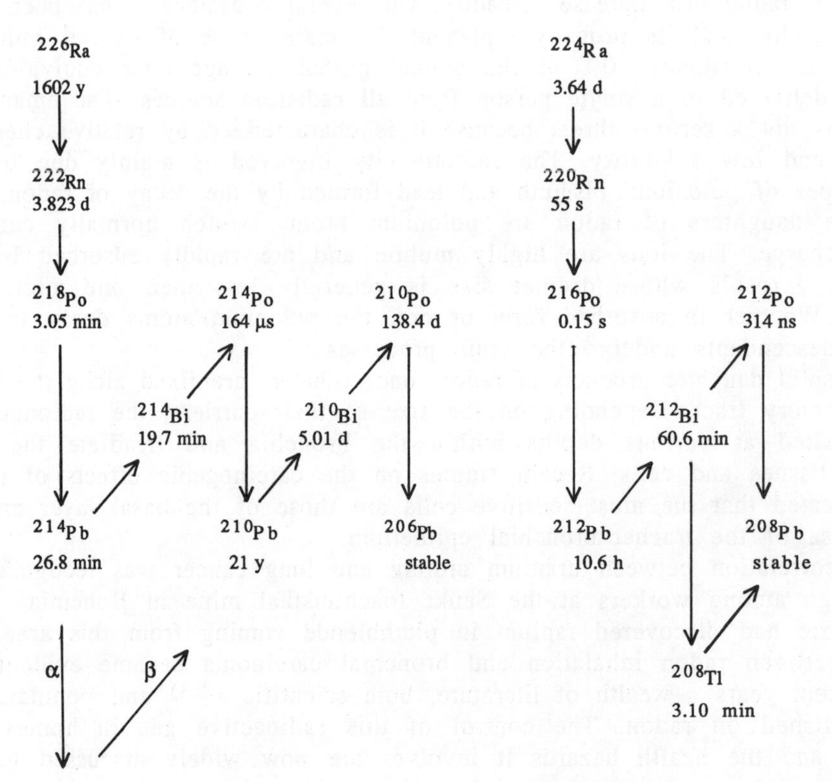

Owing to the 4-second half-life of ^{219}Rn (actinon) and to the low abundance of ^{235}U (0.7%), this third natural emanation isotope will not be considered. ^{220}Rn (thoron) in the thorium family is the most abundant of the three natural emanations, but with a half-life of 55 s its steady concentration is very small. Nevertheless, it cannot be overlooked because its decay chain contains the relatively long-lived ^{212}Pb, which in certain cases may be the major contributor to internal irradiation.

The most important emanation is ^{222}Rn (the true "radon"), a member of the abundant (99.3 %) ^{238}U series. Although its rate of release from soils is only one hundredth that of thoron, the half-life of 3.8 days ensures a much higher steady concentration in the environment. The radiological impact of radon is related to the two short-lived alpha emitters ^{218}Po and ^{214}Po.

2. From radium to radon

Radon is ubiquitous, being present in the atmosphere and in all soils, as well as in the ocean and river waters. This does not imply that radium, its parent, exhibits the same widespread distribution, since ^{222}Rn can be transported a long way from its source. Global averages for the concentrations of ^{226}Ra are given as several tens of Bq per kg of soil and 2 Bq per cubic meter of ocean water[5]; in certain mineral waters the amount may be 1000 times higher. At any given time, the radon content of the atmosphere is 10^{18} Bq, and its concentration near the surface of the earth is 2.9 Bq per m^3. The global average value of the emission rate is 1.6×10^{-2} Bq m^{-2} s^{-1}. With the possible return to coal as a primary source of energy production, these figures are likely to increase.

2.1. Nascent radon

Since several members among the progeny of radon are alpha emitters, it is appropriate to summarize the immediate consequences of the transmutations involved. The recoil energy of the daughter atom is readily computed from momentum conservation; its value is roughly 100 keV on average. Formally, emission of an alpha particle leaves the daughter with a charge which is two units less than that of the parent nuclide. Divalent radium ions Ra^{2+} can be readily converted to the zero-valent radon atom, but the expected transition from radon to a polonium atom bearing two negative charges is not generally observed.

The ionization processes which accompany the α decay have been reviewed by Wexler [6]. Perturbation of the electronic core and the loss of electrons may result from the velocity acquired by the daughter atom, from direct interaction of the expelled α particle with the electron core, or from shake-off due to the sudden change of the nuclear charge. However, the probability that these effects will occur appears to be rather small. The electron affinity of the atom and ensuing reactions with the surroundings will have a much more prominent role in determining the resulting charge of the nucleogenic species.

2.2. Radon release

When radon nuclides are born from α decay of radium iotopes in a finite-sized solid medium, they can escape either by direct ejection or by diffusion. Flügge and Zimens [7] were the first to elaborate a theory of the "emanating power", i.e. the aptitude of a radiferous medium to release the noble gas. The radon nuclides are ejected from their host if the site of radium decay is located close to the surface. When the recoil atom ends its trajectory inside the medium, it can still escape by a thermal diffusion process. Both mechanisms have been amply discussed by several authors (e.g. ref. 8) for many types of grain geometries and radium distributions.

Very recently [9], the recoil-emanation theory has been applied to radon release from mineral grains; this is a more realistic case in relation to radioecology. The distribution of radium, the radon's parent, has an important effect on the recoil emanation. It is itself determined by preceding recoil processes which begin with the decay of the ancestors of the radioactive series. Even if the latter (uranium and thorium) were formed homogeneously in a geological medium, the successive decays may displace the descendants. Eventually radium is fixed on thin layers of accessory minerals, thus becoming attached to the surface of various geological materials which enhances the release of radon.

The recoil energies of ^{222}Rn and ^{220}Rn are 86 keV and 103 keV respectively and the corresponding ranges in air are 64 and 103 mm. In a dry granulous material, radon recoil atoms can cross the pore space and become embedded in an adjacent grain. The ensuing "recoil implantation" may not be definitive, since again the thermal radon atom may diffuse to the surface and escape slowly into the intergranular space. Radiation damage may enhance the exit process.

Both theoretical considerations and experiments indicate that the fate of radon in soils, which is the main source of the gas in the indoor environment, is markedly affected by the presence of water[10]. In the first place, water in the pore space can act as a stopping medium (the recoil range of Rn in water is typically 75 nm) and hinder the embedding mechanism mentioned above. As a result, the release of radon is enhanced.

Another important role of water is to act as an etching agent of the recoil damage created by the embedded recoil radon along its path. This effect may also help to release the emanation. The relative importance of the two roles of water depends on the grain size and on porosity. The emanating fraction, defined as the ratio of mobile radon to total radon, is approximately four times larger in water-saturated soil than in a dry medium.

It should be noted that radon is the "ideal" species for any theoretical model of the purely mechanical effects of radioactive recoil since chemical combinations along the recoil trajectory or of the thermalized atom are in principle ruled out. The possibility of recoil synthesis of radon compounds has been discussed [11], but it remains to be proven.

3. From radon to polonium

3.1. Nascent polonium

The following discussion refers to the first step in the radon family: the decay of ^{222}Rn to ^{218}Po. Numerous experiments have proven that most of the Po atoms are born as positive ions. In dry air a good estimate of the initial yields is 88% for Po^+ and 12% for neutral Po atoms. It is assumed that the recoiling species is still in the charged state at the end of its path.

The fate of Po is intimately related to the positive charge. A convenient parameter for characterizing ions in air is the mobility. This represents the change in velocity of the ion in an electric field; it depends on the charge of the ion and is inversely proportional to its mass. Alternatively, the ions can be described by their diffusion coefficient, i.e. the product of the mobility and the thermal energy of the ion. The diffusion coefficient of Rn in air is 0.1 $cm^2\ s^{-1}$. That of a single Po atom, with similar size and mass, would be expected to be about the same; in reality, however, Po and other daughters of Rn have much smaller diffusion coefficients of the order of 0.05 $cm^2\ s^{-1}$. In terms of mobility, these daughter products behave like ordinary atmospheric ions. On the average, 75% of the ions have mobilities in the range (0.25 to 1.5) $\times 10^{-4}\ m^2\ V^{-1}\ s^{-1}$. These observations suggest that the nascent Po ions undergo charge transfer and clustering reactions.

3.2. Attached and unattached Po

It has been known for a long time that the daughter products of Rn can be classified into two categories. The first is the "unattached" fraction which includes mobile ions, molecules and small clusters with diffusion coefficients from (0.01 to 0.1) x $10^{-4}\ cm^2\ s^{-1}$. The second category comprises the daughter products attached to aerosols and dust particles. The attachment is controlled by the electric charge of the ions. It is responsible for the "plate out" of the radon progeny, i.e. the deposit of airborne radon daughters onto large surfaces such as walls, furniture etc. The plate out depends on environmental conditions: concentration of aerosols, air moisture, presence of trace gases and the properties of surfaces.

The unattached fraction is mainly responsible for the fixation of the radioactive daughters in the respiratory tract. Paradoxically, purification of air in a dwelling by removal of dust by filtration and electrostatic precipitation increases the radiation dose delivered to the lungs. In the presence of inert dust particles, the radon progeny is attracted to and attached to these particles. It has been evaluated that for a given number of atoms, the unattached radon daughters will produce 30 to 40 times the dose expected for the plate out fraction. An understanding of the electric behaviour of the decay products may be useful in developing control methods for indoor radon.

3.3. Neutralization of the polonium ion

Once formed, the Po ions can disappear by radioactive decay, neutralization, condensation-plate out on aerosols and by deposition in unattached form. The probability of the last three processes is highly dependent on the properties of the environment, as is revealed by the numerous discrepant values reported in the literature for the lifetime and diffusion coefficients of the Po ions. Increases as well as decreases of the diffusion coefficients with increasing humidity have been claimed.

The mean lifetime of ^{218}Po is 260 s. In an outdoor situation, in which plate out is not significant, the lifetime of Po ions has been estimated at 12 s. The competition between neutralization and fixation of the ion on condensation nuclei has been evaluated for typical situations, with the result that the lifetime increases with decreasing number of condensation nuclei. Thus, the attachment to aerosols prevails over neutralization.

The mechanism of neutralization has been discussed by several authors [12,13]. In the atmosphere, hot Po recoils undergo 10^8 collisions per s and are rapidly thermalized. The actual charge and chemical form of the species at the end of the recoil path depend on the ionization potential (IP) of the species, on the nature, concentration, IP and electron affinity of gases in the environment, and on the clustering of polar molecules around positive ions.

The behaviour of ^{218}Po has been investigated extensively [12-13]. In general, the diffusion coefficient of Po is taken as an indication of the degree of neutralization of the radon daughter. For a free ion the coefficient is of the order of 0.03 $cm^2\ s^{-1}$ and for a neutral species about twice this value. The actual mechanism of the neutralization can be inferred from the variation of the diffusion coefficient under controlled composition of the gaseous environment. Two processes have been proposed:

a) Charge transfer in the collision of the recoil ion with a substrate molecule A:

$$Po^+ + A \dashrightarrow Po + A^+$$

b) Neutralization by an electron or a negative ion:

$$Po^+ + M^- \text{ (or } e^-) \dashrightarrow Po + M$$

The first process requires a species A with an IP below that of Po, which amounts to 8.43 eV. Such species (e.g. organic molecules) are hardly available in sufficient amounts apart from laboratory conditions. In the atmosphere, it is unlikely that Po^+ can be neutralized by collision with neutral molecules [13]. On the other hand, in the presence of oxygen, the radon daughter exists in the form of the dioxy ion PoO_2^+ rather than as elemental Po. The reaction of Po with oxygen to form the neutral dioxide PoO_2 releases 3.7 eV. The IP of the latter has been deduced from the molecular diffusion coefficient in a variety of gaseous additives and has been found to lie between 10.35 and 10.53 eV. Thus, in dry N_2 (IP 15.58 eV) and O_2 (IP 12.10 eV) neutralization by charge transfer is precluded and the diffusion coefficient of polonium is of the order of 0.03 $cm^2\ s^{-1}$, which is characteristic of a charged species. However, with NO_2 (IP 9.79 eV) or NO (9.25 eV) additives, neutralization of the dioxide ion by charge transfer is complete as confirmed by a diffusion coefficient of ca 0.07 $cm^2\ s^{-1}$. On the other hand, nitrogen dioxide is inoperant in an atmosphere of dry N_2 since polonium oxide cannot be formed.

The second process accounts for the neutralization of the radon daughter as, for example, in the presence of water. It is well established that the fraction of initially charged Po decreases with increasing relative humidity. Since charge transfer from PoO_2^+ to H_2O (IP 12.36 eV) is not possible, and since water is a poor electron scavenger, the neutralization involves an electron-scavenging mechanism by another species, i.e.

$$M + e^- \longrightarrow M^-$$

followed by a recombination of the negative ion with the charged radon daughter. It is expected that the rate of this process should increase with the concentration of the electron scavenger.

The dual neutralization mechanism has been verified experimentally [13]. In dry N_2, the direct electron transfer from traces of NO_2 to charged Po is precluded. With increasing concentration of nitrogen dioxide, a good electron scavenger, one observes an increase of the diffusion coefficient of Po and the neutralization through NO_2^- is complete for 700 ppb of the scavenger. In dry O_2 on the other hand, neutralization is complete for the smallest amount (50 ppb) of NO_2 introduced. Thus, in the atmosphere at least two ways are available for the neutralization of the radon daughter.

Small negative ions are ubiquitous in the atmosphere. Their concentration is determined, among other means, by the rate of ion-pair production by cosmic rays and radioactive decay due to natural radioactive substances. Thus, it is adequate to consider possible effects of self-radiolysis of the decay site of radon. A single α particle emitted by ^{222}Rn produces about 150 000 ion pairs. The recoiling Po itself is a highly ionizing particle. In addition to the discussed mechanisms, neutralization can also occur through the high local ion density. This process is more likely to occur in radon-rich air, such as in uranium mines. Radiolysis is also expected to influence the further fate of PoO_2, which may react with nitrogen oxides produced by the α bombardment of air and become transformed into a basic nitrate.

3.4 Clustering of unattached polonium

The range of diffusion coefficents found in the literature suggests that Po appears as clusters. The radon daughter is surrounded by several dozen molecules of a condensable species from the air such as H_2O, NO_2 or SO_2. The mechanism of clustering has been widely investigated (e.g. ref. 14) and the theory of cluster formation has been applied to the specific cases of ^{218}Po and ^{212}Pb [15].

Clustering involves a charged Po species since the formation of neutral H_2O clusters is thermodynamically impossible. The rate of agglomeration of molecules around the Po ion is fast; depending on the relative humidity it requires 5 to 0.5 ms, i.e. a time much shorter than the radioactive half-life of any natural radon isotope. Once seeded, the cluster grows up into an aerosol droplet which may eventually condense.

It is well known that radiations can promote the formation of condensation nuclei even in initially particle-free ambient air, provided a minimum dose is deposited. Because of the higher LET of the recoil atom as compared to that of the emitted α particle, the ion density is higher along the Po track. The recoil atom comes to rest in a region where microphysical and chemical processes favour the formation of radiolytic seeds.

The actual mechanism has been established from the clustering rate in various atmospheres [16]. Humidity plays a key role. The first step is the radiolysis of water with the formation of OH radicals. If the latter are scavenged by species such as NO or butanol, the formation of condensation nuclei is precluded. In the presence of reduced species such as sulfur dioxide, the strongly oxidant OH radicals produce SO_3, which upon hydrolysis forms readily condensable sulfuric acid that either combines with other molecules or condenses on existing aerosols. The droplets coagulate and become ultrafine particles which incorporate Po. It is assumed that the minimum size of ultrafine particles for initiating condensation is 3 nm. This scheme is supported by the observed increase in density and size with increasing concentration of SO_2. Similar processes intervene in the fixation on aerosols of the cosmogenic radionuclides ^{7}Be, ^{32}P and ^{35}S.

3.5 Plate out polonium

A part of the radon daughter which is neither free nor fixed on aerosols becomes attached to large surfaces such as walls and constitutes the plate out fraction. This form has been extensively investigated [17,18,19] and mathematical models have been established [20]. The degree of plate out depends on the aerosol and dust concentrations, humidity, presence of trace gases and the surface properties. The charge of the radon daughter, as discussed above, probably favours the plate out deposit. The plate out rates of the free radon daughters are about 200 times higher than the corresponding values for the radioactive aerosols. Radon and thoron progeny seem to have different behaviours with respect to plate out [17].

4. The granddaughters of radon

All immediate daughters of radon are α emitters. As before, the behaviour of the radioactive lead isotopes formed in the decay of Po is controlled by the recoil and charge of the nucleogenetic atoms. In this case, however, the α emitter is a solid bound to an aerosol or to a cluster rather than a gaseous, chemically inert gas. Thus one is led to examine the probability that the Pb atom is recoil-detached from the cluster whereby it may subsequently become incorporated again in another cluster or aerosol. The fraction of ^{214}Pb which is charged is about 4 times higher than that for ^{218}Po and the average mobility of the lead atom ten times lower. The average value of the recoil factor [18], defined as the probability of desorption from a particle surface, is about 0.5.

Owing to the 3.05 min half-life of ^{218}Po, monitoring of this nuclide is limited; further information on the behaviour of the ^{222}Rn daughter products is gained from the 26.8 min ^{214}Pb. Interestingly enough, the aerosols loaded with ^{214}Pb and 10.6h ^{212}Pb (from 0.16 ms ^{216}Po) have different size distributions[14], the shorter-lived nuclides from the Rn chain being associated on the average with larger-sized aerosols than in the case of nuclides from the longer-lived thoron chain. The origin of this so called "^{214}Pb shift" is a recoil effect.

As seen above, the time required for attachment of ^{218}Po to an aerosol or coagulation with other molecules is much shorter than the half-life. If the diameter of the aerosol were much smaller than the recoil range (about 0.1 mm) of the Pb daughter, complete recoil loss would occur. The probability of loss would decrease with increasing size of the aerosol. In fact, part of the ^{214}Pb is recoil-detached from the smaller aerosols by mechanisms already described and is again and definitely incorporated into a new generation of aerosols. In the case of ^{216}Po, the half-life is too short to allow a substantial attachment and most of the nuclides would decay before forming an aerosol. Hence ^{212}Pb has only one opportunity of becoming involved in a condensation process, and the net effect is the shift of the average aerosol size from 0.16 mm for ^{214}Pb to 0.13 mm for ^{212}Pb. This reflects the recoil-induced depletion of ^{214}Pb of the smaller aerosols [14] and the fact that this nuclide undergoes more than one condensation

5. To the terminal stable lead isotopes

The Pb isotopes described in the previous section, lead in two successive β decays to ^{214}Po and ^{212}Po. The recoil energy associated with the β emission (and with that of the concomitant γ) does not exceed a few eV. The nucleogenic Po atoms will essentially remain at the site of the lead granddaughters, so that the behaviour of ^{214}Pb and ^{212}Pb actually reflects that of the aerosols loaded with the α emitters.

The story of the thoron progeny ends with the ^{212}Pb aerosol. In the case of radon, a further recoil-induced redistribution of 22 y-^{210}Pb isotope formed by α decay of ^{214}Po (10^{-4} s) is predictable. Once detached by recoil from its original aerosol, ^{210}Pb can be fixed on pre-existing particles or coagulate in the course of radiation induced chemical reactions in the recoil track. The presence of the long-lived lead isotope in large aerosols is attributed to growth after condensation.

The atmospheric flux of ^{210}Pb from the decay of radon is 15 atoms cm^{-2} s^{-1}. This value has been derived from the activity of the loaded aerosols. The fall-out ^{210}Pb, together with the part formed by decay of ^{226}Ra in solution, is found only in surface ocean waters. It is rapidly removed from deeper layers by adsorption onto sinking particulates or coprecipitates with ferric hydroxide or insoluble oxides. The oxidation state of ^{210}Pb is not further related to the after-effects of the decay of ^{214}Bi-^{214}Po and is fixed by geochemical processes. On the other hand, the 140 d granddaughter ^{210}Po resulting from two β decays is often found to be out of radioactive equilibrium with ^{210}Pb. This rupture is a consequence of preferential adsorption of polonium on particulate matter and depends on different chemical properties rather than on recoil effects.

The terminal lead isotopes in the three natural radioactive families are of great importance in geochemistry. Speciation of the stable end products cannot be achieved but it has been found that the Pb^{2+}/Pb^{4+} ratio of ^{210}Pb can depend on the type of mineral [21]. The possible role of hot atom effects in the rupture of equilibrium among the long-lived nuclides in the radon chain and in the determination of the chemical state of individual members is obscured by overlapping chemical and geochemical processes.

6. Conclusion

The radon progeny represents a unique case for which chemical effects of radioactive decays have radioecological implications. The fixation of harmful α emitters on aerosols and dust particles, a step preliminary to their incorporation in living bodies, is a consequence of recoil and charge-formation events triggered by transmutation. A better knowledge of the mechanisms involved would be helpful in deriving methods for reducing indoor airborne radon-decay products.

References

1. "Radon and its Decay Products. Occurrence, Properties and Health Effects", P.K. Hopke, Ed., ACS Symposium Series 331, Am. Chem. Soc. Washington DC, (1987), 609 p.
2. "Radon", Proceed. 24th Ann. Meet. National Council on Radiation Protection and Measurements, Harley, N. M. Ed. Bethesda, MD, (1989), 314 p.
3. Crameri, R., Burkart, W. : Radiat. Phys. Chem., 34, 251 (1989).
4. Adloff, J.P. : Radiochim. Acta, 23, 137 (1976).
5. Cohen, B.L.: Progress in Nuclear Energy, 4, 1 (1979)
6. Wexler, S.:"Actions Chimiques et Biologiques des Radiations", M. Haïssinsky, Ed., Series VIII, 105 (1965), Masson, Paris.
7. Flügge, S., Zimens, K.E. : Z. Phys. Chem., B42, 179 (1939).
8. Balek, V. : Thermochimica Acta, 22, 1 (1977)
9. Semkow, T.M. : Geochim. Cosmochim. Acta, 54, 425 (1990); Geophys. Res. Lett. (1990), in press.
10. Fleischer, R.L.: Geochim. Cosmochim. Acta, 47, 779 (1983).
11. Adloff, J.P. Radiochim. Acta, 6, 1 (1966).
12. Goldstein, S.D., Hopke, P.K. : Environ. Sci. Technol., 19, 146 (1985)
13. Busigin, A., Van der Vooren, A.W., Babcock, J.C., Phillips, C.R.: Health Phys., 40, 333 (1981).
14. Bondietti, E.A., Papastefanou, C., Rangarajan, C.: ref.1 p.377.
15. Raes, F.: Health Phys., 49, 1177 (1985).
16. Chu, K.D., Hopke, P.K., Knutson, E.O., Tu, K.W., Holub, R.F.: ref.1 p. 365.
17. Bigu, J. : ref.1 p. 272.
18. Porstendörfer J., Reineking, A., Becker K.H.: ref.1 p. 285.
19. George, A.C., Knutson, E.O., Tu, K.W. : Health Phys., 45, 439 (1983).
20. Knutson, E.O., George A.C., Frey J.J., Koh, B.R.: Health Phys. 45, 445 (1982);
21. Rowland, F.S., Hathaway, L., Kambara, T. : "Chemical Effects of Nuclear Transformations", IAEA, Vienna, 1961, Vol. II, p.255.

8.2 Hot Atom Chemistry and Severe Accident of Water Cooled Fission Reactor

Masakatsu SAEKI
Department of Chemistry, Japan Atomic Energy Research Institute,
Tokai-mura, Naka-gun, Ibaraki-ken 319-11, Japan

1. Introduction

The large inventories of fission products and transuranium elements in the cores of nuclear reactors are potential hazards associated with severe core damage accidents. Among these radioactive elements, iodine, cesium and tellurium are classified as the most hazardous ones, because they have relatively high volatility, and can be released into the primary coolant system. Especially, iodine is potentially most significant due to its large fission yield and its chemical and biological behavior. In this chapter, therefore, the chemical behavior of iodine will be emphasized. Hot atom chemistry is expected to supply basic knowleges in understanding the behavior of such radioactivities.

The first release of iodine from a nuclear reactor was experienced at Windscale in 1957.[1] In the accident, the chemical form of iodine released was mainly elemental iodine (I_2), because the atmosphere during the accident was oxidative and dry. However, it was impressed by this accident that iodine was probably released in elemental form in any reactor accident. Therefore, the behavior of iodine in a reactor accident was mainly examined using elemental iodine until the accident of unit 2 at Three Mile Island (TMI-2), which was very severe.

In the TMI-2 accident, about 40 % of the radioactive iodine present in the core escaped from the nuclear fuel into the containment building. However, only a very limited amount of the radioiodine was found in the environment as well as the inside atmosphere of the containment building.[2] This meant that the solubility in water of the chemical form released must be higher than that of elemental iodine. After extensive efforts, it was believed that the most probable chemical form would be cesium iodide, CsI.

2. Release behavior of fission products

The studies have been carried out using commercial light water reactor fuel or simulated fuel (fissium) in several national institutes, in order to determine the release rates and the predominant chemical forms of the volatile fission products as functions of temperature, heating time, test atmosphere and fuel characteristics.[3-12]

By the experiments of ORNL, in which spent fuel was heated up to 2,300 K in a flowing mixture of steam and helium, it was revealed that the fractional release of krypton, iodine and cesium were similar in all tests and varied from about 2% in 30 min at 1,700 K to a maximum of about 60% in 20 min at 2,300 K.[3-6] Similar results were reported from the Severe Fuel Damage Test which was conducted in the Power Burst Facility at the Idaho National Engineering Laboratory using a test assembly of 28 PWR-type fuel rods.[7-9] In Fig. 1, the experimental results from ORNL[5] are compared with the results of the US-NRC review[13]. The ORNL group believed the data depicted by the dashed line in Fig. 1 are more typical of the conditions of these tests. From these experimental evidences, it can be concluded that the fractional release rates of volatile fission products including noble gases are lower than that expected from the estimating techniques before the TMI-2 accident.

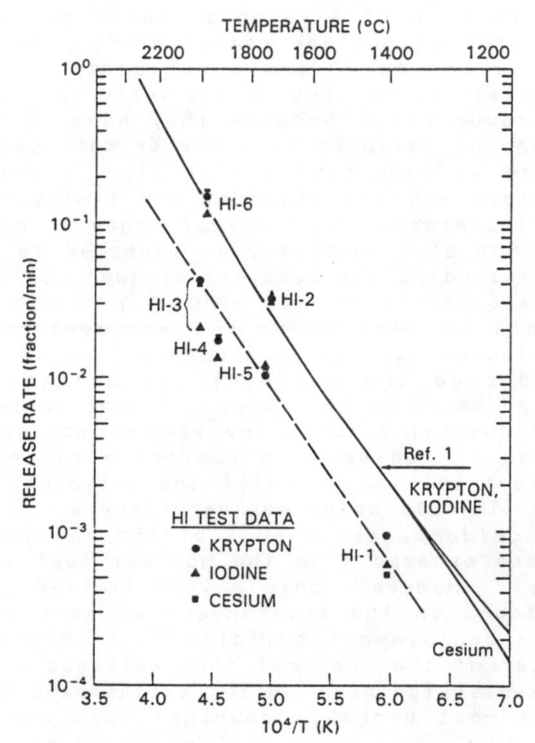

Fig. 1 Inverse temperature dependence of HI test data, compared with NRC review data.

The chemical forms of the fission products were determined by several methods. The most popular method is thermochromatography which is often used for real fuel tests. The characterization of the chemical forms was made according to their deposition profiles on a thermal gradient tube (TGT). Deposition patterns of fission products in the fuel tests are compared with those of known compounds in control tests. Considering the following facts, it was concluded that the most probable chemical form of released iodine would be cesium iodide (CsI); (1)both elements deposited in the same temperature range, (2) almost equal quantities of cesium and iodine were detected in the region, (3) the peak location was similar to those obtained for CsI in the control tests. It is understood that the iodine was released already in the form of CsI or CsI formed instantly upon the fuel. For the former concept, it has been reported that CsI formation occurred in microbubbles which were produced in the fuel matrix for fuel burnups in excess of about 5000 MWD/t.

Furthermore, the leachability of fission products deposited on a TGT was conducted using H_2O, NaOH and HNO_3. Water was quite effective in removing cesium from deposition samples which were provided under severe fuel damage accident conditions, in an atmosphere of hydrogen and steam. This means that the chemical forms of other fission products possessed high solubility. Since cesium is about 10 times more abundant than iodine, the chemical form of cesium other than CsI was probably CsOH.

The release rate of tellurium and barium varied strongly with the extent of cladding oxidation.[10,11] This was noticed at first in KfK. Tellurium released from UO_2 fuel reacted with the zircaloy cladding and was retained on it forming mainly zirconium tellurides ($ZrTe_2$). With increasing oxidation of zirconium by steam, the resulted telluride decomposed into metal oxides, ZrO_2 and TeO, which accelerated the release of tellurium. Contrarily, barium behaved inversely to the tellurium; because the free energy of oxide formation is larger for ZrO_2 than for BaO, metallic zirconium is able to reduce the BaO released from the fuel and convert it into more volatile elemental form. Thus, the release rate of barium is higher before the cladding of the fuel is oxidized.

As described above, the release behavior of fission products during a severe accident mainly obeyed the thermodynamics in a similar manner for the eactions often observed in the studies of HAC.

3. Alternation of chemical form after fission product release

In outpile experiments, the chemical products released from UO_2 fuel were immediately quenched, and they would keep their original chemical forms. However, during a severe accident of a nuclear reactor, the temperature of the atmosphere may change quickly. Many attempts have been made to predict the predominant chemical forms of fission products in the gas phase under such an indefinite atmosphere.[14-19] The most common method was a calculation applying equilibrium thermodynamics. The results of such calculations are independent of the initial chemical form released, and depend only on the system temperature, pressure and the concentrations of elements. Since the accuracy of the thermodynamic data base is in general quite good, the accuracy of these calculation is usually good.

At elevated temperature, the equilibrium may be achieved in a short period. But, there are three points to be considered regarding the validity of the prediction; (1) the reaction kinetics in a system are sufficiently rapid to ensure that equilibrium is reached, (2) the calculation does not include the radiolysis, and (3) all significant species have to be considered. In order to confirm the point of (1), some attempts have been made. The results show that the approach to equilibrium is sufficiently fast at temperatures more than 1000K, and the validity of thermodynamic calculations is conframed for predicting the chemistry.[16,17-19] However, the accuracy of this kind calculation is usually less than that of an equilibrium calculation. Thus, many efforts have been made to devise a kinetic data base for the relevant thermal and radiolytic reactions.[20-22]

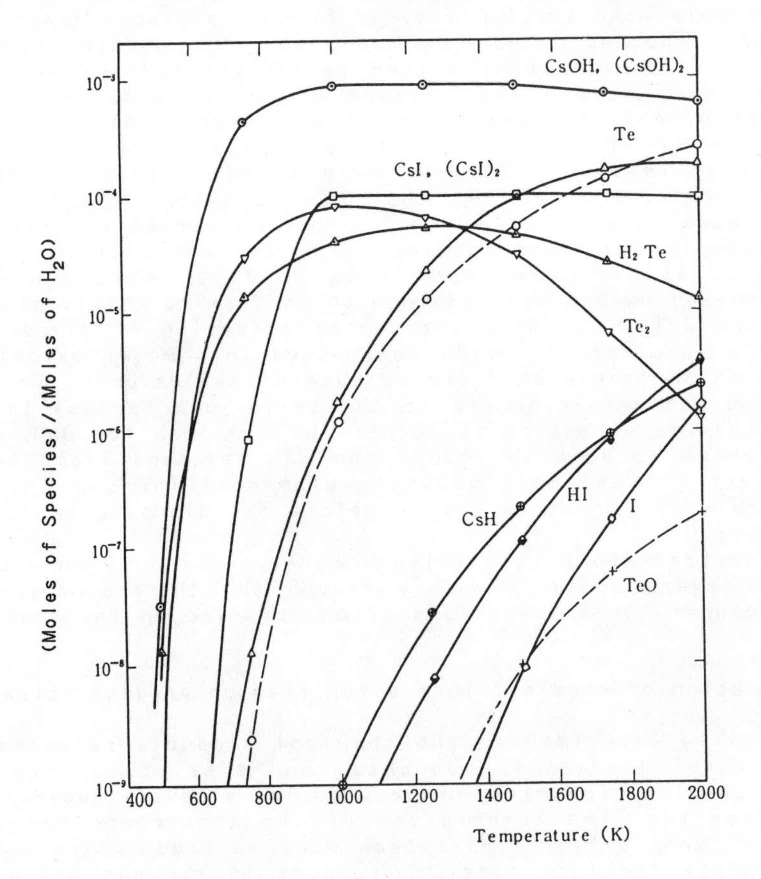

Fig. 2 Molar Fraction of Gas-Phase Species ($H/O = 4$, $Cs/H_2O = 10^{-3}$, 10 atm)

Numerous computer programs have been reported for calculating thermodynamic equilibrium compositions.[15, 23-25] This method computes the equilibrium composition by the direct minimization of the system free energy. The total Gibbs free energy of a system can be expressed.

$$G_T = \sum_i n_i (G^0_i + RT\ln a_i), \quad (1)$$

where G_T = total Gibbs free energy,
n_i = moles of species i,
G^0_i = standard Gibbs free energy of species i,
R = ideal gas law constant,
T = absolute temperature,
A_i = activity of species i.

The minimum total Gibbs free energy is calculated by solving the above equation after suitable modifications for computation.

An example is shown in Fig. 2,[19] which was calculated using SOLGASMIX-PV.[24] The parameters for the calculation are as follows, the ratios are [Cs]/[I] = 10, [Te]/[I] = 2, [Cs]/[water vapor] = 10^{-5}, respectively, and the total pressure is 10 atm. From these computed results, it is revealed that the most stable chemical form of iodine is CsI in the temperature range from 500 to 1400 K and the form of cesium is CsOH for the whole range of temperature calculated. It is also ascertained that the concentration of the elemental form of iodine is zero for the whole range of temperature, although its concentration was thought as dominant in WASH-1400.[26]

4. Long term alternation of chemical form of iodine in water

As mentioned in the preceding section, the most probable final species of iodine released during an accident is always cesium iodide regardless of the initial chemical form. The final form of the remaining cesium is CsOH. These species are easily washed out by the containment spray system and they instantly dissociate to yield iodide ion, I^-, and cesium ion, Cs^+. As is already well known, the chemical forms of iodine in the aqueous phase are very complicated, since iodine has a wide spread of oxidation states. Thus, the long term contributions to the iodine source term will depend on the changes in chemical form giving volatile species in water.

Several calculations were reported on the radiation dose rate in the suppression pool under a severe accident. The results are focused on the order of 10^6 rad h^{-1} (10^4 Gy h^{-1}).[27,28] A realistic estimation for the maximum aqueous iodine concentration might be 10^{-4} mol dm^{-3}, assuming that one-fourth to one-half of the iodine inventory (ca.15 kg) would be dissolved in 4×10^2 m^3 of water.[29]

Under such a high radiation field the water sustains radiolysis. The initial process of water radiolysis is expressed by the following equation.

$$H_2O \rightsquigarrow OH(2.7), e^-_{aq}(2.7), H(0.6), H_2O_2(0.7), H_2(0.45), \quad (2)$$

where the figures in parentheses are the initial G values.[30,31] The products include both highly reactive oxidizing and reducing species.

As is easily understood, the interactions between these radiolysis products and the dissolved iodine species are complex. For the iodine and water system, hydrated electrons are always reducing and OH radicals are oxidizing. The other important radiolysis products are H_2O_2 molecules and H atoms, which can be either reducing or oxidizing, depending on the pH.[31] If iodine is initially present as iodide ion, oxidation will proceed until back reactions reducing the oxidized I_2 or IO_3^- species balance the oxidation rate. The equilibrium reached will depend on a variety of factors, such as pH, the concentration of iodine and other impurities.

A typical example is shown in Fig. 3.[30] As is seen in the figure, the yields of I_2 and IO_3^- have maxima after a small dose of irradiation, and I^- species finally recovers the initial concentration. In this research area, good progress has been made over the last 4 years on the study of the effect of gamma-radiation on iodine species in higher oxidation states, such as, HIO and IO_3^-.[31-34] Although oxidation of I^- to the I_2 and HIO states is sufficiently understood, experimental studies are still required to elucidate the mechanism of formation of the higher oxidation states.

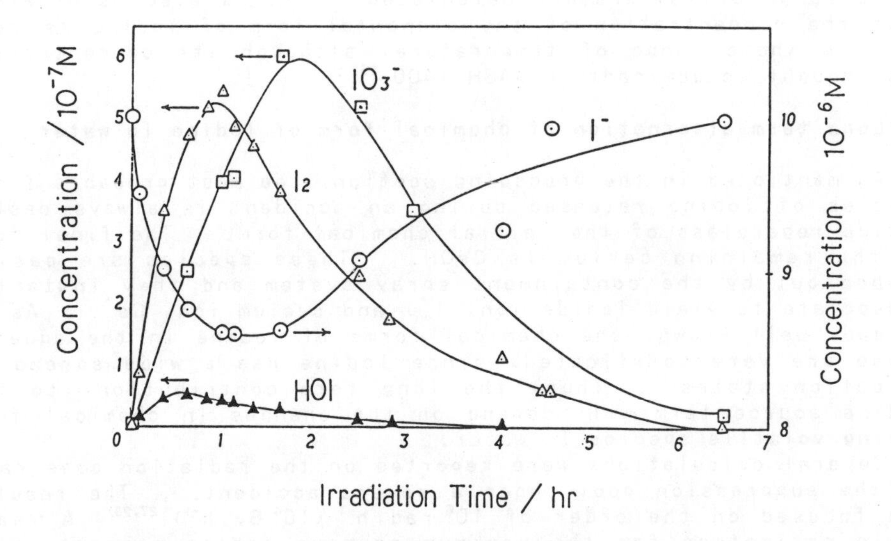

Fig. 3 Variation of iodine species with irradiation time in semi-batch deaerated system.
([I^-]=10^{-5} M, 3.8×10^3 Gy hr^{-1}, ambient temp., neutral pH (unbuffered))

One of the most perplexing aspects of the behavior of iodine following reactor accidents is the formation of volatile organic iodides. Many laboratory and larger scale experiments have been carried out relevant to the prediction of organic iodides behavior for a long time. Main results of these experiments have been summarized in some comprehensive reviews[27,31,35-37] up to 1986.

The author and his coworkers have also studied extensively the formation mechanisms of organic iodides under various circumstances.[38-44] The series of experiments has revealed that organic substances existing in the vicinity are the predominant carbon source, and their decomposition is a key process leading to the formation of organic iodides. The resulted organic radicals react with elemental iodine as follows:

$$R \rightsquigarrow R' + CH_3 \quad (3)$$

$$I^- + OH \longrightarrow I + OH^- \quad (4)$$

$$I + I \longrightarrow I_2 \quad (5)$$

$$CH_3 + I_2 \longrightarrow CH_3I + I \quad (6)$$

This reaction sequence is actually identical with the scavenging reaction technique which is often used in HAC.

As is clear from the mechanism, three factors are important in forming organic iodides in severe accidents of light water reactors. These are (1) radiation, (2) iodine as I_2 and (3) organic materials as source of organic radicals. The studies for the behavior of organic iodides are still continued.[45-48] Substantial progress was made in understanding the organic iodide chemistry, however, additional studies are required to obtain quantitative data which can be used in the establishment of models or computer-codes to predict the behavior of iodine in various accidents.

5. Hot atom chemistry of iodine and decay of precursor

As is well known, the origin of the hot atom chemistry (HAC) is the so called "Szilard-Chalmers' reaction". Thus, the HAC of iodine has been extensively studied for various reaction systems. Among many papers, it is reported that the iodine ions (I^+) in excited states always play important roles in reactions in the gaseous phase.[49-54] The yield of CH_3I was more than 70% in the case of the $^{125}Xe(EC)^{125}I$ and CH_4 system.[54] However, it was reduced to less than 0.5% under radiation field (dose rate : 2×10^4 Gy/h). The following reaction sequences were proposed to explain the results.

$$^{125}I^+ + CH_4 \longrightarrow (CH_4{}^{125}I)^+ \quad (7)$$

$$(CH_4{}^{125}I)^+ + CH_4 \longrightarrow CH_3{}^{125}I + CH_5{}^+ \quad (8)$$

$$(CH_4{}^{125}I)^+ + e^- \longrightarrow CH_4 + {}^{125}I \quad (9)$$

The competition between the reactions (8) and (9) leads to the conclusion that the reaction of iodine ions in excited states is unimportant under high radiation field, such as severe reactor accident, unless an electron scavenger is present. In the presence of an electron scavenger reaction (10) will occur in competition with reaction (9), and the yield of the organic iodide will increase after reaction (8)

$$SF_6,\ I_2,\ \text{or}\ O_2 + e^- \longrightarrow SF_6^-,\ I_2^-,\ \text{or}\ O_2^- \qquad (10)$$

In order to study the behavior of iodine newly formed from tellurium, ^{132}Te precipitated on copper wire was examined.[55] It was observed that almost all the newly formed iodine could not leave the surface of the copper, that is, more than 99 % of iodine atoms remained there. However, the fraction of organic iodides was 97 $\pm$ 2 % of the total iodine found in the gaseous phase. The absolute yield of organic iodide was 0.15 $\pm$ 0.05 % and was hardly affected by the concentration of methane when the atmosphere was diluted with nitrogen. Even in pure He or in vacuum(ca.10^{-1} Pa), the yield was the same as that obtained in methane.

When $Cu^{131}I$ was used as an iodine source, as little as 0.005% of ^{131}I was converted into $CH_3{}^{131}I$. Therefore, the beta-decay process of ^{132}Te itself plays an important role in the formation of the organic iodides. By assuming the organic impurities as the carbon source for the organic iodide, the above results can be consistently explained as follows. In the emission of the beta-ray of ^{132}Te, the ^{132}I forms in an excited state. The subsequent deexcitation is accompanied by the emission of conversion electrons, following an Auger process. The energy deposition of these electrons of relatively low energy is localized near the resulting ^{132}I atom. The radiolysis of organic impurities existing nearby provides radicals, which can react with the ^{132}I, leading to the formation of organic iodides.

$$\text{Organic impurities (R)} \xrightarrow{\text{beta-ray}} R' + CH_3 \qquad (11)$$

$$^{132}I + CH_3 \longrightarrow CH_3{}^{132}I \qquad (12)$$

Organic iodides are possibly formed from the iodine and tellurium deposited on surfaces, although the total amount of organic iodides formed from iodine deposited on surfaces in high radiation-field may not be large.

6. Conclusion

The main conclusions to be drawn in each section are as follows.

During a severe accident of a water cooled fission reactor, the fractional release of volatile fission products including noble gases is lower than that expected from the current source term estimating techniques. The most probable chemical form of the released iodine would be cesium iodide (CsI). The concentration of elemental iodine is zero for the whole range of temperature.

After CsI is dissolved into a suppression pool, iodide ion will be oxidized by the radiolysis products of water. Although oxidation of I^- to the I_2 and HIO states is sufficiently understood, experimental studies are still required to elucidate the mechanism of formation of the higher oxidation states and organic iodides.

References

1) Morewitz, H. A.: Nucl. Technol., 53, 120 (1981).
2) Pelletier, C. A., Voilleque, P. G., Thomas, C. D., Daniel, J. A., Schlomer, E. A., Noyce, J. R.: GEND-028, (March 1983).
3) Osborne, M. F., Lorenz, R. A., Norwood, K. S., Wichner, R. P.: "Proc. Intern. Meeting on Light Water Reactor Severe Accident Evaluation", 1983, p.4.1-1.
4) Collins, J. L., Osborne, M. F., Lorenz, R. A., Norwood, K. S.,Travis, J. R., Webster, C. S.: ORNL/TM-9316, (February 1985).
5) Osborne, M. F., Collins, J. L., Lorenz, R. A.: Nucl. Technol.,78, 157 (1987).
6) Lorenz, R. A., Collins, J. L.: NUREG/CP-0078, p.4-69 (1987).
7) Osetek, D. J., Vinjamuri, K., Kudera, D. E., Hobbins, R. R.: "Proc. Intern. Meeting on Light Water Reactor Severe Accident Evaluation", 1983, p.4.3-1.
8) Cronenberg, A. W., Appelhans, A. D., MacDonald, P. E., Rest, J., Lorenz, R. A.: ibid. p. 4.5-1.
9) Cronenberg, A. W., Osetek, D. J., Reed, P. R.: NUREG/CP-0078, p.6-59 (1987).
10) Albrecht, H., Wild, H.: "Proc. Intern. Meeting on Light Water Reactor Severe Accident Evaluation", 1983, p.4.2-1.
11) Albrecht, H.: Radiochim. Acta, 133 (1987).
12) Schlenger, B. J., Dunn, P. F., Herceg, J. E., Simms, R., Horton, E. L., Baker, L. Jr., Ritzman, R. L.: NUREG/CP-0078, p.2-65 (1987).
13) U. S. Nuclear Regulatory Commission, "Technical Bases of Estimating Fission Product Behavior During LWR Accidents", NUREG-0772, (June 1981).
14) Besmann, T. M., Lindemer, T. B.: Nucl. Technol., 40, 297 (1978).
15) Garisto, F.: AECL-7782, (November 1982).
16) Paquette, J., Sunder, S., Torgerson, D. F., Wren, C. J., Wren, D. J.: Water Chemistry 3. BNES, London, 1983, p.71.
17) Wren, D. J.: AECL-7781, (April 1983).
18) Cubicciotti, D., Sehgal, B. R.: Nucl. Technol., 65, 266 (1984).
19) Severe Core Damage Accident Research and Analysis Task Force : JAERI-M 84-055 (1984).
20) Evans, G. J., Melnyk, A., Paquette, J., Sagert, N. H.: "The LIRIC Database/Model", Proc. 2nd Intern. Conf. on Containment Design and Operation, 1990.
21) Buxton, G. V., Greenstock, C. L., Helman, W. P., Ross, A. B.: J. Phys. Chem., 17, 513 (1988).
22) Wren, D. J., Sagert, N. H.: Private Communication.
23) Eriksson, G.: Acta Chem. Scand., 25, 2651 (1971).
24) Besmann, T. M.: ORNL/TM-5775, (April 1977).
25) Uchida, M.: JAERI-M 84-143, (August 1984).
26) U. S. Nuclear Regulatory Commission, "Reactor Safety Study, An Assessment of Accident Risk in U. S. Commercial Nuclear Power Plants", WASH-1400, (1975).
27) Postma, A. K., Zavadoski, R. W.: WASH-1233, (October 1972).
28) Beahm, E. C., Shockley, W. E., Weber, C. F.: IAEA-SM-281/41, (November 1985).
29) Campbell, D. O., Malinauskas, A. P.: Nucl. Technol., 53, 111 (1981).
30) Ishigure, K., Shiraishi, H., Okuda, H., Fujita, N.: Radiat. Phys. Chem., Intern. J. Radiat. Appl. Instum. Part C, 28, 601 (1986).
31) Wren, D. J., Paquette, J., Wren, J. C., Clough, P. N., Starkie, H. C.: AECL-9089, (1987).
32) Deane, A. M., Potter, P. E., Ed.: "Proc. Specialists' Workshop on Iodine Chemistry in Reactor Safety", AERE R 11974 (January 1986).

33) Vikis, A. C. Ed.: "Proc. 2nd CSNI Workshop on Iodine Chemistry in Reactor Safety", AECL-9923 (March 1989).
34) Lucas, M.: Nucl. Technol., 82, 157 (1988).
35) Mishima, J.: BNWL-319, (June 1966).
36) Beahm, E. C., Shockley, W. E., Culberson, O. L.: NUREG/CR-4327
37) Deane, A. M.: AERE R 12359, (March 1988).
38) Numakura, K., Saeki, M., Tachikawa, E.: J. Nucl. Sci. Technol., 10, 367 (1973).
39) idem, ibid., 10, 762 (1973).
40) Saeki, M., Numakura, K., Tachikawa, E.: Intern. J. Appl. Radiat. Isotopes, 25, 407 (1974).
41) Tachikawa, E., Saeki, M., Nakashima, M.: J. Inorg. Nucl. Chem., 39, 749 (1977).
42) Tachikawa, E., Nakashima, M.: Intern. J. Appl. Radiat. Isotopes, 28, 417 (1977).
43) Saeki, M., Tachikawa, E.: Radiochem. Radioanal. Lett., 40, 17 (1979).
44) Nakashima, M., Saeki, M., Aratono, Y., Tachikawa, E.: Intern. J. Appl. Radiat. Isotopes, 32, 397 (1981).
45) Beahm, E. C., Wang, Y., Wisbey, S. J., Shockley, W. E.: Nucl. Technol., 78, 34 (1987).
46) Lutz, J. B., Kelly, J. L.: ibid., 80, 431 (1988).
47) Deane, A. M., Davies, C. P.: AERE R 13526, (November 1989).
48) Paquette, J., Ford, B. L.: Radiat. Phys. Chem., Intern. J. Radiat. Appl. Instrum., Part C, 36, 353 (1990).
49) Rack, E. P., Gordus, A. A.: J. Chem. Phys., 34, 1855 (1961).
50) Nicholas, J. B., Yoog, M., Rack, E. P.: Radiochim. Acta, 19, 124 (1973).
51) Schroth, F., Adloff, J. P.: J. Chim. Phys., 61,1373 (1964).
52) Loberg, M. D., Welch, M. J.: J. Am. Chem. Soc., 95, 1073 (1973).
53) Schleiffer, J. J., Certout, G.: Radiochim. Acta, 20, 59 (1973).
54) Saeki, M., Tachikawa, E.: Bull. Chem. Soc. Jpn., 50, 1762 (1977).
55) Saeki, M., Tachikawa, E.: Radiochem. Radioanal. Letters, 40,17 (1979).

8.3 Fusion Reactor and Hot Atom Chemistry

Hiroshi KUDO
Japan Atomic Energy Research Institute, Tokai-mura, Ibraki-ken, 319-11 Japan

1. Introduction

The energy source of the Sun is provided by the nuclear fusion of four hydrogen atoms, the most important sequence of which is known as the PPI chain:

$$H + H \rightarrow D + e^{+} + \nu \quad (1)$$
$$D + H \rightarrow {}^{3}He + \gamma \quad (2)$$
$${}^{3}He + {}^{3}He \rightarrow {}^{4}He + 2D \quad (3)$$

Utilization of nuclear energy liberated from fusion reactions will lead to an ultimate solution of energy problems in the future, and enormous efforts have recently been made aimed at development of a fusion reactor or controlled thermonuclear reactor (CTR). The nuclear reactions of prime interest for CTR are as follows:

$$D + T \rightarrow {}^{4}He + n + 17.48\ MeV \quad (4)$$
$$D + D \rightarrow {}^{3}He + n + 3.27\ MeV \quad (5)$$
$$D + D \rightarrow T + H + 4.04\ MeV \quad (6)$$
$$D + {}^{3}He \rightarrow {}^{4}He + H + 18.34\ MeV \quad (7)$$

Of these reactions, first-generation fusion reactors likely utilize the deuterium-tritium (D-T) reaction which gives rise to 14-MeV neutrons and 3.5-MeV α particles, since the reaction has the highest cross section at low energies and the highest Q value.[1] Even for the D-T reaction, however, the necessary temperature for ignition and for maintaining the burning condition is of the order of 10^8 K or 10 keV. In the past decade most developments have been made towards the generation of hot plasmas of hydrogen isotopes. The progress of plasma confinement technology attained with large tokamak devices such as JT-60 (Japan), TFTR (USA) and JET (EC) is shown in Fig. 1. To construct a fusion reactor, however, further progress is required, including research in the fields of materials science and fuel-cycle technology. Although the natural abundance of deutrium would ensure a sufficient supply of this isotope for the fueling of fusion reactors, tritium with negligible abundance is to be

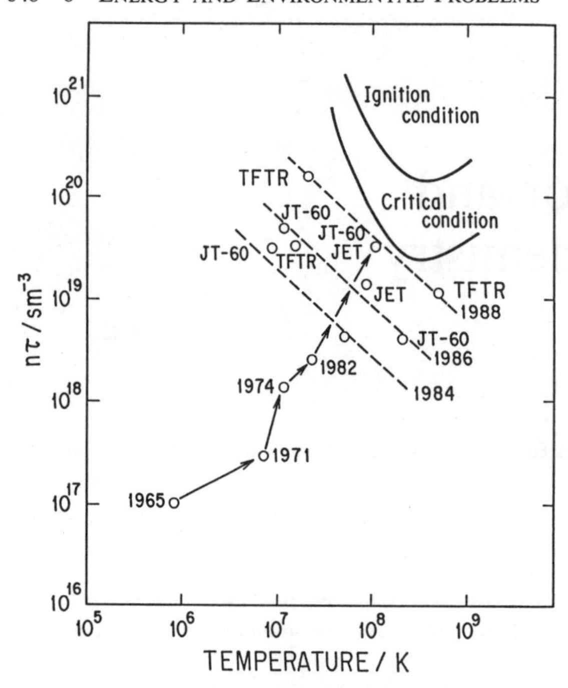

Fig. 1. Progress of high temperature plasma confinement technology with large tokamak devices.

artificially produced and any practical fusion reactor will have to breed at least as much tritium as it consumes. The amount of tritium required for a CTR is estimated to be more than 3 kg (30 MCi)[2] and various kinds of radiochemical problems as well as technological problems on the safe handling of tritium should be solved in the course of CTR development. Tritium is an essential component of a fusion reactor and the chemistry of tritium would attract great interest for radiochemists. The basic concept of the plasma fueling and exhaust systems of a D-T fusion reactor is illustrated in Fig. 2. In a tokamak reactor, for example, the thermonuclear reaction takes place in the plasma confined in the vacuum vessel. The energy produced by the D-T reaction is partly transported by the 14-MeV neutrons. In addition, electromagnetic radiation and particles (neutrals as well as ions) with kinetic energies up to the keV range will leave the plasma zone. The "first wall" which separates the vacuum zone from the blanket will receive a heavy energy load. The blanket is designed to play the following roles; (1) heat generation, (2)tritium breeding and (3) radiation shield for superconducting magnet outermost. The fast neutrons reaching the blanket will lose their energy and produce new tritium through $^{7}Li(n,n'\alpha)T$ and $^{6}Li(n,\alpha)T$ reactions (breeding). The generated heat will be removed and eventually converted into electric energy. From a hot-atom chemical point of view, particular attention would be paid to the chemistry of the first wall (plasma-wall-interaction); i.e., chemical sputtering, chemical effects of implantation, hot surface chemistry and plasma-driven permeation of hydrogen isotopes. As to the reaction of tritium in lithium-bearing meterials of the blanket, the final states of recoil tritium would be independent of the primary species and classical thermodynamics and kinetics of thermal species will govern the behavior of the tritium, although the chemical effects of nuclear transformation obviously enter the scene in the very first stage of exposure to

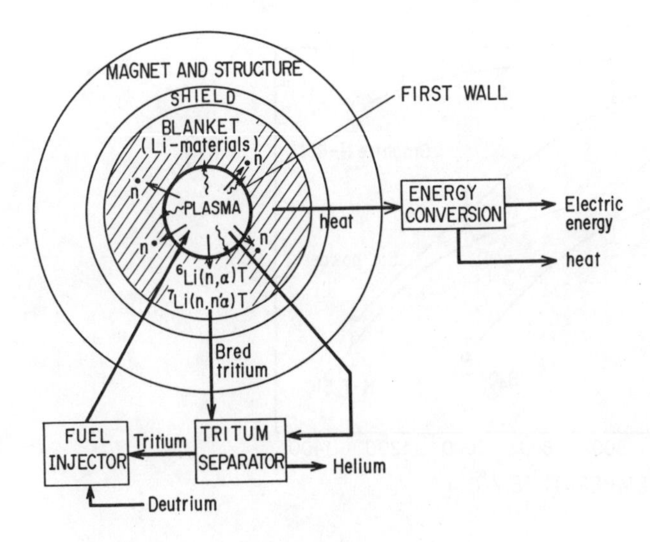

Fig. 2. Basic concept of fueling cycle of D-T fusion reactor.

neutrons.

Another interesting subject would be muon catalyzed fusion (μCF) which was first discussed by A. Sakharov in 1948, several years before any concepts of hot fusion were suggested. Although the idea of energy applications was discarded for a long time because no way was recognized of efficient use of the muon within its lifetime of 2.2μs, only recent discovery of the resonance mechamism of ddμ and dtμ mesic molecule formation has shed light on the μCF study again. In recent experiments at LAMPF (USA), PSI (Switzerland) and UT-MSL/KEK (Japan), fusion yields exceeding 100 per muon were observed for the liquid deuterium-tritium system. The μCF has become a research of quite new interest and is rapidly developing in theory, experiment and future applications.[3]

2. Tritium in Plasma-Wall-Interaction (PWI)

The erosion of the CTR first wall (vacuum wall) by energetic particles from the plasma is considered to be the main source of impurity for the plasma. Since high-Z impurities would have the most significant effect on plasma performance, the use of low-Z material has been suggested for structural components which are in direct contact with the plasma; e.g., limiters in tokamak devices.[4-6] Graphite is an important candidate for first wall components and, in fact, graphite and carbide coatings are most widely used in today's fusion machines.[7, 8]

In a D-T fusion reactor, the kinetic energy of the tritium at the first wall will be below keV and only a very small fraction would have kinetic energies in the 200 keV range. The kinetic energy is comparable with the recoil energy of tritium produced by the ^{3}He(n,p)T reaction. Hence, this nuclear reaction can be a useful tool for simulation experiments to investigate the fate

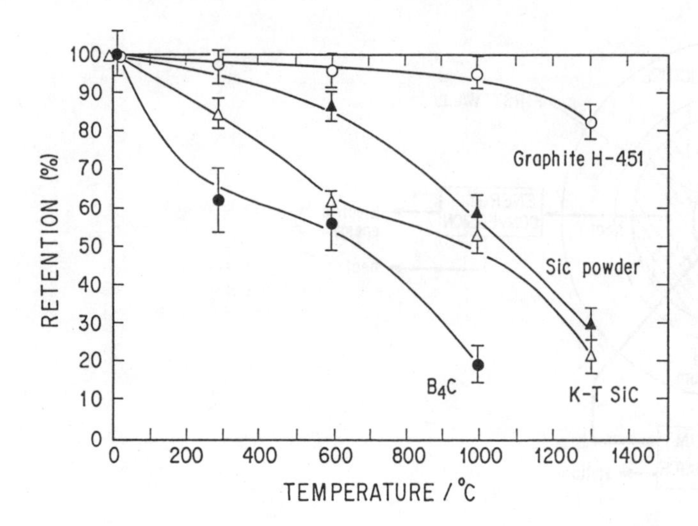

Fig.3 Tritium retention in graphite, SiC and B_4C as a function of the heating in a vacuum at various temperatures for 30 min.

of tritium and hydrogen species incorporated into low-Z materials such as graphite, SiC, B_4C and TiC, all first wall candidates.

The first result of the simulation experiment with the nuclear recoil technique has been reported by Dietz et al.[9] Almost all of tritium atoms produced by the $^3He(n,p)T$ reaction with the initial kinetic energy of 195 keV were incorporated into graphite and only a small fraction (10^{-5}) of the total tritium was observed in the gas phase (90% HT and 10% CH_3T). In addition, more than 20% of the total tritium was retained in the graphite matrix even when the material was kept in a hydrogen atmosphere for 10 min at 1200 ℃ before combustion. The result suggests that stable C-T bonds are formed and that the graphite may act as a serious sink for tritium in the first wall.

Boothe and Ache reported that the energetic tritium was strongly bound to graphite and was not released even at 1000 ℃, if the graphite had been throughly degassed and annealed prior to tritium bombardment by means of the $^3He(n,p)T$ reaction.[10] Subsequent treatment of these samples with H_2, H_2O or NH_3 at elevated temperatures leads to the release of up to 47% of the tritium in the form of HT and CH_3T, with minor amounts of tritiated higher hydrocarbonds present. The result also implies that the continuous buildup of the tritium in the graphite could lead to a serious problem with regard to the tritium inventory of the fusion reactor, although the contamination of the plasma resulting from the reactions of energetic tritium species with graphite would be a lesser problem since tritium is mainly released in the form of HT.

These authors have extended the simulation experiment to other low-Z materials such as SiC and B_4C.[11,12] The results on the tritium retention are shown in Fig. 3. When the SiC, degassed and annealed at 1400℃ prior to tritium bombardment, was heated to 1350 ℃ in a vacuum, about 40% of the tritium was released in the form of HTO. Most of the remaining tritium was retained in the material. Treatment of degassed samples with H_2O and H_2 at

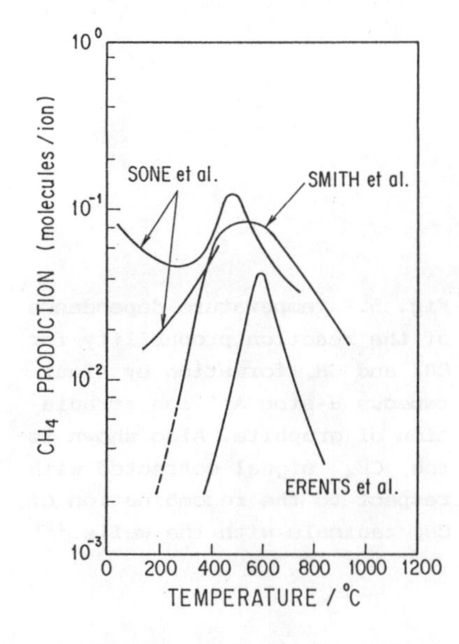

Fig. 4. Temperature dependence of CH_4 production for hydrogen incident on graphite. The incident ion species are H^+ (20 keV) by Erents et al., H^+ (1 keV) by Sone et al. and H_2^+ (5 keV) by Smith et al.[21]

temperatures up to 1000 ℃, after tritium bombardment, led to the release of 45% of the tritium as HT and CH_3T. From the degassed B_4C the tritium was rapidly released from the material as HT, CH_3T and HTO upon heating to 1000 ℃ in a vacuum. The oxygen sources were considered to be SiO_2 or $-Si(OH)_n$, B_2O_3 or $B(OH)_n$ and HBO_2 or H_3BO_3 on the surface of the materials.

The results of these experiments indicate that the energetic fraction of hydrogen isotopes escaping the plasma of CTR would initially be bound in the SiC and B_4C matrices. However, these species can subsequently be released back into the plasma at elevated temperatures in the form of HTO, HT and CH_3T, if no hydrogen sources are introduced into the system. Under actual CTR operation conditions, where the flux of D^+ and T^+ which reach the first wall is estimated to vary from 10^{13} to 10^{16} cm^{-2} with kinetic energies between a few eV and keV,[13,14] an accumulation of hydrogen species on or near the surface can be expected. In this case the implanted energetic tritium would be released predominantly in the form of HT and CH_3T if the wall is kept at temperatures higher than 600 ℃. At lower temperatures SiC would act as a sink for tritium in fusion reactors.

Another tool available for the study of PWI is a particle accelerator which generates the beam with energies from a few eV to 200 keV. Flaskamp et al.[15,16] have bombarded tritium and hydrogen (~0.3 eV) on graphite targets and measured the sticking coefficient. The graphite was revealed to act as a sink for thermal tritium atoms up to the fluence of 10^{17} cm^{-2}. The finding of temperature dependence of CH_4 formation during hydrogen ion (10 keV) bombardment on graphite by Busharov et al.[17] has stimulated the work on chemical sputtering. Such experiments have been extended by Feinberg and Post,[18] Erents et al.[19], Sone et al,[20] and Smith et al.[21] The temperature dependence of CH_4 production on a graphite surface is shown in Fig. 4. Erents et al. have proposed a model that holds two "sink" terms to describe the concentration of adsorbed hydrogen. The first of these terms relates to thermal desorption of hydrogen and the second term allows for ion induced desorption of hydrogen. The overall CH_4 production rate is assumed to be directly proportional to

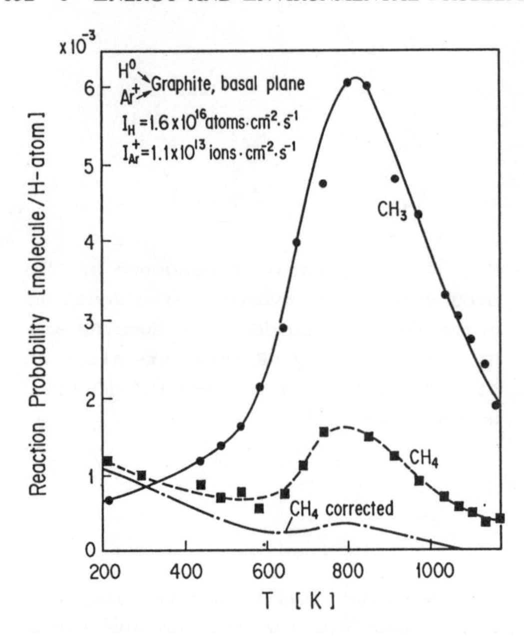

Fig. 5. Temperature dependence of the reaction probability for CH_3 and CH_4 formation by simultaneous H-atom/Ar^+ ion irradiation of graphite. Also shown is the CH_4 signal corrected with respect to the recombination of CH_3 radicals with the walls.[22)]

surface hydrogen coverage. Recently, it has been found that the chemical erosion of graphite by bombardment with atomic hydrogen alone significantly differs from that with energetic ions. The simultaneous bombardment of the graphite with atomic hydrogen and a small portion of energetic particles drastically increases the chemical erosion resulting in similar erosion behavioras in the case of energetic hydrogen ion alone.[22, 23)] This strong synergistic effect is important for understanding the physical and chemical processes involved in the erosion. Vietzke et al.[22)] have reported that the predominant reaction product on graphite induced by atomic hydrogen/energetic ion (5 keV Ar^+) bombardment was the CH_3 radical whereas the main product was CH_4 when irradiated with H_2^+, as shown in Fig. 5. From the mass spectrometric observation of the reaction products on graphite by H^0/D_2^+ irradiation, they conclude that the reaction of energetic hydrogen ions occurs at the inner surfaces and leaves the graphite through open channels whereas CH_3 is formed at the surface by irradiation with H^0/energetic ions. In both cases, CH_4 would be formed through the recombination of CH_3 with the walls.

Regarding the safety aspects of tritium plasmas, on the other hand, permeation of hydrogen isotopes through plasma facing materials has extensively been studied by a number of research groups. In 1978 Perkins and Noda[24)] reported interesting evidence that when a thin stainless steel foil was irradiated with energetic H^+ ions the hydrogen permeability increased by one to two orders of magnitude compared with exposure to hydrogen gas. The enhancement of hydrogen permeation was also found in such experiments as atomic-hydrogen bombardment,[25)] glow-discharge,[26)] and exposure to hydrogen plasmas.[27, 28)] The phenomenon, called a plasma-driven permeation (PDP), was first discussed in terms of difference in the depth of hydrogen species implanted into materials. Namely, high-energy hydrogen atoms or ions, which penetrate deeper than thermal ones, would play a significant role to enhance the permeation rate. However, recent experimental results have contained a variety of evidence which is not necessarily explained in this way.[29] No differences are reported in the diffusivity between high-energy and thermal hydrogen species. The surface conditions of materials would govern the PDP. Namely, glow-discharge and chemical sputtering with plasmas probably make the surface clean, so that the permeation rate increases.

3. Tritium in Blanket Materials

For the purpose of tritium breeding a fusion reactor blanket contains lithium which appears to be the only element suitable for tritium breeding. Of many lithium-bearing materials, only a few types of materials would be the most promising for practical use. For blanket materials, a number of performance requirements can be used as a measure of the relative merits of candidates; i.e., (1)tritium breeding ratio, (2) chemical and physical stability, (3) tritium recovery, (4) materials compatibility, (5) thermophysical property or thermal conductivity and (6) safety.

Table 1 lists the candidate materials of current interest. Lithium metal and $Li_{17}Pb_{83}$ will be used in the liquid state (liquid blanket) and the oxidic materials with a higher melting point such as Li_2O are the candidate for solid-state blankets.[2,30] Since both the $^6Li(n,\alpha)T$ and $^7Li(n,n'\alpha)T$ reactions contribute to the tritium breeding, the high lithium-atom density is favorable for the blanket materials. A neutronic calculation for Li_2O blankets with lithium of natural isotopic composition indicates that 2/3 of the total tritium is produced from ^6Li and 1/3 from ^7Li.[31] Despite the relatively low lithium-atom density, $Li_{17}Pb_{83}$ can give a viable tritium breeding rate because of an excellent neutron multiplication by the (n,2n) reaction in the constituent lead.[32]

Table 1
Tritium breeder candidates of current interest

Type of blanket	Material	Properties		
		Melting point (K)	Density (g/cm^3)	Li-atom density ($10^{22}/cm^3$)
Liquid blanket	Li	459	0.53	4.4
	$Li_{17}Pb_{83}$	508	9.5	0.56
Solid-state blanket	Li_2O	1711	2.023	8.16
	$LiAlO_2$	1883	2.61	2.38
	Li_5AlO_4	1320	2.22	5.34
	Li_2SiO_3	1474	2.52	3.38
	Li_4SiO_4	1529	2.39	4.81
	Li_2TiO_3	1820	3.46	3.80
	Li_2ZrO_3	1873	4.15	3.27
	Li_8ZrO_6	1568	2.99	5.93

The tritium recovery from tritium breeding materials is a key factor in establishing the viability of a blanket concept and an important consideration in selecting the potential candidate materials. In this respect Kudo et al. have studied the chemical behavior of tritium produced by the $^6Li(n,\alpha)T$ reaction in a variety of lithium-bearing materials, with emphasis on the thermal release behavior of tritiated species.[33-45] Table 2 lists the chemical form of tritium released from neutron-irradiated lithium compounds on heating in a vacuum. From the oxidic materials the tritium was released mainly in the form of HTO, while HT was the predominant species released from materials which contained no oxygen. Small amounts of CH_3T and $C_2H_{2n-1}T$ (n=1,2,3) were released from all the materials examined. The hydrocarbon fractions released from Li_2C_2 were not as large as anticipated when the material was well degassed before the neutron irradiation.

In Table 3 listed are the valence states of tritium in solids of lithium-bearing materials, analyzed with a radiometric method. The tritium produced in neutron-irradiated Li_2O crystals existed in three valence states of T^+, T^- and T^0. The initial abundance of these species were 67-77%, 23-31% and <2%, respectively, although only the T^+ state of tritium was found in the unirradiated Li_2O crystal in which tritium was thermally doped under equilibrium with gaseous HT. In neutron-irradiated LiOH crystals nearly 100% of tritium

Table 2
Chemical forms of tritium released from neutron-irradiated lithium compounds on heating in a vacuum

Material[a]	Neutron fluence (cm^{-2})	Upper temp.[b] (K)	% of total tritium			
			HTO	HT	CH_3T[c]	Retention
Li_2O	$5.4x10^{16}$	873	99.1	0.4	0.3	0.2
	$3.6x10^{16}$	873	98.0	0.9	1.0	0.1
	$8.1x10^{16}$	873	97.6	1.8	0.5	0.1
	$8.9x10^{17}$	873	93.4	5.6	0.8	0.1
γ-$LiAlO_2$	$2.5x10^{16}$	1173	94.4	1.6	4.0	-
Li_2SiO_3	$2.5x10^{16}$	1173	97.1	2.5	0.4	0.01
Li_4SiO_4	$2.5x10^{16}$	1173	98.6	1.2	0.1	0.04
Li_2ZrO_3	$2.5x10^{16}$	1173	99.0	0.7	0.3	-
Li_8ZrO_6	$2.5x10^{16}$	1073	91.1	2.2	5.7	1.0
LiH	$2.5x10^{16}$	1023	0.3	99.4	0.3	0.1
Li_2C_2	$6.0x10^{15}$	973	1.2	95.8	3.0	0.01
Li_3N	$3.0x10^{15}$	1223	1.1	98.6	0.2	0.1
LiAl	$3.0x10^{16}$	1073	5.3	93.2	1.2	0.3
Li_7Pb_2 ingot	$2.5x10^{16}$	1163	2.6	95.2	1.8	0.4

a) All but ingot mateirals are crystalline powders.

b) The materials were heated for 20 min at each temperature which was raised stepwise from 373 K to the upper one at 100 K interval.

c) Includes small amounts of C_2HT and C_2H_3T.

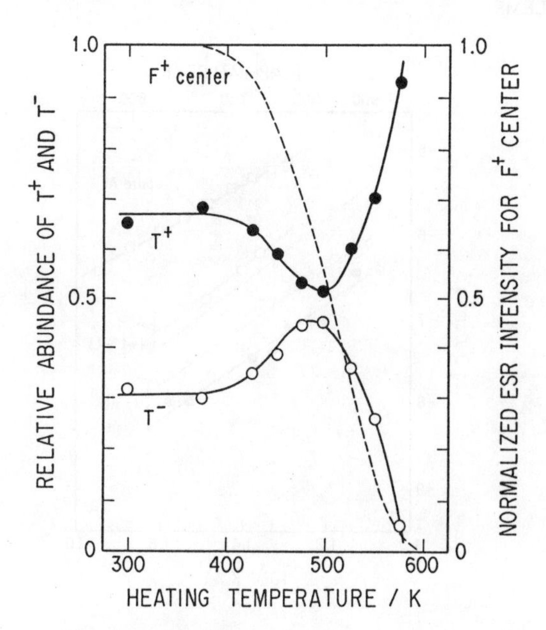

Fig. 6. Change of T^+ and T^- abundances through thermal annealing of Li_2O crystals irradiated with neutrons to $2.5x10^{16}$ cm^{-2} and annihilation of the F^+ center.[41)]

was in the T^+ state. On the contrary, almost all of the tritium was found in the T^- state in LiH crystals irradiated with neutrons. The presence of T^+ in LiOH and T^- in LiH crystals would be understood by considering the affinity of H^+ for O^- and H^- for Li^+ in these crystals. The presence of T^- in neutron-

Table 3
Valence state of tritium produced in neutron-irradiated lithium-bearing compounds

Material	Neutron fluence (cm^{-2})	Initial abundance (%) T^+	T^-	T^0
Li_2O	$2.5x10^{15}$	75.8	22.2	2.0
	$8.3x10^{17}$	77.2	22.0	0.8
Li_2O_2	$2.5x10^{16}$	100	0.01	0.01
LiOH	$2.5x10^{16}$	100	0.01	-
Li_3N	$2.5x10^{16}$	98.2	1.4	0.4
LiH	$2.5x10^{16}$	1.3	97.8	0.9
LiD	$2.5x10^{16}$	1.8	97.6	0.9
Li_2C_2	$2.5x10^{16}$	14.9	80.2	4.9
Li_7Pb_2	$2.5x10^{16}$	1.8	97.7	1.2
Unirradiated[a)]				
Li_2O		99.9	-	0.1
LiOH		100	-	0.01

[a)] The tritium was thermally doped.

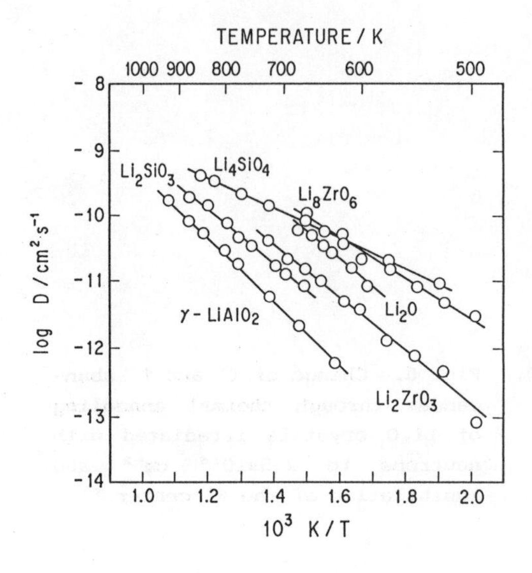

Fig. 7. Diffusivity of tritium (T^+) in oxidic ceramic materials irradiated with neutrons.[46)]

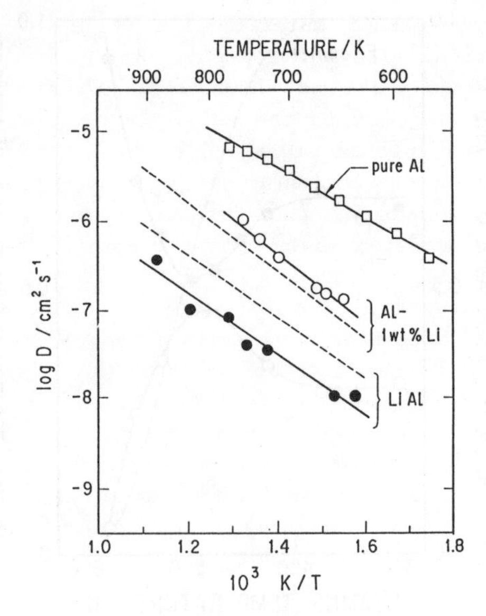

Fig. 8. Diffusivity of tritium (T^-) in LiAl, Al-1 wt%Li alloy and pure aluminum metal: the broken lines are values calculated from a trapping model.[48)]

irradiated Li_2O is ascribed to the presence of positive radiation damage in the crystal. Namely, F^+ centers (oxygen-ion vacancy occupied by one electron) would play roles in neutralization of T^- ions in Li_2O crystals. Figure 6 depicts the change of T^+ and T^- abundances through thermal annealing of Li_2O crystals irradiated with neutrons to the fluence of 2.5×10^{16} cm^{-2}, in comparison with the feature of the F^+-center annihilation in Li_2O crystals. The presence of T^- species become less probable with decreasing concentration of F^+ centers, and almost all of the T^- state of tritium are eventually converted to the T^+ state when the neutron-irradiated Li_2O crystals are heated above 570 K, in which temperature region the HTO(g) release rate is controlled by the diffusion of tritium ion (T^+).

The HTO(g) release processes in oxidic ceramic materials is explained by a mixed regime effect where the bulk diffusion and solid-surface reaction of tritium competes for overall control of the process. In Li_2O crystals, for instance, the HTO(g) release rate below 570 K is controlled by the dissociation of LiOT formed at the solid surface, and the diffusion of T^+ ions in the crystal become the rate-determining step at higher temperature. The diffusivities of T^+ ions in Li_2O, $LiAlO_2$, Li_2SiO_3, Li_4SiO_4, Li_2ZrO_3 and Li_8ZrO_6 crystals are compared in Fig. 7. The order of the tritium diffusivity in these oxidic materials was $D(Li_8ZrO_6) \geqq D(Li_4SiO_4) > D(Li_2O) > D(Li_2ZrO_3) > D(Li_2SiO_3) > D(LiAlO_2)$. The tritium diffusivity increases with an increase of the Li-atom density in the oxidic materials.[46,47] On the contrary, in metallic materials such as Li-Al alloys the tritium diffusivity decreases with an increase of the Li-atom density,[48] as shown in Fig. 8. The opposite tendencies are ascribed to the difference in the valence state of diffusing tritium. In the oxidic materials the tritium migrates in the T^+ state, and the presence of Li^+ would moderate the interaction of T^+ with O^{2-} in the matrix. In metallic materials, on the other hand, the tritium migrates in the T^- state, and a trapping effect associated with strong affinity of Li^+ for T^- would impede the diffusion of tritium.

With a few exceptions, above mentioned studies have been performed on lithium-bearing materials irradiated with neutrons to the fluence of 10^{15}-10^{18} cm^{-2} (the tritium concentration in the range of 1-100 appm). The experiments with more realistic fluences ($\sim 10^{20}$ cm^{-2}) of the fusion reactor environments will be needed for the practical design of tritium recovery systems. Recently, a number of research programs are proceeding on the engineering aspects of tritium recovery under fusion reactor conditions.[49] In this article, however, reference has been made only to fundamental studies on chemical behavior of tritium in candidate blanket materials.

4. Helium and Tritium in Muon-Catalyzed Fusion (μCF)

Nuclear fusion reactions of Eqs. (1)-(7) occur when the two nuclei are within a few fm (10^{-15} m). Under moderate conditions, however, nuclei with positive charge hardly appoarch each other because of the strong Coulomb repulsion. Although a hydrogen atom with an orbital electron is neutral, the atomic radius is as large as 50 pm. In D_2 molecules, for example, the equilibrium internuclear distance is 74 pm. In this case the fusion rate is estimated to be as low as 10^{-70} to 10^{-60} s^{-1}. When negative muon (μ^-) is replaced for the electron in the deuterium atom, the diameter of neutralized muonic atoms is reduced to about 1/200 of normal deuterium atoms, because the mass of μ^- is 207 times as heavy as electrons. In muonic molecules, $dt\mu$, the internuclear distance

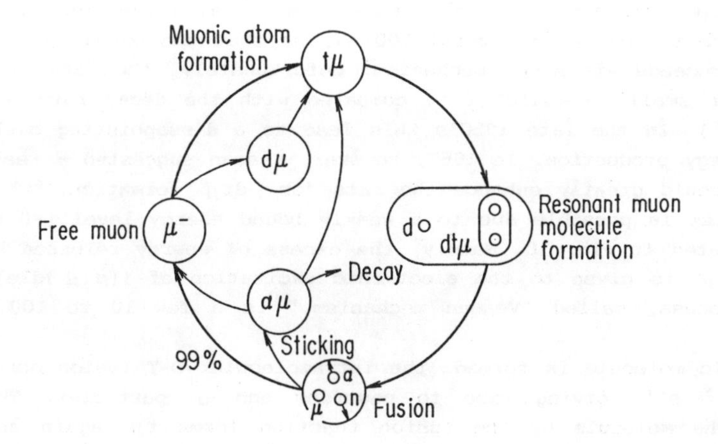

Fig. 9. Schematic expression of a muon-catalyzed-fusion cycle in D-T mixtures.

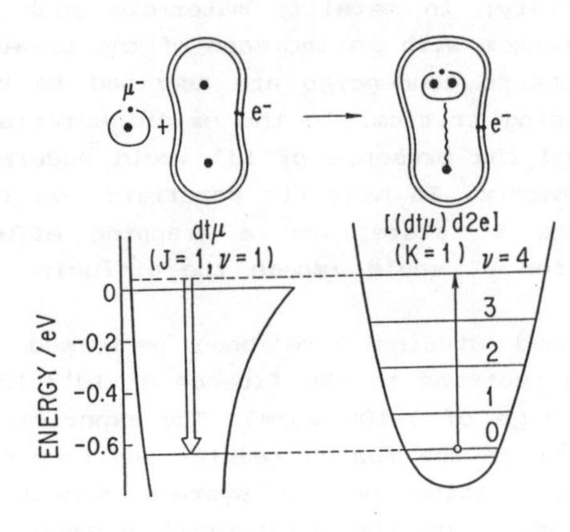

Fig. 10. Level schemes of resonant $dt\mu$ formation.

between the deuterium and tritium nuclei becomes about 500 fm and then the fusion rate is enhanced to approximately 10^{12} s^{-1}. The lifetime of the muon is 2.2 μs, but the fusion yields exceeding 100 per muon have been experimentally observed for liquid deuterium-tritium systems in several laboratories.[50-54] The muon is one of the cosmic rays but intense muon beams for laboratory research are produced by accelerators. Namely, bombardment of protons or heavy ions with 300 MeV or more of kinetic energy on Be or Li targets gives rise to pions (π^+, π^-). The pions with 26 ns of lifetime decay to muon (μ^+, μ^-). Negative muon (μ^-) is obtained only through the decay of negative pion (π^-) in a vacuum. Figure 9 shows a cycle of the muon catalyzed fusion (μCF) in a deuterium-tritium (DT) mixture at the atomic density of liquid hydrogen ($4.22 \times 10^{22}/cm^3$). Negative muons from an accelerator thermalize in the mixture and quickly form muonic atoms $d\mu$ or $t\mu$ of the ground state within 10^{-10} s. These muonic atoms are tiny and neutral. Since the ground-state energy level of $t\mu$ is deeper by 48 eV than that of $d\mu$, the $d\mu$ transfers to $t\mu$ in 10^{-8} s^{-1}, colliding with the surrounding DT and T_2 molecules.

The neutral $t\mu$ easily penetrates into D_2 or DT molecules and interact with the deuterium nuclei to form muonic $dt\mu$ molecules. Binding energies of muonic hydrogen atoms are typically of several 100 eV, so that the normal process of $dt\mu$ formation proceeds via Auger mechanism. Unfortunately, the rate of Auger process is rather small ($\sim 5 \times 10^4$ s^{-1}) compared with the decay rate of muon ($\lambda_0 = 4.5 \times 10^5$ s^{-1}). In the late 1950's this lead to a dissapointing disbelief of μCF for energy production. In 1967, however, Vesman suggested a resonance mechanism which could greatly enhance the rate for $dt\mu$ formation.[55,56] The resonance mechanism is possible due to a weakly bound energy level (-0.64 eV) of $dt\mu$ illustrated in Fig. 10. Namely, the excess of energy released by the formation of $dt\mu$ is given to the electronic excitation of $[(dt\mu)d2e]$. The rate of this process, called "Vesman mechanism," is a few 10 to 100 times higher than λ_0.

Once the muonic molecule is formed, the intramolecular D-T fusion occurs at the rate of 10^{12} s^{-1}, giving rise to neutrons and α particles. The μ^- liberated from the molecule by the fusion reaction forms $t\mu$ again and the μCF cycle continues. The cycle number of μCF in the lifetime of μ^- (2.2 μs) depends upon the μ^- sticking on α particles. Determination of the sticking

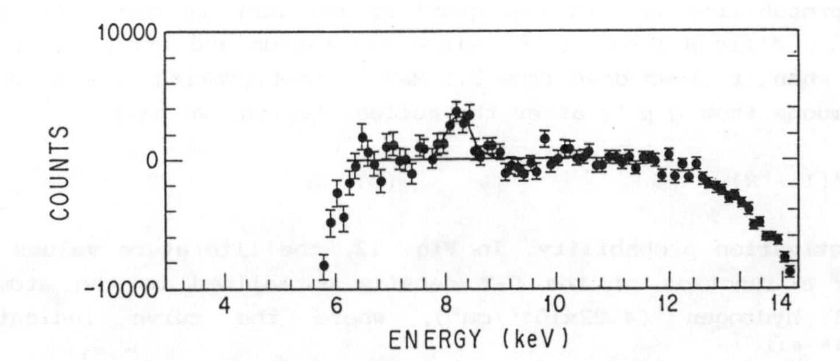

Fig. 11. X-ray spectrum observed for $\alpha\mu$ moving with the kinetic energy of 3.5 MeV after μCF in D-T mixtures. The peak energy is 8.23 keV and the Doppler broadning is 0.53 keV.[57]

probability (ω_s) is essential in evaluating the possibility of energy production with the μCF, and a number of studies have been carried out with a focus on the determination of ω_s.[50-54]

Recently, Nagamine et al. have carried out experiments aimed at the direct determination of ω_s through measurement of X rays from muonic helium ($\alpha\mu$). Figure 11 shows the X-ray spectrum of $\alpha\mu$ observed for the μCF in a liquid D_2-30%T_2 mixture at 20 K. The peak energy at 8.234 ± 0.008 keV was identified to be the characteristic X ray from $\alpha\mu$ and its width (FWHM) of 0.53 ± 0.10 keV agreed well with the theoretical Doppler broadning for $\alpha\mu$ moving at 3.5 MeV of kinetic energy. The initial sticking probability (ω_s^0) obtained was 0.39 ± 0.14%.[57]

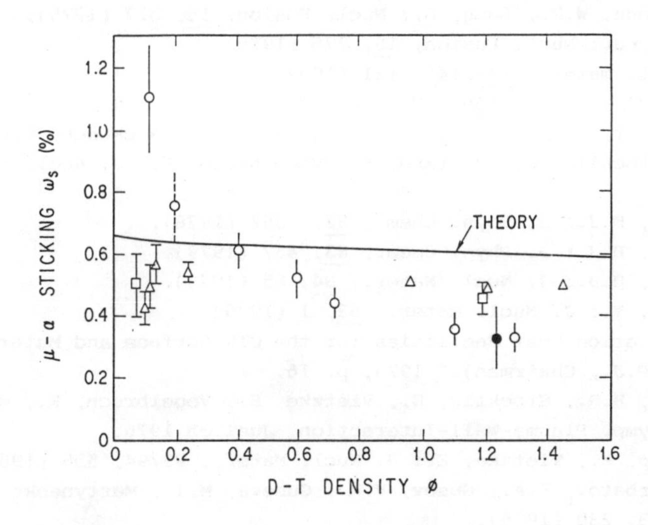

Fig. 12. Observed α-sticking probabilities (ω_s) plotted against the density of D-T mixtures: ○ LAMPF,[50, 51] □ and △ PSI,[52, 53] and ● UT-MSL/KEK.[57] The curve is from theories.

Final sticking probability ω_s is the quantity relevant to the catalysis cycle. The value ω_s differs from ω_s^o, since excitation and stripping processes act on $\alpha\mu$, when it slows down from 3.5 MeV to rest. Taking into account the shaking-off of muons from $\alpha\mu$'s after the nuclear fusion, we have

$$\omega_s = \omega_s^o(1 - R), \quad (8)$$

where R is the reactivation probability. In Fig. 12, the literature values of ω_s are plotted as a function of the D-T density normalized to the atomic density of liquid hydrogen ($4.22\times10^{22}/cm^3$), where the curve indicates theoretical values.[58-61]

In a hot-atom chemical point of view, it would be interesting to examine the α-sticking behavior of μ^- as well as reactivation processes, since $\alpha\mu$ or proton-like helium muonide ($He\mu^+$) is considered to pick up one electron forming $He\mu^0$ atoms. Yoshihara et al. have discussed chemical processes of He species attached to a negative muon and estimated reaction rates of hydrogen homologues (muonium, hydrogen and $He\mu^0$ atoms) with O_2, NO and C_2H_4.[62-64] They have pointed out that O_2, NO and C_2H_4 impurities contained in a μCF system would act as effective scavengers for thermal $He\mu^0$ atoms.

References

1. Post, R.F.: Ann. Rev. Nucl. Sci., 20, 509 (1970).
2. INTOR Group: "International Tokamak Reactor," Phase Two A, Part III, IAEA, Vienna (1988).
3. Petitjean, C.: Fusion. Eng. Des., 11, 255 (1989).
4. Kulcinski, G.L., Conn, R.W., Lang, G., Wittenberg, L., Kesner, J., Kummer, D.C.: UWFDM-108 (1974).
5. Kulcinski, G.L., Conn, W.R., Lang, G.: Nucl. Fusion, 15, 327 (1975).
6. Conn, R.W., Kesner, J.: Nucl. Fusion, 15, 775 (1975).
7. Winter, J.: J. Nucl. mater., 145-147, 131 (1987).
8. Dietz, K.J.: J. Nucl. Mater., 155-157, 8 (1988).
9. Dietz, K.J., Geissler, E., Waelbröch, F., Kirschner, J., Nickosch, E.A., Tschesich, K.G., Stöcklin, G., Vietzke, E., Vogelbtuch, K.: J. Nucl. Mater., 63, 167 (1976).
10. Boothe, T.E., Ache, H.J.: J. Phys. Chem., 82, 1362 (1978).
11. Boothe, T.E., Ache, H.J.: J. Phys. Chem., 83, 457 (1979).
12. Boothe, T.E., Ache, H.J.: J. Nucl. Mater., 84, 85 (1979).
13. Conn, R.W., Kesner, Y.: J. Nucl. Mater., 63, 1 (1976).
14. Kaminski, M.: "Radiation Test Facilities for the CTR Surface and Materials Program (Persani, P.J., Chairman)," 1975, p. 16.
15. Flaskamp, K., Ihle, H.R., Stöcklin, G., Vietzke, E., Vogelbruch, K., Wu, C.H.: Proc. Int. Symp. Plasma-Wall-Interaction, Juelich 1976.
16. Hucks, P., Flaskamp, K., Vietzke, E.: J. Nucl. Mater., 93/94, 558 (1980).
17. Busharov, N.P., Gorbatov, E.A., Gusev, V.M., Guseva, M.I., Martynenko, Y.V.: J. Nucl. Mater., 63, 230 (1976).
18. Feinberg, B., Post, R.S.: J. Vac. Sci. Technol., 13, 443 (1976).
19. Erents, S.K., Braganza, C.M., McCraken, G.M.: J. Nucl. Mater., 63, 399 (1976).

20. Sone, K., Ohtsuka, H., Abe, T., Yamada, R., Obara, K., Tsukakoshi, O., Narusawa, T., Satake, T., Mizuno, M., Komiya, S.: Proc. Int. Symp. Plasma-Wall-Interaction, Juelich 1976, Pergamon Press 1977, p. 323.
21. Smith, J.N., Meyer Jr., C.H.: J. Nucl. Mater., 76/77, 193 (1978).
22. Vietzke, E., Flaskamp, K., Philipps, V.: J. Nucl. Mater., 128/129, 545 (1984).
23. Philips, V., Yietzke, E., Erdweg, M., Flaskamp, K.: J. Nucl. Mater., 145-147, 292 (1987).
24. Perkins, H.K., Noda, T.: J. Nucl. Mater., 122/123, 349 (1978).
25. Waelbroeck, F., Dietz, K.J., Wienhold., P., Winter, J., Alikhan, I., Nerkens., H., Rota, E.: J. Nucl. Mater., 93/94, 839 (1980).
26. Winter, J., Waelbroeck, F., Wienhold, P., Schelske, T.: J. Nucl. Mater., 111/112, 243 (1982).
27. Kerst, R.A., Swansiger, W.A.: J. Nucl. Mater., 122/123, 1499 (1984).
28. Takagi, I., Komori, T., Fujita, H., Higashi, K.: J. Nucl. Mater., 136, 278 (1985).
29. Takagi, I., Komori, T., Aoi, H., Fujita, H., Higashi, K: Proc. Int. Symp. on Fusion Reactor Blanket and Fuel Cycle Technol., Univ. Tokyo, Tokai (1986).
30. Sako, K., Ohta, M., Yamato, H., Hiraoka, T., Tanaka, K., Asami, N., Mori, S.: JAERI-M 5502 (1973).
31. Hiraoka, T.: JAERI-M 5147 (1973).
32. Meier, W.R.: UCRL-87499 (1982).
33. Kudo, H., Tanaka, H., Amano, H.: J. Inorg. Nucl. Chem., 40, 363 (1978).
34. Kudo, H.: J. Nucl. Mater., 87, 185 (1979).
35. Kudo, H., Tanaka, K.: J. Chem. Phys., 72, 3049 (1980).
36. Kudo, H., Okuno, K.: J. Nucl. Mater., 101, 38 (1981).
37. Kudo, H., Kushita, K., Okuno, K: J. Nucl. Mater., 116, 78 (1983).
38. Okuno, K., Kudo, H.: J. Nucl. Mater., 116, 82 (1983).
39. Kudo, H., Okuno, K,: Radiochim. Acta, 33, 223 (1983).
40. Kudo, H., Okuno, K,: J. Nucl. mater., 133/134, 192 (1985).
41. Okuno, K., Kudo, H.: J. Nucl. Mater., 138, 31 (1986).
42. Okuno, K., Kudo, H.: J. Nucl. Mater., 138, 210 (1986).
43. Okuno, K., Nagame, Y., Kudo, H.: J. Less-Common Met., 119, 211 (1986).
45. Kudo, H., Okuno, K.: J. Nucl. Mater., 155-157, 524 (1988).
46. Okuno, K., Kudo, H.: Fusion Eng. Des., 8, 355 (1989).
47. Kudo, H.: Radiochim. Acta, 50, 71 (1990).
48 Hayashi, T., Okuno, K., Kudo, H., Amano, H.: J. Less-Commom Met., 141, 169 (1988).
49. Kurasawa, T., Watanabe, H., Roth, E., Vollath, D.: J. Nucl. Mater., 155-157, 544 (1988).
50. Jones, S. E.: Muon Cat. Fusion, 1, 21 (1987).
51. Caffrey, A.J., Anderson, A.N., Van Sichen, C.DeW., Watts, K.D.: Muon Cat. Fusion, 1, 53 (1987).
52. Petitjean, C., Breunlich, W.H., Cargnelli, M., Kammel, P., Marton, J., Nägele, N., Pawlek, P., Scrinzi, A., Werner, J., Zmeskal, J.: Muon Cat. Fusion, 1, 89 (1987).
53. Petitjean, C., et al.: Muon Cat. Fusion, 2, 37 (1988).
54. Nagamine, K., Matsuzaki, T., Ishida, K., Hirata, Y., Watanabe, Y., Kadono, R., Miyake, Y., Nishiyama, K., Jones, S.E., Maltrud, H.R.: Muon

Cat. Fusion, 1, 137 (1987).
55. Vesman, E.A.: JETP Lett., 5, 9 (1967).56. Gerstein, S.S., Ponomarev, L.I.: Phys. Lett., 72B, 80 (1977).
57. Nagamine, K., Matsuzaki, T., Ishida, K., Watanabe, Y., Sakamoto,S., Iwasaki, M., Miyake, Y., Nishiyama, K., Torikai, E., Kurihara, H., Kudo, H., Tanase, M., Kato, M., Kurosawa, K., Sugai, H., Fujie, M., Umezawa, H.: Proc. Int. Symp. Muon Catalyzed Fusion, μ CF-89, RAL-90-022 (1990) p. 27.
58. Kamimura, M.: Proc. μ CF-88 workshop, Sanibel Island, USA (1988).
59. Bogdanova, L.N., Markushin, V.E., Melezhik, V.S., Ponomarev, L.I.: Sov. J. Nucl. Phys., 50, 848 (1989).
60. Marukshin, V.E.: Muon Cat. Fusion, 3, 395 (1988).
61. Cohen, J.S.: Muon Cat. Fusion, 3, 421 (1988).
62. Yoshihara, K.: J. Radioanal. Nucl. Chem., Lett., 119, 247 (1987).
63. Yoshihara, K., Sekine, T.: J. Radioanal. Nucl. Chem., Lett., 128, 53 (1988).
64. Yoshihara, K., Miyakawa, A.: J. Radioanal. Nucl. Chem., Lett., 144, 215 (1990).

8.4 Utilization of Radioactive Decay and Hot Atom

Yasuyuki ARATONO and Shin-ichi OHNO
Japan Atomic Energy Research Institute, Tokai, Ibaraki, 319-11 Japan

1. Introduction

The energy released in radioactive decays and the energy of hot atoms can be exploited in two ways. First, the emitted radiations(α , β , γ rays) and the hot atoms which can be considered as heavy radiations with a very high LET, can be used themselves by virtue of their ionizing properties. Next, the energy of any type of radiation is eventually converted into heat in the surrounding medium. Indeed, the origin of nuclear energy for electric power generation stems from the slowing down of the "hot" fission fragments in the nuclear fuels.

On the other hand, in fusion reactors, 80 % of the energy released in the D-T reaction is carried by 14 MeV neutrons. Because of the long penetration range of neutrons in matter, many peculiar uses of these particles have been proposed, which are rather different from those envisaged for the utilization of the energy released in fission reactors.

In this chapter, the various methods which are in practical use, or which are expected to be used in the future, as well as those which were considered but not realized, will be reviewed. They comprise methods based on the radiation effects and methods relying on the heat dissipated by the radiations.

2. Utilization of Radiation from Radioactive Decay and of Fission Energy

2.1. Chemical Syntheses with Radiation Sources

The synthesis of chemical compounds based on radiation-induced reactions has been investigated with all types of radiations emitted in radioactive decays, but mostly with γ rays, and interestingly enough, also with the radiations(i.e. the fragments) appearing in the fission process.[1-4] In one sense, fission fragments are rather peculiar hot atoms, because of their broad spectrum of masses peaking at masses 92 and 144, their very high initial ionic charges and their high kinetic energies distributed over a wide range. For these reasons, the initiation of unique chemical reactions with high yields were expected.

The idea of "chemonuclear reactors" in which the fission fragments and other radiations from a fission reactor could be used for the production of chemicals has attracted radiation chemists since a long time.[5] The radiochemical yields(G values) of various products formed in the radiation field of reactor have been measured.[1-5] The most attractive reaction was the production of H_2 from water, which could serve as a fuel or as a raw material in the chemical industry.

However, the energy efficiency for fission fragments appeared to be only 5%.[1] The highest energy efficiency of 29.4% was obtained for the conversion of CO_2 to O_2 and to CO which are the starting compounds for the preparation of many industrial products.[1]

The main problems encountered with the "fissio-chemical" synthesis are the neutron activation of the starting material and of the products, and the contamination of the latter with uranium and fission products. For these reasons, it was concluded that the fission-induced chemical synthesis presents no economic advantages over conventional processes.

Experimental and theoretical studies on the release of radiolytic H_2 from reprocessed fission waste solutions containing large amounts of long-lived radionuclides such as ^{90}Sr and ^{137}Cs were reported by Sauer et al.[6] An estimate of the part of the fission energy available for the decomposition of the waste solution has been made with following assumptions: 12% of the fission energy is released as decay energy of the fission products, 90% of the activity of the fission products decay before processing, 50% of the radiation energy is absorbed in the solution. It results that 0.6% of the fission energy can be used for the decomposition of water. With $G(H_2) = 2.5$ and a combustion heat of H_2 equals to 3 eV it is found that 7.5% of absorbed energy can be converted to combustion heat. Finally the overall yield of formation of H_2 from the fission energy is only 0.05% and the authors concluded that the production of H_2 from fission waste solution was not profitable.

Although the radiation-chemical syntheses have not yet been used for the synthesis of commercial products the possible application of fusion reactor has been discussed recently.[7,8]

2.2. Utilization of Radiation as a Source of Heat and for Electric Power Generation

2.2.1 Heat Sources

In a condensed medium, charged particles and hot atoms lose their kinetic energy by elastic and inelastic collisions with the constituting atoms, producing locally small regions of elevated temperature, called hot zones or thermal spikes.[9,10] The calculated temperatures at the center of these regions are 10000 K and 400 K in the tracks of fission fragments and α particles, respectively. Radioactive nuclides which have been used as a source of heat or for the generation of electric power are shown in Table 1.

Table 1. Typical nuclides used for heat source or/and power generation

Nuclide	Half life (year)	Specific activity (Bq/kg)	Thermal output (W_{th})	Radiation (MeV)
^{90}Sr	28.5	5.14×10^{15}	0.96	2.27
^{137}Cs	30.0	3.22×10^{15}	0.42	0.51
^{238}Pu	87.7	6.33×10^{14}	0.55	5.5

The Apollo-11 space probe launched in 1969 for the lunar exploration contained two ^{238}Pu heat sources, each with a thermal output of 15 W, for the purpose to warm the seismometer.[11]

The high temperature gas-cooled nuclear reactor(HTGR) has been developed in several countries as the most promising multi-purpose heat source.[12] A peculiar feature of the reactor is the temperature of the coolant gas helium, typically 1000-1300 K, high enough to consider the production of H_2 by steam reforming from CH_4, thermochemical process, or by high temperature electrolysis of water vapor(HTE). The pilot plant "EVA-ADAM" located in Germany was constructed for testing the feasibility of the production of H_2-CO by steam reaction with CH_4, as well as its transport and uses.[13,14] Based on the experience gained with EVA, a new project named "Integral Energy System, IES" has been started for developing a new source of energy combining processes based on nuclear and solar energy.[15] In Japan, the "High Temperature Engineering Testing Reactor, HTTR" is under construction and will be in operation in 1995.[16] Engineering studies will be concentrated on the production of H_2 using the heat of 1223K coolant temperature.

2.2.2 Generation of Electricity

a) Radioisotope Thermal Generator(RTG)[11,17]

The main radionuclide used in RTG is ^{238}Pu and its most spectacular application was for interplanetary exploration. The scientific instruments used on the moon during the 1969 Apollo-12 mission were powered by a SNAP 27 containing 2.6 kg of ^{238}Pu, which generated 1480 W of thermal power and 74 W of electric power. A still more powerful RTG called MHW(Multi-Hundred Watt) was developed for the two Voyager spacecrafts launched in 1977. Advanced RTG's such as GHS(General Purpose Heat Source) for the Galileo spacecraft and DIPS(Dynamic Radioisotope Power System) are under development in the USA for future missions.

A second important application of RTG is in the field of medical treatment. Isotopically very pure ^{238}Pu is necessary so that the human body is not exposed to unnecessary radiation from radioactive impurities. Sources containing 150-180 mg of ^{238}Pu which deliver an electric power of 0.2 to 0.4 mW are generally used. Other potential medical applications include a brain pacemaker to stop epileptic seizures and a nuclear energy-powered artificial heart.

b) Electronuclear Power Reactor

The most immediate conversion of the heat of nuclear energy to electricity is realized in nuclear power reactors. The kinetic energy of the fission fragments is first converted to heat by the slowing down process in the fuel and next to electricity. The overall conversion efficiency is 30-40%.

The commercial power reactors in operation are classified into two categories, i.e., water-cooled and gas-cooled reactors.[18] In the former type, light(H_2O) or heavy(D_2O) water is used both as a moderator of the neutrons and as a coolant; they are known as LWR(Light Water Reactor) and HWR(Heavy Water Reactor), respectively. In LWR the fuel is UO_2 enriched to 3-4% in ^{235}U. LWR's are in operation in USA, France, Germany, USSR etc.; in 1990 their number was 326, with a production of $2.8x10^8$ W electricity, representing about 80% of the total output of all power reactors.[19] HWR's are found in Canada, with 18 reactors fueled with natural uranium and known as "CANDU".[19] The first commercial CO_2 gas-cooled power reactor(GCR) was put in operation in UK in 1956 and later on 24 stations were constructed. Also in UK, an advanced type of GCR, the "AGR", was developed and installed in 14 plants.[19]

3. Utilization of Fusion Energy

The very fast neutrons from the D-T fusion, because of their long range, can be used outside of the reactor core. The FAME program, "Fusion Applications And Market Evaluation" has been developed by GA Technologies for LLNL and US DOE for the evaluation of the applications and of the potential market of fusion energy.[7] Among many possible applications,[7,8,20,21] the production of H_2 was considered as the most important, based on conventional or innovative methods as shown below.[22,23]

3.1. Improvement of Conventional Methods : Exploitation of Heat

These topics have been investigated at BNL, LLNL, Westinghouse Electric Corp. and GA Technologies Inc.. The studies at BNL and at Westinghouse Electric Corp. were focussed on the application of the tokamak fusion reactor STARFIRE to HTE in the combined design "HYFIRE".[24] The research developed at LLNL and by GA Technologies Inc. is based on sulfur-iodine thermochemical process, in connection with the LLNL tandem mirror reactor designed as a part of the "Mirror Advanced Reactor Study"(MARS).[25] Originally these two processes were conceived for the application of a fission reactor, but it was concluded that they were feasible for fusion reactors as well.

3.2. Innovative Aspects : Application of Heat or/and Radiolysis

Many innovative concepts for the utilization of fusion energy were proposed in the 1970's and the early 1980's,[7,8,20,21] among others the decomposition of water on refractory ceramics heated by the absorption of 14 MeV neutrons or in thermochemical process. Since the previous review by Ohno,[26] in which these concepts were discussed, nothing new has appeared. Although these ideas have received much attention, no experimental attempt has been made for the obvious reason that the conditions for sustained fusion reaction have not yet been realized.

3.3. Hot Atom Chemistry Considerations for the Utilization of Fusion Energy

The chemical reactions due to fusion neutrons are triggered by the atoms displaced in the slowing down process of the neutrons. Thus, they are similar to those produced by nuclear recoil atoms(hot atoms) or by fast moving (accelerated) particles.

The production of H_2 from H_2O in a redox cycle initiated by solar energy is considered as very promising.[27] The cycle more often investigated is shown below.

$$Fe_3O_4 \longrightarrow 3FeO + 1/2O_2 \quad (1)$$
$$3FeO + H_2O \longrightarrow Fe_3O_4 + H_2 \quad (2)$$

$$H_2O \longrightarrow H_2 + 1/2O_2 \quad (3)$$

It is known that the reduction of Fe(III) by solar heat (reaction 1) proceeds at a temperature above 2500 K, while reaction (2), 450 K. As said previously, displaced atoms, alike hot atoms, form thermal spikes in which the host material is radiolized. If this happen in Fe_3O_4 under the action of fast neutrons, it can be anticipated that the reduction takes place at a temperature below that predicted from thermodynamic considerations.

Experimental informations on the reduction of Fe(III) by the energetic particles released in the $^6Li(n, \alpha)^3H$ reaction have been gained from Mössbauer spectroscopy of neutron irradiated α-$LiFeO_2$.[28] The Mossbauer spectrum shows the formation of magnetite with an initial radiochemical yield G=0.001. From a comparison with thermal annealing experiments it was concluded that magnetite results from the thermal and radiolytic effects caused by the energetic α (2.1 MeV) and tritium(2.7 MeV) particles.

The chemical effects induced by 40 keV He^+ ions in hematite (α-Fe_2O_3) were investigated by conversion electron Mössbauer spectroscopy.[29] Magnetite was formed in amounts increasing with the fluence of the particle beam. From the experimental data, and computer simulation of the slowing down and of the scattering of He ions using the TRIM program,[30] the initial G value was calculated to be about 10^{-4}, which corresponds to about 1 Fe_3O_4 per He^+ ion.

4. Applications of Radioactive Decay

4.1. Measurement of Short Nuclear Decay Times[31,32]

The blocking of charged particles in single crystals has been applied to the measurement of the lifetime of excited compound nuclear states. Maruyama et al. were the first to observe the effect of nuclear lifetimes on the distribution of measured nuclear reaction products which were blocked by lattice atoms in a study of the inelastic scattering of protons in germanium crystals.[33,34] Gibson and Nielsen have applied the technique to the measurement of the reaction time of fission induced by protons in uranium oxide crystals.[31] The method is based on the measurement of the charged particles emitted by the excited nucleus located in normal lattice site in a monocrystal; nuclear lifetimes in the range 10^{-14} to 10^{-18} s are accessible.

The crystal is irradiated by a particle beam of several MeV. The excited compound nucleus formed in a nuclear reaction recoils out of the lattice site with an initial velocity of the order of 10^6 m s^{-1}. If its lifetime is 10^{-17} s, the excited nucleus travels over an average distance of 0.01 nm before decaying. If the decay products are emitted at distances larger than the vibrational amplitude of the lattice atoms, they are not as effectively blocked from channeling in the planar or axial directions as they would if they were not recoiling. From the magnitude of the changes the mean recoil distance can be deduced, and knowing the particle velocity, also the lifetime. By this method, a fission lifetime of $0.6\text{x}10^{-6}$ s was determined for the excited Np nuclei formed by the bombardment of an UO_2 crystal with 10 MeV pro-tons. Many other reactions including $^{72}Ge(p,p')^{72}Ge^*$, $^{27}Al(p,\alpha)^{24}Mg$ and $^{31}P(p,\alpha)^{28}Si$ have been studied in the same way. Lifetimes below 10^{-18}s will become accessible with refinements of the method, such as the cooling of the crystals in order to reduce the thermal vibrations, or the use of heavy ions of higher energy which will increase the recoil energy.

4.2. Use of Nuclear Reaction to Pump a Potential Gamma-ray Laser

The development of lasers in the sub-nanometer wavelength range is still a major scientific challenge.[35] A γ-ray laser must rely on the Mössbauer effect in order to prevent the Doppler broadening of the very narrow nuclear resonance lines. For this purpose, a single crystal rather than an amorphous or polycrystalline material must be used. Aiming at the realization of γ-ray laser works are now in progress at, for instance the Los Alamos National Laboratory (LANL) in following areas: nuclear level schemes, isomer production and separation, interlevel transition mechanisms, wave modes, superradiance in crystals. While the development of γ-ray laser is an interdisciplinary project, the lasing must be driven by a nuclear process, such as a neutron induced nuclear reaction. The half-life of the excited state will probably lie in the 1 to 1000 ns interval. If recoilless emission conditions can be realized, the stimulated emission cross section will be enhanced to the million barn range. The attenuation can be greatly reduced by performing an isotope separation of the excited nuclei, followed by implantation into a favorable host in a time short compared to the isomeric half-life. The required neutron beam intensity has been discussed.[36] The spallation neutron source at LANL operates with 1 GeV proton pulses with a width of a few tenths of a μs. The resulting neutron output is about 10^{15} per pulse, or an average of 10^{16} neutrons per s. This facility makes neutron capture γ-ray spectroscopy accessible, a step towards a γ-ray laser.

4.3. Inverted Doppler Shift Attenuation Methods for the Determination of the Stopping Power of Swift Ions

The stopping power cross sections of elements and compounds for fast moving ions are important parameters in the study of the interaction of energetic particles with materials. They were determined by Neuwirth et al. for Li ions produced by the $^{10}B(n,\alpha)^{7}Li^{*}$ reaction in various materials.[37,38] The Doppler shift of the 478 keV photon emitted by Li^{*} at any time is a measure of the instantaneous velocity of the ion, from which the energy loss and hence the stopping cross section can be determined. The targets consisted of very thin boron films evaporated on metal foils. The cross section was measured with a 1% accuracy in the 80-840 keV energy range using an (α,γ) coincidence method. The authors concluded that in this range the cross sections are proportional to the velocity of the Li ions as predicted by the LSS theory, but that the Bragg rule is not generally valid.

5. Conclusion

Radioactive decay and hot atoms have been used in many fields of fundamental science and technology dealing with nuclear phenomena. Hot atom chemistry will promote a better understanding of the mechanisms involved and will lead to a rise in traditional applications as well as in the development of new technologies, especially those related to fusion. Although the start of commercial operation of fusion reactors cannot yet be fixed, it is not premature to investigate the potential applications of 14 MeV neutrons.

References

1. Steinberg, M., Beller, M., Powell, J. R.: BNL-18866 (1974).
2. Tabata, Y.: "CRC Hand Book of Radiation Chemistry" (Y. Tabata, Ed.) CRC Press, Boca Raton, Ann Arbor, Boston, 1991, p. 605.
3. Ikezoe, Y., Sato, S.: Bull. Chem. Soc. Jpn., 48, 3111(1975).
4. Sato, S., Ikezoe, Y., Shimizu, S.: Radiat. Phys. Chem., 18, 741(1981).
5. Juppe, G.: Eur. Spectra, 8, 39(1969).
6. Sauer, M. C., Hart, E. J., Flynn, K. F., Gindler, J. E.: ANL-76-46 (1976).
7. Schultz, K. R., Engholm, B. A., Bourque, R. F., Cheng, E. T., Schaffer M. J., Wong, C. P. C.: Fusion Technology, 10, 1279(1986).
8. Bourque, R. F., Schultz, K. R.: GA-A18658 (1987).
9. Harbottle, G.: "Chemical Effects of Nuclear Transformations in Inorganic Systems" (G. Harbottle and A. G. Maddock, Ed.) North-Holland Publishing

Company, Amsterdam, New York, Oxford, 1979, p. 39.
10. Mozumder, A.: "Advances in Radiation Chemistry, Vol. 1" (M. Burton and J. L. Magee, Ed.) Wiley-Interscience, New York, London, Sidney, Toronto, 1969, p. 51.
11. "Space Nuclear Power"(J. A. Angelo, Jr and D. Buden, Ed.) Orbit Book Co., Malabar, Fl. 1985.
12. "The High-Temperature Reactor and Nuclear Process Heat Applications" (K. Kussmaul Ed.) North-Holland Physics Publishing , Amsterdam, 1984.
13. Singh, J., Niessen, H. F., Harth, R., Fedders, H., Reutler, H., Pankin, W., Muller, W. D., Harms, H. G.: Nucl. Eng. Design, 78, 179(1984).
14. Hohlein, B., Niessen, H., Range. J., Schiebahn, H. J. R., Vorwerk. M., ibid., 78, 241(1984).
15. Hohlein, B., Fedders, H.: "Hydrogen Energy Progress VII, Vol.3, Proceedings of the 7th World Hydrogen Energy Conference, Moscow, U.S.S.R," (Veziroglu, T. N., Protsenko, A. N. Ed.) 1988, p. 1821.
16. Tanaka, T.: Genshiryoku kougyou(Nuclear Engeneering), 36(4), 58(1990) (in Japanese).
17. "Nuclear Energy, third edition" (R. L. Murray, Ed.) Pergamon Press, Oxford, New York, Beijing, Frankfurt, Sao Paulo, Sydney, Tokyo, Toronto, 1988 p. 244.
18. "Operating Experience with Nuclear Power Stations in Member States in 1988" International Atomic Energy Agency, Vienna, 1989.
19. "Sekaino genshiryokuhatsudenno doukou" Japan Atomic Industrial Forum, Inc. 1990 p. 52(in Japanese).
20. GA project staff, GA-A15371, 1979.
21. Kouts, H.: J. Fusion Energy, 2, 253(1982).
22. Booth, L. A., Conf-770593, 1977.
23. Fillo, J. A.: BNL-28627, 1980.
24. Fillo, J. A., Powell J. R., Benenati, R., Malick F.: Nucl. Technol./Fusion, 4, 184(1983).
25. UCRL-53480-Vol.2, 1984.
26. Ohno, S.: "Hot Atom Chemistry" (T. Matsuura, Ed.) Kodansha, Tokyo (and Elsvier Amsterdam), 1984, p. 512.
27. Bilgen, E., Bilgen, C.: Int. J. Hydrogen Energy, 7, 637(1982).
28. Aratono, Y, Sagawa, C., Nakashima, M., Saeki, M., Sato, T.: Chem. Letters, 35(1990).
29. unpublished results.
30. Biersack J. P., Haggmark. L. G.: Nuclear Instruments and Methods, 174 257(1980).
31. Gibson, W. M., Maruyama, M.: "Channeling" (D. V. Morgan Ed.) John Wiley & Sons, London, 1973, p. 349.
32. Gibson, W. M., Maruyama, M., Hashimoto, Y., Kanter, E. P., Temmer, G. M., Keddy, R. J., Mingay, D. W., Sellchop, J. P. F.: Nucl. Phys., A317, 313(1979).
33. Maruyama, M., Tsukada, K., Ozawa, K., Fujimoto, F., Komaki, K., Mannami, M., Sakurai, T.: Phys. Lett., B29, 414(1969).
34. idem : Nucl. Phys., A145, 581(1970).
35. Baldwin, G. C., Trammel, G. T.: Bull. Am. Phys. Soc., 32, 1042(1987).
36. Bowman,C. D.: LA-UR-87-2898, 1987.
37. Neuwirth, W., Pietsch, W., Richter, K., Hauser, U.: Z. Physik, A275, 209 (1975).
38. idem, ibid, A275, 215(1975).

Author Index

Underlined numbers indicate the first page of a contribution herein

D

E

F

S

Subject Index

Notes:

(1) Page numbers with hyphen but without subsequent number indicate that the subjects continue over a number of pages in the sub-chapters.

(2) Choice of names for substances and nuclides was restricted for reasons of space.

S

Acknowledgments

Permissions to reproduce the following copyright materials are gratefully acknowledged.

AMERICAN CHEMICAL SOCIETY, WASHINGTON

Source	Section	Figure	Page
J. Phys. Chem., 95, 7338 (1991) (J. R. Kempton *et al.*) Fig. 4, 5	3.8	Fig. 1	(p.238)
		Fig. 2	(p.238)
J. Am. Chem. Soc., 92, 3480 (1977) (A. E. Richardson *et al.*) Fig. 1	4.2	Fig. 1	(p.289)
J. Phys. Chem., 84, 687 (1980) (Au.) Fig. 1	4.2	Fig. 3	(p.293)
Acc. Chem. Res., 11, 433 (1978) (G. A. Kenney-Wallace) Fig. 2	5.2	Fig. 1	(p.404)
Acc. Chem. Res., 14, 138 (1981) (L. Kevan) Fig. 2	5.2	Fig. 3	(p.406)
J. Phys. Chem., 92, 4277 (1988) (P. J. Possky *et al.*) Fig. 3	5.2	Fig. 4	(p.408)
J. Phys. Chem., 88, 1200 (1984) (I. A. LaVerne and R. H. Schuler) Fig. 1, 5	5.6	Fig. 3	(p.439)
		Fig. 4	(p.440)

AMERICAN INSTITUTE OF PHYSICS, NEW YORK

Source	Section	Figure	Page
J. Chem. Phys., 67, 4866 (1977) (Au.) Fig. 1	3.1	Fig. 1	(p.138)
J. Chem. Phys., 89, 6226 (1988) (Au.) Fig. 2, 9, 10	3.1	Fig. 4	(p.141)
		Fig. 5, 6	(p.142)
J. Chem. Phys., 89, 6238 (1988) (Au.) Fig. 9	3.1	Fig. 7	(p.144)
J. Chem. Phys., 93, 5719 (1990) (Au.) Fig. 2, 5, 10, 12, 20(a) and (b), and 27(a) and (b)	3.1	Fig. 2	(p.137)
		Fig. 8	(p.148)
		Fig. 10	(p.149)
		Fig. 12a	(p.151)
		Fig. 12b	(p.152)
J. Chem. Phys., 85, 1931 (1986) (Au.) Fig. 9	3.3	Fig. 2	(p.170)
J. Chem. Phys., 84, 5575 (1986) (Au.) Fig. 4	3.3	Fig. 3	(p.172)
J. Chem. Phys., 79, 671 (1983) (Au.) Fig. 5	3.5	Fig. 3	(p.196)
J. Chem. Phys., 74, 1401 (1981) (Au.) Fig. 2, 1, 9	3.6	Fig. 1	(p.219)
		Fig. 2, 3	(p.220)
J. Chem. Phys., 66, 5790 (1977) (Au.) Fig. 1	3.9	Fig. 1	(p.253)
J. Chem. Phys., 60, 680 (1974) (Au.) Fig. 1, 2, 4	4.1	Fig. 11, 12	(p.277)
		Fig. 13	(p.278)
J. Chem. Phys., 64, 4926 (1976) (R. G. Manning *et al.*) Fig. 1	4.2	Fig. 2	(p.290)
J. Chem. Phys., 52, 2950 (1970) (K. Yoshihara and H. Kudo) Fig. 3	4.3	Fig. 6	(p.314)
J. Chem. Phys., 92, 3980 (1990) (J. V. Coe *et al.*) Fig.1	5.2	Fig.6	(p.410)

AMERICAN NUCLEAR SOCIETY, INC., ILLINOIS

Source	Section	Figure	Page
Nucl Technol., 78, 157 (1987) (M. S. Osborne *et al.*) Fig. 3	8.2	Fig. 1	(p.638)

AMERICAN PHYSICAL SOCIETY, NEW YORK
Phys. Rev., B, 38, 1 (1988) (Au.) Fig.1 — 5.9 Fig. 1 (p.465)

THE CHEMICAL SOCIETY OF JAPAN, TOKYO
Bull. Chem. Soc. Jpn., 52, 3271 (1979) (Au.) Fig. 1 — 2.9 Fig. 1 (p.128)
Bull. Chem. Soc. Jpn., 43, 2745 (1970) (Au.) Fig. 4 — 5.6 Fig. 2 (p.438)
Bull. Chem. Soc. Jpn., 47, 1113 (1974) (Au.) Fig. 3 — 5.6 Fig. 5 (p.441)
Bull. Chem. Soc. Jpn., 62, 576 (1989) (T. Kobayashi) Fig. 3 — 6.1 Fig. 9 (p.480)
Bull. Chem. Soc. Jpn., 61, 2785 (1990) (Au.) Fig. 6 — 6.1 Fig. 13 (p.485)

LES EDITIONS DE PHYSIQUE, FRANCE
Rev. Phys. Appl., 22, 1755 (1987) (Y. Gauduel *et al.*) Fig. 4 — 5.2 Fig. 2 (p.405)

ELSEVIER SCIENCE PUB. CO., AMSTERDAM
Surface Sci., 222, 491 (1984) (Au.) Fig. 3 — 3.2 Fig. 4 (p.161)
Chem. Phys., 45, 261 (1980) (Au.) Fig. 5 — 3.3 Fig. 1 (p.169)
Surface Sci., 147, 227 (1984) (Au.) Fig. 2 — 5.9 Fig. 2 (p.467)
J. Less Common Metals, 141, 169 (1988) (Au.) Fig. 3 — 8.3 Fig. 8 (p.656)

ELSEVIER SEQUDIA, A.S.,LAUSANNE
Fusion Eng. and Design, 8, 355 (1989) (Au.) Fig. 2 — 7.3 Fig. 7 (p.656)

Gmelin-Institut, FRANKFURT
Gmelins Handbook of Inorganic Chemistry, Vol. A4, p.199 (1989) (Au.) Fig. 52 — 7.4 Fig. 5 (p.581)

J. C. BALZER AG, SWITZERLAND
Hyperfine Interactions, 56, 1533 (1990) (T. Kobayashi *et al.*) Fig. 3, 4 — 6.1 Fig. 8 (p.479)
Hyperfine Interactions, 56, 1527 (1990) (C. Hennen *et al.*) Fig. 2 — 6.1 Fig. 12 (p.483)

THE JAPAN RADIATION RESEARCH SOCIETY, KYOTO
J. Radiat. Res., 26, 334 (1985) (K. Shinohara *et al.*) Fig. 1 — 7.3 Fig. 3 (p.561)

THE JAPAN SOCIETY OF APPLIED PHYSICS, TOKYO
Jap. J. Appl. Phys., 24, 129 (1985) (Au.) Fig. 3 — 5.5 Fig. 4 (p.428)

JAPAN RADIOISOTOPE ASSOCIATION, TOKYO
Radiosotopes, 33, 1 (1984) (Au.) Table 2 — 5.7 Table 2 (p.445)

JOHN WILEY & SONS PUB., NEW YORK
"Kinetics of Nonhomogeneous Processes", ed. by G. R. Freeman, John-Wiley & Sons, New York, 1987, Fig. 5.24, 5.25 — 5.3 Fig. 1, 2 (p.417)

J. RADIOANAL. NUCL. CHEM., HUNGARY

J. Radioanal. Nucl. Chem, Articles, 147, 207 (1991) (Au.) Fig. 3	2.7	Fig. 4	(p.110)
Radiochem. Radioanal. Lett., 18, 291 (1974) (Au.) Fig. 1	4.1	Fig. 3	(p.271)
J. Radioanal. Nucl. Chem. Lett., 126, 273 (1988) (Au.) Fig. 1	4.8	Fig. 1	(p.369)
Radiochem. Radioanal. Lett., 26, 5 (1974) (Au.) Fig. 2	4.8	Fig. 2	(p.369)
J. Radioanal. Nucl. Chem. Lett., 144, 195 (1990) (Au.) Fig. 3, 4	6.1	Fig. 4,5	(p.477)
J. Radioanal. Nucl. Chem. Lett., 136, 257 (1989) (Au.) Fig. 1, 2	6.1	Fig.10,11	(p.481)
J. Radioanal. Nucl. Chem. Articles., 142, 101 (1990) (Au.) Fig. 1, 2, 3	7.5	Fig. 1	(p.590)
		Fig. 2	(p.593)
		Fig. 3	(p.595)

MACMILLAN MAGAZINES LTD., LONDON

Nature, 312, No. 5994, 535 (6 Dec., 1984) (Au.) Fig. 2	7.5	Fig. 4	(p.597)

MARUZEN CO., TOKYO

"Aisotoupu Binran", Japan Radioisotope Association, Ed., (1984) (Au.) Fig. 11,14	5.6	Fig. 1	(p.488)

ELSEVIER SCIENCE PUB. CO. INC., NEW YORK

J. Luminescence, 21, 311 (1980) (N. A. Atari) Fig. 4	5.5	Fig. 2	(p.426)
J. Luminescence, 15, 227 (1977) (Au.) Fig. 1, 2	5.5	Fig. 3	(p.427)
Nucl. Instr. Meth., 178, 437 (1980)(Au.) Fig. 4 and Table 1	5.7	Fig. 1	(p.444)
		Table 1	(p.445)
J. Nucl Mat., 76/77, 193 (1978) (J. N. Smith *et al.*) Fig. 3	7.3	Fig. 4	(p.651)
J. Nucl Mat., 128/129, 545 (1984) (E. Vietke *et al.*) Fig. 5	7.3	Fig. 5	(p.652)
J. Nucl Mat., 138, 31 (1986) (Au.) Fig. 4	7.3	Fig. 6	(p.655)

PERGAMON plc., OXFORD

Nucl. Tracks Radiat. Meas., 16, 283 (1989) (Au.) Fig. 2, 3	5.7	Fig. 2	(p.445)
		Fig. 3	(p.447)
J. Phys. Chem. Solid, 49, 921 (1988) (M. Devillers *et al.*) Fig. 1	6.1	Fig. 2	(p.475)
Radiat. Phys. Chem., 28, 601 (1986) (K. Ishigure *et al.*) Fig. 8	8.2	Fig. 3	(p.642)

THE PHYSICAL SOCIETY OF JAPAN, TOKYO

J. Physical Soc. Jpn., 53, 4109 (1989) (F. Asai *et al.*) Fig. 1, 2	6.4	Fig. 3,4	(p.509)

R. ORDENBOURG VERLAG GMBH, MUENCHEN

Source	Section	Figure (page)
Radiochim. Acta, 47, 119 (1989) (Au.) Fig. 3, 5	2.5	Fig. 2 (p.81), Fig. 3 (p.82)
Radiochim. Acta, 35, 37 (1984) (Au.) Fig. 1, 2	2.7	Fig. 1 (a,b) (p.108)
Radiochim. Acta, 26, 147 (1979) (Au.) Fig. 11	2.7	Fig. 2 (p.108)
Radiochim. Acta, 33, 3 (1983) (Au.) Fig. 4	2.7	Fig. 2 (p.128)
Radiochim. Acta, 52/53, 269 (1991) (Au.) Fig. 2	4.1	Fig. 15 (p.279)
Radiochim. Acta, 43, 61 (1988) (Au.) Fig. 2, 1	4.2	Fig. 4 (p.297), Fig. 5 (p.298)
Radiochim. Acta, 33, 21 (1983) (H. H. Connen *et al.*) Fig. 1	4.2	Fig. 6 (p.300)
Radiochim. Acta, 49, 17 (1990) (Au.) Fig. 1	4.3	Fig. 1 (p.308)
Radiochim. Acta, 38, 125 (1984) (K. Sasaki *et al.*) Fig. 3	4.3	Fig. 4 (p.372)
Radiochim. Acta, 47, 177 (1989) (Au.) Fig. 8,9,6(partly, with alterations), 5(partly,with alterations), 11	7.4	Fig. 1,2 (p.578), Fig. 3 (p.579), Fig. 4 (p.580), Fig. 6 (p.581)
Radiochim. Acta, 52/53, 269 (1991) (Au.) Fig. 3, 1	7.4	Fig. 5 (p.581), Fig. 7 (p.582)

SPRINGER VERLAG, HEIDELBERG

Source	Section	Figure (page)
J. Phys. D., Appl. Phys., 7, 2412 (1974) (Au.) Fig. 1	5.5	Fig. 1 (p.424)

TOKYO METROPOLITAN UNIVERSITY, TOKYO

Source	Section	Figure (page)
Doctral Thesis, p. 31 and 31, 991 (T. Sato) Fig. 31, 32	6.1	Fig. 6 (p.478), Fig. 7 (p.478)